RESEARCH IN
PROTOZOOLOGY

RESEARCH IN PROTOZOOLOGY

In Four Volumes

EDITED BY

TZE-TUAN CHEN

Professor of Zoology
University of Southern California
Los Angeles, California

VOLUME 3

THE QUEEN'S AWARD
TO INDUSTRY 1966

PERGAMON PRESS

OXFORD · LONDON · EDINBURGH · NEW YORK
TORONTO · SYDNEY · PARIS · BRAUNSCHWEIG

Pergamon Press Ltd., Headington Hill Hall, Oxford
4 & 5 Fitzroy Square, London W.1

Pergamon Press (Scotland) Ltd., 2 & 3 Teviot Place, Edinburgh 1

Pergamon Press Inc., 44–01 21st Street, Long Island City, New York 11101

Pergamon of Canada, Ltd., 207 Queen's Quay West, Toronto 1

Pergamon Press (Aust.) Pty. Ltd., Rushcutters Bay, Sydney, N.S.W.

Pergamon Press S.A.R.L., 24 rue des Écoles, Paris 5ᵉ

Vieweg & Sohn GmbH, Burgplatz 1, Braunschweig

First edition 1969

Library of Congress Catalog Card No. 66–22364

08 003236 2

CONTENTS

PREFACE

LIKE Volumes 1 and 2, this volume contains chapters dealing with several subjects: Cytology, Genetics, Parasitology, and Fibrillar Systems. As before, it is impractical to include only related chapters.

The editor wishes to express his gratitude to the contributors for their dedicated efforts toward making this volume a contemporary resource of needed information.

Again, as in previous volumes, Dr. Ruth Stocking Lynch has contributed her help in the editing of these chapters.

I am indebted to the Board of Consultants, including Drs. William Balamuth, A. C. Giese, R. F. Kimball, Norman D. Levine, William Trager, and D. H. Wenrich for their assistance in the making of decisions on matters of importance to the preparation of this collection.

Finally, I wish to acknowledge the cooperation of the staff of Pergamon Press in New York and in Oxford, England.

Los Angeles, California

T. T. CHEN

THE MACRONUCLEUS OF CILIATES

I. B. Raikov

Institute of Cytology of the Academy of Sciences,
Leningrad F-121, USSR

CONTENTS

2

I. INTRODUCTION

The ciliates differ sharply from the great majority of other protozoans in their *nuclear dualism*, the simultaneous presence in the cell of two or more nuclei belonging to two clearly different types: *micronuclei* and *macronuclei*. The micronuclei are usually small and compact. They divide by mitosis, and during the sexual processes (conjugation or autogamy) they undergo meiosis and give rise to pronuclei. After conjugation, autogamy, and other similar processes connected with destruction of the old macronucleus, the nuclear apparatus, including the macronucleus, is always reconstructed at the cost of the synkaryon derivatives, i.e., finally at the cost of micronuclear division products. Cases of transformation of a vegetative micronucleus into a macronucleus without meiosis and karyogamy are also known ("endomixis"). Thus, micronuclei can be transformed into macronuclei, while the opposite process—formation of micronuclei from macronuclear fragments—is improbable.†

For a long time the ciliate macronucleus was considered unique, with no analogies among nuclei of other Protozoa nor even among cell nuclei in general. The unusually large chromatin content of the macronucleus, its capability for multiple and unequal divisions, the apparent amitotic nature of its division, and the obvious dependence on it of the vegetative cell functions led Schaudinn, Popoff, and Goldschmidt, at the beginning of this century, to create a theory of "two chromatins" (see, e.g., ref. 71). According to this theory the macronucleus has a non-chromosomal structure and contains a special type of chromatin, a genetically inert but physiologically active "trophochromatin". The normal, genetically active chromatin ("idiochromatin") was thought to be confined to the micronucleus.

Further development of protozoan cytology, especially during the last two decades, resulted in the revision of these ideas and permitted a description of the macronuclear structure in terms of modern karyology and cytogenetics. Now the macronucleus is considered *highly polyploid* and all its DNA chromosomal. Yet the question of the spatial arrangement of numerous chromosomes and of whole genomes within the macronucleus is far from being solved. At the same time it has been discovered that macronuclei of some lower (mainly marine) ciliates remain diploid; investigation of these forms may throw light on the origin and evolution of nuclear dualism in Ciliata.

† The only recorded exception to this rule[235] will be discussed on page 41.

Reviews at least partially concerned with the macronucleus have been published repeatedly. Some of them are out of date,[11] while others are too brief or deal only with some of the problems related to the macronucleus.[47, 62, 70, 75, 77, 82, 88, 90, 171, 175, 176, 188, 194, 250] The present review aims to fill this gap and to examine as thoroughly as possible the modern achievements in the study of the ciliate macronucleus.

The author wishes to acknowledge the valuable cooperation of the following persons who placed at his disposal originals of their published and/or unpublished micrographs and drawings: Dieter Ammermann, Tübingen, West Germany (Fig. 14B); Alfred M. Elliott, Ann Arbor, Michigan, USA (Fig. 36); Marina A. Frenkel, Leningrad, USSR (Fig. 30); Joseph G. Gall, New Haven, Connecticut, USA (Fig. 19B); Margaret N. Golikowa, Leningrad, USSR (Fig. 14A); Karl G. Grell, Tübingen, West Germany (Figs. 13, 33, 49); Byron C. Kluss, Long Beach, California, USA (Figs. 5 and 19C); Viktor F. Mashansky and Lilia N. Vinnichenko, Leningrad, USSR (Fig. 4); Tatjana N. Mosevich, Leningrad, USSR (Figs. 3D and 25A); Maria A. Rudzinska, New York, USA (Fig. 6); August Ruthmann, Tübingen, West Germany (Fig. 34); Viktor Schwartz, Tübingen, West Germany (Figs. 15 and 22); B. R. Seshachar, Delhi, India (Fig. 7); and Emile Vivier, Lille, France (Figs. 8 and 9). The author's gratitude is also due to Drs. D. M. Prescott and G. E. Stone (Denver, Colorado, USA), who kindly sent him the text of their chapter which is to appear in the second volume of this series, and to Drs. J. Frankel, R. H. Gavin (Iowa City, Iowa, USA), and G. G. Holz, Jr. (Syracuse, New York, USA), for communicating some of their unpublished material.

II. MORPHOLOGY AND CYTOCHEMISTRY OF THE MACRONUCLEUS

This section as well as sections III to VIII deals only with data concerning typical polyploid macronuclei. The peculiarities of the diploid macronuclei of certain lower ciliates will be considered separately in section IX, devoted to evolution of the macronucleus.

1. Number, Form, and Size of Macronuclei

The macronuclei are highly diverse morphologically (Fig. 1). Most ciliates have one macronucleus, usually of a comparatively simple form: spherical, oval, elongate, etc. (Fig. 1A). Such macronuclei are characteristic mainly of small and medium-size ciliates.

Very common are horseshoe-shaped or C-form macronuclei (Fig. 1B); a long, irregularly wound ribbon form also occurs (Fig. 1C, D). A longitudinally stretched macronucleus is often separated by constrictions into many nodes, becoming moniliform (Fig. 1E). And in a number of ciliates the

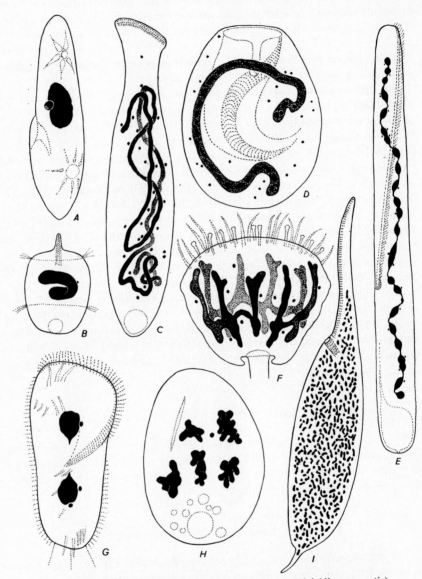

Fig. 1. Morphological diversity of infusorian macronuclei (diagrammatic).
A—*Paramecium caudatum*, B—*Didinium nasutum*, C—*Spathidium spathula*,
D—*Bursaria truncatella*, E—*Spirostomum minus*, F—*Ephelota gemmipara*,
G—*Stylonychia mytilus*, H—*Schizokaryum dogieli*, I—*Dileptus anser*. A–G
and I—originals; H—after Poljansky and Golikowa.[174]

macronucleus acquires a complicated branched form (Fig. 1 F). This type is common in Suctoria; in certain members of this group, e.g. in *Gorgonosoma arbuscula*, the spectacularly branching macronucleus repeats the branching of the tree-shaped body.[260]

Some members of nearly all taxonomic groups of ciliates have several macronuclei (Fig. 1 G, H). As a rule these are formed by division or fragmentation of a single macronuclear anlage of the exconjugant. In cases of intense fragmentation the macronucleus may consist of several hundred or even thousands of small parts (Fig. 1 I).

A relationship between macronuclear form and systematic position of the ciliate is not always clear. Certainly in some specialized ciliate taxa the macronuclei may be more or less constant in type (C-shaped in Peritricha, etc.). But far more often the macronuclear form varies even within small groups. Thus in the genus *Stentor* there are species with moniliform, rod-shaped, and rounded macronuclei; in *Dileptus*, species with fragmented, moniliform, and elongate macronuclei. At the same time, the macronuclear form may become convergently similar in totally unrelated ciliates: e.g., moniliform macronuclei occur in *Dileptus monilatus*, *Helicoprorodon gigas* (Gymnostomatida), and in many Heterotrichida; C-shaped in *Didinium* and in Peritricha; and highly fragmented in *Dileptus anser* and *Urostyla grandis*. Such examples might be quoted almost indefinitely. They indicate a great lability of the macronuclear form during evolution and the presence of many independent parallel series of morphological changes of these nuclei in different groups of ciliates.

In many cases sharp changes of the macronuclear form occur even at different stages of the life cycle of a single species. For instance, in *Magnifolliculina*, adult sedentary specimens have a rounded macronucleus while vermiform swarmers have a moniliform macronucleus.[275] In the adult form of *Chromidina elegans* (Apostomatida) the macronucleus is a complex network from which some fragments may separate. But in young buds formed at the posterior end of the ciliate the macronucleus condenses into a simple elongate body. During growth of the bud the macronucleus becomes netlike again.[285] Such cases may be considered recapitulations of the ancestral macronuclear shape occurring in young stages of specialized forms.

The size of the macronucleus is usually considerable, and in large ciliates it may be very large; the macronucleus of *Spirostomum ambiguum* is more than 2 mm long. Generally there is a definite proportionality between the body size and the macronuclear size; moreover, in large infusorians not only the volume but also the surface of the highly irregular macronucleus is greatly increased. Undoubtedly this is related to the high biochemical activity of the macronucleus (see section VIII).

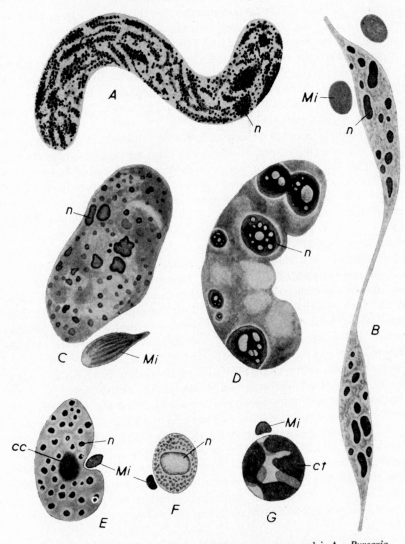

FIG. 2. Internal structure of some homomerous macronuclei. A—*Bursaria truncatella*, Mann's stain, × 1100; after Poljansky.[172] B—*Helicoprorodon gigas*, methyl green–pyronin, × 2300 (original). C and D—*Paramecium bursaria* (C—in normal culture, D—after 8 days starvation), methyl green–pyronin, × 1350; after Egelhaaf.[56] E—*Prorodon teres*, methyl green–fuchsin S; after Kasanzeff.[119] F—*Colpoda steinii*, Feulgen, × 1800; after Reichenow.[205] G—*Colpoda cucullus*, Feulgen, × 1800; after Reichenow.[205] *Mi*—micronuclei, *n*—nucleoli, *ct*—chromatin trabeculae, *cc*—chromatin condensation.

2. Structural and Chemical Components of the Macronucleus

The macronucleus of ciliates contains the same main structural components which characterize the nuclei of other Protozoa and cell nuclei in general: nuclear membrane, karyolymph, chromatin elements, and nucleoli. But the interrelation of these components in the macronucleus differs from that in other protozoan and metazoan nuclei. The chromatin elements, containing DNA, are very prominent in the macronucleus and usually fill its whole volume, leaving no space for the "free" karyolymph, which can be discerned only with difficulty. The nucleolar apparatus of the macronucleus is also often developed very strongly (Fig. 2). Consequently, in classification of protozoan nuclei, the macronuclei are usually treated as a special category of "massive nuclei".

A. Macronuclear Envelope

Under the light microscope the macronuclear envelope generally looks like a thin membrane uniformly encircling the whole nucleus (Fig. 2). Cytochemical investigation of the envelope is difficult because of its thinness. It usually gives positive reactions for total protein.

Electron microscopy shows that the macronuclear envelope generally has a typical structure,[23, 58, 59, 112, 185, 186, 201, 207, 213, 215, 220, 294, 305] consisting of two membranes, each 70 to 100 Å thick and obviously corresponding to unit membranes (although a three-layered structure has never been demonstrated on macronuclear envelope material). The outer and the inner membranes are separated by a perinuclear space. The envelope is perforated by numerous pores, 400 to 450 Å in diameter (Fig. 3A, B; see also Figs. 4, 5, 8). At the pore edges the inner membrane is, as usual, continuous with the outer one. On tangential sections the pores appear as dark circles, the so-called annuli (Fig. 3C). In *Nassula ornata*[201] and *Ophryoglena bacterocaryon*[207] central granules, 150 to 200 Å in diameter, may be seen in the center of each annulus; their nature remains obscure.

Under the light microscope, the macronuclear envelope in *Nassula ornata* appears rather thick and clearly basophilic, the basophilia depending on presence of RNA.[192] Electron microscopy shows that this basophilia is probably connected not with the nuclear envelope proper but with a peculiar perinuclear layer of dense cytoplasm, about 0.25 μ thick, which adheres to the outer side of the nuclear envelope (Fig. 3A–C). This layer is a plexus of fine channels, bound with single membranes, and contains many ribosomes.[201]

Electron micrographs often show signs of lability of the macronuclear envelope. In *Nassula ornata*[201] protrusions of the outer membrane of the nuclear envelope extend into the perinuclear layer. These blebs seem to

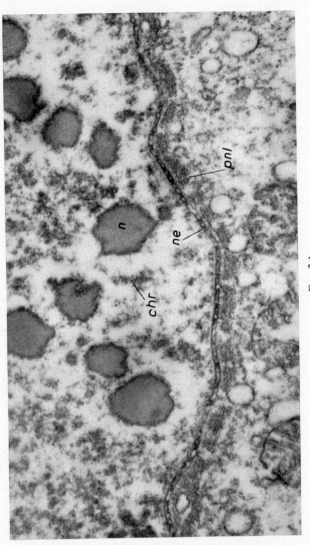

Fig. 3 A

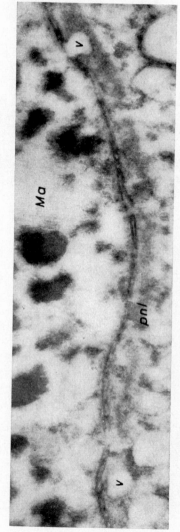

Fig. 3 B

Fig. 3. Ultrastructure of the macronuclear envelope. A—transverse section of the macronuclear envelope of *Nassula ornata*, × 24,000 (original). B—blebbing of the outer macronuclear membrane in *Nassula*, × 41,500 (original). C—annuli in an oblique section of the macronuclear envelope of *Nassula*, lead citrate staining, × 29,000; after Raikov.[201] D—blebbing of both macronuclear membranes in *Ichthyophthirius*, × 20,000 (original by T. N. Mosevich). *Ma*—macronucleus, *n*—nucleoli, *chr*—macronuclear chromatin threads, *ne*—macronuclear envelope, *pnl*—perinuclear cytoplasmic layer, *v*—vacuoles separating from the outer membrane.

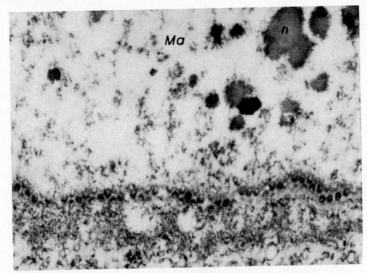

FIG. 3 C

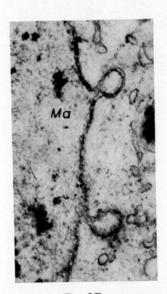

FIG. 3 D

separate, forming vacuoles (Fig. 3 B). The latter are bound with a single membrane carrying ribosomes on its outer surface, and are identical with vacuoles of the granular endoplasmic reticulum. In *Mesnilella trispiculata* granules of unknown nature, 800 to 900 Å in diameter, appear in the peri-nuclear space and then in blebs separating from the outer macronuclear membrane.[186] In *Ichthyophthirius multifiliis* the blebbing process involves both membranes of the macronuclear envelope,[152] resulting in separation of small vesicles bound with a double membrane (Fig. 3D).

Direct continuity of the membranes of the macronuclear envelope with those of the endoplasmic reticulum channels have been observed in rare cases only,[142] e.g., in *Paramecium caudatum* (Fig. 4). Far more frequently this connection seems to be a dynamic one and to express itself in separation of vacuoles of the endoplasmic reticulum from the outer membrane of the macronucleus.

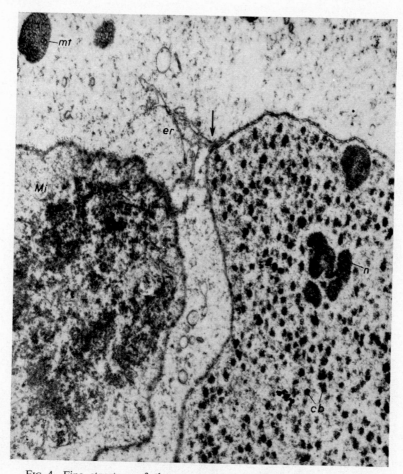

FIG. 4. Fine structure of the macronucleus of *Paramecium caudatum*. × 24,000 (original by V. F. Mashansky and L. N. Vinnichenko). The macronucleus contains chromatin bodies (*cb*) and nucleoli (*n*); the *arrow* indicates connection of the outer macronuclear membrane and the endoplasmic reticulum channels (*er*); micronucleus at left (*Mi*); *mt*—mitochondrion.

Very little is known about permeability of the macronuclear envelope. According to Dass and Devi[33] the envelope of the *Spirostomum* macronucleus is permeable to ribonuclease, a protein with molecular weight about 13,000. It is not known whether the RNase molecules penetrate through pores of the nuclear envelope.

B. CHROMATIN ELEMENTS

Even the first Feulgen reaction studies of ciliates[108, 205, 296] showed that in almost all forms investigated the macronucleus displays a sharply positive nucleal reaction. Numerous later studies invariably confirmed

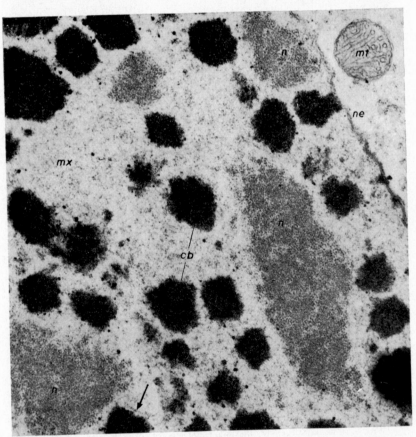

FIG. 5. Ultrastructure of the macronucleus of *Euplotes eurystomus.* × 24,000, lanthanum acetate and uranyl acetate staining. After Kluss.[134] Note ribosome-like granules in the nucleoli (*n*), fibrillar structure of the chromatin bodies (*cb*), and fibrils of the nuclear matrix (*mx*); coiled fibril at *arrow; ne*—nuclear envelope, *mt*—mitochondrion.

this[†] so that at present the conspicuously high DNA content of the macronuclei may be considered as a firmly established fact. Under the light microscope the macronuclear chromatin usually appears to consist of densely packed small (less than 1 μ) granules which stain brightly with the Feulgen reaction and uniformly fill the whole nucleus. The macronuclear chromatin of several (but not all) ciliate species proved to contain not only DNA but also RNA. For example, a high RNA content has been found by Moses[150] in the macronucleus of *Paramecium caudatum*.

The protein components of the macronuclear chromatin are represented mainly by basic proteins of the histone type, which stain with fast green at high pH.[1, 64, 192, 257] The chromatin is also rich in arginine.[210] The question whether it contains non-histone proteins is not yet sufficiently investigated. On one hand, Fauré-Fremiet[64] did not find them in the chromatin granules of the macronucleus of *Dysteria*, but on the other hand, the total content of non-histone proteins in the macronucleus of *Paramecium* is so high[150] that their at least partial localization in the chromatin may be supposed.

Electron microscopy of the macronuclei shows that in most species two types of intranuclear bodies can be distinguished (Figs. 4, 5, 8): the smaller, compact, electron-dense elements ("small bodies"), and the larger elements, usually of granular ultrastructure ("large bodies").[58, 59, 67, 134, 142, 213, 217, 219, 220, 269, 294] Neither the "small" bodies, nor the "large" are bound by any membranes. The "small" bodies are by far more numerous; their size ranges from 0.05 to 1 μ, usually about 0.1 to 0.2 μ; they probably correspond to chromatin elements while the "large" bodies seem to be nucleoli. The "small" bodies usually have an irregular shape (Figs. 4, 5, 8); often one gets the impression that they are sections of threadlike or rod-like structures (e.g., in *Tetrahymena pyriformis*—Fig. 36A, C). In other cases the chromatin ("small") bodies have more regular outlines—for instance, in *Tokophrya infusionum* (Fig. 6A, B). The identity of these bodies with Feulgen-positive chromatin granules visible under the light microscope has been shown in the latter species by direct comparison of electron micrographs with Feulgen stained light microscopical sections;[220] this was possible because the chromatin bodies are very big in this species. In *Tetrahymena*, Gorovsky[300] demonstrated by means of electron microscopic cytochemistry that the "small" bodies contain DNA. The presence of DNA in the "small" bodies of the macronucleus of *Paramecium caudatum* and *P. aurelia* has been demonstrated by the following experiment. Starvation or ultraviolet irradiation is followed by a concentration of the nucleoli in the center of the macronucleus, while the Feulgen-positive material remains at its periphery. Electron microscopy of such macronuclei shows that the

† As already pointed out above, we leave aside here the lower ciliates with diploid macronuclei.

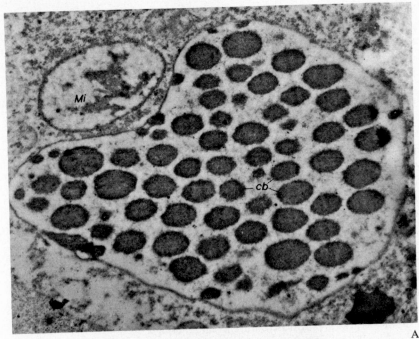

A

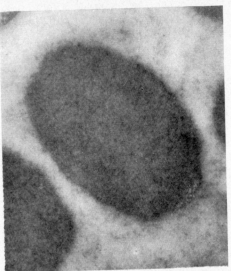

B

FIG. 6. Ultrastructure of the macronucleus of *Tokophrya infusionum*. A—General view showing large macronuclear chromatin bodies (*cb*); micronucleus (*Mi*) at upper left; × 8100. B—single chromatin body at higher magnification (× 55,000). C—longitudinal section through a honey-comb structure in the macronucleus of a senile animal (× 43,000). A and B after Rudzinska,[219] C after Rudzinska and Porter.[220]

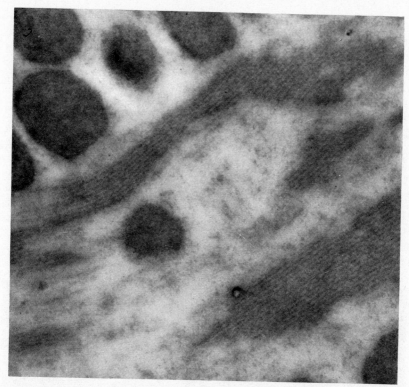

FIG. 6C

"small" bodies are now localized in the Feulgen-positive zone only, and the agglomeration of Feulgen-negative RNA-containing nucleoli corresponds in electron micrographs to a mass of "large" bodies.[41, 142] The opposite view, according to which DNA might be localized in the "large" bodies of the *Paramecium* macronucleus,[112] is now abandoned by its authors.[113]

When the electron microscopical resolution is sufficiently high, it is possible to see that the macronuclear chromatin bodies are formed of densely packed twisted microfibrils of about 100 Å in diameter (Figs. 5, 6B, 8B). This has been shown in *Euplotes*,[67, 134] *Tokophrya*,[219] and *Paramecium*.[142] Thus, the fine structure of the chromatin bodies proves to be like that of chromosomes: the main structural component of the latter is also represented by 100 Å thick fibrils consisting of DNA and histone (for reviews see refs. 151, 206). Therefore many investigators[42, 58, 220] are inclined to consider the chromatin ("small") bodies as macronuclear chromosomes.

The chromatin bodies of the macronucleus of *Tokophrya* undergo interesting changes in old individuals and in the overfed.[217, 219, 220] The size of the chromatin bodies strongly increases and many of them become hollow; later on, several bodies fuse into polymorphous chromatin masses which show a particular ultrastructure: long parallel tubes filled with less electron-dense material, resembling to some extent a honeycomb. In longitudinal sections (Fig. 6C) the walls of the tubes look like parallel lines spaced at 230 Å. The significance of this structure remains unknown; perhaps it might be related to degenerative changes of the macronuclear chromatin involving a transition of the latter into a paracrystalline state.

In certain ciliates the structure of the macronuclear chromatin differs somewhat from that just described. In *Blepharisma intermedium* and *Spirostomum ambiguum*, according to Seshachar,[243, 305] the macronucleus contains no small chromatin bodies but distinct thread-like structures, 0.05 to 0.2 μ thick, which become sectioned in various directions (Fig. 7A). This is also the case in *Blepharisma undulans*.[302] The fine structure of these threads is, however, the same as that of chromatin bodies; they are composed of 100–150 Å thick microfibrils. Seshachar considers these structures to be macronuclear chromosomes; with the aid of centrifugation or cyanide treatment he succeeded in obtaining bundles of very fine Feulgen-positive fibers

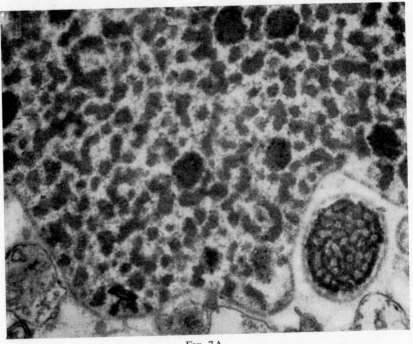

FIG. 7A

FIG. 7. Thread-like chromatin structures in the macronucleus of *Blepharisma intermedium*. A—electron micrograph; micronucleus at lower right; × 16,000 (original by B. R. Seshachar). B—photomicrograph of bundles of chromatin threads isolated after 0.05 M KCN treatment, Feulgen staining, × 520; after Seshachar.[243]

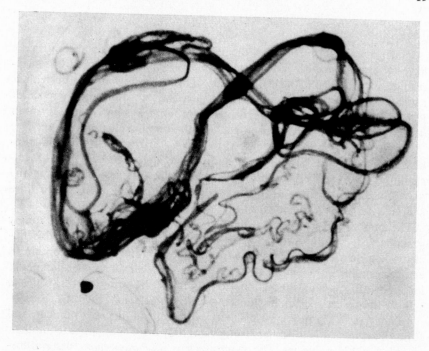

FIG. 7B

from the macronuclei of *Blepharisma* and *Spirostomum* (Fig. 7B). These fibers seem to be identical with the thread-like 0.05 μ to 0.2 μ thick structures observed with the electron microscope. Centrifugation or treatment with a despiralizing agent like cyanide appears to cause straightening of these threads and transformation of the whole macronucleus into a bundle of fibers.

No small bodies are present in the macronucleus of *Nassula ornata*.[201] The chromatin of the *Nassula* macronucleus consists of loose fibrillar and granular material; however, sections of threads, about 0.1 μ thick, are discernible in it (Fig. 3A). The latter threads are bundles of 100 Å thick microfibrils similar to those in the small bodies of macronuclei of other ciliates. But in *Nassula* they are considerably more loosely packed.

Another type of macronuclear structure was recently found by Jurand and Bomford[301] in the parasitic suctorian *Podophrya parameciorum*. The center of the macronucleus is occupied here by a large nucleolus with radial "spokes". Large strips of Feulgen-positive electron-dense material are radially arranged in the peripheral part of the macronucleus (between the nucleolar "spokes"). These strips are as dense as the usual "small" bodies but are much larger. They are also larger than micronuclear chromosomes of *Podophrya*.

C. Nucleoli

Under the light microscope the nucleoli of the macronucleus usually have an appearance of Feulgen-negative basophilic bodies (Fig. 2) far exceeding in size the chromatin granules. The basophilia of the nucleoli is usually completely destroyed with ribonuclease, indicating the presence of RNA. With this method, RNA in high concentrations has invariably been demonstrated in the macronuclear nucleoli of numerous ciliate species.[56,153, 192, 208, 209, 233, 257] In addition to RNA, a great quantity of non-histone protein can always be demonstrated cytochemically in the nucleoli.[64, 192, 257] The question of the presence of basic proteins in the macronuclear nucleoli is not yet solved; probably there is no [257] or little histone type protein there.

The number and size of the nucleoli in the macronucleus (Fig. 2) is strongly variable.[119, 296] In rare cases no nucleoli have been found in this nucleus—e.g., in *Stentor*.[282] In some species, the macronucleus may contain an enormous number of tiny nucleoli (Fig. 2A), in others, a smaller number of larger, usually polymorphous nucleoli (Fig. 2B). In certain forms (*Colpoda steinii*) the macronucleus has one big central nucleolus (Fig. 2F).

In relation to the physiological state of the animal, the size, number, and form of the nucleoli may differ strongly not only from one species to another, but also within a species. The macronucleus of *Paramecium bursaria* normally (Fig. 2C) contains many small nucleoli, but during starvation (Fig. 2D) the latter fuse into several large vacuolated masses.[56] Fusion of nucleoli into larger aggregates has also been reported in other *Paramecium* species (*P. caudatum, P. aurelia*) during starvation [92] and ultraviolet irradiation.[125] Small nucleoli of the macronucleus of *Tetrahymena pyriformis*, which are characteristic of the logarithmic growth phase of the culture, fuse into larger bodies during the stationary phase.[20] In *Telotrochidium* nucleoli appear in the macronucleus only during the period of cyst formation.[44]

The nucleolar apparatus of the macronucleus reacts not only to long-lasting influences, such as prolonged starvation, but also undergoes definite cyclical changes even with the usual daily feeding. As shown by Vivier with the light [277] and the electron [279] microscopes, the macronuclear nucleoli of *Paramecium caudatum* before feeding are small, numerous, and comparatively simple in shape (Fig. 8A). Soon after feeding they fuse groupwise into larger aggregates of complex shape (Fig. 8B). These complex nucleoli disintegrate again into simple ones 9 to 18 hours later.

Two main submicroscopic components have been demonstrated electron microscopically in the nucleoli ("large bodies") of the macronucleus: granules about 150–200 Å in diameter, resembling cytoplasmic ribosomes, and densely packed thin fibrils of about 50 Å in diameter. The interrelation of these two components may be quite various. In some species the granular component predominates (Fig. 5) while the fibrils are almost or completely

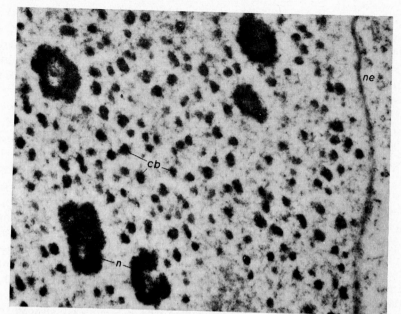

FIG. 8 A

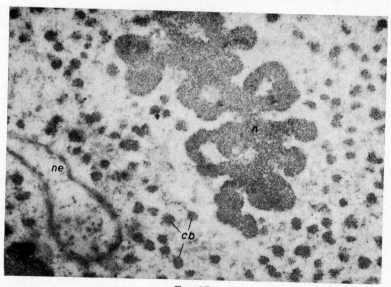

FIG. 8 B

FIG. 8. Ultrastructural changes of macronuclear nucleoli in *Paramecium caudatum* in relation to feeding. × 24,000. After Vivier.[279] A—simple nucleoli (*n*) before feeding; B—formation of complex nucleoli (*n*) by agglomeration of simple ones several hours after feeding; *cb*—chromatin bodies, *ne*—nuclear envelope.

invisible [*Haptophrya plethodonis*,[183] *Euplotes eurystomus*[134]]. In other forms the nucleoli are mainly fibrillar [*Blepharisma*[243]]. In still other ciliates both components are visible: in *Mesnilella trispiculata* the peripheral parts of the nucleoli consist of fibrils and the central parts of ribosome-like granules.[186] In *Tetrahymena pyriformis* the components have the opposite localization: the nucleolar cortex of granules, and the core of fibrils.[20, 299, 300] In *Nassula ornata*, ribosome-like granules are at the nucleolar periphery while the core appears homogeneous (Figs. 3A, C; 26B; 27), although some micrographs suggest that the core consists of a mass of densely packed fibrils.[201]

Two types of macronuclear nucleoli may be distinguished electron microscopically, the compact and the reticular, with all transition states between them. Nucleoli of the compact type are characterized by a relatively simple form and by absence of strong vacuolization (Figs. 3A, C; 5; 7A); their centers are often occupied by single vacuoles, or they assume a cup-like form, as in *Paramecium* (Figs. 8A, 9). Reticular nucleoli are characterized by considerable vacuolization, by a complex, frequently branched form, and by a more loose structure (Fig. 8B). They are usually much larger than the compact nucleoli.

Typical compact nucleoli have been described in *Haptophrya gigantea*[185] and *Ophryoglena bacterocaryon*,[207] typical reticular nucleoli in *Anoplophrya commune*.[184] Adopting this classification, we must nevertheless bear in mind that macronuclear nucleoli are extremely labile structures, and that a transition from compact nucleoli to reticular ones and the reverse are both possible within a few hours (Fig. 8A, B).

The nucleoli sometimes come into close contact with the macronuclear envelope. In *Tetrahymena* (Fig. 36A, C) the cup-like nucleoli are usually localized just beneath the envelope.[20, 59, 215, 299] A similar contact has also been found in *Haptophrya*.[183]

D. KARYOLYMPH

As mentioned above, in the majority of macronuclei the karyolymph is almost invisible under the light microscope: these nuclei seem to be entirely filled with chromatin granules and nucleoli. However, in species with less chromatin in the macronucleus, e.g., in *Colpoda steinii* (Fig. 2F), the karyolymph can be discerned as a homogeneous or a slightly structured (after fixation) Feulgen-negative matrix surrounding the chromatin elements. In electron micrographs this matrix can be seen in practically every macronucleus. It fills the spaces between chromatin bodies and usually looks like a reticulum of very fine (less than 100 Å) twisted fibrils, probably protein in nature (Figs. 4, 5, 8). At many points the matrix fibrils can be seen to enter both the chromatin bodies and the nucleoli, thus interconnecting all structural elements of the macronucleus (Figs. 5, 8). In the macronucleus of

Euplotes, Kluss[134] found helical fibrils of unknown nature, embedded in the matrix (Fig. 5, arrow).

Little is known of the chemical composition of the macronuclear karyolymph. It seems to be mainly protein.† Until now, no work has involved the isolation of chromatin, or nucleolar, or karyolymph fractions from homogenized macronuclei. The exact localization of macronuclear enzymes, for example, is unknown; on grounds of pure analogy with metazoan nuclei they may be supposed to be localized in the karyolymph.

Of the cell enzymes only phosphatases have been revealed in the macronucleus and these results, obtained with cytochemical methods only, are rather contradictory. Alkaline and acid phosphatases have been repeatedly found in macronuclei of various ciliates,[154] but these results were obtained with the Gomori reaction, which is likely to give diffusion artifacts, and the matter needs reinvestigation. With the azo coupling method no alkaline phosphatase could be found in the macronucleus of *Tetrahymena*, but ATPase was discovered there.[68] Negative reaction for acid phosphatase in the macronucleus of *Nyctotherus cordiformis*, observed in winter, changes to positive in summer.[236] Other macronuclear enzymes remain unstudied.

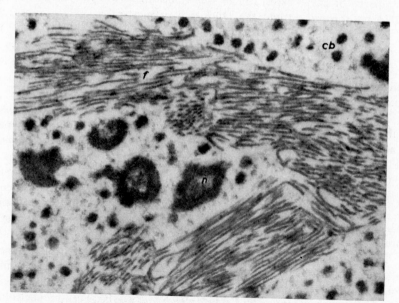

FIG. 9. Fibrillar inclusions of unknown nature (*f*) in the macronucleus of *Paramecium caudatum*; *cb*—chromatin bodies, *n*—nucleoli. Electron micrograph, × 24,000. After Vivier and André.[280]

† Peculiar carbohydrate-protein bodies, about 1 μ large, were recently found in the karyolymph of the macronucleus of *Blepharisma*.[302]

Completely apart stands the unusual structure observed by Vivier and André[280] in the karyolymph of the macronucleus in certain strains of *Paramecium caudatum*. During many generations (for more than 4 years) the macronuclei contained strange Feulgen-negative zones. Electron microscopy showed the karyolymph of these macronuclei to contain large bundles of parallel, approximately 250 Å thick fibers (Fig. 9). Unlike the fibrils normally appearing during macronuclear division (see below, p. 59), these fibers are not tubular, but solid. The fiber bundles are pyroninophilic, but their basophilia is RNase-resistant. They give positive reactions for total protein and negative ones for basic proteins. Possibly these fibers are intranuclear parasites.

3. Homomerous and Heteromerous Macronuclei

According to their internal structure, polyploid macronuclei of the ciliates can be easily divided into two large groups: the *homomerous* and the *heteromerous*. The above description of the macronuclear structural components refers mainly to homomerous macronuclei; in these there is no differentiation into sharply different zones. But in the heteromerous macronuclei (Fig. 10) two parts, or karyomeres, can be clearly distinguished: the comparatively DNA-poor *paramere* and the DNA-rich *orthomere*.

A. STRUCTURAL TYPES OF HOMOMEROUS MACRONUCLEI

The homomerous macronuclei are characteristic of the vast majority of ciliates. The variety of their outer morphology has been discussed above (p. 5). Their internal organization is also various.

The most widespread type of homomerous macronuclei is the most variable in outer shape; all macronuclei shown in Fig. 1 belong to this type. Their chromatin and nucleoli are more or less uniformly distributed (Fig. 2A–C).

Other types of homomerous macronuclei occur more rarely, only in some specialized taxa or even in single species. For example, the macronucleus of *Prorodon teres* (Fig. 2E) contains a central condensation of chromatin which is sharply Feulgen-positive and devoid of nucleoli. The latter are present only in the peripheral region of the macronucleus.[119]

The macronuclei of most members of the family Colpodidae deviate rather strongly from the main type of homomerous macronuclei. In this family there are at least three aberrant patterns of the macronuclear structure. The first one is represented by *Colpoda steinii* with one large central nucleolus and peripheral chromatin granules (Fig. 2F). The second and most common pattern[17, 124] differs in the lobed form of the central nucleolus and the irregular trabeculae of the peripheral chromatin (Fig. 2G). However, it has been shown electron microscopically that the lobed nucleolus of *Colpoda cucullus* is in reality a dense group of many subunits.[121] The third pattern, the most aberrant one, occurs in the macronucleus of *Woodruffia metabolica*.[61, 109] Here all chromatin elements are united into two ribbon-like bands embedded in the Feulgen-negative "matrix" of the macronucleus.

B. STRUCTURE OF HETEROMEROUS MACRONUCLEI

Heteromerous macronuclei characterize only one specialized branch of Holotricha, which leads from the family Chlamydodontidae through Dysteriidae to the order Chonotrichida.[43, 64] Two structural patterns of heteromerous macronuclei are obvious: that with juxtaposed orthomere and paramere (Fig. 10A), and that with concentric disposition of the karyomeres and complete encircling of the paramere by the orthomere (Fig. 10B). The paramere and the orthomere are always well delimited from each other, although electron microscopy failed to show any separating membrane.[116]

The structure and cytochemistry of the heteromerous macronucleus have been studied most thoroughly in *Dysteria monostyla* (Fig. 10A) by Fauré-Fremiet,[64] who also introduced the terms "heteromerous", "orthomere", and "paramere". The orthomere in this species lies behind the paramere, and appears to be filled with a mass of Feulgen-positive granules (or "DNA-microsomes", according to Fauré-Fremiet). Embedded in them, especially

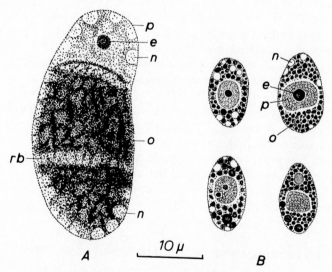

FIG. 10. Structure of heteromerous macronuclei. Feulgen staining, × 1800. A—macronucleus of the juxtaposed type of *Dysteria monostyla;* redrawn after a photomicrograph of Fauré-Fremiet.[64] B—macronuclei of the concentric type of *Chilodonella cucullus:* variations of the endosome; after Reichenow. [205] O—orthomere, *p*—paramere, *e*—endosome, *n*—nucleoli, *rb*—reorganization band.

at the nuclear periphery, are Feulgen-negative nucleoli. The nucleoli contain RNA and non-histone proteins, while basic proteins are confined to the "DNA-microsomes". Thus the structure of the orthomere is basically the same as that of homomerous macronuclei. In most nuclei the orthomere is crossed by a faintly Feulgen-positive reorganization band (Fig. 10A, rb), which will be discussed below (p. 44).

The structure of the paramere is much more aberrant. In living animals it appears homogeneous, its center occupied by a small body giving a bright Feulgen reaction—the so-called endosome (Fig. 10A, e). The periphery of the paramere contains nucleoli. With Feulgen the matrix of the paramere stains faintly and diffusely; no "DNA-microsomes" are present in this part of the nucleus. The paramere contains much non-histone protein.

Basically, the heteromerous macronucleus of the juxtaposed type found in *Spirochona* has the same structure.[270] The macronucleus of *Chlamydodon pedarius*, of the same type, differs at the light microscopical level only by the structure of its orthomere; instead of "DNA-microsomes", it contains fine filaments composing a Feulgen-positive network.[114, 115] The macronucleus of this species is presently the only one among heteromerous macronuclei which has been investigated electron microscopically,[116] unfortunately with a relatively low resolution. The filaments of the orthomere proved to be about 0.1 μ thick and showed signs of coiling. Kaneda[116] interpreted these filaments as chromonemata. They seem to consist of 100–150 Å thick microfibrils. The matrix of the paramere is composed of interlacing 250 to 300 Å thick threads. The endosome is formed by the same threads, more densely packed; the threads seem to be continuous with those of the matrix. Whether DNA is localized in these threads remains unknown.

The best studied heteromerous macronucleus of the concentric type is that of *Chilodonella*.[140, 141, 205, 239, 240, 303] The structure of its karyomeres is practically the same as that in macronuclei of the juxtaposed type. The peripheral orthomere is filled with Feulgen-positive chromatin grains (Fig. 10B) and contains some basophilic nucleoli. The central paramere is faintly and diffusely Feulgen-positive. In most cases it contains a brightly Feulgen-positive endosome lying at its center or displaced to one side (Fig. 10B, e). The presence of the endosome seems to depend on the stage of the division cycle (p. 63).

III. DEVELOPMENT OF THE MACRONUCLEAR ANLAGE

A study of the history of the development of the adult macronucleus is essential to an understanding of its structure. It is well-known that after conjugation or autogamy the macronucleus usually develops from a division product of the diploid synkaryon (more rarely of a haploid hemikaryon). The general pattern of nuclear behavior in the exconjugants is considered elsewhere (Vol. 4). In the present section we are interested mainly with changes in the internal structure of the macronuclear anlage during its development.

In spite of considerable diversity in the course of development of the macronuclear anlage in various ciliate species, four main stages of its development may be established as expressed in some form in most of the species investigated. Rarely, one of the stages may fall out completely or become poorly pronounced. At the first stage chromosomes appear in the anlage; at the second stage the chromosomes undergo endomitosis leading to polyploidy (or sometimes become polytene as a result of endoduplication); at the third stage the chromosomes become despiralized, and the anlage acquires a vesicular appearance; finally, at the fourth stage, polyploidization recommences, nucleoli appear, and the anlage acquires the form of the adult macronucleus.

1. Early Stages

In almost all forms studied the early stages of macronuclear development proceed uniformly, strongly resembling a mitotic prophase (Figs. 11A; 12A, B). Very thin, thread-like, tangled chromosomes appear, causing this stage to be often called the spireme stage [Stentor,[156] Euplotes,[274] Bursaria,[172] Nyctotherus,[72, 288] Ephelota,[74, 78] Stylonychia,[5] and others]. Sometimes the chromosomes of this stage are longitudinally split, looking like double parallel threads [Chilodonella,[141] Climacostomum,[168] Fabrea[60]].

Later on the chromosomes usually shorten and become well delimited from each other, as in Ephelota (Fig. 12C) or Stylonychia.[5, 74, 78] In other cases no shortening occurs but the spireme threads fragment into what are probably small chromosomes arranged in a chain-like manner (Fig. 11B, C). This suggests that in these forms the spireme threads are linear aggregates of several chromosomes, and not single chromosomes [Bursaria,[172] Climacostomum[168]].

Finally, in a small number of ciliates the stage of threadlike chromosomes (spireme) is absent [Spirochona,[270] Vorticella[155]].

2. Polyploidization Stage

In many ciliates the condensed chromosomes, which appear by the end of the stage described above, start autonomous endomitotic reproduction. In Bursaria, Poljansky[172] succeeded in observing two rapidly successive endomitotic cycles. During the first cycle single chromosomes of the macronuclear anlage split longitudinally, forming "dyads" (Fig. 11D, E), and during the second cycle the "dyads" transform into "tetrads" (F). But the process goes no further: the "tetrads" begin to distort, some of them fuse into a Feulgen-positive karyosome (G), while others gradually disappear (H).

2*

In the macronuclear anlage of *Ephelota*, Grell[74, 78] demonstrated that single chromosomes undergo at least three successive endomitotic duplications. The chromosomes here are longer than in *Bursaria*, and their longitudinal splitting is more distinct (Fig. 12D). After the second endomitotic cycle, bundles of four parallel chromosomes are formed (Fig. 13), and after the third cycle there are approximately 30 bundles of eight chromosomes each (Fig. 12E). Later some of the chromosome bundles of this species also fuse into a chromatin karyosome, while some disappear (F).

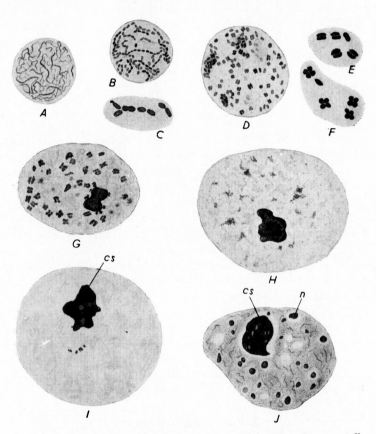

FIG. 11. Development of macronuclear anlagen in *Bursaria truncatella*. After Poljansky.[172] A—spireme stage; B—fragmentation of spireme threads into chromosomes; C—chromosome chains at higher magnification; D—chromosome splitting into dyads and tetrads; E, F—dyads and tetrads at higher magnification; G—deformation of dyads and tetrads, appearance of a chromatin karyosome; H—disappearance of dyads and tetrads; I—achromatic (karyosomal) stage; J—appearance of chromatin and nucleoli in the anlage of a 10-day-old exconjugant. Sections; A, B, D and G–J—× 1100; C, E and F—× 3170; A–I—iron hematoxylin, J—methyl green–pyronin; *cs*—karyosome, *n*—nucleoli.

Separate stages of endomitotic duplication of single chromosomes of the macronuclear anlage have also been observed in a number of other ciliates [*Stentor*,[156] *Climacostomum*,[168] *Fabrea*,[60] etc.].

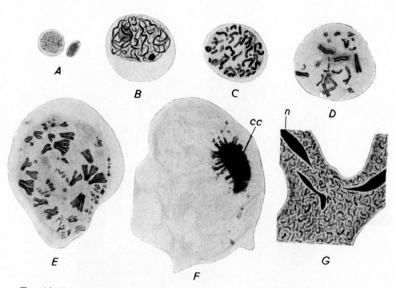

FIG. 12. Development of the macronuclear anlage in *Ephelota gemmipara*. After Grell.[74,78] A—early spireme stage (micronucleus at right), B— spireme stage, C—condensation of chromosomes, D—polyploidization stage (first endomitosis), E—bundles of eight chromosomes after the third endomitosis, F—achromatic stage with a collective chromocenter (*cc*), G—part of the macronuclear anlage during the formative phase: appearance of nucleoli (*n*) and of chromosomes. Iron hematoxylin stained sections, × 1250.

Quite recently the existence of another type of chromosome behavior in the macronuclear anlage—that of polytenization of its chromosomes— has been discovered. This phenomenon was found independently and almost simultaneously by Golikowa[72] in *Nyctotherus cordiformis*, by Ammermann[5] in *Stylonychia mytilus*, and by Alonso and Pérez-Silva[2, 3] in *Stylonychia muscorum* and some other Oxytrichidae.

In *Nyctotherus cordiformis* there is no shortening of the thread-like chromosomes of the early macronuclear anlage. On the contrary, the spireme thread remains very long, and only two free ends of it may be found in the ball. On this ground Golikowa concludes that all the chromosomes of the macronuclear anlage become connected end-to-end into one composite chromosome. Later on, the anlage grows and the spireme thread gradually becomes thicker. This stage had been observed by Wichterman[288] and called by him a "spireme-ball", but he failed to give it a correct interpretation.

Golikowa found that the thick spireme thread displays a pattern of alternating transverse Feulgen-positive and Feulgen-negative bands (Fig. 14 A), very similar to the banding of the giant salivary gland chromosomes of Diptera. She succeeded in showing that the dark bands consist of chromomeres lying in one plane. Thus the macronuclear anlage of *Nyctotherus*

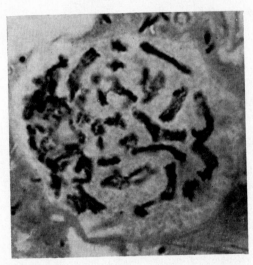

FIG. 13. Polyploidization stage of the macronuclear anlage in *Ephelota:* bundles of four endomitotic chromosomes in each. × 1300. After Grell.[78]

seems to contain only one giant polytene chromosome, formed by a chain-like connection of all the chromosomes of the initial genome and by subsequent polytenization. This stage lasts in *Nyctotherus* for more than two weeks. After that, the giant chromosome appears to split longitudinally into numerous non-polytene chromosomes.

In *Stylonychia mytilus*,[5] unlike *Nyctotherus*, the chromosomes of the early spireme are single. A phase of condensation follows, the chromosomes becoming compact and situated at the periphery of the anlage. At this stage, the number of chromosomes still remains unchanged: it is diploid (~250) in anlagen developing from diploid synkarya, and haploid (~100–150) in anlagen originating from haploid hemikarya. But the DNA content of the anlage is already four times the initial content, which points toward a beginning polytenization of the chromosomes. Later, the chromosomes despiralize, forming threads, and probably uniting end-to-end into one or two chains, i.e., composite chromosomes. In any case, at later stages very few free ends of the thread can be found (just as in *Nyctotherus*). The composite chromosomes become polytene and ribbon-like, with transverse banding (Fig. 14 B). At this stage the DNA content of the macronuclear anlage is 14 times higher than that of the micronucleus. There is no RNA in the giant chromosomes. The polytene chromosomes are most strongly developed in anlagen originating from haploid hemikarya (Fig. 14B).

In *Stylonychia muscorum*, no detailed description of the macronuclear anlagen development has so far been published. Here also the giant polytene

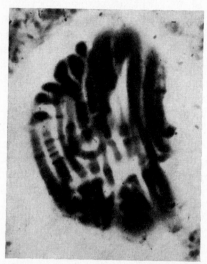

FIG. 14A

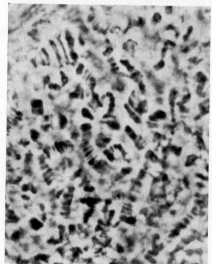

FIG. 14B

FIG. 14. Polytene chromosomes in developing macronuclei. A—section through the macronuclear anlage of *Nyctotherus cordiformis*, iron hematoxylin staining, × 2000; after Golikowa.[72] B—part of a macronuclear anlage of *Stylonychia mytilus* developing from a haploid hemikaryon; phase contrast, × 1700; after Ammermann.[5]

chromosomes are ribbon-like, with transverse bands.[3] But the number of polytene chromosomes in this species is 50–60; moreover, the chromosomes differ in length and banding pattern. This suggests that in *S. muscorum*, unlike the two species described above, the single chromosomes of the anlage do not unite into composite chromosomes. However, the possibility of artificial fragmentation of the composite chromosomes should not be excluded here, since the authors worked with the squash technique.

Beyond any doubt, polytene chromosomes have been seen in the macronuclear anlagen of some other ciliates without an understanding of their significance. This includes all descriptions of dense balls formed by thick spireme threads in macronuclear anlagen [*Metopus*,[159] *Euplotes*,[274] etc.]. Reinvestigation of these cases is needed.

Finally, there exists a series of ciliates where the polyploidization stage is not morphologically expressed. The chromosomes of the early anlage partially fuse here into a Feulgen-positive karyosome, partially become despiralized and lost in the karyolymph; i.e., the anlage passes directly to the third stage, omitting the second one. Such are, first of all, the species of *Paramecium*,[38, 56, 93, 133, 169, 226] and also *Vorticella campanula*.[155]

3. Achromatic Stage

This stage, sometimes called interphasic or karyosomal, usually follows the polyploidization stage (but in some cases directly follows the spireme stage). During this stage the macronuclear anlage becomes homogeneous, without any visible chromosomes, and stains faintly and diffusely with the Feulgen method. In most cases it contains, however, a sharply Feulgen-positive karyosome (Figs. 11 H, I; 12 F).

In *Bursaria*[172] the transition to the achromatic stage is accompanied by a strong increase in the volume of the anlage. The chromosomal tetrads become gradually distorted and seem to dissolve in the karyolymph (Fig. 11 G, H), except one agglomeration of tetrads (D) which fuses into a Feulgen-positive karyosome (G–I). In the middle of the achromatic stage (I) the matrix of the anlage is practically Feulgen-negative.

Chromatin karyosomes within homogeneous, faintly staining macronuclear anlagen have been described in many ciliates, mainly among Heterotrichida [*Stentor*,[156] *Climacostomum*,[168] *Fabrea*[60]]. In the suctorian *Ephelota*, according to Grell,[74, 78] the endomitotic chromosomes gradually become thinner and disappear, while the karyosome is formed by fusion of certain parts of many chromosomes. The ends of the latter protrude for some time from the surface of the karyosome (Fig. 12 F). Therefore Grell considers the karyosome to be a collective heterochromatic chromocenter, and interprets the disappearance of the chromosomes as their despiralization (i.e., transition to interphase), and not as their destruction.

In *Paramecium bursaria*, the chromosomes of the early anlage omit endomitosis, one end of each chromosome despiralizing and fading in the karyolymph, the other ends fusing into a collective heterochromocenter.[56] In *P. caudatum* the karyosome is formed in a similar way.[93, 133, 226] The karyosome does not exist long in *Paramecium* species; it soon dissolves, and the anlage becomes perfectly homogeneous and very faintly Feulgen-positive. No karyosome is formed in *Vorticella*.[155]

Thus until recently all data were consistent with the assumption that the chromosomes of the macronuclear anlage (a diploid set in forms without polyploidization stage or a polyploid set when the latter is present) pass into interphasic state during the achromatic stage and therefore become invisible, while the heterochromatic regions fuse into the karyosome. More striking are the recent results of Ammermann,[5] who photometrically measured the DNA content during this stage in *Stylonychia mytilus*. As described above, the achromatic stage here is preceded by the stage of polytene chromosomes and the DNA content of the macronuclear anlage is 14 times that of a diploid micronucleus. As the polytene chromosomes fragment into isolated blocks which rapidly disappear, and the anlage enters the achromatic stage (there is no karyosome in *Stylonychia*), its DNA decreases abruptly (approximately to 1/14), thus returning to the level of a diploid micronucleus. The volume of the anlage also decreases during this time. Ammermann tentatively explains this phenomenon by destruction of most of the chromonemata formed during polytenization, only two haploid genomes remaining intact in the macronuclear anlage. The fate of DNA lost by the anlage is not yet known, and therefore no conclusions can be drawn now as to the possible significance of this surprising phenomenon of abortive polytenization. Quantitative studies of the DNA content during the achromatic stage of macronuclear development in other ciliates are also needed.

4. Feulgen-positive Stage

The achromatic stage is followed by a stage of macronuclear anlagen development characterized by several processes occurring simultaneously or in one or another sequence; among these processes are intense DNA synthesis, nucleoli appearance, and transformation of the shape of the anlage into the shape of the mature macronucleus. This stage is also called the formative phase ("Formbildungsphase" of German authors).

The DNA synthesis usually starts throughout the whole volume of the anlage, which becomes distinctly Feulgen-positive and begins to incorporate tritiated thymidine.[12] In some ciliates, the Feulgen-positive karyosome persists to the beginning of this stage, e.g. in *Bursaria* (Fig. 11 J), but it usually is resorbed earlier. Small thread-like chromosomes reappear in the anlagen of certain forms, their number already high (*Ephelota*, Fig. 12 G).

But in most ciliates the chromosomes are not distinct at this stage, the chromatin of the anlage looking homogeneous or finely granular (Fig. 11 J). The DNA synthesis proceeds until the very end of the development of the anlagen, and it is during this stage that the main mass of DNA of the mature macronucleus is synthesized. Some studies have followed the course of the synthesis microphotometrically. The DNA content usually grows steadily, reaching very high values by the end of macronuclear development [*Chilodonella*,[239] *Epistylis*,[246, 247] *Trichodina*,[255] *Paramecium aurelia*[291]].

Changes in volume of the macronuclear anlage are not always parallel with changes in DNA content. For instance, in *Chilodonella* the anlage at first so grows that its DNA concentration diminishes in spite of constant increase in DNA quantity. Then the anlage decreases to the size of the adult macronucleus.[239] A similar phenomenon has been described in *Epistylis articulata* during "regeneration" of the macronucleus from the micronucleus[244, 247] but not during its development after conjugation.[246]

It seems reasonable to expect DNA synthesis at this stage to be accompanied by manifold endomitotic duplication of the chromosomes of the anlage, but this was seldom observed, perhaps due to the small size and poor visibility of the chromosomes. So far only Saito and Sato[226] have succeeded in observing endomitoses during this stage in *Paramecium caudatum*. Interesting enough it is just this species that has no early phase of polyploidization (before the achromatic stage). Ammermann's[5] data on *Stylonychia mytilus* also point to a connection between DNA synthesis and chromosome replication in the late anlagen. After the achromatic phase, the macronuclear anlage becomes stretched, and five pairs of reorganization bands, one after another, pass through it (from the ends towards the middle of the anlage). It is well known that in mature macronuclei reorganization bands are connected with DNA replication in the chromosomal elements (see below, p. 44). Ammermann showed that the passage of each pair of bands through the macronuclear anlage is followed by a doubling of the DNA content, so that by the end of the development the DNA quantity of the anlage is 32 times the diploid quantity (which remained after destruction of the polytene chromosomes). The passage of several pairs of reorganization bands has also been noticed in the macronucleus of *Stylonychia muscorum*.[4]

The nucleoli, containing RNA, usually make their first appearance in the macronuclear anlage either by the very end of the achromatic stage (*Bursaria, Ephelota, Stylonychia*), or at the beginning of the Feulgen-positive stage (Figs. 11 J, 12 G). More rarely they appear in the middle or by the end of the latter (*Climacostomum, Nyctotherus*). Before this, i.e., during the polyploidization stage and all or nearly all the achromatic stage, the anlage contains no RNA.[5, 56, 72, 93, 172]

It is probable that at least the first nucleoli appearing in the anlage are formed by specific chromosomes of each of the genomes of the anlage. For example, in *Paramecium bursaria*, in which no polyploidization stage precedes the achromatic stage, only two nucleoli appear at first in each macronuclear anlage, a number corresponding to the number of haploid genomes.[56] In *Stylonychia mytilus* also, where only two haploid genomes are preserved during the achromatic stage, only two nucleoli are initially formed while in the anlage developing from a haploid hemikaryon only one nucleolus appears.[5] In species where the early stage of polyploidization is pronounced (*Bursaria, Ephelota*, etc.), many nucleoli appear simultaneously in the developing anlage.

According to Ehret and Powers,[57] three successive generations of nucleoli are formed in the macronuclear anlagen of *Paramecium bursaria*. The last generation is the definitive one. Many nucleoli seem to be extruded into the cytoplasm during macronuclear development; this has also been found in *Paramecium putrinum* by Jankowski.[107]

The only published electron microscopical investigation of the macronuclear anlagen development[113] was on *Paramecium aurelia*, and deals mainly with changes in the nucleolar apparatus. Achromatic stage anlagen appear homogeneous until dense bodies appear which then fuse into sponge-like aggregates containing RNA. These disintegrate into the well-known "large bodies" (see p. 20), i.e., definitive macronuclear nucleoli.

During the Feulgen-positive stage, sometimes at its very beginning but more often by its end, the macronuclear anlage begins to acquire the form characteristic of the mature macronucleus. Before this stage, the anlagen in nearly all ciliates are spherical or ellipsoidal. The changes in shape of the growing anlage are of course more pronounced in species with a complicated form of the macronucleus. They may involve longitudinal stretching of the anlage (*Vorticella, Bursaria*), nodulation (*Blepharisma*), branching (*Ephelota*), division into two (*Stylonychia*) or more parts, etc. Sometimes fusion of several anlagen into one macronucleus may also occur at this stage [*Didinium*,[178] *Stentor*,[156] *Climacostomum*,[168] *Fabrea*,[60] *Blepharisma*,[14] etc.]. Cases of fusion of the macronuclear anlage with fragments of the old macronucleus have also been described in several species of *Euplotes*.[66, 203, 274] However, Katashima[120] did not confirm the existence of this phenomenon in *E. harpa*, and Sonneborn[250] failed to obtain genetic evidence for its existence in *E. patella*.

Several conclusions may be drawn from the above. During development of the macronuclear anlagen of most ciliates there are definite signs either of polyploidization proceeding by endomitotic replication of whole chromosomes, or of polytenization of the chromosomes. Probably ciliates have in principle two phases of polyploidization, the primary one (2nd stage of anlagen development, according to our classification), and the secondary one (4th stage), separated by the achromatic stage. The secondary phase is pronounced in all ciliates studied, but the primary phase is often absent; it is absent in *Paramecium* but usually present in Spirotricha. The mode of

2a*

polyploidization during the primary and secondary phases may differ even within a species; for instance, until now polytenization has been described for only the primary phase.

The primary phase of polyploidization is also distinguished by the apparent metabolic inertness of the chromosomes which do not produce RNA or nucleoli. In contrast is the metabolic activity of the chromosomes during the secondary phase when they synthesize RNA and store it in nucleoli. This activation must occur sometime during the achromatic stage. The exact significance of this stage is far from clear, but its invariable presence points toward the assumption that just here some chromosomal transformations must proceed, preparing for the secondary polyploidization phase. In certain cases the achromatic stage may include even the destruction of a number of genomes formed during the primary phase of polyploidization.[5]

IV. EVIDENCE FOR POLYPLOIDY AND CHROMOSOMAL STRUCTURE OF THE MACRONUCLEUS

The above examined data on endomitoses and DNA accumulation in developing macronuclear anlagen are clear support for the theory of a highly polyploid macronucleus. This theory was originally advanced in 1941 by Piekarski[171] and Geitler.[70] Sonneborn[250, 251] arrived at the same conclusion on grounds of experimental cytogenetic investigations, especially those concerning macronuclear regeneration. The theory of polyploidy of the macronucleus has been further developed and supplemented in the works of Grell and his students,[75, 77, 82, 88, 90, 99] of Fauré-Fremiet,[62] Poljansky, Raikov,[175, 176, 188, 194, 200] and some other authors. Additional evidence for macronuclear polyploidy are (a) the ability of the macronucleus to regenerate, (b) the high DNA content of adult macronuclei, and (c) the presence therein of numerous endomitotically duplicating chromosomes.

1. Ability of the Macronucleus to Regenerate

The astonishing ability of a small fragment of the macronucleus to regenerate a normal whole has been known since Gruber's and Balbiani's first experiments on merotomy of ciliates (1885–93). This phenomenon is most clearly expressed in forms having, like *Stentor*, a moniliform macronucleus where a single node, approximately 1/10 to 1/20 of the original macronucleus, can regenerate a normal nucleus.[232, 264, 265] The node stretches, grows, and becomes subdivided into several smaller nodes. Later, the size and number of nodes of the regenerated macronucleus becomes normal for the given strain.

In many ciliates, especially among Suctoria and Astomatida, multiple or unequal divisions of the macronucleus occur during budding of the animal (see Fig. 17, p. 43). Each bud receives a fraction of the mother cell's nucleus which, during growth of the bud (or metamorphosis of the swarmer) grows to the size of the mother nucleus. This is also a manifestation of the ability of a small fragment of the macronucleus to regenerate a whole.

Macronuclear regeneration may occur also during conjugation and autogamy,[248, 250] fragments of the old macronucleus developing into both morphologically and genetically normal nuclei. This phenomenon will be considered in more detail below (p. 70, Fig. 32).

The vast majority of nuclei are known to be incapable of repairing any significant damage involving loss of a part of the genome, a consequence of the template type of chromosome reproduction. The regenerating ability of the macronucleus indicates that the fragment capable of regeneration contains at least one complete diploid genome which, by means of repeated endomitoses, reconstructs the whole macronucleus. Since such fragments are very small as compared to the whole macronucleus (about 1/40 in *Paramecium aurelia*), the macronucleus obviously contains many genomes, i.e., is polyploid. According to Sonneborn,[250] the macronucleus may contain a great number of diploid subnuclei capable of autonomous reproduction. According to Grell,[82, 88, 90] the macronucleus is a typical example of a polyenergid nucleus in M. Hartmann's[96, 97] sense, i.e., of a nucleus containing many similar and to a certain degree autonomous subunits.

2. DNA Content of Macronuclei

When it became known that the DNA content of a chromosome set is relatively constant within a species and that the degree of nuclear polyploidy varies directly with the amount of nuclear DNA, attempts at quantitative determination of macronuclear DNA began. These determinations are based on the idea that high quantity of DNA in the macronucleus (as compared to that of the diploid micronucleus of the same species) not only indicates macronuclear polyploidy but also allows determination of degree of polyploidy. However, a certain difficulty remains since ciliate micronuclei are by no means always diploid. As shown by Chen,[27, 27a] they may be heteroploid in various strains of the same species, and may differ in size, chromosome number, and DNA content. In such cases it is very difficult to decide which strain has a diploid micronucleus. This circumstance is naturally a source of error in determination of the polyploidy degree of the macronucleus, usually leading to underestimation of the latter. In *Paramecium* species the micronuclear heteroploidy is especially frequent.[25, 27, 38]

Until now, measurements of the DNA content of infusorian nuclei have been done only by photometrical methods, usually after Feulgen staining. The results of these studies are brought together in Table 1.

Table 1 shows that in all cases the quantity of DNA is many times higher in the macronucleus than in the micronucleus. The degree of polyploidy of the macronucleus may vary in different species over an extremely wide range—

TABLE 1. MEAN RATIO OF DNA CONTENTS OF MACRO- AND MICRONUCLEI, AND MEAN DEGREE OF MACRONUCLEAR POLYPLOIDY IN SOME CILIATES

Species	$\dfrac{\text{DNA of Ma}}{\text{DNA of Mi}}$	Degree of macronuclear polyploidy	References
Paramecium bursaria	8.2	$16\,n$[a]	24
Paramecium putrinum	11.5	$23\,n$[a]	24
Tetrahymena limacis	7.5–45[b]	15–$90\,n$[b]	53
Tetrahymena rostrata	15–45[b]	30–$90\,n$[b]	53
Chilodonella uncinata	32	$64\,n$	239
Stylonychia mytilus	32	$64\,n$	5
Paramecium caudatum	25–30	50–$60\,n$[a]	281
The same	40	$80\,n$[a]	150
The same	64	$128\,n$[a]	15
The same	26, 27, 30, 42, 44, 46, 50, 66, 74, 80[c]	52–$160\,n$[a]	25
Tetrahymena patula	75–450[b]	150–$900\,n$[b]	53
Nassula ornata	115	$230\,n$	202
Nassulopsis elegans	125.5	$251\,n$	199
Euplotes eurystomus	200	$400\,n$	69
Trichodina cottidarum	242, 290, 376, 426, 758[c]	484–$1516\,n$	255
Paramecium calkinsi	280	$560\,n$	24
Metaradiophrya varians	290	$580\,n$	149
Metaradiophyra gigas	330	$660\,n$	149
Paramecium aurelia	430	$860\,n$	290
Paramecium woodruffi	441	$882\,n$	24
Metaradiophyra lubrici	660	$1320\,n$	149
Bursaria truncatella	2620	$5240\,n$	222
Ichthyophthirius multifiliis, mature trophont	6300	$12{,}600\,n$	276
The same, swarmer	24	$48\,n$	276
Spirostomum ambiguum	6575	$13{,}150\,n$	163

[a] Degree of polyploidy possibly underestimated due to micronuclear heteroploidy.
[b] Several ploidy classes within one strain.
[c] Figures for several strains or populations.

from $16\,n$ to more than $13{,}000\,n$. It is practically impossible to find any relation between degree of macronuclear polyploidy and systematic position of the ciliate: within one genus, *Paramecium*, this degree varies from $16\,n$ to $882\,n$, while phylogenetically unrelated forms may have a common degree of polyploidy (*Chilodonella* and *Stylonychia*). In general, the degree of macronuclear polyploidy seems to depend on the relation between volume of cytoplasm and volume of micronucleus. Polyploidization of the developing macronucleus probably stops when the DNA content reaches a certain amount relative to the volume and to the activity of the cytoplasm. The number of endomitoses necessary to reach this DNA level will be the greater the larger the cytoplasmic volume and the smaller and DNA-poorer the initial diploid synkaryon derivate (and consequently the micronucleus). In accordance with this interpretation, we find the highest macronuclear polyploidy degrees in large ciliates having small micronuclei (*Bursaria, Spirostomum*). In forms so far investigated the number of endomitoses during macronuclear development appears to vary from 3 to 12–13.

In most macronuclei, especially in those with high degrees of polyploidy, the number of genomes deviates from the series 16–32–64–128–256–512, etc. Such deviations may follow endomitoses that are asynchronous or that involve only a part of the genomes; such endomitoses seem to occur during late stages of the polyploidization of the macronuclear anlagen. Or the deviation may follow an unequal distribution of DNA during macronuclear division (see p. 58).

The intraspecific variation of the macronuclear polyploidy degree is often very large. Among strains of *Paramecium caudatum* the macronuclear DNA content, according to Cheissin et al.,[25] varies widely. But the quantity of DNA in the micronuclei may also vary from one strain to another, indicating heteroploidy of the micronucleus. According to Blanc,[15] different syngens of *P. caudatum* differ in the absolute quantity of DNA in both macronuclei and micronuclei, but the relation between the DNA contents of the two types of nuclei within all syngens studied is constant. In three species of *Tetrahymena*[53] the amount of DNA in the micronucleus is species-specific while the macronuclei fall into several classes of DNA content: in *T. limacis* the DNA values of different classes are divisible by 15 n, in *T. rostrata* by 30 n, and in *T. patula* by 150 n. Three classes of macronuclear DNA content have also been described in *Paramecium aurelia*.[29]

3. Chromosomes in Mature Macronuclei

The manifold increase in the DNA content of the macronucleus, as compared with the micronucleus, is a serious argument for macronuclear polyploidy. But for complete assurance, it must be shown that the macronuclear DNA is localized in chromosomes and does not represent a special non-chromosomal "trophochromatin". Before 1940–50, a widespread idea held that all chromosomes become destroyed during the achromatic phase of macronuclear anlage development, and that the so-called "secondary chromatin", synthesized after this stage, was non-chromosomal. However, during recent years much evidence has shown that all the chromatin of the mature macronucleus is chromosomal. This conforms to the theory of macronuclear polyploidy and disproves the theory of "trophochromatin".

As shown above (p. 17), electron microscopical studies of the macronuclear chromatin show that DNA-containing "small" bodies have the same ultrastructure as chromosomes; they are composed of 100 Å thick micro-

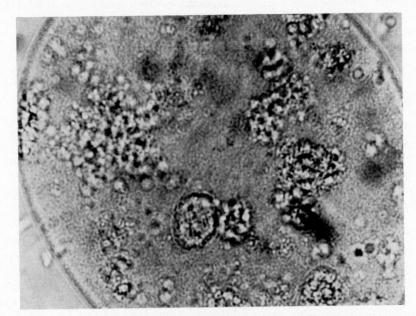

FIG. 15 A

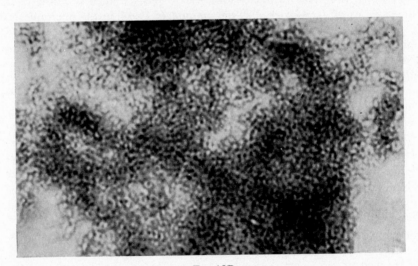

FIG. 15 B

FIG. 15. Chromosomes in the adult macronucleus of *Paramecium bursaria*. After Schwartz.[235] A—tangled thread-like chromosomes in an isolated unfixed and unstained macronucleus, × 1880 (the refringent structures are nucleoli). B—isolated unfixed chromosomes stained with methyl green–pyronin (× 2400).

fibrils. In many views the "small" bodies look like sections of thread-like structures (Fig. 36 A, C); or instead of "small" bodies the macronucleus contains definite filaments resembling despiralized chromosomes (Fig. 7 A). Thus, ultrastructural data do not contradict our picture of the chromosomal structure of the macronucleus.

Under the light microscope, observation of the macronuclear chromosomes is rather difficult; their small diameter, great number, and dense packing usually make the macronuclear chromatin appear granular. Only in some favorable species or with some special methods is fibrillar nature shown. Positively Feulgen-staining threads, interpreted as chromosomes, were first described by Grell[76, 79] in macronuclei of the suctorians *Tachyblaston* and *Tokophrya*, and by Kimball[126] in *Paramecium aurelia*. These threads filled the whole macronucleus; in living *Tokophrya* their coiled structure could be seen.

A detailed study of the macronuclear chromosomes of *Paramecium bursaria* has been carried out by Schwartz.[234, 235] He worked mainly with isolated unfixed macronuclei, treating them with various reagents and enzymes to produce swelling or dissolution of the protein nuclear matrix. In such unstained nuclei a huge number of tangled knotty threads could be seen (Fig. 15 A). They were also present inside the nucleoli. Staining (Fig. 15 B) showed that just these threads contained DNA. During conjugation of amicronucleate paramecia long chromatin strands, resembling polytene chromosomes of colchicinized micronuclei, appear in macronuclei,[235] also arguing for the presence of chromosomes. Finally, the same paper contains the only so far unrefuted description of the formation of micronuclei, capable of mitosis, from small macronuclear fragments during prolonged cultivation of amicronucleate clones. If this astonishing observation is confirmed, it also would argue for the presence of normal chromosomes in the macronucleus.

Thread-like chromosomes containing DNA have been observed by Sato and Saito in macronuclei of *Tetrahymena*,[229] *Paramecium caudatum*,[225,228] *Spirostomum*[227] and *Vorticella*.[224] In *Vorticella* they have been recorded also by Mügge.[155] Rod-like chromosomes have been found by Ruthmann[221] in *Loxophyllum* (Fig. 34). In *Bursaria* long Feulgen-positive threads form the macronuclear chromatin; these threads are oriented parallel to each other and spirally to the long axis of the macronucleus.[223] Chromatin filaments of the orthomere of the heteromerous macronucleus of *Chlamydodon*[114-6] have been described above (p. 26).

These observations seem to provide adequate proof that all macronuclear DNA is bound to chromosomes, and that the macronucleus is highly polyploid.

V. MACRONUCLEAR DIVISION

1. Types of Macronuclear Division

The most widespread type of macronuclear division is a separation into halves (Fig. 16), a division which looks amitotic and for a long time was so considered. With this type of division, daughter macronuclei usually do not differ significantly in either size or DNA content. Two phases of this division can usually be distinguished: stretching (Fig. 16A) and constriction (B). This division is usually preceded by mitosis of the micronucleus (or the micronuclei), and is, as a rule, accompanied by transverse division of the cytoplasm (Fig. 16).

However, the macronucleus is capable of other types of division, with daughter macronuclei much smaller than half of the mother macronucleus growing up to the size of the latter during their subsequent development ("natural regeneration" of the macronucleus). This happens during multiple simultaneous division, when several buds separate from the mother cell at

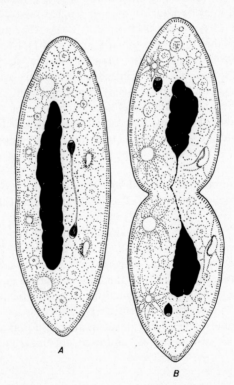

A

B

FIG. 16. Macronuclear division in *Paramecium caudatum*. A—stretching phase, B—constriction phase. Feulgen reaction (original).

the same time, each receiving a branch of the macronucleus (Fig. 17A), and also during successive budding, when buds pinch off one after another (Fig. 17B). Both types are common among Suctoria. Unequal macronuclear division during linear budding, characteristic of Astomatida (Fig. 17C), also belongs to this type.

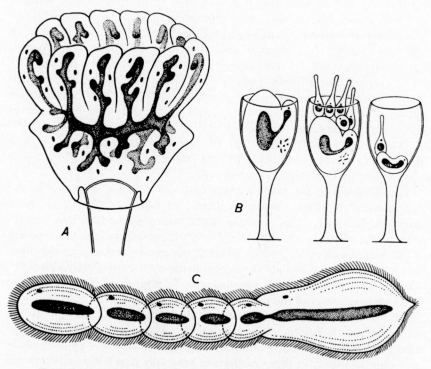

FIG. 17. Unequal and multiple division of the macronucleus. After Grell.[77] A—simultaneous multiple division in *Ephelota gemmipara;* B—successive multiple division in "*Dactylophrya*-stages" of the parasitic suctorian *Tachyblaston ephelotensis;* C—unequal division in *Anoplophrya* (Astomatida).

2. Preparation of the Macronucleus for Division

A. DNA Replication

DNA replication is one of the earliest events preceding macronuclear division. Exactly as in the vast majority of nuclei of other organisms, the synthesis of DNA in the macronucleus always proceeds during the interval between two cell divisions. Usually this interval is divided into three periods: the presynthetic (G_1), the period of DNA synthesis (S), and the postsynthetic (G_2).

During recent years the synthesis of DNA during the macronuclear division cycle has been studied in many ciliates either with techniques of DNA photometry or with autoradiography after incorporation of labeled thymidine. DNA synthesis in the macronucleus and problems of its control are thoroughly examined in the chapter by Prescott and Stone (Vol. 2, Chapter II), and we need only point out some of its more general features.

The S period may occupy various portions of the interval between two macronuclear divisions: at its beginning, in the middle, or near the end. In the first case the G_1 period is very short or even absent [*Tetrahymena pyriformis*, strain HS,[179] *Paramecium trichium*,[95] *Nassulopsis elegans*[199]]. In the second case all three periods, G_1, S, and G_2, are well represented [most strains of *Tetrahymena pyriformis*,[21, 144, 146, 281, 299] *Spathidium spathula*[289]]. In the third case the G_2 period undergoes complete or partial reduction [*Paramecium caudatum*,[26, 281, 297] *P. aurelia*,[13, 127, 128, 290] *Euplotes eurystomus*,[182] *Bursaria truncatella*[222]]. The length of these periods also varies within a species and strain according to culture conditions, and may be changed experimentally.[298, 304]

The S period in the macronucleus may not coincide with that in the micronucleus in either time of beginning of synthesis[146, 182] or in its duration. As a rule, DNA synthesis in the macronucleus lasts much longer than in the micronucleus.[146, 182, 199, 290] Especially long is the S period in the macronucleus of *Stentor*, where it occupies practically all the interdivision interval, the periods G_1 and G_2 being almost completely absent.[94] This phenomenon might be connected with asynchrony of DNA replication in separate genomes of the highly polyploid macronucleus.

Before division the macronuclei of all Hypotrichida, as well as the orthomeres of the heteromerous macronuclei of certain Holotricha, undergo a peculiar reorganization. Faintly staining bands, the so-called reorganization bands, appear in these nuclei and gradually pass completely through them. In *Euplotes*, for instance, two reorganization bands appear simultaneously at the ends of the C-shaped macronucleus (Fig. 18), move to meet each other in the middle of the latter, and then disappear.[274] In *Aspidisca*, however, the direction of movement of the reorganization bands is exactly the opposite.[258] When there are several macronuclei, reorganization bands appear simultaneously in all (Fig. 23A), even if their number exceeds a hundred, as in *Urostyla grandis*.[187]

In heteromerous macronuclei of the juxtaposed type there is only one reorganization band; it appears at the boundary of orthomere and paramere and moves to the free end of the orthomere (Figs. 10A, 28B, C). The paramere undergoes no reorganization.[64, 114, 115, 270]

The structure of the reorganization band has been thoroughly studied by Turner[274] in *Euplotes* (Fig. 19A). It consists of two zones, the forward, homogeneous, rather brightly Feulgen-positive zone (or solution plane), and the rear, very faintly staining zone (or reconstruction plane). Outside the reorganization band, the macronucleus contains chromatin bodies of variable size which disappear in the forward zone. The rear zone is not sharply delimited from the reorganized part of the macronucleus: tiny chromatin granules appear in this zone and gradually grow larger as the reorganization band moves away.

The nucleoli usually disappear in the reorganization band, and the RNA content becomes sharply decreased in the reorganized macronuclear region.[161]

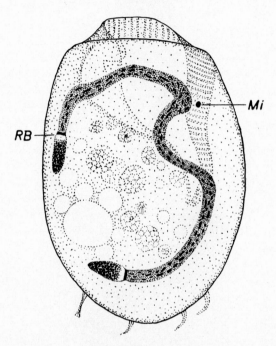

FIG. 18. *Euplotes eurystomus* with reorganization bands (*RB*) in the macronucleus. Ventral view; *Mi*—micronucleus. Iron hematoxylin staining, × 540. After Turner.[274]

The significance of the reorganization bands remained unknown until Gall[69] discovered that DNA is synthesized in these structures and nowhere else. Tritiated thymidine becomes incorporated in the DNA of only those segments of the macronucleus through which the reorganization bands passed during incubation with the precursor (Fig. 19 B). Gall also showed photometrically that DNA and histone concentrations become approximately doubled in the reorganized parts of the nucleus. Therefore the reorganization bands are now often called replication bands.

With shorter incorporation periods and higher autoradiographic resolution Prescott and Kimball[180, 181] succeeded in demonstrating that in

Euplotes DNA is synthesized only at the leading edge of the rear zone of the reorganization band. Protein synthesis occurs simultaneously with DNA replication, as can be judged by H³-histidine,[180, 181] H³-lysine, and H³-arginine[304] incorporation into the reorganization band. As suggested by Prescott and Kimball, this protein may be of the histone type; but Ringertz

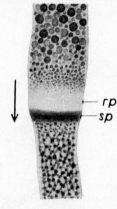

Fig. 19 A

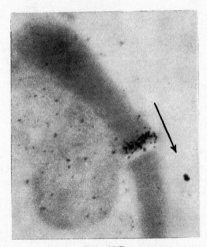

Fig. 19 B

Fig. 19. Reorganization band of *Euplotes eurystomus*. A—light microscopical picture, safranin staining, × 2400; after Turner.[274] B—autoradiograph after H³-thymidine incorporation during 3 hours, azure B staining, × 1300; after Gall.[69] C—ultrastructure of the reorganization band, 0.1 M FeCl₃ staining, × 11,000; after Kluss.[134] The *arrows* indicate direction of movement of the bands; *sp*—solution plane (forward zone), *rp*—reconstruction plane (rear zone), *cb*—chromatin bodies, *n*—nucleoli, *f*—network of twisted microfibrils in the forward zone, *sz*—DNA synthesis zone, *ne*—nuclear envelope, *mt*—mitochondrion.

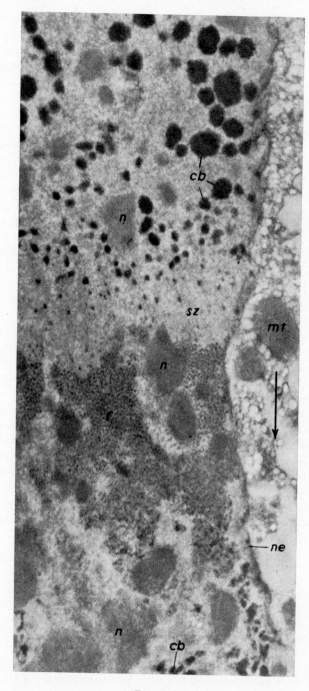

Fig. 19 C

and Hoskins[304] showed that practically all types of macronuclear proteins become doubled at the passage of the reorganization band. The forward zone of the band has a greater dry mass and greater protein concentration than either the unreorganized or reorganized parts of the nucleus.[304] On the other hand, the zone of DNA synthesis seems to be highly hydrated, since interferometry shows little dry matter therein.[180, 181, 304]

Electron microscopy of the reorganization band of *Euplotes*[67, 134, 213] showed that just ahead of the forward zone the macronuclear chromatin bodies (see p. 15 and Fig. 5) disintegrate, liberating their densely packed 110 Å thick microfibrils. The forward zone itself consists of an organized network of such twisted microfibrils (Fig. 19C). The transition to the rear zone is very sharp: the 110 Å microfibrils abruptly disappear, probably splitting into very thin subfibrils with a diameter of less than 50 Å and a very low electron density. It is in just this zone that DNA replication takes place; this has been confirmed by Stevens[256] with electron microscopic autoradiography. At the posterior edge of the rear zone small chromatin bodies reappear and rapidly grow in size, probably due to aggregation of fibrils behind the DNA synthesis zone (Fig. 19C).

Migration of the reorganization bands in *Euplotes* takes from 8 to 12.5 hours, i.e., from 40 to 75 per cent of the generation time.[67, 182, 304]† Thus the synthesis of DNA in the hypotrich macronucleus is not only extended in time, as in most ciliates, but also in space, not occurring at once throughout the macronucleus, but proceeding gradually along it. Progressive development of DNA synthesis, only probable in other ciliate macronuclei, is evident here.

In some cases the macronuclear division takes place without preceding DNA replication, thus resembling fragmentation. This seems to be especially characteristic of ciliates having a stage of hypertrophic growth followed by a stage of repeated palintomic divisions of the encysted tomont, giving rise to many tomites. In *Ichthyophthirius*[276] only the first three or four of the 10 divisions rapidly following one another occur with preceding DNA replication, while during the last six or seven divisions no DNA synthesis is observed in the macronuclei. As a result, the macronuclear ploidy degree falls from 12,600 n in a mature trophont to 48 n in a swarmer.

B. Duplication of Macronuclear Chromosomes

Sooner or later, the DNA replication in the macronucleus obviously must become morphologically expressed as endomitotic duplication of its chromosomes, just as DNA synthesis in the interphase of an ordinary mitotic cycle precedes chromosome splitting in metaphase.

---

† The rate of progression of the reorganization bands is not constant. In *Euplotes*, they move (and DNA synthesis proceeds) four times faster during the last 20 per cent of the S period than during the first 80 per cent of it.[304]

Chromosome duplication can be observed not only during macronuclear anlagen development (see p. 27) but in some ciliates also in each division cycle of mature macronuclei. The thread-like chromosomes found by Sato and Saito in the macronuclei of *Tetrahymena, Paramecium,* and *Vorticella* (see p. 41) undergo a cycle of spiralization and endomitotic duplication during the interdivision interval. In *Tetrahymena* the doubling of chromosomes takes place during the last 30 minutes before division, the daughter chromosomes lying parallel to each other.[229] The timing of DNA synthesis is not known in the strain used ("*T. geleii* W"), but keeping in mind that in all other strains of *T. pyriformis* (= *geleii*) macronuclear DNA synthesis occurs in the middle or at the beginning of the interdivision interval, one may suppose that endomitotic chromosome duplication takes place here during the G_2 period. On the other hand, in *Paramecium caudatum* the macronuclear chromosomes become longitudinally split at the beginning of the interdivision interval, i.e., in the G_1 period; at first the chromatids appear relationally coiled, during the interdivision interval they uncoil, and just before division they coil again, this time independently, forming parallel daughter chromosomes.[225] Probably the duplication of chromosomes shifts here from the end of one interdivision interval to the beginning of the next one: in this species there is no G_2 period,[26] and thus no time for chromosome doubling before division. The behavior of macronuclear chromosomes in *Vorticella* appears to be similar.[224]

In the orthomere of the heteromerous macronucleus of *Chlamydodon,* Kaneda[114-6] observed the thread-like "chromonemata" become double just before nuclear division, after passage of the reorganization band (which is probably also connected here with DNA replication, as in hypotrichs), i.e., during the G_2 period.

The chromatin threads in the *Bursaria* macronucleus[223] and the rodlike chromosomes in that of *Loxophyllum* (Fig. 34)[221] are also usually paired; however, the time of their duplication is not yet known.

The clearest pictures of endomitoses have been observed by Raikov[192] in the macronucleus of *Nassula ornata.* The nondividing macronucleus of this species contains peculiar elongated Feulgen-positive strands, 5 to 10 μ long and 1–2 μ thick (Fig. 20A). The strands are interconnected in a loose network and immersed in a Feulgen-negative karyolymph. Shortly beforedivision, the macronucleus swells considerably, and its chromatin strands stretch into sinuous, Feulgen-positive, long threads interpreted as chromosomes (more exactly as composite chromosomes, as will be shown below— pp. 57, 79).

Only segments of these threads can be seen in sections. Soon the threads become longitudinally split into two chromatids (endoprophase stage), and then the chromatids separate completely and become independent parallel chromosomes (endoanaphase stage—Fig. 20B). It is interesting that during this time the micronuclei are in anaphase. Later, the daughter chromatin

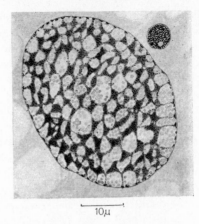

FIG. 20 A

10μ

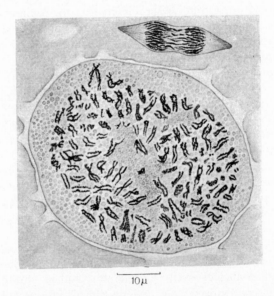

FIG. 20 B

10μ

FIG. 20. Endomitotic replication and division of the macronucleus of *Nassula ornata.* × 1150. After Raikov.[192] A—non-dividing macronucleus showing interconnected chromatin strands and many nucleoli; micronucleus at upper right. B—endomitosis of the chromatin strands; micronuclear anaphase at top. C—beginning of macronuclear stretching: radial position of daughter chromatin strands, fibrils of the pushing body in the center, micronucleus at lower left. D—macronuclear division with central pushing body; three micronuclei are seen. A–C—Feulgen–light green, D—methyl green–pyronin.

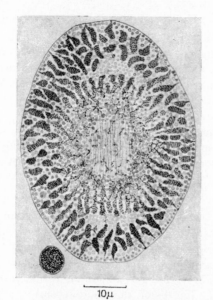

FIG. 20 C

10μ

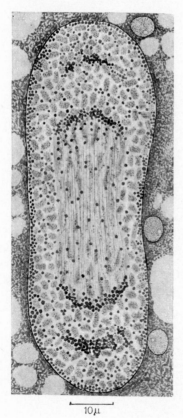

FIG. 20 D

10μ

threads again become condensed into chromatin strands, and the macronucleus starts dividing (Fig. 20C, D).

The macronucleus of *Nassulopsis elegans* behaves in quite a similar
way.[199] It has been shown in this species that DNA replication occurs in
the macronucleus in the first half of the interdivision interval. Consequently,
splitting of macronuclear chromosome threads takes place in Nassulidae
during the G_2 period.

The DNA synthesis and the following endomitotic duplication of the
macronuclear chromosomes obviously result in doubling of the polyploidy
degree of the macronucleus by the beginning of its division.

C. MACRONUCLEAR CONDENSATION

In most ciliates having a complexly shaped macronucleus (stretched,
moniliform, branched, etc.), the macronucleus condenses immediately before
division into a comparatively simple body, a spherical, ovoid, or slightly
irregular one. In *Spirostomum*, for example, separate nodes of the moniliform
macronucleus (Fig. 21 A) fuse into a continuous ribbon (B), which shortens
into a compact mass (C). Later, the macronucleus stretches again (D) and

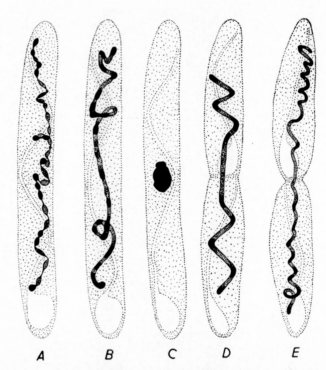

A   B   C   D   E

FIG. 21. Condensation (A–C) and division (D, E) of the macronucleus of
Spirostomum ambiguum. × 75. After Doflein and Reichenow.[45]

divides simultaneously with the cytoplasm (E). Its nodulation occurs only after cytokinesis.[55, 164] The behavior of moniliform macronuclei of *Stentor*,[282] *Fabrea*,[60] *Blepharisma*,[100, 147] *Loxophyllum*,[221] *Homalozoon*,[40] *Dileptus cygnus*,[73] and other ciliates is the same.

In the ribbon-like macronucleus of *Bursaria* a longitudinal row of condensed chromatin clumps appears before it shortens. During its shortening, these so-called condensation centers fuse with each other and finally completely fill the nucleus.[223]

When several macronuclei are present (Fig. 23 A) these usually fuse into one (B) which then condenses into a compact body (C). This divides into the two nuclei of the daughter animals, and each of these nuclei divides one or several times more (D–G). This process persists even when the number of macronuclei is very high, e.g., in *Urostyla grandis*.[187]

The significance of macronuclear condensation is not clear. According to Weisz,[283, 284] during the interdivision interval the posterior nodes of the macronuclei of *Stentor* and *Blepharisma* gradually lose their ability to support regeneration. In this case the macronuclear condensation might serve to smooth out this morphogenetic gradient. However, the studies of Tartar[263, 264] did not confirm morphogenetic inequality of different parts of the macronucleus of *Stentor* and *Condylostoma*.

It deserves attention, that macronuclear condensation always occurs after the DNA replication. This has been shown, in particular, in *Stentor*,[94] *Bursaria*[222] and *Spirostomum*.[163] This relationship is most clearly expressed in the Hypotrichida, where macronuclear shortening begins only after passage of the reorganization bands. In *Euplotes*, the ends of the macronucleus, having already accomplished DNA replication, begin to condense first.[130, 274] On the other hand, in *Aspidisca*, where the reorganization bands move from the middle to the ends of the nucleus, it is the middle region of the nucleus that condenses first.[258] Maximum condensation of the macronucleus is attained only after the reorganization bands disappear. If there are several macronuclei, the reorganization bands pass through each one separately (Fig. 23 A), after which the nuclei begin to fuse [e.g., in *Diophrys*, *Stylonychia*,[258] *Urostyla*,[187] etc.].

Less clear is the relation between endomitotic duplication of the macronuclear chromosomes and macronuclear shortening. Both processes seem to occur at approximately the same time after DNA replication. Possibly the significance of macronuclear condensation is that it in some way assures the splitting of its chromosomes. For instance, it might facilitate changes in spatial arrangement of its chromosomes or of whole genomes. Such an interpretation is favoured by the mixing up of the *Euplotes* macronuclear contents during condensation; the labeled DNA, previously confined to two small segments of the macronucleus, becomes dispersed throughout the condensed nucleus[130] (see Fig. 4 in the chapter by Prescott and Stone, Vol 2, Chapter II). This problem deserves further investigation.

Predivisional macronuclear condensation does not take place, however, in all ciliates. For instance, the numerous macronuclei of *Dileptus anser* do not fuse, each one dividing independently.[110] The seven macronuclei of *Conchophthirius steenstrupii* do the same.[212] And within a single colony of *Epistylis articulata* some zooids divide with macronuclear condensation, others without.[32] The significance of these variations is unknown.

3. Structural Changes in the Macronucleus during Division

A. NUCLEOLAR APPARATUS

The macronuclear nucleoli change most frequently just before division or at its beginning. For instance, in *Paramecium bursaria* the large nucleoli of the non-dividing nucleus (Fig. 22A) disintegrate into small granules during the stretching phase (B). Later, they completely disappear and the RNA content of the macronucleus drops almost to zero. But at late stages of division RNA reappears in the macronucleus, at first in diffuse form.[233] Complete disappearance of nucleoli during macronuclear division has been reported also in *Fabrea*,[60] some Ophryoglenidae,[153] *Loxophyllum*,[221] *Dileptus cygnus*,[73] and other ciliates. In *Paramecium putrinum* the nucleoli become fragmented during division but do not disappear entirely.[107]

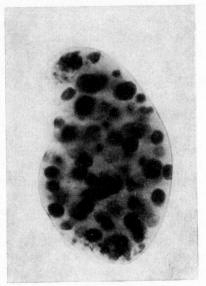

FIG. 22A

FIG. 22. Isolated unfixed macronuclei of *Paramecium bursaria*, methyl green–pyronin staining, × 1000. After Schwartz.[233] A—non-dividing macronucleus with large nucleoli; B—nucleolar fragmentation during macronuclear stretching (the bodies adhering to the nucleus are zoo-chlorellae).

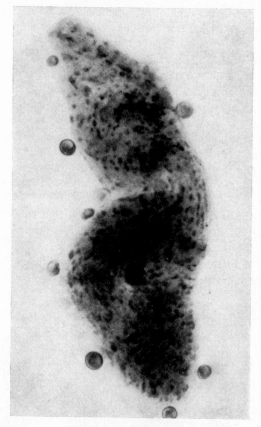

FIG. 22 B

In *Kahlia simplex* (Hypotrichida) the nucleoli and the RNA disappear at passage of the reorganization band and reappear only in daughter macro-nuclei.[161] On the other hand, in *Euplotes* the nucleoli are re-formed immedi-ately after passage of the reorganization band (Fig. 19 C).

In some other ciliates nucleoli are retained during division, but become stretched along the dividing nucleus. Finally, in certain species there are no appreciable changes of the nucleoli during macronuclear division.

B. Chromatin Elements

The most usual change of the macronuclear chromatin during division is from a uniformly granular appearance to a striated, as if the chromatin granules became aligned in the direction of macronuclear stretching (Fig. 23). This phenomenon has been observed in many ciliates.[11, 144, 187] Some-times fusion of the chromatin granules into longitudinal strands has been described, e.g., during budding of the suctorian *Solenophrya*.[102] Each row of granules seems to divide transversely when the daughter nuclei separate (Fig. 23E).

The alignment of chromatin granules into rows may be interpreted in two ways. First, it might follow the establishment of longitudinal connections between the granules (or the manifestation of preexisting connections) with the chains interpreted as composite chromosomes, and the granules (or small bodies of the electron microscopists) interpreted as single chromosomes. Second, the alignment of granule smight follow the appearance of longitudinal bundles of achromatic substance in the macronucleus, the chromatin granules being pushed into the spaces between them. As will be shown below (p. 58), such achromatic bundles are present in dividing macronuclei.

Interesting is the behavior of the chromatin elements during macronuclear division in reproduction cysts of Colpodidae. The large central nucleolus dissolves and the macronuclear chromatin forms characteristic stellate aggregates well delimited from each other. In *Colpoda steinii* (Fig. 24), eight chromatin aggregates appear; during two successive cell divisions they

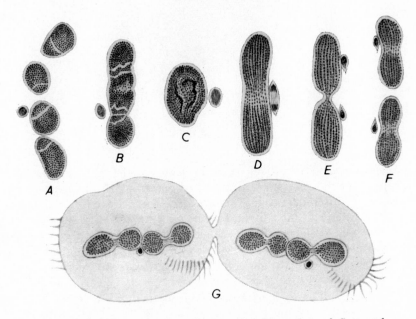

FIG. 23. Condensation and division of the macronucleus of *Gastrostyla steinii*, hemalum staining, × 640. After Weyer.[287] Note longitudinal rows of chromatin granules (D–F). A—reorganization bands in each of the four macronuclei; B—fusion of macronuclei; C—maximum condensation stage; D–E—first, F—second, G—third division of the macronucleus. Each daughter animal receives four macronuclei.

segregate among the daughter macronuclei, at first by fours, then by twos. Piekarski[170] supposed these aggregates to be macronuclear genomes which segregate during nuclear division.

In other Colpodidae, the number of chromatin aggregates may be different.[17] Only four of them appear in *Colpoda duodenaria*, segregating by twos during the only division.[266] On the other hand, in *Colpoda maupasi* there are more than 70 aggregates, which become distributed among eight daughter macronuclei during three successive cell divisions in the cyst.[166] Very high is the number of chromatin aggregates in *Tillina magna* (Fig. 30). Unfortunately, not yet studied photometrically is the degree of macronuclear polyploidy in Colpodidae, whether it is proportional to the number of chromatin aggregates, or what the DNA content of one aggregate is as compared with the micronucleus. Therefore whether the aggregates are haploid, diploid, or polyploid is unknown.

During macronuclear division in *Woodruffia*, both of the thick chromatin bands permanently present in the non-dividing nucleus divide transversely without fusing with each other. Each daughter macronucleus receives a half of each band.[61] The interpretation of this process remains obscure.

As pointed out above (p. 49), the macronuclei of *Nassula ornata* and *Nassulopsis elegans* contain peculiar chromatin strands replicating by endo-

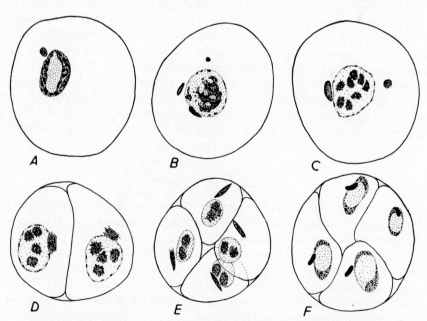

Fig. 24. Appearance (A–C) and segregation (D, E) of macronuclear chromatin aggregates during two successive divisions in reproduction cysts of *Colpoda steinii*. F—reconstruction of the normal macronuclear structure. Feulgen reaction, × 1050. After Piekarski.[170]

mitosis before nuclear division. During division the strands show maximum shortening and assume spindle-like or barrel-like shapes. Often they appear spirally striated, suggesting that they are a tightly coiled thread (Fig. 20C, D). In this condition, the chromatin strands segregate at random between the daughter nuclei.[192] Counting of the chromatin strands, carried out in *Nassulopsis elegans*, showed that their number is close to 128 before endomitosis and to 256 after it. The degree of macronuclear polyploidy in this species, determined independently by DNA measurement, approaches $256\,n$ during the G_1 period and $512\,n$ during the G_2 period. A comparison of these figures demonstrates that the chromatin strands of Nassulidae must be diploid chromosome aggregates.[199] Possibly, this might also be the case in Colpodidae.

Thus there are grounds for assuming that in certain ciliates not separate chromatin bodies or chromosomes but larger aggregates are segregation units during macronuclear division; at least in one case they have been shown to be diploid. It is possible that such phenomena are much more widely spread but in the majority of ciliates proceed in a masked form.

Photometric DNA measurements show that even during ordinary binary division the macronuclear chromatin material is by no means always precisely halved. Small (up to 14 per cent) differences in the DNA content of sister macronuclei have been found in *Tetrahymena* by McDonald.[144] In *Bursaria*,[222] unequal DNA distribution at macronuclear division occurs more often and is much more pronounced (up to 1 : 2.4). These differences are not compensated during the next DNA synthesis period. On the contrary, according to Ruthmann,[222] they accumulate and lead to a very wide diversity of ploidy degree of the macronuclei within a clone. Similar phenomena have been found also in *Spirostomum*.[163] If we assume that whole genomes, identical to each other, are segregation units of the macronuclear chromatin, then unequal distribution of the DNA between the daughter nuclei could follow random genome segregation.

C. Kinetic Elements

In certain ciliates mitosis-like patterns of macronuclear division involving formation of spindle-like figures were described long ago—e.g., in *Conchophthirius*[212] and in many forms with heteromerous macronuclei.[261] But it was difficult to generalize these observations. Schwartz[234] showed for the first time that during division of *Paramecium bursaria* a birefringent substance appears in the macronucleus which has no apparent "spindle". The character of the birefringence indicates the presence of some fibrous structures oriented along the stretching macronucleus. The birefringent substance can be dissolved with proteases and HCl, exactly as can both micronuclear spindle fibers and the protein matrix of the non-dividing macronucleus, and it seems to be formed at the cost of this matrix. On the basis of his observations, Schwartz concludes that the dividing macronucleus contains a diffuse "pushing body" of fibrillar nature, and that stretching of the whole nucleus follows the longitudinal growth of this body.

In the macronucleus of *Nassula ornata*, the "pushing body" is spatially delimited from other nuclear components and has been observed by Raikov[192] with the ordinary light microscope. It appears as a small bundle of protein fibers in the center of the macronucleus at the very beginning of macronuclear stretching (Fig. 20C). During macronuclear elongation, the pushing body rapidly grows and assumes a cylindrical shape, consisting as before of longitudinal protein fibers (Fig. 20D). At late division stages, the pushing body stretches strongly and occupies the bridge between the two daughter nuclei.

Now rapidly accumulating are electron microscopical data which show that dividing macronuclei always contain longitudinally oriented submicroscopic fibrils. These fibrils have tubular ultrastructure and a diameter of 150–200 Å. Undoubtedly it is these fibrils which give birefringence to the dividing macronucleus. Such fibrils have been found by Roth and co-workers in the constriction region of the dividing macronuclei of *Stylonychia*,[214] *Tetrahymena*[215] and *Diplodinium*.[216] According to Mosevich,[152] the tubular filaments in the dividing macronucleus of *Ichthyophthirius multifiliis* are collected into several thick wavy bundles (Fig. 25A). The "pushing body" of the macronucleus of *Nassula ornata*, studied by Raikov,[201] also consists of tubular 150–180 Å thick fibrils lying parallel to each other and along the

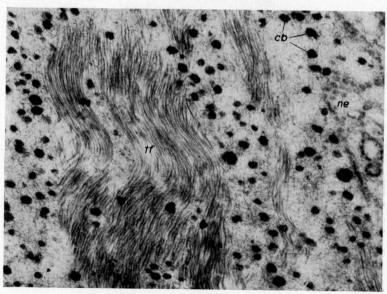

FIG. 25A

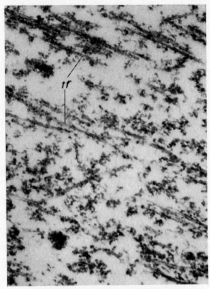

FIG. 25 B

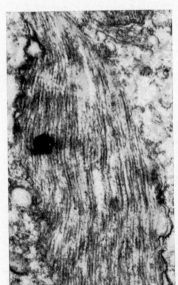

FIG. 25 C

FIG. 25. Ultrastructure of kinetic elements of the dividing macronucleus.
A—bundles of tubular fibrils (*tf*) in the dividing macronucleus of *Ichthyoph-thirius; cb*—chromatin bodies, *ne*—nuclear envelope with pores; × 16,000
(original by T. N. Mosevich). B—tubular fibrils (*tf*) in the pushing body of
the dividing macronucleus of *Nassula*, × 49,000; after Raikov.[201] C—tubular fibers of the micronuclear mitotic spindle in *Nassula*, × 15,000; after
Raikov.[201]

stretching nucleus (Fig. 25 B). These fibrils closely resemble the fibers of the micronuclear mitotic spindle of the same species (Fig. 25 C). Fibrils of the same type have also been observed in the macronuclei of *Ophryoglena bacterocaryon*[207] and *Euplotes*.[310] Carasso and Favard[23] showed that in the dividing macronucleus of *Campanella umbellaria* tubular fibrils, about 200 Å in diameter, appear at first as isolated units, then rapidly aggregate into bundles of 20–25 fibrils in each. At first the bundles are randomly directed, but during macronuclear stretching they become oriented parallel to each other and along the macronucleus. By the end of division, the tubular fibrils disappear.

It is well known that the mitotic spindle of various animal and plant cells consists of just such tubular proteinous fibrils. Consequently, the ciliate macronuclei during division contain a kinetic component fully comparable with spindle fibers.

This homology is supported by experiments using the mitotic inhibitor mercaptoethanol. As known, mercaptoethanol suppresses mitotic spindle formation, blocking the establishment of intermolecular disulfide bonds.[143] Holz[101] (and also personal communication) showed that this agent suppressed or strongly impaired the macronuclear division in *Tetrahymena*, so that one of the daughter animals received no macronucleus or an unusually small macronucleus. These observations have been extended by Gavin and Frankel (personal communication) on two other strains of *Tetrahymena*. According to them, mercaptoethanol may disturb the regular formation and orientation of the macronuclear fibrillar elements. These experiments show that the tubular fibrils of the macronucleus are biochemically comparable to spindle fibers.

No attachment of tubular fibrils to chromatin elements of the macronucleus has ever been observed. This, as well as the form and position of the "pushing body" in *Nassula* (Fig. 20 C, D), suggests that the tubular fibrils of the macronucleus correspond not to chromosomal fibers, but to continuous fibers of the mitotic spindle. Elongation of the whole macronucleus probably follows the elongation of the fibrils. In the majority of ciliates, the fibrils are dispersed throughout the macronucleus or collected into small bundles only, and therefore are invisible with the light microscope, but in certain forms (e.g., in *Nassula*) they unite into one large compact "pushing body".

D. NUCLEAR ENVELOPE

All available electron microscopical data demonstrate that the macronuclear envelope is not destroyed during division, but persists as two membranes bearing numerous pores.[23, 59, 201, 215, 216]

With the light microscope, Raikov[192] found that before division in *Nassula ornata* the macronuclear envelope becomes distinctly double, the distance between the two "sheets" attaining 1–2 µ (Fig. 26A). Soon the outer "sheet" disintegrates (Fig. 20B), and the macronucleus starts dividing with an ordinary, single (at the light microscopical level!) envelope (Fig. 20C). An electron microscopical investigation of this unusual phenomenon[201] showed that the disintegrating outer sheet is in reality not the nuclear envelope proper, but the perinuclear layer of dense cytoplasm usually adhering to it (see above, p. 9). Before division, the perinuclear layer loosens, moves away from the nuclear envelope to a distance of 1–2 µ and gradually disintegrates into its components, i.e., into vacuoles and channels of the granular endoplasmic reticulum and into numerous free ribosomes (Fig. 26B). But the two membranes of the nuclear envelope proper persist throughout macronuclear division. During late division stages, the perinuclear layer is re-formed by separation of membrane-bound vacuoles and channels from protrusions of the outer macronuclear membrane (Fig. 27). At the same time, numerous free ribosomes appear near the nuclear envelope. Condensation of all these structures into a dense plexus leads to the formation of a new perinuclear layer.

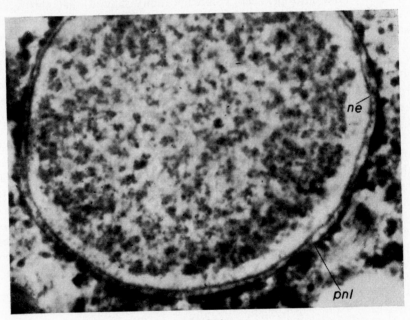

FIG. 26A

FIG. 26. Separation of the perinuclear cytoplasmic layer (*pnl*) from the macronuclear envelope (*ne*) of *Nassula* before division. A—photomicrograph, endoprophase stage; iron hematoxylin stained section, × 1800; after Raikov.[192] B—electron micrograph, × 24,000; after Raikov.[201] *Ma*—macronucleus, *n*—nucleoli, *r*—ribosomes, *er*—vacuoles of the endoplasmic reticulum.

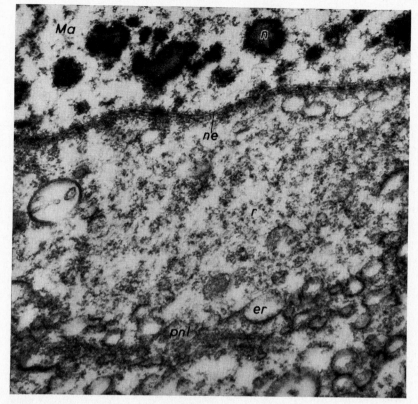

FIG. 26 B

E. DIVISION OF HETEROMEROUS MACRONUCLEI

During division the heteromerous macronuclei undergo rather complicated changes not yet altogether clear. In this category belong almost all mitosis-like patterns of macronuclear division. Sometimes the division of heteromerous macronuclei externally resembles mitosis so vividly that terms "metaphase", "anaphase", etc. have been used for its stages.[114] But it is not mitosis, since absent here is the principal feature of mitotic division, the regular segregation of sister chromatids into daughter nuclei. Therefore these terms should not be applied to heteromerous macronuclei.

As an example, let us consider the macronuclear division in *Spirochona gemmipara*.[270] At the beginning of the interdivision interval the paramere contains no endosome (Fig. 28A), but by the end of the interval the endosome is formed, and a reorganization band passes through the orthomere (Fig. 28B, C). Shortly before division the orthomere begins to envelop the paramere (D), so that the macronuclear structure changes from the juxta-

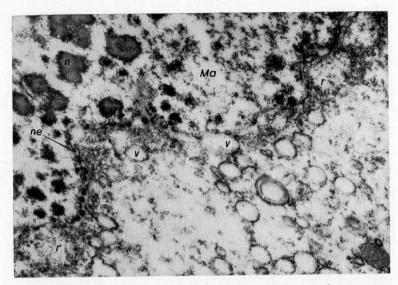

Fig. 27. Re-formation of the perinuclear cytoplasmic layer at late stages of macronuclear division in *Nassula*. Electron micrograph showing separation of vacuoles (*v*) from the outer membrane of the nuclear envelope (*ne*), and accumulation of ribosomes (*r*) on the outer side of it. *Ma*—macronucleus, *n*—nucleoli. × 24,500. After Raikov.[201]

posed type to the concentric one (E). Then the chromatin of the orthomere aggregates into longitudinal strands which become localized at the surface of the middle part of the stretching nucleus while the substance of the paramere, which occupied the center of the nucleus, becomes gradually squeezed towards the poles of the division figure and forms two polar caps (F, G). During late division stages, the chromatin strands of the orthomere seem to divide transversely, and a small chromatin aggregation appears on the nuclear constriction, which possibly arises from the endosome (H). This aggregation divides into two granules which are extruded into the cytoplasm just after division (Fig. 28 I).

Very similar is the macronuclear division in *Spirochona elegans*,[261] *Dysteria monostyla*,[64] *Chlamydodon pedarius*,[114] and *Allosphaerium paraconvexa*.[43] The division of heteromerous macronuclei of the concentric type appears to be more simple. In *Chilodonella*[140, 141, 303] the endosome divides first, followed by constriction of the paramere. The chromatin granules of the orthomere fuse into twisted threads or a continuous network, and then the whole macronucleus divides.

It should be pointed out that there is nothing unusual in the behavior of the orthomere. Granular chromatin strands can also be observed during division of homomerous macronuclei (see Fig. 23). Much more peculiar is the behavior of the paramere and endosome. According to Kaneda[115]

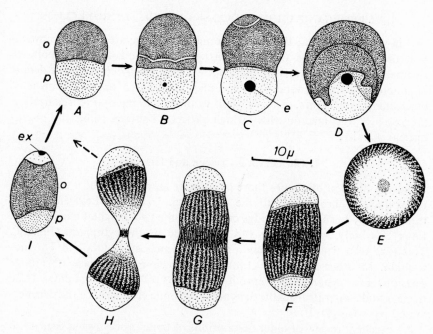

FIG. 28. Division of the heteromerous macronucleus of *Spirochona gemmipara* (diagrammatic). × 1600. After Tuffrau.[270] A–I—successive stages; *o*—orthomere, *p*—paramere, *e*—endosome, *ex*—extrusion body.

and Dobrzańska-Kaczanowska,[43] during stretching of the macronucleus of *Chlamydodon* and *Allosphaerium* (stages F–G on Fig. 28) the substance of the paramere, occupying the center of the macronucleus, plays the role of a "pushing body" or division spindle and has a finely fibrillar structure. Unfortunately, dividing heteromerous macronuclei have never been studied electron microscopically. If these observations are confirmed, we shall be obliged to consider the paramere as a specialized nuclear zone which gives rise, during division, to the fibrillar pushing body. While in *Nassula* the latter is distinct only during division, in heteromerous macronuclei the protein material destined to form the pushing body seems to be permanently separated from other nuclear components.[43]

Let us draw some conclusions. The macronuclear division cycle is a regular alternation of endomitosis and of random segregation of complete genomes. A kinetic element, similar to continuous fibers of the mitotic spindle, takes part in the macronuclear division. All structural components of the macronucleus undergo profound changes during division, showing that macronuclear division is a much more complex process than a simple pulling into two parts.

VI. REORGANIZATION PROCESSES IN THE MACRONUCLEUS

It is well known that the old macronucleus degenerates during conjugation and autogamy (see Vol. 4). Extensive examination of these phenomena is outside the field of this chapter, but we shall briefly consider the details of macronuclear degeneration, since they are related to the problem of macronuclear structure. And we shall examine the internal reorganization processes of the macronucleus which proceed unaccompanied by micronuclear activity.

1. Chromatin Extrusion and Hemixis

During division of ciliates there may occur an extrusion of a part of the macronuclear chromatin into the cytoplasm. Usually a Feulgen-positive residual body forms on the bridge connecting the two daughter macronuclei. Later this body becomes free and is resorbed by the cytoplasm (Fig. 29). This type of extrusion is common among Hymenostomatida and Thigmotrichida. In other cases, the chromatin extrusion takes place only after division. For instance, in reproduction cysts of most Colpodidae large nuclear buds separate from the daughter macronuclei (Fig. 30 C) and degenerate by pycnosis (D, E).

An excellent review of older descriptions of these processes has been given by Woodruff.[292] Since that time, chromatin extrusion of the first type (on

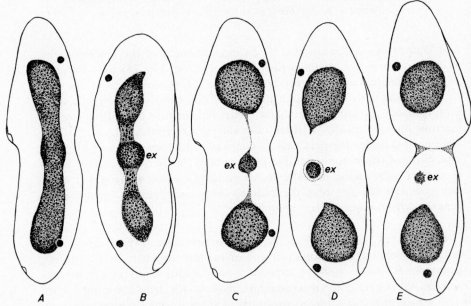

FIG. 29. Macronuclear division with chromatin extrusion in *Ancistruma isseli*. × 630. After Kidder.[123] A–C—formation, D–E—resorption of the extrusion body (*ex*). Feulgen reaction (A, C) and Borrel stain (B, D, E).

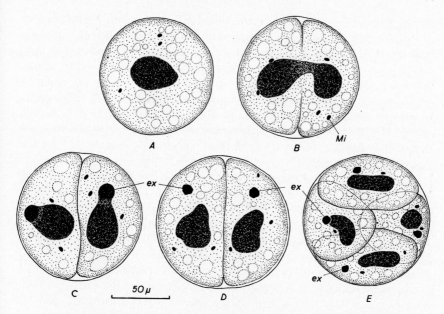

Fig. 30. Chromatin extrusion from the macronucleus in reproduction cysts of *Tillina magna*. Feulgen reaction, × 320 (original by M. A. Frenkel). A—encysted animal; B—first division; C, D—chromatin extrusion after the first division; E—chromatin extrusion after the second division; *ex*—extrusion bodies, *Mi*—micronuclei.

the connecting bridge) has been reported in *Tetrahymena*,[51, 231] *Glaucoma*,[31] *Colpidium*,[35] *Frontonia*,[34] *Ophryoglena*,[22, 230] *Porpostoma*, *Philaster*,[153] *Disematostoma*,[273] and some ciliates from sea urchins.[9] Chromatin extrusion of the second type (after division) has been described in *Ichthyophthirius*,[153] many Colpodidae,[8, 17, 166, 167] and *Conchophthirius curtis*.[10]

The size of the extrusion body may vary considerably; in *Tetrahymena limacis* it contains from 1/58 to 1/4 of the macronuclear DNA, in *T. patula* from 1/23 to 1/6 of it.[54] The DNA synthesis in this body, judging by tritiated thymidine incorporation, continues in *Tetrahymena limacis*,[52] but in *T. rostrata*[53] and *T. pyriformis*[306] stops immediately after body formation is complete.

Quite unusual is the behavior of the extrusion body formed on the macronuclear connecting bridge of *Nassulopsis lagenula*, according to Tuffrau.[271] Here it is not resorbed but regenerates a normal macronucleus; it is the old macronucleus of the daughter animal receiving the extrusion body which degenerates. This phenomenon has been called *parahemixis*.

Extrusion of Feulgen-positive fragments from the macronucleus may also occur without any relation to division. Diller[36] described this phenomenon

3a*

for the first time in *Paramecium aurelia* and called it *hemixis*. He distinguished four types of hemixis: A—splitting of the macronucleus into large
fragments usually segregating at subsequent cell divisions and regenerating
into normal macronuclei; B—extrusion of small fragments, which usually
become resorbed; C—combination of both processes; and D—complete
disintegration of the macronucleus into small fragments with lethal effect.
At present, hemixis is known to occur also in *P. caudatum*,[37, 278] *P. polycaryum*,[39] *P. jenningsi*,[148] *Balantidium elongatum*,[257] *Blepharisma undulans*,[165] *Euplotes woodruffi*,[103] three species of *Epistylis*,[237] and in
Tokophrya infusionum.[218]

Related to hemixis is the extrusion of a chromatin bud from the macronucleus in resting cysts of many Colpodidae. In *Colpoda duodenaria*[266]
extrusion is preceded by formation of four chromatin aggregates in the
macronucleus (Fig. 31 B), just as division is preceded in the same species.
Two aggregates get into the extrusion body (C, D), which degenerates by
pycnosis (E–H). In this case, the chromatin extrusion in resting cysts may
be interpreted as abortive macronuclear division (with destruction of one
of the daughter nuclei). However, in other Colpodidae the extrusion body
receives much less than a half of the macronuclear chromatin, and the
chromatin aggregates cannot be clearly seen.[8, 17, 124, 167] In the latter case
it is hardly possible to consider the chromatin extrusion a suppressed division; it may more accurately be homologized with hemixis.

Three viewpoints can be distinguished as to the significance of chromatin
extrusion. The first one considered these processes a "purification" of the
macronucleus from "waste products" of the metabolism of chromatin.[122]
It is of purely historical interest. According to the second one, chromatin
extrusion is a means of transportation of DNA into the cytoplasm, where

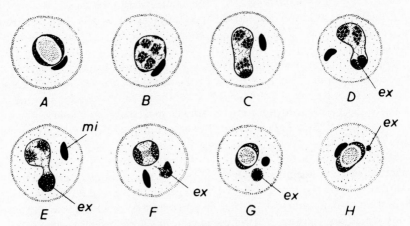

FIG. 31. Chromatin extrusion in resting cysts of *Colpoda duodenaria*.
Feulgen reaction, × 2400. After Taylor and Garnjobst.[266] A–H—successive stages; *ex*—extrusion body, *mi*—micronucleus.

DNA "converts" into the RNA necessary for growth and protein synthe-ses.[31, 238] From the position of modern biochemistry, such a "conversion" is highly improbable. Besides, neither viewpoint takes into account the chromosomal nature of macronuclear DNA nor that chromatin extrusion must alter the chromosomal and/or genomic composition of the macro-nucleus. But it is from just this circumstance that the third hypothesis, advanced by Fauré-Fremiet,[62] proceeds. According to it, chromatin extrusion and hemixis may serve to adjust the polyploidy degree of the macronucleus. It is known that a tendency towards hyperpolyploidization and hypertrophy of the macronucleus appears during clonal senescence in certain ciliates. Hyperploidy probably arises as a result of the repeated replication of DNA (and chromosomes) during a single interdivision interval in all or some macronuclear genomes. In *Euplotes* the reorganization bands sometimes pass through the macronucleus twice;[130] in *Tetrahymena* the DNA content of the macronucleus is much higher during the stationary phase than during the logarithmic one.[144] Additional DNA is also syn-thesized in *Tetrahymena* after ultraviolet irradiation, the excess DNA then being eliminated in especially large extrusion bodies during the next three divisions.[306] And it is in senile clones that hemixis occurs more fre-quently.[218, 278] According to Faure-Fremiet, the significance of chromatin extrusion and of hemixis is the destruction of "excess" macronuclear genomes and the restoration of a normal nucleocytoplasmic relation. This viewpoint seems presently to be the most probable one. It is indirectly supported also by the usual absence of any clonal senescence during vegeta-tive reproduction in just those species which have regular chromatin extru-sion (*Tetrahymena, Ophryoglena, Colpoda*).

2. Macronuclear Condensation without Division

Macronuclear condensation of the type that precedes division (p. 52) sometimes occurs without any connection with division. It is observed during the so-called physiological reorganization, which occurs quite regularly in *Stentor*,[232, 264, 282] *Spirostomum*,[55] and other ciliates and consists of dedifferentiation and subsequent redifferentiation of the peris-tome. The number of macronuclear nodes usually changes after physiologi-cal reorganization. It is possible that condensation is here merely a mecha-nism of alteration of the number of nodes, but it is equally possible that physiological reorganization is accompanied by endomitosis of macro-nuclear chromosomes.

Macronuclear condensation takes place also during regeneration.[55, 264] Sometimes condensation and re-nodulation of the macronucleus is repeated several times during regeneration in *Stentor*, the macronuclear size and the number of nodes increasing after each condensation. Here it is especially probable that condensation in some way ensures the endomitoses in the regenerating macronucleus.

In resting cysts of many Hypotrichida, several macronuclei fuse into a single one.[177, 287] This phenomenon is perhaps analogous to macro-nuclear condensation during physiological reorganization.

3. The Macronucleus during Conjugation and Autogamy

As known, the old macronucleus degenerates during the sexual processes and a new one is formed from a synkaryon derivative.

There are two main patterns of macronuclear degeneration in ciliates: without fragmentation and with fragmentation. The latter pattern is the more frequent one.

Macronuclear degeneration without fragmentation is usually described as pycnosis. In this case, the macronucleus gradually decreases in size and its chromatin becomes homogeneous and stains very intensely with the Feulgen method. Macronuclear degeneration of this type is known to occur in *Chilodonella*,[140, 240] *Colpidium*,[35] *Tetrahymena*,[204] *Paramecium bur-saria*,[56] and some other species.

Degeneration of the macronucleus involving its fragmentation usually begins with its deformation. The nucleus forms protrusions and often assumes the shape of a loose skein consisting of thick, irregularly wound strands. The skein stage is characteristic of many *Paramecium* species,[38, 39, 104, 107] of macroconjugants of *Epistylis*,[32] *Vorticella*,[155] etc. Later on, the skein disintegrates into rounded fragments which become dispersed and gradually resorbed in the cytoplasm. In ciliates with moniliform macronuclei (e.g., *Stentor*), there is usually a simple fragmentation of the nuclear chain into separate nodes[60, 156] but in *Blepharisma undulans* the macronucleus condenses into a compact body before fragmentation.[14] The stretched macronuclei of *Bursaria* and *Euplotes* divide into separate segments without preceding condensation.[172, 203, 274]

In at least some ciliates the macronuclear fragments do not undergo any irreversible changes for a long time, remaining capable of regeneration into normal macronuclei. This phenomenon was first obtained experimentally in *Paramecium aurelia* by Sonneborn.[248, 250] Heating of the exconjugant to 38°C retards development of the macronuclear anlage and it does not divide during the second metagamic division of the exconjugant, but goes entirely into one of the daughter animals (Fig. 32, stage 2). In the other animal, devoid of macronuclear anlagen, a gradual regeneration is begun by the fragments of the old macronucleus. The latter segregate during several cell divisions (stages 3 to 5), until animals are formed having only one macro-nuclear fragment, which by that time has attained the size of a normal macronucleus and acquired the ability to divide (stage 6).

Sometimes macronuclear regeneration in the exconjugants also occurs spontaneously. Its frequency is sharply increased in strains having the recessive gene *am* in homozygous condition. In ciliates with this genotype the process of macronuclear division is seriously impaired. During the first

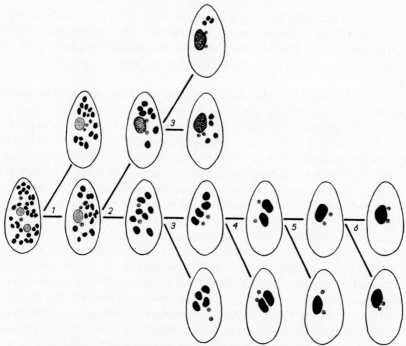

FIG. 32. Diagram of macronuclear regeneration in exconjugants of *Paramecium aurelia*. After Sonneborn.[250] 1 to 6—successive cell divisions; small circles with a dot are micronuclei, large dotted circles are macronuclear anlagen, black bodies are macronuclear fragments.

divisions of the exconjugant many individuals receive no new macronuclei and fragments of the old one, still present in the cytoplasm, regenerate normal new ones.[158, 252]

Macronuclear regeneration has also been obtained experimentally in *Paramecium woodruffi*[104] and in the suctorian *Cyclophrya katharinae*,[135] but the attempt failed in *P. caudatum*.[162]

As pointed out above (p. 37), the phenomenon of macronuclear regeneration is an important argument for macronuclear polyploidy. The ability of the fragments to regenerate shows that each of them contains one or several complete genomes capable of endomitotic replication. The resorption of the macronuclear fragments is apparently not autonomous, but somehow induced by the developing anlage of the new macronucleus. As soon as this influence ceases, the fragments stop resorption and begin regeneration.

In this respect the question about cytochemical changes in degenerating macronuclear fragments is of interest. In *Paramecium aurelia* there is no DNA synthesis in macronuclear fragments, judging by the absence of H^3-thymidine incorporation.[12] The DNA content of the fragments gradually decreases, as shown photometrically in *Epistylis*.[246] No quantitative data are presently available showing what part of the DNA must be lost to make the degeneration of the fragments irreversible. The mechanism of DNA destruction is also obscure. Possibly acid phosphatase takes part in this process, since it appears in degenerating macronuclear fragments of *Nyctotherus*.[236]

The RNA synthesis continues in macronuclear fragments of *Paramecium aurelia* for a long time, as shown by H^3-uridine or H^3-cytidine incorporation.[129] In macronuclear fragments of *Paramecium putrinum*, Jankowski[107] observed an active formation of RNA-rich nucleoli and their extrusion into the cytoplasm. Probably the inhibitory influence of the macronuclear anlagen on the fragments is directed upon destruction of DNA but not on RNA synthesis. The macronuclear fragments usually contain high quantities of RNA; and the RNA content of the cytoplasm of the exconjugants also increases.[90, 240, 291] Such observations have been frequently interpreted as direct "conversion" of the macronuclear DNA into RNA (e.g., ref. 245). In connection with this interpretation, as well as with the fact that loss of DNA by the fragments is more or less parallel to the DNA synthesis in macronuclear anlagen, Seshachar[238] and Gromowa[93] advanced a hypothesis about transfer of DNA from the old macronucleus into the new one. According to it, the DNA of the macronuclear fragments is not destroyed but converted into RNA, which migrated via the cytoplasm into the growing macronuclear anlage, where it becomes re-converted into DNA.

This hypothesis is in disagreement with modern knowledge of synthetic mechanisms and conversion possibilities of the nucleic acids, and therefore cannot be accepted in its original version. Now we can speak only about possibility of reutilization of low molecular fragments of DNA of the old macronucleus (probably of single nucleotides) during DNA replication in macronuclear anlagen. This possibility has been explored with autoradiographic methods, but the results are still difficult to interpret unequivocally. According to McDonald,[145] reutilization of DNA fragments takes place only in starving exconjugants of *Tetrahymena*, the material for DNA synthesis in the fed ones being of exogenous origin. According to Berech and Wagtendonk,[12] there is no reutilization at all in *Paramecium aurelia*, neither in fed nor in starving exconjugants.

VII. THEORIES OF MACRONUCLEAR STRUCTURE

1. The Macronucleus and Its Division from the Genetic Viewpoint

Examination of infusorian genetics, exceeding the limits of this review, is given in Preer's chapter (Chapter II). Here we are interested only with the question about use of genetic methods for analysis of the macronuclear structure.

It is now well known that the macronucleus contains genes determining the entire phenotype of the ciliate, in particular the mating type, the possible array of antigenic types, the maintenance and quantity of cytoplasmic kappa and other particles, etc. The dependence of the phenotypic characters on genes of the macronucleus has been best shown by Sonneborn's experiments[249, 250, 253] using macronuclear regeneration (see p. 70) to obtain strains with genetically different macronucleus and micronucleus. Only the parent genotype of the regenerated macronucleus became phenotypically manifested in these strains, though it was homozygous by a recessive gene, and the micronucleus contained the dominant allele. Micronuclear genes do not become phenotypically expressed at all and remain, according to Sonneborn, in an inactive state. Also the usual, but not invariable,[150] absence of RNA from the micronuclei[56, 192, 221] argues for inactivity of the micronuclear genes. The mechanism of inactivation of these genes is not yet known. Since it is presently supposed that histones can act as gene repressors, the data of Alfert and Goldstein[1] may be of interest. They showed that the micronucleus of *Tetrahymena* contains 67–74 per cent more histone per DNA unit than the macronucleus.

Numerous genetic studies also showed that the macronuclear genotype remains, as a rule, unchanged during long-term cultivation of the caryonides (leaving aside the possible mutations). Therefore the genes of the macronucleus must be normally reproduced and distributed among the daughter nuclei in such a way that both nuclei receive a complete set of genes.

The question arises whether macronuclear division is amitotic. Amitosis is usually defined as nuclear division in the interphase state, i.e., without preceding spiralization of chromosomes and their regular segregation. After amitosis, the daughter nuclei become aneuploid. This type of nuclear division is frequent in specialized tissue cells.

With this definition of amitosis, macronuclear division cannot be called amitotic. The macronuclear chromosomes surely leave the interphasic state and undergo a duplication cycle during division. Genetic data indicate that division of the polyploid macronucleus is accompanied by precise distribution of the genetic material and does not lead to aneuploidy or loss of genes even after many generations.

How can the precise distribution of genetic material be assured during macronuclear division? A priori either of two methods might be followed:

1. The genetic identity of the daughter macronuclei might be assured by purely statistical laws, with random segregation of separate chromosomes. The macronuclear polyploidy degree being sufficiently high, the daughter nuclei might receive a number of complete chromosome sets throughout a series of generations. But they would also receive a steadily increasing number of incomplete genomes; in other words, during clonal reproduction aneuploidy would increase, until it touched all or nearly all macronuclear genomes. This would lead to degeneration of the macronucleus. Since certain amicronucleate clones of *Tetrahymena* have already lived more than 30 years, this mechanism is hardly the real one. In any case, as pointed out

by Grell[77] and Heckmann,[99] this hypothesis requires additional postulates about compensatory processes which might correct the growing macronuclear aneuploidy. Asynchronous duplication of lacking chromosomes and/or elimination of excess ones could be such processes, but they have not been shown to occur. Chromatin extrusion phenomena (p. 66) might perhaps be related to elimination of surplus chromosomes,[62] but it is very difficult to conceive of a mechanism which might collect in the extrusion body all such chromosomes from the whole nucleus. Therefore it is more probable, that not surplus chromosomes, but excess genomes are eliminated during chromatin extrusion, i.e., that the latter serves to regulate not aneuploidy, but hyperpolyploidy of the macronucleus (see p. 69).

2. The genomes within the macronucleus may be in some way separated from each other, either morphologically or spatially, and therefore behave as segregation units during macronuclear division. If chromosomes of each genome are distinct from chromosomes of other genomes, the division of the polyploid macronucleus would result in distribution of complete chromosome sets among the daughter nuclei—the so-called *segregation of genomes.* [75, 77, 88, 90, 99, 250, 251] In this case no aneuploidy would arise and the genetic identity of the daughter nuclei would be assured even during random segregation of genomes, because all the latter are identical to each other, being formed from a single genome of the synkaryon derivative by means of endomitotic polyploidization during macronuclear anlage development.

Recognition of this latter mechanism is the basis of both principal theories of macronuclear structure—the theory of subnuclei by Sonneborn and the theory of composite chromosomes by Grell— which we will now consider.

2. The Theory of Subnuclei

In 1947, Sonneborn[250] advanced the idea that the macronucleus may consist of a great number of diploid *subnuclei,* delimited from each other by some kind of envelopes. The subnuclei were thought to be capable of autonomous reproduction by mitosis, and during macronuclear division to segregate at random between the daughter nuclei.

This theory is irreproachable from the genetic standpoint: it is supported by all the peculiarities of inheritance of the characters determined by macronuclear genes. Diploidy of the segregation units at macronuclear division is shown by the absence of homozygous specimens during long cultivation of clones with heterozygous macronuclei.[98, 157, 254] Macronuclear regeneration also supports this position.

However, until recently all attempts by morphological methods have failed to find anything like subnuclei. No membranes of separate subnuclei have been found electron microscopically in the macronucleus. No signs of small mitotic figures in the macronucleus have been observed with the light or with the electron microscope. Therefore many morphologists have answered negatively the question as to the presence of subnuclei within the macronucleus. Still, Raikov[199] recently succeeded in showing that the chromatin strands, visible in the macronucleus of Nassulidae, are diploid and become segregation units during macronuclear division, thus corresponding to the notion of subnuclei (see p. 58). But they replicate by endomitosis, not by mitosis, and are devoid of envelopes,[201] which forces us to modify the original theory of subnuclei, as will be discussed below (p. 79).

3. The Theory of Composite Chromosomes

The theory of composite chromosomes, ensuring genome segregation in a highly polyploid nucleus, was originally devised by Grell,[80] not for ciliate macronuclei but for the primary nucleus of the radiolarian *Aulacantha scolymantha*. This nucleus is very big and contains a huge number (more than 1000) of rather large chromosomes. Shortly before nuclear division, the chromosomes undergo spiralization and become longitudinally split, but during division both chromatids of each chromosome get into the same daughter nucleus. Thus, according to Grell, the nuclear division of *Aulacantha*, though resembling mitosis externally, is not mitosis, but is segregation of genomes.† But here the same question arises as in the case of macronuclei: how do the chromosomes of each genome keep together during nuclear division?

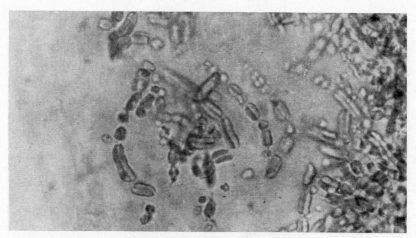

FIG. 33. Composite chromosomes of the radiolarian *Aulacantha scolymantha* (endometaphase stage). Part of a compressed acetocarmine stained central capsule, × 1500. After Grell.[80]

† This conclusion of Grell has been criticized by Cachon-Enjumet,[19] but in a recent paper Grell and Ruthman[91] continue to defend their position and strengthen it with new arguments.

A detailed study of the chromosomes of *Aulacantha* showed that at certain stages of the spiralization cycle they appear as segments, connected end-to-end (Fig. 33). The segments have distinctly different lengths and are longitudinally split. Grell believes that the segments are the true chromosomes while the chains are whole genomes, where the individual chromosomes are interconnected end-to-end. He calls such formations *composite chromosomes* ("Sammelchromosomen"). All composite chromosomes are homologous and their number equals the ploidy degree of the nucleus. If all this is true, the division cycle of the *Aulacantha* nucleus appears to be an alternation of endomitosis with genome segregation. During endomitosis, the composite chromosomes split longitudinally as a whole, i.e., without dis-

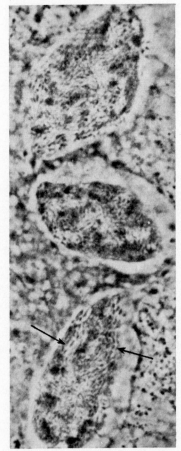

Fig. 34 A

FIG. 34. Paired composite chromosomes (at *arrows*) in the nodes of the moniliform macronucleus of *Loxophyllum meleagris*. Acetic alcohol fixation, phase contrast. A—× 1760, B—× 1950. After Ruthmann.[221]

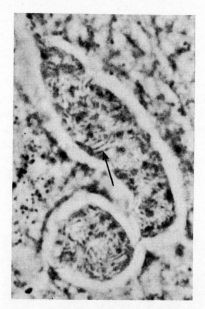

FIG. 34B

integrating into segments (single chromosomes). During nuclear division the composite chromosomes segregate at random. Since they are homologous this would not lead to aneuploidy.

Later, Grell[77, 89, 90] suggested that the same mechanism could well explain the structure and division of the infusorian macronucleus. At first this assumption was based on pure analogy but later, evidence for existence of composite chromosomes in the macronucleus began to accumulate. Ruthmann[221] observed junction of rod-like chromosomes into chains in the macronucleus of *Loxophyllum* (Fig. 34A, B). Each segment of a chain is split longitudinally, so that parallel pairs of identical chains arise. This fact confirms the possibility of endomitotic replication of whole composite chromosomes without their disintegration into individual segments, i.e., true chromosomes. During endomitotic duplication of the chromatin bodies (chromosomes) of the macronucleus of *Tokophrya*, they become arranged in parallel rows (Fig. 35A, B), as shown by Rudzinska.[219] Possibly they are connected into composite chromosomes as well.

Ruthmann and Heckmann[223] demonstrated that the longitudinal thread-like chromosomes of the *Bursaria* macronucleus are much longer than micronuclear chromosomes could be even at complete despiralization. These threads probably extend from one end of the stretched macronucleus to the other, and may correspond to composite chromosomes.

If this is true, it is easy to understand the significance of macronuclear condensation before division (see p. 52). A simple constriction of the elongate nucleus into two parts would lead to transverse rupture of all the composite chromosomes—i.e., to sharp aneuploidy of all genomes at once. It may be supposed that during macronuclear condensation the composite chromosomes become spiralized and shortened into compact segregation units, while sister composite chromosomes, formed by endomitosis, become separated. The shortened composite chromosomes segregate between the daughter nuclei, where they again stretch into long threads. Supporting this interpretation is the longitudinal contraction of these chromatin threads into the chromatin condensation centers (p. 53), which in *Bursaria* appear at the beginning of the macronuclear condensation.[223]

Possibly *Euplotes* also has composite chromosomes stretched along the macronucleus. In this case, passage of reorganization bands might signify asynchrony of DNA synthesis along each composite chromosome. Such

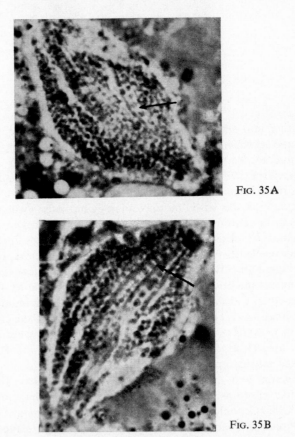

FIG. 35A

FIG. 35B

FIG. 35. Endomitotic duplication of chainwise arranged chromatin bodies (at *arrows*) in the macronucleus of *Tokophrya infusionum*. Phase contrast, × 1800. A and B—two focal planes. After Rudzinska.[219]

ideas (though without mention of the composite nature of chromosomes) have been developed by Gall,[69] who compared the DNA synthesis in the *Euplotes* macronucleus with the well-known asynchrony of DNA synthesis along mammalian chromosomes.

Finally, the theory of composite chromosomes is supported by the observations of Golikowa[72] and Ammermann,[5] who found that the chromosomes in developing macronuclear anlagen of *Nyctotherus* and *Stylonychia* are not only polytene, but also composite (p. 29, 30).

The question whether macronuclear composite chromosomes are haploid or diploid is not yet solved. As mentioned above (p. 74), genetic data argue for diploidy of macronuclear segregation units (whether subnuclei or composite chromosomes). But diploidy of segregation units may be a result not only of diploidy of composite chromosomes as such, but also of pairwise parallel union of haploid composite chromosomes resembling somatic conjugation.[90, 199] Somatic conjugation of composite polytene chromosomes has been actually observed by Golikowa[72] in the macronuclear anlage of *Nyctotherus*, but Ammermann[5] failed to find it in *Stylonychia*.

Let us draw some conclusions. Both theories proceed from the assumption that macronuclear chromosomes are united in groups corresponding to genomes. But they consider different aspects of the macronuclear structure. The theory of subnuclei is based mainly on genetic data and has a more abstract character, while the theory of composite chromosomes lays stress upon clarification of the cytological mechanisms of chromosome union and genome replication.

According to this author's opinion, there are no serious discrepancies between the theories of Sonneborn and of Grell. In any case, Raikov's[192, 199] observations may be interpreted in the light of either theory. In Nassulidae, each diploid chromatin strand, or subnucleus (see p. 58), stretches before division into a long thread which splits longitudinally (Fig. 20A, B). This thread may be interpreted as an endomitotically doubling composite chromosome (or a pair of composite chromosomes in the state of somatic conjugation).

A united theory of macronuclear structure may be created through synthesis of the two theories. For such a synthesis one must assume that subnuclei are identical with diploid composite chromosomes (or with pairs of haploid ones). The subnuclei have no membranes and usually no compact shape (with rare exceptions like Nassulidae), but look like long tangled threads. This explains why for a long time they failed to be discovered morphologically. The subnuclei replicate not by mitosis, but by endomitotic longitudinal splitting of the entire composite chromosome, without its breaking up into single chromosomes. The integrity of the genomes is thereby maintained throughout the entire cycle of macronuclear division. The subnuclei, or the composite chromosomes, segregate at random during macro-nuclear division. This does not lead to aneuploidy, since all composite chromosomes are homologous.

A number of questions concerning the macronuclear structure remain obscure. Here are some of them: Are the composite chromosomes diploid or haploid? If they are haploid, do they undergo a somatic conjugation? Are single chromosomes joined into a composite chromosome in a definite or a random sequence? How are the single chromosomes attached to each other? Further investigation of these problems is very desirable.

VIII. ROLE OF THE MACRONUCLEUS IN SYNTHETIC PROCESSES

As mentioned above, the macronucleus is a physiologically active nucleus, connected in one or another way with almost all metabolic processes of the ciliate. In amacronucleate animals, digestion of food very soon stops; pos-sibly, the synthesis of digestive enzymes depends on macronuclear genes. Amacronucleate body fragments never regenerate even if they contain micronuclei.[232] In most cases the presence of even a small piece of the macronucleus assures complete regeneration.[6, 232, 259, 264, 265, 284] The influence of the macronucleus on regeneration is species-specific: in *Stentor*, the interspecifically grafted macronucleus does not support regeneration of the cytoplasmic structures of the foreign species.[262] Regeneration seems to depend on species-specific gene products supplied by the macronucleus— probably on messenger RNA. This supposition is supported by the immediate inhibition of regeneration which follows blocking of the RNA synthesis in the macronucleus of *Euplotes* (by vancomycin or aza-uracil), though DNA synthesis continues.[293] In a similar way, inhibition of the macronuclear RNA synthesis in *Tetrahymena* with actinomycin D during the second half of the interdivision interval suppresses oral morphogenesis and division.[309] The dependence of the infusorian phenotype on macronuclear genes, shown by Sonneborn (see p. 73), also provides evidence for activity of the genetic apparatus of this nucleus.

In the light of modern knowledge about mechanisms of genic activity, we have to expect the macronucleus to synthesize considerable amounts of RNA and to give them off to the cytoplasm. This expectation has been fully con-firmed. The RNA synthesis in macronuclei is examined in detail in the chap-ter by Prescott and Stone (Vol. 2, Chapter II). Therefore we shall confine ourselves to a short summary of autoradiographic data discussed by Prescott and Stone, but examine more thoroughly the morphological pictures re-lated to macronuclear RNA synthesis.

Autoradiographic data show that the macronuclei of *Tetrahymena*[179, 180] and *Paramecium aurelia*[128] intensely synthesize RNA. The synthesis of RNA proceeds, unlike that of DNA, during the entire interdivision interval, either with a constant speed (*P. aurelia*), or more rapidly by the end of the interval (*Tetrahymena*), or more rapidly at its beginning (*Paramecium trichium*[95]). In *Euplotes*, RNA is synthesized throughout the macronucleus, both ahead and behind the reorganization band. But in the reorganization band itself, i.e., during DNA replication, there is no RNA synthesis.[180, 181, 256]

With short incorporation periods, only macronuclear RNA becomes labeled, the label appearing much later in the cytoplasm. When ciliates with pulse-labeled macronuclear RNA are placed in a non-radioactive medium, all labeled RNA is transferred to the cytoplasm rather soon;[128, 180] (see Figs. 17a and 17b in the chapter by Prescott and Stone). Amacronucleate fragments of *Tetrahymena* synthesize no RNA,[180] and amacronucleate *P. aurelia* very little.[131] From this it may be concluded that in ciliates all the RNA of the cell is of macronuclear origin.

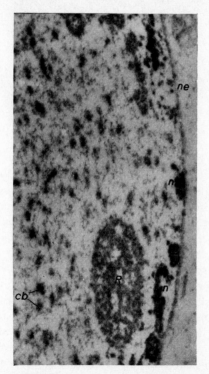

Fig. 36A

Fig. 36. Electron micrographs of the macronucleus of *Tetrahymena pyriformis*. After Elliott *et al.*[59] A—RNA bodies (*R*) and nucleoli (*n*) before nuclear division, × 13,600; B—RNA body at higher magnification (× 32,000); C—shifting of RNA bodies (*R*) to the macronuclear periphery and separation of blebs (*bl*), containing nucleoli (*n*) and RNA body material, from the macronucleus; × 8000. *Ne*—macronuclear envelope, *cb*—chromatin bodies, *mt*—mitochondria.

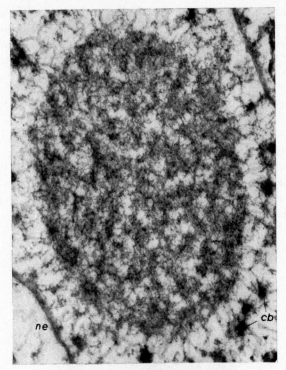

FIG. 36B

Autoradiography usually gives no indication as to what macronuclear structures are actually the sites of RNA synthesis. However, Stevens,[256] with electron microscopic autoradiography, showed that RNA precursors are incorporated in both chromatin bodies and nucleoli of the *Euplotes* macronucleus. And light microscopic observations by Ruthmann and Heck-mann[223] showed that tiny RNA particles adhere to chromatin threads (composite chromosomes?) of the macronucleus of *Bursaria*. In this case, RNA seems to be produced by specific loci of the chromatin threads.

Ruthmann[221] observed in *Loxophyllum*, that some chains of rod-like macronuclear chromosomes give positive cytochemical reactions for RNA, while other chains (composite chromosomes) of the same macronuclear node give negative ones. He supposes that at each given moment only a part of the macronuclear genomes is engaged in RNA synthesis. The proportion of RNA-producing composite chromosomes increases during macronuclear division. It is not yet clear whether this RNA is later transferred to the nucleoli, or is synthesized there independently.

The mechanism of transition into the cytoplasm of the RNA synthesized in the macronucleus is still little known. Elliott and co-workers[59] studied it in *Tetrahymena* with the electron microscope. Shortly before division

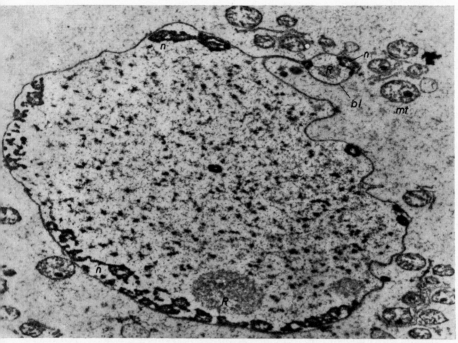

Fig. 36 C

(both the normal and the synchronized) large RNA containing bodies appear in the macronucleus (Fig. 36A). They contain no protein, thus differing from peripheral nucleoli, and have a fibrillar ultrastructure (Fig. 36B). Later on, the RNA bodies shift to the macronuclear periphery and disintegrate there, probably giving some RNA to the nucleoli. At the same time, the macronuclear envelope begins to form numerous blebs containing nucleoli and the residues of RNA bodies (Fig. 36C). These blebs become separated from the macronucleus.

However, in another strain of *Tetrahymena pyriformis* Flickinger[299] failed to confirm formation of RNA bodies and blebbing of the macronuclear envelope at any stage of the normal cell cycle. The basis of these differences in unknown.

Extrusion of nucleoli from the macronucleus has also been described in *Paramecium bursaria*[57] and *P. putrinum*,[107] but how they pass through the nuclear envelope is not known. Finally, in *Chlamydodon pedarius* a transition through pores of the nuclear envelope of ribosome-like granules from the macronuclear nucleoli has been reported.[117]

Cytoplasmic protein synthesis depends on RNA of macronuclear origin. Immediately after enucleation the incorporation of labeled precursors into cytoplasmic protein decreases by 50 per cent in *Tetrahymena*[180] and by 70–80 per cent in *Paramecium aurelia*.[131] In amacronucleate fragments of

Tetrahymena, the protein synthesis continues to decrease and gradually comes to zero approximately 8 hours after enucleation. By that time, the RNA content of the fragments has decreased by approximately 50 per cent. These data suggest that protein synthesis depends on some special RNA fraction which becomes exhausted earlier than other RNA fractions, probably on messenger RNA.

Little is known about protein synthesis in the macronucleus itself. Its extent can be estimated by the changes in the dry weight of the macronucleus, which can be measured by interferometry. In *Paramecium aurelia,* the macronuclear dry weight grows mainly during the second half of the interdivision interval.[132] In *Euplotes,* a twofold increase of the macronuclear dry weight is correlated with the passage of the reorganization bands, indicating that protein doubling occurs simultaneously with DNA replication.[304] No data are available about transition of macronuclear proteins into the cytoplasm.

IX. EVOLUTION OF THE MACRONUCLEUS

The preceding sections have shown that the polyploid macronucleus of the ciliates has a very complex internal organization. How could such a nucleus originate during phylogenesis?

To solve this problem, we have to answer the following three questions: (a) By what ways and at what stages of evolution did the ciliates acquire the nuclear dualism, i.e., the nuclear differentiation into macro- and micronuclei? (b) When and how did the macronuclear polyploidy arise—simultaneously with the nuclear dualism or later? (c) What may be the origin of such a peculiar type of macronuclear division as genome segregation: did it originate by transformation of mitosis or otherwise?

For a long time the ciliates were considered quite uniform in their nuclear apparatus, and the survival of any early phylogenetic stages of macronuclear development unlikely.†

However, comparative investigations of the last decade showed that a considerable number of ciliates have an aberrant nuclear apparatus. All these, without exception, belong to the lower holotrichs; most of them are representatives of a peculiar and probably very ancient interstitial fauna of marine sand. As will be shown below, we have reason to consider their nuclear apparatus primitive. According to the structure of their nuclei, they fall into two unequal groups. The smaller group includes homokaryotic ciliates (i.e., those without nuclear dualism). The larger group includes heterokaryotic ciliates (i.e., those which have nuclear dualism) with diploid macronuclei, unlike most ciliates which have polyploid macronuclei.

---

† We leave aside the Opalinidae, which were formerly included in the Ciliophora and often considered primitive ciliates devoid of nuclear dualism (hence the very name Protociliata). However, according to recent data, Opalinidae are more related to the flagellates than to the ciliates,[28, 286] and in any case they are not an ancestral group among Ciliophora.

1. Homokaryotic Ciliates

Only one genus of homokaryotic ciliates—*Stephanopogon*—is presently known, including two species, *S. mesnili* and *S. colpoda*. These marine forms belong to the lowest group of the ciliates, the Holotricha Gymnostomatida Rhabdophorina.

The absence of any nuclear dualism was originally discovered in *S. mesnili* by Lwoff,[138] who assigned much phylogenetic significance to this form, considering it related to the homokaryotic ancestors of the ciliates. Later, Lwoff[139] studied in detail the whole life cycle of *S. mesnili*. His results were so unusual that many investigators hesitated to accept them. But Dragesco[49] showed them to be correct for both *S. mesnili* and the other species, *S. colpoda*. I also had an opportunity to examine a series of preparations of *Stephanopogon colpoda*,† and I can confirm that the nuclear apparatus of this species is not differentiated into macronuclei and micronuclei (Fig. 37).

The life cycle of *S. colpoda* includes a stage of hypertrophic growth without cell division and a stage of multiple division within a reproduction cyst. The smallest of the active specimens have two identical nuclei (Fig. 37A). During growth of the trophont, the number of nuclei increases by mitoses (B, C). The mitotic nuclear divisions are often asynchronous, especially in animals with a considerable number of nuclei (C). The largest of the active forms have up to twelve and even sixteen nuclei. The mature trophonts encyst and within each cyst the cytoplasm separates (syntomy) into the number of parts equal to the number of nuclei (Fig. 37D). Later, but still before excystment, the single nucleus of each tomite divides mitotically into two (E), after which the buccal organoids become redifferentiated. Young binucleate individuals leave the cyst (Fig. 37A).

The nuclei of *Stephanopogon* are similar to the nuclei of some small amebae. They have a large central nucleolus and peripheral fine-granular chromatin (Fig. 37A, C, D). During nuclear division (Fig. 37F) the nucleolus does not dissolve, but divides by simple constriction ("promitosis" of the older authors—see ref. 11). After division of the nucleolus, very thin chromosomes appear in the equatorial region of the spindle (Fig. 37C, F), and two groups of them migrate toward the poles.

The life cycle of *S. mesnili* is, according to Lwoff,[139] practically the same. Unfortunately, sexual processes in *Stephanopogon* have never been studied, and even their existence is in doubt.

Phylogenetically, how shall we view the nuclear apparatus of *Stephanopogon*? In principle, two interpretations are possible: (1) Following Lwoff, we may consider the absence of nuclear dualism to be primary, i.e., consider these ciliates to be true homokaryotic forms. Or (2) we may suppose that

† These preparations were made by Dr. A. Cantacuzène (Roscoff, France) and brought to Leningrad by Professor G. Poljansky. I wish to express to them my sincere gratitude.

originally they were heterokaryotic ciliates and lost their nuclear dualism secondarily by reduction of one of the two categories of nuclei.

The primary nature of the homokaryotic nuclear apparatus of *Stephano-pogon* is favored by the very primitive systematic position of this genus, as well as by the structural difference of its nuclei from both micronuclei and

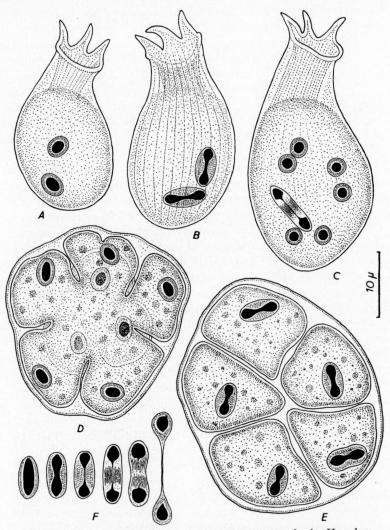

Fig. 37. Stages of the life cycle of *Stephanopogon colpoda*. Hemalum staining, × 1700 (original from preparations by A. Cantacuzène). A—young binucleate animal, B—division of its nuclei, C—multinucleate trophont with an asynchronous mitosis of one of the nuclei, D—syntomy of the encysted tomont into eight mononucleate tomites, E—mitosis of the nucleus of each tomite. F—stages of mitosis.

macronuclei of higher ciliates. Its nuclei differ from the micronuclei by the presence of nucleoli, and differ from the macronuclei by the definitely vesicular type of structure and the mitotic type of division. It is true that externally the nuclei of *Stephanopogon* resemble the diploid macronuclei of certain lower heterokaryotic ciliates (see below, p. 88). But diploid macronuclei do not divide, while *Stephanopogon* nuclei divide by mitosis. It is unlikely that the nuclei of *Stephanopogon* were ever diploid macronuclei which, after loss of the micronuclei, reacquired mitotic ability, since differentiation of somatic diploid nuclei seems to be irreversible (see p. 107). These facts make unlikely a secondary origin for the homokaryosis of *Stephanopogon*. The nuclear apparatus of this ciliate seems to correspond to the primitive condition.

The presence of homokaryotic primitive forms among the lower holotrichs provides evidence that nuclear dualism arose within the class Ciliata, i.e., later than the complex of other features characterizing the ciliates.

2. Ciliates with Diploid Macronuclei

Presently known among the lower Holotricha are almost 100 species of heterokaryotic ciliates which have macronuclei of a quite peculiar structure, bearing no resemblance to the above described structure of the polyploid macronuclei. This is the case in all representatives of the families Trachelocercidae (genera *Trachelocerca*, *Tracheloraphis*, and *Trachelonema*), Loxodidae (genera *Loxodes* and *Remanella*), and Geleiidae (genus *Geleia*), as well as in all members of the genera *Kentrophoros*, *Ciliofaurea*, and *Cryptopharynx*, of which the systematic position is not yet clear.[48, 49, 189, 190, 193] Except for the genus *Loxodes* with three or four fresh water species, nearly all these ciliates belong to the interstitial fauna of marine sand.

Studies of the karyology of ciliates of this group began with *Loxodes*. As early as 1876 Bütschli,[18] and thereafter Balbiani,[7] Joseph,[111] Kasanzeff,[118] and Rossolimo[211] noticed the unusual structure of the macronuclei of *Loxodes* and succeeded in gaining a correct understanding of its nuclear changes during division. The nuclear apparatus of some Trachelocercidae was examined by Lebedew,[136] but he failed to interpret correctly both nuclear structure and nuclear behavior during cell division. He failed also to find the micronuclei. Therefore Lebedew's paper is now of purely historical interest.

For a long time the nuclei of *Loxodes* have been considered an isolated curious exception, and the nuclei of the Trachelocercidae a peculiar "protozoological riddle", no phylogenetic significance being attributed to either case. The similarity between the nuclei of *Loxodes* and *Trachelocerca* also remained unnoticed, mainly because the nuclei of the latter have been described incorrectly. Only after Lebedew's errors were rectified and a rather wide distribution of the nuclear apparatus of the *Loxodes-Trachelocerca* type became known, did its study with modern methods begin. At present, due mainly to investigations of Fauré-Fremiet, Raikov, Dragesco, and Torch, the nuclear apparatus is being studied in detail in three species of *Loxodes*,[63, 190] five species of *Tracheloraphis*,[50, 189, 267] three species of *Remanella*,[195, 196] three species of *Geleia*,[191, 197] and one species of *Kentrophoros*.[63]

A. STRUCTURE OF THE NUCLEAR APPARATUS

All ciliates considered here have more than one macronucleus. The minimum number of nuclei met with in these forms—two macronuclei and one micronucleus—occurs, e.g., in *Loxodes rostrum*, *Remanella granulosa* (Fig. 42 A), and *R. rugosa* (Fig. 43 A). Here the macronuclei lie one behind the other with the micronucleus between them. *Loxodes striatus* has two macronuclei located at a distance from each other, and two micronuclei, one near each macronucleus (Fig. 38). In many Trachelocercidae the whole nuclear apparatus, consisting of several macronuclei and several micronuclei, is collected in the middle of the body into a compact "nuclear group" (Fig. 44). The micronuclei usually lie near the center of the group while the macronuclei lie at its periphery. In all families there are many multinucleate forms with up to several dozen of both macronuclei and micronuclei. These numerous nuclei may be freely scattered through the cytoplasm, as in *Loxodes magnus* (Fig. 39), or may be collected into several nuclear groups consisting of a relatively constant number of macronuclei and micronuclei (e.g., in *Tracheloraphis discolor* or *T. caudatus*[50, 193]).

Among the various species, the micronuclei of all these forms differ only in size, having almost identical structure. They are compact and sharply Feulgen-positive (Fig. 40 A), their membrane usually tightly applied to the chromatin mass and, with the light microscope, visible only during mitosis. The chromatin fills the micronucleus, looks homogeneous, and stains with methyl green and also with toluidine blue (Fig. 40 B) and other basic stains. Ribonuclease treatment leaves the micronuclear stainability unchanged, while deoxyribonuclease destroys its stainability with Feulgen and methyl green indicating that the micronuclei are rich in DNA and lack RNA. They contain also much basic protein as well as some non-histone protein.[189-91, 195-7]

The micronuclei of these ciliates have been little studied electron microscopically; in *Tracheloraphis caudatus* such study has shown the micronucleus surrounded by an envelope consisting of two membranes, and filled with a densely packed fibrillar material obviously corresponding to the chromatin (Fig. 45).

Thus, the micronuclei of the ciliates considered here seem to be more or less similar structurally and chemically to those of the ciliates in general.

The structure of the macronuclei is, on the other hand, rather unusual. These nuclei are comparatively small, rarely exceeding 10–15 μ in diameter. Their form may vary from spherical to oval, elongate, or bean-shaped

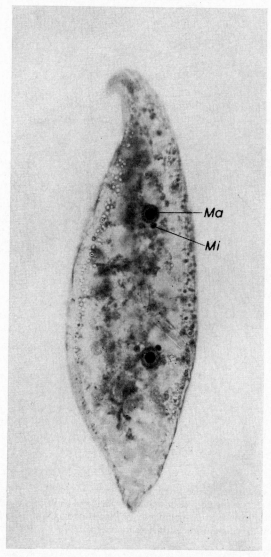

FIG. 38. *Loxodes striatus* showing two macronuclei (*Ma*) and two micronuclei (*Mi*). Hemalum stained whole mount, × 600 (original).

(Figs. 40, 42, 43), but they never have the complexity characteristic of the
macronuclei of many higher ciliates (ribbon-like, moniliform, branched,
etc.). Their structural diversity depends mainly on their nucleolar apparatus.
They all have one common feature—they are comparatively poor in DNA,
thus differing sharply from the polyploid macronuclei of the majority of
ciliates.

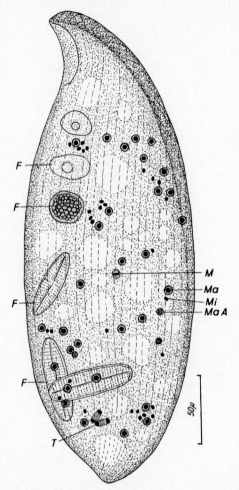

FIG. 39. *Loxodes magnus* containing thirty macronuclei (*Ma*), thirty micro-nuclei (*Mi*), three macronuclear anlagen (*MaA*) and showing asynchronous micronuclear mitoses; one metaphase (*M*) and two telophases (*T*); *F*—food inclusions. Hemalum stained whole mount, × 360. After Raikov.[190]

As an example, let us consider a macronucleus of *Loxodes magnus*.[190] This is a comparatively small (about 7 μ in diameter), spherical nucleus possessing a large central nucleolus (Fig. 40). It stains rather faintly with Feulgen, the Feulgen-positive structures being localized at the nuclear periphery in the form of small granules (Fig. 40A). These granules also stain with methyl green. RNase and DNase tests show that all the DNA of the macronucleus is localized in these granules, and that they contain no or very little RNA. Basic proteins may also be demonstrated in them. Another category of peripheral granules (micronucleoli) are Feulgen-nega-

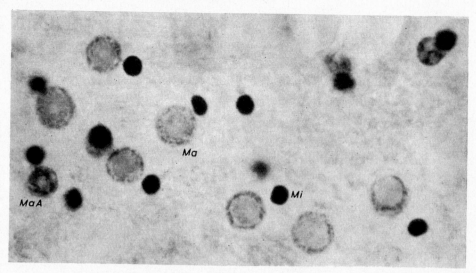

FIG. 40 A

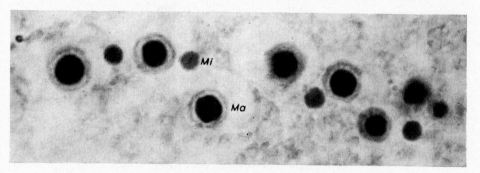

FIG. 40 B

FIG. 40. Nuclei of *Loxodes magnus* (× 1500). A—Feulgen–light green; after Raikov *et al.*[202]; B—toluidine blue (original). *Ma*—macronuclei, *Mi*—micronuclei, *MaA*—macronuclear anlagen.

tive and RNA-containing. Thus, the quantity of chromatin in a *Loxodes* macronucleus is moderate, in no way comparable with the huge amount of chromatin in the polyploid macronuclei. As a result, the very type of macronuclear structure is diverse, not massive but vesicular, with a central nucleolus and well expressed karyolymph (Fig. 40), resembling the nuclei of some amebae more than the macronuclei of the Infusoria.

The small DNA content proved to be a feature common to macronuclei of all species of this group. In some species the DNA is finely dispersed through the macronuclear karyolymph, which then gives a faint, diffuse, or finely granular Feulgen reaction (*Loxodes, Geleia*). In other species, the

4*

chromatin is concentrated in larger granules or in a few chromocenters, the remaining karyolymph being Feulgen-negative (*Remanella rugosa*, many Trachelocercidae—Figs. 46, 48). There is a clear parallelism between the size and the DNA content of the micronuclei on the one hand and the quantity of Feulgen-positive material in the macronuclei on the other. The species with large, brightly Feulgen-staining micronuclei also have macronuclei with more DNA [*Tracheloraphis dogieli*,[189] *Loxodes magnus*[190]], while in species with small micronuclei the Feulgen-positive structures of the macronuclei are almost invisible, e.g., in *Geleia* species.[191, 197] In general, visual estimation of the DNA content of macronuclei of many species leaves a clear impression that within a species the amount of DNA in one macronucleus and one micronucleus is approximately equal.

Proceeding from these observations, Raikov[188, 189] supposed that the macronuclei of the lower ciliates considered here do not become polyploid, but retain a diploid chromosome set and correspondingly a diploid DNA content.

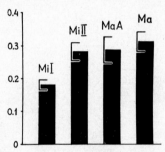

FIG. 41. Mean DNA content of G_1 micronuclei (*Mi I*), G_2 micronuclei (*Mi II*), macronuclear anlagen (*MaA*) and adult macronuclei (*Ma*) of *Loxodes magnus* (in arbitrary units). Three standard errors are shown in both directions of the mean. After Raikov et al.[202]

This idea has been recently verified in *Loxodes magnus*[202] using microphotometrical methods of DNA determination. The results are presented in Fig. 41. The adult macronuclei (*Ma*), as well as the developing ones (*MaA*), proved to contain practically the same amount of DNA as micronuclei in the G_2 phase (*Mi II*). Thus, the macronuclei of *Loxodes* (and probably of all other ciliates of this group) are actually diploid.

A strong development of the nucleolar apparatus in the diploid macronuclei indirectly indicates a high metabolic activity in them. These macronuclei usually have one large central nucleolus—e.g., in all species of *Loxodes* (Figs. 38, 39, 40), in *Remanella granulosa* (Fig. 42 A), *Geleia nigriceps*,[191] and some Trachelocercidae.[193] In other species, the macronuclei contain a small number (2–4) of comparatively large nucleoli, e.g., in *Tracheloraphis caudatus* (Fig. 45), *T. margaritatus* (Fig. 46), etc. Finally, in some forms there are many nucleoli scattered in the macronuclear karyolymph (*Remanella*) *rugosa*—Fig. 43 A). The nucleoli are especially numerous (several dozen) in the macronuclei of *Geleia orbis* and *G. murmanica*.[197]

The nucleoli of the diploid macronuclei are rather uniform cytochemically. They are always strongly basophilic (Fig. 40 B), the basophilia being RNase-sensitive. Thus they are rich in RNA. They also contain high concentrations

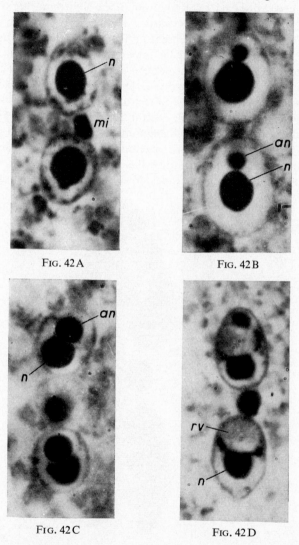

FIG. 42 A   FIG. 42 B

FIG. 42 C   FIG. 42 D

FIG. 42. Nucleolar cycle in macronuclei of *Remanella granulosa*. Iron hematoxylin (A–C) and hemalum (D) staining, × 3000. After Raikov.[195] A—simple nucleoli (*n*) in both macronuclei; B–C—growth of additional nucleoli (*an*); D—dissolution of additional nucleoli forming RNA-vacuoles (*rv*); *mi*—micronucleus.

of proteins. Their reaction for basic proteins is usually weakly or moderately positive.[190, 191, 195]

With relation to the idea of high metabolic activity of the diploid macronuclei, morphological pictures, suggesting passage of RNA from macronuclear nucleoli into cytoplasm, are of considerable interest. Such phenomena have been observed by Raikov in *Geleia nigriceps*,[191] *G. orbis, G. murmanica*,[197] *Remanella granulosa, R. rugosa*,[195] and *R. multinucleata*.[196] They seem to be absent in Trachelocercidae and in *Loxodes*.

Cyclical changes of the nucleolar apparatus appear periodically in *Remanella granulosa*. In each given moment approximately 15 per cent of the animals in a population are involved. During the intervals between two nucleolar cycles, which seem thus to last longer than the cycles themselves, both macronuclei have one simple central nucleolus (Fig. 42 A). The changes begin with the appearance, in each macronucleus, of an additional nucleolus (B), which rapidly increases in size, reaching that of the main nucleolus (C). At the same time, the additional nucleolus becomes surrounded with a clear vacuole which then contacts the inner side of the nuclear membrane, where-

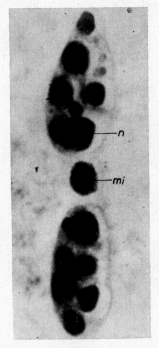

FIG. 43 A

FIG. 43. Nucleolar cycle in macronuclei of *Remanella rugosa*. Hemalum (A, B) and mercuric bromphenol blue (C) staining, × 2400. After Raikov.[195] A—usual nucleoli (*n*) in both macronuclei, B—formation of RNA-vacuoles (*rv*), C—complete dissolution of nucleoli; *mi*—micronucleus.

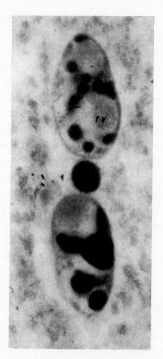

FIG. 43 B

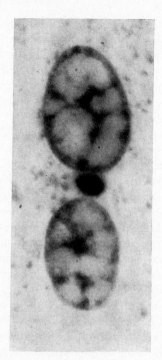

FIG. 43 C

upon the nucleolus loses its sharp outline, as if dissolving in the contents of the vacuole (D). RNA and protein can be demonstrated cytochemically in the latter. Further on, the intensity of the reactions for these substancet diminishes in the vacuole, being preserved for the longest time in that pars of it, which is adjacent to the macronuclear envelope (Fig. 42 D). This produces the impression that the RNA-rich material of the additional nucleolus, in a finely dispersed state, gradually migrates from the macronucleus into the cytoplasm. Accumulations of RNA, possibly of macronuclear origin, are sometimes met with in the cytoplasm adjacent to the macronuclei.

In *Remanella rugosa*, the nucleolar changes seem to last relatively longer since they involve a larger proportion of individuals (~46 per cent) at each given moment. As already mentioned, normal macronuclei of this species contain up to 10 nucleoli (Fig. 43 A). The changes begin with dissolution of some nucleoli, leading to the formation of several RNA-containing vacuoles within the macronucleus (Fig. 43 B). Finally, all nucleoli dissolve (Fig. 43 C), and the RNA disappears from the vacuolar contents, probably migrating into the cytoplasm.

No connection of the nucleolar cycles with cytokinesis could be found in either *R. granulosa* or *R. rugosa*. During one interdivision interval, they are probably repeated more than once.[195]

In *Geleia orbis* and *G. murmanica*, large "spherules", rich in RNA and protein, are formed among the numerous small nucleoli of the macronuclei. Later on, they dissolve, giving rise to RNA-containing intranuclear vacuoles. Unlike *Remanella*, in both *Geleia* species the passage of RNA from the macronuclear vacuoles into the cytoplasm proceeds not by diffuse "filtration", but by pouring of the vacuole contents out of the nucleus through a gap in the nuclear envelope.[197]

Finally, in *Geleia nigriceps* the RNA-containing "spherule" does not dissolve in a vacuole but leaves the macronucleus as a unit through a rupture of the nuclear envelope. Shortly after extrusion, the "spherule" may be observed in the cytoplasm. It is of interest that these "RNA-spherules" are formed inside the large central nucleolus and only later pass at first into the karyolymph, then into the cytoplasm. Moreover, a relation between the nucleolar cycle and cytokinesis could be established in *G. nigriceps*: the "spherules" leave the macronuclei shortly before cell division.[191]

These data support the hypothesis concerning the high metabolic activity of the diploid macronuclei. These nuclei seem to be engaged in active synthesis of RNA which then migrates into the cytoplasm in one way or another.

Quite recently, RNA synthesis in diploid macronuclei has been shown in direct autoradiography. Torch[268] showed the macronuclei of *Tracheloraphis* sp. to incorporate tritiated cytidine and uridine (the label probably accumulating in the nucleoli). In the cytoplasm, the labeled RNA appeared much later. The macronuclear RNA synthesis can be blocked with actinomycin D,[307] but the cytoplasm continues, though slowly, to incorporate H^3-uridine. Thus, *Tracheloraphis* seems to possess a nucleus-independent cytoplasmic system of RNA synthesis.

In the macronuclei of many Trachelocercidae, very peculiar crystalloids appear. They usually have an elongated shape (cylindric or prismatic), and lie free in the karyolymph. There is usually one per macronucleus. I observed them in *Trachelocerca coluber* (Fig. 44), *Tracheloraphis prenanti*, *T. incaudatus*, and other species. These crystalloids show a high protein content, judging by cytochemical reactions (Fig. 44), and probably consist of a crystalline protein. Their function remains obscure. No extrusion of these crystalloids into the cytoplasm has ever been observed. They show some basophilia, but whether they contain RNA is not clear. In any case, if RNA is present, it must have a very high turnover stability, since Torch[268] failed to find any incorporation of RNA precursors in macronuclear crystalloids of *Tracheloraphis* sp. even with 24 hours of incubation.

Electron microscopical studies of diploid macronuclei are just beginning. Mashansky[142] investigated the macronuclei of *Loxodes rostrum* and found the central nucleolus to consist of a compact plexus of electron dense fibers, about 200–300 Å in diameter. Besides the main nucleolus, many small additional nucleoli were seen among the peripheral chromatin elements, obviously corresponding to the RNA-positive granules of light microscopy.[190] The most interesting fact reported by Mashansky is that no chromatin ("small") bodies, so characteristic of the polyploid macronuclei (see above, p. 15), are present in the peripheral Feulgen-positive area of a *Loxodes* macronucleus. The chromatin elements of the latter are represented by tangled 150–200 Å thick fibrils, which enter both main and additional nucleoli.

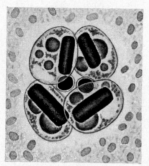

FIG. 44. The nuclear group of *Trachelocerca coluber*; four macronuclei containing nucleoli and protein crystalloids, and two micronuclei. Mercuric bromphenol blue staining, × 2300 (original).

Quite recently, the author of this review together with J. Dragesco began an electron microscopic study of the nuclei of *Tracheloraphis caudatus*. The nuclear apparatus of this species is formed of many nuclear groups, each consisting of four macronuclei and two micronuclei. Figure 45 shows a section of one of the nuclear groups. The macronuclei (as well as the micronuclei) are surrounded by double porous membranes. Moreover, a third membrane, the outermost one, surrounds the whole nuclear group. Probably it is this membrane which holds the nuclei together. The macronuclear nucleoli, both large and small, consist of densely packed ribosome-like granules and possibly some fibrils as well. The macronuclei lack chromatin ("small") bodies, just as in *Loxodes*. The chromatin elements are poorly delimited from the karyolymph; they seem to consist of a network of thin twisted fibrils about 100 Å in diameter.

Thus, the ultrastructure of the diploid macronuclei differs significantly from that of polyploid nuclei. In their fine structure, diploid macronuclei are more like the vesicular nuclei of other protozoan and metazoan cells, where the chromatin elements also consist of a loose network of chromosomal microfibrils (for reviews see refs. 151, 206).

B. NUCLEAR BEHAVIOR AT CELL DIVISION

The second remarkable peculiarity of the macronuclei of this group of lower ciliates (besides their diploidy) is their lack of any kind of division. They never divide; during cytoplasmic division they are distributed between the daughter animals, resulting in a decrease in their number. The normal

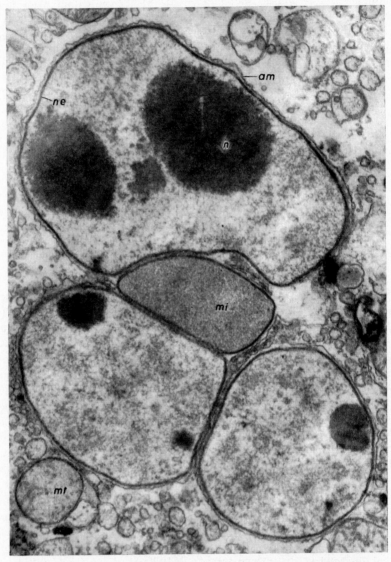

Fig. 45. Electron micrograph of a section through one of the nuclear groups of *Tracheloraphis caudatus*. Three macronuclei and one micronucleus (*mi*) are seen; *ne*—macronuclear envelope, *am*—additional membrane surrounding the nuclear group, *n*—nucleolus, *mt*—mitochondrion. Lead hydroxide staining, × 15,000 (original by Raikov and Dragesco).

number is restored by transformation of several micronuclei, reproducing by mitosis, into macronuclei. Thus, development of macronuclear anlagen occurs in lower ciliates with diploid macronuclei in a regular manner during the cycle of each cell division, while in most higher ciliates it takes place only after conjugation or autogamy.

The absence of macronuclear division and the transformation of micronuclei into macronuclei were observed for the first time in *Loxodes* by Bütschli.[18] It is now recognized that this peculiarity is common to all species with diploid macronuclei.

In multinucleate forms, the nuclei are usually segregated at random during cytokinesis, the daughter animals often receiving diverse numbers of both macronuclei and micronuclei. This seems to be one of the conditions leading to the wide variability in number of nuclei in such species (e.g., in *Remanella multinucleata* there may be from seven to thirty-five macronuclei). During division in *Tracheloraphis margaritatus*[189] both macronuclei and micronuclei become randomly distributed between the daughter individuals (Fig. 46); micronuclear mitoses are rare during plasmotomy. The nuclei of multinucleate *Tracheloraphis dogieli*,[189] *Loxodes magnus*,[63, 190] *Remanella multinucleata*,[63, 196] and *Geleia murmanica*[197] behave during cell division in exactly the same way.

The diploid macronuclei do not synthesize DNA; this absence of DNA replication may be closely related to the absence of macronuclear division. The absence of macronuclear DNA synthesis has been shown autoradiographically in *Tracheloraphis* sp. by Torch,[268] who failed to obtain any macronuclear incorporation of H^3-thymidine. The DNA of the diploid macronuclei obviously has a very high metabolic stability: all the DNA of a given macronucleus comes directly from the micronucleus, from which the former has developed, and is never renewed during the life-span of the macronucleus.

In multinucleate species, the reorganization of the nuclear apparatus, restoring the normal number of macronuclei, usually occurs during the interval between two cell divisions. The micronuclei reproduce by mitoses, usually asynchronous mitoses (Fig. 39). This asynchrony of micronuclear mitoses has been confirmed microphotometrically in *Loxodes magnus*; the population of micronuclei in each specimen proved to be nearly always a mixture of nuclei undergoing the G_1, S, and G_2 periods of the mitotic cycle.[202] Some mitoses may occur during cytokinesis as well, but their frequency is not higher than that during the interdivision interval. In *Tracheloraphis dogieli*, the micronuclear mitoses are more synchronized, but never fully; about 70 per cent is average.

The morphology of micronuclear mitosis has been studied in *Loxodes*,[190, 211] *Tracheloraphis margaritatus*, *T. dogieli*,[189] and some other species (Fig. 48, B, C, E). The spindle is intranuclear in all cases (the micronuclear envelope does not dissolve); no centrioles are visible. The micronuclear

4a*

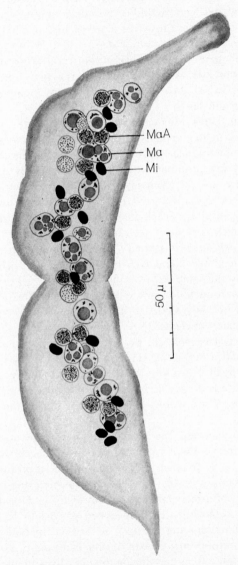

FIG. 46. Division of *Tracheloraphis margaritatus*. Passive segregation of macronuclei (*Ma*), micronuclei (*Mi*) and macronuclear anlagen (*MaA*) between the daughter animals. Feulgen–light green, × 660. After Raikov.[189]

chromosomes are numerous, rod-like; they split longitudinally in metaphase. The diploid chromosome number in *Tracheloraphis margaritatus* and *T. dogieli* is approximately 68, in *T. phoenicopterus*, 34, in *Trachelocerca coluber*, 52 to 56 (Fig. 48).

The mitoses lead to an increase in the number of micronuclei; later, some of these transform into macronuclear anlagen. In multinucleate species the development of the anlagen is also asynchronous; it may occur at every moment of the cell division cycle (including cytokinesis itself—Fig. 46). The number of macronuclear anlagen varies widely from one specimen to another; and in a single animal, several anlagen may be at different stages of development.

The development of a macronuclear anlage begins with a marked swelling of the micronucleus and the simultaneous appearance in it of thin thread-like chromosomes ("spireme" phase). This phase resembles mitotic prophase. Then the chromosomes condense, and chromatin granules may be seen in the anlage (Fig. 46). These granules are probably shortened chromosomes or their heterochromatic regions. At this stage, the anlage still contains no nucleoli and no RNA.

Unlike macronuclear development in higher ciliates, no signs of endomitotic duplication of the chromosomes of the anlagen could be found during development of diploid macronuclei. According to photometrical data, there is also no DNA synthesis in developing macronuclei.[202] During further development of the anlagen, their volume grows still more. In some species, the chromatin granules become dispersed (possibly the chromosomes uncoil), while in others they fuse into larger blocks or chromocenters characterizing the adult macronuclei. At the same time, small Feulgen-negative nucleoli, containing RNA, appear in the macronuclear anlagen (Fig. 40A). The nucleoli grow rapidly; in *Loxodes* they fuse with each other into the large central nucleolus.

As a result of transformation of some micronuclei into macronuclei, the number of the latter becomes supplemented, so that there is no progressive decrease in number of nuclei in successive cell generations.

It is obvious that at least some of the micronuclei divide more than once during each interval between two cell divisions. If the macronuclear number is twice that of the micronuclei (and this is frequent in *Loxodes magnus* and other multinucleate species), all the micronuclei must divide twice during this interval. Indeed, if immediately after cell division a specimen possessed $2x$ macronuclei (Ma) and x micronuclei (Mi), then after two mitoses of all the micronuclei it will have $2x$ Ma and $4x$ Mi; $2x$ Mi being transformed into macronuclear anlagen (MaA), the nuclear number will become $2x$ Ma, $2x$ MaA and $2x$ Mi. Finally, after the end of the anlagen development there will be $4x$ Ma and $2x$ Mi, double the initial number.

In species with a small and constant number of nuclei, the micronuclear mitoses and the formation of macronuclear anlagen are usually strictly synchronous and occur during cytokinesis. Let us consider as examples *Loxodes rostrum* and *L. striatus*.[188, 190]

In *Loxodes rostrum* (Fig. 47A), the two macronuclei of the mother animal become segregated during cytokinesis in such a way that each daughter receives one. The single micronucleus divides mitotically twice in succession, each daughter animal receiving two micronuclei. One of the latter transforms into a macronuclear anlage by the end of cytokinesis. After completion of the macronuclear development the initial number of nuclei—two macronuclei and one micronucleus—becomes restored.

In other species having the same number and position of nuclei, the nuclear reorganization proceeds exactly in the same manner, e.g., in *Geleia nigriceps*,[191] *G. orbis*,[197] *Remanella rugosa* and *R. granulosa*.[195]

In *Loxodes striatus* (Fig. 47B) the sequence of nuclear events is somewhat different. Both mother micronuclei divide once, forming four so that each daughter receives two mother micronuclei and one mother macronucleus. One of the micronuclei gives rise to the anlage of the second daughter macronucleus, while the other micronucleus divides to form the two daughter micronuclei.

Thus the two macronuclei of every specimen of *Loxodes rostrum* or *L. striatus* are of different age; one of them is the old macronucleus, received from the mother animal, while the other is the young macronucleus, formed during the last cell division. To avoid unnecessary complication of the diagram (Fig. 47), the young macronucleus in the anterior daughter cell is posterior, while in the posterior daughter cell the young macronucleus is anterior. In reality, in both species (and also in *Geleia orbis*, *G. nigriceps*, *Remanella rugosa*, and *R. granulosa*) the young macronucleus is always anterior, since the whole nuclear group of the anterior daughter animal turns with the macronuclear anlage forward before plasmotomy is complete.

The macronuclei of *L. magnus* are also of different age. This circumstance was first pointed out by Fauré-Fremiet,[63] who stated the inapplicability to *Loxodes* of the term "caryonide".

In species with the whole nuclear apparatus united into a compact group, the reorganization processes are in principle similar. For example, the nuclear group of *Trachelocerca coluber* consists of four macronuclei and two micronuclei (Fig. 48A). At the beginning of cytokinesis both micronuclei divide mitotically (B, C), and the nuclear group splits into the two groups of the future daughter animals (D and D'). Here also, the macronuclei are distributed without division, so that each daughter nuclear group consists at first of two macronuclei and two micronuclei (D). Later, both micronuclei divide mitotically for the second time (Fig. 48E), resulting in the formation of four micronuclei in each daughter group (F). Two of them, and exactly those which lie farther from the old macronuclei, transform into macronuclear anlagen (G). As usual, the anlagen at first contain chromatin granules and no nucleoli; they also show no signs of endomitosis. Nucleoli appear in

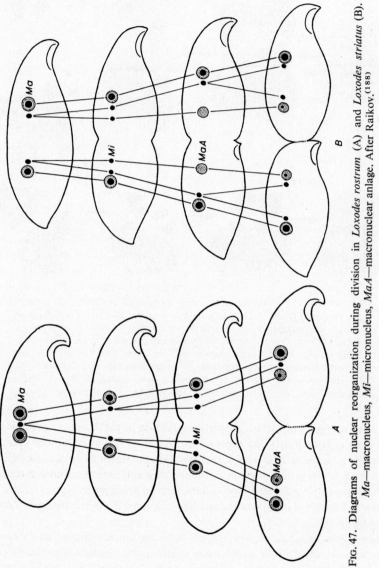

FIG. 47. Diagrams of nuclear reorganization during division in *Loxodes rostrum* (A) and *Loxodes striatus* (B). *Ma*—macronucleus, *Mi*—micronucleus, *MaA*—macronuclear anlage. After Raikov.[188]

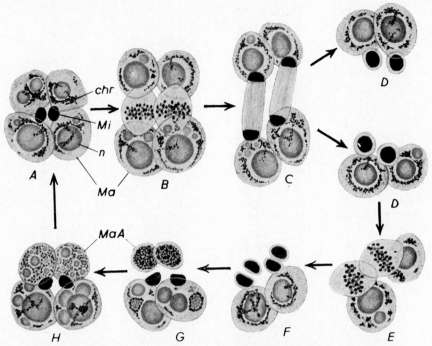

FIG. 48. Nuclear reorganization during division of *Trachelocerca coluber*.
Feulgen–light green, × 2300 (original). A—nuclear group of a non-dividing
animal; B—metaphase, C—telophase of the first mitosis of both micronuclei; D and D′—separation of the daughter nuclear groups; E—metaphase of the second micronuclear mitosis (here and further only one
daughter nuclear group is shown); F—stage after the second mitosis; G,
H—formation and growth of the macronuclear anlagen (*MaA*). *Ma*—
macronucleus, *Mi*—micronucleus, *n*—nucleoli, *chr*—macronuclear chromatin elements.

growing anlagen only after complete separation of the daughter animals (H);
the normal constitution of the nuclear groups is restored in the daughter
animals. Exactly as in *Loxodes*, the macronuclei here are always of different
age: the nuclear group of every specimen contains two macronuclei received
from the mother cell, and two others formed from micronuclei at the last
division. Exactly the same is the nuclear behavior during division in *Tracheloraphis* sp.[267]

The question about longevity of individual macronuclei also deserves
attention. As shown above, the macronuclei pass, during cell division, from
one generation into another, being only "diluted" by newly forming
macronuclei. The question is whether a macronucleus may pass in such a
way through an indefinite number of generations, or whether its longevity is
restricted. Fauré-Fremiet[63] observed in *Loxodes magnus* pycnotic macronuclei, which he considered to be senile and degenerating. Raikov[190]

confirmed these observations and showed that pycnotic macronuclei form, at average, 2 to 10 per cent of the total number of macronuclei in *L. magnus*. Provided the number of old macronuclei is halved at each cell division, such a relation indicates that individual macronuclei live as long as four to seven cell generations.

In *Loxodes striatus*, having two macronuclei, a nuclear anomaly is sometimes met:[190] the micronucleus lying near the posterior macronucleus divides asynchronously, and one of the daughter micronuclei gives rise to the anlage of a third macronucleus. This phenomenon may be connected with periodical replacement of the old macronucleus, which in this species is always the posterior. Degenerating macronuclei have also been observed in *Geleia murmanica*.[197]

Thus, in all species of ciliates having diploid macronuclei, every cell division is accompanied by a peculiar nuclear reorganization, including extra divisions of some or all micronuclei and the transformation of a number of these derivatives into macronuclei. Fauré-Fremiet[63] pointed out that such a reorganization process corresponds to the notion of "endomixis". In fact, "endomixis" is usually defined as transformation of a micronucleus into a macronucleus without meiosis and karyogamy. Therefore he proposed to say that each division of the ciliate is accompanied here by "endomixis". The author of the present review formerly used this terminology.[188-90] But presently it appears to me more correct to avoid using here the term "endomixis", since this term has been used for a long time to designate processes of a completely different origin, namely, the secondarily agamic processes of the type of diploid parthenogenesis, leading to a periodical replacement of a polyploid macronucleus. Undoubtedly these processes evolved by abbreviation of the sexual processes, conjugation or autogamy (loss of meiosis and karyogamy; see Ref. 105). Though in *Paramecium* there is no typical "endomixis", but only autogamy,[36, 250] processes of this kind may occur in some higher ciliates,[106] and the term "endomixis" should, to avoid confusion, be reserved for them only. As to the lower ciliates with diploid macronuclei, their nuclear reorganization during each division, though involving macronuclear anlagen development, has nothing in common with nuclear behavior at conjugation and therefore cannot be termed "endomixis". Conjugation has been studied in *Loxodes*,[16] *Tracheloraphis phoenicopterus*,[189] and *Trachelocerca coluber*.[198]

C. Primitivity of the Diploid Macronuclei.
Comparison with Nuclear Dualism in Foraminifera

A question may arise whether the diploid macronuclei correspond to a primitive level of development of the nuclear dualism in ciliates, or whether these nuclei are secondarily simplified, originating phylogenetically from the usual polyploid macronuclei. Fauré-Fremiet[63, 65] has repeatedly supported the latter hypothesis, basing it on the fact that the never-dividing macronuclei are characteristic mainly of members of the interstitial fauna of marine sand. He considers these nuclei highly specialized and secondarily simplified due to adaptation of the ciliates to dwelling in the sand. The author of the present review develops, however, the other viewpoint, according to which the diploid macronuclei are primitive and phylogenetically more ancient than the polyploid macronuclei of the majority of ciliates. The structural similarity of diploid macronuclei of various lower ciliates is considered not convergence, but a result of common origin. Extant species of ciliates with diploid macronuclei seem, using the figurative expression of Grell,[88] to be peculiar "karyological relicts".

The following considerations argue for primitivity of the diploid macronuclei.

First, macronuclei of this type exist only in the lower groups of ciliates, while the more highly organized sand-dwelling forms (Heterotrichida, Hypotrichida) always have typical polyploid macronuclei. The family Trachelocercidae belongs to the lowest group among the Ciliata—to Holotricha Gymnostomatida Rhabdophorina. The family Loxodidae has also been included for a long time in the Rhabdophorina, but according to the latest data it seems to be related to primitive Cyrtophorina.[272] The systematic position of the Geleiidae is not altogether clear;[49, 160] in any case they are also representatives of the lower Holotricha, perhaps related to primitive Hymenostomatida.

Second, the diploid macronuclei are not restricted to any single specialized systematic group. The families Trachelocercidae, Loxodidae, and Geleiidae are hardly closely related. They have rather different types of oral and ciliary apparatus. Therefore it is natural to suppose that these systematically isolated groups of ciliates with diploid macronuclei are actually remnants of a much wider spectrum of forms. As to the secondarity of the diploid macronuclei, it would be very difficult to understand how simple convergence could bring about such far-reaching similarities in the structure and reorganization of the nuclear apparatus.

Third, the interstitial sand fauna retains many primitive forms, not only of Protozoa, but also of Metazoa (turbellarians, crustaceans, etc.). The psammophilous biotope may have been one of the ecological niches favoring survival of ancient primitive forms, which became supplanted in other biotopes by higher organized forms.

Fourth, the diploid macronuclei are not confined to sand fauna—they are also met in typical fresh-water pond species of *Loxodes*. Therefore, the diploid macronuclei could hardly originate by convergence under the action of ecological proximity of unrelated forms.

Fifth, it is difficult to imagine a formation of diploid nuclei through "simplification" of polyploid ones. In its phylogenetical aspect, polyploidization seems to be an irreversible process.

Therefore it appears probable that diploid macronuclei of lower ciliates originated from ordinary diploid nuclei of homokaryotic forms like *Stephanopogon* which underwent some irreversible change and, as a result, lost their ability to divide, becoming physiologically active somatic nuclei. We call this change *primary differentiation of somatic nuclei*, in contrast to the next step in phylogenetic development of the nuclear apparatus—that of macronuclear polyploidization.

Remarkably enough, the primary differentiation of somatic nuclei evidently took place quite independently in some Sarcodina, namely in the diploid agamonts of certain Foraminifera. The foraminiferan nuclear dualism was discovered and thoroughly studied during the last decade by Grell and co-workers in some members of the family Rotaliidae belonging to the genera *Rotaliella, Metarotaliella, Rubratella,* and *Glabratella*[29, 30, 81, 83-86, 89, 295, 308] (for reviews see refs. 87, 88, 90). Recently, the nuclear dualism has also been found in planktonic Globigerinidae.[137]

The foraminiferan life cycle is known to be an alternation of a sexual generation with an asexual generation. Individuals of the sexual generation (the gamonts) are haploid, while animals of the asexual generation (the agamonts) are diploid. The gamonts usually have only one nucleus (Fig. 49A, a). The mature gamont fragments into numerous gametes; before this, the haploid nucleus of the gamont divides mitotically many times forming the nuclei of the future gametes. The gametes pair and give rise to diploid zygotes. In species of *Rotaliella*, the nucleus of the zygote divides mitotically twice, forming four genetically identical diploid nuclei of the young agamont. At first these nuclei are also identical morphologically. But with the beginning of growth of the agamont, the nuclei become differentiated: one of the four nuclei comes out of the initial chamber into younger chambers, increases in size, and forms a large nucleolus (Fig. 49A, b). This nucleus is called the *somatic* nucleus, and the three nuclei remaining in the initial chamber, the *generative* nuclei. The latter remain small, compact, and devoid of nucleoli. After the end of the growth period of the agamont, the generative nuclei enter meiosis (Fig. 49B). Their homologous chromosomes conjugate, forming bivalents (Fig. 49B, a). The first meiotic division results in *Rotaliella* with six generative nuclei, the second meiotic division (Fig. 49B, b) results in *Rotaliella* with twelve haploid nuclei. A cytoplasmic region separates around each nucleus, forming haploid agametes which will give rise to gamonts.

During the meiotic divisions of the generative nuclei, the somatic nucleus degenerates in one way or another. In *Rotaliella heterocaryotica* and *Metarotaliella parva* it becomes pycnotic and is gradually resorbed.[81, 83, 89, 308] In other species, chromosome condensation occurs in it simultaneously with the meiotic prophase in the generative nuclei. But homologous chromosomes in the somatic nucleus do not conjugate, remaining univalent (Fig. 49B, a). During the second meiotic division of the generative nuclei, the envelope of the somatic nucleus disintegrates, the univalent chromosomes become dispersed in the cytoplasm and resorbed (Fig. 49 B, b). Such is the fate of the somatic nuclei in *Rotaliella roscoffensis*,[84] *Rubratella intermedia*,[85] and *Glabratella sulcata*.[86]

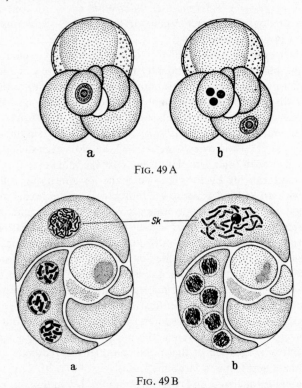

a   b

Fig. 49 A

a   b

Fig. 49 B

Fig. 49. Nuclear dualism in Foraminifera. A—*Rotaliella heterocaryotica;* a—gamont (no nuclear dualism), b—agamont with three generative and one somatic nucleus; after Grell.[81] B—agamonts of *Rotaliella roscoffensis;* a—generative nuclei in diakinesis of the first meiotic division, chromosomes of the somatic nucleus (*Sk*) do not conjugate; b—generative nuclei in metaphase of the second meiotic division, chromosomes of the somatic nucleus scattering in the cytoplasm; after Grell.[83]

The number of somatic and generative nuclei may be different in different species, since the number of divisions of the zygote nucleus may vary. In *Rotaliella* and *Metarotaliella* there are usually three generative and one somatic nucleus, in *Rubratella*, five generative and one somatic. In *Glabratella*, the initial number of nuclei of the agamont is highly variable (from four to twenty-four, more often ten to sixteen). Here, only one somatic nucleus is differentiated at first, but later, with growth of the agamont, a second one is formed, then a third, and sometimes even a fourth and fifth.

The differentiation of somatic nuclei is not accompanied by their poly-ploidization. This has been demonstrated by the photometrical studies of Zech,[295] who showed that the somatic nuclei of *Rotaliella heterocaryotica* contained the same amount of DNA as the diploid generative nuclei but much more RNA and protein.

The latter fact speaks for a high metabolic activity of the somatic nucleus. There are also direct proofs of this activity. For instance, in *Rotaliella roscoffensis*[84] degeneration of all generative nuclei sometimes occurs; nevertheless, such agamonts, with only a somatic nucleus, grow normally. However, they die later when the somatic nucleus degenerates after the end of the growth period, as usual. These observations also show that differentiation of the somatic nucleus is irreversible: even in the absence of generative nuclei it does not undergo normal meiosis and give rise to nuclei of agametes. A similar phenomenon has sometimes been observed in *Glabratella sulcata*,[86] where, if the initial number of nuclei of a young agamont is very small (two to four), all the nuclei may become somatic. It also occurs in *Rotaliella heterocaryotica* after experimental destruction of all generative nuclei by ultraviolet microbeam; the agamont grows quite normally but dies after degeneration of the somatic nucleus.[29] These phenomena indicate that it is the somatic nucleus which supports the growth of the agamont, the generative nuclei probably remaining inactive during this period. It may be supposed that differentiation of nuclei into generative and somatic is based on processes of differential gene activation in nuclei with identical genotypes.

Also interesting is the mechanism of differentiation of the somatic nuclei.[87, 90] If the somatic nucleus of *Rotaliella heterocaryotica* is destroyed with an UV microbeam[30] or removed by microsurgical methods,[295] a new somatic nucleus develops from one of the remaining generative nuclei. This experiment may be repeated twice with the same result. This indicates that somatic and generative nuclei are not determined during division of the zygote nucleus; on the contrary, each generative nucleus may in principle become a somatic nucleus. Grell[87, 90] advanced a hypothesis according to which differentiation of somatic nuclei is stimulated by a certain "differentiating substance" accumulating in the cytoplasm of the agamont. The four nuclei of the young agamont may have a somewhat different threshold sensitivity to this substance. The most sensitive nucleus begins to differentiate into a somatic nucleus. This first somatic nucleus probably begins at once to inhibit differentiation of any further nuclei (perhaps through binding or inactivation of the "differentiating substance"). Such a feedback mechanism prevents transformation of all nuclei into somatic nuclei. Elimination of the somatic nucleus erases its inhibiting action, and then a new somatic nucleus differentiates. In *Glabratella*, however, the inhibitory action of a single somatic nucleus seems to be insufficient, and further somatic nuclei are formed later.

Obviously there is much in common between somatic nuclei of Foraminifera and diploid macronuclei of lower ciliates. Both are formed agamically
from generative nuclei. Both remain diploid. Both form large nucleoli and
produce a considerable amount of RNA. Both are differentiated irreversibly.
Finally, the somatic nuclei of foraminiferans, exactly as diploid macronuclei,
lose their ability to divide (in this case meiotically), and are doomed to
ultimate degeneration. In both cases, the nuclear differentiation appears to
be based on similar processes of epigenetic character (differential activation of
certain genes).

It is quite possible that the feedback mechanism regulating differentiation
of the somatic nuclei of foraminiferans exists also in ciliates; during division
of many lower ciliates the macronuclear anlagen develop from just those
micronuclei which lie farther from the old macronuclei (e.g., Fig. 48 G),
suggesting that the old macronuclei produce some substance inhibiting
transformation of the nearer micronuclei into macronuclear anlagen. We
have only to assume that the inhibiting substance has a restricted ability of
diffusion.

Thus the parallelism between the somatic nuclei of Foraminifera and the
diploid macronuclei of Ciliata is very close. It is possible that the two types
of nuclei also arose phylogenetically by similar ways. There are no forms
with polyploid somatic nuclei among foraminiferans, so the origin of their
diploid somatic nuclei by "simplification" of polyploid nuclei is out of the
question, and their origin from ordinary diploid nuclei by means of primary
differentiation is credible. And it is probable that diploid ciliate macronuclei
originated in a similar way.

The above data allow us to conclude that the nuclear apparatus of the
Trachelocerca–Loxodes–Remanella–Geleia type actually corresponds to an
early stage in the phylogenetic development of the nuclear dualism retained
in a number of lower ciliates, especially those inhabiting marine sand.

3. Hypothesis of Origin and Evolution of Nuclear Dualism in Ciliates

The studies of lower ciliates, performed mainly during the last decade, offer
an approach to the solution of the question of the origin of nuclear dualism
in ciliates. Earlier evidence was insufficient. The hypothesis set forth below
is based on the recognition of the primitive character of both the homokaryotic nuclear apparatus of *Stephanopogon* and the diploid macronuclei
of *Trachelocerca*, *Loxodes*, and other similar forms. The arguments for
primitivity of these two types of nuclei were examined above (pp. 86, 106).

One of the early hypotheses of the origin of the infusorian nuclear apparatus was advanced by Lwoff.[139] In his opinion, the primitive ciliates did not
at first possess nuclear dualism but had a nuclear apparatus of the *Stephanopogon* type, with a later gradual "hypertrophy" (enrichment with chromatin
and nucleolar material) of some of their nuclei into macronuclei, with their
mitotic type of division transforming little by little into amitosis.

Lwoff's hypothesis leaves, however, no place for ciliates with diploid macronuclei, which were, at that time, poorly known. Besides, this hypothesis was put forward before the highly polyploid nature of the macronucleus of most ciliates was known. Thus the relationship between the origin of nuclear dualism and the polyploidization of the macronuclei also remained obscure.

The present ideas on the evolution of the nuclear dualism of the ciliates are somewhat different.[175, 176, 188, 189, 194, 200] Nuclear dualism obviously arose earlier than polyploidy of the macronucleus and went through three definite stages of phylogenetic development. Both lower stages have representatives, which have survived as "karyological relicts".

The first and most primitive stage of phylogenetic development is characterized by complete *absence of nuclear dualism*, although other characters of the class Ciliata (the oral and the ciliary apparatus) are already well developed. *Stephanopogon*, a surviving member of this group, clearly shows a tendency toward multinuclearity. Probably many of the homokaryotic ciliates were multinucleate. This is quite understandable, since polymerization of nuclei and various cell organoids is a main principle of progressive evolution in the Protozoa, as shown by Dogiel.[46, 47, 173] Their progressive evolution is usually accompanied by increase in body size and activation of metabolism, especially cellular syntheses. This activation and growth must be supported by a higher production of RNA, best ensured by an increase in the quantity of genic material in the cell. And increase in genic material is most simply attained by transition to multinuclearity. Many homokaryotic protozoans reaching large dimensions are actually multinucleate (*Pelomyxa* among amebae, *Actinosphaerium* among heliozoans, many Polymastigida, etc.).

The second stage of phylogenetic development is characterized by the appearance of nuclear dualism with *a primary differentiation* of the genetically identical nuclei into somatic (macronuclei) and generative (micronuclei). The generative nuclei remain totipotent, but the somatic nuclei become irreversibly differentiated with complete loss of ability to divide and a fate of ultimate degeneration. At this stage, the somatic nuclei are still diploid. The ciliates Trachelocercidae, Loxodidae, Geleiidae, and some others belong to this group. Quite independently, the same stage of development of nuclear dualism was reached by heterokaryotic Foraminifera.

In its evolutionary aspect, the primary differentiation of diploid nuclei into generative and somatic should apparently be interpreted as a kind of "division of labour", which allows the physiological activity of the somatic nuclei (especially RNA production) to increase at the cost of loss of the ability of the genetic material to reproduce itself. The principle of nuclear polymerization remains valid: polymerization involving both micronuclei and macronuclei occurs regularly, especially in large forms like *Loxodes magnus*. The number of somatic nuclei is supplemented at the cost of the generative nuclei during the reorganization processes accompanying cell division.

The third and highest stage of evolution of the nuclear dualism is characterized by *polyploidization* of the somatic nucleus (macronucleus). This stage has been reached by ciliates only; the majority of the ciliates belong to it. The increase in quantity of genetic material is now attained not by increasing the number of *nuclei*, but by increasing the number of *genomes* within a polyploid macronucleus. This ensures synthesis of a large quantity of gene products (primarily RNA) by one large nucleus. Apparently the process of polymerization has passed from the level of nuclei to the level of genomes. The tendency toward multinuclearity is, as a rule, no longer expressed; on the contrary, the number of macronuclei is in most cases reduced to one. In other words, polymerization of genomes within the macronucleus makes possible oligomerization (reduction of number) of the somatic nuclei themselves. Forms with a single polyploid macronucleus may have some evolutionary advantages over multinucleate forms characterized by a certain "decentralization" of the organism (i.e., by decrease in the level of morphophysiological integration).

Simultaneously with its polyploidization, the macronucleus reacquires the ability to divide. Since diploid macronuclei do not divide, it is evident that division of polyploid macronuclei could arise only *de novo*, and not by a gradual transformation of mitosis. The very type of macronuclear division—segregation of genomes—is such that it could not originate before macronuclei became polyploid.

How could the phylogenetic transition of macronuclei from diploid to polyploid be accomplished? This question is still completely obscure. In principle, we have two possibilities.

(1) The chromosomes of the diploid macronuclei might reacquire the ability of replication, without their nuclei reacquiring the ability to form normal mitotic spindles. This would direct chromosome reproduction onto the endomitotic way and result in polyploidization of the macronucleus. In this case, a polyploid macronucleus would be homologous with one diploid macronucleus of the lower forms.

Or, (2) macronuclear polyploidy might arise by fusion of many diploid somatic nuclei, the genomes of the diploid nuclei remaining more or less separated, and the whole complex of fused nuclei very labile, easily fragmenting into its component units. In the course of evolution, this fragmentation might give rise to genome segregation. In this case, a polyploid macronucleus would correspond to the entire sum of diploid macronuclei of a lower ciliate.

Both possibilities are purely speculative. So far we have no means of testing them. But it may be said now that a tendency toward fusion of diploid macronuclei is well expressed in lower ciliates. The nuclear groups of many Trachelocercidae (see p. 88) often fuse into the so-called "*complex nucleus*" surrounded by one membrane, the outlines of individual macronuclei disappearing. The micronuclei are included in the complex nucleus and may be seen near its center (Fig. 50A).

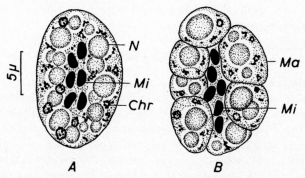

FIG. 50. The complex nucleus of *Tracheloraphis phoenicopterus*. Feulgen–light green. × 2300. After Raikov.[193] A—intact complex nucleus, B—fragmentation of the complex nucleus. *Ma*—macronuclei, *Mi*—micronuclei, *Chr*—macronuclear chromatin, *N*—nucleoli.

These Trachelocercidae complex nuclei are very labile. Environmental changes usually provoke their fragmentation into the component macronuclei, with the micronuclei lying in the middle of the morula-like accumulation of the macronuclei (Fig. 50B). During division, the complex nucleus usually becomes fragmented with the daughter nuclear groups fusing again into complex nuclei after division is completed. Such a nuclear apparatus has been studied in detail in *Tracheloraphis phoenicopterus*;[189] it occurs also in many other Trachelocercidae as well as in *Kentrophoros latum* and *K. uninucleatum*.[193]

The complex nuclei of Trachelocercidae are evidently polyploid formations. The nucleus of *Tracheloraphis phoenicopterus* (Fig. 50) consists of approximately twelve macronuclei, thus being 24-ploid. But this polyploidy is a transient phenomenon. The sharpest difference between the complex nuclei and the true polyploid macronuclei is that the micronuclei always get inside the former and never inside the latter. Therefore complex nuclei are not homologous to macronuclei of higher ciliates. Such formations seem to be a blind branch of evolution of the nuclear apparatus of lower ciliates, an "unsuccessful attempt of polyploidization". But the very existence of such an "attempt" shows that other, in the evolutionary sense more successful, types of fusion of diploid macronuclei might have occurred. One such type, where macronuclei fused, leaving the micronuclei outside, might have given rise to polyploid macronuclei of all extant higher ciliates.

In conclusion, we may answer with considerable degree of probability the three questions posed at the beginning of this section: (1) Nuclear dualism arose within the class Ciliata by epigenetic differentiation of some of the diploid nuclei into somatic nuclei, with simultaneous loss of their ability to divide. (2) The polyploidy of the macronucleus originated considerably later than the nuclear dualism. (3) The segregation of macronuclear genomes arose not by a gradual modification of mitosis, but anew, only after the macronucleus became polyploid.

4. Conclusion

Formation of highly polyploid nuclei certainly played a progressive role in the evolution of some higher protozoan taxa. As an example we may cite the radiolarians—a highly organized group of Sarcodina. Still more advantageous in the evolutionary sense seems to be a combination of polyploidy with nuclear dualism, characteristic of most ciliates. Polyploidization, though giving advantages (a larger amount of gene products), is fraught with danger for the cell, primarily the danger of disturbance of the precise mechanisms of distribution of genic material during division. Forms possessing a nuclear dualism are not subject or are less subject to this danger, since they always have a "reserve" genome in the micronucleus which can assure replacement of the unbalanced macronucleus. Forms with such a nuclear apparatus will have some survival advantages. This is probably one of the conditions favoring the flourishing state of the ciliates among the extant protozoans.

The ciliates reached the highest level of organization among Protozoa. It is probably the unicellular nature of protozoans itself which fixes a limit to their further complication. The numerous genomes of metazoan somatic cells are highly independent from each other; therefore these cells have wide possibilities of multiplication, of further differentiation in various directions, and of union into systems of higher order—i.e., tissues and organs. In infusorian macronuclei, on the contrary, the somatic genomes are bound by a common nuclear envelope and a common cytoplasm; the possibilities for increase in number of genomes are limited, and differentiation of genomes within the macronucleus, though occurring sometimes (e.g., in the case of unstable caryonides of *Tetrahymena*—see ref. 157), finds no strong development. In this sense, it may be said that the evolutionary possibilities of the ciliates and of protozoans in general are limited by their unicellularity. Quoting the figurative expression of Fauré-Fremiet,[62] they are "prisoners of their unicellularity".

X. ACKNOWLEDGMENTS

The following publishers, societies, or journals have kindly granted permission for the reproduction of illustrations: Academic Press Inc. (Fig. 32); Akademische Verlagsgesellschaft Geest u. Portig K.-G. (Fig. 17); *Biological Bulletin* (Fig. 29); *Bulletin Biologique de la France et de la Belgique*

(Fig. 28); Gauthier-Villars et Cie (Fig. 9); Gerontological Society Inc. (Figs. 6A, B, and 35); Publishing House of the Czechoslovak Academy of Sciences (Fig. 8); Rockefeller Institute Press (Figs. 5, 6C, 19B, C, and 36); Society of Protozoologists (Figs. 7B and 10A); University of California Press (Figs. 18 and 19A); VEB Georg Thieme (Figs. 15 and 22); VEB Gustav Fischer Verlag (Figs. 2A, C, D, F, G, 10B, 11–14, 20, 21, 23, 24, 26A, 33, 34, 39, 46, 49A); Wistar Institute of Anatomy and Biology (Fig.31); *Zeitschrift für Naturforschung* (Fig. 49B).

REFERENCES

1. ALFERT, M., and GOLDSTEIN, N. (1955) Cytochemical properties of nucleoproteins in *Tetrahymena pyriformis*; a difference in protein composition between macro- and micronuclei. *J. Exper. Zool.* **130**, 403–21.
2. ALONSO, P. (1965) Polytene chromosomes in oxytrichous ciliates. In *Progress in Protozoology* (Abstr. 2nd Int. Conf. Protozool. London) 230.
3. ALONSO, P., and PÉREZ-SILVA, J. (1965) Giant chromosomes in Protozoa. *Nature*, **205**, 313–4.
4. ALONSO, P., and PÉREZ-SILVA, J. (1965) Conjugation in *Stylonychia muscorum* Kahl. *J. Protozool.* **12**, 253–8.
5. AMMERMANN, D. (1965) Cytologische und genetische Untersuchungen an dem Ciliaten *Stylonychia mytilus* Ehrenberg. *Arch. Protistenk.* **108**, 109–52.
6. BALAMUTH, W. (1940) Regeneration in Protozoa: a problem of morphogenesis. *Quart. Rev. Biol.* **15**, 290–337.
7. BALBIANI, E. G. (1890) Étude sur le Loxode. *Ann. Micrograph.* **2**, 401–31.
8. BEERS, C. D. (1946) History of the nuclei of *Tillina magna* during division and encystment. *J. Morphol.* **78**, 181–200.
9. BEERS, C. D. (1948) The ciliates of *Strongylocentrotus droebachiensis*: incidence, distribution in the host, and division. *Biol. Bull.* **94**, 99–112.
10. BEERS, C. D. (1963) A comparison of two methods of chromatin extrusion from the macronucleus of *Conchophthirus curtis* Engl. *Trans. Amer. Microscop. Soc.* **82**, 131–7.
11. BĚLAŘ, K. (1926) Der Formwechsel der Protistenkerne: eine vergleichendmorphologische Studie. *Ergebn. Fortschr. Zool.* **6**, 235–654.
12. BERECH, J., and WAGTENDONK, W. J. VAN (1962) An autoradiographic study of the macronuclear changes occurring in *Paramecium aurelia* during autogamy. *Exper. Cell Res.* **26**, 360–72.
13. BERGER, J. D., and KIMBALL, R. F. (1964) Specific incorporation of precursors into DNA by feeding labeled bacteria to *Paramecium aurelia*. *J. Protozool.* **11**, 534–7.
14. BHANDARY, A. V. (1960) Conjugation in *Blepharisma undulans americanum*. *J. Protozool.* **7**, 250–5.
15. BLANC, J. (1963) Étude cytophotométrique sur la teneur en acide désoxyribonucléique de l'appareil nucléaire chez plusieurs variétés de *Paramecium caudatum*. *Exper. Cell Res.* **32**, 476–83.
16. BOGDANOWICZ, A. (1930) Über die Konjugation von *Loxodes striatus* (Engelm.) Penard and *Loxodes rostrum* (O.F.M.) Ehrenb. *Zool. Anz.* **87**, 209–22.
17. BURT, R. L., KIDDER, G. W., and CLAFF, C. L. (1941) Nuclear reorganization in the family Colpodidae. *J. Morphol.* **69**, 537–61.
18. BÜTSCHLI, O. (1876) Studien über die ersten Entwicklungsvorgänge der Eizelle, die Zelltheilung und die Conjugation der Infusorien. *Abhandl. Senckenberg. Naturforsch. Ges.* **10**, 213–452.
19. CACHON-ENJUMET, M. (1961) Contribution à l'étude des Radiolaires phaeodariés. *Arch. Zool. Expér. Génér.* **100**, 151–238.

20. CAMERON, I. L., and GUILE, E. E., JR. (1965) Nucleolar and biochemical changes during unbalanced growth of *Tetrahymena pyriformis*. *J. Cell Biol.* **26**, 845–55.

21. CAMERON, I. L., and STONE, G. E. (1964) Relation between the amount of DNA per cell and the duration of DNA synthesis in three strains of *Tetrahymena pyriformis*. *Exper. Cell Res.* **36**, 510–4.

22. CANELLA, I. R., and TRINCAS, L. (1961) Ciclo vitale e nucleare di *Ophryoglena singularis* sp. n. (Ciliata, Holotricha, Hymenostomata). *Pubbl. Civ. Museo Storia Nat. Ferrara*, **5**, 1–44.

23. CARASSO, N., and FAVARD, P. (1965) Microtubules fusoriaux dans les micro- et macronucleus de Ciliés péritriches en division. *J. Microscopie*, **4**, 395–402.

24. CHEISSIN, E. M., and OVCHINNIKOVA, L. P. (1964) A photometric study of DNA content in macronuclei and micronuclei of different species of *Paramecium*. *Acta Protozool.* **2**, 225–36.

25. CHEISSIN, E. M., OVCHINNIKOVA, L. P., and KUDRIAVTSEV, B. N. (1964) A photometric study of DNA content in macronuclei and micronuclei of different strains of *Paramecium caudatum*. *Acta Protozool.* **2**, 237–45.

26. CHEISSIN, E. M., OVCHINNIKOVA, L. P., SELIVANOVA, G. V., and BUZE, E. G. (1963) (Changes of the DNA content in the macronucleus of *Paramecium caudatum* in the interdivision period). *Acta Protozool.* **1**, 63–69 (in Russian with English summary).

27. CHEN, T. T. (1940) Polyploidy and its origin in *Paramecium*. *J. Hered.* **31**, 175–84.

27a. CHEN, T. T. (1940) A further study on polyploidy in *Paramecium*. *J. Hered.* **31**, 249–51.

28. CORLISS, J. O. (1955) The opalinid infusorians: flagellates or ciliates? *J. Protozool.* **2**, 107–14.

29. CZIHAK, G. (1964) Experiments on nuclear differentiation in the foraminifer *Rotaliella heterocaryotica* Grell by means of UV microirradiation. *Exper. Cell Res.* **35**, 372–80.

30. CZIHAK, G., and GRELL, K. G. (1960) Zur Determination der Zellkerne bei der Foraminifere *Rotaliella heterocaryotica*. *Naturwissenschaften*, **47**, 211–2.

31. DASS, C. M. S. (1950) Chromatin elimination in *Glaucoma pyriformis* Ehrbg. *Nature*, **165**, 693.

32. DASS, C. M. S. (1953) Studies on the nuclear apparatus of peritrichous ciliates. Part I. The nuclear apparatus of *Epistylis articulata* (From.). *Proc. Nat. Inst. Sci. India*, **19**, 389–404.

33. DASS, C. M. S., and DEVI, R. V. (1962) The action of ribonuclease on the nucleic acid system of *Spirostomum ambiguum*. *Quart. J. Microscop. Sci.* **103**, 37–40.

34. DEVI, R. V. (1960) The nuclear apparatus of *Frontonia leucas* (Ehrbg.). *Proc. Nat. Inst. Sci. India*, B **26**, 269–77.

35. DEVIDÉ, Z. (1951) Chromosomes in Ciliates (Euciliata and Opalinidae). *Bull. Internat. Acad. Yougosl. Sci. Beaux-Arts Zagreb*, n. sér. **3**, 75–114.

36. DILLER, W. F. (1936) Nuclear reorganization processes in *Paramecium aurelia*, with description of autogamy and "hemixis". *J. Morphol.* **59**, 11–67.

37. DILLER, W. F. (1940) Nuclear variation in *Paramecium caudatum*. *J. Morphol.* **66**, 605–33.

38. DILLER, W. F. (1948) Nuclear behavior of *Paramecium trichium* during conjugation. *J. Morphol.* **82**, 1–52.

39. DILLER, W. F. (1958) Studies on conjugation in *Paramecium polycaryum*. *J. Protozool.* **5**, 282–92.

40. DILLER, W. F. (1964) Observations on the morphology and life history of *Homalozoon vermiculare*. *Arch. Protistenk.* **107**, 351–62.

41. DIPPEL, R. V., and SINTON, S. E. (1963) Localization of macronuclear DNA and RNA in *Paramecium aurelia*. *J. Protozool.* **10**, Suppl., 22–3.

42. DIPPEL, R. V., and SONNEBORN, T. M. (1957) Structure of the *Paramecium aurelia* macronucleus as revealed by electron microscopy. *Proc. Indiana Acad. Sci.* **66**, 60.

43. DOBRZAŃSKA-KACZANOWSKA, J. (1963) Comparaison de la morphogenése de Ciliés: *Chilodonella uncinata* (Ehrbg.), *Allosphaerium paraconvexum* sp. n. et *Heliochona scheuteni* (Stein). *Acta Protozool.* **1**, 353–94.

44. DODD, E. E. (1962) A cytochemical investigation of the nuclear changes in the cyst cycle of the ciliate *Telotrochidium henneguyi*. *J. Protozool.* **9**, 93–7.

45. DOFLEIN, F., and REICHENOW, E. (1953) *Lehrbuch der Protozoenkunde.* 6-te Auflage. VEB Gustav Fischer Verlag, Jena.

46. DOGIEL, V. (1929) Polymerisation als ein Prinzip der progressiven Entwicklung bei Protozoen. *Biol. Zbl.* **49**, 451–69.

47. DOGIEL, V. A. (1965) *General Protozoology.* 2nd ed., revised by G. I. POLJANSKY and E. M. CHEISSIN. Clarendon Press, Oxford.

48. DRAGESCO, J. (1960) Les Ciliés mésopsammiques littoraux (systématique, morphologie, écologie) *Trav. Stat. Biol. Roscoff,* n. sér. **12**, 1–356.

49. DRAGESCO, J. (1963) Compléments à la connaissance des Ciliés mésopsammiques de Roscoff, I. Holotriches. *Cahiers Biol. Mar.* **4**, 91–119.

50. DRAGESCO, J., and RAIKOV, I. (1966) L'appareil nucléaire, la division et quelques stades de la conjugaison de *Tracheloraphis margaritatus* (Kahl) et *T. caudatum* sp. nov. (Ciliata, Holotricha). *Arch. Protistenk.* **109**, 99–113.

51. DYSART, M. P. (1959) Macronuclear chromatin extrusion in the ciliate genus *Tetrahymena*. *J. Protozool.* **6**, Suppl. 17–18.

52. DYSART, M. P. (1960) Study of macronuclear chromatin extrusion in *Tetrahymena limacis* using tritiated thymidine. *J. Protozool.* **7**, Suppl., 10–11.

53. DYSART, M. P. (1963) Cytochemical and quantitative DNA analyses of the macronucleus and its extrusion body in species of *Tetrahymena*. *J. Protozool.* **10**, Suppl., 8.

54. DYSART, M. P., CORLISS, J. O., and DE LA TORRE, L. (1962) Comparative DNA measurements in two species of *Tetrahymena*. *J. Protozool.* **9**, Suppl., 17.

55. EBERHARDT, R. (1962) Untersuchungen zur Morphogenese von *Blepharisma* und *Spirostomum*. *Arch. Protistenk.* **106**, 241–341.

56. EGELHAAF, A. (1955) Cytologisch-entwicklungsphysiologische Untersuchungen zur Konjugation von *Paramecium bursaria* Focke. *Arch. Protistenk.* **100**, 447–514.

57. EHRET, C. F., and POWERS, E. L. (1955) Macronuclear and nucleolar development in *Paramecium bursaria*. *Exper. Cell Res.* **9**, 241–57.

58. ELLIOTT, A. M. (1963) The fine structure of *Tetrahymena pyriformis* during mitosis. In *The Cell in Mitosis* (Symposium), Academic Press, New York and London, 107–21.

59. ELLIOTT, A. M., KENNEDY, J. R., and BAK, I. J. (1962) Macronuclear events in synchronously dividing *Tetrahymena pyriformis*. *J. Cell Biol.* **12**, 515–31.

60. ELLIS, I. M. (1937) The morphology, division and conjugation of the salt-marsh ciliate *Fabrea salina* Henneguy. *Univ. Calif. Publ. Zool.* **41**, 343–88.

61. EVANS, F. R. (1944) A study of nuclear reorganization in the ciliate *Woodruffia metabolica*. *J. Morphol.* **74**, 101–29.

62. FAURÉ-FREMIET, E. (1953) L'hypothése de la sénescence et les cycles de réorganisation nucléaire chez les Ciliés. *Rev. Suisse Zool.* **60**, 426–38.

63. FAURÉ-FREMIET, E. (1954) Réorganisation du type endomixique chez les Loxodidae et chez les *Centrophorella*. *J. Protozool.* **1**, 20–7.

64. FAURÉ-FREMIET, E. (1957) Le macronucleus hétéromere de quelques Ciliés. *J. Protozool.* **4**, 7–17.

65. FAURÉ-FREMIET, E. (1961) Quelques considérations sur les Ciliés mésopsammiques a propos d'un récent travail de J. Dragesco. *Cahiers Biol. Mar.* **2**, 177–86.

66. FAURÉ-FREMIET, E., GAUCHERY, M., and TUFFRAU, M. (1954) Les processus de l'enkystement chez *Euplotes muscicola* Kahl. *Bull. Biol. France Belg.* **88**, 154–67.

67. FAURÉ-FREMIET, E., ROUILLER, C., and GAUCHERY, M. (1957) La réorganisation macronucléaire chez les *Euplotes*. Étude au microscope électronique. *Exper. Cell Res.* **12**, 135–44.

68. FENNELL, R. A., and DEGENHARDT, E. F. (1957) Some factors affecting alkaline phosphatase activity in *Tetrahymena pyriformis* W. *J. Protozool.* **4**, 30–42.

69. GALL, J. G. (1959) Macronuclear duplication in the ciliated protozoan *Euplotes*. *J. Biophys. Biochem. Cytol.* **5**, 295–308.

70. GEITLER, L. (1941) Das Wachstum des Zellkerns in tierischen und pflanzlichen Geweben. *Ergebn. Biol.* **18**, 1–54.

71. GOLDSCHMIDT, R., and POPOFF, M. (1907) Die Karyokinese der Protozoen und der Chromidialapparat der Protozoen- und Metazoenzelle. *Arch. Protistenk.* **8**, 321–43.

72. GOLIKOWA, M. N. (1965) Der Aufbau des Kernapparates und die Verteilung der Nukleinsäuren und Proteine bei *Nyctotherus cordiformis* Stein. *Arch. Protistenk.* **108**, 191–216.

73. GOLIŃSKA, K. (1965) Macronucleus in *Dileptus cygnus* and its changes in division. *Acta Protozool.* **3**, 143–52.

74. GRELL, K. G. (1949) Die Entwicklung der Makronucleusanlage im Exkonjuganten von *Ephelota gemmipara* R. Hertwig. *Biol. Zbl.* **68**, 289–312.

75. GRELL, K. G. (1950) Der Kerndualismus der Ciliaten und Suctorien. *Naturwissenschaften* **37**, 347–56.

76. GRELL, K. G. (1950) Der Generationswechsel des parasitischen Suktors *Tachyblaston ephelotensis* Martin. *Zeitschr. Parasitenk.* **14**, 499–534.

77. GRELL, K. G. (1953) Der Stand unserer Kenntnisse über den Bau der Protistenkerne. *Verhandl. Deutsch. Zool. Ges. Freiburg* 1952, 212–51.

78. GRELL, K. G. (1953) Die Konjugation von *Ephelota gemmipara* R. Hertwig. *Arch. Protistenk.* **98**, 287–326.

79. GRELL, K. G. (1953) Die Struktur des Makronucleus von *Tokophrya*. *Arch. Protistenk.* **98**, 466–8.

80. GRELL, K. G. (1953) Die Chromosomen von *Aulacantha scolymantha* Haeckel. *Arch. Protistenk.* **99**, 1–54.

81. GRELL, K. G. (1954) Der Generationswechsel der polythalamen Foraminifere *Rotaliella heterocaryotica*. *Arch. Protistenk.* **100**, 268–86.

82. GRELL, K. G. (1956) *Protozoologie*. Springer Verlag, Berlin-Göttingen-Heidelberg.

83. GRELL, K. G. (1956) Über die Elimination somatischer Kerne bei heterokaryotischen Foraminiferen. *Zeitschr. Naturforsch.* **11** b, 759–61.

84. GRELL, K. G. (1957) Untersuchungen über die Fortpflanzung und Sexualität der Foraminiferen. I. *Rotaliella roscoffensis*. *Arch. Protistenk.* **102**, 147–64.

85. GRELL, K. G. (1958) Untersuchungen über die Fortpflanzung und Sexualität der Foraminiferen. II. *Rubratella intermedia*. *Arch. Protistenk.* **102**, 291–308.

86. GRELL, K. G. (1958) Untersuchungen über die Fortpflanzung und Sexualität der Foraminiferen. III. *Glabratella sulcata*. *Arch. Protistenk.* **102**, 449–72.

87. GRELL, K. G. (1958) Studien zum Differenzierungsproblem an Foraminiferen. *Naturwissenschaften*, **45**, 25–32.

88. GRELL, K. G. (1962) Morphologie und Fortpflanzung der Protozoen. (Einschließlich Entwicklungsphysiologie und Genetik). *Fortschr. Zool.* **14**, 1–85.

89. GRELL, K. G. (1962) Entwicklung und Geschlechtsdifferenzierung einer neuen Foraminifere. *Naturwissenschaften*, **49**, 214.

90. GRELL, K. G. (1964) The protozoan nucleus. In *The Cell* (*Biochemistry, Physiology, Morphology*), eds. J. BRACHET and A. MIRSKY, Academic Press, New York and London, **6**, 1–79.

91. GRELL, K. G., and RUTHMANN, A. (1964) Über die Karyologie des Radiolars *Aulacantha scolymantha* und die Feinstruktur seiner Chromosomen. *Chromosoma*, **15**, 158–211.

92. GROMOWA, E. N. (1941) (The action of external factors on the structure of the macronucleus in *Paramecium caudatum*). *Zool. Zhurnal* (*Moscow*), **20**, 187–97 (in Russian).

93. GROMOWA, E. N. (1948) (The dynamics of nucleic acids during conjugation in *Paramecium caudatum*). *Doklady Acad. Nauk SSSR*, **63**, 73–5 (in Russian).
94. GUTTES, E., and GUTTES, S. (1960) Incorporation of tritium-labeled thymidine into the macronucleus of *Stentor coeruleus*. *Exper. Cell Res.* **19**, 626–8.
95. HANSON, E. D., and TWICHELL, J. B. (1962) Autoradiographic study of the time of DNA and RNA synthesis in *Paramecium trichium*. *J. Protozool.* **9**, Suppl., 11.
96. HARTMANN, M. (1909) Polyenergide Kerne. Studien über multiple Kernteilung und generative Chromidien bei Protozoen. *Biol. Zbl.* **29**, 481–7, 491–506.
97. HARTMANN, M. (1952) Polyploide (polyenergide) Kerne bei Protozoen. *Arch. Protistenk.*, **98**, 125–56.
98. HECKMANN, K. (1963) Paarungssystem und genabhängige Paarungstypdifferenzierung bei dem hypotrichen Ciliaten *Euplotes vannus* O. F. Müller. *Arch. Protistenk.* **106**, 393–421.
99. HECKMANN, K. (1964) Der Zellkern der Protozoen, Tatsachen und Probleme. *Verhandl. Anat. Gesell. München 1963* (*Anat. Anz.*, **113**, Suppl.), 4–31.
100. HELSON, L., PECORA, P., and HIRSHFIELD, H. I. (1959) Macronuclear changes in a strain of *Blepharisma undulans* during the divisional cycle. *J. Protozool.* **6**, 131–5.
101. HOLZ, G. G., JR. (1958) Mercaptoethanol and *Tetrahymena*. *Biol. Bull.* **115**, 354.
102. HULL, R. W. (1954) The morphology and life cycle of *Solenophrya micraster* Penard 1914. *J. Protozool.* **1**, 93–104.
103. IKEDA, A. (1955) (Studies on *Euplotes woodruffi* Gaw. in Japan. II. Hemixis). *Zool. Mag. (Jap.)*, **64**, 326–9 (in Japanese with English summary).
104. JANKOWSKI, A. V. (1961) (The process of conjugation in the rare salt water *Paramecium, P. woodruffi*). *Doklady Acad. Nauk SSSR*, **137**, 989–92 (in Russian).
105. JANKOWSKI, A. V. (1962) (The conjugation processes in *Paramecium putrinum* Clap. et Lachm. II. Apomictic reorganization cycles and the system of mixotypes). *Cytology (USSR)*, **4**, 435–44 (in Russian).
106. JANKOWSKI, A. V. (1962) (Nuclear reorganization of the endomixis type in clones of *Cyclidium glaucoma* O.F.M.). *Nauchnye Doklady Vysshej Shkoly, Biol. Nauki*, No. 4, 14–9 (in Russian).
107. JANKOWSKI, A. V. (1966). (The conjugation processes in *Paramecium putrinum* Clap. et Lachm. IX. On "necrochromatin" and the functional significance of macronuclear fragmentation). *Cytology (USSR)*, **8**, 725–35 (in Russian with English summary).
108. JIROVEC, O. (1927) Protozoenstudien. II. Die Nuclealreaktion bei einigen Protozoen. *Arch. Protistenk.* **59**, 550–61.
109. JOHNSON, W., and LARSON, E. (1938) Studies on the morphology and life history of *Woodruffia metabolica*, spec. nov. *Arch. Protistenk.* **90**, 383–92.
110. JONES, E. E. (1951) Encystment, excystment, and the nuclear cycle in the ciliate *Dileptus anser*. *J. Elisha Mitchell Sci. Soc.* **67**, 205–18.
111. JOSEPH, H. (1907) Beobachtungen über die Kernverhältnisse von *Loxodes rostrum* O.F.M. *Arch. Protistenk.* **8**, 344–68.
112. JURAND, A., BEALE, G. H., and YOUNG, M. R. (1962) Studies on the macronucleus of *Paramecium aurelia*. I. (With a note on ultraviolet micrography). *J. Protozool.* **9**, 122–31.
113. JURAND, A., BEALE, G. H., and YOUNG, M. R. (1964) Studies on the macronucleus of *Paramecium aurelia*. II. Development of macronuclear anlagen. *J. Protozool.* **11**, 491–7.
114. KANEDA, M. (1960) The structure and reorganization of the macronucleus during the binary fission of *Chlamydodon pedarius*. *Jap. J. Zool.* **12**, 477–91.
115. KANEDA, M. (1961) On the division of macronucleus in the living gymnostome ciliate, *Chlamydodon pedarius*, with special reference to the behaviors of chromonemata, nucleoli and endosome. *Cytologia (Tokyo)*, **26**, 89–104.

116. KANEDA, M. (1961) Fine structure of the macronucleus of the gymnostome ciliate, *Chlamydodon pedarius*. *Jap. J. Genet.* **36**, 223–34.

117. KANEDA, M. (1961) On the interrelations between the macronucleus and the cytoplasm in the gymnostome ciliate *Chlamydodon pedarius*. *Cytologia (Tokyo)*, **26**, 408–18.

118. KASANZEFF, W. (1910) Zur Kenntnis von *Loxodes rostrum*. *Arch. Protistenk.* **20**, 79–96.

119. KASANZEFF, W. (1928) Beitrag zur Kenntnis der Großkerne der Ciliaten. *Trudy Osoboi Zool. Lab. i Sevastopol. Biol. Stancii AN SSSR*, ser. 2, N. 11, 1–30.

120. KATASHIMA, R. (1953) Studies on *Euplotes*. II. Macronuclear reorganization process, double and giant animals from two-united exconjugants. *J. Sci. Hiroshima Univ.*, ser. B, div. 1 (Zool.), **14**, 57–71.

121. KAWAKAMI, H., and YAGIU, R. (1963) (The electron microscopical study of the change of fine structures in the ciliate, *Colpoda cucullus*, during its life cycle. I. The trophic stage). *Zool. Mag. (Jap.)*, **72**, 89–96 (in Japanese with English summary).

122. KIDDER, G. W. (1933) Studies on *Conchophthirius mytili*. I. Morphology and division. *Arch. Protistenk.* **79**, 1–24.

123. KIDDER, G. W. (1933) On the genus *Ancistruma* Strand (*Ancistrum* Maupas). I. The structure and division of *A. mytili* Quenn. and *A. isseli* Kahl. *Biol. Bull.* **64**, 1–20.

124. KIDDER, G., and CLAFF, C. (1938) Cytological investigation of *Colpoda cucullus*. *Biol. Bull.* **74**, 178–97.

125. KIMBALL, R. F. (1949) The effect of ultraviolet light upon the structure of the macronucleus of *Paramecium aurelia*. *Anat. Rec.* **105**, 543.

126. KIMBALL, R. F. (1953) The structure of the macronucleus of *Paramecium aurelia*. *Proc. Nat. Acad. Sci. USA*, **39**, 345–7.

127. KIMBALL, R. F., and BARKA, T. (1959) Quantitative cytochemical studies on *Paramecium aurelia*. II. Feulgen microspectrophotometry of the macronucleus during exponential growth. *Exper. Cell Res.* **17**, 173–82.

128. KIMBALL, R. F., and PERDUE, S. W. (1962) Quantitative cytochemical studies on *Paramecium*. V. Autoradiographic studies of nucleic acid synthesis. *Exper. Cell Res.* **27**, 405–15.

129. KIMBALL, R. F., and PERDUE, S. W. (1964) Synthesis of RNA by fragments of the old macronucleus in *Paramecium aurelia* undergoing autogamy. *J. Protozool.* **11**, Suppl., 33.

130. KIMBALL, R. F., and PRESCOTT, D. M. (1962) Deoxyribonucleic acid synthesis and distribution during growth and amitosis of the macronucleus of *Euplotes*. *J. Protozool.* **9**, 88–92.

131. KIMBALL, R. F., and PRESCOTT, D. M. (1964) RNA and protein synthesis in amacronucleate *Paramecium aurelia*. *J. Cell Biol.* **21**, 496–7.

132. KIMBALL, R. F., VOGT-KÖHNE, L., and CASPERSSON, T. O. (1960) Quantitative cytochemical studies on *Paramecium aurelia*. III. Dry weight and ultraviolet absorption of isolated macronuclei during various stages of the interdivision interval. *Exper. Cell Res.* **20**, 368–77.

133. KLITZKE, M. (1915) Ein Beitrag zur Kenntnis der Kernentwicklung bei den Ciliaten. *Arch. Protistenk.* **36**, 215–35.

134. KLUSS, B. C. (1962) Electron microscopy of the macronucleus of *Euplotes eurystomus*. *J. Cell Biol.* **13**, 462–5.

135. KORMOS, J., and KORMOS, K. (1960) Experimentelle Untersuchung der Kernveränderungen bei der Konjugation von *Cyclophrya katharinae* (Ciliata, Protozoa). *Acta Biol. Acad. Sci. Hung.* **10**, 395–419.

136. LEBEDEW, W. (1909) Über *Trachelocerca phoenicopterus* Cohn. *Arch. Protistenk.* **13**, 71–114.

137. LEE, J. J., FREUDENTHAL, H. D., KOSSOY, V., and BÉ, A. (1965) Cytological observations on two planktonic Foraminifera, *Globigerina bulloides* D'Orbigny, 1826, and *Globigerinoides ruber* (D'Orbigny, 1839) Cushman, 1927. *J. Protozool.* **12**, 531–42.

138. LWOFF, A. (1923) Sur un infusoire cilié homocaryote à vie libre. Son importance taxonomique. *C.R. Acad. Sci. Paris*, **177**, 910–3.

139. LWOFF, A. (1936) Le cycle nucléaire de *Stephanopogon mesnili* Lw. (Cilié homocaryote). *Arch. Zool. Expér. Gén.* **78**, 117–32.

140. MACDOUGALL, M. S. (1925) Cytological observations on gymnostomatous ciliates, with a description of the maturation phenomena in diploid and tetraploid forms of *Chilidon uncinatus. Quart. J. Microscop. Sci.* **69**, 361–84.

141. MACDOUGALL, M. S. (1936) Étude cytologique de trois espèces du genre *Chilodonella* Strand. Morphologie, conjugaison, réorganisation. *Bull. Biol. France Belg.* **70**, 308–31.

142. MASHANSKY, V. F. (1963) (Electron microscopical study of the macronuclei of some ciliates). *Morphol. i Physiol. Prostejshikh* (Collection of papers No. 3 of the Inst. of Cytology, Acad. Sci. USSR), Moscow, Leningrad, 3–8 (in Russian).

143. MAZIA, D. (1958) SH compounds in mitosis. I. The action of mercaptoethanol on the eggs of the sand dollar *Dendraster excentricus. Exper. Cell Res.* **14**, 468–94.

144. MCDONALD, B. B. (1958) Quantitative aspects of deoxyribose nucleic acid (DNA) metabolism in an amicronucleate strain of *Tetrahymena. Biol. Bull.* **114**, 71–94.

145. MCDONALD, B. B. (1959) The fate of DNA in degenerating macronuclei of exconjugants of *Tetrahymena. J. Protozool.* **6**, Suppl., 17.

146. MCDONALD, B. B. (1962) Synthesis of deoxyribonucleic acid by micro- and macronuclei of *Tetrahymena pyriformis. J. Cell Biol.* **13**, 193–203.

147. MCLOUGHLIN, D. K. (1957) Macronuclear morphogenesis during division of *Blepharisma undulans. J. Protozool.* **4**, 150–3.

148. MITCHELL, J. B., JR. (1963) Nuclear activity in *Paramecium jenningsi* with reference to other members of the *aurelia* group. *J. Protozool.* **10**, Suppl., 11.

149. MORAT, G. (1965) Étude cytophotometrique des teneurs en ADN chez quelques espèces de Ciliés astomes du genre *Metaradiophrya* Heid. *Arch. Zool. Expér. Gén.* **105**, 201–14.

150. MOSES, M. J. (1950) Nucleic acids and proteins of the nuclei of *Paramecium. J. Morphol.* **87**, 493–536.

151. MOSES, M. J. (1964) The nucleus and chromosomes: a cytological perspective. In *Cytology and Cell Physiology*, 3rd ed., ed. G. H. BOURNE, Academic Press, New York and London, 423–558.

152. MOSEVICH, T. N. (1967) New data on fibrillar structures in the macronucleus of the ciliate *Ichthyophthirius multifiliis. Acta Protozool.* (in press).

153. MUGARD, H. (1948) Contribution à l'étude des Infusoires hyménostomes histiophages. *Ann. Sci. Nat. (Zool.)*, sér. 11, **10**, 171–268.

154. MUGARD, H. (1951) Phosphatase alcaline chez les Infusoires ciliés. *Bull. Soc. Zool. France*, **76**, 39–41.

155. MÜGGE, E. (1957) Die Konjugation von *Vorticella campanula* (Ehrbg). *Arch. Protistenk.* **102**, 165–208.

156. MULSOW, W. (1913) Die Conjugation von *Stentor coeruleus* und *Stentor polymorphus. Arch. Protistenk.* **28**, 363–88.

157. NANNEY, D. L. (1964) Macronuclear differentiation and subnuclear assortment in ciliates. In *Role of Chromosomes in Development*, Academic Press, New York, 253–73.

158. NOBILI, R. (1961) L'azione del gene *am* sull'apparato nucleare di *Paramecium aurelia* durante la riproduzione vegetativa e sessuale in relazione all'età del clone et alla temperatura di allevamento degli animali. *Caryologia*, **14**, 43–58.

159. NOLAND, L. E. (1927) Conjugation in the ciliate *Metopus sigmoides. J. Morphol. Physiol.* **44**, 341–61.

160. Nouzarède, M. (1965) Étude de quelques ciliés mésopsammiques de la famille des Geleiidae Kahl. In *Progress in Protozoology* (Abstr. 2nd Internat. Conf. Protozool. London), 210–1.

161. Ördögh, F. (1959) Kernteilung in *Kahlia simplex* (Ciliata, Protozoa). *Acta Biol. Acad. Sci. Hung.* **10**, 127–39.

162. Ossipov, D. V. (1966) (On the problem of macronuclear regeneration in *Paramecium caudatum*). *Cytology* (*USSR*), **8**, 108–10 (in Russian with English summary).

163. Ovchinnikova, L. P., Selivanova, G. V., and Cheissin, E. M. (1965) Photometric study of the DNA content in the nuclei of *Spirostomum ambiguum* (Ciliata, Heterotricha). *Acta Protozool.* **3**, 69–78.

164. Padmavathi, P. B. (1955) Observations on the nuclear apparatus of *Spirostomum ambiguum*. *J. Zool. Soc. India*, **7**, 91–100.

165. Padmavathi, P. B. (1960) Hemixis in *Blepharisma undulans* (Ciliophora: Spirotricha). *Naturwissenschaften*, **47**, 383.

166. Padnos, M. (1962) Cytology of cold induced transformation of octogenic reproductive cysts to resting cysts in *Colpoda maupasi*. *J. Protozool.* **9**, 13–20.

167. Padnos, M., Jakowska, S., and Nigrelli, R. F. (1954) Morphology and life history of *Colpoda maupasi*, Bensonhurst strain. *J. Protozool.* **1**, 131–9.

168. Peshkovskaja, L. S. (1936) (Changes of the nuclear apparatus of *Climacostomum virens* during conjugation). *Biol. Zhurnal* (*Moscow*), **5**, 207–20 (in Russian with English summary).

169. Peshkovskaja, L. S. (1941) (Changes of the nuclear apparatus during conjugation in some holotrichous ciliates). *Trudy Inst. Cytol., Histol. i Embryol.* **1**, 19–27 (in Russian).

170. Piekarski, G. (1939) Cytologische Untersuchungen an einem normalen und einem Mikronucleus-losen Stamm von *Colpoda steinii* Maupas. *Arch. Protistenk.* **92**, 117–30.

171. Piekarski, G. (1941) Endomitose beim Großkern der Ziliaten? Versuch einer Synthese. *Biol. Zbl.* **61**, 416–26.

172. Poljansky, G. (1934) Geschlechtsprozesse bei *Bursaria truncatella* O. F. Müll. *Arch. Protistenk.* **81**, 420–546.

173. Poljansky, G. (1965) Morphological regularities of the progressive evolution in Protozoa. In *Progress in Protozoology* (Abstr. 2nd Int. Conf. Protozool. London), 17–8.

174. Poljansky, G. I., and Golikova, M. N. (1957) (On ciliates of the sea urchin intestine. II. New ciliate genus from *Strongylocentrotus droebachiensis* of the Murman coast). *Trudy Leningrad. Obsz. Estestvoisp.* **73**, 138–42 (in Russian).

175. Poljansky, G. I., and Raikov, I. B. (1960) (The role of polyploidy in the evolution of Protozoa). *Cytology* (*USSR*), **2**, 509–18 (in Russian).

176. Poljansky, G., and Raikov, I. (1961) Nature et origine du dualisme nucléaire chez les Infusoires ciliés. *Bull. Soc. Zool. France*, **86**, 402–11.

177. Pomrjaskinskaja, N. (1940) (Observations on cysts of the hypotrichous ciliate *Oxytricha hymenostoma*). *Uchenye Zapiski Leningr. Gos. Pedagog. Inst. im. Gerzena*, **30**, 93–132 (in Russian).

178. Prandtl, H. (1906) Die Konjugation von *Didinium nasutum* O.F.M. *Arch. Protistenk.* **7**, 229–58.

179. Prescott, D. M. (1960) Relation between cell growth and cell division. IV. The synthesis of DNA, RNA, and protein from division to division in *Tetrahymena*. *Exper. Cell Res.* **19**, 228–38.

180. Prescott, D. M. (1962) Nucleic acid and protein metabolism in the macronuclei of two ciliated Protozoa. *J. Histochem. Cytochem.* **10**, 145–53.

181. Prescott, D. M., and Kimball, R. F. (1961) Relation between RNA, DNA, and protein synthesis in the replicating nucleus of *Euplotes*. *Proc. Nat. Acad. Sci. USA*, **47**, 686–93.

182. PRESCOTT, D. M., KIMBALL, R. F., and CARRIER, R. F. (1962) Comparison between the timing of micronuclear and macronuclear DNA synthesis in *Euplotes eurystomus*. *J. Cell Biol.* **13**, 175–6.

183. PUYTORAC, P. DE (1959) Structures et ultrastructures nucléolaires et périnucléolaires du macronoyau intermitotique des Ciliés Haptophryidae. *C.R. Acad. Sci. Paris*, **249**, 1709–11.

184. PUYTORAC, P. DE (1961) Observations sur l'ultrastructure *d'Anoplophrya commune* de Puyt., Cilié parasite du Ver *Eophila savignyi* (G. et H.). *C.R. Soc. Biol.* **155**, 783–6.

185. PUYTORAC, P. DE (1963) Contribution à l'étude des Ciliés astomes Haptophryidae Cépède, 1903 (Cytologie, ultrastructure, taxonomie). *Ann. Sci. Nat.* (*Zool.*), sér. 12, **5**, 173–210.

186. PUYTORAC, P. DE (1963) Observations sur l'ultrastructure du Cilié astome: *Mesnilella trispiculata* K. *J. Microscopie*, **2**, 189–96.

187. RAABE, H. (1947) L'appareil nucléaire *d'Urostyla grandis* Ehrbg. Partie II. Appareil macronucléaire. *Ann. Univ. Mariae Curie-Sklodowska*, sér. C, **1**, 133–70.

188. RAIKOV, I. B. (1957) (Reorganization of the nuclear apparatus in ciliates and the problem of the origin of their binuclearity). *Vestnik Leningrad. Univ.*, No. 15, 21–37 (in Russian with English summary).

189. RAIKOV, I. B. (1958) Der Formwechsel des Kernapparates einiger niederer Ciliaten. I. Die Gattung *Trachelocerca*. *Arch. Protistenk.* **103**, 129–92.

190. RAIKOV, I. B. (1959) Der Formwechsel des Kernapparates einiger niederer Ciliaten. II. Die Gattung *Loxodes*. *Arch. Protistenk.* **104**, 1–42.

191. RAIKOV, I. B. (1959) (Cytological and cytochemical peculiarities of the nuclear apparatus and division in the holotrichous ciliate *Geleia nigriceps* Kahl). *Cytology* (*USSR*), **1**, 566–79 (in Russian).

192. RAIKOV, I. B. (1962) Der Kernapparat von *Nassula ornata* Ehrbg. (Ciliata, Holotricha). Zur Frage über den Chromosomenaufbau des Makronucleus. *Arch. Protistenk.* **105**, 463–88.

193. RAIKOV, I. B. (1962) Les Ciliés mésopsammiques du littoral de la Mer Blanche (URSS), avec une description de quelques espèces nouvelles ou peu connues. *Cahiers Biol. Mar.* **3**, 325–61.

194. RAIKOV, I. B. (1963) On the origin of nuclear dualism in ciliates. In *Progress in Protozoology* (*Proc.* Ist *Internat. Congr. Protozool. Prague*, 1961), 253–8.

195. RAIKOV, I. B. (1963) (Nuclear apparatus and division of *Remanella granulosa* Kahl and *R. rugosa* Kahl [Holotricha, Gymnostomatida]). In *Morphol. i Physiol. Prostejshikh* (Collection of papers No. 3 of the Inst. of Cytology, Acad. Sci. USSR), Moscow, Leningrad, 20–34 (in Russian).

196. RAIKOV, I. B. (1963) The nuclear apparatus of *Remanella multinucleata* Kahl (Ciliata, Holotricha). *Acta Biol. Acad. Sci. Hung.* **14**, 221–9.

197. RAIKOV, I. B. (1963) (The nuclear apparatus of holotrichous ciliates *Geleia orbis* Fauré-Fremiet and *G. murmanica* Raikov). *Acta Protozool.* **1**, 21–30 (in Russian with English summary).

198. RAIKOV, I. B. (1963) (Some stages of conjugation of the holotrichous ciliate *Trachelocerca coluber*). *Cytology* (*USSR*), **5**, 685–9 (in Russian).

199. RAIKOV, I. B. (1964) DNA content of the nuclei and the nature of macronuclear chromatin strands of the ciliate *Nassulopsis elegans* (Ehrbg.). *Acta Protozool.* **2**, 339–55.

200. RAIKOV, I. B. (1965) (New data on polyploid nuclei in Protozoa). In *Polyploidija i Selekcija* (*Proc. Conf. on Polyploidy Leningrad, 1963*), Moscow, Leningrad, 134–42 (in Russian).

201. RAIKOV, I. B. (1966) Elektronenmikroskopische Untersuchung des Kernapparates von *Nassula ornata* Ehrgb. (Ciliata, Holotricha). *Arch. Protistenk.* **109**, 71–98.

202. RAIKOV, I. B., CHEISSIN, E. M., and BUZE, E. G. (1963) A photometric study of DNA content of macro- and micronuclei in *Paramecium caudatum, Nassula ornata* and *Loxodes magnus. Acta Protozool.* **1**, 285–300.

203. RAO, M. V. N. (1964) Nuclear behavior of *Euplotes woodruffi* during conjugation. *J. Protozool.* **11**, 296–304.

204. RAY, CH. (1956) Meiosis and nuclear behavior in *Tetrahymena pyriformis. J. Protozool.* **3**, 88–96.

205. REICHENOW, E. (1928) Ergebnisse mit der Nuclealfärbung bei Protozoen. *Arch. Protistenk.* **61**, 144–66.

206. RIS, H. (1961) Ultrastructure and molecular organization of genetic systems. *Canad. J. Genet. Cytol.* **3**, 95–120.

207. ROQUE, M., PUYTORAC, P. DE, and SAVOIE, A. (1965) *Ophryoglena bacterocaryon* sp. nov., Cilié holotriche péniculien (cytologie, ultrastructure, cycle). *Arch. Zool. Exper. Gén.* **105**, 309–44.

208. ROSKIN, G. I., and GINSBURG, A. S. (1944) (Zymonucleic acid of the protozoan cell). *Doklady Acad. Nauk SSSR*, n. ser. **42**, 362–5 (in Russian).

209. ROSKIN, G. I., and GINSBURG, A. S. (1944) (Protoplasmic basophilia in Protozoa in connection with the presence of zymonucleic acid in the cell). *Doklady Acad. Nauk SSSR*, n. ser. **43**, 126–9 (in Russian).

210. ROSKIN, G., and STRUVE, M. (1953) (Cytochemical differences of the protoplasm of different species of Protozoa). *Doklady Acad. Nauk SSSR*, **93**, 151–3 (in Russian).

211. ROSSOLIMO, L. L. (1916) (Observations on *Loxodes rostrum* O.F. MÜLLER). *Dnevnik Zool. Otdel. Imper. Obsz. Ljubit. Estestvozn., Antropol. i Etnogr.*, n. ser. **3**, No. 4, 1–18 (in Russian with French summary).

212. ROSSOLIMO, L., and JAKIMOWITSCH, K. (1929) Die Kernteilung bei *Conchophthirius steenstrupii* St. *Zool. Anz.* **84**, 323–33.

213. ROTH, L. E. (1957) An electron microscope study of the cytology of the protozoan *Euplotes patella. J. Biophys. Biochem. Cytol.* **3**, 985–1000.

214. ROTH, L. E. (1960) Observations on division stages in the protozoan hypotrich *Stylonychia.* In *Vierter Internat. Kongr. Elektronenmikr. Berlin, 1958*, Verhandlungen, Springer Verlag, Berlin-Göttingen-Heidelberg, **2**, 241–4.

215. ROTH, L. E., and MINICK, O. T. (1961) Electron microscopy of nuclear and cytoplasmic events during division in *Tetrahymena pyriformis*, strains W and HAM 3. *J. Protozool.* **8**, 12–21.

216. ROTH, L. E., and SHIGENAKA, Y. (1964) The structure and formation of cilia and filaments in rumen Protozoa. *J. Cell Biol.* **20**, 249–70.

217. RUDZINSKA, M. A. (1956) Further observations on the fine structure of the macronucleus in *Tokophrya infusionum. J. Biophys. Biochem. Cytol.* **2**, Suppl., 425–8.

218. RUDZINSKA, M. A. (1956) The occurrence of hemixis in *Tokophrya infusionum. J. Protozool.* **3**, Suppl., 3–4.

219. RUDZINSKA, M. A. (1961) The use of a protozoan for studies on aging. II. The macronucleus in young and old organisms of *Tokophrya infusionum*: light and electron microscope observations. *J. Gerontol.* **16**, 326–34.

220. RUDZINSKA, M. A., and PORTER, K. R. (1955) Observations on the fine structure of the macronucleus of *Tokophrya infusionum. J. Biophys. Biochem. Cytol.* **1**, 421–8.

221. RUTHMANN, A. (1963) Die Struktur des Chromatins und die Verteilung der Ribonucleinsäure im Makronucleus von *Loxophyllum meleagris. Arch. Protistenk.* **106**, 422–36.

222. RUTHMANN, A. (1964) Autoradiographische und mikrophotometrische Untersuchungen zur DNA-Synthese im Makronucleus von *Bursaria truncatella. Arch. Protistenk.* **107**, 117–30.

223. RUTHMANN, A., and HECKMANN, K. (1961) Formwechsel und Struktur des Makronucleus von *Bursaria truncatella. Arch. Protistenk.*, **105**, 313–40.

224. SAITO, M. (1961) A note on the duplication process of macronuclear chromosomes in a peritrichous ciliate, *Vorticella campanula*. *Jap. J. Genet.* **36**, 184–6.
225. SAITO, M., and SATO, H. (1961) (Morphological studies on the macronuclear structure of *Paramecium caudatum*. II. Structural changes of the macronucleus during the division cycle). *Zool. Mag. (Jap.)*, **70**, 73–80 (in Japanese with English summary).
226. SAITO, M., and SATO, H. (1961) (Morphological studies on the macronuclear structure of *Paramecium caudatum*. III. On the development of the macronucleus in the exconjugant). *Zool. Mag. (Jap.)*, **70**, 81–88 (in Japanese with English summary).
227. SATO, H. (1963) The structural changes of the macronuclear constituents during the division cycle in ciliated Protozoa. In *Proc. XVIth. Internat. Congr. Zool. Washington, D.C.* **2**, 294.
228. SATO, H., and SAITO, M. (1958) (Morphological studies on the macronuclear structure of *Paramecium caudatum*. I. Macronuclear constituents in interphase). *Zool. Mag. (Jap.)*, **67**, 249–58 (in Japanese with English summary).
229. SATO, H., and SAITO, M. (1959) (Morphological study on the macronuclear structure in interphase and prefission stage of *Tetrahymena geleii* W.). *Zool. Mag. (Jap.)*, **68**, 209–14 (in Japanese with English summary).
230. SAVOIE, A. (1961) *Ophryoglena hypertrophica* n. sp. (Ciliata Hymenostomatida). *J. Protozool.* **8**, 324–34.
231. SCHERBAUM, O. H., LOUDERBACK, A. L., and JAHN, T. L. (1958) The formation of subnuclear aggregates in normal and synchronized protozoan cells. *Biol. Bull.* **115**, 269–75.
232. SCHWARTZ, V. (1935) Versuche über Regeneration und Kerndimorphismus bei *Stenor coeruleus* Ehrbg. *Arch. Protistenk.* **85**, 100–39.
233. SCHWARTZ, V. (1956) Nukleolenformwechsel und Zyklen der Ribosenucleinsäure in der vegetativen Entwicklung von *Paramecium bursaria*. *Biol. Zbl.* **75**, 1–16.
234. SCHWARTZ, V. (1957) Über den Formwechsel achromatischer Substanz in der Teilung des Makronucleus von *Paramecium bursaria*. *Biol. Zbl.* **76**, 1–23.
235. SCHWARTZ, V. (1958) Chromosomen im Makronucleus von *Paramecium bursaria*. *Biol. Zbl.* **77**, 347–64.
236. SERGEJEVA, G. I. (1964) (Activity of acid phosphatase at different stages of the life cycle of *Nyctotherus cordiformis* (Ehrbg.) Stein (Ciliata)). *Acta Protozool.* **2**, 163–71 (in Russian with English summary).
237. SESHACHAR, B. R. (1946) Nuclear reorganization in *Epistylis*. *Current Sci.* **15**, 198.
238. SESHACHAR, B. R. (1947) Chromatin elimination and the ciliate macronucleus. *Amer. Nat.* **81**, 316–20.
239. SESHACHAR, B. R. (1950) The nucleus and nucleic acids of *Chilodonella uncinatus* Ehrbg. *J. Exper. Zool.* **114**, 517–44.
240. SESHACHAR, B. R. (1953) Metachromasy of the ciliate macronucleus. *J. Exper. Zool.* **124**, 117–30.
241. SESHACHAR, B. R. (1960) Effect of centrifugation on the macronucleus of *Spirostomum* and *Blepharisma*. *Nature*, **186**, 333–4.
242. SESHACHAR, B. R. (1963) Experiments with the ciliate macronucleus. In *Progress in Protozoology* (Proc. 1st Internat. Congr. Protozool. Prague, 1961), 275–7.
243. SESHACHAR, B. R. (1964) Observations on the fine structure of the nuclear apparatus of *Blepharisma intermedium* Bhandary (Ciliata: Spirotricha). *J. Protozool.* **11**, 402–9.
244. SESHACHAR, B. R., and DASS, C. M. S. (1953) Macronuclear regeneration in *Epistylis articulata*. *Quart. J. Microscop. Sci.* **94**, 185–92.
245. SESHACHAR, B. R., and DASS, C. M. S. (1953) Evidence for the conversion of desoxyribonucleic acid (DNA) to ribonucleic acid (RNA) in *Epistylis articulata* From. (Ciliata: Peritricha). *Exper. Cell Res.* **5**, 248–50.
246. SESHACHAR, B. R., and DASS, C. M. S. (1954) The macronucleus of *Epistylis articulata* From. during conjugation: a photometric study. *Physiol. Zool.* **27**, 280–6.

247. SESHACHAR, B. R., and DASS, C. M. S. (1954) Photometric study of desoxyribonucleic acid (DNA) synthesis in regenerating macronucleus of *Epistylis articulata* From. *Proc. Nat. Inst. Sci. India*, **20**, 656–9.

248. SONNEBORN, T. M. (1940) The relation of macronuclear regeneration in *Paramecium aurelia* to macronuclear structure, amitosis and genetic determination. *Anat. Rec.* **78**, Suppl., 53–54.

249. SONNEBORN, T. M. (1946) Inert nuclei: inactivity of micronuclear genes in variety 4 of *Paramecium aurelia*. *Genetics*, **31**, 231.

250. SONNEBORN, T. M. (1947) Recent advances in the genetics of *Paramecium* and *Euplotes*. *Adv. in Genetics*, **1**, 263–358.

251. SONNEBORN, T. M. (1949) Ciliated Protozoa: cytogenetics, genetics, and evolution. *Ann. Rev. Microbiol.* **3**, 55–80.

252. SONNEBORN, T. M. (1954) Gene-controlled, aberrant nuclear behavior in *Paramecium aurelia*. *Microbial Genet. Bull.* **11**, 24–25.

253. SONNEBORN, T. M. (1954) Is gene *K* active in the micronucleus of *Paramecium*? *Microbial Genet. Bull.* **11**, 25–26.

254. SONNEBORN, T. M., SCHNELLER, M. V., and CRAIG, M. F. (1956) The basis of variation in phenotype of gene-controlled traits in heterozygotes of *Paramecium aurelia*. *J. Protozool.* **3**, Suppl., 8.

255. STEIN, G. A. (1964) (The life cycle of *Trichodina cottidarum* Dogiel, 1948 (Peritricha, Urceolariidae); a photometric study of DNA changes in the macronucleus). *Acta Protozool.* **2**, 357–65 (in Russian with English summary).

256. STEVENS, A. R. (1963) Electron microscope autoradiography of DNA and RNA syntheses in *Euplotes eurystomus*. *J. Cell Biol.* **19**, No. 2, 67A.

257. SUKHANOVA, K. M. (1960) (Cytophysiology of the life cycles of the ciliates of the genus *Balantidium* from amphibians). In *Voprosy Cytol. i Protistol.* (Collection of papers No. 1 of the Inst. of Cytol., Acad. Sci. USSR), Moscow-Leningrad, 285–312 (in Russian).

258. SUMMERS, F. M. (1935) The division and reorganization of *Aspidisca lynceus*, *Diophrys appendiculata*, and *Stylonychia pustulata*. *Arch. Protistenk.* **85**, 173–208.

259. SUMMERS, F. M. (1941) The protozoa in connection with morphogenetic problems. In *Protozoa in Biological Research*, eds. G. N. CALKINS and F. M. SUMMERS, Columbia Univ. Press, New York, 772–817.

260. SWARCZEWSKY, B. (1928) Zur Kenntnis der Baikalprotistenfauna. Die an den Baikalgammariden lebenden Infusorien. I. Dendrosomidae. *Arch. Protistenk.* **61**, 349–78.

261. SWARCZEWSKY, B. (1928) Beobachtungen über *Spirochona elegans* n. spec. *Arch. Protistenk.* **61**, 185–222.

262. TARTAR, V. (1953) Chimeras and nuclear transplantations in ciliates, *Stentor coeruleus* X *S. polymorphus*. *J. Exper. Zool.* **124**, 63–103.

263. TARTAR, V. (1957) Equivalence of macronuclear nodes. *J. Exper. Zool.* **135**, 387–401.

264. TARTAR, V. (1961) *The biology of Stentor*. Pergamon Press, Oxford, London, New York, Paris.

265. TARTAR, V. (1963) Extreme alteration of the nucleocytoplasmic ratio in *Stentor coeruleus*. *J. Protozool.* **10**, 445–61.

266. TAYLOR, C., and GARNJOBST, L. (1941) Nuclear reorganization in resting cysts of *Colpoda duodenaria*. *J. Morphol.* **68**, 197–213.

267. TORCH, R. (1961) The nuclear apparatus of a new species of *Tracheloraphis* (Protozoa, Ciliata). *Biol. Bull.* **121**, 410–1.

268. TORCH, R. (1964) Autoradiographic studies of nucleic acid synthesis in a gymnostome ciliate, *Tracheloraphis* sp. *J. Cell Biol.* **23**, No. 2, 98A.

269. TSUJITA, M., WATANABE, K., and TSUDA, S. (1957) Electron microscopy of thin sectioned nuclei in *Paramecium*. *Cytologia* (*Tokyo*), **22**, 322–7.

270. TUFFRAU, M. (1953) Les processus cytologiques de la conjugaison chez *Spirochona gemmipara* Stein. *Bull. Biol. France Belg.* **87**, 314–22.

271. TUFFRAU, M. (1962) Les processus régulateurs de la "caryophthisis" du macronucleus de *Nassulopsis lagenula* Fauré-Fremiet 1959. I. Cycle évolutif. *Arch. Protistenk.* **106**, 201–10.

272. TUFFRAU, M. (1963) Les structures infraciliaires et la stomatogénèse chez les *Loxodes*. In *Progress in Protozoology* (Proc. 1st Internat. Congr. Protozool. Prague, 1961), 278–80.

273. TUFFRAU, M., and SAVOIE, A. (1961) Étude morphologique du Cilié hyménostome *Disematostoma colpidioides* von Gelei, 1954. *J. Protozool.* **8**, 64–8.

274. TURNER, J. P. (1930) Division and conjugation in *Euplotes patella* Ehrbg., with special reference to the nuclear phenomena. *Univ. Calif. Publ. Zool.* **33**, 193–258.

275. UHLIG, G. (1964) Die Folliculiniden der Deutschen Bucht I. *Magnifolliculina* n.g., eine interessante Formengruppe der Epifauna des Sandgrundes. *Helgol. Wiss. Meeresuntersuch.*, **11**, 92–109.

276. USPENSKAJA, A. V., and OVCHINNIKOVA, L. P. (1966) (Changes of DNA and RNA content during the life cycle of *Ichthyophthirius multifiliis*). *Acta Protozool.* **4**, 127–41. (In Russian with English summary).

277. VIVIER, E. (1960) Cycle nucléolaire en rapport avec l'alimentation chez *Paramecium caudatum*. *C.R. Acad. Sci. Paris*, **250**, 205–7.

278. VIVIER, E. (1960) Contribution à l'étude de la conjugaison chez *Paramecium caudatum*. *Ann. Sci. Nat. (Zool.)*, **2**, 387–506.

279. VIVIER, E. (1963) Étude au microscope électronique des nucléoles dans le macronucleus de *Paramecium caudatum*. In *Progress in Protozoology* (Proc. 1st Internat. Congr. Protozool. Prague, 1961), 421.

280. VIVIER, E., and ANDRÉ, J. (1961) Existence d'inclusions d'ultrastructure fibrillaire dans le macronucleus de certaines souches de *Paramecium caudatum* Ehr. *C.R. Acad. Sci. Paris*, **252**, 1848–50.

281. WALKER, P., and MITCHISON, J. (1957) DNA synthesis in two ciliates. *Exper. Cell Res.* **13**, 167–70.

282. WEISZ, P. B. (1949) A cytochemical and cytological study of differentiation in normal and reorganizational stages of *Stentor coeruleus*. *J. Morphol.* **84**, 335–64.

283. WEISZ, P. B. (1949) The role of specific macronuclear nodes in the differentiation and the maintenance of the oral area in *Stentor*. *J. Exper. Zool.* **111**, 141–56.

284. WEISZ, P. B. (1954) Morphogenesis in Protozoa. *Quart. Rev. Biol.* **29**, 207–29.

285. WERMEL, E. (1928) Untersuchungen über *Chromidina elegans* (Foett.) Gond. *Arch. Protistenk.* **64**, 419–45.

286. WESSENBERG, H. (1961) Studies on the life cycle and morphogenesis of *Opalina*. *Univ. Calif. Publ. Zool.* **61**, 315–70.

287. WEYER, G. (1930) Untersuchungen über die Morphologie und Physiologie des Formwechsels der *Gastrostyla steinii* Engelmann. *Arch. Protistenk.* **71**, 139–228.

288. WICHTERMAN, R. (1937) Division and conjugation in *Nyctotherus cordiformis* (Ehr.) Stein (Protozoa, Ciliata) with special reference to the nuclear phenomena. *J. Morphol.* **60**, 563–611.

289. WILLIAMS, D. B. (1964) Ultraviolet resistance and macronuclear DNA synthesis in *Spathidium spathula*. *J. Protozool.* **11**, Suppl., 26.

290. WOODARD, J., GELBER, B., and SWIFT, H. (1961) Nucleoprotein changes during the mitotic cycle in *Paramecium aurelia*. *Exper. Cell Res.* **23**, 258–64.

291. WOODARD, J., WOODARD, M., and GELBER, B. (1964). Cytochemical studies of conjugation in *Paramecium aurelia*. *J. Cell Biol.* **23**, No. 2, 125 A.

292. WOODRUFF, L. L. (1941) Endomixis. In *Protozoa in Biological Research*, eds. G. N. CALKINS and F. M. SUMMERS, Columbia Univ. Press, New York, 646–65.

293. Yow, F. W. (1961) Effects of nucleic acid synthesis inhibitors on morphogenesis in *Euplotes eurystomus*. *J. Protozool.* **8**, Suppl., 20.

294. Zebrun, W. (1957) An electron microscopic investigation of nuclear and cytoplasmic structures in *Tetrahymena rostrata*. *J. Protozool.* **4**, Suppl., 22.

295. Zech, L. (1964) Zytochemische Messungen an den Zellkernen der Foraminiferen *Patellina corrugata* und *Rotaliella heterocaryotica*. *Arch. Protistenk.* **107**, 295–330.

296. Zinger, J. A. (1929) (Materials on morphology and cytology of freshwater ciliates). *Russkij Arch. Protistol.* **8**, 51–90 (in Russian with German summary).

297. Blanc, J. (1965) Etude cytophotométrique des périodes de duplication de l'acide désoxyribonucléique dans l'appareil nucléaire de *Paramecium caudatum*. *Protistologica*, **1**, No. 2, 11–5.

298. Cameron, I. L., Padilla, G. M., and Wysinger, B. M. (1965) Regulation of the DNA-synthetic period within the cell cycle of *Tetrahymena pyriformis*. In *Progress in Protozoology* (Abstr. 2nd Internat. Conf. Protozool. London), 236–7.

299. Flickinger, C. J. (1965) The fine structure of the nuclei of *Tetrahymena pyriformis* throughout the cell cycle. *J. Cell Biol.* **27**, 519–29.

300. Gorovsky, M. A. (1965) Electron microscopic cytochemistry of isolated nuclei of *Tetrahymena*. *J. Cell Biol.* **27**, No. 2, 37 A.

301. Jurand, A., and Bomford, R. (1965) The fine structure of the parasitic suctorian *Podophrya parameciorum*. *J. Microscopie*, **4**, 509–22.

302. Kennedy, J. R. (1965) The morphology of *Blepharisma undulans* Stein. *J. Protozool.* **12**, 542–61.

303. Radzikowski, S. (1965) Changes in the heterometric macronucleus in division of *Chilodonella cucullulus* (Müller). *Acta Protozool.* **2**, 233–8.

304. Ringertz, N. R., and Hoskins, G. C. (1965) Cytochemistry of macronuclear reorganization. *Exper. Cell Res.* **38**, 160–79.

305. Seshachar, B. R. (1965) The fine structure of the nuclear apparatus and the chromosomes of *Spirostomum ambiguum* Ehrbg. *Acta Protozool.* **3**, 337–43.

306. Shepard, D. C. (1965) Production and elimination of excess DNA in ultraviolet-irradiated *Tetrahymena*. *Exper. Cell Res.* **38**, 570–9.

307. Torch, R. (1965) The effects of actinomycin D on RNA synthesis in the ciliate, *Tracheloraphis* sp. In *Progress in Protozoology* (Abstr. 2nd Internat. Conf. Protozool. London), 232.

308. Weber, H. (1965) Über die Paarung der Gamonten und den Kerndualismus der Foraminifere *Metarotaliella parva* Grell. *Arch. Protistenk.* **108**, 217–70.

309. Whitson, G. L., Padilla, G. M., and Elrod, L. H. (1964) Morphogenesis, RNA synthesis, and actinomycin D inhibition in synchronized *Tetrahymena pyriformis*. *J. Cell Biol.* **23**, No. 2, 102 A.

310. Wise, B. N. (1965) Fine structure of *Euplotes*: filaments, vesicles, and kinetosomes. *J. Cell Biol.* **27**, No. 2, 113 A–114 A.

GENETICS OF THE PROTOZOA

JOHN R. PREER, JR.

Department of Biology, University of Pennsylvania

CONTENTS

I. INTRODUCTION

The genetics of the Protozoa is the genetics of organisms far larger and more complex than the viruses and bacteria, yet still a step below multicellular forms. The peculiar advantages of the Protozoa for genetic work include a wealth of complex cellular organelles, a diversity of nuclear processes, large, easily handled individuals, and the possibility of crossing differentiated lines of cells. Protozoan geneticists, particularly since 1937 when Sonneborn discovered mating types, have made important contributions in a number of fundamental areas of genetics. These include mechanisms of differentiation, cytoplasmic inheritance, genetic aspects of the physiology of the life cycle, and radiation genetics.

Indeed, the major portion of our present knowledge of the kinds of mechanisms responsible for non-Mendelian inheritance has been obtained from work on the Protozoa. First, the work on kappa and its relatives in *Paramecium* led us to the realization that external organisms may become part of the genetic system of cells, and once integrated they become part of the cell—no matter what their origin. Subsequent work on viruses and episomes has confirmed this view, and recent work on the fine structure of the DNA-containing regions in mitochondria and chloroplasts has led to a revival of the suggestion that they too have had an external origin. Second, the work on mating types, serotypes, and the life cycle in *Paramecium* has shown that alternate states of activation or repression of nuclear genes may be determined (often under the control of cytoplasmic influences) and inherited for innumerable generations. Finally, the studies on cortical variation in ciliates have provided sound experimental evidence for the current notion that pre-existing cellular structure and modifications in it may control the formation of new organelles in a truly hereditary way. And now, as the problems of DNA structure and its role in specifying the structure of proteins are elucidated, we may expect that more and more attention will be given to the genetic aspects of the control of gene action and the determination of cytoplasmic organization, problems which have long occupied the attention of protozoan geneticists.

While most geneticists over the years have been preoccupied with problems of genetic structure, recombination, mutation, and the synthesis of biologically important molecules, protozoan geneticists have investigated problems peripheral to these areas of study. This situation has arisen from the disadvantages of most protozoa (*Chlamydomonas* is an exception) for study in these areas—disadvantages such as complex nutritional requirements, a lack of techniques for screening and isolating rare mutants, and, until Sonneborn's discovery of mating types, inadequate control over the mating process.

Protozoan genetics is one of the oldest branches of genetics. Investigations go back to the pioneering studies of Maupas[403, 404] in the late 1800's, and numerous investigations which were carried out in the early 1900's. When Jennings published his review of the genetics of the Protozoa in 1929[275] his bibliography contained 259 references. Protozoan genetics in its early years was primarily concerned with the constancy of the clone and with the origin of clonal diversity, particularly in relation to the life cycle. These earlier studies were thoroughly reviewed by Jennings and are not considered in detail here. One of their chief contributions was firm experimental evidence for the principle of the constancy of the clone, a principle which we recognize as a consequence of mitosis. Many hereditary variations were encountered by the early workers, but their hereditary basis was generally not discovered. Jollos distinguished between permanent diversities and dauermodifications, long-lasting environmentally induced hereditary changes which eventually disappeared. A few of the heterogeneous phenomena considered as dauer-modifications are discussed in this chapter, but for details the reader is referred to Jennings' reviews.[275, 279]

Jennings' review of 1929[275] was the first comprehensive review of protozoan genetics. In 1941 Jennings brought his review up to date.[279] Sonneborn[629] reviewed the genetics of *Paramecium* and *Euplotes* in 1947, and soon thereafter added a review of the genetics and evolution of ciliated Protozoa covering the years 1946 to 1949.[634] Catcheside's *The Genetics of Microorganisms* was published in 1949.[86] G. H. Beale's excellent book on the genetics of *Paramecium aurelia* appeared in 1954.[45] Kimball in 1955[319] reviewed the effects of radiation in Protozoa. The genetics of the Protozoa was reviewed by Preer for the years 1947 to 1956.[505] In 1957 Sonneborn considered species problems in the Protozoa[646] and in 1959, kappa and related particles in *Paramecium*.[649] In 1957 Beale reviewed the serotype system of *Paramecium*.[47] In 1960 the genetics and cytology of *Chlamydomonas* were discussed by Levine and Ebersold[364] and certain cytological and genetic problems in Protozoa were reviewed by Nanney and Rudzinska.[461] In 1961 Beale and Wilkinson published a review of antigenis variation in unicellular organisms.[51] Biochemical genetics of the algae wal considered by Ebersold in 1962.[141] In 1964 Sager discussed cellulas heredity in *Chlamydomonas*[563] and Kimball reviewed physiologicra genetics of the ciliates.[328] Finally, the chemical genetics of the Protozoa wca reviewed by Allen in 1966.[12]

II. THE ORGANISMS

The Protozoa include numerous organisms useful for genetic analysis. This section considers only the few major forms which have been studied genetic-ally, with some general information concerning species, culture, special genetic techniques, lists of Mendelian genes, linkage relations, and nuclear processes.

A. Amebae

Early work on protozoan genetics includes studies on variation in the shelled amebae *Difflugia, Arcella,* and *Centropyxis*. More recently special attention has been devoted to *Amoeba proteus* and *A. discoides* and to a lesser extent, *A. dubia*. The three species are generally very similar and are differentiated primarily on the basis of form and number of pseudopods. A recent study of proteins in *A. proteus* and *A. discoides* by Kates and Goldstein[303] revealed only one minor antigenic difference. However, a number of character differences have been discovered by Judin, Danielli, and coworkers and are considered in Section VIII, H. Crosses are not possible in *Amoeba* but experimental nuclear transfer has been perfected. An ameba is held in a micromanipulator with a specially fabricated hooked needle and its single nucleus pushed out through the cell membrane with a second needle. The donor ameba is now brought into contact with the enucleated cell and its nucleus is pushed through the cell membranes of both cells. This process has been shown to transfer practically no cytoplasm.

Amoeba has large numbers of small chromosomes. The very high degree of resistance to X-radiation suggests that it may be polyploid.[483] Amebas are generally cultured in an inorganic salt solution and fed living protozoans such as *Tetrahymena* and *Chilomonas*. There are in the cytoplasm of *A. proteus* DNA-containing[495a] bodies which are considered symbionts by Roth and Daniels.[548]

B. Heliozoans

Variations in *Actinophrys sol* were studied by Bělař in the 1920's[55, 56] and by Jollos in 1934,[291] but there has been no recent work on the genetics of heliozoans. Meiosis and nuclear fusions occur within cysts. Occasionally more than one individual may enter a single cyst. Thus, crosses between variant clones, although never attempted, should be possible. *A. sol* can be cultured in an inorganic salt solution and fed green flagellates.

C. Trypanosomes

Studies on trypanosomes and their relatives have been concerned with induced loss of the kinetoplast, changes in antigenic properties, and reports of DNA induced transformation. Much of the work has involved *Trypanosoma gambiense* and *T. rhodesiense*, the agents of African sleeping sickness, *T. cruzi*, which causes Chagas disease or South American trypanosomiasis, and *T. evansi*, pathogenic in a number of different mammals. A hemoflagellate, *Leishmania*, normally reproducing in the blood of mammals or in their insect intermediate hosts, has been cultured *in vitro*.[706] Characteristic changes in morphology and metabolism in different hosts and *in vitro* have recently been the subject of a number of studies[707] and are considered in Section VIII, D. Meiosis and nuclear fusions have not been described.

D. Euglena

Studies on the genetics of *Euglena gracilis* have been devoted primarily to chloroplast inheritance. *E. gracilis* can be cultured on a simple defined medium.[217] If grown in the dark, it loses its green color. Changed back to light, its green color reappears. Although there have been reports of sexuality in certain species of *Euglena*, only asexual reproduction is found in the strains of *E. gracilis* in use today.

E. Chlamydomonas and its Relatives

Investigations on *Chlamydomonas* began with Pascher[490, 491] in 1916. He crossed two "species" and obtained 2:2 segregations within tetrads. Between 1931 and 1955 F. Moewus published some forty papers on the genetics of *Chlamydomonas* and related forms such as *Polytoma, Protosiphon*, and *Brachiomonas*. (For an excellent bibliography see ref. 212). The work has been reviewed a number of times.[279, 526, 622, 638] Moewus' investigations were very extensive, dealing with sexuality, biochemical genetics, crossing over, dauermodifications, and mutation. He claimed to have mapped some seventy genetic loci. But his work has been very severely criticized and numerous attempts to repeat it have always failed.[492, 610, 213, 554, 227, 537, 494, 704] There is no question that Moewus did much to stimulate work on *Chlamydomonas*, but it is also clear that his claims cannot be accepted without independent confirmation. For this reason, Moewus' results will not be considered further in this chapter.

More recently, work on *Chlamydomonas* has been concerned primarily with the three species, *C. reinhardi, C. moewusii* and *C. eugametos*. The latter two species are very closely related and Bernstein and Jahn[59] report that they mate with each other and should be considered different strains of *C. eugametos*. The sixteen-celled colonial species, *Gonium pectorale*[682, 682a] and *Pandorina morum*[110, 111] have also been studied recently. In *Chlamydomonas, Gonium*, and *Pandorina* mating is between haploid plus and minus mating types, which fuse to form the zygote. Fifteen different complementary pairs of mating types have been found in *Pandorina*. Stein has found a number of poorly defined syngens in *Gonium* (see Section II, F, 2 for a discussion of the term "syngen"). Meiosis in *Chlamydomonas* and in *Gonium* yields tetrads; but in *Pandorina* meiosis is comparable to oogenesis in higher forms, two polar bodies and one viable haploid individual resulting. In all three genera mating type is determined by a pair of alleles at a single locus (except in a few monoecious strains of *Pandorina*). In *Chlamydomonas* and *Gonium* the meiotic products in the unordered tetrads consequently show

2 : 2 segregation for plus and minus mating types, while in *Pandorina* one half the meioses yield plus gametes and one half yield the minus type. Mating types in a number of species of *Eudorina* (16 to 128-celled colonies) have been investigated recently by Goldstein.[211a] Most clones are heterothallic, each producing either ova or sperm. Some species have more than one syngen, there being at least four in *Eudorina elegans*. In *E. elegans* and in *E. illinoisensis* sex in heterothallic strains is determined by a pair of alleles at one mating type locus. Interspecific matings occur, but most, if not all, lead to considerable nonviability in further generations.

    C. reinhardi is the most thoroughly investigated species. It may be cultured on simple inorganic salts in the light. The medium may be supplemented with acetate for the recovery of photosynthetic mutants, or yeast extract or other supplements for the growth of auxotrophic mutants. The addition of sodium acetate to the medium makes it possible to culture *C. reinhardi* in the dark, but *C. moewusii* can grow only in the light.[371] *C. reinhardi* retains its green color when grown in the dark.[568] Certain mutants of *C. reinhardi* cannot be grown in the dark, even on supplemented medium, while others lose their chlorophyll in the dark and regain it when returned to the light. *Chlamydomonas* may be cultured on agar, where it grows without flagella. Replica plating may be used and has proved an important technique in the isolation of mutants.

    Plus and minus haploid cells of *C. reinhardi* in reactive condition pair or clump by their flagella. Soon after clumping the members of each pair fuse to yield a zygote with two nuclei and four flagella. Zygotes are then generally plated on agar where they lose their flagella, undergo nuclear fusion, and develop a thick wall. In crosses it is useful to take advantage of the fact that vegetative cells are killed by chloroform, while zygotes are resistant. Zygotes may be induced to mature and germinate by placing them at 25°C in the light for a day (500 ft-candles), then five days in the dark, and finally a day in fresh medium in the light. During this period two meiotic divisions yield four haploid cells. Occasionally a third mitotic division occurs and eight rather than four cells are liberated from the zygote. Techniques for separating members from the tetrad are reviewed by Levine and Ebersold.[364] Cultures produced by these cells may be induced to acquire mating reactivity (mature into gametes) by starving them for nitrogen. Although in *C. reinhardi*, *C. eugametos*, and *C. moewusii* reactive cells of opposite mating type are of the same size, in other species of *Chlamydomonas* they may be very different.

    The chromosomes of *Chlamydomonas* are small and difficult to observe. *C. reinhardi* has been reported to have a haploid number of 18 ± 2, chromosomes by Schaechter and DeLamater[577] and 16 by Wetherell and Krauss.[722] A haploid number of eight has been reported by Buffaloe,[76] six to eight by Levine and Folsome,[365] and eight by Sager.[561] Sixteen inkage groups are reported by Hastings *et al.*[229] Because of the difficulty in observing the chromosomes of *Chlamydomonas,* it is likely that the chromosome number will have to be established by genetic techniques.

It has been reported that polyploidy may be induced in *Chlamydomonas* by colchicine[77, 722] and by high light intensity.[77] Return to the original conditions of colchicine-free medium and lower light intensity brought about a return to haploidy. The work on colchicine reported in one of the papers[722] has been criticized by Levine and Ebersold[364] and the reader is referred to their paper for the details which are beyond the scope of this review.

Ebersold[142] has reported the occurrence of diploid strains of *C. reinhardi.* The allele for the minus mating type is found to be dominant, and mitotic recombination occurs.

A large number of mutations have been described in *C. reinhardi, C. moewusii* and *C. eugametos.* Those which have given 2 : 2 segregations in

TABLE 1. GENES IN CHLAMYDOMONAS REINHARDI*

Phenotype	Symbol	Number of loci	Reference
mating type (+ or −)	*mt*	1	610
paralyzed flagella	*pf*	16	144, 563, 229
paralyzed flagella (central fibers disrupted)	*pro*$_1$	1	525
paraminobenzoic acid-requiring	*pab*	2	164
nicotinamide-requiring	*nic*	6	164, 144, 229
thiamin-requiring	*thi*	7	164, 144, 563
arginine-requiring	*arg*	4	164, 229
suppressor of arginine requirement	*su*^{arg}	1	229
acetate-requiring	*ac*	35	164, 144, 360, 359, 357, 229, 563
suppressor of acetate requirement	*su*^{ac}	1	229
inability to use nitrate as N source	*No*$_3$	1	563
streptomycin resistance	*sr-1*	1	556, 573
paromycin resistance	*pr-1*	1	203
neamine resistance	*nr-1*	1	203
canavine resistance	*can*	1	229
amplification of streptomycin resistance	*A*	1	573
methionine sulfoximine resistance	*msr*	1	557
actidione resistance	*act*	1	563
yellow green	*ygr*	1	557
pale green	*pgr*	1	557
brown	*br*	1	557
eye spot lacking	*ey*	1	228
small colonies	*sc*	1	228
slow growth	*sg*	1	228
raised colony		1	140

* Linkage map is given in Fig. 1.

TABLE 2. GENES IN CHLAMYDOMONAS MOEWUSII

Phenotype	Symbol	Number of loci	Reference
mating type (+ or −)	mt*	1	372
twinning	t†	1	372
paralyzed flagella	p	1	372
paraminobenzoic acid-requiring	a*	1	372
thiamin-requiring	b	1	372
non-photosynthetic	n	1	372
lazy	l†	1	372
volutin	v	1	372

* a and mt are linked.[372]
† t and l are linked.[372]

TABLE 3. GENES IN CHLAMYDOMONAS EUGAMETOS

Phenotype	Symbol	Number of loci	Reference
mating type (+ or −)	*sex*	1	213
thiamin-requiring	*th*	1	213
paraminobenzoic acid-requiring	*pab*	3	213
purine-requiring	*pur*	1	213
nicotinamide-requiring	*nic*	5	213, 436, 438
resistance to 3-acetyl pyridine	*apy*	2	436
modifier of *nic* loci	*mod*	1	438

tetrads and therefore probably represent single gene mutations are given in Tables 1, 2 and 3. A genetic map of *C. reinhardi*, modified from Ebersold et al.[144] Sager[563] and Hastings et al.,[229] is given in Fig. 1 (p. 244).

1. TETRAD ANALYSIS IN CHLAMYDOMONAS

Tetrads consist of the four haploid products of meiosis. Occasionally a final mitotic division yields eight products, but tetrad analysis is not hampered by the presence of two of each of the meiotic nuclei. In some fungi, such as *Neurospora crassa*, the linear arrangement of meiotic products with no overlapping of spindles makes it possible to determine which nuclei are descended from each of the two products of the first division. In such ordered tetrads, the arrangement of meiotic products makes it possible to state whether each pair of different alleles segregates at the first or second meiotic division. Such information is useful, for if centromeres segregate at the first meiotic division, one-half the percentage of second division segregation is a measure of the gene–centromere distance. In the unordered tetrads of *Chlamydomonas* the arrangement of meiotic products yields no information on division of segregation. However, if a determinant which always segregates at the first meiotic division is known and included as a marker, the division of segregation of other segregating genes in the tetrad is easily determined.

C. reinhardi has at least three such markers: one is the ac-17 locus (see Fig. 1) reported by Ebersold et al.,[144] which is very close to the centromere in linkage group III; another is pf-2, 0.5 units from its centromere in linkage group XI; and the last is the y_1 determinant which always segregates at the first meiotic division, yet is not associated with any of the known linkage groups (see Section VIII, F). Although they are useful in determining gene–centromere distances, they have only limited value in the study of chromatid interference. This is true because of the possibility that rare apparent second division segregations of a gene may be scored because of rare second division segregations of the markers. It might be noted, however, that this difficulty could be avoided by using more than one such marker which normally segregates at the first division.

One-factor crosses in tetrads, of course, yield precise 2 : 2 segregations. 2 : 2 segregations do not, however, prove Mendelian factors in Chlamydomonas, for the factor y_1 segregates 2 : 2 and yet does not belong in any one of the linkage groups of C. reinhardi.

Two-factor crosses such as AB × ab yield three types of unordered tetrads: PD, or parental ditype (AB, AB, ab, ab); NPD, or non-parental ditype (Ab, Ab, aB, aB); and T or tetratype (AB, Ab, aB, ab). If two genes are linked with each other the number of PD is expected to be greater than NPD, for PD may be obtained without crossovers, while four strand double crossovers are required to produce NPD.[493] Non-linkage is indicated if PD is equal to NPD or if NPD is more frequent than 1 NPD to 4 T. (See Ref. 40 for discussion.) It has been demonstrated (see Ref. 487) that recombination frequencies obtained from random strands are a more efficient test of linkage than are the data obtained from tetrads, but tetrads are often the method of choice because of their greater usefulness in obtaining data on interference, in locating the position of the centromere, and in establishing genetic independence. Map distances are generally estimated by utilizing the frequency of tetratypes and a suitable mapping function (see Ref. 40). Confidence limits are also tabulated by Barratt et al.[40] Distances obtained from tetrad tetratype frequencies are not readily combined with distances based on recombination frequencies, for to do so, assumptions concerning interference must be made. Most mapping in Chlamydomonas has utilized tetratype frequencies.

Methods for the location of centromeres in the analysis of unordered tetrads have been considered by a number of workers, the most general treatment being that of Whitehouse.[725]

The papers by Whitehouse[723, 724] and Papazian[487] are helpful in studies on chromatid and chiasma interference, which are best made with more than two factors. In C. reinhardi Ebersold and Levine[143] found positive chiasma interference and no evidence of chromatid interference in linkage group I.

F. Ciliates

1. GENERAL FEATURES

Ciliates have one or more diploid micronuclei and a compound macronucleus containing many sets of genes. The organization of the macronucleus is the subject of a special chapter in this book and it is considered briefly in a later section in this chapter. Most ciliates reproduce by binary fission in which the micronuclei undergo mitosis and the macronuclei divide amitotically. A number of special nuclear processes occur and they will be described presently.

2. THE SPECIES

The strains of ciliates are often referred to as stocks. Each stock represents the descendants of a single protozoan, generally isolated from a stream or pond. The members of a stock may undergo sexual reorganization and thereby differ from a clone which consists of the asexual progeny of a single cell. Most individuals may be classified as one of many possible mating types. If contact between different individuals of complementary mating types in reactive condition occurs, then pairing and conjugation follows. All of the mating types complementary to each other (often two, frequently several) constitute a mating group whose individuals are capable of mating with all other types within the group, but not with individuals belonging to other groups. The mating groups actually constitute distinct biological species. Since they are very similar in morphological and physiological characteristics they constitute sibling species. Their sexual isolation is virtually complete, for although certain mating types show cross reactions (usually weak) with non-homologous types, their progeny generally die in F-1 or F-2.[646, 656, 96] Although it is now accepted procedure to designate sibling species by binomial names,[405] for practical reasons this course has not been followed in the Protozoa. Consequently, we shall use Sonneborn's term "syngen"[646] to designate the protozoan sibling species characterized by complementary mating types. For a stimulating statement of the arguments in favor of binomial names for sibling species (particularly within *Paramecium*) see Hairston.[220a] The syngens were originally called "varieties". Syngens recognized in the major forms which have been studied genetically follow.

Fourteen syngens have been found in *Paramecium aurelia*, number 1 containing mating types I and II, number 2 corresponding to mating types III and IV, etc., through type XXVIII.[646, 648]

Sixteen syngens have been found in *Paramecium caudatum*, each with a pair of complementary types.[205-211, 240]

Three syngens have been found in *Paramecium multimicronucleatum*, each with a pair of complementary types.[646, 648]

Paramecium bursaria has multiple complementary mating types. Eight complementary types have been found in syngens 2 and 6, four in syngens 1 and 3, and two in syngen 4. Syngen 5 consists of one stock which has not yet mated with any other strain (see Ref. 278, 284, 95, 98, 98a, 596, 70).

Nine syngens have been found in *Tetrahymena pyriformis*, each with multiple mating types. Syngen 2 has eleven mating types, syngen 3 has eight, syngen 1 has seven, syngen 9 has five, syngens 7 and 12 have four, syngens 4, 8, 11, and 6 have three, syngens 5 and 10 have two.[156, 454, 455, 157, 158, 219, 486b, 485, 159a, 257a]

One syngen has been found in *Euplotes crassus*; it contains five complementary mating types.[237]

Euplotes patella has at least one syngen. It consists of six complementary mating types.[309, 314]

One syngen has been found in *Euplotes vannus*; it consists of five complementary mating types.[235, 236]

One syngen has been found in *Euplotes minuta*; it consists of seven complementary mating types.[478, 478a, 600a]

3. CULTURE

Methods of culture and genetic analysis in *P. aurelia* have been reviewed in detail by Sonneborn.[635] *Paramecium* and *Tetrahymena* are generally cultured in a buffered extract of baked lettuce or grass which has been inoculated the day before use with a strain of some favorable bacterium such as *Aerobacter aerogenes*. *E. patella* has been cultured in a rye grain infusion containing *Chilomonas*.[312] Marine forms such as *E. vannus, E. crassus*, and *E. minuta* are cultured on algae in sea water.[237] *Tetrahymena* grows well in a sterile medium containing proteose peptone and yeast extract and also on a completely defined medium.[307] *P. caudatum*[535] has also been cultured on a completely defined medium. *P. aurelia* and *P. multimicronucleatum* may be cultured on partially defined media.[413, 286]

4. CONJUGATION

Conjugation in *P. aurelia* can be briefly summarized as follows. (See Ref. 45 for a more detailed account.) The two micronuclei in each conjugating animal undergo two meiotic divisions yielding eight haploid products. A variable number of these nuclei now undergo a third division, a mitotic division. All but two of the products are destined to be lost. The two survivors, the gametic nuclei, are sisters of the third division, the mitotic division. One of the two in each animal migrates to the other conjugant. The haploid nuclei then fuse to form a diploid syncaryon. Soon after fusion the conjugants separate from each other. During and following the meiotic divisions, the macronucleus spins out into a long skein and breaks into some 20 to 40 more or less spherical fragments. After separation of the conjugants, the syncarya divide twice mitotically. Two of the nuclei in each exconjugant develop into macronuclei and two remain as micronuclei. Binary fission now occurs, accompanied by mitosis of the micronuclei and segregation of the new macronuclei (as well as the old macronuclear fragments). Each of the four paramecia now has two micronuclei, one new macronucleus, and 10 to 20 fragments of the old macronucleus. The old fragments segregate at random at succeeding fissions, their average number per animal dropping by one-half at each cell division. Each of the exconjugants derived from a pair thus gives rise to a clone (the progeny of a single animal). Since each exconjugant has in it two independently-formed new macronuclei which are segregated at the first division, the two subclones formed by each exconjugant at that division are given a specific designation, "caryonide". Thus, the paramecia descended from each conjugating pair constitute two clones or four caryonides. Occasionally more than two new macronuclei are formed and then there are more than two caryonides per clone, one for each new macronucleus. In caryonidal inheritance the newly forming macronuclei may undergo a "genetic determination" at the time of their formation and the resulting caryonides may possess alternative traits.

In considering the genetic consequences of conjugation in *P. aurelia*, it should be remembered that the two gametic nuclei are formed in each conjugant by mitosis from a single meiotic product; the two in each conjugant should, therefore, be haploid and genetically identical. When genotype *AA* conjugates with *aa*, the two gametic nuclei in the paroral cone of the *AA* conjugant just prior to fusion will both be *A*. Since the *aa* conjugant produces two *a* gametic nuclei, fusion yields in each conjugant an *A* and an *a* nucleus which fuse to form a diploid *Aa* synkaryon. The F-1 nuclei of the exconjugants, which all arise from the synkarya, are therefore *Aa*. If an *Aa* ciliate undergoes conjugation, the probability is 1/2 that the two gametic nuclei in a single conjugant will both be *A*, and 1/2 that they will both be *a*. Consequently, in the cross of *Aa* × *Aa*, one expects that in 1/4 of the conjugating pairs of ciliates, the gametic nuclei in both conjugants will be *a*, and the resulting F-2 exconjugants will both be *aa*; similarly, 1/4 of the pairs should produce *AA* F-2 exconjugants; and in 1/2 of the pairs one expects that the two gametic nuclei in one conjugant will be *A* and in the other conjugant both will be *a*, so that exconjugants will all be *Aa*. The single factor F-2 ratio expected is thus the classical 1*AA* : 2*Aa* : 1*aa* for pairs, each exconjugant being like its mate. Backcross ratios and ratios involving greater numbers of Mendelian differences may be predicted with ease. It is interesting to note that no matter what the genotype of two conjugants, the two exconjugants have identical nuclear genes.

Conjugation in other ciliates is similar to that in *P. aurelia* but varies in a number of details. For example, in *Euplotes* an additional mitotic division precedes the three pregametic divisions. Of genetic importance is the fact that gametic nuclei are not always sisters in *Euplotes*.[236, 237] Consequently, the two exconjugants from each pair may have different genetic constitutions. Two macronuclear anlagen are generally formed in *P. aurelia*, *P. bursaria*, and *T. pyriformis*. In *P. caudatum* and *P. multimicronucleatum* four anlagen are produced. *Euplotes* normally has only one anlage. If more than one anlage is normally produced, they segregate at the fissions following conjugation until each animal has only one. Similarly, if exconjugants regularly have more than the final number of micronuclei, they also segregate without dividing until the normal number is reached.

Occasionally the migratory nuclei are not exchanged, the sister nuclei fuse in the paroral cone region, and the processes continue as in true conjugation. Wichterman[728] called the phenomenon cytogamy. Genetically it is equivalent to autogamy, now to be described.

5. AUTOGAMY

Depending upon the stock and nutritive conditions, some 10 to 30 fissions after the last nuclear reorganization (conjugation or autogamy), *P. aurelia* when starved undergoes autogamy. The process is exactly like conjugation, except that it occurs in single animals, without exchange of nuclei.[127] The syncaryon is formed simply by the union of the two haploid nuclei. Autogamy is generally induced in the laboratory by taking advantage of the fact that starvation favors autogamy and feeding inhibits it. Paramecia are cultured at a rapid multiplication rate by copious feeding for a number of fissions, then starved. If enough fissions have elapsed since the last nuclear reorganization up to 100 per cent of the paramecia will go into autogamy.

If Aa undergoes autogamy, the probability that the two identical gametic nuclei are A is 1/2, the probability that they are a is also 1/2. Completion of the process yields a ratio of autogamous animals of $1AA : 1aa$. Each autogamous animal yields two caryonides. It is important to note that autogamy makes all loci homozygous.

Recently autogamy has been reported in *Euplotes minuta*, but details have not yet been described.[600a]

6. MACRONUCLEAR REGENERATION

Occasionally at conjugation, cytogamy, or autogamy, in *P. aurelia*, newly forming macronuclear anlagen fail to develop properly. The frequency of abortive development is higher in lines homozygous for the gene *am*. It may be increased to very high levels by exposing conjugants of *P. aurelia* to high temperature for a short period at the critical time. As a result, the macronuclear fragments instead of degenerating, enlarge as they are segregated to new paramecia during the succeeding fissions. Eventually they develop into full-fledged macronuclei, one per paramecium, and thereafter divide normally at binary fission. Frequently the previously arrested new macronuclear anlagen will recover and also segregate to individual paramecia—some cells obtaining their macronuclei from the new anlagen, some from the old regenerating macronucleus. Sonneborn[620] called the process macronuclear regeneration.

If *Aa* starts into autogamy or conjugation and macronuclear regeneration occurs, segregating macronuclear regenerate lines will still be *Aa*, while segregating lines descended from the macronuclei which have developed from the products of syncarya will be of their expected constitution— 1/2 *AA* and 1/2 *aa*. All types may be distinguished if the genes show incomplete dominance. The process has been useful in studies of macronuclear differentiation, macronuclear stucture, and in studies of the relative contribution of macronuclei and micronuclei to the phenotype.

7. Cytoplasmic Transfer

At conjugation in *P. aurelia* there are three points of attachment between mates, an anterior "hold-fast" region, one at the paroral cone region and a third (Sonneborn, unpublished) just posterior to the paroral cone. When exconjugants separate, they normally do so first at the anterior hold-fast region, and then at the posterior regions. Normally the time between separation at the anterior hold-fast region and complete separation of conjugants, which occurs when they separate posteriorly, is only 2 or 3 minutes; under such circumstances little or no cytoplasm is transferred. A more extensive cytoplasmic bridge formed at the paroral cone region will be evidenced by a longer time required for separation and more cytoplasm transferred. This process is called delayed separation and the amount of time between separation at the anterior region and separation at the paroral cone makes it possible to measure the relative amount of cytoplasm transferred.

Cytoplasmic exchange carrying kappa from killers to kappa-free paramecia was studied by Sonneborn.[625, 626] He developed the technique of delayed separation as a measure of cytoplasmic exchange using kappa as an index of transfer. Since kappa is not transferred during normal separation times, it is assumed that little or no cytoplasm is normally transferred. Long delayed separations may produce very broad cytoplasmic bridges in *P. aurelia* and very extensive amounts of cytoplasm exchanged. The use of homologous antiserum makes delayed separation easy to obtain and control. Higher serum concentrations readily induced partial permanent fusions, or double animals.

McDonald[391a] has shown that in *Tetrahymena pyriformis*, syngen 1, massive cytoplasmic exchange is normal.

8. Abnormal Nuclear Behavior

A number of cytogenetic abnormalities have been reported in ciliates. A few with genetic significance in *P. aurelia* are as follows. Diller in 1936[127] described several types of macronuclear modifications under the name hemixis, but the processes were not under experimental control. One type of hemixis was probably macronuclear regeneration (then unknown). It is likely that more than one syncaryon may sometimes be formed.[644] Sonneborn[642] has described a strain which fails to form new macronuclear anlagen; lines homozygous for the gene am undergo irregular nuclear division leading to amacronucleates and to macronuclear regeneration (see Table 4). Haploid micronuclei have been described by Sonneborn[642] and by Kimball and Gaither.[333] (Chen, Ref. 96a, was the first to report haploidy in ciliates with an account of haploid nuclei in opalinids.)† Nonviability in interstock crosses has been attributed to aneuploidy by Dippell.[130] Finger[170] has invoked aneuploidy to explain the appearance of heterozygotes following autogamy. Finally, it is clear that non-viability in crosses of haploid by diploid results from aneuploidy.[333]

One of the difficulties in genetic work with *Tetrahymena pyriformis* is the necessity of frequent conjugation and selection for maintainance of highly viable lines. Stocks often lose their micronuclei and then usually (but not always) die. When stocks which are not highly viable are crossed, genomic exclusion has been observed by Nanney,[450] Allen,[8] and Nanney and Nagel:[458] abnormal nuclear behavior causes all the nuclei of a given pair to arise from the meiotic products of one of the mates. Allen[12] reports that two rounds of mating are involved, the second occurring because retention of the old macronucleus (induced by abnormal nuclear development) is a regular part of the first; details of the process have not been published. While the micronuclei of *T. pyriformis* are normally diploid, haploid strains were found by Clark and Elliott[103, 104] and the micronuclei in such strains fail at meiosis just as in *P. aurelia*. Complete nonviability in crosses of stocks within syngen 5 of *T. pyriformis* has been reported by Ray,[527] apparently resulting from multispindle prezygotic divisions.

9. CHROMOSOMES

The chromosomes of *P. aurelia*, like those of most ciliates, are small, numerous, and difficult to distinguish. Dippell[130] has reported haploid numbers of 33 to 51 in different stocks.

Although the chromosomes of *P. bursaria* are numerous, they are somewhat more favorable for cytological study than those of *P. aurelia*. Chen[91, 92, 93] has described polyploid series with diploid numbers ranging from about 80 to several hundred.

The most favorable form for cytological studies, however, is *Tetrahymena pyriformis*. A haploid number of five chromosomes has been demonstrated by Ray[528] in syngens 1, 2, 4, 5, 6, and 9.

---

† Some investigators consider opalinids to be flagellates; they have only one kind of nucleus.

10. GENES

Published records of genes in *P. aurelia* appear in Table 4. A similar listing for *T. pyriformis* is found in Table 5. Allen[9] reports that the esterase locus *E-1* and the *mt* locus are linked with a recombination frequency of about 25 per cent. Possible linkage of two mutants determining temperature sensitivity in *P. aurelia*, syngen 4, is discussed by Igarashi.[257b] Igarashi's finding that temperature sensitive mutants may be isolated in large numbers and that numerous loci are involved opens the door for serious studies of linkage and mapping in *P. aurelia*.

The four mating types of *P. bursaria*, syngen 1 are determined by two loci, one with two alleles, one with three.[603, 599, 599a] The eight mating types of syngen 2 are determined by three of alleles.[70]

Hiwatashi found in *P. caudatum*, syngen 3[250] and possibly in syngen 12[243, 245] that mating type appears to be determined by one pair of alleles showing simple dominance. In the case of syngen 3, the allele for mating type VI is dominant to that for V. One stock of mating type VI was found to be homozygous, another heterozygous. A pair of alleles showing no dominance controls the specifically different forms of serotype F in stocks Ma 1 and Ys 3 of syngen 3.[249]

In syngen 2 of *P. multimicronucleatum* crosses between "cyclers" (stocks having circadian rhythm controlling mating type—see section VIII, J, 4, c) and "non-cyclers" show the presence of a dominant gene *C* for cycling and its recessive allele, *c*, for non-cycling, according to Barnett.[35, 37]

Single loci with multiple alleles were found to determine mating type in *E. patella* by Kimball,[309, 313] in *E. vannus* by Heckmann,[235, 236] in *E. crassus* by Heckmann,[237] and in *E. minuta* by Nobili.[478]

III. GENETIC ANALYSIS IN UNIPARENTAL REPRODUCTION

A. General Methods

For the most part, genetic technique has involved crosses of sexually reproducing forms. The use of methods of analysis based on asexual reproduction, however, is often necessary and desirable. First, many protozoans (as well as other organisms) reproduce exclusively asexually. Second, the nature of the differences between different lines of a clone can be examined only by such techniques. This problem is particularly important in considering the genetics of cellular differentiation in multicellular forms, particularly when cells can be grown in tissue culture. Third, such methods are essential in the study of non-Mendelian inheritance. Genetic analyses involving sexual reproduction are often adequate to establish the existence of non-Mendelian inheritance, but they are unable to resolve it into components, as they do so admirably in the case of genes. Fourth, techniques of asexual reproduction must be used in considering the nature of the ciliate macronucleus, for it is normally destroyed at sexual reproduction.

TABLE 4. GENES IN PARAMECIUM AURELIA

Syngen	Phenotype	Symbol	Reference
1	Mating type I vs. caryonidal determination of mating types I and II	mt	619, 79, 80
	Specificity of immobilization antigen D	d	43
	Specificity of immobilization antigen G	g	43
	Specificity of immobilization antigen S	s	43
	Cytoplasm "clear" because of absence of crystals	cl, tr (two loci)	318, 78 318
	"Dumpy" body form	dp	
	Loss of mu particles	m_1, m_2 (two loci)	196
	Normal, rather than slow growth	sl	84
	Modifier of mt	IN^I	79
2	Temperature sensitive	t	506
	Abnormal trichocyst	tr	507
	Loss of kappa	k	30a
	Specificity of immobilization antigen C	c	170
	Production and specificity of immobilization antigen E	e	172
	Specificity of antigen 5	v	112
	Normal, instead of reduced level of antigen 5	r	112
4	Specificity of immobilization antigen A	a	631
	Specificity of immobilization antigen D	d	641, 399
	Specificity of immobilization antigen E	e	644, 400
	Specificity of immobilization antigen M	m	399
	Porduction of immobilization antigen F	f	631
	Stability and specificity of immobilization antigen H	h	636, 654, 536
	Clear	cl	113
	Thin	th	663, 673
	No delayed separation	dl	735a
	Temperature sensitive	ts (several loci)	257b, 257c
	Lethal		639
	Unequal distribution of nuclei at cell division	am	640, 470, 466, 471, 467, 474, 469

TABLE 4. *(continued)*

Syngen	Phenotype	Symbol	Reference
4	Loss of kappa	k, s_1, s_2 (three loci)	623, 28, 29
	Specificity of antigen 5	v	292
	"Snaky", incomplete fission yielding chains of abnormal paramecia	sn, ds (two loci)	394, 395
7	Mating type XIII vs. caryonidal determination of mating types XIII and XIV	mt, n (two loci)	701, 702, 699
8	Loss of mu	m	592, 355
	Loss of lambda	l	583
9	Specificity of immobilization antigen X	x	518
	Specificity of immobilization antigen G	g	518

TABLE 5. GENES IN TETRAHYMENA PYRIFORMIS

Syngen	Phenotype	Symbol	Reference
1	Ability to produce mating types II-VII vs. I-III and V-VI in different frequencies	mt^*	456, 445
	Tiny (lethal)	t	484, 7
	Fat (lethal)	f	484, 7
	Serotypes A, C, D and E	H	457
	Esterases	$E\text{-}1^*$	6
	Esterases	$E\text{-}2$	6
	Acid phosphatases	$p\text{-}1$	13
2	Pyridoxine independent	p	154
8	Mating type	mt	485
9	Serine independent	s	155

* mt and $E\text{-}1$ are linked.[9]

Several methods of analysis involving asexual reproduction have been used in various organisms. The first method, somatic recombination, is apparently possible in *Chlamydomonas*.[142] A second, DNA mediated transformation, has been claimed for the trypanosomes and will be considered in Section IV of this chapter. A third technique is nuclear transplantation, used in the amebas (Section VIII, H). A fourth method is the grafting of a portion of the cortical cytoplasm removed from one cell to another, i.e., the technique utilized so effectively by Tartar[698] in studies of development in *Stentor* and in a modified form by Sonneborn and Beisson.[650] A fifth, an allied technique used on *Amoeba* by Hawkins *et al.*[231] and on *Paramecium* by Koizumi and Preer[347a] is the use of a micro-syringe and micromanipulator to transfer cytoplasm from one cell to another. Many transfers of kappa, the bacteria-like symbiont of *Paramecium aurelia*, have been made in this manner.

The seventh, and clearly the major technique of studying heredity in asexual reproduction is that of the analysis of segregation in clones. The remaining portion of this section will be devoted to this topic.

B. The Meaning of Heredity in Clones

Jennings many years ago[274] in a study of *Paramecium* pointed out that there are three causes of variations. He noted that those variations due to life cycle differences may be eliminated from consideration simply by measuring characteristics in the same stage of the life cycle. Non-inherited differences due to prior exposure of organisms to different environments may, he noted, be identified and distinguished from hereditary differences by culturing cells in identical environments. Diversities which persist under identical conditions have an hereditary basis; those which disappear are due to prior differences in their environments. Jennings was, of course, enunciating the basic working definition of heredity for all organisms as well as protozoans. Later[275] he observed that the long-term life cycle differences observed in the ciliated protozoa should also be looked upon as hereditary. The notion that long lasting, but not permanent, differences are the province of genetics was also maintained by Jollos[289, 290] in his theory of dauermodifications (see Section VIII, O). How long must a difference persist during culture under uniform environmental conditions to be judged hereditary? Although this question has no absolute answer, the following considerations are useful. One may, at least, eliminate those differences which result from the time required for an excess of a substance acquired in one environment to be diluted out in a new environment, assuming its net rate of synthesis or entrance into the cell stops in the new environment. After one fission in the new environment there should be 1/2 of the original molecules in each cell; after two fissions, 1/4; after three fissions, 1/8; and after sixty fissions, 2^{-60}. Preer[507] noted that all cells must have less than 2^{60} molecules per cell, so it is evident that 60 fissions which produce 2^{60} cells should dilute out the original molecules of any substance. Kimball[315] also pointed out that a depleted substance which begins synthesis at a rate of one doubling per cell division must acquire 1/2 of its final concentration after one fission; 3/4, after two; 7/8, after three; etc. Thus, any cellular diversity persisting through 60 fissions, the maximum number of generations required for complete molecular turnover, clearly does not represent a slow approach to equilibrium by one of these two simple mechanisms.

C. Mathematical Models of Clonal Segregation

The time and rate at which pure variant lines segregate within a clone can often be measured. Sometimes the initial conditions can be varied or controlled. The analysis of segregation in clones consists of the fitting of such times and rates of segregation to mathematical models. Suppose, for example, that a hereditary change occurs in some one of a number of cytoplasmic or nuclear determinants. Assume that these units continue to multiply and that they are segregated more or less randomly at cell division. No variants among the daughter cells should be produced at first, but eventually pure lines should appear in many subclones. The time and rate of appearance will depend upon the number of such subunits, their rate and mode of multiplication, as well as their manner of segregation at cell division. There have been a number of attempts to analyze clonal segregations among the cells of higher organisms, from this point of view, for example by Michaelis,[412] and Auerbach,[21] as well as in lower organisms. The segregation encountered when randomly segregated cellular elements increase more slowly than the cells is another similar problem which requires a similar approach. It is intended in the material which follows to call attention to those mathematical solutions which have been developed. The relevant biological problems are cited only to provide background; they will be considered in more detail later.

A statement of the problem, sufficiently general to include all the cases so far investigated is as follows: Cells, nuclei, or chromosomes start with m_1 particles or subunits of type 1, m_2 particles of type 2, m_3 particles of type 3, etc., for a total of n types, and a total of N particles. Before cell division each particle, on the average, increases by a factor of f, so that there are now fN particles. At cell division the particles are distributed at random to the two cells. In some cases particles are assumed to segregate independently of each other. In others, particularly in the case when $f = 2$, it is desirable to assume that each cell receives exactly N of the $2N$ particles in the parent cell. The mathematical problem is to relate the parameters to the probability of a cell at a given later generation having been freed of some one or more types of particles (and, hence, becoming "pure" for the remaining types). Although no general solution is available, a number of special cases have been solved and applied to specific data and will now be considered. It is of interest to note the similarity and even identity of some of the models—a fact not generally pointed out by the authors.

1. THE DILUTION OF KAPPA AND METAGONS

There is only one type of particle, $m_1 = N$, all other types being absent. $f \leq 2$, so the mean number of particles per cell either stays constant or decreases with increasing numbers of fissions. Particles are distributed at random, and independently of each other. For different values of f and N

what is the probability, P, that after a given number of fissions a cell will have zero particles? This problem has received two solutions. The first was obtained by Otter and reported and applied by Preer[501] to the case of kappa particles multiplying more slowly than paramecia. P, the fraction of paramecia with no kappa particles, was measured experimentally, and from it, f (designated k by them), and N were calculated. Experimentally determined values of log ($-$log P) were plotted against the number of fissions. Since the slope of the line was shown to be log $f/2$, f is easily found. N is computed by a process of iteration using an equation given in the paper.[501] Methods of allowing for logistic increase of particles, and methods for the calculation of the effects of increase by multiples of three, four, etc., rather than by two, are given.

The second solution to this problem was obtained by Reeve[531] and Reeve and Ross.[532, 533] The iterative procedures require the use of a digital computer and treat only the case of increase by doubling of the individual particles. However, a method for the consideration of non-random distribution of particles (two models) and of computing variances of parameters is provided. Reeve and Ross were apparently unaware of the work of Otter.

2. RANDOM ASSORTMENT OF SUBUNITS IN THE CILIATE MACRONUCLEUS

Schensted[579] considered the possibility of diploid macronuclear subunits which might segregate to give pure lines for mating type. Her model was later applied to other characteristics as well. Two types of units were postulated: $m_1 = k$, $m_2 = N - k$, total number N. Units double between each cell division, so $f = 2$. At each cell division the $2N$ units are segregated at random but not independently of each other; it is assumed that each new cell has exactly N units. She showed that when segregation approaches completion (all clones pure) the fraction of clones of one of the two types approaches k/N, the fraction of subunits of that type in the original nucleus. Thus, a simple way of experimentally determining k/N is provided. Schensted also showed that the rate, r, at which cells deficient for either of the two types should arise from cells which have both types, approaches a limiting value as the number of fissions increases and that this limiting value is dependent only on N; that is, $r = 1/(2N - 1)$ where r is the number of pure cells arising at a given fission divided by the number of mixed cells present before the fission. She showed how to compute the rate r for different values of k and N after different numbers of fissions. A digital computer is necessary for the computations. r has been measured by Allen and Nanney (see Section VIII, J, 6, a) and used to calculate a value, N, of 45 macronuclear subunits in *Tetrahymena*. Data on the approach to equilibrium of r, starting with different input ratios, k/N, were shown by Nanney to agree with Schensted's theoretical curves for $N = 45$.

Kimball and Householder[308] considered the case of haploid macro-nuclear units, each of which was assumed to contain a non-allelic recessive mutation following radiation. The rate of attainment of homozygosity (assumed to induce death) was measured. Since each of the subunits was different, $m_1 = m_2 = m_n = 1$. The rate of attainment of homozygosity (loss of all types but one) was calculated for values of N up to five. The data did not fit the calculated values, and it was evident that higher values of N would not fit either.

A model of senescence was treated mathematically by Kimura.[341] He assumes that the macronuclear subunit is the chromosome itself, and that the chromosomes in the polyploid macronucleus are distributed amitotically at each fission. It is also assumed that complete loss of any one of the many kinds of chromosomes leads to senescence and death. There are n chromosomes in each of the haploid sets, thus $m_1 = m_2 = m_3 = m_n$. There are m sets and $mn = N$ total chromosomes. Each chromosome duplicates before division, so $f = 2$. At each fission the 2N chromosomes are distributed at random so that each new cell has exactly N chromosomes (the case of independent segregation, in which it is not necessary to assume that each new cell has exactly N chromosomes, is also considered). What is the probability that one or more of the n chromosome types has been eliminated after a given number of fissions? Kimura provides a solution for large N and high probabilites of loss, which he states agrees with the data of Sonneborn and Schneller.[670] Similar agreement is obtained for the case of independent segregation. It should be noted, however, that this model postulated by Kimura is not compatible with that assumed by Schensted. Discussion of the ciliate macronucleus is given in Section IX of this chapter.

It should be noted that in the case of independent segregation an exact solution to the model proposed by Kimura can be obtained from the above work of Otter reported by Preer.[501] Otter's treatment makes it possible to tabulate for $f = 2$ and for any initial number of units, the probability of a cell having no units after different numbers of fissions. If these units are considered to be the m chromosomes of a given type, one from each haploid set, Otter's treatment gives the probability of elimination of all the chromosomes of that type. The probability of the failure of elimination of all of one or more of the n types of chromosomes is then easily computed.

3. Random Assortment of Chromosomal Subunits

The chromosome is considered to be multistranded with one mutant and a number of wild type strands. Thus, two types of units, or chromosomal strands, are postulated. The first is a single mutant strand, so $m_1 = 1$; the second is the nonmutated type and $m_2 = N - 1$. Units double between divisions, so $f = 2$. At each cell division the 2N units are segregated at random so that each new cell has exactly N units. Kimura[341] has presented equations which relate the rate of production of cells pure for the mutant type with numbers of fissions for N up to 16. He has also presented a method for a solution when N is large. The data of Friedrich-Freska and Kaudewitz[185] on P-32 induced damage in *A. proteus* were consistent with $N = 16$. It should be pointed out, however, that the model proposed here is not consistent with the semiconservative replication of chromosomes demonstrated for higher organisms.

It is interesting to note that this problem is a special case of the problem discussed in number 2 above (the case in which $k = 1$) which was investigated by Schensted;[579] neither appears to have been aware of the work of the other. In the same paper, Kimura also considers the more general model that Schensted investigated, in which k may have any value between 0 and N. However, a complete solution is given only for large values of N.

IV. DNA INDUCED TRANSFORMATION

DNA induced transformation has been reported in *Trypanosoma gambiense* and *T. evansi* by Inoki and coworkers.[266, 271] The character followed is resistance to p-rosaniline. Resistance may be manifested as an increased ability of the trypanosomes to survive in mice injected with the drug and as an increased resistance to the action of the drug in producing kinetoplast-free forms (see Section VIII, D). (In cases studied with the electron microscope it is clear that the kinetoplast is not completely lost, but greatly modified in structure. See Ref. 707. Hence, so-called kinetoplast-free forms are properly called "dyskinetoplastic".)

In *T. gambiense*, the injection of p-rosaniline into the host animals, mice, yields dyskinetoplastic forms which are unable to reproduce. The injection of small but increasingly larger doses of p-rosaniline leads to resistant strains which contained kinetoplasts.[265] Not only can the resistant organisms survive in high concentrations of p-rosaniline, but the frequency of dyskinetoplastic forms does not increase when the host animals are exposed to the drug.

In *T. evansi* p-rosaniline also yields dyskinetoplastic forms but in this case they are able to reproduce. Furthermore, it appears that the action of the drug is merely to select spontaneous dyskinetoplastic forms rather than directly induce them (see Section VIII, D). Continued exposure of *T. evansi* to p-rosaniline yields forms able to survive in the drug, but lacking in kinetoplasts.

Resistance of the trypanosomes to the action of p-rosaniline in increasing the frequency of kinetoplast loss is the character which Inoki and coworkers attempted to transfer by transformation. Kinetoplast-containing sensitives are exposed to homogenates of resistants (prepared by freeze-thawing), injected into mice, and the mice injected with p-rosaniline. The frequency of the dyskinetoplastic forms is found to be much reduced by the presence of the homogenates. Normal high frequencies of dyskinetoplastic forms are obtained if the homogenate is pretreated with DNAse (but not RNAse or proteolytic enzymes) or if a homogenate of sensitive trypanosomes is used. Transformation of resistance can occur from *T. gambiense* to *T. evansi* or from *T. evansi* to *T. gambiense*—even though the resistant strain of *T. evansi* is dyskinetoplastic. Because the homogenates of resistant dyskinetoplastic forms are effective, it is concluded that kinetoplast DNA is not involved. The magnitude of the reduction in frequency of dyskinetoplastic forms after exposure to homogenates is characteristic of the recipient, not the donor. Standard errors are reported and the data are statistically significant.

V. PROBLEMS OF CROSSING OVER

A. Crossing Over in the Two-Strand Stage

The fact that crossing over occurs in the four-strand stage is well documented.[540] In tetrad analysis, crossing over in the four-strand stage is clearly shown by the existence of tetratypes involving linked genes. If crossing over in the two-strand stage occurs, then it would result in non-parental ditype tetrads. However, occasional non-parental ditypes may just as well be explained by four-strand double crossing over in the four-strand stage. Moewus, on the basis of tetrad data, reported[420, 421] that in *Chlamydomonas eugametos* crossing over occurs in the two-strand stage at temperatures below 5°C and in the four-strand stage at higher temperatures. A number of workers have unsuccesfully tried to repeat these observations. Ebersold[140] found no evidence for crossing over in the two-strand stage in *C. reinhardi* at either 5°C or 26°C. Gowans[213] was unable to get germination of *C. eugametos* at 5°C, and at 13°C and higher temperatures obtained no evidence for crossing over in the two-strand stage. Lewin[372] found crossing-over at the four-strand stage but not two-strand stage in *C. moewusii*.

Excesses of non-parental ditype tetrads at higher temperatures in *C. reinhardi*, however, were reported by Eversole and Tatum[165] and Ebersold.[140]. Attempts by Ebersold and Levine[143] to confirm such excesses in linkage group I in *C. reinhardi*, however, were not successful. It must be concluded that there is no confirmed evidence of crossing over in the two-strand stage in *Chlamydomonas*.

B. Interference

Ebersold and Levine[143] showed that chiasma interference is positive within the one mapped arm of linkage group I of *C. reinhardi*. They used the markers *arg-1*, *arg-2*, *pab-2*, and *thi-3* (see Fig. 1). No evidence for chromatid interference was obtained.

6*

C. Gene Conversion

Gene conversion, unlike ordinary crossing over, yields non-reciprocal recombinants. It has been studied extensively in yeast, *Neurospora*, and a number of other organisms. Its mechanism is not known. Aberrant tetrads yielding segregations other than 2 : 2 are characteristic of gene conversion. However, 3 : 1 and 4 : 0 tetrads may also result from a number of other processes such as crossing over within complex loci, aneuploidy, fusion of more than two gametes, or asynchronous postmeiotic division in tetrads followed by loss of some of the products. These alternative explanations can be ruled out only if well marked chromosomes are available.

Aberrant ratios are occasionally observed in *Chlamydomonas* and it is possible that they arise by gene conversion. Moreover, Levine and Ebersold[362] report that their frequency is increased by ultraviolet irradiation of one of the mating types before a cross. Roman and Jacob[545] report that aberrant segregation during mitotic recombination in yeast is increased by ultraviolet irradiation. Nevertheless, the occurrence of gene conversion in *Chlamydomonas* remains exceedingly doubtful. Levine and Ebersold,[364] for example, point out that further matings involving aberrant segregants found after radiation sometimes yield alleles which were thought to be absent in the segregants, but which were present in the original parents of the segregants, suggesting that the radiation led to extra chromosomes. Doubts about the occurrence of gene conversion in *Chlamydomonas* are further increased by the observation that triple fusions at mating have been observed by Sager;[557] these would, of course, yield aberrant ratios within tetrads. Furthermore, Levine and Ebersold[364] have reported that in matings obtained from mixtures of three different mutant strains, some tetrads produce clones with characteristics of all three parents. It must be concluded that no good evidence has been obtained for gene conversion in *Chlamydomonas*.

D. Chelating Agents and Crossing Over

Noting that the DNA of suspensions of sperm was disrupted by a chelating agent, Mazia[406] suggested that segments of nucleoprotein in the chromosome may be held together by divalent metal ions. This suggestion gave particular pertinence to a number of studies testing the effect of chelating agents and calcium and magnesium ions on crossing over, chromosome breakage, and chromosome structure. Eversole and Tatum[165] found that exposure of gametes of *Chlamydomonas reinhardi* to the chelating agent EDTA (ethylenediamine tetracetic acid) resulted in increase of the frequency of crossing over between *arg*-1 and *arg*-2 (linkage group I, Fig. 1) from 6 to 59 per cent. In a much larger study Levine and Ebersold[363] found no significant effect of EDTA on the crossover frequency. The results of the two studies show clear statistically significant differences. The problems of the difference between the two studies and the status of the effect of EDTA on crossing over in *Chlamydomonas* remain unresolved. Nevertheless, studies of the effect of divalent ions and chelating agents on other organisms have shown significant effects on both crossing over[357, 681, 306] and on chromosome breakage.[678, 679, 680] The significance of the EDTA effects, however, has been very seriously questioned. Several workers[358, 305] have emphasized that the action of chelating agents and divalent ions may be so indirect that it may yield little information concerning the problems of crossing over and chromosome structure.

VI. GENES AND METABOLISM

A search for biochemical mutants has been carried out only in *Tetrahymena* and *Chlamydomonas*, two of the few protozoans genetically investigated which can be grown on defined media. In *Tetrahymena* only two auxotrophs have been isolated, one requiring pyridoxine, the other serine. Surprisingly, both are reported (see Table 5) to be dominant to their wild type alleles for independence. The scarcity of auxotrophs in *Tetrahymena* may be attributed to the complex nutritional requirements of wild type and to a lack of satisfactory methods for screening and isolating mutants.

In contrast to *Tetrahymena*, *Chlamydomonas* can be cultured on a simple medium, and replica plating facilitates the isolation of mutants. Although the search for biochemical mutants has been more successful in *Chlamydomonas* than in *Tetrahymena*, there is still a peculiar paucity of amino acid-requiring mutants. Nutritional mutants have been found only for paraminobenzoic acid (three loci), thiamin (six loci), nicotinamide (five loci), arginine (two loci), purines (one locus), and carbon source (a number of loci). The two groups of mutants whose study has led to interesting information concerning intermediary metabolism are mutants affecting photosynthesis and the synthesis of nicotinamide, both of which will now be considered.

A. Nicotinamide Metabolism in Chlamydomonas

The characteristics of nicotinamide-requiring mutants at three loci in *C. reinhardi* reported by Eversole[164] indicate that synthesis of nicotinamide is by the familiar tryptophan pathway[717] via kynurenine and 3-hydroxyanthranilic acid. Studies on six loci in *C. eugametos* by Nakamura and Gowans[213, 436, 437, 438] suggest the same pathway, but clear responses to intermediates were not obtained. More recent work by these workers [437, 438] on a new series of nicotinamide mutants (five loci) in *C. eugametos* indicates that quinolenic acid is probably an intermediate, three loci causing blocks after quinolenic acid, the other two before. This latter result is surprising since presumably only one biochemical step follows quinolenic acid.[438] Mutants blocked at the two loci concerned with syntheses prior to quinolenic acid have not been found to utilize any of the earlier intermediates.

A modifying gene[438] present in one of the nicotinamide requiring mutants prevents the utilization of quinolenic acid or nicotinic acid. It has been suggested[438] that the modifier acts to prevent the operation of a transport system.

Mutants at two loci show increased resistance to 3-acetyl-pyridine, a structural analogue of nicotinamide. apy-1 liberates an excess of nicotinic acid into the medium; apy-2 is only partially resistant, and liberates little or no excess nicotinic acid. Neither is linked with the auxotrophic mutants. One possible explanation for the action of the apy mutants is that the apy mutant genes desensitize an early enzyme of the pathway to feedback inhibition and thereby lead to overproduction of nicotinic acid. However, the fact that the apy mutants are not allelic with any of the auxotrophic mutants has led Nakamura and Gowans[436] to reject this explanation. Instead, they suggest that the apy mutations are inactive alleles of regulator genes which normally act to repress the nicotinamide synthesizing enzymes. Another suggestion[438] is that the apy-1 mutants represent defects in the nicotinamide and nicotinic acid transport system. Such defects would lead to resistance by a failure in the accumulation of intracellular 3-acetylpyridine and secondarily to a liberation and overproduction of nicotinic acid.

B. Genetic Control of Photosynthesis in Chlamydomonas

Comparison of metabolic pathways in different organisms has played an important part in our knowledge of photosynthesis. Investigations of the properties of mutants which have impaired photosynthetic activities have also proved of use. Mutants of several algae such as Chlorella and Scenedesmus have been studied from this point of view. Our knowledge of the genetics of Chlamydomonas reinhardi makes it a favorable organism for such studies, and a number of mutants have been investigated. First, several pigment deficient mutants will be described, then a number of photosynthetic mutants whose defects are not so obvious will be considered.

C. reinhardi normally retains chlorophyll and normal chloroplast structure while grown in the dark on acetate. The mutant y_1 (probably cytoplasmic; see Section VIII, F) is green in the light and yellow in the dark. Sager[560] found that dark grown y_1 contained protochlorophyll along with a small amount of chlorophyll. In the light the protochlorophyll declined and chlorophyll increased. Hence, Sager suggests that protochlorophyll is a precursor of chlorophyll as in other organisms (see Ref. 67 for a review of chlorophyll synthesis in algae). A brown mutant[557] appears to be blocked at a step preceding protochlorophyll, for it accumulates protoporphyrin 9.

A mutant, y-2, has been the subject of recent studies by Hudock, Levine and others.[255, 256, 349] The mutant y-2, like y_1, loses its chlorophyll and its chloroplast degenerates when cultured in the dark but reverts to normal when returned to light. Krinsky and Levine[349] found that in the dark y-2 synthesizes much less carotenoid than does wild type. Hudock and Levine[255] followed photosynthetic nucleotide reductase, ribulose diphosphate carboxylase, and chlorophyll during transitions between darkness and light. The two enzymes decreased in the dark, but more slowly than chlorophyll. Their synthesis also lagged behind chlorophyll increase when returned to the light. It was suggested that critical amounts of chlorophyll may exert a regulatory function over the development of chloroplast lamellae and the enzymes necessary for photosynthetic activity. However, treatment with chloramphenicol[256] during regreening did not inhibit chlorophyll synthesis but did inhibit the development of normal chloroplast structure and photosynthesis. Thus, while chlorophyll synthesis may be important in controlling the development of the photosynthetic apparatus, its presence is only one of the necessary conditions.

Chance and Sager[88] and Sager and Zalokar[575] studied a pale green mutant (number 95) of *C. reinhardi* which was unable to grow in the light. It contained about 1/15 the chlorophyll and 1/200 the carotenoid content of the normal green strain. It was apparently able to photosynthesize, taking up carbon dioxide and liberating oxygen. Thus, the carotenoids (except possibly in small amounts) are not essential for these activities.

An extensive series of investigations on normal green photosynthetic mutants has been carried out by Levine and coworkers, and their work will now be summarized. *C. reinhardi* will grow in the light, with no other source of carbon than CO_2, which it reduces photosynthetically. It will grow in the dark if reduced carbon is added. A convenient form is acetate. Many mutants have been isolated[360] which cannot reduce CO_2 in the light but which can grow if acetate is provided.

Six acetate requiring photosynthetic mutants have been studied in some detail. They are ac-20 (linkage group XIII), ac-115 (linkage group I), ac-141 (linkage group III), ac-21 (linkage group XI), ac-206 (linkage group XIV), and ac-208 (linkage group III). Ac-141 and ac-208 lie about ten units apart on opposite sides of their centromere in linkage group III. The properties of ac-115 and ac-141 appear to be identical, so that there are only five kinds of mutants. None can fix CO_2 photosynthetically. All have chlorophyll and only minor modifications in carotenoids.

The points at which the blocks to photosynthesis are located have been sought in terms of the current widely held theory that there are two photochemical acts in higher plants and algae: one (system I) in which the absorption of light by chlorophyll leads to the reduction of triphosphopyridine nucleotide (NADP) which in turn is used in the fixing of CO_2, and a second (system II) in which the absorption of light by chlorophyll leads to the oxidation of water, liberating O_2. The two systems are linked because electrons removed from water are passed through intermediates, including plastocyanin, cytochrome b_6, and cytochrome f, to NADP. The fact that the photosynthetic mutants may be explained in terms of this theory, of course, provides support for the theory.

Ac-20[369] fails in photosynthesis because it lacks ribulose diphosphate carboxylase activity. Its phosphoribulokinase and phosphoriboisomerase activities are normal. It is the first such mutant of this type and provides excellent supporting evidence for the theory[41] that the enzyme is essential for photosynthetic carbon dioxide fixation *in vivo*.

The properties of whole cells and of cell fractions have led to the conclusion that the other mutants represent blocks at four different points in the photosynthetic electron transport chain. Two of the mutants (ac-21 and ac-115) are essentially like wild-type in their chloroplast structure, quantities of chlorophyll *a* and *b*, photosynthetic pyridine nucleotide reductase (PPNR), pyridine nucleotide transhydrogenase, diphosphopyridine nucleotide (DPN or NAD) and NADP linked cytochrome *c* reductase, plastocyanin, cytochrome *c*, and cytochrome b_6.[304, 359, 370, 368, 366, 361, 367, 609] These characteristics have not been reported upon for ac-206 and ac-208. Points of difference between the mutants and wild type are summarized in Table 6.

The block represented by mutants ac-115 and ac-141 are thought to involve the action of chlorophyll in system II. This conclusion is supported by the fact that the mutants are unable to carry out the Hill reaction, in which the liberation of oxygen depends on elements of system II. Furthermore, these same mutants can photoreduce NADP (a function of system I) if an electron donor is available in the form of reduced DPIP (2,6-dichlorophenol indophenol) and ascorbate to keep it reduced. In addition, the mutants can carry out cyclic photophosphorylation with PMS (phenazine methosulfate) or with vitamin K_3 and FMN (flavin mononucleotide). Cyclic phosphorylation utilizes system I, as well as part, at least, of the electron carrier system linking the two systems. It is also noted that the slow electron paramagnetic resonance signal is missing in these mutants. It has been suggested by Weaver and Bishop[719] and Allen et al.,[2] primarily on the basis of a study of mutants in *Chlorella* and *Scenedesmus*, that the broad slow signal (S or I) is associated with system II, and that the fast narrow signal (R or II) is concerned with system I. The fact that ac-115 and ac-141 do not produce the slow signal and seem deficient in system II, supports these conclusions. The reduction in level of plastoquinones raises the question of whether their reduction in quantity could be a primary cause of the photosynthetic defect. Plastoquinones apparently function as electron carriers after the absorption of light in system II and are necessary for the Hill reaction. However, Levine[361] points out that the reduction in amount in these mutants is probably not sufficient to block completely the Hill reaction.

The Hill reaction can be produced with ac-21, showing that system II operates. Mutant ac-21 can also photoreduce NADP using DPIP and ascorbate

Table 6. Properties of Photosynthetic Mutants in Chlamydomonas Reinhardi

| | Photosynthetic CO_2 fixation (whole cells) | Photoreduction of NADP from H_2O | Photoreduction of NADP with DPIP and ascorbate | Photoreduction of CO_2 with H_2 | Hill reaction | | | Cyclic phosphorylation with PMS | Ribulose diphosphate carboxylase | Cytochrome f | Plastocyanin | Plastoquinone | Carotenoids | Slow EPR signal I |
					Ferricyanide	DPIP	Parabenzoquinone							
ac-20	No 369	Yes 369						Yes 369	No 369					
ac-21	No 359	No 368, 367	Yes 367	No 361	Yes 370, 368	Yes 367	Slightly reduced 359	No 361	Normal 359	Normal 367, 609		Normal 367, 609	Modified 361, 349	Normal 366
ac-115 and ac-141	No 370	No 368, 367	Yes 367	Yes 361	No 368, 367	No 367	No 367	Yes 361	Normal in ac-115 255	Increased 367, 609		Decreased 367, 609	Modified 361, 349	Absent 366
ac-208	No 361, 211b	No 361, 211b	No 361, 211b	No 361	Much reduced 361, 211b	Reduced 361, 211b		Reduced 361, 211b		Normal 211b	None 211b			Normal 361
ac-206	No 211b	No 211b	Yes 211b		Much reduced 211b	Reduced 211b		Yes 211b		None 211b	Normal 211b			

as a source of electrons, indicating that system I is also operable. Consequently, it is suggested by Levine that ac-21 is blocked in the electron transport chain between the two light reactions. This suggestion is supported by the fact that both slow and fast EPR signals are produced by the mutant. The fact that cyclic phosphorylation with PMS or with vitamin K_3 and FMN does not occur with ac-21, yet that NADP is photoreduced by DPIP and ascorbate suggests that ac-21 is blocked at a point between the places of entry of electrons into the electron transport chain in the two reactions.

Recently Gorman and Levine[211b] have established the points of the blocks in mutants ac-206 and ac-208. Their experiments on these two mutants have resulted in a significant contribution to our understanding of the photosynthetic electron transport chain in *C. reinhardi*. Ac-206 lacks cytochrome f and has a normal level of plastocyanin, while ac-208 lacks plastocyanin and has a normal level of cytochrome f. Both cytochrome f and plastocyanin are known to function in the electron transport chain carrying electrons from system II to system I; however, it has not been known whether the two carriers lie in parallel or in series. Since neither mutant can photoreduce NADP from water, it is evident that the two lie in series. Furthermore, the data indicate that the sequence in the electron transport chain must be system II, cytochrome f, plastocyanin, system I. This conclusion may be deduced from the following considerations. First, ac-206 lacks cytochrome f, and can photoreduce NADP when DPIP and ascorbate are present; therefore in this reaction the site of entry of electrons must be after cytochrome f. Second, with ac-208, which lacks plastocyanin, NADP cannot be photoreduced in the presence of DPIP and ascorbate; the electrons therefore must enter at or before plastocyanin. It follows that cytochrome f must precede plastocyanin. Gorman and Levine point out that the absence of noncyclic photosynthetic phosphorylation coupled to ferricyanide, and the presence of cyclic phosphorylation catalyzed by PMS (though much reduced in the case of ac-208) in the two mutants indicate that the site of photosynthetic phosphorylation is probably on the system I side of cytochrome f and plastocyanin.

VII. RADIATION GENETICS

Radiation has been of use in protozoan genetics in a number of ways. These include the production of mutants, studies on crossing over in *Chlamydomonas*, investigations of ploidy levels, assessment of the relative roles of nucleus and cytoplasm in heredity, the study of symbionts, considerations of the role of the ciliate gullet in inheritance, and investigations of aging in ciliates. Most of these studies have utilized radiation as a tool, and most of them are considered elsewhere in this paper. In this section we consider work bearing on the genetic effects of radiation, the repair of premutational injury, and the mechanism of radiation induced mutation.

A. Genetic Effects of Radiation

It is not likely that the immediate death observed after large doses of radiation can be ascribed to damage to the genetic systems of cells. Delayed fissions after radiation, generally only temporary, may also be excluded as a genetic effect. Death occurring a few fissions after radiation may or may not be genetic. Unless there were special methods for ascertaining the nature of such death, it will not be considered here.

In ciliates, with which most of the radiation studies have been performed, mutations in the macronucleus have not been detected. Presumably because of the many sets of genes in the macronucleus, ciliates are able to survive very large doses of radiation. Mutations induced in the diploid micronuclei, including lethals, do not appear until the organisms undergo conjugation or autogamy and have their macronuclei replaced by products of the micronuclei. If experiments are arranged so that a number of fissions elapse between radiation and autogamy, only permanent inherited effects will appear at autogamy. As described below, death after autogamy is the standard method of measuring micronuclear mutations in ciliates.

Several kinds of radiation induced effects will be considered: cytoplasmic mutation, changes in ploidy, aberrant nuclear behavior, mutation, and chromosomal aberrations.

1. Cytoplasmic Mutation

Mottram[426, 427] reported radiation induced abnormalities in amicronucleate *Colpidium*. Since macronuclear mutations are not known, it was suggested that the effects were cytoplasmic, but decisive evidence is not available. Schaeffer[578] reported inherited changes in size in the multinuclear *Amoeba chaos* following X-irradiation. Kimball[319] pointed out that in view of the multinucleate condition it is difficult to see how gene mutations or chromosomal aberrations are involved. But decisive evidence is not available in this instance either. Paramecia have been freed of the cytoplasmic symbiont kappa by X-rays[503] and nitrogen mustard.[187] It is also likely that serotypes in *Paramecium* may be induced to change by treatment with ultraviolet radiation.[630] It should be noted, however, that the induction of serotype change is not very specific, there being numerous other factors causing changes (see Section VIII, K, 1, c). Hanson[224, 226] has shown that an ultraviolet microbeam directed at one of the two gullets of double paramecia often leads to reorganization of animals as singles, implying that cortical elements of heredity may be caused to change by radiation.

Most of the observations, however, indicate that radiation is not very effective in producing visible cytoplasmic mutations either in Protozoa or in other organisms.[726, 727] Thus, *Paramecium* can be given many times the amount of radiation needed to induce almost 100 per cent death at the next autogamy without producing harmful effects or death before autogamy. Furthermore, Kimball and Gaither[334] showed directly that death at conjugation after radiation is nuclear and not cytoplasmic. They found that crosses of unirradiated diploids with irradiated amicronucleates gave the same results as crosses of unirradiated diploids with unirradiated amicronucleates. Radiation induced mutations affecting chloroplast characters in *Chlamydomonas* have all shown $2:2$ segregation in crosses[574] and are, therefore, probably gene mutations. The only mutants thought to be cytoplasmic which give $2:2$ segregations are the y_1 mutants in *Chlamydomonas* (see Section VIII, F). Although y_1 mutants occur spontaneously and can also be readily induced by streptomycin, they have not been reported to occur in high frequency after radiation. Most cytoplasmic mutations in *Chlamydomonas* give $4:0$ segregations and radiation has not been found to induce them.

2. CHANGES IN PLOIDY

Buffaloe[77] reported that when *Chlamydomonas eugametos* and *C. moewusii* were cultured under light of 800 foot-candle intensity rather than 100 foot-candle, cells multiplied more slowly, enlarged, and became polyploid. Treatment of *C. reinhardi* and *C. chlamydogama* was ineffective.

MacDougall[392, 393] radiated the ciliate *Chilodonella uncinatus* with ultraviolet light. Although adequate statistical data were not available to prove induction, triploids and tetraploids were reported.

The studies of Kimball and coworkers[333, 334, 336] with X-rays and Sonneborn et al.[663] with ultraviolet light indicate occurrence of changes in chromosome number in *Paramecium*. Thus, conjugation between normal and irradiated paramecia often yields haploids whose nuclei are formed exclusively from the normal mate. Haploids are fully viable, but at autogamy they yield abnormal meioses, aneuploidy, and nonviability.

3. ABERRANT NUCLEAR BEHAVIOR

As indicated above, radiation damaged nuclei in *Paramecium* often fail to function as gametic nuclei.[663, 333, 334, 336] Damaged meiotic products are at a selective disadvantage when they compete with undamaged products in entering the paroral cone region to form gametic nuclei.[334, 336] If entrance does occur, the stationary nucleus will function; but the migratory nucleus often fails to enter the mate. These conclusions are based primarily on genetic studies of marked stocks and to a lesser extent on cytological investigations. Sonneborn et al.[663] suggest that ultraviolet radiation slows the meiotic process and may throw the conjugation processes in radiated and unirradiated mates out of synchrony. On the other hand, X-irradiation does not result in lack of synchrony according to Kimball and Gaither.[334] It is likely[328] that these aberrant nuclear activities, together with the complication of interaction between nonallelic mutations,[316] are responsible for the complex breeding results described by Geckler[188] for nitrogen mustard and Mitchison[414] for ultraviolet light.

Elliot and Clark[153] and Clark and Elliot[103, 104] showed that X-irradiation of one of the mates in *Tetrahymena* also can lead to aberrant nuclear behavior and haploidy.

4. Mutation and Chromosomal Aberration

The standard method of measuring the induction of micronuclear mutations in *Paramecium aurelia* is to treat, allow a period of multiplication, induce autogamy so that the old macronuclei are replaced by products of the micronuclei and, after a few days, check for survival and rate of multiplication. This method was developed by Powers,[498, 499] Kimball,[316, 317] and Geckler.[188] Kimball[339] isolates 25 autogamous cells from the progeny of each treated cell and records the proportion (p) of clones with normal growth for each group of 25. In order to equalize the variance of p, a complex arc sin transformation (see Ref. 339) is used to obtain y. y varies from 2.6 to 0 as p varies from 1 to 0. y for treated lines is then subtracted from the value of y for the untreated controls to yield M. M is found to increase linearly with dose and is, therefore, taken to be proportional to the number of mutations. It has not been possible to determine the value of the constant of proportionality because of gene interactions and selection for meiotic products free of mutation (see above).

This method should detect both dominant and recessive lethals. On the basis of the amount of nonviability in the F-1 of crosses between irradiated and unirradiated paramecia, Kimball and Gaither[334] conclude that dominant lethals are low in frequency. Therefore, the quantity measured by M is primarily the frequency of induction of recessive lethals. The question of whether the recessive lethals represent "point" mutations or chromosomal aberrations will be considered after a discussion of repair mechanisms and radiation sensitivity.

B. Repair Mechanisms and Radiation Sensitivity

It now appears clear that most primary radiation lesions are reversible. For reviews see Hollaender[253, 254] and Sobels.[613] The mutation frequency may be reduced many-fold by suitable treatments. The phenomenon is observed with ultraviolet and with ionizing radiation, with point mutation and with chromosomal breakage. One repair mechanism is almost certainly enzymatic. A photoreactivating enzyme appears to act by breaking ultraviolet-induced thymine dimers.[552, 589, 587, 736] Four factors affecting mutation rate, some of which clearly involve repair mechanisms, will now be considered.

1. THE OXYGEN EFFECT

In *Paramecium*, as in other organisms, oxygen increases the yield of X-ray induced mutations.[320, 331] The atmosphere is important only during the time of radiation. Consequently, it is likely that oxygen affects only the very first stage in the production of lesions. One mechanism which has been proposed to account for the oxygen effect is that there is an increased production of H_2O_2 under higher oxygen tensions, and that the H_2O_2 acts as a mutagen. However, Kimball and coworkers[320, 338] obtained no mutagenic action of H_2O_2 on the rate of occurrence of X-ray induced mutants. Hearon and Kimball[233] calculated that intranuclear X-ray-induced H_2O_2 concentrations were considerably below the doses obtained by adding H_2O_2 to the medium and found to be without effect. Thus, H_2O_2 does not appear to be involved with the oxygen effect, nor does it induce mutations in *Paramecium*.

2. PHOTOREACTIVATION

Kimball and Gaither[330] showed that photoreactivation is effective in *P. aurelia* after ultraviolet light, but not after X-rays. It follows that, while thymine dimer formation may be a major cause for mutations induced by ultraviolet light, it is not for those induced by X-rays.

3. THE CELL CYCLE

Because of the efforts of Kimball and collaborators[335, 321, 322, 325, 339] the relation between mutation rate and the cell cycle is probably better known for *P. aurelia* than for any other organism. Immediately after fission at the beginning of Gl paramecia are found to be relatively sensitive to X-rays. During micronuclear Gl (lasting about $2\frac{1}{2}$ hours under the conditions employed by Kimball) their sensitivity increases continuously until it is some 35 per cent greater than it was at the beginning of Gl. During S ($\frac{1}{2}$ hour) there is a dramatic drop in sensitivity to approximately 1/10 of its value at the end of Gl. Sensitivity remains low during G 2 (about 1 hour) and then rises again during mitosis ($1\frac{1}{2}$ hours). Similar patterns have been found for ultraviolet light, alpha particles, Pu^{239}, and nitrogen mustard, all agents which react with the chromosomes. 5-bromodeoxyuridine, as would be predicted, induces mutation only when present in S.

4. METABOLIC INHIBITORS AND STARVATION

When paramecia in the stationary phase in Gl are treated with X-rays, the longer food is withheld after radiation, the fewer the mutations observed.[337] The number of mutants can be reduced to about one-third the number obtained when radiation is administered immediately before S.[325] Post-irradiation treatments with any of a number of compounds (caffeine, iodoacetate, chloramphenicol, and streptomycin) which inhibit metabolism and delay cell division[335] similarly decrease the number of mutations.

Disappearance of premutational damage continues after irradiation up until S, when damage becomes fixed.[337, 335, 333]

In spite of the fact that starvation and metabolic inhibitors decrease the number of mutations, the *rate* of disappearance of premutational damage is actually decreased by such treatments.[335, 325] This apparent anomaly is explained by the fact that these treatments delay S, thereby allowing more time for loss of premutational damage. The increased time more than compensates for the reduced rate of disappearance of damage.

Does the disappearance of premutational injury result from active repair processes? Or does it result from interference with a sequence of events which leads from the initial lesion to the final mutation? Kimball favors the first possibility. He[325] points out that as the time between radiation and S increases, damage decreases. This finding is in agreement with the idea of repair, and contrary to what would be expected if mutation follows from the initial lesions through a series of stages.

It is of interest to look at the relation between mutation rate and the cell cycle, on the assumption that the initial lesions are constant in number and that the apparent variations in sensitivity result from the repair of damage. Thus, the steady increase in apparent sensitivity during Gl would be due to there being progressively shorter time for repair between radiation and S, when mutations become fixed. The drop to 1/10 of the peak value at S indicates that most (at least 9/10) of the lesions can be repaired. Only the unexpectedly high sensitivity during prophase requires further explanation. Kimball and Perdue[339] point out that at least part of this discrepancy may be accounted for on the basis of the "splint" hypothesis[705]—the notion that double chromosomes in G 2 are more stable and hence better able to reconstitute until they separate in prophase.

C. The Mechanism of Radiation Induced Mutations

As noted above, Kimball finds that repair of premutational damage in *P. aurelia* continues after radiation up until the time of chromosomal duplication at S, when damage becomes fixed. Kimball *et al.*[335] estimate that the half-life for one-hit lesions which become fixed at S is of the order of hours. Kimball[324] also finds evidence (to be considered presently) for a relatively small number of breaks (leading to two-hit chromosomal aberrations) whose half-life under comparable conditions is of the order of minutes. Chromosomal breaks leading to one-hit aberrations would be expected to have the same half-life as breaks leading to two-hit aberrations. Therefore Kimball concludes that the bulk of the mutations, the one-hit lesions fixed at S, since they have a longer half-life, are not due to chromosomal breakage. This conclusion is reinforced by the fact that work on other organisms shows that the ability of broken chromosomes to undergo restitution is not terminated at S. Kimball[324] suggests that the one-hit lesions may be "point" mutations and that their fixation at duplication means that the initial damage results in misreplications at S.

Evidence for two-hit chromosomal aberrations is obtained from dose rate and fractionation studies.[324, 325] In log phase paramecia, more mutations are produced when a constant dose of X-rays is given during a short interval of time than when it is given over a longer period of time.[325] This result is interpreted to mean that two-hit effects are important, and that joining of broken ends into new rather than the original configurations is enhanced by shorter and more intense treatments. However, log phase paramecia show no effect of fractionation of dose; presumably because rejoining of broken ends occurs in such paramecia in only a few minutes and is, therefore, essentially completed during radiation and before the intervals (one and a half hours or more) during which radiation is not given. In stationary phase paramecia precisely the opposite relations were obtained. Less mortality was noted when the dose was fractionated (6 to 7 hours between fractions) than when a constant dose was given. No differences were found when a constant dose was given in times ranging between three and 100 minutes. These results are consistent with the view that rejoining in stationary phase, unlike that in log phase, occurs very slowly over a period of several hours. Therefore, in the stationary phase two-hit chromosomal aberrations (e.g., intrachromosomal deletions, translocations, inversions) probably make up a significant component of the lethal and reduced fission rate effects. Kimball showed that the breakage and reunion hypothesis gives not only a qualitatively satisfactory explanation, as described above, but that the explanation is also quantitatively satisfactory. He estimates that the half-life of breaks in log phase is no more than 25 minutes and probably no more than a minute or two.

The fraction of the mutants which result from breakage and non-breakage phenomena will depend upon the various conditions which determine the amount of reversal of the initial lesions. Paramecia irradiated a short time before S will have little time for repair and hence, a large number of misreplication mutations. Paramecia irradiated a long time before S will have more time for repair of damage leading to misreplication and fewer such mutants. Rejoining of broken ends, which occurs rapidly, will be essentially the same in the two groups.

Kimball[323, 326] has shown that in *Paramecium aurelia* X-irradiation in Gl usually yields mutations which are found in all the progeny at subsequent mitoses. This result indicates that all the preexisting strands are mutated. A small fraction of the cases represent one-half mutants. These results agree with the work on spermatozoa of *Drosophila*[16, 435, 85] and the mouse.[553] It is, therefore, likely that X-ray mutagenesis results from changes in both strands of the DNA double helix. Changes such as double strand breaks or base pair rotations have been suggested by Kimball.[323, 326]

Chemical mutagens as well as X-rays, alpha particles, and ultraviolet light cause reversible premutational lesions. Kimball[327] has found that the number of lethals induced by nitrogen mustard and triethylene melamine is reduced by pretreatments (before S) and by increases in the interval between exposure to the mutagens and S. Although part of the damage produced by triethylene melamine is reparable through mitosis, it is all fixed at S.[329] Triethylene melamine, unlike X-rays, produces predominantly fractional mutations.[329]

While it is generally assumed that the harmful effects of radiation on chromosomes result from absorption of energy in or near the chromosome, it is of interest to note that part of the deleterious action of P^{32} incorporated into DNA is thought to arise from its transmutation into S^{32}. Thus, Powers[498] found P^{32} more effective than Sr^{89}, Sr^{90}, and R^{90} in the medium. The possibility that this effect might be due to higher intranuclear concentrations of P^{32} than of the other elements was considered by Rubin.[549] He calculated that the localization of P^{32} in the nucleus could not account for more than a small fraction of the large effect observed. Hence, the replacement of P by S or perhaps the removal of P by recoil may account for a portion of the harmful effects.

VIII. NON-MENDELIAN PHENOMENA

The phenomena considered under the fourteen topics in this section all show hereditary differences which cannot be explained in Mendelian terms. Our knowledge of these cases in Protozoa constitutes a large portion of what is known about inherited cellular differentiations and non-Mendelian inheritance in all organisms. Three kinds of non-Mendelian inheritance can be recognized: inheritance involving extrachromosomal DNA, inheritance due to a role of preexisting structure in determining new structure, and inheritance due to stable differences in gene expression.

The first five topics (algal symbionts, kappa and its relatives, chloroplasts, kinetoplasts, and mitochondria) all deal with structures which contain DNA. They constitute a spectrum of forms which begins with intracellular symbionts and culminates in normal cellular organelles. Although it cannot be said with certainty that the DNA in all of these structures is self-reproducing, it is likely, first, because the only known mechanism of DNA synthesis involves self-determination, and second, because it has been shown that chloroplast DNA is replicated semi-conservatively. The similarities in fine structure of the nucleic acid containing regions of chloroplasts and mitochondria with those regions in bacteria and blue-green algae have resulted in a revival[542, 462, 464, 463] of the idea advanced by Altmann and others[17, 408, 166, 496, 718] many years ago that mitochondria and chloroplasts are descendants of ancient cytoplasmic symbionts. On this view kappa and its relatives would be more modern and less well-integrated symbionts, most having lost their capacity for self-reproduction outside their hosts.

The next three topics (non-chromosomal elements of heredity in *Chlamydomonas*, the "mo" element in *Paramecium*, and cytoplasmic inheritance in ameba) are not sufficiently well-known for them to be classified with certainty, but the non-chromosomal elements of heredity in *Chlamydomonas* probably have nucleic acid as their basis, and the other two may also.

The second kind of non-Mendelian inheritance is represented by the ciliate cortex. It constitutes the only certain evidence for the currently popular notion (see, for example, Green and Hechter Ref. 215) of a role of structure and pattern in inheritance. It might be argued, at least for viruses and in the main for bacteria too, that genetics ends once the proper sequences of bases and amino acids have been synthesized in their proper amounts. However, the work of Landmann and associates (see Landmann and Halle Ref. 350) suggests that the cell wall in bacteria contains genetic elements, for treatment with agents known to interfere directly with the cell wall induces true-breeding L forms free of cell walls. Work on the complex structures of Protozoa has shown clearly that preformed structures and patterns of structures are important in determining the characteristics of organisms. Although the chemical and biological bases of such phenomena are almost completely unknown, the facts to be presented in this section make it clear that the presence of self-reproducing macromolecules cannot provide an adequate explanation of the situation. Discovery of the mechanisms responsible for these phenomena apparently leads into important but little understood problems of growth and development. We will also find suggestions that the DNA in structures does not explain fully the self-reproducing properties of those structures. Likewise, the genetic basis for the "mo" element and for cytoplasmic inheritance in *Amoeba* could just as well be explained by a genetic role of structure.

The third kind of non-chromosomal inheritance is illustrated by the next series of topics (mating type, antigenic type, enzymes in *Tetrahymena*, and life cycle changes in the ciliates). All involve differences in gene expression. The last two topics, calcium chloride resistance and temperature adaptation, while not sufficiently well-known for classification, may also be examples of differential gene action. The well-known hypothesis of Jacob and Monod[272] asserts that genes are "turned off" by the action of intracellular repressor substances whose synthesis is under the control of still other genes. The action of a repressor substance depends upon the presence of a competent operator site adjacent to the gene whose action is modified. Changes in gene action (other than those due to gene mutation) are due to environmentally induced activations or inactivations of repressor substances. The experimental basis for this hypothesis rests primarily upon studies of induction and repression of enzyme synthesis in bacteria. The observed changes in gene action are, for the most part, fully reversible, non-hereditary, and dependent upon the environment.

It might appear that this hypothesis of the control of gene action should be the starting point in any attempt to explain differential expression of genes. However, in all of the cases of differential gene expression considered in this section, the variations, although often induced by the environment, are hereditary changes persisting long after the environmental stimulus has been removed. Many of the changes seen in cellular differentiation in multicellular forms have often been cited as similar examples. One of the first attempts at a molecular model was given by Delbrück[126] in an attempt to explain the serotype system in *Paramecium*. More recently, a number of hypothetical schemes yielding stable systems and incorporating the operator–repressor theory have been constructed by Jacob and Monod.[273]

The only example of a stable difference in gene action with a satisfactory molecular explanation seems to be a very specialized case, that of "maintenance" or "preinduction" of β-galactosidase in *Escherichia coli*.[108, 481] "Unadapted" cells growing in a medium in which an inducer is absent or in very low concentration lack a permease (which facilitates the entrance of inducer) and β-galactosidase. When unadapted cells are placed in a medium rich in inducer, the inducer brings about the development of permease and β-galactosidase and the cells are said to be adapted. When unadapted cells are placed in a medium which has a specific low concentration of inducer, they and their descendants remain unadapted. But when adapted cells are placed in the same medium they and their descendants remain adapted. The low concentration of inducer is sufficient to enable adapted cells with permease to absorb enough inducer to insure the continued production of permease and β-galactosidase, but is insufficient for unadapted cells without permease.

Nanney[448] has noted that three types of repression may be distinguished among ciliates. The first is *intra-locus repression*, illustrated by caryonidal inheritance of mating types. We shall see that homozygous nuclei may be "determined" at the time of their formation for some one of several possible mating types—all apparently under the control of one mating type locus. The second type is *inter-locus repression*, exemplified by the inheritance of serotypes in *Paramecium*. Within homozygous lines a different locus is expressed in each different serotype. *Allelic repression* results when one allele represses another in heterozygotes. The inheritance of H serotypes in *Tetrahymena*, of different C antigens in syngen 2 of *P. aurelia*, and of phosphatase- and esterase-determining alleles in *Tetrahymena* are all examples of allelic repression. It is also possible that dominance among the mating type alleles in *Euplotes* (and perhaps *P. bursaria* too) might be due to allelic repression, for we shall see that "selfing" in *Euplotes* may result from shifts in allelic expression. Attention has been centered recently upon allelic repression because of the work on X chromosomes in mammals,[38, 39, 386, 387, 60] which indicates that if the alleles in one X chromosome in a cell are active, those in the other are not. All of these cases of repression in ciliates are sensitive to environmental treatments of some kind. But all have the property of great stability under most conditions. In many cases, it has been shown that the seat of the hereditary basis determining stable repression is the nucleus itself. In some cases, it is found that the nucleus, in turn, is controlled by the cytoplasm at certain critical stages of nuclear development. In no case is a molecular explanation known. Possible mechanisms are considered in connection with certain of the phenomena.

It should be noted that the demonstration that any cellular structure is self-reproducing in the genetic sense, requires a demonstration that the properties of the structure as measured by cytological means are identical with the properties of the structures as measured by genetic techniques. The property of visible self-reproduction, while providing strong evidence, is not adequate, for it is conceivable that all of the properties of a structure may be controlled by other elements. Furthermore, *de novo* origin may also occur. Nor does the fact that the characters of certain cytoplasmic particles show cytoplasmic inheritance prove that the genetic determinants lie within the particles rather than in other cytoplasmic elements. Proof that a given organelle has genetic continuity is not easily obtained. The classic case, of course, is the demonstration that the gene is located on the chromosome. Kappa was first recognized as a genetic element and its properties (dependence on nuclear genes, mutability, size, number of particles, multiplication rate) were studied by genetic techniques, particularly the mathematical techniques of uniparental reproduction reviewed in Section III, C. When cytoplasmic particles were later observed, it was necessary, in order to establish identity, to show that the cytological particles paralleled the genetic particles in number, size, and multiplication rate, especially during experimental manipulation.[503] Special evidence is thus needed in establishing genetic continuity for any of the various cellular organelles, such as chloroplasts, mitochondria, and kinetosomes.

A. Algal Symbionts in Ciliates

Symbiotic algae have been reported in a wide variety of organisms including many Protozoa—naked and shelled amebas, Foraminifera, Radiolaria, Heliozoa, flagellates, and numerous ciliates. See Buchner,[75] Caullery,[87] Fuller,[186] Droop,[136] and Karakashian and Siegel[301a] for reviews. Among the ciliates are *Stentor, Frontonia, Ophrydium, Trichodina, Paraeuplotes, Paramecium bursaria* and many others.

Protozoa sometimes lose their algae spontaneously. X-rays have been used by Wichterman[730] to eliminate the algae from *P. bursaria*. Jennings[277] eliminated them from *P. bursaria* by providing an excess of food to the paramecia, thereby allowing the ciliates to multiply faster than the algae until algae-free cells were produced. This last process is facilitated, according to Siegel,[597] by keeping cultures in the dark. Starvation in darkness is also effective.[301]

Reinfection of *P. bursaria* may be obtained by exposing algae-free cells to suspensions of algae.[482, 601, 597, 69] Algae for this purpose may be obtained by homogenizing the ciliates or by taking them from cultures.

Algae also seem to be released at a low rate from *P. bursaria* and may be found in the culture medium in which algae-containing paramecia are cultured.[597]

Different stocks of *P. bursaria* with the same algal strain differ in the concentration of algae which they can support,[300] in their ability to maintain algae in the dark,[597] and in the degree of stimulation of their growth provided by algae.[300] Recently, Karakashian and Karakashian[299] have studied the ability of algae-free paramecia to take up free-living algae. Two strains differing markedly in this respect were reported to show aberrant results in crosses which suggest non-genic inheritance of susceptibility. Bomford[69] also observed differences in the ability of different stocks to take up algae. He could find no evidence, however, for the existence of genotypes unable to support algae.

The algae from *P. bursaria* resemble the genus *Chlorella*. Most, but not all, may be cultured in bacteria-free medium.[373, 301] *P. bursaria* has been infected not only with the *Chlorella*-like species from paramecia, but also with *Chlorella*-like species from *Hydra* and from hypotrichs, with free-living *Chlorella*, with *Stichococcus*, with *Selenastrum*, with *Scenedesmus*, and with *Hormidium*.[300, 301, 482] Bomford[69] also reports that *P. bursaria* may be infected with a yeast. Many other cases of cross-infection from one species to another have been discovered.[136, 301] Strains of *Chlorella* vary in their ability to maintain themselves in the dark, in their ability to infect,[597, 301, 69] and in the amount of stimulation they provide to the growth of their hosts.[300, 301]

The symbiotic relationship has been investigated by a number of investigators.[731, 729, 300, 301] For example, Karakashian[300] compared the properties of *Chlorella*-free and *Chlorella*-containing strains of *P. bursaria*. At high concentrations of bacteria, which are used for food, the strains are alike. However, at lower bacterial concentrations both growth rate and maximum population density are higher in the algae-containing strains. Furthermore, the symbionts are able to maintain the host paramecia in the light in the absence of bacteria.[519] The possibility that algae grow in the medium and provide food does not seem to explain the results, for Karakashian (personal communication) finds that the density of algae in the medium does not appear sufficiently great. Furthermore, the algae from *Hydra* cannot be cultured, yet as intracellular symbionts they support growth of paramecia.

B. Kappa and Its Relatives

Since Sonneborn's exhaustive review[649] of kappa and related particles in 1959 (128 pages, 143 references) nearly 50 papers have been published on the subject. The following account briefly summarizes the present state of the problem.

Kappa and its relatives include all of the known bacteria-like symbionts in the cytoplasm of *Paramecium*. They constitute an important link in our understanding of the bridge between parasitism and heredity.[119] They were, in fact, first recognized by Sonneborn[623] as genetic elements. They qualify as such because they are self-reproducing, mutable, and determine certain properties of the cells in which they are found. On the other hand, they have many of the properties of organisms. Preer and Stark[517] found that they look like bacteria in the light microscope. Dippell[132] and Beale and Jurand[48] noted their resemblance to bacteria in the electron microscope. Preer[500] and later Sonneborn[627] found that their reproduction can be dissociated from that of *Paramecium*. Sonneborn[631, 632] also discovered that they are infective. And, finally, most natural strains of paramecia are free of them. The best evidence is more recent. Van Wagtendonk[712] reports that lambda can reproduce on a complex cell-free medium. And kappa itself has been shown by Kung[349a] to respire and utilize glucose and sucrose *in vitro*. The presence in kappa of the biochemical apparatus required for such a sophisticated metabolism clearly eliminates the possibility that it is a virus. A virus with the complex enzymatic and structural apparatus necessary to carry out the glycolytic and citric acid pathways (as kappa appears to do) and thereby obtain energy from glucose would better be defined as a cell! Furthermore, it does not appear that kappa is a cell organelle of intrinsic origin. One of the most complex organelles known is the mitochondrion and even it lacks the numerous enzymes necessary for the glycolytic pathway. Although we could postulate that natural selection has resulted in a unique organelle containing the whole respiratory machinery in paramecia (completely without parallel in all of biology), the simple assumption that kappa is a symbiont fits the facts just as well or better. The revival of the old theory that chloroplasts and mitochondria (see Section VIII, C, D, and E) are descendants of ancient symbiotic organisms suggests the perspective in which kappa and its relatives should properly appear. Evolutionarily, kappa and its relatives represent a more recent symbiosis. Integration has proceeded beyond the stage of free-living organisms. Although *Paramecium* probably benefits from the association under many conditions, the particles have not become essential for *Paramecium*, as *Paramecium* has become for the particles.

1. THE PARTICLES

It was shown by Preer and Stark[517] that the particles (designated by letters of the Greek alphabet) may be observed by washing paramecia free of bacteria,[234] crushing them between a slide and a coverslip, and observing under the "bright" phase microscope. Table 7 lists the particles in a number of different stocks.

Kappa, discovered by Sonneborn[623] using genetic techniques, was the first particle to be found. Paramecia which possess kappa are killers, liberating toxic particles into the medium. The presence of kappa insures that a killer will be resistant to its own toxin. The toxic particles kill sensitive strains of paramecia lacking the particles and also they usually kill killers which contain different kinds of particles.[619, 128, 129, 501, 504] That some of the kappa particles in every population contain one (rarely more) refractile or R bodies was discovered by Preer and Stark.[517] Such kappa particles are called "brights" or B particles because they appear bright in the bright phase contrast microscope.[517, 649] The remainder of the kappa particles are called "non-bright" or N particles. N particles are self-reproducing[517, 666, 611, 430] and give rise to B particles. It was shown by Preer et al.[516] and confirmed by Smith[611] and Mueller[430] that B particles are the toxic particles (called P particles by Sonneborn,[649]) which kill sensitives when liberated into the medium. R bodies have a highly characteristic morphology (see below) and serve to distinguish kappa particles not only from the other related particles (lambda, mu, etc.) in *Paramecium*, but from all known biological entities. In this connection, it is felt by this reviewer that particles which kill but which do not have R bodies should be given a designation other than kappa. A number of so-called kappa particles (such as those in syngens 6 and 8—see Table 1) should be reexamined with this point in mind. The characteristic prelethal states undergone by affected sensitives (spinning, vacuolization, cytoplasmic extrusions, etc.) make it possible to distinguish many different kinds of kappa by their specific toxic actions. Sensitives usually require about 2 hours or more to show an effect after being exposed to the toxic particles, and death may require much longer, depending upon the strains of killers and sensitives.

Lambda particles kill in only a few minutes.[667, 582a] They are very large, and do not contain R bodies. Sigma[667, 582a] is similar to lambda in its rapid killing action, but it is distinguished morphologically by its sinuous form. The particles in the syngen 2 killer stock SG reported by Nobili[475] have not been described, but their very rapid killing suggests that the particles may be more like lambda or sigma than kappa.

Mu particles, found in mate-killers, were discovered by Siegel[590–593] and later studied further by Levine[354, 355] and Beale.[46] They do not contain R bodies. No toxic action is produced by the fluid in which matekillers have lived or by homogenates of mate-killers. Instead, after conjugation, sensitive mates either die or produce a limited number of progeny which die. Apparently, a toxin is transferred from mate-killer to sensitive. Nuclear transfer is not required, but cell to cell contact is needed. Electron microscope observations by Beale and Jurand[48] revealed no nucleus within mu.

The pi particles of Hanson[222, 223, 516] are probably kappa mutants; they produce no toxic action on sensitives nor do they protect their host from the toxic action of kappa. They contain no R bodies. Nu particles, reported by Sonneborn et al.[667] are the only particles found in syngen 5. They are naturally occurring forms similar to pi.

The buoyant density of the DNA from a number of the particles has been determined starting with the demonstration by Smith-Sonneborn et al.[612] that 51 kappa has a density of 1.696 (nuclear DNA of stock 51 has a density of 1.688). Behme[52] reports for stock 138 mu a DNA density of 1.700; stock 540 mu is 1.701; stock 239 lambda, 1.708; and stock 114 sigma, 1.704. Preer (unpublished) finds the density of stock 7 kappa DNA to be 1.698. These diverse ratios, taken with the very different morphology of the particles and their great differences in killing action, suggest that the particles are quite diverse phylogenetically.

2. Genetic Control

In the presence of certain *Paramecium* genotypes the particles are not maintained. Sonneborn[623] found that kappa of stock 51 of syngen 4 is maintained in that stock in the presence of the genotype KK. When paramecia of the genotype Kk are obtained from a cross with kk (derived from the sensitive stock 32), Chao[89, 90] found that Kk usually has only about half as many kappa as there are in KK. This same relation has been reported by Balsley[30a] for stock 7 of syngen 2. The kk clones derived from autogamy in killer heterozygotes lose kappa altogether after a few fissions. Sonneborn[630] and Balbinder[28] showed that stock 29 has two pairs of genes S_1S_1 and S_2S_2 which increase the likelihood of kappa loss. Genes known to affect particle maintenance, along with the stocks from which they are derived are given in Table 8. The kappa particles in stock 214 are not excluded by the genes which exclude 299 lambda. Similarly, Balsley[30a] has found that the kk genotype of syngen 2 which excludes kappa does not exclude sigma. Nobili[468, 473] finds that kappa does not multiply in amacronucleate paramecia, but killing activity can increase.

TABLE 7. KAPPA AND ITS RELATIVES IN PARAMECIUM AURELIA

Syngen	Particle	Stocks (and References)
1	Mu	540 (46), 548 (646), 551 (646)
2	Kappa	7 (619), 8 (619), 34 (649), 36 (501), 50 (501), 193 (649), 249 (649), 292 (649), 308–2 (517), SG (475)
	Sigma	114 (667)
4	Kappa	47 (129), 51 (623), 116 (649), 139 (649), 169 (649), 277 (649), 298 (649)
	Lambda	239 (667)
5	Nu	87 (667), 314 (667)
6	Kappa	225 (645)
8	Kappa	214 (645)
	Lambda	216 (667), 229 (667), 299 (582)
	Mu	130 (355), 131 (355), 138 (592)

Mutations of kappa often occur spontaneously and many have been isolated. Dippell[128, 129] studied a number of stock 51 kappa mutants and demonstrated that their properties were controlled by changes in the genetic apparatus of kappa, not of *Paramecium*. Her mutants differed from wild type in the characteristic prelethal stages induced in sensitives and in the maximum multiplication rate which the kappas could maintain. Mutations to non-killer pi particles have already been noted, and several other mutants have also been described. These include mutants resistant to aureomycin[150] and a mutant which can no longer kill, has no brights, but is resistant to its original killing substance.[732, 431, 432]

TABLE 8. GENES LEADING TO LOSS OF SYMBIOTIC PARTICLES IN PARAMECIUM AURELIA

Syngen	Stock	Genotype	Particle excluded	Reference
1	513	$m_1m_1m_2m_2$	540 mu	196
2	1010	kk	7 kappa	30a
4	32	kk	51 kappa	623
	29	$S_1S_1S_2S_2$*	51 kappa	28
8	214	ll	299 lambda	583
	137	mm	138 mu	592

* The more S alleles present, the greater the probability of loss of kappa.

3. LOSS OF PARTICLES

Stock cultures of paramecia occasionally spontaneously lose their particles. It was shown by Preer[501] that the maximum multiplication rate of some strains of particles (not others) is less than that of their *Paramecium* hosts. Excess feeding of such cultures leads to a decline in kappa concentration until increasing proportions of cells are completely freed of particles, and, of course, remain permanent sensitives. It was shown that so long as a paramecium has even one particle, the full number may be regenerated during reduced feeding. Estimates of kappa multiplication rate and number were shown to be possible by an examination of the kinetics of loss (see Section III, A, 1). These studies came at a time when kappa had not been observed cytologically, and was known only genetically. They played an important part in the cytological demonstration of the particles. They also suggested that other cytoplasmic entities might be subject to a similar form of analysis.

A number of other treatments are also capable of eliminating particles from paramecia. These include temperature extremes,[225, 503, 627, 635, 662] X-rays,[502, 503, 441] ultraviolet irradiation[320a] nitrogen mustard,[188] aureomycin,[150] streptomycin (Preer, unpublished), penicillin,[713] chloromycetin,[73, 150, 734] terramycin,[734, 150] 2,6-diaminopurine[684, 734, 221] and 8-azaguanine.[198]

4. INFECTION

When particle-containing and particle-free paramecia conjugate, particles are not usually transferred to the particle-free mate. Occasionally, however, transfer does occur, and as indicated earlier, kappa transfer has served as a guide in working out measures and techniques of controlling cytoplasmic transfer in *Paramecium*.

Infective transfer was obtained by Sonneborn when he exposed sensitives of the proper genotype to homogenates of killers and found that sensitives acquired kappa and finally became killers themselves.[631, 653] The conditions for kappa uptake have been defined by several studies.[696, 697, 428] More recently it has been shown by Sonneborn, Mueller, and Smith[666, 430, 611] that infection may be obtained with non-bright kappa particles, but not with bright particles. All of these infections have been accomplished by transferring stock 51 kappa into sensitive stocks of syngen 4. All other combinations have failed[649] except for one. Van Wagtendonk *et al.*[712] report that lambda from stock 299 cultured free of paramecia may infect lambda-free strains of the same stock.

Recent studies utilizing cytoplasmic transfer achieved by microinjection, however, have been successful in making one other transfer. Koizumi and Preer[347a] have transferred syngen 2, stock 7 kappa into syngen 4, kappa-free stock 51.

5. SYMBIOTIC RELATIONS

The particles have a number of effects on the paramecia which contain them. Thus it has been known for some time that killer strains of stock 51 are unable to live in certain axenic media in which sensitive strains of paramecia thrive.[712] More recently, media which allow 51 killers to multiply have been found by Soldo.[614] Of particular interest is Soldo's[615] finding that 299 lambda killers will grow on axenic medium free of folic acid, but that the stock 299 particle-free strain requires folic acid. The story was completed recently by the discovery of van Wagtendonk *et al.*[712] that folic acid is not a requirement of stock 299 lambda in cell-free culture, suggesting that lambda may be able to supply the folic acid requirement of its host.

Reports by van Wagtendonk and Simonsen[714, 604, 605, 606] that the respiration rate of kappa-containing killers of stock 51 is greater than that of sensitive stocks have not been confirmed for other killers by Levine and Howard[356] or Preer.[505] Nobili[468, 473] has reported that amacronucleate stock 51 killers do not survive as long as amacronucleate stock 51 sensitives.

Perhaps the most striking effect, however, is that in every case the particles afford complete protection against the toxic action for which they are responsible. The effect is generally quite specific, and different killers kill each other.[619, 501, 504] Dippell[129] found several instances of paramecia containing mutant kappas which could kill each other, yet were immune to their own toxic actions. Immunity must be very closely tied to the production of toxic activity. Still, the mutant kappa of Widmayer[732] referred to above, which has no R bodies and yet is resistant, shows that R-containing kappa particles are not necessary for protection.

The resistance of sensitives to the toxic action of killers is also affected by a number of other factors: temperature at which the sensitives have been cultured (Preer, unpublished), stage in life cycle,[623, 632, 129] the presence of a functional ingestory apparatus and macronucleus,[472, 649] syngen and stock differences[206, 582, 617, 618] which in one case have been shown to be due to polygenic inheritance,[504] serotype,[25, 27] and nutritive condi-ion.[627] Butzel and coworkers[81, 82] have found that treatment of sensitives with either detergents, NaN_3, DNP, or chloramphenicol increases their resistance to stock 51 killer substance. They conclude that both protein synthesis and energy producing mechanisms in the sensitives are essential for the manifestation of killing action.

6. TOXIC ACTIVITY

Mu particles produce a toxin which appears to act on the nuclei of sensi-tives, and it can only be transmitted by cell to cell contact.[590, 591, 593] Nothing is known about the nature of the presumed toxins.

The toxic action associated with lambda of stock 299 of *P. aurelia* has recently been studied by Butzel *et al.*[83] The killing substance can be found in the cell-free fluid in which killers have lived. It is labile and associated with easily sedimented particles, possibly lambda itself.

The substance responsible for the toxic activity of kappa has also never been obtained in solution. It is found in the fluid in which killers have lived and in homogenates in the form of discrete particles (called P particles by Sonneborn, see Ref. 649). Austin,[22, 23, 24] Sonneborn *et al.*[665, 662] and Nobili[475] have shown that a single P particle is sufficient to kill a single paramecium.

Preer *et al.*[516] showed that the P particle of stock 7 killers is the kappa particle which contains the R body. This finding was confirmed by Smith[611, 612a] and Mueller[430] for stock 51 killers. Furthermore, it has been recently demonstrated that the lysis of R-containing particles of stock 7 killer by deoxycholate[515] or by ultrasonic[513] yields intact R bodies which are fully active killing particles. When stock 51 R-containing kappa particles are disrupted, however, all killing activity is invariably lost.[513]

The isolated R body from stock 7 thus contains all the killing activity of the R-containing (or B) kappa particles. R bodies have been studied by Hamilton and Gettner,[221] Dippell[132] and Rudenberg,[550] and shown by electron microscopy to consist of tubes of about one-half micron length and width, with walls consisting of some ten rather thin layers. It has now been found by Mueller,[429] Anderson et al.[18] and Preer et al.[513] that the R body has the form of a roll of tape which can suddenly (less than a second) unroll to produce a long twisted ribbon. Preer et al.[513] showed that isolated R bodies of stock 7 and stock 51 show a number of differences. Those from stock 7 generally unroll from the outside when treated with sodium lauryl sulfate or occasionally spontaneously; they are unaffected by pH changes. R bodies from stock 51 are unaffected by sodium lauryl sulfate, but when the pH is lowered to 6.0 and below, they unwind from the inside. And when the pH is again raised to 7.0 and above, they quickly wind back up again, from the inside. It is speculated[18, 513, 432a] that the unwinding of the R body is important in delivering the toxic substance to its site of action in sensitives. The chemical nature of the R body is unknown.

The chemical nature of the killing substance has been investigated by means of the action spectrum for ultraviolet light inactivation by Setlow and Doyle[588] and with the use of enzymes by van Wagtendonk.[709, 710] Although considerable evidence was gained indicating that a protein is involved, these data have been made largely irrelevant by the more recent findings. All of the studies ultilized stook 51 kappa, and as pointed out above, all that is needed to inactivate the P particle of stock 51 is to disrupt the outer membrane of the B particle. The matter needs reinvestigation. Whether the poison is the R body in stock 7 or whether it is adsorbed to the R body is not known. Whether it is distinct from the R body in stock 51, or merely inactivated by rupture of the B particle and exposure to the outside medium is also unknown.

7. THE METAGON

In 1961 Gibson and Beale[196] reported on crosses which indicated that the syngen 1 mate-killer stock 540 was of genotype $M_1M_1M_2M_2$ and that sensitive stock 513 was $m_1m_1m_2m_2$ (hereafter designated mm). When $M_1m_1m_2m_2$ or $m_1m_1M_2m_2$ (either will hereafter be designated Mm) undergoes autogamy half the exautogamous paramecia stay mate-killers and the other half lose their mu and become sensitives. It was reported in 1962 by Gibson and Beale[197] that increasing percentages of the exautogamous recessive mm paramecia were found to lose mu with successive fissions, These percentages in one experiment were: 1 to 7 fissions, 0 per cent; 8 fissions, 5 per cent; 9, 17 per cent; 10, 32 per cent; 11, 61 per cent; 12, 71 per cent; 13, 79 per cent; 14, 85 per cent; 15, 93 per cent. Other data were similar. In those paramecia which retained mu, the mu concentrations stayed high until loss, when their number suddenly dropped to zero within a fission. A similar pattern of loss was observed by Chao[89] in 1953 for stock 51 kappa. It was postulated by Gibson and Beale that the mu particles are dependent upon a hypothetical particle called the metagon. Paramecia of genotype Mm have many metagons but when the genotype changes to mm, metagons are no longe ·synthesized and become progressively diluted out. The entire mu population depends upon the metagon for its maintenance. So when the last metagon disappears from each line of descent, all of the mu particles quickly disappear. A number of lines of evidence have been presented in support of this hypothesis. In one experiment[197] paramecia were cultured for fifteen fissions after induction of autogamy in *Mm* and mated to sensitives. Those animals which killed their mates were those which still had mu. These were isolated and allowed to undergo three fissions. Each of the resulting eight paramecia was now examined for mu particles. If the metagon hypothesis were correct, each group of eight should have at least one, but usually not more than one killer, for each of the isolated paramecia which gave rise to the octet should have had at least one, but not often more than one metagon. This prediction was beautifully confirmed as follows: 0 octets had 0 killers;32 octets had 1; 5 octets had 2; 1 octet had 3; and no octets had more than 3. Direct examination revealed that when mu was lost, it disappeared from 1 to 6 hours after the fission in which the metagon was presumed to be lost. If the metagons do not increase after *Mm* becomes *mm*, but are distributed at random among the paramecia at successive fissions, then their number can be easily estimated. Assuming a Poisson distribution, from the 32 per cent of the paramecia freed of metagons at the 10th fission (see above), the mean number of particles among the 2^{10} or 1024 paramecia is about one, and the total number of metagons must be about 1000, and that number must also have been the starting number. Reeve[531] and Reeve and Ross[532, 533] have analyzed the data statistically and concluded that they fit the hypothesis fairly well (but not in an entirely satisfactory manner) provided that one assumes a slow multiplication rate of metagons—a probability of 1/5 of a metagon division during a *Paramecium* interfission interval. The kinetics of dilution was found to be highly reproducible, completely unaffected by starvation, temperature, and type of culture medium.

Evidence that the metagon is cytoplasmic was provided by comparing the results[197] of crossing (with and without cytoplasmic exchange) "eleventh-fission" animals (*mm* paramecia derived by autogamy from *Mm* mate-killers eleven fissions previously) with "fifteenth fission" animals (derived in a similar way fifteen fissions previously). When exconjugants were isolated and allowed to undergo three fissions and the resulting octets examined for mu, it was found that the octets derived from the "fifteenth fission" exconjugants contained more killers when cytoplasmic exchange had occurred than when it had not.

In 1963 Gibson and Beale[198] showed that metagons could be destroyed by ribonuclease. The evidence is as follows. First, mate-killers treated with ribonuclease permanently lose their mu. How can one determine whether this effect is on metagons or on mu? The cross (without cytoplasmic exchange) of untreated "seventh fission" paramecia with untreated "eleventh fission" animals yields few killers among octets produced from isolated "eleventh fission" exconjugants because they have only a few metagons and receive none from their mates. In the same cross, if cytoplasmic exchange occurs, metagons pass into the eleventh fission exconjugants from the seventh fission mates and they yield many killers within octets derived from both exconjugants. The cross of ribonuclease treated seventh fission paramecia with untreated eleventh fission animals (with cytoplasmic exchange) yielded few killers in octets derived from either exconjugant— apparently ribonuclease had destroyed the metagons. Furthermore, many killers were obtained in octets from both exconjugants after treated seventh fission animals were crossed (with cytoplasmic exchange) to *MM* sensitives (which, of course, contained many metagons). Direct examination of ribonuclease treated mate-killers revealed that mu remained in the killers after treatment until division, and then disappeared before the next division. In the same study it was reported that 8-azaguanine caused complete destruction of mu particles in mate-killers even before division. It was shown that 8-azaguanine acts by destroying mu, not by destroying metagons. A cross (with cytoplasmic exchange) of 8-azaguanine treated seventh fission killers to untreated eleventh fission animals produced octets from both exconjugants with numerous mu particles. The required metagons could only have come from the 8-azaguanine treated paramecia.

In 1964 accounts of a number of remarkable discoveries appeared. First Gibson and Beale[199] found an assay for extracted metagons. Metagon depleted paramecia (either ribonuclease treated mate-killers or eleventh fission animals) are treated with extracts suspected of having metagons. If metagons are absent in the extract, very few killers arise from the treated animals; but if metagons are present, many killers arise. Although whole homogenates of mate-killers did not show positive tests, microsomes, ribosomes, and RNA extracts of microsomes did. Furthermore, data are presented which indicate that metagons are disassociated from ribosomes in low magnesium ion concentrations and reaggregated when the magnesium ion concentration is raised. Further evidence for the RNA nature of the isolated metagon is found in its sensitivity to RNAse, resistance to DNAse and association with an RNA-containing zone in electrophoresis.[195]

These results led to the possibility that the metagon might be messenger RNA produced by the M genes. Gibson and Sonneborn[200, 201] have shown the likelihood of this possibility by studies on hybridization using the Bolton and McCarthy[68] technique. It is reported that metagons hybridize well with DNA from *M*-containing paramecia, less well with DNA from *mm* paramecia. A number of other DNA's (*Didinium*, mu, *Tetrahymena*, and *Aerobacter aerogenes*) also hybridized very poorly or not at all.

Most remarkable of all are the reports by Gibson and Sonneborn[200, 201, 664, 653, 194] that metagons, as well as kappa and mu, are self-reproducing in *Didinium*. Thus, the metagon, messenger RNA in *Paramecium*, is a virus in *Didinium*. It was found that the ciliate *Didinium* which feeds on *Para-*

mecium can maintain kappa of stock 51 and mu of stock 540 in its cytoplasm if fed initially with a killer and thereafter with sensitives. Different stocks of *Didinium* vary in their ability to harbor symbionts. After being fed *MM* killers or sensitives and then placed on a steady diet of *mm* paramecia for as many as 1000 generations, didinia continue to have metagons. Loss of both metagons and mu is said to occur at encystment of *Didinium*.[194] Extracts were tested by the methods already described. Hybridization tests showed that the metagons do not hybridize with DNA from *Didinium*. Further evidence that the metagon is a primary product of the *M* gene in *Paramecium*, yet a self-reproducing particle in *Didinium* comes from the report by Gibson (quoted in Ref. 653) on the effects of actinomycin D (assumed to inhibit messenger RNA synthesis in *Paramecium*—Ref. 534) and guanidine hydrochloride (assumed to prevent RNA primed RNA synthesis—Ref. 31). Actinomycin D inhibits metagon production in *Paramecium*, but not in *Didinium*. Guanidine hydrochloride inhibits metagon production in *Didinium*, but not in *Paramecium*.

Sonneborn has recently[653] reported that McManamy (unpublished) and Beale (unpublished) have both found variations in the time of loss of mu 540 after autogamy in *Mm* mate-killers. These findings are in marked contrast to the original results of Gibson and Beale who found not only great uniformity, but an independence from environmental effects, as noted above. Attempts by Yeung[737] to determine whether there are metagons associated with stock 51 kappa have revealed similar variations. These variations are also puzzling because the earlier work on stock 51 kappa by Chao (as noted above) yielded kinetics of loss like the original work of Gibson and Beale on 540 mu. Sonneborn[653] also reports that McManamy (unpublished) has found great variability in loss of mu in studies on the mate-killers of syngen 8. Apparently, there are still unknown sources of variability in conditions influencing symbiont loss which were not found initially. These conditions need elucidation, for the *in vitro* tests for metagons depend on adequate control of such factors.

The recent report that the guanine plus cytosine content of metagons is very high[201] appears to have been in error.[653]

The discovery of stable messenger RNA which can become self-reproducing in another organism is completely without parallel and its significance hardly requires comment. In view of the difficulties in controlling mu loss, however, a final evaluation should not be attempted until further work has been done.

8. KAPPA-LIKE FORMS IN SPECIES OTHER THAN PARAMECIUM AURELIA

It has been noted that both 51 kappa and 540 mu can be introduced into *Didinium*. Sonneborn has also reported[653] that the kappas of stocks 7 and 51 and the mu particles of the syngen 8 mate-killer stocks 130 and 138 will survive in certain stocks of *Dileptus*—a form which also eats paramecia.

Takayanagi and Hayashi[694] have recently described a killer stock of *Paramecium polycaryum*. However, no symbionts were discovered. The same is true for the killers of *P. bursaria*.[94, 97, 135] Preer (unpublished) has recently found kappa-like particles in a new killer discovered by Siegel and Heckmann[600a] in *Euplotes minuta*.

Numerous cases of kappa-like particles in the cytoplasm of various protozoans have been reported and are reviewed by Sonneborn[649] and Kirby.[342] The particles found in *E. patella* and *E. eurystomus* by Fauré-Fremiet[167] are of particular interest. Exposure of the *Euplotes* to penicillin resulted in loss of the particles followed by death of the *Euplotes*. Fauré-Fremiet argues that it is likely that the death of the *Euplotes* was caused by loss of the symbionts, for other strains of *Euplotes* were able to withstand much higher doses of penicillin. Obviously, kappa-like symbionts are very widespread among the Protozoa.

C. Chloroplasts

It has long been known that nuclear genes may control the properties of chloroplasts. For example, the gene mutations of *Chlamydomonas* which affect photosynthesis (see Section VI, B) demonstrate this fact. It has also been known for many years that chloroplast characteristics may show cytoplasmic inheritance. Although it is often assumed that the demonstration of cytoplasmic determinants of plastid characters means that such determinants lie within the chloroplasts, this conclusion is not necessarily valid. It is theoretically possible that some or all the cytoplasmic determinants may lie outside the chloroplasts. However, the design of experiments which make a choice possible has proved very difficult. We shall first review the information pertaining to the matter in Protozoa, and then at the close of this section return to the general question.

1. CHLOROPLAST INHERITANCE IN CHLAMYDOMONAS

Chlamydomonas reinhardi has only one chloroplast. Many mutations affecting chloroplast characteristics have been detected. They fall into three categories. First are gene mutations which show 2 : 2 tetrad segregations and map onto one of the known linkage groups. Second are the acetate-requiring streptomycin-induced mutations of Sager which show 0 : 4 or 4 : 0 tetrad segregations. They are clearly cytoplasmic and are considered in some detail in Section VIII, F. Third, are the y_1 yellow mutants.[557, 561, 574] They segregate 2 : 2 in tetrads, always show segregation at the first meiotic division, but do not map on any known linkage group. They, too, are considered in Section VIII, F. The site of the physical basis for both of these types of non-Mendelian inheritance is unknown, but the chloroplasts are a possibility.

Extensive investigations of chloroplasts have been undertaken with *Euglena gracilis*, and we shall now devote most of this section to *Euglena*.

2. Non-hereditary Light-controlled Bleaching and Greening
in Euglena

Euglena gracilis has about 8 to 12 plastids when grown in the light according to Lyman *et al.*[385] and Gibor and Granick.[191] Chloroplasts remain separate for the most part when grown under conditions of 12 hours light and 12 hours darkness, but fuse to form a single chain when grown in a rich medium under continuous light.[191, 214] When wild type cells are cultured in the dark, they undergo non-hereditary "bleaching", chloroplasts degenerating into proplastids. Proplastids, according to Epstein and Schiff,[162] are small granules about one micron in diameter. Degeneration required about 144 hours (eight generations in the experiments described by Ben-Shaul *et al.*[57] However, on return to light new chloroplasts develop from the proplastids.

The number of proplastids in dark grown cells has been estimated by Lyman *et al.*[385] on the basis of cytological observations of Epstein and Schiff[162] to be about 30. However, Gibor and Granick[191] state that there are 30 to 40 proplastid *particles* with 3 to 4 particles contained in each proplastid, i.e., only about 10 proplastids per cell. On the basis of a sudden threefold increase in number of discs in developing proplastids exposed to light, Ben-Shaul *et al.*[58] postulate that the proplastids fuse in groups of three after 8 to 14 hours to form about 10 plastids. About 72 hours were required for complete development into plastids. However, Granick[214] reports that after 5 hours cells with only 10 proplastids are present. Thus it appears that there are on the order of about 30 granules capable of developing chlorophyll, but there is conflicting evidence on whether or not in dark grown cells they are organized into some 10 proplastids.

Development of chloroplasts from proplastids is repressed if utilizable carbon sources are added to the medium.[19]

3. Inducers of Hereditary Bleaching in Euglena

The bleaching induced by darkness is not permanent, but permanent hereditary bleaching may occur spontaneously or may be induced. Spontaneous mutants appeared in a frequency of 0.1 per cent in the studies of Robbins *et al.*[543] and (in a different medium) of 1 to 2 per cent in studies of Granick.[214] Spontaneous mutants include not only white strains but stable pale greens and cultures with other characteristics as well. It was discovered by Provasoli *et al.* in 1948[522] that permanent hereditary bleaching may be induced by exposure to streptomycin. Since that time a number of treatments have been found to produce the same effect: high temperature,[520] ultraviolet light,[385, 521, 120] antihistamines,[218, 740] erythromycin,[145] kanamycin,[146] *o*-methylthreonine,[1] a number of nitrofurans,[388, 389] and nitrosoguanidine.[390]

4. Characteristics of Bleached Strains of Euglena

Hereditarily bleached strains may be cultivated for many cell generations (presumably indefinitely) without reversion. Gibor and Granick[190, 192] and Moriber et al.[422] have reported that bleached strains still have proplastids, but that they are unable to differentiate into mature chloroplasts. Bleached strains have been compared to the colorless flagellate, Astasia. Astasia, too, has been reported to have structures resembling proplastids.[541] Recently, it was shown that a bleached strain of Euglena investigated by Leff et al.[353] and Edelman et al.[147] had only nuclear DNA. There was a complete absence of the characteristic DNA found in Euglena chloroplasts and in wild type euglenas bleached by growth in darkness.

5. Experiments on the Nature of Bleaching in Euglena

The production of permanently bleached lines after a short exposure to streptomycin was studied by deDeken-Grenson and Messin.[122] After treatment cultures were maintained in liquid medium and then plated onto agar after various numbers of cell divisions. With increasing numbers of fissions in liquid medium, the proportion of bleached cultures on plates was observed to increase. Attempts to interpret segregation frequencies in terms of a model of segregating self-reproducing plastids were complicated by variations in sensitivity to streptomycin, dependent on the physiological condition of the cells; cell death also proved a complicating factor. Moreover, there were serious difficulties in assessing the relative contibutions of temporary and permanent inhibition of the multiplication of the hereditary basis for plastid formation. Later, deDeken-Grenson and Godts[121] repeated these experiments carrying them for longer periods of time. Now it was found that the percentage of green colonies on the plates, while dropping very low in platings taken after the first few fissions in liquid medium, in later platings increased to high levels. This result suggested that green clones outgrow white clones in liquid medium; but artificial mixtures maintained constant proportions in liquid medium, disproving this explanation. It must be concluded that the genetic basis for the chloroplasts undergoes partial recovery after streptomycin treatment in liquid medium but does not recover (or, does not recover as well) on agar.

deDeken-Grenson and Godts[121] also studied bleaching induced by streptomycin, high temperature, and ultraviolet irradiation by following individual cells in micro-drops isolated at various times after treatment. They argued that if the treatment induced some chloroplasts to mutate, then most treated cells should have a mixture of normal and mutated chloroplasts. Such cells should segregate both green and white subclones at subsequent fissions. However, the authors noted a paucity of lines containing both white and green cells, even when isolations were made soon after treatment. Streptomycin treatment, for example, gave out of 60 isolates, 47 pure green, 13 pure white, no mixed; high temperature gave of 41 isolates,

16 pure green, 23 pure white, and 2 mixed; ultraviolet radiation gave of 16 isolates, 7 pure green, 5 pure white, and 4 mixed. They point out that the whole complex of plastids in each cell acts as a unit. The observations can be accounted for if one assumes first that these treatments destroy the genetic basis for many of the chloroplasts, and second that there is no reduction in the reproductive rate of chloroplasts which are not destroyed. The genetic elements determining chloroplasts in most cells are either all irreversibly damaged by treatment, or one or more recover and regenerate the full complement. They also note that certain isolations made several fissions after treatment were completely free of chloroplasts, yet produced pure green clones on multiplication. It follows that in these cases the chloroplasts were destroyed, but not their hereditary basis. The treatments can alter the phenotype without permanently changing its hereditary basis, and that hereditary basis must, therefore, not always lie within the normal green chloroplast in the progeny of treated green cells. The possibility that it lies in a proplastid-like degenerate chloroplast produced by the treatment, however, should be considered. And, in fact, the possibility that normal green cells also contain proplastids should not be overlooked.

Brawerman and Chargaff[71] also studied the frequency of bleached cells in the descendants of euglenas which had been kept at high temperature for a short time and then returned to low temperature. The percentages of permanently bleached cells were higher if higher fission rates were maintained after the exposure to high temperature than if lower fission rates occurred. They concluded that the cytoplasmic genetic elements essential for chloroplasts were reduced in quantity and hence were diluted out before recovering from the high temperature in the more rapidly multiplying clones. They estimated that if the heat treatment caused a complete but temporary cessation of multiplication of the cytoplasmic elements then their initial number was more than 400. But, if the high temperature caused a reduced multiplication rate, then the number could be much less. Data were not obtained to which the mathematical models of clonal analyses considered above (Section III) could be applied and no way of deciding between these alternatives is possible.

Lyman et al.[385] reported a similar study in which ultraviolet light was used to inactivate the ability of both light and dark grown Euglena to produce chloroplasts. Inactivation kinetics indicated a "30-hit" curve for both light and dark grown cells, the light grown cells being more resistant. These results suggest that there are 30 genetic units which must be inactivated to permanently bleach *Euglena*. Since several dozen proplastids or proplastid units have been observed in dark grown cells,[162] they postulated that each of the approximately 10 chloroplasts is formed by the fusion of about three proplastids.

Information of a different kind concerning the number of genetic units involved in bleaching was presented by Schiff et al.[580] Dark grown cells were given sufficient ultraviolet radiation to produce 100 per cent albino colonies in the absence of photoreactivation, and 0 per cent albino colonies after photoreactivation. Now let us assume that the irradiated genetic units, in the absence of light, are unable to divide, but are merely segregated to progeny during further cell division in the dark. Starved non-multiplying cells should remain capable of developing chloroplasts and they do. Multiplying cells should be capable of developing chloroplasts at first and then, as increasing numbers of cells are produced which lack irradiated genetic elements, they should lose their ability to develop chloroplasts and they do. Furthermore, examination of the kinetics of loss of ability to become reactivated should provide a means of estimating the starting number of genetic units. If it is further assumed that cells with less than two photoreactivable entities yield albino cells (an assumption required to make the theoretical and observed reactivation curves have the same shape), the number of genetic units is calculated to be 10 to 12. To reconcile this result with the number of 30 calculated above,[385] they assume aggregation of genetic units. It might be noted, however, that all results are brought into substantial agreement by assuming that dark grown cells have about 10 proplastids, each with 3 to 4 particles (as postulated by Gibor and Granick, Ref. 191). The 30 or so particles would be the units of ultraviolet inactivation and the 10 proplastids would be the units of segregation, which develop into the 10 plastids when exposed to light.

Lyman et al.[385] reported that the ultraviolet action spectrum for bleaching had a peak at 260 millimicrons and a shoulder at 280 millimicrons, suggesting that the genetic unit is nucleoprotein.

The basis for the hereditary changes induced by ultraviolet bleaching has been clearly shown to be cytoplasmic. Gibor and Granick[190] used an ultraviolet microbeam to show that irradiation of the nucleus did not produce bleaching, while irradiation of the cytoplasm did. It should also be noted that many of the other aspects of the induction of bleached lines (such as high frequency of induction) are at variance with what we expect of chromosomal inheritance.

Schiff et al.[581] showed that ultraviolet irradiated dark grown cells exposed to red (non-photoreactivating) light, developed chloroplasts before becoming permanently bleached. Even though the radiation has caused damage which will lead to a loss of the self-reproduction of chloroplast determinants, those determinants may still function to produce chloroplasts from proplastids.

6. THE DNA OF CHLOROPLASTS

A number of workers have obtained evidence suggesting that chloroplasts contain DNA. Although much of the older work is subject to alternative interpretations, (see Ref. 542 for references and discussion), more recent work leaves very little doubt that DNA is present in chloroplasts.[542, 343, 193, 32, 569, 555] Gibor and Izawa,[193] for example, found that isolated chloroplasts could be freed of contaminating nuclear DNA by treating them with DNAse, while chloroplasts and chloroplast DNA were unaffected. The demonstration that chloroplast DNA has a different buoyant density (and, hence, a different base content) from that of nuclear DNA completes the demonstration (see Table 9).

Three or four bands of DNA from *Euglena gracilis* have been found in cesium chloride centrifugation studies. The first is presumed to be nuclear, for it is present in much higher concentration than the others. Its density is 1.707 to 1.708.[147, 529, 148, 530, 72, 353] It has a melting point between 89°C and 92°C,[147, 72] and contains 48 to 51 per cent guanine plus cytosine [529, 147), 148] and approximately 2 per cent 5-methyl cytosine.[72, 529]

The other bands of DNA from *Euglena* are "satellite" bands and represent only a small fraction of the total. The chloroplast DNA has a density of 1.684 to 1.686.[72, 353, 529, 530, 148] The evidence which indicates that it is associated with chloroplasts is, first, its high concentration in cell fractions rich in chloroplasts,[147] and second, the fact that it is absent in chloroplast-free mutants.[148, 353, 530] It shows the characteristic changes in density and optical density when heat denatured which indicate that it is double stranded.[147, 148, 529] It has a melting temperature of 78° to 82°C, [147, 72] and it contains about 26 to 28 per cent guanine plus cytosine and no detectable 5-methyl cytosine.[147, 148, 72] Chloroplast DNA is estimated at some 2 to 4 per cent of the total DNA.[72] The DNA which can be isolated from a single chloroplast of *Euglena* is about 10^{-14} g according to Brawerman and Eisenstadt[72] and 1.2×10^{-16} g according to Edelman *et al.*[147] Gibor and Izawa[193] give 10^{-16} g per plastid in *Acetabularia* and Gibor and Granick[192] estimate 10^{-15} to 10^{-16} g DNA per plastid in higher plants. By way of reference, 10^{-16} g of DNA is sufficient to code some 100 proteins of molecular weight 30,000; the coliphages contain about 2×10^{-16} g DNA per phage. The molecular weight of chloroplast DNA is some 20 to 40×10^6. It has also been noted[72] that the RNA base content of ribosome-like bodies of chloroplasts is very similar to the base content of chloroplast DNA, suggesting that chloroplast RNA is coded by chloroplast DNA.

One other satellite band of density 1.690 to 1.692[148, 72, 530] has been found in *Euglena*; it may be mitochondrial. Still another band of unknown origin with a density 1.694 may be present in chloroplast-free mutants.[530]

The density of the main DNA of *Chlamydomonas* (presumably nuclear) has been estimated as 1.723,[102] 1.726 (computed from base composition by Sager and Ishida, see Ref. 569), and 1.728.[685] Analysis shows 62 per cent cytosine plus guanine.[569] Satellite DNA is double stranded with a density of 1.695[102] or 1.702 (computed from base composition by Sager and Ishida[569]). Its guanine plus cytosine content is 39 per cent.[569] The satellite represents about 1 to 5 per cent[102, 569] of the total extractable cellular DNA or 10^{-14} g per chloroplast.[569] It is shown to be associated with isolated chloroplasts.[569] Evidence has also been obtained indicating that chloroplasts contain the necessary enzymatic machinery for DNA primed RNA synthesis and protein synthesis.[343, 152, 584]

7. DO CHLOROPLASTS HAVE GENETIC CONTINUITY?

The first of a number of arguments concerning this question is that chloroplasts may be observed directly to reproduce by division in many algae (see, for example, Ref. 216). The argument is particularly credible in algal cells which have only one chloroplast. In most cases, however, occasional *de novo* origin as well is not ruled out. The ability of most chloroplasts to exist in the minute proplastid state and even to be formed exclusively from proplastids, as in higher plants, makes the elimination of *de novo* origin on cytological grounds virtually impossible. It should also be noted that even if chloroplasts and proplastids arise exclusively by division, the proportion of their characteristics determined by genetic elements within rather than outside themselves is still not specified. Nevertheless, the observation that chloroplasts may be seen to divide does constitute a strong argument in favor of genetic continuity.

A second argument, and in the writer's opinion, potentially the best, is the observation that the number of genetic units determining proplastid or plastid existence is equal to the number of observable cytological units. The best cases are the estimates in *Euglena* of 30 ultraviolet inactivable genetic units[385] and 10 genetic segregational units capable of light reactivation[580] which correspond to 30 observable proplastids and 10 developing chloroplasts. A second example, in the higher plant *Epilobium*, was studied by Michaelis.[412] He concluded from the patterns of segregation of white cells in leaves that there were two sorts of cytoplasmic genetic segregational units. One was judged to correspond to the number of plastids. The other type was much more numerous and was, therefore, assumed to lie in a nonchloroplast cytoplasmic genetic system. The chief difficulty with this approach, however, is the great difficulty in obtaining accurate independent cytological and genetic estimates of the number of units involved. These difficulties are reflected in the conflicting data and *ad hoc* assumptions reviewed above for *Euglena*. (See also the discussion at the beginning of Section VIII.)

A third argument is that the occurrence of single cells which contain more than one kind of chloroplast indicates that chloroplasts must have genetic properties.[715] Generally, the argument lacks force, for it is easy to imagine that a specific intracellular environment (determined by the interaction of environmental, cytoplasmic, and nuclear elements) could provide conditions near a threshold which might cause some plastids to develop in one way, others in another. Nevertheless, strong evidence is provided by the work of Woods and DuBuy (see Ref. 539 for a review) who observed microscopically as many as four plastid types in a single cell of *Nepeta*, and by the work of Stubbe (see Ref. 105 for a review) who found three microscopically distinct types in a single cell of *Oenothera*. It might also be noted that the failure to find cells with more than one plastid type in chimeras likewise does not provide evidence that plastids are not self-producing. For it is entirely possible that in a mixed population of plastids, substances may diffuse from one mutant type to the other, causing all to be alike.

Fourth, it is frequently argued that because chloroplast characters are inherited cytoplasmically, the units of cytoplasmic inheritance responsible for chloroplasts must lie within the chloroplasts themselves. This, of course, need not be the case; the units may be localized in the cytoplasm outside the chloroplast.

Fifth, the argument that chloroplast mutation occurs more frequently than nuclear gene mutations and is caused by different mutagens indicates only that we are dealing with non-chromosomal mutations; it does not show that the mutations lie within the chloroplast.

Sixth, the existence of DNA with a unique base composition in chloroplasts provides very strong evidence that chloroplasts have genetic properties. As far as we know, pre-existing DNA always serves as the determinant for the bases in newly formed DNA. The recent report by Chiang *et al.*[101] that chloroplast DNA is replicated semiconservatively supports this view. Nevertheless we must still reckon with the possibility that chloroplast DNA is synthesized in the nucleus.

Of particular interest are the reports[353, 148, 530] that bleached *Euglena* mutants, unlike light or dark grown *Euglena*, have no chloroplast (or proplastid) DNA while others[190, 192, 422] report that bleached *Euglena* mutants do have proplastids. Note, also, the report by Lang[351] which indicates that *Polytoma* (a colorless relative of *Chlamydomonas*) has plastids visible in the electron microscope. Perhaps some mutants have proplastids and others do not.Otherwise, we must assume that the proplastids which are free of DNA have an unknown genetic basis which could be either nuclear or cytoplasmic. The only evidence which might support a genetic mechanism within DNA-free proplastids is the possibility that they are visibly self-duplicating; but satisfactory evidence of this kind has not been obtained. And it is not clear that proplastid-free strains exist. Hence, there is no more reason to believe that DNA-free proplastids determine their own properties than do any other cellular organelle. It is quite possible that their entire structure is determined by the nucleus.

If the proplastids of bleached strains are free of DNA, since they are morphologically similar to the proplastids of dark-grown *Euglena*, then it may be that chloroplast DNA is inactive when in the wild type dark-grown proplastids. One of the effects of light on *Euglena*, then, would be to control the state of activity of proplastid and chloroplast DNA.

D. Kinetoplasts

In trypanosomes and relatives a large body below the flagellar kinetosome or basal body is variously known as the kinetoplast, the blepharoplast, the kinetonucleus, and the parabasal body. Electron microscope studies show its similarity to a mitochondrion.[683, 551] When *Leishmania donovani* is in its leishmania form within the cells of its vertebrate host, the kinetoplast is relatively small.[707] The leishmania form has high lactate dehydrogenase activity and lacks cytochrome.[348] On infecting an insect host a number of changes in morphology and physiology occur, and it transforms into its leptomonad or extracellular form. Lactic dehydrogenase content goes down, cytochrome appears and the kinetoplast enlarges and develops cristae. Changes in hosts during the life cycle of *Trypanosoma* also produce changes in the kinetoplast and in the respiratory and other physiological properties of the parasites.[707, 716]

Kinetoplasts contain DNA, as shown by the Feulgen and other stains and by uptake of tritiated thymidine. For a bibliography see Ref. 707. The DNA of the kinetoplast represents some 10 per cent of the total cell DNA according to Simpson.[607] In *L. enrietti* kinetoplast DNA was obtained pure by treating osmotically shocked cells with DNAse. This procedure destroyed the nucleus and nuclear DNA without harming the kinetoplast. The kinetoplast DNA was found by duBuy et al.[139] to have a buoyant density of 1.699, that of the nucleus being 1.721. In *L. tarentolae* Simpson[607] found a major band of DNA (presumably nuclear) with a density of 1.716 and a minor band (representing 10 per cent of the major, hence, presumably kinetoplast) with a density of 1.703.

At least one species of trypanosomes is free of kinetoplasts and dyskineto-plastic forms arise spontaneously in many. The appearance of dyskineto-plastic forms during treatment of the mammalian hosts with drugs such as *p*-rosaniline and acriflavin has been known for many years.[721, 285, 495, 260] The production of kinetoplast-free flagellates has been obtained *in vitro* by Robertson,[544] Mühlpfordt[433, 434] and Trager and Rudzinska.[708] Dyskinetoplastic forms are often non-viable or, at least, greatly altered in their ability to infect different hosts. Electron microscopy shows that kinetoplasts in dyskinetoplastic forms appear to lack DNA, yet still retain much of their structure.[434, 708] The case is remarkably similar to that of the DNA-free proplastids of Euglena (see above).

The response of the kinetoplasts of *T. gambiense* and *T. evansi* to *p*-rosaniline is of particular interest because of the claims by Inoki and co-workers (see Section IV) that resistance to *p*-rosaniline-induced kinetoplast loss is subject to DNA-mediated transformation in those species. They report that when *T. gambiense* (Welcome strain) is cultured in mice a few (less than 1 per cent) of the individuals are found to lack kinetoplasts. However, dyskinetoplastic strains of *T. gambiense* cannot be established.[260]

If p-rosaniline is injected into mice after injection of *T. gambiense*, the frequency of dyskinetoplastic forms increases to around 15 to 20 per cent. Inoki[260] presents three lines of evidence which indicate that in *T. gambiense* the increase is due to induction, and not to selection of the dyskinetoplastic forms already present. First, dyskinetoplastic clones cannot be established from isolations and no dividing forms containing two nuclei and no kinetoplast can be observed, i.e., dyskinetoplastic forms cannot reproduce. Second, during dye treatment, increase in dyskinetoplastic forms occurs simultaneously with increase in forms bearing two kinetoplasts—hence, misdivision is thought to be at least partly responsible for the origin of dyskinetoplastic forms. The number of forms with two kinetoplasts decreases as dye treatment continues, indicating that kinetoplast division is inhibited.[265]

T. evansi (Taiwan strain) also produces dyskinetoplastic forms, but unlike *T. gambiense*, it can give rise to pure dyskinetoplastic strains.[270] Dyskinetoplastic forms are usually found in a spontaneous frequency of about 5 per cent in *T. evansi*, and Inoki states that care must be observed in making passages in order to prevent the complete loss of the kinetoplast from the stock. p-rosaniline injected into mice after injection of *T. evansi* also yields high frequencies of dyskinetoplastic forms.[270] It is probable (see Inoki et al.[270]) that in *T. evansi* selection is the primary mechanism of increase of dyskinoplastic forms and not induction as in *T. gambiense*.

The kinetoplast has long been known to be a visibly self-duplicating body[252, 716] and has been assumed to have genetic continuity. The observed self-duplication of the kinetoplast, the apparent induction by drugs of dyskinetoplastic strains in high frequency, and the presence of DNA support the argument that the kinetoplast is a genetic structure.

E. Mitochondria

Mitochondria have been considered visibly self-reproducing for many years (see, for example, discussion by Guillermond[220]). On the other hand, there have been numerous reports of *de novo* origin. Speculations that mitochondria have genetic continuity have been supported by the existence of cytoplasmic mutants in yeast[160, 161] and *Neurospora* (see Ref. 717) which show modifications in the cytochromes and other enzymes of mitochondria. Two new kinds of evidence have recently provided strong evidence that mitochondria are self-reproducing: the presence of DNA in mitochondria and the random distribution of radioactive label to new mitochondria reproducing in unlabelled medium.

DNA in mitochondria from chick fibroblasts was demonstrated by Chèvremont et al.[100] Nass and coworkers[462, 465] and Swift and collaborators [691, 692, 693, 344] on the basis of electron microscopy have reported the presence of DNA fibers in mitochondria from a number of different organisms. DNA in the mitochondria of *Tetrahymena* has been demonstrated autoradiographically by Parsons[488, 489] and by Stone and Miller.

7a   RP III

TABLE 9. DNA DENSITIES

	Nucleus	Mitochondria	Chloroplast	Kinetoplast
Paramecium aurelia Syngen 4, stock 51	1.688–1.689 (689, 612)	1.702 (689)		
Tetrahymena pyriformis, Strain ST	1.688 (689)	1.682 (689)		
Tetrahymena pyriformis, Strain GL	1.688 (686)	1.684 (686)		
Tetrahymena pyriformis, Syngen 4, stock UM 981	1.692 (686)	1.686 (686)		
Tetrahymena pyriformis, Syngen 9, stock TC	1.690 (686)	1.684 (686)		
Chlamydomonas reinhardi	1.723 (102) 1.726 (569) 1.728 (685)		1.702 (569) 1.695 (102)	
Leishmania enrietti	1.721 (139)			1.699 (139)
Leishmania tarentolae	1.716 (607)			1.703 (607)
Euglena, gracilis	1.707–1.708 (147, 148, 529, 530, 72, 353)	1.690–1.692 (148, 72, 530)	1.684–1.686 (72, 529, 530, 147, 148, 353)	
Chick	1.698 (692, 523)	1.707 (523)		
Rat	1.698 (687)	1.698 (687)		
Neurospora crassa	1.712–1.713 (382, 690, 381)	1.701 (382)		
Yeast	1.700 (703)	1.685 (703)		
Phaseolus aureus	1.691 (688)	1.706 (688)		
Swiss chard	1.689 (344)	1.705 (692)	1.700 (344)	
Brassica rapa	1.692 1.700 (satellite) (688)	1.706 (688)	1.695 (688)	
Ipomoea batatas	1.692 (688)	1.706 (688)		

The finding that the DNA from mitochondria may be isolated and that it generally has a buoyant density different from that of nuclear and chloroplast DNA completes the picture. Determinations have been made on a number of organisms (see Table 9). The DNA is double stranded and of high molecular weight. Luck[381] reports a maximum molecular weight of 13×10^6 for purified DNA in *Neurospora* and Suyama[686] finds a maximum molecular weight of 42×10^6 for purified DNA in *Tetrahymena*. Although fragmentation is always a possibility, the fact that crude DNA from carefully lysed mitochondria shows the same molecular weight has led Suyama to suggest, as a working hypothesis, that this is the size of the native double strand. One double strand would, therefore, have a weight of 0.7×10^{-16} g. Densities differ in different organisms. They may be similar to nuclear DNA or occasionally quite different. Suyama and Preer[689] measured the amount of DNA extractable from the mitochondria of *Tetrahymena* and found it to be 3.7×10^{-16} g per mitochondrion. They estimated that the amount in *Paramecium* and *Phaseolus aureus* is similar. Nass et al.[465] found that 1×10^{-16} g of DNA per mitochondrion could be extracted from isolated mitochondria of the rat. Tewari et al.[703] estimated 1×10^{-16} g in yeast mitochondria. Taking Suyama's molecular weight and amount of DNA per mitochondrion, some five double strands should be present, each about one-third as large as the amount of DNA in bacteriophage T-2.

Evidence has also been obtained by Luck[381] which indicates that mitochondria have a DNA dependent RNA polymerase, see also Kalf[298]and Wintersberger.[735] Perhaps the first convincing evidence that mitochondria are self-reproducing was provided by Luck in 1963.[380] He labelled the mitochondria of *Neurospora* with radioactive choline and showed that in subsequent growth in non-radioactive medium, label was distributed uniformly among all mitochondria. Confirmation is found in the distribution of labelled mitochondria of different densities.[381] Recently, a very beautiful study of mitochondria in *Tetrahymena* was carried out by Parsons[488,489] using pulse-labelling with tritiated thymidine. Mitochondria became labelled at any stage of the cell cycle (unlike nuclei). Furthermore, the label was distributed uniformly to all mitochondria during four generations in unlabelled medium. Parson's experiments provide excellent evidence that mitochondrial DNA is synthesized in the mitochondria rather than in the nucleus.

Finally, the evidence for considering the kinetoplast of trypanosomes a self-reproducing structure also applies here, for it is clear that the kinetoplast is a specialized mitochondrion, as pointed out above.

F. Non-chromosomal Elements of Heredity in Chlamydomonas

Two patterns of non-Mendelian inheritance in *Chlamydomonas* have been studied by Sager and coworkers in *C. reinhardi*. The first pattern consists of non-mappable factors which always show segregation at the first meiotic division to yield 2 : 2 tetrads. It is shown by the y_1 mutants.[557, 561, 574]

7a*

Wild type *C. reinhardi* cultured in the dark are green. y_1 mutants are yellow when cultured in the dark but become green in the light. Crosses between wild type and y_1 mutants segregate two green and two yellow clones from each tetrad, and it can be deduced (see section on tetrad analysis above) that segregation is always at the first meiotic division. They are not linked to any of the sixteen known linkage groups.[561, 229] They could be very close to the centromere on an unknown linkage group, but this possibility becomes steadily less likely as *C.reinhardi* becomes better known genetically.

y_1 mutants arise spontaneously; the proportion of y_1 mutants in wild type strains is commonly around 10^{-3} to 10^{-4}. Growth of streptomycin-resistant clones (sr-500, to be discussed presently) on streptomycin-containing agar yields high proportions of y_1 mutants. Although the time of appearance of the mutants varies considerably, in general long periods of growth in contact with streptomycin are required for the appearance of most of the mutants. For this reason the hypothesis of selection of spontaneous mutants cannot be rigorously tested by experiments such as the Luria and Delbruck[383] fluctuation test. Such tests are also complicated by the presence of spontaneous mutants. However, the low mortality and very high frequency of new y_1 mutants leaves little doubt that true induction occurs. The induced mutants are often unstable and can give rise to both stable and unstable clones. Different y_1 clones may also differ in their growth rate and in other characteristics.

Because of their peculiar pattern of inheritance and susceptibility to induction by streptomycin (a known inducer of non-chromosomal mutations— see below), Sager concludes that y_1 mutants are non-chromosomal. She also[561] notes that their pattern of inheritance can be accounted for if they are determined by a structure of which there is only one per cell, which segregates at the first meiotic division, and which divides at subsequent cell divisions. That structure could be the chloroplast but some unknown unit structure is not ruled out.

The second kind of non-chromosomal inheritance in *C. reinhardi* yields 0 : 4 or 4 : 0 tetrads. It has been extensively studied by Sager and others.[556, 558, 559, 562–567, 570, 571, 573, 574, 202, 203, 203a] It was first encountered in a study of streptomycin mutants. Wild type is sensitive to streptomycin (ss). Sr-100 (originally designated ss-1) can multiply in 100 micrograms of streptomycin per milliliter; sr-500 (originally called sr-2) is resistant to 500 micrograms per milliliter; and sr-1500 is resistant to 1500 micrograms per milliliter. In addition, a streptomycin dependent mutant, sd, grows optimally in 100 micrograms per milliliter. Sr-100 turns out to be determined by a simple Mendelian factor about 15 units from the centromere in linkage group IX.[573] The inheritance of sr-500 is characteristic of all the non-chromosomal mutants except y_1. In a cross of sr-500 by ss, all the clones are sr-500 if the plus mating type parent was sr-500 and the minus, ss. But if the plus parent was ss and the minus sr-500, all clones derived from the meiotic products are ss (with rare exceptions to be discussed presently). In other words, progeny are always like the plus mating type parent. Sd behaves in the same way when crossed to ss.[573] Sd ss zygotes will not germinate without streptomycin, so sd shows zygotic dominance. Sr-1500 follows the same pattern of inheritance as sr-500 and sd. It is known only in the minus mating type and is not transmitted to the progeny after crossing it with ss or sr-100 plus mating type gametes.[573] The mutant gene A (amplifier) has no apparent effect in ss, but very markedly increases the streptomycin resistance of sr-100, sr-500, and sd. Sr-500 A can withstand more than 2 milligrams per milliliter of streptomycin.

The explanation for the peculiar unilateral transmission is unknown. It clearly means non-chromosomal inheritance, however. Evidently, certain elements in the minus mating type do not contribute to the zygote in spite of the apparently equal participation of both types in mating. This conclusion is, perhaps, somewhat less surprising if it is recalled that in some species of *Chlamydomonas* the two mating types are markedly different in size, and hence contribute unequally to the zygote.

Sr-500 mutants have not arisen spontaneously. They are induced by growth in streptomycin-containing medium. This conclusion is supported by the Luria and Delbruck[383] fluctuation test and the Newcombe respreading test.[562, 204] It is significant that the same tests indicated that the sr-100 gene mutations arise by selection of pre-existing mutants, not by induction. Transient resistance to streptomycin was induced in some 5 per cent of the cells exposed for a short time to 500 micrograms per milliliter of streptomycin.[562] Such phenocopies could multiply for some 13 to 19 doublings longer than normal wild type in 300 micrograms per milliliter.

Sager has found that streptomycin induces not only y_1 yellow mutants and streptomycin mutants, but also numerous other types of non-chromosomal mutants.[562, 564, 567] These include green acetate-requiring strains, leaky acetate-requiring strains some of which can grow on yeast extract, auxotrophs which can grow only on yeast extract, and lethals. Gillham[203] has also found non-chromosomal neamine-resistant and neamine-requiring mutants. Two of the acetate mutants which have been studied extensively are ac_1 which is a leaky acetate mutant and ac_2 which has an absolute acetate requirement. The technique of induction is to culture sr-500 mutants on complete streptomycin-containing agar (the same conditions used to obtain y_1 mutants) and screen the treated colonies for altered phenotypes. A sample of some 20 of these mutants when crossed to wild type all showed the same pattern of inheritance characteristic of sr-500; i.e., $0:4$ or $4:0$ tetrads in reciprocal crosses.[564] Gillham[203] reports that nitrosoguanidine will induce both chromosomal and non-chromosomal mutations.

Exceptional zygotes, in which a trait borne by the minus mating type is transmitted, are occasionally produced.[202, 570, 564] For example, in a cross of sd mt^+ x ss mt^- on streptomycin-free agar at 25°C, about 0.1 per cent ss clones can be found. Similarly, in the reciprocal cross ss mt^+ x sd mt^- on streptomycin-containing agar, exceptional sd clones are found. If zygotes are placed at 37°C, the percentage of exceptional zygotes obtained rises to about 1 per cent. Such clones are found to segregate both parental types at later vegetative fissions. If crosses involving two non-chromosomal determinants are made[570, 572, 564] (for example, sd ac^+ mt^+ x ss ac^- mt^- on streptomycin-free acetate-containing agar), exceptional clones are obtained which later show vegetative segregation for both pairs of non-chromosomal factors (sd and ss; ac^+ and ac^-). All combinations appeared in crosses involving ss, sd, sr, ac_1, ac_2, and ac^+. In unselected crosses ac_1 and ac_2 segregated 1 : 1 as did the sd and sr pair. Segregation continues through a number of fissions after meiosis and may occur earlier for some pairs of characters than for others.

In exceptional clones from a cross of sd x sr, rare ss segregants were obtained. They behaved like normal ss lines in further crosses and apparently arise by recombination between sd and sr determinants.[572] Similar ac^+ lines were obtained from crossing ac_1 and ac_2. Furthermore, in the same cross, *in lines producing* ac^+, the reciprocal type $ac_1 - ac_2$, which could recombine with neither parent, was also found. Other lines which appear to represent a number of different recombinants between sd and sr were obtained.

The fact that the recombinants between sd and sr occur in very low frequency of course suggests that they are linked (probably within a single functional unit). Gillham[203, 203a] also finds low recombinant frequencies in both coupling and repulsion in crosses involving differences in resistance to neamine (also non-chromosomally determined) and streptomycin, indicating that the determinants of these characters are linked with each other. (The apparent degree of linkage, however, is different in coupling and in repulsion). On the other hand, in crosses of ss ac^- x sd ac^+ the four combinations (ss ac^-, ss ac^+, sd ac^-, and sd ac^+) segregate in exceptional clones in approximately equal frequencies[570]—so streptomycin and the ac determinants are not linked.

Thus, recombination within as well as between different pairs of non-chromosomal genes can occur. Furthermore, the results may be interpreted to mean linkage as well as independent assortment between different markers. Sager[566] argues that this finding suggests recombination between portions of nucleic acid molecules; but the chemical basis and cellular localization of the determinants is still unknown.

G. The "Mo" Element in Paramecium

Numerous cases of abortive cytokinesis in *Paramecium* have been described (see Ref. 731 for a review). Animals fail to separate completely at binary fission and the two daughters remain attached end to end. Additional abortive divisions produce chains of cells and other abnormal forms. Normal single forms may be cut off from such chains, but the aggregate itself is unable to reproduce. Maly[394-398] has studied two such abnormal strains of stock 51 of syngen 4 of *P. aurelia*. One is called "snaky", the other, "monster". The phenotypes of these two strains are practically identical.

"Snaky" was first discovered and analyzed by Sonneborn (unpublished) and later by Maly.[394] The trait is due to a single recessive gene, *sn*, with variable penetrance and expressivity.

The inheritance of the "monster" or "mo" characteristic[394] is more complex. Crosses between mo and normals gave F-1 clones which varied markedly in respect to the character. Occasionally the individual exconjugants from a single pair maintained the same characteristics which they had before conjugation, indicating cytoplasmic inheritance (the possibility of cytogamy was eliminated by a gene marker). More often, exconjugants were alike, sometimes showing a high frequency of monster formation, sometimes low. Autogamy in all F-1 clones, however, invariably led to the production of both mo and normal clones in F-2 by autogamy. In most cases, 1 : 1 F-2 segregations were obtained, but in others there was a marked excess of either normal or of mo clones. To explain these results, Maly suggested that the mo strain is homozygous for the recessive gene *ds* which induces a cytoplasmic factor to mutate to a mo-determining form, and that the cytoplasmic factor may or may not be transferred at conjugation. When it is not, no immediate change is seen and exconjugants are like the parents for a period. When it is transferred exconjugants are alike. Maly found that it is sometimes transferred independently of kappa. Deviations from 1 : 1 ratios were explained by *dsds* lines whose cytoplasmic determinants have not yet mutated and by *DsDs* lines which contain the mutant autonomous cytoplasmic element. Elimination of the autonomous cytoplasmic factor from *DsDs* lines often occurs spontaneously and could be eliminated by selection for normals. Thus, in a group of F-2 lines which gave an excess of monster forming clones, selection for normals gave a number of clones from which monsters could not be permanently eliminated (presumably *dsds*) and other clones from which monster formation could be permanently eliminated (presumably *DsDs*). The susceptibility of the original mo strain (*dsds*) to selection for monster-forming ability is ascribed to changes in concentration of mo-determining cytoplasmic elements. Maly notes the similarity between the *ds* gene hypothesized here and the *iojap* gene of Rhoades[538] which induces a cytoplasmic chloroplast-determining element to mutate in maize.

The expression of the mo and snaky characters may be repressed by low oxygen tension, by carbon monoxide (reversible by light), and 2,4-dinitrophenol.[395] It is enhanced under certain conditions by iodoacetic acid. Maly concludes that the character is due to an oxygen sensitive step in glycolysis in the mutant. It has also been found[396] that EDTA increases monster formation in the mo and snaky strains. The effect is reversed by ferrous and cobalt ions, which are also able to normalize the two strains in the absence of EDTA. Because the activity of aldolase is inhibited by EDTA and reversed by ferrous and cobalt ions in a similar fashion, Maly suggests that aldolase in the two mutant strains is defective. In support of this hypothesis he finds[397] that the reaction products of aldolase, triose phophates, aid in normal separations in the snaky strain. Fructose 1,6-diphosphate, the substrate of aldolase, was ineffective as expected. Furthermore, Maly[398] has more recently reported that the aldolase activity of crude extracts of snaky animals cultured under aeration is only one-half to one-tenth that of snaky grown in unaerated cultures. No effect of aeration on the aldolase activity of wild type was found. And finally, the aldolase of wild type and of snaky apparently may be distinguished on DEAE-Sephadex columns.[398] Nothing is known of the physical basis of the postulated cytoplasmic factor.

H. Cytoplasmic Inheritance in Amoeba

Variations in the shelled amebas, *Difflugia*, *Arcella*, and *Centropyxis* were studied by earlier workers. All of this work has been reviewed in some detail by Jennings.[275] Differences in shell form were often encountered and could be made greater by selection under appropriate conditions. Differences tended to disappear when selection was relaxed, but under some circumstances persisted for many generations. Genetic analysis suffered from the lack of mating processes in these forms, and in most instances we know nothing of the mechanisms involved.

One exception is that of the number of teeth surrounding the mouth in *Difflugia*, studied by Jennings[276] Variations in the number of teeth sometimes occurred and were inherited. Furhermore, damage to the teeth brought about by micropmanipulation, generally led to inherited abnormalities. Jennings explained this phenomenon by assuming a direct role of the old mouth in the formation of the new. When *Difflugia* undergoes division, one of the daughters extends from the old shell and secretes a new shell while in close juxtaposition to the old. Thus, the teeth in the old mouth appear to provide a template for the new.

Danielli, Judin, and others have studied inheritance in *Amoeba* by transferring nuclei from one ameba to an enucleated ameba by micromanipulation.[376, 377, 118, 115, 116, 117, 232, 231, 230, 296, 109] In this way the relative contributions of nucleus and cytoplasm may be assessed. The work has so far been restricted to strains of *Amoeba proteus* and *A. discoides*. One of the major obstacles encountered in the work is the difficulty in obtaining clearcut character differences. Results are summarized in Table 10.

It is found that in nuclear-cytoplasmic "hybrids" between two strains many of the characters always correspond to the strain from which the nucleus was taken: ethyl alcohol resistance, methionine resistance, development of resistance to antiserum, and quantity of free α-alanine. In these cases there is no evidence of cytoplasmic control. Nuclear diameter, on the other hand, follows the cytoplasm almost exclusively in the "hybrids" between *A. proteus* (large nucleus) and *A. discoides* (small nucleus), the amebas with *A. proteus* nucleus and *A. discoides* cytoplasm having small nuclei, and the reciprocal hybrids (*A. discoides* nucleus and *A. proteus* cytoplsm) having large nuclei. Differences between *A. proteus* and *A. discoides* in pseudopod form and overall cell shape are found by Danielli and coworkers to be intermediate in hybrids and, hence, must be controlled partly by nuclear and partly by cytoplasmic elements. However, somewhat similar differences between different strains of *A. proteus* according to Judin[296] are due to nucleus alone.

TABLE 10. DIFFERENCES IN AMOEBA STUDIED BY NUCLEAR TRANSPLANTATION

Character	Strains	Inheritance	Reference
Pseudopod form	*A. proteus*	Nuclear	296
Ethyl alcohol resistance	*A. proteus*	Nuclear	296
Methionine resistance	*A. proteus*	Nuclear	296
Ability to survive isolation	*A. proteus*	Nuclear	296
Nuclear diameter	*A. proteus* vs *A. discoides*	Mainly cytoplasmic, partly nuclear	376 377
General shape and pseudopod form	*A. protweus* vs *A.* discoides	Mainly cytoplasmic, partly nuclear	376 377
General shape in antiserum	*A. proteus* vs *A. discoides*	Partly cytoplasmic, partly nuclear	116
Development of resistance to antiserum	*A. proteus* vs *A. discoides*	Nuclear	116
Amount of free α-alanine	*A.proteus*, strain Z vs strain T4	Nuclear	232
Streptomycin sensitivity	*A. proteus* and *A. proteus vs A. discoides*	Cytoplasmic and Nuclear	109

Attempts to confirm the work on nuclear size have been undertaken by simply transferring cytoplasm by microinjection from one species to the other.[231, 230] Injections of *A. discoides* (small nucleus) cytoplasm into *A. proteus* (large nucleus) yields small nuclei; the injected *A. discoides* cytoplasm, amounting to about 6 to 10 per cent of the whole protoplasm, is able to exert its effect in spite of the presence of the full complement of *A. proteus* cytoplasm and nucleus. Hawkins *et al.*[231] also report the very surprising and unexplained result of the reciprocal cytoplasmic transfer, *A. proteus* cytoplasm (6 to 10 per cent) into *A. discoides*. In this case, the small amount of *A. proteus* cytoplasm in *A. discoides* yields the large nuclear size characteristic of *A. proteus*.

Streptomycin resistance is found[109] to have an unusual behavior in "hybrids". *A. proteus* strain T-1 is classed as "sensitive", strain D as "moderately resistant", and strain Z is "resistant". *A. discoides* strain T-1 is also resistant. Interstrain "hybrids" within *A. proteus* are all sensitive. Since the hybrids have the characteristic of the nuclear "parents" in some instances and the characteristic of the cytoplasmic in others, both cytoplasmic and nuclear control is postulated. All hybrids between resistant *A. discoides* and less resistant strains of *A. proteus* tend to be somewhat intermediate but more like the resistant parent. Here, too, both cytoplasmic and nuclear factors are postulated. Studies on uptake of streptomycin suggest that *A. discoides* (unlike resistant strains of *A. proteus*) owes its greater resistance to a reduced permeability to streptomycin.

The basis for these cytoplasmically determined differences is unknown. Danielli has suggested that the role of the cytoplasm here is to provide structural templates for the synthesis of new structures. It might be noted, however, that *Amoeba proteus* contains DNA-bearing particles which have been called symbionts.[548] It would be of interest to study the cytoplasmic differences in particle-free strains if they can be obtained. It might also be noted that Nanney[451] has pointed out that the method of nuclear transfer does not make it possible to distinguish between cytoplasmic inheritance and cytoplasmic action in inducing long-lasting nuclear-changes.

I. The Ciliate Cortex

Certain elements of the ciliate cortex such as the gullet[224, 226] and the kinetosomes (basal bodies)[384] have long been thought to have genetic properties. We will see in this section that the complex pattern of structures in the cortex plays a major role in determining new patterns during cell reproduction. Modifications in the pre-existing pattern lead to modifications in the newly forming patterns. The assumption that individual structures such as kinetosomes or individual molecules such as DNA are self-reproducing is inadequate to describe the results. The ordering or arranging of new structures under the influence of the old, Sonneborn calls "cytotaxis".[652] The process is called "macrocrystallinity" by Weiss[720] and "patterned growth" by Sager.[567] No attempt is made here to give a balanced review of the morphological, developmental, and genetic factors involved in the subject of the ciliate cortex. The techniques of the experimental cytologist have for many years proved most powerful in attacking these problems and the reader is referred to Chapter I, "Morphogenesis in Protozoa", by Vance Tartar in volume II of this series for a review of this work. The reader is also referred to Tartar's book on *Stentor*[698] and Hanson's paper on oral structures in *Paramecium*.[226] Many of the older related papers were reviewed by Sonneborn in a paper[650] on the genetics of the cortex. Here we will be concerned primarily with a series of recent papers by Sonneborn and his collaborators[657–661, 650, 652, 733, 54, 53, 123, 124, 125] in which are described a number of beautiful experiments on the genetics of the cortex in *Paramecium*.

It might also be noted that *Paramecium* is somewhat aberrant among ciliates in its rather low capacity to readjust its surface organelles toward the normal pattern after damage. On the other hand, it is just this property which makes it particularly appropriate for the application of genetic techniques.

In the material which follows we will consider first the normal cortical morphology in *Paramecium*, next the properties of a number of cortical mutants and finally, the general principles which can be drawn.

Sonneborn[650] defines the cortex in *P. aurelia* as the outer one or two microns of the cell consisting of the outermost membranes and the gelated ectoplasm. It contains repeating cortical unit structures. See Ehret and Powers[151] for a review of the cortex of *P. aurelia*. Each cortical unit consists of one or two kinetosomes with associated cilium and kinetodesmal fiber, a parasomal sac, and membranes. Kinetodesmal fibers run anteriorly and to the right of the kinetosomes; the parasomal sac is also located to the right of the kinetosomes. ("Right" is clockwise to the observer when he looks at the anterior end of the ciliate in polar view.)

The recent studies of Dippell[133, 134] lead to the conclusion that increase in cortical units is accomplished by the appearance of new kinetosomes, cilia, and parasomal sac at definite positions within an old cortical unit, followed by partitioning of the old unit to yield two or more new units. It had been formerly thought by Ehret and deHaller[149] that new cortical units originate internally and are interpolated between the old units.

Rows of cortical units, called kineties, make up the cortex. A trichocyst tip is inserted in the cortex at the anterior and posterior junctions between cortical units. Six fields of kineties may be defined: dorsal, anterior left, anterior right, posterior left, posterior right, and circumoral (or vestibular). See Sonneborn[650] and Beisson and Sonneborn.[53]

The left and right fields of kineties on the ventral surface are collectively known as the oral segment, and they meet on a midventral line or suture. The suture is separated into anterior and posterior segments by the circumoral region and gullet. The cytopyge or anal opening is on the posterior suture. The two contractile vacuole openings lie on a meridian in the dorsal field of kineties. The complex gullet, or cytopharynx, includes: a dorsal wall, consisting of the quadrulus (four kineties or rows of kineties); a left wall, consisting of a dorsal and ventral peniculus (four rows each); a right wall consisting of an outer endoral kinety, and an interior group of modified kineties called the ribbed wall.

A number of cortical mutants (defining "mutant" as a form which is hereditarily different from wild type) have been reported. The first of these is the double animal or doublet. Doubles have been known for many years and in many ciliates, such as *Glaucoma, Colpidium, Leucophrys, Stentor*, and others. Sonneborn[650] gives a review. Doubles may arise at conjugation by failure of cells to separate. The presence of antiserum during conjugation makes it easy to induce doubles in *Paramecium*.[635] Doubles in *P. aurelia* as described by Sonneborn[650] have two complete sets of fields and associated structures. Ventral and dorsal areas lie 90° apart, each pair of homologous areas 180° apart. Although doubles sometimes segregate singles, they may be maintained indefinitely with selection. Sonneborn and Dippell[657] showed by crossing singles and doubles, marked with suitable genic and cytoplasmic markers, with and without cytoplasmic exchange, that neither the fluid cytoplasm nor genes are responsible for the difference between singles and doubles. Furthermore, macronuclear differentiations were eliminated as a possibility by experiments involving macronuclear regeneration: no change was encountered in double by single crosses when a double derived its macronucleus from a fragment of the old macronucleus of the single to which it was mated. The conclusion is that the hereditary basis for the difference lies within the fixed cortex.

The second cortical mutant is the triple, described by Sonneborn and Dippell[658] Although triples can be maintained by selection, they divide much more slowly than singles. Quadruples can be formed, but cannot be maintained, and fusion of sutures often occurs.

The third cortical mutant was described by Sonneborn and Dippell[657, 660] and by Sonneborn[650]. It was produced spontaneously when an animal separated abnormally from another at conjugation and incorporated a portion of its partner's cortex. It contained two oral segments (including ventral fields, sutures, mouths, gullets and cytopyges) but only one dorsal field including one set of contractile vacuoles. Frequently, a third cytopyge appeared at the junction of the left posterior kinety field of one oral segment with the right posterior kinety field of the second oral segment.

The fourth cortical mutant first appeared spontaneously.[659, 650] It is a typical double, except for the fact that the mouth and gullet and circumoral kinety field on one oral meridian is lacking; cytopyge, sutures, and the remaining ventral fields remain. Beisson and Sonneborn[53] reported that this mutant could be induced by cutting off the anterior mouth- and gullet-containing portion of one of two animals connected by a cytoplasmic bridge

Some naturally occurring stocks and some mutant strains, in contrast to the two-type stocks just described, are always pure for only one mating type (type I), and are called one-type stocks. They are homozygous for the allele mt^I which is recessive to the allele found in homozygous two-type stocks, $mt^{I,II}$. This was the first Mendelian factor found in ciliated protozoans and its behaviour was shown by Sonneborn to provide genetic evidence for the cytological events of conjugation, autogamy, and macronuclear regeneration.

The temperature sensitive stage and, hence, very probably the normal time of macronuclear anlagen determination, has been shown to be just before, or early in anlagen formation.[619]

Butzel[80] suggests that the mating type I substance (or its precursor) is synthesized first in the cell. It (or its precursor) is then transformed into the mating type II substance in the presence of an active $mt^{I,II}$ allele; the mt^I allele being incapable of effecting the change. This view is supported by the fact that mutations yielding pure mating type I determining alleles occur often, but mutations yielding pure mating type II determining genes have never been found. On this view the nuclear differentiation for mating type I or II is a change toward inactivity or activity of the macronuclear $mt^{I,II}$ gene. Once the repressed or derepressed state of the gene is determined, that state is inherited for the life of the macronucleus. Beale[45] suggests that the elements determining activity or inactivity are contained within the "macronuclear sap" and Nanney[443] suggests that the mechanism is a series of competing reactions (see, for example, Ref. 273). It is not inconceivable, however, that gene activity is determined by the structural state of the chromosome and that such states may be self-perpetuating. (See, for example, Ephrussi,[161a] Sonneborn,[649a] and Brink.[72a, 72b]) At any rate, speculations on the nature of the differentiation are only useful at this time if they lead to new experimental approaches, for there is little or no available information in molecular terms which is relevant to the problem.

b. *Tetrahymena pyriformis, syngen 1*

Allen, Nanney, and coworkers[3, 443, 445, 454, 455, 456] have found that in strains homozygous for the allele mt^B, mature caryonides ordinarily have been determined to exhibit some one of the six complementary mating types II–VII. In strains containing the alleles mt^A, mt^C, or mt^D, the choice is among the five types I, II, III, V, VI. The frequencies of the five types are different in each of the strains homozygous for the alleles, mt^A, mt^C, and mt^D.

It was once considered possible[440] that nuclear differentiations of mating type represented gross changes in chromosome numbers, such as changes in ploidy in the macronucleus. A number of lines of evidence have made this view unlikely. (See Nanney [442] for a review.) One of these was the finding that nuclear differentiations in the case of syngen 1 of *Tetrahymena pyri-*

formis involved a choice not between just two alternative mating types but among many.

c. *P. multimicronucleatum, syngen 2*

Caryonidal inheritance of phase (see above, Section VIII, J, 2) of mating type in cycling lines (35, 37) has been reported within syngen 2 of *P. multimicronucleatum.*

5. CARYONIDAL INHERITANCE AND THE CYTOPLASMIC STATE

a. *Paramecium aurelia,* typical Group B syngens

In the group B syngens (2, 4, 6, 7, 8, 10, and 12) of *P. aurelia*, caryonidal inheritance is almost but not quite obscured by the major role of the cytoplasm in determining that the new macronuclei will usually maintain the mating type of the paramecia in which they are formed. Change in mating type is thus much less frequent than in syngen 1 of *P. aurelia*. Selfers, to be discussed below, are also found frequently in the group B syngens.

The effect of the cytoplasm is striking, as seen in a cross of mating types VII and VIII of syngen 4. Exconjugant clones generally show no change in mating type, the VII exconjugant producing a clone of type VII and the VIII exconjugant producing a clone of type VIII. Changes of type, often to selfers, occur when cytoplasmic exchange occurs. An analysis of the products of the first few fissions after conjugation by Nanney[442] showed that clones segregate into VII or VIII or selfer at the first fission, indicating caryonidal inheritance. A clear demonstration that mating types VII and VIII are really under nuclear and not solely cytoplasmic control was provided by Sonneborn[642] who induced cytoplasmic exchange and macronuclear regeneration in a cross of VII by VIII containing marker genes. Macronuclei newly forming from micronuclei often changed type, but macronuclei regenerating from old fragments always retained the mating type of the macronuclei from which they came. So in syngen 4, the macronucleus determines the mating type, and the macronucleus in turn is determined by the cytoplasm in which it is formed. Nanney[443] suggests that the elements of the postulated steady state system of determination (see above) spill over into the cytoplasm in the group B varieties and are able to penetrate and determine the newly forming macronuclei.

Temperature has been shown to affect the ratio of the two complementary mating types in syngen 4 under certain conditions, high temperature increasing the frequency of mating type VIII.[442, 444] It has not been determined what stage is temperature sensitive, but estimates of the stage sensitive to transferred cytoplasm[642] indicate that nuclei may remain sensitive fairly late in their development. Sonneborn[642] has also observed that crosses of normal animals with amicronucleates yields abnormally high frequencies of the mating type of the normal animal among the original amicronucleate exconjugants. It is suggested that the micronuclei are already partially determined by the normal animal before migrating into the amicronucleate.

b. *Paramecium aurelia, syngen 7*

The fact that macronuclear anlagen become determined for mating type VII when developing in VII cytoplasm, and VIII when developing in VIII cytoplasm, suggests a high degree of specificity with, perhaps, the mating type substance itself playing a role in the process of determination. The facts of mating type determination in syngen 7, however, show that mating type and the cytoplasmic state which determines mating type may be independent of each other. Taub[699-702] has found that in paramecia bearing the dominant N and $mt^{XIII, XIV}$ alleles at the two mating type loci, type XIII cytoplasm determines that anlagen will become determined for XIII, and type XIV cytoplasm determines that anlagen will become determined for XIV—typical group B inheritance. If either the ultraviolet induced recessive n or the naturally occurring recessive mt^{XIII} is present in homozygous condition the paramecia are always type XIII. Conjugation or autogamy in animals having the N allele, but heterozygous at the mt locus show that the mt^{XIII} (but not the n) allele has a curious dominant second effect—it causes a carrier's cytoplasm to be XIV-determining, irrespective of whether the carrier is type XIII or XIV. The $mt^{XIII, XIV}$ allele on the other hand allows the cytoplasm to be either XIII- or XIV-determining. Neither of the alleles at the n locus has the effect. So it is clear that the mating type substance or one of its specific precursors is not the effective cytoplasmic determinant of mating type. This same conclusion was suggested by earlier work of Nanney[442, 444] who found that selfing cultures in syngen 4 of *P. aurelia,* which were predominantly of one type, often produced the complementary type at conjugation.

Taub[702] notes that the mechanism suggested by Butzel for syngen 1 (see above) may be applied and extended to account for the facts of mating type inheritance in syngen 7. The mating type XIII substance or its precursor is transformed into the type XIV substance in the presence of N and $mt^{XIII, XIV}$ alleles, provided they are active. The n and mt^{XIII} alleles are ineffective in making the pathway operate, so animals homozygous for these alleles are always type XIII. Furthermore, a repressor of the pathway is sometimes present, and when it is, animals cannot be type XIV. Establishment of the continuing production (or absence) of the repressor constitutes nuclear differentiation. The repressor may be active sometimes, inactive at others. It has the potentiality of becoming established in all circumstances but one: in the presence of the mt^{XIII} allele (even when the mt locus is heterozygous) no repressor is produced. The hypothesis is consistent with the results of other crosses which reveal that type XIII paramecia homozygous for $mt^{XIII, XIV}$ and n may sometimes be in the XIII-determining state (presence of repressor) and sometimes in the XIV-determining state (no repressor).

c. *Stylonychia putrina*

Downs[135a] has suggested that the results of crosses between different mating types in *S. putrina* may be explained on the basis of cytoplasmic effects on the determination of macronuclear anlagen. However, as he points out, the data are not decisive and further work is needed.

d. *Tetrahymena pyriformis, syngens 6, 7 and 9*

The pattern of mating type inheritance in syngen 6,[720a] syngen 7,[486b] and syngen 9[155] follows the pattern of the typical group B syngens of *P. aurelia*. However, gene markers have not been present in the work on syngens 6 and 7 and it has not been possible to determine whether normal conjugation with nuclear exchange has occurred. Details of the work on syngen 9 have not been published.

6. SELFING

Selfing may occur when mating type changes do not occur synchronously in all lines of descent. This is found, for example, in *P. multimicronucleatum* during the daily shifts in type (see above). Another example found in syngen 1 of *P. aurelia* by Kimball[311, 314] and later in syngen 3 by Sonneborn[619] is due to a lag in expression of a newly determined mating type. It was shown that the change from mating type II to I (not the reverse) occurred only after a lag of a few fissions. Since different animals in the culture actually change at slightly different times, both types are present during change, and selfing may occur.

Many selfers, however, breed true as selfers, i.e., isolations from selfing clones give rise to new cultures which also self. At least two mechanisms appear to be responsible for such selfing: segregation of macronuclear subunits and variations in genic expression. Each will now be considered.

a. *Segregation of Macronuclear Subunits*

A number of studies[310, 598a, 440, 442, 444] has been concerned with the selfers in syngens 1 and 4 of *P. aurelia*. Nanney[440] has suggested that selfers might result from vegetative segregation of macronuclear subunits, some determined for one mating type, others for the complementary type. Nanney[442] attempted to test this hypothesis in the following ways. Macronuclear anlagen (in a two-type stock of syngen 1 of *P. aurelia*) which would ordinarily determine different mating types were induced to fuse by starving exconjugants (see Ref. 629). Selfers arose, as predicted by the hypothesis. Furthermore, macronuclear regeneration in selfers in which a new macronucleus is regenerated from a small fragment might be expected to yield homogeneous nuclei and stable mating types. This prediction was verified.[455] Nevertheless, the possibility that changes in gene expression constitute a major factor in changes of mating type of group B syngens of *P. aurelia* is clearly not eliminated.[444]

Studies of selfers in syngen 1 of *Tetrahymena pyriformis* have also been carried out by Nanney, Allen, and coworkers.[455, 15, 579, 453, 448, 452] The analyses have been performed (a) on strains homozygous for an allele allowing types I, II, III, V, and VI; (b) on strains homozygous for an allele allowing types II, III, IV, V, VI, and VII; and (c) on heterozygotes which may show any one of the seven types. Many caryonides contain animals of more than one mating type and are classed as selfers. Most selfers contain cells of only two mating types, but some consist of as many as four mating types. Isolations from selfing clones often give rise to selfing lines, but stable or "pure" lines are occasionally segregated from selfers. Within clones of dual potentiality the sum of the rates of appearance of the two pure types (the rate of stabilization) comes to equilibrium after a number of fissions. The rate of stabilization has been measured and found to have a value of 0.0113 stabilizations per generation. This value was found to be the same in the two dual combinations tested, V–VI and I–VI. A mathematical treatment by Schensted[579] (see Section III, C, 2) assumes that a newly formed macronucleus has some subunits determined for one mating type, other subunits determined for another. Each subunit is assumed to form an identical one before cell division. At cell division equal numbers of subunits are assumed to go to the two new cells, with all possible distributions of the two kinds of subunits being equally likely. It is found that the segregation rate of 0.0113 corresponds to a subunit number of 45 and the hypothesis fits the observed data very well. Detailed comparisons between the theory and the observed rates of stabilization early in the life of selfer clones also show no discrepancies.

The chief observation unexplained by the segregation theory of selfing is the fact that the rate of stabilization is markedly increased by starvation of selfers.[455] Allen and Nanney[15] point out that if starvation reduced the number of subunits, an increased rate of stabilization would be observed. However, at variance with this explanation is the fact that the efficiency of starvation in increasing the rate of stabilization is not the same for I–VI and V–VI selfers. It appears to the reviewer that starvation might act by simply causing differentiated subunits to redifferentiate and change their type.

After some 60 to 100 fissions, most of the cells have become pure because segregation of macronuclear subunits has been largely completed.[453] Accordingly, the ratio of the different pure types within caryonides at this time should reflect the ratio of different subunits in macronuclear anlagen earlier when determination of subunits occurred. Thus, determination of one subunit for type V and another for type VI at the two subunit stage should after 100 generations, yield equal numbers of pure V and pure VI, as well as some selfing lines. Nanney and Allen observed that many caryonides yielded very unequal ratios of types, indicating that determination must have occurred rather late, many as late as the 32 unit stage. However, since determination occurs late, one might expect subunits to be determined for many different types. But, as already indicated, such is not the case, for usually only two, occasionally three or four types, segregate from any given caryonide. Nanney and Allen, therefore, conclude that there is an interaction among subunits in any anlage during determination; there is a strong tendency for subunits to be determined alike. The situation may be compared to the tendency for separate anlagen within the same cell to be determined alike in the group B syngens of *Paramecium aurelia*.

Work on serotypes and other systems in *Tetrahymena* reviewed elsewhere in this chapter reinforce the subunit hypothesis. These various lines of evidence are brought together below in the section on the macronucleus.

b. *Variations in Gene Expression*

In *P. aurelia* and syngen 1 of *T. pyriformis* selfers appear early in the life cycle and often segregate pure types. As we have seen, considerable evidence suggests that selfing in these forms results from segregation of macronuclear subunits at binary fission. Heckmann[237] finds, however, that in *E. crassus*, after conjugation, lines undergo long periods of mating type stability with selfing appearing late in the life cycle. Selfing is induced by exposing hetero-zygotes (but not homozygotes) to low temperature. Heckmann suggests, therefore, that selfing represents the expression of the normally recessive allele in the old and in cold-treated lines.

The selfers observed by Jennings[280] in *P. bursaria* also appear late in the life cycle, and Heckmann[238] suggests that they may also result from the same mechanism. The selfers of *P. bursaria* need reinvestigation, but, as noted above, they have not been observed in the more recent studies of Siegel and collaborators.[599]

In syngen 12 of *P. caudatum* Hiwatashi[245] found selfers which occur late in the life cycle. He found that the direction of change of mating type could be influenced by the amount of nutrient provided. More recently Hiwa-tashi[251] has reported that homogenates of paramecia may induce stable lines to become selfers. It does not seem likely that macronuclear segregation can explain such environmental effects.

The rapidity of the changes in mating type observed in syngen 5 of *P. aurelia* by Bleyman[64, 65] also are not readily explained by the segregation hypothesis. Nor does it appear likely that the pattern of segregation of pure types shown by the selfers of syngen 5 can be explained without invoking changes in gene expression.

Finally, the effect of starvation in reducing selfing in *Tetrahymena*[455] may well be an example of a change in gene expression, as noted above.

7. Conclusions

The synthesis of mating type substances is under the control of nuclear genes. The expression of these genes depends upon environmental factors (such as temperature), upon circadian rhythms, upon long-lasting life cycle changes, and upon nuclear "states" of activity or inactivity. Agents known to inhibit protein and RNA synthesis in other organisms prevent the expression of the mating type genes. This finding suggests that when the genes are not expressed they are repressed very early in the sequence of reactions leading from gene to character, possibly at the level of the chromosome itself. This view is supported by the fact that the site of the long-lasting differentiations of mating type is the nucleus, not the cytoplasm. Nevertheless, the cytoplasm does have a role in the stable nuclear differentiations, for just as the nucleus determines the cytoplasm, the cytoplasm in many cases may determine the nucleus at the time of macronuclear formation.

The "states" of nuclear activity may be extremely long-lasting, hundreds of generations, and in many cases, for the life of the nucleus. In other cases, the "states" may change back and forth from active to inactive with great ease. Activity of certain elements is often accompanied by inactivity of others; or, in other cases, all elements may be correlated and act alike. In any case, it is clear that mechanisms of intranuclear communication exist. It has also been found that the many examples may be classified as showing intralocus repression or interallelic repression (see introductory material at the beginning of Section VIII).

Of greatest interest, perhaps, is the mechanism by which the many instances of hereditary repressions and activations may operate. Two possibilities have been suggested. They are, first, repressor substances or steady state reactions operating within the nuclear membrane, and second, three-dimensional alterations in chromosomal structure which are perpetuated. But no experiments have dealt with these problems at the molecular level and the possible mechanisms are only speculations at this time. (See discussion under VIII, J, 4, a).

Perhaps, the main significance of the work on mating types is that it establishes firmly the fact that highly stable modifications in the activity of genes can occur, and that these states of activity may be perpetuated during cellular reproduction.

K. Immobilization Antigens

1. PARAMECIUM AURELIA

a. Serotypes

It was discovered many years ago by Rössle[546, 547] that when paramecia are placed in a suitable dilution of homologous antiserum they are immobilized. Cilia are agglutinated and, if the serum is sufficiently strong, paramecia die. Jollos[289] found that resistant variants appear after paramecia are so exposed. Sonneborn,[624] using *P. aurelia*, confirmed that resistant lines are indeed induced by antiserum and do not arise simply by selection. Later, Sonneborn[630] injected resistant lines of *P. aurelia*,

8*

syngen 4, into rabbits and obtained antiserum which would immobilize the "resistant" lines, but not the original clones of paramecia. He was thus able to show that the "resistants" were in fact new "serotypes" with new specificities. He found within each stock a number of different serotypes (A, B, C, etc.), some induced and some spontaneous, each immobilized by its homologous antiserum and not by antiserum against the other types. The appearance of new serotypes, as we shall see later, results not from mutation, but from stable changes in the expression of genes.

Perhaps the most thoroughly investigated protozoan serologically is stock 51 of syngen 4 of *P. aurelia*. Serotypes A, B, C, D, E, G, H, I, J, N, Q, and U[636, 26] have been found in stock 51. As in other stocks of *Paramecium*, individual paramecia are generally of one type only, i.e., they react with only one diagnostic serum. One exception is the case of a paramecium transforming from one serotype to another, when it goes through a transitory stage in which it reacts well with antiserum directed against both the old and the new types.[42] Another exception is a very unusual one analyzed by Margolin.[399] Paramecia of stock 172 of syngen 4 were able to react as serotypes D and M simultaneously. Margolin was able to show that the simultaneous manifestation depended specifically upon the m^{172} allele (see below).

If normal control serum in which complement has been inactivated by heating at 55–60°C for one-half hour is diluted to 1/25th full strength, it has no effect on paramecia in the standard 2-hour test period.[635] Antiserum prepared against paramecia of a given serotype, however, generally immobilizes the animals of that serotype in concentrations as low as 1/1000 or lower. In higher concentrations such as 1/25 or 1/50 some sera may "cross-react" with paramecia of a non-homologous serotype. As discussed below, cross-reactions may occur because of the presence of cross-reacting antibody induced by the presence of more than one kind of immobilization antigen molecules in the individual paramecia of the serotype used for injection.[177, 586] In many cases it is due to a close chemical relationship between different serotype-determining antigen molecules such that at least some of the antibody formed in response to one antigen can react with a related antigen.[30] Thus, serotypes A, B, G, and Q in stock 51 often cross-react and form one related group and types D and J also cross-react and are related.[511] Numerous similar relations have been observed in other stocks.[30, 399] Most serotypes within a stock, however, show little or no serological cross-reaction with others.

When Sonneborn investigated stocks other than stock 51, many of the same serotypes were found, some were missing, and new ones were encountered. Thus, stock 29 of syngen 4 manifested types A, B, C, D, F, G, H, and J.[636, 508] Each stock was found to be capable of producing a characteristic spectrum of serotypes. Although many of the serotypes in different stocks are indistinguishable, such as B in stocks of syngen 4, most show slight differences in titer when tested with appropriate sera. Thus, 29 A can be distinguished from 51 A by certain diagnostic sera. Such sera immobilize both types when concentrated, but immobilize only one at somewhat greater dilutions. The cross-reactions between different serotypes within a stock, however, are generally much weaker than the cross-reactions between homologous types in different stocks. Bishop[62] has compared the cross-reactions obtained by different serological techniques and found that the magnitude of cross-reaction depends upon the technique used, precipitation in gel and absorption techniques giving greater cross-reactions than immobilization reactions. Somewhat similar results had been reported by Finger.[169]

b. Inheritance of Serotypes

Sonneborn[630, 633] found that although environmental conditions are important in serotype determination, the expression of a given serotype (such as A) rather than one of the possible alternatives (such as B) has a hereditary basis. At 32°C all types of stock 51 transform to A, and at 17°C all types of stock 51 transform to B. But at intermediate temperatures under one set of environmental conditions many types are stable, breeding true for their original serotypes for many hundreds of generations. Therefore the alternative serotypes within a stock are hereditarily diverse. Although many serotypes cannot be maintained stably except under rather specialized conditions, there is no reason to suspect that their mechanism of determination is any different from those groups of serotypes whose members breed true to type under one common set of environmental conditions.

Sonneborn found[630, 633] that in crosses of stable types of syngen 4, such as 51 A with 51 B, the original conjugants of serotype A produced exconjugant clones of type A, and the original conjugants of serotype B produced exconjugant clones of serotype B. If cytoplasmic exchange occurred, however, the two exconjugant clones from individual pairs were sometimes both A, sometimes both B, and sometimes one or both were mixed, containing both A and B paramecia. No change was encountered later at subsequent autogamies. So the genetic basis for the hereditary expression of one rather than an alternative serotype within a stock is clearly not Mendelian. It is evident that during conjugation, at least, there is a cytoplasmic determinant important in the choice of what serotype will be manifested. The nature of the action of that determinant will be considered in more detail presently.

Inheritance of differences between the serotypes of different stocks is Mendelian. Two kinds of differences are known, the ability of a stock to manifest a given serotype, and specific differences between homologous serotypes. Sonneborn[636] reports that the difference between the ability of stock 29 of syngen 4 to produce serotype F and lack of this ability in stock 51 is determined by a simple Mendelian factor. Finger[170] has reported similar inheritance of the ability of stocks of syngen 2 to produce serotype E (not homologous with the E of syngen 4). In the case of serotype E, the allele for the ability to produce the serotype is dominant. Finger and Heller[175] also observed that crosses between stocks capable of manifesting E and others unable to manifest E produce F-1 lines with serotype E of modified specificity—showing that the allele for no E is, nevertheless, capable of contributing E specificities in hybrids. Numerous cases of specifically different homologous serotypes under the control of multiple alleles have been described. The first case discovered was a gene determining 29 A and its allele determining 51 A. In fact, most serotypes which have been carefully investigated have shown alleles in different stocks which control their specificity. (See Table 4). An exception is that of serotype B in syngen 4 which has been examined in many stocks but which has exhibited no differences. It was found by Reisner[536] that the allele governing specificity of serotype H in syngen 4 was allelic with the gene controlling ability of that serotype to be expressed. No more than one locus has ever been shown to be concerned with a given serotype and all loci governing different serotypes are unlinked. The data, then, are consistent with the hypothesis that there is a genetic locus corresponding to each serotype and the locus determines both the capacity for the serotype to be expressed and its specificity. Genes which affect the stability of serotypes under different environmental conditions are also known and they will be considered in the next section.

The role of environment, cytoplasm, and genes in determining serotypes was first elucidated by Sonneborn in syngen 4. The same relations were shown by Beale[43] in syngen 1 in a somewhat different way. Stocks 60 and 90 both manifest serotype G at 25°C and D at 29°C. The two G's and also the two D's are specifically rather different, however, and may be easily differentiated by means of sera made against the different types. Crosses show that there are two loci involved, one for the two G serotypes and one for the two D serotypes. The genotype of stock 60 may be represented as $g^{60}g^{60}d^{60}d^{60}$ and the genotype of stock 90 as $g^{90}g^{90}d^{90}d^{90}$. When paramecia are G, the g alleles are being expressed; when they are D, the d alleles are expressed. When G (cultured at 25°C) is placed at 29°C or when D (cultured at 29°C) is placed at 25°C, serotypes change to the type stable at the new temperature, but only after a long lag of up to 60 fissions. This lag makes it possible to investigate the role of cytoplasm and genes in serotype determination in the following way. 90 G is crossed with 60 D (from 29°C) at 25°C and the exconjugant clones are cultured at 25°C. When tests are made before the fifth fission, no change in type is shown, because of cytoplasmic lag. After five fissions, however, the new genotypes come to expression; the original 60 D exconjugant clones show a hybrid reaction indicating that the cells contain both 60 D and 90 D antigens; similarly, the original 90 G exconjugant clones show the hybrid 90 G–60 G reaction. Thus the new alleles which have migrated into each conjugant respond to the new cytoplasm (not the new temperature) in which they find themselves and act accordingly. Eventually, however, the temperature prevails and new proto-plasmic states are established. Thus, all animals become hybrid G. When the experiments are carried out at 29°C the final phenotype in all lines is hybrid D.

It is clear that the expression of one rather than an alternative serotype determining gene within a stock has a hereditary basis. It is important to know whether this hereditary basis is localized within the cytoplasm or within the nucleus, and the remainder of this section will be devoted to a consideration of this question. The results of Sonneborn and those of Beale were originally interpreted to mean that the hereditary system determining gene expression is cytoplasmic. And, indeed, there is no question but that this is true during conjugation, for the patterns of inheritance at conjugation, with and without cytoplasmic exchange, can be interpreted in no other way. However, a more complex alternative hypothesis also fits the facts. It may be that the hereditary system determining gene expression resides in the macronucleus, and the cytoplasm may be active only in influencing the macronuclei when they are being newly formed at conjugation or autogamy. Indeed, this latter hypothesis has been clearly demonstrated in the case of mating type inheritance in syngen 4 of *P. aurelia*,[642, 442, 444] and Butzel[80] and Nanney[443] have pointed out the similarities between mating type and serotype determination. For example, when serotypes A and B and mating types VII and VIII of stock 51 syngen 4 are both followed in a cross in which some pairs undergo cytoplasmic exchange and others do not, the patterns of inheritance are remarkably similar. Moreover, a number of lines of evidence favor a nuclear rather than a cytoplasmic basis for serotypes and they will now be enumerated.

First, Finger and Heller[174] have shown that migratory micronuclei appear to be partly predetermined for serotype in accordance with the phenotype of the paramecia from which they came (reminiscent of Sonne-born's finding[642] that migratory gametic micronuclei at conjugation are partly determined for mating type in accordance with the cytoplasm from which they came). The evidence involves hybrids between stocks of syngen 2 which manifest different kinds of serotype E and also different kinds of C. Hybrids of the same genotype differ in respect to the degree they resemble one or the other of the allelic types (such as 197E or 72E) and these differ-ences are often perpetuated for many generations. Thus, crosses in syngen 2 between stock 197 (genotype $e^{197}e^{197}$) and stock 72 ($e^{72}e^{72}$) yield F-1 clones of genotype $e^{197}e^{72}$ which differ from each other in the expression of the two alleles. If both parents manifest the E antigen when crossed, both alleles tend to function in the F-1. But if a serotype other than E is being manifested by one of the parents and E is being shown by the other parent, then the *e* allele present in the E parent tends to be favored in the F-1 heterozygotes which show serotype E. Migratory nuclei coming from non-E conjugants tend not to be expressed. If significant amounts of cytoplasm are not exchanged (and there is no evidence for cytoplasmic exchange here), then the nuclei have been already partially determined for serotype. Second, the finding by Jollos,[289] Sonneborn,[624] Beale,[45] Skaar,[608] and Dryl[137, 138] that serotypes tend to change more frequently at nuclear reorganization than at binary fission is predicted by the theory of nuclear states of determination. Third, Preer et al.[512] showed that the transformation of 51B to 51A at high temperature at conjugation occurs much more frequently in lines whose macronuclei are descended from new anlagen than in lines whose macronuclei are descended by macronuclear regeneration from fragments of the old macronucleus. The possibility exists, however, that special secondary effects of macronuclear regeneration favor serotype B over A in stock 51.

Perhaps the only argument which might be advanced in favor of a strict cytoplasmic determination of serotypes different from mating type determination is the fact that change of serotype generally occurs more frequently and is more susceptible to environmental influences than is the case with mating types. Normally, mating types change only at anlagen formation. But the recent experiments of Heckmann[237] and others (see above) on mating type "selfers" indicate that alternative genes may frequently change or be induced to change in their activity. We cannot be certain whether the hereditary mechanism controlling gene action in serotype determination resides within the nucleus (and, at times, within the cytoplasm) like mating type determinants, or whether it is exclusively cytoplasmic. But in this reviewer's opinion, the evidence favors the former interpretation. No facts make it necessary to postulate a new mechanism different from the one already demonstrated for mating types.

c. Serotype Transformation and Stability

It has already been noted that serotype stability is influenced by the environment. One of the best known and most important factors is temperature. Certain types appear at high temperature, such as A of syngen 4[633] and E of syngen 2.[170] Other types are stable at lower temperatures, such as B and H of syngen 4[633] and G of syngen 2.[170] Beale has found that in stocks of syngen 1, S is stable at low temperature, G at intermediate temperature, and D at high temperature. This order of serotype stability in respect to temperature has been found to hold for many stocks of syngen 1.[45] Although serotypes tend to be most stable over a limited range, Sonneborn et al.[688] and Margolin[400] found that the order of serotypes in respect to temperature stability was not always the same in different stocks of syngen 4.

Serotype stability is also influenced by a number of other factors such as fission rate (determined by food supply), the type of dessicated leaves used for the culture medium (grass, lettuce, etc.), salt concentration, growth in bacteria-free versus bacteria-containing medium, etc. (See reviews by Beale,

Refs. 45, 47.) One curious finding concerning serotype stability is the fact that the past history of a clone has an effect on its stability.[608, 400] Some such changes are related to the number of fissions since autogamy or conjugation, but others are due to previous nutritive conditions or other factors. Effects of this latter kind may persist for as many as 20 days at maximum fission rate. Their basis is completely unknown. One possibility is that the genetic "state" determining serotype is different from the serotype itself—just as Taub[702] (see above) found to be the case in mating type determination in syngen 7 of *P. aurelia*.

The stability of a given serotype is strongly influenced by nuclear genes. Sonneborn et al.[668] showed that in syngen 4 the alleles which determine the specificity of a given serotype are important in determining its stability. Beale[44] had previously reported the same for syngen 1. Sonneborn et al.[668] also found that loci other than the specificity locus are important in determining a serotype's stability. In most, if not all cases these loci proved to be genes determining the presence and absence or specificity of other serotypes.

A number of different agents are capable of inducing serotype change. Jollos[289] reported that paramecia were induced to become resistant to a serum by exposure to that serum. The induction of transformation from one serotype to another by antiserum was reported by Sonneborn[621] and studied in detail by Beale.[42] It was at first thought that the action of specific serum in inducing change might indicate that the immobilization antigens themselves represent an element in the genetic "state" responsible for serotype inheritance, antiserum inactivating antigens by combining with them. Skaar,[608] however, showed that some serotypes are actually stabilized by exposure to homologous antiserum. Furthermore, the wide variety of physiological agents capable of inducing serotype change suggests that homologous serum may act indirectly by virtue of its generally harmful effect on paramecia. The many factors known to induce serotype transformation include enzymes such as trypsin and chymotrypsin,[315, 711] patulin,[27] high salt concentrations,[45] X-rays and ultraviolet light,[630, 669, 637] and many others. Recently, Finger and Heller[176] have reported that paramecia secrete substances into the cultures in which they live which stabilize or induce change to their own serotype. These preliminary observations, if substantiated by future work, could be of great importance in understanding the chemical basis of repression in serotype determination.

Serotype transformation is accompanied by the loss in titer of a serotype to one serum and the concomitant increase in titer to the new one.[42, 30] In at least one case, however, it has been reported[674] that loss of reactivity to the old serotype does not occur until after reactivity to the new serotype has been achieved. Balbinder and Preer[30] followed the transformation of 28G (stable at low temperature in stock 28 of syngen 2) to 28E when paramecia were changed from 12 to 31°C. The amount of E antigen per cell as judged by gel diffusion tests was found to increase exponentially until transformation was complete at the end of two fissions. Although cell division is generally required for transformation, Austin et al.[27] have reported that the change of 51 D to B, when induced by patulin, may occur without cell multiplication.

d. Chemistry

Finger[169] showed that the immobilization antigens are soluble and can be detected in gel diffusion precipitation tests. Preer[508, 509] was able to isolate the immobilization antigens and show that they are proteins.

Preer[510] reported a molecular weight of 240,000 for syngen 4 antigen 51 A, based on sedimentation and diffusion. Bishop and Beale[63] isolated the immobilization antigens of several serotypes of syngen 1 and Bishop[61] reported a molecular weight of about 250,000 for antigen 60 D of syngen 1 using the Archibald approach to equilibrium method. Jones[293] reported molecular weights of 240,000–260,000 for antigens D and G of syngen 1 using both the short column low speed equilibrium technique (see Yphantis,[739]) and the sedimentation and diffusion method. Steers[677] used the high speed equilibrium centrifugation technique of Yphantis[739] and reported that the molecular weight of antigen 51 A is 310,000 $\pm$ 20,000. Steers' rather high value is somewhat surprising in view of the previous lower estimates. However, the methods of Preer, of Bishop and Beale, and of Jones apparently did not include extrapolation of all the experimentally determined parameters used in the calculations to zero protein concentration. This is particularly important, for the immobilization protein shows a strong concentration dependence. Steers (personal communication) has also used the short column low speed equilibrium technique and obtained a molecular weight of about 240,000. The high speed Yphantis method used by Steers yields a "zero concentration" value, and the molecular weight of 310,000 must, therefore, be considered the best estimate.

On the basis of the rather high frictional ratio (1.8) and high intrinsic viscosity (0.11) of antigen 51 A, Preer[510] suggested that the molecule was probably fibrous. Mott[425] has recently investigated the immobilization antigens of syngen 1 with the electron microscope and found that one of them appears hexagonal in outline, some 100–200 Ängstroms in diameter. However, the hydrodynamic data of Preer do not clearly indicate a fibrous protein, nor has the possibility of molecular aggregation been ruled out by Mott.

Amino acid analyses by Steers[676, 677] and by Jones[293] show an unusually high half-cystine content. Furthermore, both Steers and Jones find no free SH groüps in the native protein, so that each molecule contains a very large number of S–S bonds. Reduction and alkylation of sulfur-containning groups yields fragments which, according to Jones, are variable from one preparation to the next. This author (unpublished) has obtained the same result. Steers, however, has been able to achieve rather consistent preparations with subunits of about 35,000 molecular weight. Consideration of the data from peptide mapping leads both Jones and Steers to the conclusion that the molecule is a dimer, if the molecular weight is about 250,000. Thus, it might be represented by two α chains, two β chains and two γ chains $(\alpha_2\beta_2\gamma_2)$, although Jones notes that one can be sure only that there is more than one kind of chain. If, on the other hand, the molecular weight is around 310,000 (as it seems to be), then both Jones' and Steers' data indicate that the molecule is a trimer. Steers suggests that the molecule is a trimer consisting of three non-identical chains—$\alpha_3\beta_3\gamma_3$, nine chains in all.

Investigations of the number and kinds of antigens found in heterozygotes are also pertinent to a consideration of the number of subunits. Finger and coworkers[125, 179] have studied the hybrid antigens produced by heterozygotes for alleles determining different C and also different E antigens in syngen 2. In both cases, at least four hybrid antigens different from the parental types were distinguished. Since serotype C hybrids are unusual in that the mutual exclusion mechanisms which normally operate between loci operate between the c alleles, their finding of clonal differences in the antigenic constitution of hybrids was to be expected. They concluded that there must be at least three non-identical chains—α, β, and γ—a conclusion consistent with the chemical findings.

Jones[294] studied the $d^{60}d^{90}$ hybrid and concluded that it contained at least one parental (60D) protein amounting to about 50 per cent of the total antigen. The remaining 50 per cent consisted of at least two species of hybrid molecules. His results can be explained on the basis of a minimum of two non-identical chains (e.g., α and β), combined at random. However, it was also necessary to postulate that the chains are not made in equal amounts.

The alternative serotype antigens within a stock have been investigated chemically. Preer[511] reported that serotypes of syngens 2 and 4 differ in solubility in ammonium sulfate and also that similarities in solubility reflect similarities in immunological relationships. Bishop and Beale[63] showed that antigens D, G, and T of syngen 1 migrate at different rates on starch gel, and Steers,[675] using Tiselius free electrophoresis found that antigens A and B of stock 51, syngen 4, have slightly different isoelectric points. Bishop and Beale[63] also found that certain syngen 1 serotypes could be separated chromatographically on calcium phosphate columns. Radical differences in peptide maps following tryptic digestion were reported by Steers[676] for serotypes A, B, and D of syngen 4 and later confirmed by Jones and Beale[295] for G and D serotypes of syngen 1. Amino acid differences between serotypes of the same stock have also been reported by Steers[676, 677] and by Jones.[293]

Differences between two A types were not found in the peptide maps of Steers,[676] but nine different D types, several of which have been demonstrated to be determined by alleles at one locus, were distinguished in peptide maps by Jones and Beale.[295] Five of the types could not be distin-

8a*

guished serologically but nevertheless showed peptide differences. There was a strong correlation between serological relationship and similarity of peptides. This close correlation was interpreted to mean[295] that the antigenic sites are found throughout large portions of the molecule. Finger et al.[178, 171] using serological gel diffusion tests investigated the antigenic sites on five different types of C antigens in syngen 2 and found that the specificities could be accounted for by postulating a total of seven determinants, each specifically different type having some combination of three or more of the determinants.

e. Localization

Beale and Kacser[49] treated whole paramecia with fluorescein-labelled antibody and showed that the immobilization antigen is associated with the cilia and pellicle. Preer and Preer[514] found that in homogenates and in isolated cell fractions most of the extractable immobilization antigen was obtained from the cilia and body wall. Beale and Mott[50] treated sections of paramecia with labelled antibody and confirmed that the immobilization antigen is associated with the surface, and not with internal regions. Mott[423, 424, 425] treated whole paramecia with ferritin conjugated antibody and then sectioned and observed with the electron microscope. Her work makes it clear that the immobilization antigen forms a layer which coats the surface of the cilia and pellicle. Since it was shown by Preer (unpublished) that about 30 per cent of the protein of isolated cilia is the immobilization protein, it can be calculated that the layer on the cilium would have to be some 200 to 300 Ängstroms thick. The work of Mott is consistent with such a distribution. Mott also followed the antigen during transformation. She found that the new antigen appeared first on the pellicle in isolated sites. The sites enlarged, covering first the pellicle, then the cilia.

f. Secondary Antigens

Sonneborn[630, 633] postulated that cross-reactions between serotypes might be due to the presence of secondary antigens, immobilization antigens capable of eliciting antibody formation, but not capable of entering into the immobilization reaction. Although subsequent experiments caused Sonneborn to doubt this view,[634] evidence in support of the existence of secondary antigens was provided later by both him and others.[636, 177] Balbinder and Preer,[30] studying the strongly cross-reacting serotypes G and E of stock 28 of syngen 2 of P. aurelia by means of gel diffusion techniques, concluded that the cultures of serotype G which they studied did not contain secondary antigens. The work on isolated immobilization antigens of stock 51 has also revealed no secondary antigens.[509, 510, 511] Furthermore, secondary antigens should have been apparent were they present in the electrophoretic and other studies reported by Steers.[675] Recent confirmation of Sonneborn's original hypothesis, however, has been provided by Finger and coworkers.[177, 586] They have produced evidence, by means of gel diffusion tests, that secondary antigens do occur in certain cases. For example, secondary G is sometimes present in serotype E, and E is present as a secondary antigen in G. They find that the presence of a secondary antigen is sporadic in those cases in which it can occur. It can involve closely related antigens such as G and E of syngen 2, or it can on occasion involve unrelated antigens such as G and C. Seed *et al.*[586] also find that the relative amounts of primary and secondary antigens which can be extracted from different centrifugal fractions is not constant. It appears that the cellular distribution of secondary antigen is not identical with primary. They suggest that much (but not all) secondary antigen is internal.

g. *Function*

The function of the immobilization antigens is unknown but several lines of evidence suggest that they are indispensable. First, exposure to high concentrations of homologous serum kills paramecia. Finger and Heller[175] report that low concentrations of serum also kill if the protein synthesizing system of the paramecia is made nonfunctional (presumably with inhibitors). Second, no paramecia have ever been found which lack immobilization antigens. And finally, natural selection preserves a large number of genetic sites, all concerned with the production of the immobilization proteins. The fact that the surface of *Paramecium* is coated with the protein suggests that it may somehow act as a buffer between the cell surface and the environment. Perhaps it influences membrane permeability or controls the access of certain substances to the membrane. A hint is provided by Austin and collaborators[25, 27] who have presented evidence indicating that different serotypes vary in resistance to the antibiotic patulin and to the killer substance.

h. *Conclusions*

The stable differences in gene expression manifested by the serotypes are of particular interest. Obviously the cytoplasm can determine whether a gene can come to expression or not. Once expressed, it continues to be expressed and the manifestation of other alternative serotype determining genes is repressed. The hypotheses proposed to account for serotype determination assume some sort of feedback mechanism in the sequence of reactions leading from nucleus to antigen. These consist of either a repression of competing reactions or of an autocatalytic effect coupled with substrate competition. It may well be that the mechanism operates at the level of the nucleus, and resides in the cytoplasm only during periods of nuclear reorganization, just as in the case of mating type. The results on secondary antigens imply that the site of antigen localization may also play an important role in serotype determination.

The question of the chromosomal location of the determinants of the different antigenic subunits is open. But the fact that there is only one specificity locus for a given serotype suggests that all subunits are specified at one chromosomal locus, and that each serotype is specified separately and completely by its own locus. The locus may, of course, be a group of closely linked cistrons each specifying a different polypeptide subunit. If more than one locus were involved in specifying the amino acid sequence of a single serotype antigen, then we would have to make the assumption that certain regions of the molecule never carry the antigenic determinants. As discussed above, the very strong correlations between peptide maps and serological specificity make this assumption unlikely.

2. PARAMECIUM CAUDATUM

Koizumi[345, 346, 347] and Hiwatashi[249] have studied serotypes in syngens 3 and 12. Crosses between serotypes in syngen 12[249] show no change in type, just as in *P. aurelia*. Two specifically different F serotypes in syngen 3 are determined by alleles.[249] Koizumi[347] isolated the immobilization antigens and found their physical properties similar to those of *P. aurelia*, with one exception. The sedimentation coefficient of the antigens of *P. caudatum* was greater and the diffusion coefficient smaller. The molecular weight calculated from sedimentation and diffusion was 340,000, some 50 per cent greater than that obtained by similar methods on the immobilization antigens of *P. aurelia*. Thus, the serotype system of *P. caudatum* appears very similar to that in *P. aurelia*, except for the somewhat larger antigen molecule in the former.

3. TETRAHYMENA PYRIFORMIS

A number of different serotypes (H, R. L, etc.) have been described and studied in *T. pyriformis*.[375, 264, 401] A single inbred strain may express different types when cultured under different conditions. For example, L may be expressed below 20°C and H above 20°C. However, a given border-line temperature (such as 19°C) may allow the continued expression of both types.[264] In other words, the expression of one rather than another serotype is inherited. Inoki and Matsushiro[264] studied the inheritance of serotype differences, and inferred that the cytoplasm was involved, just as in the case of serotype differences in *P. aurelia*. More recent studies by Nanney,[449] however, indicate that true conjugation probably did not occur in the experiments of Inoki and Matsushiro. Nanney found that when pseudo-conjugants were eliminated from consideration by the use of adequate criteria, no evidence of cytoplasmic control was noted, both ex-conjugants from each pair being alike in serotype.

A number of variants of the H serotype have been found and studied in different stocks of *T. pyriformis*, syngen 1.[374, 457, 446, 448, 447, 460, 452, 459] They have been designated as Ha, Hb, Hc, etc. One genetic locus is involved, and several alleles have been demonstrated—H^A, H^C, H^D, and probably H^E and H^B. The analysis is straightforward except for the occasional appearance of an unexplained anomalous type.[447]

Heterozygotes for H alleles, however, do not breed true at vegetative reproduction. All exconjugant clones (and caryonides, too) contain some cells in which the two antigens are present and other cells in which only one is present. "Pure" types are segregated from mixed lines at a rate which, with successive fissions, approaches 0.0112 pure types per division.[457] This rate is indistinguishable from the rate of 0.0113 already cited for mating type stabilization. The similar rates suggest[457, 446] similar mechanisms. Nanney postulates, therefore, that alleles in macronuclear subunits are "determined" either for expression or lack of expression during macronuclear formation at conjugation, i.e., they show *interallelic exclusion*. After determination, the subunits are segregated at binary fission. A study of the relative frequencies of the two pure and the mixed types at different times after conjugation[459] showed that subcaryonides are much more alike than are the two caryonides from each conjugant, signifying caryonidal inheritance and thereby supporting the notion of nuclear determination. The distribution of the relative frequencies as well as some subcaryonidal fixations suggest that determination comes late in macronuclear development. Variations in environmental conditions produced no effect on the process of determination[675] but the process was influenced by the specific alleles involved, some being much more likely to be expressed than others. The interallelic exclusion in *T. pyriformis* heterozygotes is quite similar to that studied by Finger and Heller[170, 173, 174] in syngen 2 of *P. aurelia*. One important difference, however, is the complete lack of a cytoplasmic effect or of nuclear predetermination in *T. pyriformis*.

4. Trypanosoma

In the early 1900's numerous workers demonstrated that species of *Trypanosoma* are agglutinated by homologous serum and that populations often change their antigenic character during growth in their vertebrate hosts. (See review by Taliaferro, Ref. 677). In recent years the agents of African sleeping sickness, *T. gambiense* and *T. rhodesiense*, have been given particular attention. Serotypes and serotype transformation in *T. gambiense* have been studied by Inoki, Osaki, and coworkers.[258, 259, 263, 269, 268, 267, 486, 261, 262] In one strain, TG1, the original serotype, 0, and 23 variant serotypes, R_1, R_2, R_3, etc., have been described. When 0 is injected into mice, the mice soon die of the infection. However, if suitable amounts of normal human serum or plasma are also injected, the mice recover temporarily only to succumb later to some one of the relapse variant serotypes R_1, R_2, or R_3, etc. The new serotypes breed true in mice unless human serum is injected with them or unless a recovery is effected in the original mouse by the injection of human serum. In either event, the population changes to a new type, usually serotype 0. Lourie and O'Connor[378, 379] found a similar system involving 17 variants in *T. rhodesiense*.

Although this phenomenon has been known for many years, little evidence has been available to indicate whether the changes in serotype arise by induction or spontaneous mutation and selection. Inoki and coworkers present evidence that the change from R to 0 is induced. They add mouse antiserum to R serotype *in vitro* and note that the trypanosomes first agglutinate by their flagella to form clumps but that after some minutes the organisms in the clumps break apart. Inoki and coworkers report that if the free trypanosomes are now tested, they invariably are found to react as serotype 0. Furthermore, when injected into mice they breed true as serotype 0. The similarity to the serotypes of ciliates is obvious and Inoki suggests that the mechanism of serotype determination in trypanosomes is similar to that in *Paramecium*.

However, Brown reports that he is unable to repeat the *in vitro* transformation in serotype in either *T. gambiense* or *T. rhodesiense*. Brown also finds that unlike serotypes in *Paramecium*, serotypes in *T. rhodesiense* differ from each other in a number of different antigenic molecules which can be distinguished in immunoelectrophoresis. It appeares that the molecules responsible for serotype specificity in trypanosomes have not yet been identified with certainty (see also Ref. 585a).

L. Enzymes in Tetrahymena

Allen and coworkers[4, 5, 6, 9, 10, 11, 13, 14] have studied a number of enzymes in Tetrahymena using electrophoresis in gels. Three genetic loci, *E-1*, *E-2*, and *P-1*, have been reported.

The *E-1* locus is represented by two alleles *E-1*[B] and *E-1*[C]. Although many esterase bands can be demonstrated in gel electrophoresis, strains homozygous for *E-1*[B] show five specific negatively migrating esterase bands which are lacking in strains homozygous for *E-1*[C]. *E-1*[C] homozygotes, instead, show four or five positively migrating bands which are unlike those in *E-1*[B]. *E-1*[B] and *E-1*[C] enzymes, while differing in their behavior in electrophoresis, are very similar in other respects, having similar substrate sensitivity specificities and similar sensitivity to the inhibitor, eserine sulfate. The B and C isozymes are thus under the control of single alleles. It is possible that their control may be like that of the lactic dehydrogenase enzymes of vertebrates (see Markert[402]). That is, they may be compound proteins representing different combinations of more than one kind of subunit. It is also possible that there is initially only one protein specified by each allele in a homozygous strain, but then secondary modifications occur which result in alterations in the electrophoretic properties of many of the molecules. Studies show that the different isozymes within a homozygote appear at different times in the life history of a culture. Furthermore, all do not have the same intracellular distributions. If the isozymes within the B and C groups are arranged in order of electrophoretic migration, homologous forms of the B and C enzymes may be recognized. Moreover, homologous forms have been found to be similar in respect to differences in cellular localizations and in time of appearance in the growth stage, implying that the genetic difference does not extend to the function or time of synthesis.

The $E-2$ locus is also represented by a pair of alleles, $E-2^B$ and $E-2^C$. The $E-2$ esterases, unlike the $E-1$ esterases, are insensitive to eserine sulfate. Genetic work has been restricted to two which are characterized by the fact that they split only α-naphthyl butyrate. One of these is found in strains homozygous for $E-2^B$, the other is found in strains homozygous for its allele $E-2^C$.

Of the many acid phosphatases, only those under the control of the $P-1$ locus have been investigated. Strains homozygous for $P-1^A$ exhibit the A phosphatase band; homozygotes for $P-1^B$ produce the B phosphatase and two other isozymes lacking in A.

Clones heterozygous at the $E-1$, $E-2$, and $P-1$ loci, when established soon after conjugation, generally show all of the enzymes which the homozygotes manifest. Moreover, in the case of animals heterozygous at the $P-1$ locus there appear not only the parental enzymes but also new enzymes not present in the homozygotes. The appearance of new enzymes in the heterozygote has been explained by assuming that the $P-1$ phosphatases are tetramers consisting of different combinations of A and B subunits, each elaborated under the control of one of the two alleles. The five possible types are AAAA, BBBB, ABBB, AABB, AAAB, and five bands are produced by $P-1$ heterozygotes.

If heterozygous clones are maintained for many generations and new subclones are then established, it is found that considerable differentiation has taken place. Thus, after 100–200 fissions although some clones heterozygous for $E-1$ and $E-2$ have not changed, others have phenotypes like the parental homozygotes. Still others appear as if one of the two alleles is being expressed to a greater extent than the other. Heterozygotes at the $P-1$ locus are more complex. Several kinds of clones may be recognized. One kind has the maximum number of five bands while others have fewer) Clones showing only single bands (bands number 1, number 3, and number 5) are stable, others are not. (Numbers 1 and 5 are characteristic of the two homozygotes. Number 3 is a type seen only in hybrids.) The unstable clones, however, never produce subclones possessing bands which were lacking in the original unstable clone.

Allen has provided evidence that in heterozygotes the differentiations of enzyme forming ability are examples of allelic suppression. If it is assumed that one or the other allele becomes suppressed in macronuclear subunits, and that these macronuclear subunits are subsequently segregated at random at binary fission, then the differentiations are accounted for. The only difficulty is in the case of the one stable number 3 hybrid band seen in *P-1* heterozygotes; here one must assume that both alleles are expressed and that some kind of interaction results only in hybrid enzyme.

The hypothesis of allelic suppression followed by segregation of macronuclear subunits has already been proposed for both mating type and serotype determination in *Tetrahymena* (see above). Allen followed somatic differentiation in F-1 lines heterozygous for four loci: mating type, the H serotype, *E-1* and *E-2*. The stable types controlled by the loci, for the most part, were segregated at random with respect to each other. This appeared to be true even in the case of *mt* and *E-1* which are linked (25 per cent recombination). The alternative stable types for *E-1* and *E-2*, unlike *mt* and *H*, were about equal in frequency. Furthermore, stable types for *E-1* and *E-2* segregated much later than for *mt* and *H*. Nuclear determination is, therefore, held to occur many fissions later for *E-1* and *E-2* than for *mt* and *H*. Other data indicate that *P-1* is determined later than mating type and serotype, but not as late as the esterase loci. Furthermore, as predicted by the mathematical treatment of the subunit segregation hypothesis (see discussion of this point in Allen and Nanney,[15]), after some 80 fissions, unstable lines segregate the alternative stable types in equal frequency.

Allen[11] was able to show clearly that these differentiations are macronuclear. None persists through conjugation, when the old macronucleus is destroyed. But at macronuclear regeneration differentiations persist even though the new micronuclei acquire new combinations of alleles.

M. The Ciliate Life Cycle

The problem of the ciliate life cycle has been investigated for many years. In the late 1800's Maupas, Hertwig, Bütschli, and many others were concerned with the matter, and in the early 1900's Woodruff, Calkins, Jollos, and numerous others. Their work was thoroughly reviewed by Jennings in 1929[275] and 1942.[281] For a more recent discussion of many aspects of the problem, the reader is also referred to papers by Sonneborn in 1954[643] and Nanney in 1959.[445a] Only a brief summary with emphasis on recent work is given here.

After conjugation many ciliates undergo a period of immaturity during which they can multiply vigorously but are unable to conjugate. Immaturity is followed by maturity, when strains readily conjugate, are vigorous, and grow rapidly. If conjugation does not soon occur, senescence ensues, the fission rate declines, a late conjugation yields high mortality, and finally, conjugation becomes impossible and death follows. Sonneborn[643] has shown that in *P. aurelia* autogamy can substitute for conjugation in rejuvenation. As Jennings pointed out,[275] this cycle may extend over many (often hundreds) of cell divisions and clones in different stages may reproduce side by side for many generations in the same environment yet remain different. Therefore, the changes are hereditary and their mechanism should be susceptible to genetic analysis. The problem of the life cycle may be sub-divided into three problems: immaturity, the capacity to undergo autogamy, and senescence.

Immaturity following conjugation may vary from complete absence in some strains of *P. aurelia* to some 80 fissions in *T. pyriformis*, syngen 1, to hundreds of fissions in some stocks of *P. bursaria*. Variations in the length of the immature period in *P. aurelia* have been studied by Siegel[595, 598] who finds that at least one genetic locus is responsible for the differences between stocks. Hiwatashi[247] has shown that variations in the length of the immature period in *P. caudatum* syngen 12 are also probably under the control of nuclear genes.

Immature periods have already been considered in relation to mating types in *P. bursaria*. It was noted that "adolescent" lines could be accounted for by the activation of genes at one locus before the activation of those at a second, the expression of both loci being necessary for the full mating capacity. The finding that one gene may be expressed before another suggests that all cases of immaturity may represent cases of the repression of certain genes, with passage into maturity involving derepression of such genes.

On the basis of these data it is impossible to state whether the hereditary mechanism determining whether genes are repressed or expressed is cytoplasmic or nuclear. However, Siegel[598] has shown that paramecia which undergo macronuclear regeneration at conjugation (and acquire a new macronucleus from a fragment of the old) do not become immature. In contrast, true conjugants whose new macronuclei are formed from micronuclei do become immature. Since the cytoplasmic events at conjugation and macronuclear regeneration are virtually identical, it is concluded that the seat of the differentiations determining maturity and immaturity is the macronucleus, not the cytoplasm. This demonstration further reinforces our conclusion that the mechanisms which maintain immaturity and maturity operate by controlling gene expression.

Siegel[595] notes that when conjugation in *P. aurelia* occurs soon after a previous conjugation, the subsequent immature period is long; but when the intervals between conjugations are long, shorter periods of immaturity occur. He suggests that this observation explains the curious fact that immature periods after autogamy are absent—autogamy can be induced only many fissions after conjugation. The fact that the interval between conjugations is important in determining the length of subsequent intervals implies that an old macronucleus may affect the determination of a newly forming macronucleus, much as in the case of mating type inheritance in the Group B varieties of *P. aurelia*.

It is also interesting to note that the period of immaturity (measured in number of fissions) may be increased by starvation.[283] This is reminiscent of the effects of starvation on selfing (see above) reported by Nanney in *Tetrahymena*, and Hiwatashi in *P. caudatum* (see Section VIII, J, 6, b).

The capacity of *Euplotes minuta*[600a] and *P. aurelia* to undergo autogamy also shows long term cyclic variations. When some 10 to 40 fissions have intervened following conjugation or autogamy, *P. aurelia* will undergo autogamy when starved; starvation at earlier times does not lead to autogamy. The number of fissions necessary before autogamy can be induced varies with the stock. It is well-known that autogamy may be induced with no delay after macronuclear regeneration, in contrast to the many fissions required after conjugation or autogamy. This is an important fact for it suggests rather strongly that the life cycle variations in the capacity to undergo autogamy result from macronuclear differentiations.

While the passage from immaturity to maturity and the capacity to undergo autogamy probably represent variations in genic expression, the mechanism of senescence is unknown, in spite of the fact that senescence is one of the most extensively investigated aspects of protozoan genetics. If we define senescence as an increasing likelihood of death within any given time interval in organisms of increasing age (see Medawar[407]), then it is clear that many ciliates do not show senescence. But other ciliates do. A number of hypotheses have been suggested to explain senescence. A few will be considered here.

The hypothesis that aging is caused by micronuclear gene mutation was rejected by Mitchison[414] on the basis of breeding analysis involving young and old lines of *P. aurelia*. Sonneborn and Schneller[670] and Dippell,[131] however, showed that micronuclear chromosomal aberrations do contribute to death at autogamy in aged lines. Nevertheless, they conclude that the chromosomal aberrations are a secondary manifestation of aging, not a primary one, because mortality at autogamy increases much faster in old than in young lines. The hypothesis that senescence is due to macronuclear mutations was rejected by Kimball and Gaither[332] when they found that large doses of radiation failed to increase the rate of onset of reduced fission rate in aging lines of *P. aurelia*. Another possibility is that senescence results from inequalities in chromosome distribution arising from random segregation of chromosomes in a polyploid macronucleus devoid of subunits (cf. Fauré-Fremiet[168]). Although this hypothesis appears to fit the data which show an increasing rate of non-viability at conjugation[34] (see Section III, C, 2, there are a number of facts inconsistent with this view. Thus, Sonneborn and coworkers[670, 671] could find no evidence that alleles in heterozygotes in *P. aurelia* segregate in aging clones, even after macronuclear regeneration, which should make such an event more likely. Similarly, Nobili[474] quotes an unpublished experiment by Sonneborn and Tallan in which they found 538 macronuclear regenerates, all of which maintained their heterozygous condition for serotype alleles. The experiment was carried out on lines homozygous for the *am* gene which induces macronuclear regeneration. Furthermore, the study by Allen, Nanney, and Schensted (see above) supports the hypothesis that the macronucleus of *Tetrahymena* consists of subunits containing at least two complete genomes. Perhaps senescence is a manifestation of stable nuclear differentiations in the form of unfavorable gene repressions or derepressions. This hypothesis has appeared in a number of forms several times.[281, 168, 643, 598, 599b] In its favor, it should be noted that the other life cycle phenomena of maturity and ability to undergo autogamy probably have such a basis. Furthermore, many other stable nuclear differentiations in the Protozoa have been enumerated in this review. Such an explanation, of course, is equally applicable to the phenomenon of senescence in higher organisms.

N. Resistance to Calcium Chloride in Paramecium

Génermont[189] has found that the paramecia within newly established lines of *P. aurelia* of stock 90 (syngen 1) and stock 131 (syngen 8) are fairly uniform in their ability to survive the toxic effects of calcium chloride. However, after autogamy occurs, significant differences in resistance develop.

These differences were investigated further by crossing different caryonides of stock 90, expanding the exconjugants through several fissions and testing the resulting lines for calcium chloride resistance. An analysis of variance of the results revealed that exconjugant clones differed significantly from each other. It was concluded, therefore, that cytoplasmic determinants were involved in calcium chloride resistance. Second, caryonides differed significantly from each other. It was concluded that the differences in resistance were partly due to caryonidal inheritance. This conclusion is of particular interest, for calcium chloride resistance represents the only characteristic thought to be inherited caryonidally except for mating type and for a case of resistance to temperature studied by Jollos and later reinterpreted by Sonneborn (see Section VIII, 0). Third, when the analysis of variance was extended to subcaryonides, it was found that the differences between the two subcaryonides making up each caryonide were not significant. Differences between lines making up subcaryonides were also not significant. Therefore, the original inference that differences arise only during the formation of new caryonides is substantiated. The facts seem best interpreted on the basis of variations in gene expression in a fashion similar to that shown by mating type inheritance in the group A and B syngens of *P. aurelia* (see Section VIII, J, 4 and 5).

O. Temperature Adaptation

One of the classic and most remarkable studies in protozoan genetics was reported by Dallinger in 1887.[114] He began with three flagellates in mixed culture—*Monas dallingeri*, *Dallingeria drysdali*, and *Tetramitus ro-*

stratus—and attempted to adapt them to high temperature. The organisms were originally cultured at 60°F and did not survive temperatures above 78°F. Day by day the temperature was increased slowly, but as rapidly as possible without killing the cultures. Often the rate of increase had to be very slow indeed, for as the temperature rose higher and higher many critical stages occurred. During such periods the organisms became badly vacuolated. At times an increase of only a degree or two required many months. The whole experiment lasted some seven years. Finally, however, the animals were living at a temperature of 158°F. When subcultures of adapted organisms were returned to low temperature they died. Dallinger records the termination of this truly remarkable experiment as follows: "Here, with such pain as I presume is natural, I have to close the story. The accident happened, destroying the use of the instrument, and causing the whole to collapse. I preserved the sediment of my vessels, and have, as I said, begun the work again, and with precautions and suggestions begotten of experience, that I can only hope may not make that experience dearly bought." The basis for this remarkable adaptation is unknown. Dallinger's conclusion in this modern era of sophistication is, perhaps, worth quoting: "I can only claim for this fragment its suggestiveness, and its possible value as an incentive to others to treat the lower and minute forms of life in corresponding manners, and as showing that such work cannot be without value."

Jollos[287, 288, 289] reported that growth of *P. aurelia* and *P. caudatum* at 31°C induced a number of changes including resistance to high temperature. Generally, the changes disappeared at subsequent autogamy or conjugation during growth at lower temperatures. He interpreted such changes as examples of "Dauermodificationen": long-lasting changes induced by the environment, finally wearing off during culture in the absence of the inducer. No attempt will be made to review the various examples of dauermodifications in the Protozoa studied by Jollos. They include responses to a number of chemicals added to the medium as well as extremes of temperature. The reader is referred to the reviews of Jennings[275] and Sonneborn.[629] In general, it now appears that Jollos included as dauermodifications many diverse phenomena, most of which are still poorly understood. One of the most puzzling of the cases of temperature induced changes described by Jollos has been explained by Sonneborn[629] as spontaneous mutation in a gene which gave caryonidal inheritance. The mutant could have been established by natural selection during the long period of culture at high temperature.†

More recently, temperature adaptation in *P. aurelia*, syngen 1, has been studied by Franceschi.[180-4]

---

† Ossipov [486a] in a paper received too late for adequate review has shown by a variance analysis that temperature sensitivity is caryonidally inherited in P. *caudatum*.

Resistance was induced by culture for a number of days at 30 to 33°C (controls at 24°C). Tests for resistance made by measuring survival time at 42 to 52°C showed that the cultures acquired a considerably increased resistance. Return of adapted lines to temperatures below 30°C, followed by successive tests at 52°C revealed a gradual loss of resistance, rapid at first but often not complete before some fifty fissions. Contrary to Jollos' results, Franceschi found that loss of resistance did not occur at autogamy. She therefore concludes that the macronucleus is probably not involved and that the determinant is cytoplasmic. It might be noted, however, that the system of combined cytoplasmic and macronuclear determination exhibited by the inheritance of mating type in the group B syngens (see above) is not ruled out. Spontaneous mutation and selection does not seem possible in view of the uniformity of acquisition and loss of resistance, the use of isolation lines, and the small number of fissions concerned.

P. Polymorphism in Tetrahymena vorax

A number of ciliates, especially hypotrichs, undergo transformation from relatively small bacterial feeders called "microstomes" to large carnivorous "macrostomes" which feed upon ciliates of the same and other species. Although the principle change is one of size, extensive modifications in the oral region also occur. The larger oral apparatus of macrostomes makes them better adapted to their larger prey. Such changes are reversible and constitute non-inherited environmentally induced modifications.

Stable changes in the ability of different strains of *T. vorax* to undergo the microstome to macrostome transformation have been described[113a] and have been analyzed in some detail by Williams and Shaw.[733a, 585b] Williams has characterized three types of sublines, D, M, and S, all derived from one parental stock, V_2, of *T. vorax*. Although the types differ in the frequency with which they form macrostomes in axenic medium, all three produce macrostomes when washed and suspended with a suitable ciliate prey such as *T. pyriformis*. Microstomes of the D (dimorphic) type are distinguished from the others by producing high frequencies of macrostomes in axenic culture, by readily forming cysts, by their relatively large cell and nuclear size, more tailed cell form, high meridian number, highly vacuolated endoplasm, and a tendency to form a layer near the bottom in culture vessels, and the failure of phospholipids to stimulate growth. Microstomes of the M (monomorphic) type are distinguished by a much reduced multiplication rate in axenic culture and intermediate size. Microstomes of the S (small) type are distinguished by their small size; although, like type M, they rarely produce macrostomes in axenic culture, they may be easily distinguished from type M by their more rapid fission rate which is comparable to that of type D. The three types are very stable under ordinary conditions, but spontaneous changes from M to D, D to M, and S to D have been observed; S to M has not been seen. The remaining two possible changes M to S and D to S may be readily induced in high frequency by making a series of several serial subcultures in rapid succession. The new S cultures are highly stable like spontaneously produced S types. Intermediate types between D, M, and S have never been observed. Although the changes are relatively unaffected by the environment, the D to M transformation is favored by high temperature.

The basis for these transformations from one type to the other is unknown, but gene mutation is unlikely in the case of the induced changes because of their high frequency. Williams notes the parallel with mating type and serotype transformation and suggests that the phenomena may have similar underlying mechanisms. Reports by Shaw and Williams[589a, 585b] that the different types have different immobilization and precipitating antigens suggest that the types differ in genes expressed. Shaw also found an antigenic difference between microstomes and macrostomes of the same type also suggesting that changes in gene expression accompany the change from microstome to macrostome.

IX. THE CILIATE MACRONUCLEUS

Since the ciliate macronucleus is reviewed in another chapter of this volume, no detailed consideration will be given to it here. However, since several lines of genetic evidence bearing on its structure have been cited in this chapter, it is perhaps useful to bring them together for a brief summary. The presence of many sets of genes in the macronucleus has been clearly established by a comparison of the DNA content of macronuclei and micronuclei and by cytological observations on developing macronuclear anlagen. The fact that macronuclear regeneration leads to viable progeny also shows that each of the some 20 to 40 macronuclear fragments in *P. aurelia* has at least one complete set of genes. Likewise, the great resistance to radiation of the macronucleus probably arises from the many sets of genes which it contains.

According to the "grab-bag" hypothesis of the macronucleus,[314] each chromosome duplicates during every cell cycle and is segregated at random to the progeny. Accumulation of chromosomal imbalances and even the chance loss of all chromosomes of a given set should occur. These might be involved in (but certainly could not fully explain) senescence, the segregation of pure lines of mating types at binary fission, and the vegetative segregation of phenotypes corresponding to different alleles in *Tetrahymena* heterozygotes. However, two main arguments have been advanced against this hypothesis. First, some ciliates do not show senescence. It should be noted, however, that the grab-bag hypothesis does not predict that *all* lines will develop imbalances and die. Indeed few may die, for imbalances may first produce lines with reduced fission rates which may be eliminated by natural selection in favour of lines with more nearly balanced genomes. This reviewer is not aware of quantitative data on mortality and reduced fission rate in aged lines which rule out this possibility. Nevertheless, a careful consideration of the data on macronuclear regeneration in *am* homozygotes in *P. aurelia* should be made from this point of view (see Nobili[467, 471]). The second difficulty is the failure of alleles to segregate from heterozygotes after macronuclear regeneration (see Section VIII, M on ciliate life cycle). This matter has been discussed by Nobili.[474] He points out that if the level of ploidy were, say, 400n, then each of some 40 macronuclear fragments at macronuclear regeneration would contain about 10 haploid chromosomes of each set and the likelihood of obtaining some lines with one allele missing among the 538 lines observed (see description of experiment in Section VIII, M) would be appreciable. In fact, none were observed. Nevertheless, this argument leaves some room for doubt, for the estimates of numbers of genomes in macronuclear fragments certainly must have large standard errors. In fact, Woodard *et al.*[735b, 735c] have reported macronuclear ploidy levels of 860n, 1720n and 3440n in *P. aurelia*, syngen 4. Furthermore, fragments with great imbalances in chromosome numbers may produce non-viable animals which would be eliminated from consideration.

It might be worth considering a modification of the "grab-bag" hypothesis which converts it into a "partial grab-bag". Suppose the distribution of chromosomes at macronuclear division is not completely random. Perhaps, instead, there is a tendency (often not realized) for one daughter chromosome to go to one daughter animal and the other daughter chromosome to go to the other daughter animal. Such a process could lend the necessary stability observed in inheritance of traits at binary fission, yet still allow for unequal divisions of macronuclei demonstrated by MacDonald[391] in *Tetrahymena* and Kimball and Vogt-Köhne[329a] in *Paramecium*. So while the evidence against the grab-bag hypothesis, or variants of it, is considerable, it does not appear to the reviewer that it should be ignored completely at this point.

The "subunit" hypothesis of the macronucleus [629] assumes diploid, mitotically dividing, randomly segregating subnuclei. It is consistent with the lack of senescence shown by many ciliates, the high viability after macronuclear regeneration, and the data on intracaryonidal segregation in *Tetrahymena*. Although quantitative data on segregation rates have been obtained only for mating type and serotype in *Tetrahymena*, the fit of these data to the model of Nanney, Allen, and Schensted is impressive—particularly the demonstration that the rate of stabilization for both mating type and serotype are identical, as required by the theory. Furthermore, the data on segregation of isozyme phenotypes in heterozygotes fit the hypothesis in a qualitative way, at least. One difficulty is the fact that the stabilizing effect of starvation on mating type segregation rates is unexplained. This observation and others cited above in connection with caryonidal inheritance, selfing, immature periods of mating reactivity, isozyme and serotype determination make it clear that nuclei can be "determined" in both an exceedingly stable fashion (e.g., caryonidal inheritance in syngen 1 of *P. aurelia*) and in a very labile (e.g., selfers in *Euplotes*) fashion. And, as pointed out by Nanney in an earlier communication,[444] once we have accepted that mechanisms of nuclear plasticity exist why might they not account for all of the observed changes without resort to the hypothesis of segregation of differentially determined subunits? Another cause for uneasiness is the lack of cytological evidence for subunits. See, for example, the recent paper by Jurand *et al.*[297] However, the data of Raikov, reviewed by him in this volume, help here. The good quantitative fit of the data of Nanney and Allen to the predictions of Schensted remains the strongest evidence in support of the subunit hypothesis, but the theory cannot, at this point, be judged established.

A variant of the subunit hypothesis is suggested by Grell (see, for example, Ref. 217a) who postulates that the chromosomes of a set are bound together into a "compound chromosome" and segregate as a unit at macronuclear division. If the sets are diploid (perhaps brought about by somatic pairing) and segregate randomly, then this suggestion becomes genetically identical to the subunit hypothesis.

The fact that amicronucleate lines survive shows that the macronucleus is physiologically active. Is the micronucleus physiologically active? Sonneborn[628, 641] noted that paramecia whose micronuclear genotype was *KK* and whose macronuclear genotype was *kk* were unable to maintain kappa. But since the micronuclei contain only a small fraction of the amount of DNA present in the macronuclei, it may be that such tests are not sufficiently sensitive to detect micronuclear activity. Indeed, many investigators report that amicronucleate lines of ciliates are generally abnormal, being less vigorous than normal lines or even nonviable. Wells[720a] gives an excellent bibliography and summary of the many cases of amicronucleate clones and concludes that loss of the micronuclei in most instances (there being some exceptions) brings about severe changes which generally lead to death. In some cases, however, organisms are able to "readjust" and viable amicronucleate lines may arise. Thus, the evidence for activity of micronuclear genes is somewhat conflicting. However, there is little doubt that the micronuclei of some ciliates, at least, have functions during vegetative growth and reproduction.

X. CONCLUSIONS

Of the enormous number of protozoans, with their varied structures, cytological processes, and life cycles, few have been investigated genetically: *Paramecium, Chlamydomonas, Tetrahymena, Euplotes, Euglena, Trypano-*

soma, and a few amebas. Although the task of bringing new organisms under control in the laboratory is not to be taken lightly, there is every reason to believe that the effort would be worth-while. The organisms which have been studied have contributed much because of their uniqueness, and it is likely that other protozoans will do likewise.

A considerable repertoire of techniques for investigating genetic phenomena in asexual forms has now been developed— techniques such as nuclear and cytoplasmic transfer, and possibly even DNA induced transformation in trypanosomes. Somatic crossing over has been found in *Chlamydomonas,* and there would seem to be no reason why it should not be encountered elsewhere. The use of mathematical models of clonal segregation is essential for considering many phenomena of asexual reproduction. The mathematical work which has been done by Otter, Schensted, Kimura, and Reeve provides all of the necessary foundation so that the biologist with the aid of present-day computers may readily obtain solutions for particular models.

Although Protozoa have contributed little to our basic knowledge of crossing over, *Chlamydomonas* now certainly ranks with *Neurospora* and yeast in its suitability for the investigation of crossing over in true chromosomes.

Study of pigment and photosynthetic mutants in *Chlamydomonas* is only in its initial stages, but contributions are being made. If genetics has a role in the study of photosynthesis and the biosyntheis of photosynthetic pigments, then *Chlamydomonas* is certainly the organism of choice. Non-chromosomal mutants of *Chlamydomonas* are still to be investigated from this point of view.

Paramecium has played an important role in the exciting story of repair of mutational damage. The numbers and kinds of repair mechanisms are still to be discovered. *Paramecium* excels in the ease with which stages of the cell cycle can be managed, and hence is especially well suited for such studies. There is every reason to expect progress in this area.

Symbiosis and the role of kappa and kappa-like forms in genetics has been a long story full of surprises. We now believe that symbiosis and genetics and the evolution of the most basic cellular organelles such as mitochondria, chloroplasts, and kinetoplasts cannot be disentangled. And, it is likely that still more surprises lie ahead—in the nature of the many kinds of killing action, in the mechanism of the specific resistance to symbionts conferred by the symbionts themselves, in the mode of action of genes controlling symbionts, and in the story of the metagon. Furthermore, Protozoa seem as well suited as any organisms to provide material for answering the questions about the action of DNA in replication and determination of macromolecular structure in mitochondria and chloroplasts. The genetic analysis of non-chromosomal genes in *Chlamydomonas* may have opened the way to the first studies on the genetic structure and mapping of non-chromosomal determinants.

The ciliate cortex provides our first firm evidence that structure other than nucleic acid structure may play a genetic role. There is much to be learned at the biological level about this very difficult subject before it can be attacked at the molecular level. Again, Protozoa appear to be as good as, or better than, any other organisms for this task.

In the inheritance of mating type, serotype, life-cycle changes, and other traits too, the Protozoa have provided us with a wealth of examples, virtually unstudied in other organisms, which show that genes may be brought into a repressed or a derepressed state and that these states may be inherited. Much has been learned about the environmental and also the internal control of these states. Recent studies, such as those of Bomford on mating

FIG. 1. Linkage map of *Chlamydomonas reinhardi*.
Modified from references 144, 563, 229

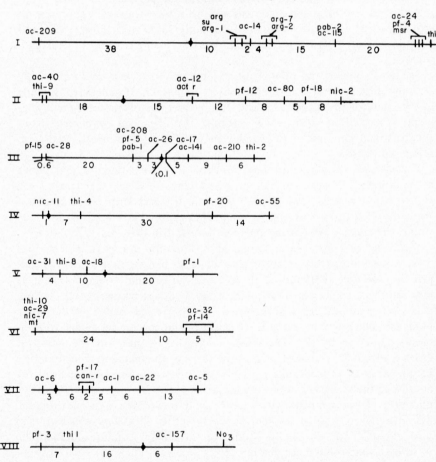

type inheritance in *P. bursaria*, seem to indicate that much is still to be learned about these phenomena at the biological level. The elucidation of the molecular mechanisms of stable repressions must be classed with the genetic role of structure as constituting two of the major problems of biology for the future.

ACKNOWLEDGMENTS

I am indebted to the Phi Beta Psi Sorority and the National Science Foundation for support of those portions of my own work which are reported in this chapter.

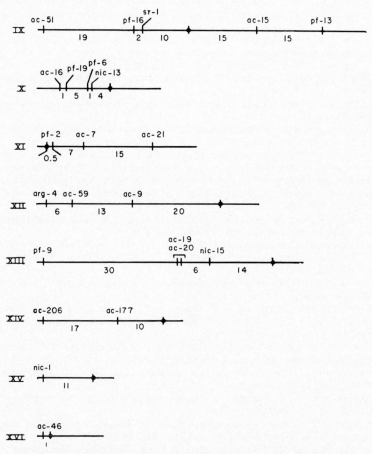

Gene symbols are given in Table 1. The order of genes within brackets is not known. Distances refer to regions between vertical lines extending below the chromosome. Centromeres are designated by solid circles.

REFERENCES

1. AARONSON, S., and BENSKY, B. (1962) o-Methylthreonine, a new bleaching agent for *Euglena gracilis. J. Gen. Microbiol.* **27**, 75–98.
2. ALLEN, M. B., PIETTE, L. H., and MURCHIO, J. C. (1962) Free radicals in photosynthetic reactions. I. Electron paramagnetic resonance signals from illuminated *Chlorella pyrenoidosa. Biochim. Biophys. Acta* **60**, 539–47.
3. ALLEN, S. L. (1956) Stabilization of unstable nuclei in *Tetrahymena pyriformis. Genetics* **41**, 632.
4. ALLEN, S. L. (1959) Strain differences in the esterases of *Tetrahymena. Anat. Rec.* **131**, 526–7.
5. ALLEN, S. L. (1960) Inherited variations in the esterases of *Tetrahymena. Genetics* **45**, 1051–70.
6. ALLEN, S. L. (1961) Genetic control of the esterases in the Protozoan *Tetrahymena pyriformis. Ann. N.Y. Acad. Sci.* **94**, 753–73.
7. ALLEN, S. L. (1961) A first case of linkage in the ciliated protozoa. *Genetics* **46**, 847–8.
8. ALLEN, S. L. (1963) Genomic exclusion in *Tetrahymena*: genetic basis. *J. Protozool.* **10**, 413–20.
9. ALLEN, S. L. (1964) Linkage studies in variety 1 of *Tetrahymena pyriformis:* A first case of linkage in the ciliated protozoa. *Genetics* **49**, 617–27.
10. ALLEN, S. L. (1964) The esterase isozymes of *Tetrahymena:* their distribution in isolated cellular components and their behavior during the growth cycle. *J. Exptl. Zool.* **155**, 349–70.
11. ALLEN, S. L. (1965) Genetic control of enzymes in *Tetrahymena. Brookhaven Symp. Biol.* **18**, 27–54.
12. ALLEN, S. L. (1966) The chemical genetics of the Protozoa. In *Chemical Zoology*, vol. 1, ed. M. FLORKIN and B. SCHEER, Academic Press Inc., New York.
13. ALLEN, S. L., MISCH, S., and MORRISON, B. M. (1963) Genetic control of an acid phosphatase in *Tetrahymena:* formation of a hybrid enzyme. *Genetics* **48**, 1635–58.
14. ALLEN, S. L., MISCH, M. S., and MORRISON, B. M. (1963) Variations in the electrophoretically separated acid phosphatases of *Tetrahymena. J. Histochem. and Cytochem.* **11**, 706–19.
15. ALLEN, S. L., and NANNEY, D. L. (1958) An analysis of nuclear differentiation in the selfers of *Tetrahymena. Am. Naturalist* **92**, 139–60.
16. ALTENBERG, E., and BROWNING, L. S. (1961) The relatively high frequency of wholebody mutations compared with fractionals induced by x-rays in *Drosophila* sperm. *Genetics* **46**, 203–11.
17. ALTMANN, R. (1890) *Die Elementarorganismen und ihre Beziehungen zu den Zellen*, Veit Co., Leipzig.
18. ANDERSON, T. F., PREER, JR., J. R., PREER, L. B., and BRAY, M. (1964) Studies on killing particles from *Paramecium:* the structure of refractile bodies from kappa particles. *J. Microscopie* **3**, 395–402.
19. APP, A. A., and JAGENDORF, A. T. (1963) Repression of chloroplast development in *Euglena gracilis* by substrates. *J. Protozool.* **10**, 340–3.
20. ARGETSINGER, J. (1965) The isolation of ciliary basal bodies (kinetosomes) from *Tetrahymena pyriformis. J. Cell Biol.* **24**, 154–7.
21. AUERBACH, C. (1951) Problems in chemical mutagenesis. *Cold Spring Harbor Symp. Quant. Biol.* **16**, 199–213.
22. AUSTIN, M. L. (1946) Contributions towards an analysis of the killing action of variety 4 killers in *Paramecium aurelia. Anat. Rec.* **96**, 514.
23. AUSTIN, M. L. (1948) The killing action and rate of production of single particles of paramecin 51. *Physiol. Zool.* **21**, 69–86.
24. AUSTIN, M. L. (1948) The killing substance, paramecin: activity of single particles. *Am. Naturalist* **82**, 51–59.

25. AUSTIN, M. L. (1951) Sensitivity to paramecin in *Paramecium aurelia* in relation to stock, serotype, and mating type. *Physiol. Zool.* **24**, 196–204.

26. AUSTIN, M. L. (1963) Progress in control of the emergence and the maintenance of serotypes of stock 51, syngen 4, of *Paramecium aurelia*. *J. Protozool.* **10**, (Suppl.), 21.

27. AUSTIN, M. L., WIDMAYER, D., and WALKER, L. M. (1956) Antigenic transformation as adaptive response of *Paramecium aurelia* to patulin; relation to cell division. *Physiol. Zool.* **29**, 261–87.

28. BALBINDER, E. (1956) Two loci controlling the maintenance and stability of the cytoplasmic factor "kappa" in stock 51, var. 4 killers of *Paramecium aurelia*. *Genetics* **41**, 634.

29. BALBINDER, E. (1959) The genotypic control of kappa in *Paramecium aurelia*, syngen 4, stock 51. *Genetics* **44**, 1227–41.

30. BALBINDER, E., and PREER, J. R. JR. (1959) Gel diffusion studies on serotype and serotype transformation in *Paramecium*. *J. Gen. Microbiol.* **21**, 156–67.

30a. BALSLEY, M. (1966) Dependence of the kappa particles of stock 7 of *Paramecium aurelia* on a single gene. *Genetics* **54**, 320.

31. BALTIMORE, D., and FRANKLIN, R. M. (1963) Properties of the mengovirus and poliovirus RNA polymerases. *Cold Spring Harbor Symp. Qant. Biol.* **28**, 105–8.

32. BALTUS, E., and BRACHET, J. (1963) Presence of deoxyribonucleic acid in the chloroplasts of *Acetabularia mediterranea*. *Biochim. Biophys. Acta*, **76**, 490–2.

33. BARNETT, A. (1959) The effect of continuous light and darkness on the mating type cycle in syngen 2 of *Paramecium multimicronucleatum*. *J. Protozool.* **6** (Suppl.), 22.

34. BARNETT, A. (1959) Effects of varying the extent and intensity of the daily exposure to light on the cycle of mating type reversals in *Paramecium multimicronucleatum*. *Science* **130**, 1412.

35. BARNETT, A. (1961) The inheritance of mating type and cycling in *Paramecium multimicronucleatum*, syngen 2. *Am. Zoologist* **1**, 341–2.

36. BARNETT, A. (1964) A circadian rhythm of mating type reversals in *Paramecium multimicronucleatum*. In *Circadian Clocks*, ed. J. ASCHOFF. North-Holland Publ. Co., Amsterdam, pp. 305–8.

37. BARNETT, A. (1966) A circadian rhythm of mating type reversals in *Paramecium multimicronucleatum*, syngen 2, and its genetic control. *J. Cell. Physiol.*, **67**, 239–70.

38. BARR, M. L. (1959) Sex chromatin and phenotype in man. *Science* **130**, 679–85.

39. BARR, M. L. (1959) Sex chromatin. *Science* **130**, 1302.

40. BARRAT, R. W., NEWMEYER, D., PERKINS, D. D., and GARNJOBST, L. (1954) Map construction in *Neurospora crassa*. *Advances in Genetics* **4**, 1–93.

41. BASSHAM, J. A., and CALVIN, M. (1957) *The Path of Carbon in Photosynthesis*, Prentice-Hall, Inc., Englewood Cliffs, New Jersey.

42. BEALE, G. H. (1948) The process of transformation of antigenic type in *Paramecium aurelia*, variety 4. *Proc. Nat. Acad. Sci., U.S.* **34**, 418–23.

43. BEALE, G. H. (1952) Antigen variation in *Paramecium aurelia*, variety 1. *Genetics* **37**, 62–74.

44. BEALE, G. H. (1952) Genetic control of gene expression in *Paramecium aurelia*. *Science* **115**, 480.

45. BEALE, G. H. (1954) *The Genetics of Paramecium aurelia*, Cambridge University Press, New York.

46. BEALE, G. H. (1957) A mate-killing strain of *Paramecium aurelia*, variety 1, from Mexico. *Proc. Roy. Phys. Soc. Edinb.* **26**, 11.

47. BEALE, G. H. (1957) The antigen system of *Paramecium aurelia*. *Intern. Rev. Cytol.* **6**, 1–23.

48. BEALE, G. H., and JURAND, A. (1960) Structure of the mate-killer (mu) particles in *Paramecium aurelia*, stock 540. *J. Gen. Microbiol.* **23**, 243–52.

49. BEALE, G. H. and KACSER, H. (1957) Studies on the antigens of *Paramecium aurelia* with the aid of fluorescent antibodies. *J. Gen. Microbiol.* **17**, 68–74.

50. BEALE, G. H., and MOTT, M. R. (1962) Further studies on the antigens of *Paramecium aurelia* with the aid of fluorescent antibodies. *J. Gen. Microbiol.* **28**, 617–23.

51. BEALE, G. H., and WILKINSON, J. F. (1961) Antigenic variation in unicellular organisms. *Ann. Rev. Microbiol.* **15**, 263–96.

52. BEHME, R. J. (1964) DNA base compositions of several symbionts in *Paramecium aurelia*. *Genetics* **50**, 235.

53. BEISSON, J., and SONNEBORN, T. M. (1965) Cytoplasmic inheritance of the organization of the cell cortex in *Paramecium aurelia*. *Proc. Nat. Acad. Sci., U.S.* **53**, 275–82.

54. BEISSON-SCHECROUN, J. (1964) Hereditary maintenance of spontaneous and provoked variations of cortical organization in *Paramecium aurelia*. *Proc. XIth Intern. Congr. Cell Biol., Excerpta Medica* **77**, 11.

55. BĚLǍR, K. (1922) Untersuchungen an *Actinophyrs sol* Ehrenberg. I. Die Morphologie des Formwechsels. *Arch. f. Protistenk.* **46**, 1–96.

56. BĚLǍR, K. (1924) Untersuchungen an *Actinophrys sol* Ehrenberg. II. Beiträge zur Physiologie des Formwechsels. *Arch. f. Protistenk.* **48**, 371–434.

57. BEN-SHAUL, Y., EPSTEIN, H. T., and SCHIFF, J. A. (1965) Studies of chloroplast development in *Euglena*. 10. The return of the chloroplast to the proplastid condition during dark adaptation. *Canad. J. Bot.* **43**, 129–36.

58. BEN-SHAUL, Y., SCHIFF, J. A., and EPSTEIN, H. T. (1964) Studies of chloroplast development in *Euglena*. VII. Fine structure of the developing plastid. *Plant Physiol.* **39**, 231–40.

59. BERNSTEIN, E., and JAHN, T. L. (1955) Certain aspects of the sexuality of two species of *Chlamydomonas*, *J. Protozool.* **2**, 81–85.

60. BEUTLER, E., YEH, M., and FAIRBANKS, V. F. (1962) The normal human female as a mosaic of X-chromosome activity; studies using the gene for G-6-PD-deficiency as a marker. *Proc. Nat. Acad. Sci., U.S.* **48**, 9–16.

61. BISHOP, J. O. (1961) Purification of an immobilization antigen of *Paramecium aurelia*, variety 1. *Biochim. Biophys. Acta* **50**, 471–7.

62. BISHOP, J. O. (1963) Immunological assay of some immobilizing antigens of *Paramecium aurelia*, variety 1. *J. Gen. Microbiol.* **30**, 271–80.

63. BISHOP, J. O., and BEALE, G. H. (1960) Genetical and biochemical studies of the immobilization antigens of *Paramecium aurelia*. *Nature* **186**, 734.

64. BLEYMAN, L. (1963) Selfing studies in stock 210, syngen 5, *Paramecium aurelia*. *J. Protozool.* **10** (Suppl.), 21–22.

65. BLEYMAN, L. (1964) Variable gene expression in *Paramecium aurelia*. *J. Protozool.* **11** (Suppl.) 29.

66. BLEYMAN, L. (1964) The inhibition of mating reactivity in *Paramecium aurelia* by inhibitors of protein and RNA synthesis. *Genetics* **50**, 236.

67. BOGORAD, L. (1962) Chlorophylls. In *Physiology and Biochemistry of Algae*, Academic Press, New York, pp. 385–408.

68. BOLTON, E., and MCCARTHY, B. (1962) A general method for the isolation of RNA complementary to DNA. *Proc. Nat. Acad. Sci., U.S.* **48**, 1390–7.

69. BOMFORD, R. (1965) Infection of algae-free *Paramecium bursaria* with strains of Chlorella, Scenedesmus, and a yeast. *J. Protozool.* **12**, 221–4.

70. BOMFORD, R. (1965) Changes of mating type in *Paramecium bursaria*. *Proc. 2nd Intern. Conf. Protozool., Excerpta Medica* **91**, 251.

71. BRAWERMAN, G., and CHARGAFF, E. (1960) A self-reproducing system concerned with the formation of chloroplasts in *Euglena gracilis*. *Biochim. Biophys. Acta* **37**, 221–9.

72. BRAWERMAN, G., and EISENSTADT, J. (1964) Deoxyribonucleic acid from the chloroplasts of *Euglena gracilis*. *Biochim. Biophys. Acta* **91**, 477–85.

72a. BRINK, R. A. (1960) Paramutation and chromosome organization. *Quarterly Rev. Biol.* **35**, 120–37.

72b. BRINK, R. A. (1964) Phase change in higher plants and somatic cell heredity. *Quarterly Rev. Biol.* **37**, 1–22.

73. BROWN, C. H. (1950) Elimination of kappa particles from "killer" strains of *Paramecium aurelia* by treatment with chloromycetin. *Nature* **166**, 527.

74. BROWN, K. N. (1963) The antigenic character of the "brucei" trypanosomes. In *Immunity to Protozoa*, ed. P.C.C. GARNHAM, A. E. PIERCE and I. ROITT, Blackwell, Oxford, pp. 204–12.

75. BUCHNER, P. (1953) *Endosymbiose der Tiere mit Pflanzlichen Mikroorganismen.* Birkhauser, Basel.

76. BUFFALOE, N. D. (1958) A comparative cytological study of four species of *Chlamydomonas. Bull. Torrey Botan. Club* **85**, 157–78.

77. BUFFALOE, N. D. (1959) Some effects of colchicine on cells of *Chlamydomonas eugametos* Moewus. *Exptl. Cell Res.* **16**, 221–31.

78. BUTZEL, JR., H. M. (1953) A morphological mutant of stock 90, variety 1, of *Paramecium aurelia. Microbial Genetics Bull.* **8**, 5–6.

79. BUTZEL, JR., H. M. (1953) Two new one-type stocks in variety 1 of *Paramecium aurelia. Microbial Genetics Bull.* **8**, 5.

80. BUTZEL, JR., H. M. (1955) Mating type mutations in variety 1 of *Paramecium aurelia,* and their bearing upon the problem of mating type determination. *Genetics* **40**, 321–30.

81. BUTZEL, JR., H. M., BROWN, L. H., and MARTIN, W. B. (1960) Effects of detergents upon killer-sensitive reactions in *Paramecium aurelia. Physiol. Zool.* **33**, 213–24.

82. BUTZEL, JR., H. M., and PAGLIARA, A. (1962) The effect of biochemical inhibitors upon the killer-sensitive system in *Paramecium aurelia. Exptl. Cell Res.* **27**, 382–95.

83. BUTZEL, JR., H. M., and VAN WAGTENDONK, W. J. (1963) Some properties of the lethal agent found in cell-free fluids obtained from cultures of lambda-bearing *Paramecium aurelia*, syngen 8, stock 299. *J. Protozool.* **10**, 250–2.

84. BUTZEL, JR., H. M., and VINCIGUERRA, B. (1957) A fission-rate mutant of stock 90, variety 1, of *Paramecium aurelia. Microbial Genetics Bull.* **15**, 7–8.

85. CARLSON, E., and SOUTHIN, J. L. (1962) Comparative mutagenesis of the dumpy locus in *Drosophila melanogaster.* I. X-ray treatment of mature sperm—frequency and distribution. *Genetics* **47**, 321–36.

86. CATCHESIDE, D. G. (1949) *The Genetics of Macroorganisms.* Pitman, New York.

87. CAULLERY, M. J. (1950). *Parasitism and Symbiosis.* Translated into English by A. M. LYSAGHT. Sidgwick and Jackson, London.

88. CHANCE, B., and SAGER, R. (1957) Oxygen and light induced oxidations of cytochrome, flavoprotein, and pyridine nucleotide in a *Chlamydomonas* mutant. *Plant Physiol.* **32**, 548–60.

89. CHAO, P. K. (1953) Kappa concentration per cell in relation to the life cycle, genotype and mating type in *Paramecium aurelia*, variety 4. *Proc. Nat. Acad. Sci., U.S.* **39**, 103–13.

90. CHAO, P. K. (1954) Present status of the study on kappa concentration per ce in *Paramecium aurelia. Microbial Genetics Bull.* **11**, 11–12.

91. CHEN, T. T. (1940) Polyploidy and its origin in *Paramecium. J. Heredity* **31**, 175–84.

92. CHEN, T. T. (1940) Conjugation in *Paramecium bursaria* between animals with diverse nuclear constitutions *J. Heredity* **31**, 185–96.

93. CHEN, T. T. (1940) A further study on polyploidy in *Paramecium. J. Heredity* **31**, 249–51.

94. CHEN, T. T. (1945) Induction of conjugation in *Paramecium bursaria* among animals of one mating type by fluid from another mating type. *Proc. Nat. Acad. Sci., U.S.* **31**, 404–10.

95. CHEN, T. T. (1946) Varieties and mating types in *Parameciumbursaria*. I. New variety and types, from England, Ireland, and Czechoslovakia. *Proc. Nat. Acad. Sci., U.S.* **32**, 173–81.

96. CHEN, T. T. (1946) Conjugation in *Paramecium bursaria*. II. Nuclear phenomena in lethal conjugation between varieties. *J. Morph.* **79**, 125–262.

96a. CHEN, T. T. (1948) Chromosomes in Opalinidae (Protozoa, Ciliata) with special reference to their behavior, morphology, individuality, diploidy, haploidy, and association with nucleoli. *J. Morph.* **83**, 281–358.

97. CHEN, T. T. (1955) Paramecin 34, a killer substance produced by *Paramecium bursaria*. *Proc. Soc. Exptl. Biol. and Med.* **88**, 541–3.

98. CHEN, T. T. (1956) Varieties and mating types in *Paramecium bursaria*. II. Variety and mating types found in China. *J. Exptl. Zool.* **132**, 255–68.

98a. CHEN, T. T. (1963) New mating types of *Paramecium bursaria* from Germany and Austria. *J. Protozool.* **10** (Suppl.), 22.

99. CHÈVREMONT, M. (1963) Cytoplasmic DNA. In *Cell Growth and Cell Division*, ed. R. J. C. HARRIS, Academic Press, New York, pp. 323–33.

100. CHÈVREMONT, M., CHÈVREMONT-COMHAIRE, S., and BAECKELAND (1959) Action de desoxyribonucléases neutre et acide sur des cellules somatiques vivante cultivées *in vitro*. *Arch. Biol. (Liège)* **70**, 811–49.

101. CHIANG, K. S., KATES, J. R., and SUEOKA, N. (1965) Meiotic DNA replication mechanism of *Chlamydomonas reinhardi*. *Genetics* **52**, 434–5.

102. CHUN, E. H. L., VAUGHAN, JR., N. H., and RICH, A. (1963) The isolation and characterization of DNA associated with chloroplast preparations. *J. Mol. Biol.* **7**, 130–41.

103. CLARK, G. M., and ELLIOTT, A. M. (1956) Nuclear behavior in haploid clones of *Tetrahymena pyriformis*. *J. Protozool.* **3** (Suppl.), 3.

104. CLARK, G. M., and ELLIOTT, A. M. (1956) The induction of haploidy in *Tetrahymena pyriformis* following x-irradiation. *J. Protozool.* **3**, 181–8.

105. CLELAND, R. (1962) The cytogenetics of *Oenothera*. *Advances in Genetics* **11**, 147–237.

106. COHEN, L. W. (1965) The basis for the circadian rhythm of mating in *Paramecium bursaria*. *Exptl. Cell. Res.* **37**, 360–7.

107. COHEN, L. W., and SIEGEL, R. W. (1963) The mating type substances of *Paramecium bursaria*. *Genetical Res.* **4**, 143–50.

108. COHN, M., and HORIBATA, K. (1959) Inhibition by glucose of the induced synthesis of the β-galactoside enzyme system of *Escherichia coli*. *J. Bact.* **78**, 601–12.

109. COLE, R. J., and DANIELLI, J. F. (1963) Nuclear-cytoplasmic interactions in the responses of *Amoeba proteus* and *Amoeba discoides* to streptomycin. *Exptl. Cell Res.* **29**, 199–206.

110. COLEMAN, A. W. (1959) Sexual isolation in *Pandorina morum*. *J. Protozool.* **6**, 249–64.

111. COLEMAN, A. W. (1963) Immobilization, agglutination and agar precipitin effects of antibodies to flagella of *Pandorina* mating types. *J. Protozool.* **10**, 141–8.

112. COOPER, J. E. (1965) An immunological, biochemical and genetic analysis of non-immobilization antigen 5 in *Paramecium aurelia*, syngen 2. Ph. D. Dissertation, University of Pennsylvania.

113. COOPER, J. E. (1965) A fast-swimming "mutant" in stock 51 of *Paramecium aurelia*, variety 4. *J. Protozool.* **12**, 381–4.

113a. CORLISS, J. O. (1953) Comparative studies on holotrichous ciliates in the *Colpidium-Glaucoma-Leucophrys-Tetrahymena* group. II. Morphology, life cycles, and systematic status of strains in pure culture. *Parasitology* **43**, 49–87.

114. DALLINGER, W. H. (1887) The president's address. *J. Roy. Micr. Soc.* **1**, 185–99.

115. DANIELLI, J. F. (1958) Studies of inheritance in amoebae by the technique of nuclear transfer. *Proc. Roy. Soc., B* **148**, 321–31.

116. DANIELLI, J. F. (1960) Cellular inheritance as studied by nuclear transfer in amoebae In *New Approaches in Cell Biology*, ed. P. M. B. WALKER, Academic Press, New York, pp. 15–22.

117. DANIELLI, J. F. (1960) Inheritance in amoebae, studied by nuclear transfer. In *Microbial Genetics*, 10th Sympos. Soc. Genl. Microbiol., London, ed. W. HAYES and R. C. CLOWES, Cambridge Univ. Press, pp. 294–300.

118. DANIELLI, J., LORCH, I., ORD, M., and WILSON, E. (1955) Nucleus and cytoplasm in cellular inheritance. *Nature* 176, 1114–5.

119. DARLINGTON, C. D. (1944) Heredity, development and infection. *Nature* 154, 164–9.

120. DeDEKEN-GRENSON, M. (1959) The mass induction of white strains in *Euglena* as influenced by the physiological conditions. *Exptl. Cell Res.* 18, 185–6.

121. DeDEKEN-GRENSON, M., and GODTS, A. (1960) Descendance of *Euglena* cells isolated-after various bleaching treatments. *Exptl. Cell Res.* 19, 376–82.

122. DeDEKEN-GRENSEN, M., and MESSIN, S. (1958) La continuité génétique des chloro. plasts chez les Euglenes. *Biochim. Biophys. Acta* 27, 145–55.

123. deHALLER, G. (1964) Altération expérimentale de la stomatogenèsis chez *Paramecium aurelia. Rev. Suisse Zool.* 71, 592–600.

124. deHALLER, G. (1964) About inheritance of morphological characteristics of the cortex in *Paramecium aurelia. J. Protozool.* 11 (Suppl.), 48.

125. deHALLER, G. (1965) Sur l'hérédité de characteristiques morphologique du cortex chez *Paramecium aurelia. Arch. Zool. Expér. Gén.* 105, 169–78.

126. DELBRÜCK, M. (1949) See discussion to paper of Sonneborn and Beale, in *Unités biologiques dousées de continuité génétique.* C.N.R.S. Paris 7, 33.

127. DILLER, W. F. (1936) Nuclear reorganization processes in *P. aurelia* with descriptions of autogamy and "hemixis". *J. Morph.* 59, 11–67.

128. DIPPELL, R. V. (1948) Mutations of the killer plasmagene kappa, in variety 4 of *Paramecium aurelia. Am. Naturalist* 82, 43–50.

129. DIPPELL, R. V. (1950) Mutation of the killer cytoplasmic factor in *Paramecium aurelia. Heredity* 4, 165–87.

130. DIPPELL, R. V. (1954) A preliminary report on the chromosomal constitution of certain variety 4 races of *Paramecium aurelia. Caryologia* 6 (Suppl.), 1109–11.

131. DIPPELL, R. V. (1955) Some cytological aspects of aging in variety 4 of *Paramecium aurelia. J. Protozool.* 2 (Suppl.), 7.

132. DIPPELL, R. V. (1958) The fine structure of kappa in killer stock 51 of *Paramecium aurelia.* Preliminary observations. *J. Biophys. Biochem. Cytol.* 4, 125–8.

133. DIPPELL, R. V. (1964) Perpetuation of cortical structure and pattern in *P. aurelia. Proc. XIth Intern. Congr. Cell Biol., Excerpta Medica* 77, 16–17.

134. DIPPELL, R. V. (1965) Reproduction of surface structure in *Paramecium. 2nd Intern. Conf. Protozool., Excerpta Medica* 91, 65.

135. DORNER, R. W. (1957) Stability of paramecin 34 at different temperatures and pH values. *Science* 126, 1243–4.

135a. DOWNS, L. E. (1959) Mating types and their determination in *Stylonychia putrina J. Protozool.* 6, 285–92.

136. DROOP, M. R. (1963) Algae and invertebrates in symbiosis. In *Symbiotic Associations,* 13th Symp. Soc. Gen. Microbiol., Cambridge Univ. Press, pp. 171–99.

137. DRYL, S. (1959) Antigenic transformation in *Paramecium aurelia* after homologous antiserum treatment during autogamy and conjugation. *J. Protozool.* 6 (Suppl.), 25.

138. DRYL, S. (1965) Antigenic transformation in relation to nutritional conditions and the interautogamous cycle in *Paramecium aurelia. Exptl. Cell Res.* 37, 569–81.

139. duBUY, H. G., MATTERN, C. F. T., and RILEY, F. L. (1965) Isolation and characterization of DNA from kinetoplasts of *Leishmania enrietti. Science* 147, 754–6.

140. EBERSOLD, W. T. (1956) Crossing over in *Chlamydomonas reinhardi. Am. J. Bot.* 43, 408–10.

141. EBERSOLD, W. T. (1962) Biochemical genetics. In *Physiology and Biochemistry of Algae*, ed. R. A. LEWIN, Academic Press, New York, pp. 731–9.

142. EBERSOLD, W. T. (1963) Heterozygous diploid strains of *Chlamydomonas reinhardi*. *Genetics* **48**, 888.

143. EBERSOLD, W. T., and LEVINE, R. P. (1959) A genetic analysis of linkage group I of *Chlamydomonas reinhardi*. *Z. Vererb.* **90**, 74–82.

144. EBERSOLD, W. T., LEVINE, R. P., LEVINE, E. E., and OLMSTED, M. A. (1962) Linkage maps in *Chlamydomonas reinhardi*. *Genetics* **47**, 531–43.

145. EBRINGER, L. (1962) Erythromycin-induced bleaching of *Euglena gracilis*. *J. Protozool.* **9**, 373–4.

146. EBRINGER, L. (1962) Side-effect of kanamycin on a green protista. *J. Antibiotics* **15**, 113–14.

147. EDELMAN, M., COWAN, C. A., EPSTEIN, H. T., and SCHIFF, J. A. (1964) Studies of chloroplast development in *Euglena*. VIII. Chloroplast-associated DNA. *Proc. Nat. Acad. Sci., U.S.* **52**, 1214–9.

148. EDELMAN, M., SCHIFF, J. A., and EPSTEIN, H. T. (1965) Studies of chloroplast development in *Euglena*. XII. Two types of satellite DNA. *J. Mol. Biol.* **11**, 769–74.

149. EHRET, C. F., and DEHALLER, G. (1963) Origin, development and maturation of organelles and organelle systems of the cell surface in *Paramecium*. *J. Ultrastructure Res.* **6** (Suppl.), 3–42.

150. EHRET, C. F., and POWERS, E. L. (1952) Antibiotic sensitivity of kappa and the influence of x-irradiation on the production of aureomycin-resistant "killers" in *Paramecium aurelia*, 51 VIII KK. *Proc. Soc. Protozool.* **3**, 14.

151. EHRET, C. F., and POWERS, E. L. (1959) The cell surface of *Paramecium*. *Intern. Rev. Cytol.* **8**, 97–133.

152. EISENSTADT, J., and BRAWERMAN, G. (1963) Incorporation of amino acids into proteins of chloroplasts and chloroplast ribosomes of *Euglena*. *Biochim. Biophys. Acta* **76**, 319–21.

152a. ELLIOTT, A. E., ADDISON, M. A., and CAREY, S. E. (1962) Distribution of *Tetrahymena pyriformis* in Europe. *J. Protozool.* **9**, 135–41.

153. ELLIOTT, A. M., and CLARK, G. M. (1956) The induction of haploidy in *Tetrahymena pyriformis* following x-irradiation. *J. Protozool.* **3** (Suppl.), 6.

154. ELLIOTT, A. M., and CLARK, G. M. (1958) Genetic studies of the pyridoxine mutant in variety 2 of *Tetrahymena pyriformis*. *J. Protozool.* **5**, 235–40.

155. ELLIOTT, A. M., and CLARK, G. M. (1958) Genetic studies of the serine mutant in variety 9 of *Tetrahymena pyriformis*. *J. Protozool.* **5**, 240–6.

156. ELLIOTT, A. M., and GRUCHY, D. F. (1952) The occurrence of mating types in *Tetrahymena*. *Biol. Bull.* **103**, 301.

157. ELLIOTT, A. M., and HAYES, R. E. (1953) Mating types in *Tetrahymena*. *Biol. Bull.* **105**, 269–84.

158. ELLIOTT, A. M., and HAYES, R. E. (1955) *Tetrahymena* from Mexico, Panama and Colombia, with special reference to sexuality. *J. Protozool.* **2**, 75–80.

159. ELLIOTT, A. M., and NANNEY, D. L. (1952) Conjugation in *Tetrahymena*. *Science* **116**, 33–34.

159a. ELLIOTT, A. M., STUDIER, M. A., and WORK, J. A. (1964) *Tetrahymena pyriformis* from several Pacific islands and Australia. *J. Protozool.* **11**, 370–8.

160. EPHRUSSI, B. (1951) Remarks on cell heredity. In *Genetics in the 20th Century*, ed. by L. C. DUNN, Macmillan, New York, pp. 241–62.

161. EPHRUSSI, B. (1953) *Nucleocytoplasmic Relations in Microorganisms*, Clarendon Press, Oxford.

161a. EPHRUSSI, B. (1956) Enzymes in cellular differentiation. In *Enzymes: Units of Biological Structure and Function*, ed. by O. H. GAEBLER, Academic Press, New York, pp. 29–40.

162. EPSTEIN, H. T., and SCHIFF, J. A. (1961) Studies of chloroplast development in *Euglena*. IV. Electron and fluorescence microscopy of the proplastid and its development into a mature chloroplast. *J. Protozool.* **8**, 427–37.

163. EPSTEIN, R. H., BOLLE, A., STEINBERG, C. M., KELLENBERGER, E., BOY DE LA TOUR, E. CHEVALLEY, R., EDGAR, R. S., SUSSMAN, M., DENHARDT, G. H., and LIELAUSIS, A. (1963) Physiological studies of conditional lethal mutants of bacteriophage T4D. *Cold Spring Harbor Symp. Quant. Biol.* **28**, 375–92.

164. EVERSOLE, R. A. (1956) Biochemical mutants of *Chlamydomonas reinhardi*. *Am. J. Bot.* **43**, 404–7.

165. EVERSOLE, R. A., and TATUM, E. L. (1956) Chemical alteration of crossing over frequency in *Chlamydomonas*. *Proc. Nat. Acad. Sci., U.S.* **42**, 68–72.

166. FAMINTZIN, A. (1907) Die Symbiose als Mittel der Synthese von Organismen. *Biol. Centralbl.* **27**, 353–64.

167. FAURÉ-FREMIET, E. (1952) Symbiontes bactériens des ciliés du genre *Euplotes*. *Compt. Rend.* **235**, 402–3.

168. FAURÉ-FREMIET, E. (1953) L'hypothèse de la sénescence et les cycles de réorganization nucléaire chez Ciliés. *Rev. Suisse Zool.* **60**, 426–38.

169. FINGER, I. (1956) Immobilizing and precipitating antigens of *Paramecium*. *Biol. Bull.* **111**, 358–63.

170. FINGER, I. (1957) The inheritance of the immobilization antigens of *Paramecium aurelia*, variety 2. *J. Genetics* **55**, 361–74.

171. FINGER, I. (1964) Use of simple gel-diffusion techniques to assign antigenic markers to native proteins. *Nature* **203**, 1035–9.

172. FINGER, I., and HELLER, C. (1962) Immunogenetic analysis of proteins of *Paramecium*. I. Comparison of specificities controlled by alleles and by different loci. *Genetics* **47**, 223–39.

173. FINGER, I., and HELLER, C. (1963) Immunogenetic analysis of proteins of *Paramecium*. IV. Evidence for presence of hybrid antigens in heterozygotes. *J. Mol. Biol.* **6**, 190–202.

174. FINGER, I., and HELLER, C. (1964) Cytoplasmic control of gene expression in *Paramecium*. I. Preferential expression of a single allele in heterozygotes. *Genetics* **49**, 485–98.

175. FINGER, I., and HELLER, C. (1964) Immunogenetic analysis of proteins of *Paramecium*. V. Detection of specific determinants in strains lacking a surface antigen. *Genetical Res.* **5**, 127–36.

176. FINGER, I., and HELLER, C. (1965) Induction of gene expression in *Paramecium* by cell-free culture fluid. *Am. Zool.* **5**, 649.

177. FINGER, I., HELLER, C., and GREEN, A. (1962) Immunogenetic analysis of proteins of *Paramecium*. II. Coexistence of two immobilization antigens within animals of a single serotype. *Genetics* **47**, 241–53.

178. FINGER, I., HELLER, C., and SMITH, J. P. (1963) Immunogenetic analysis of proteins of *Paramecium*. III. A method for determining relationships among antigenic proteins. *J. Mol. Biol.* **6**, 182–9.

179. FINGER, I., ONORATO, F., HELLER, C., and WILCOX, H. B. III (1965) Antigen structure and synthesis in *Paramecium*. *2nd Intern. Conf. Protozool., Excerpta Medica* **91**, 244.

180. FRANCESCHI, T. (1958) Modificazioni di resistenza in *Paramecium aurelia* var. 1. *Boll. Mus. Istit. Biol. Univ. Genova* **28**, 87–105.

181. FRANCESCHI, T. (1961) L'induzione della sessualita in *Paramecium* nella recerca del sistema ereditario delle Dauermodifikationen. *Boll. Mus. Istit. Biol. Univ. Genova*, **31**, 47–59.

182. FRANCESCHI, T. (1963) L'effetto dell'autogamia su linee durevolmente modificate di *Paramecium aurelia*, syngen 1. *Boll. Zool. Unione Zool. Ital.* **30**, 13–25.

183. FRANCESCHI, T. (1964) Nuovi studi sull'effetto dell'autogamia in linee durevolmente modificate di *Paramecium aurelia*, syngen 1. *Boll. Zool.* **31**, 1–14.

184. FRANCESCHI, T., and CADEMARTORI, E. (1958) Osservazioni su *Paramecium aurelia* var. 1 in allevamento a differenti temperature. *Boll. Mus. Istit. Biol. Univ. Genova* **28**, 169–82.

185. FRIEDRICH-FRESKA, VON H., and KAUDEWITZ, F. (1953) Letale Spätfolgen nach Einbau von ^{32}P in *Amoeba proteus* und ihre Deutung durch genetische Unterein-heiten. *Z. Naturforsch.* **8b**, 343–55.

186. FULLER, H. (1958) *Symbiose im Tierreich*, Wittenberg-Lutherstadt, A. ZIEMSEN.

187. GECKLER, R. P. (1949) Nitrogen mustard inactivation of the cytoplasmic factor kappa in *P. aurelia*, variety 4. *Science* **110**, 89–90.

188. GECKLER, R. P. (1950) Genetic changes induced by exposure to nitrogen mustard and their inheritance in *Paramecium aurelia*, variety 4. *Genetics* **35**, 253–77.

189. GÉNERMONT, J. (1961) Déterminants génétiques macronucléaires et cytoplasmiques controlant la résistance au chlorure de calcium chez " *Paramecium aurelia* " (souche 90, variété 1). *Ann. de Génétique* **3**, 1–8.

190. GIBOR, A., and GRANICK, S. (1962) Ultraviolet sensitive factors in the cytoplasm that affect the differentiation of *Euglena* plastids. *J. Cell. Biol.* **15**, 599–603.

191. GIBOR, A., and GRANICK, S. (1962) The plastid system of normal and bleached *Euglena gracilis. J. Protozool.* **9**, 327–34.

192. GIBOR, A., and GRANICK, S. (1964) Plastids and mitochondria: inheritable systems. *Science* **145**, 890–8.

193. GIBOR, A., and IZAWA, M. (1963) The DNA content of the chloroplasts of *Aceta-bularia. Proc. Nat. Acad. Sci., U.S.* **50**, 1164–9.

194. GIBSON, I. (1965) The replication of metagons and mu particles from *Paramecium* in another cell—*Didinium. Genetical Res.* **6**, 398–410.

195. GIBSON, I. (1965) Electrophoresis of extracts of *Paramecium aurelia* containing metagons. *Proc. Roy. Soc. (London)*, Ser. B **161**, 538–49.

196. GIBSON, I., and BEALE, G. H. (1961) Genic basis of the mate-killer trait in *Paramecium aurelia*, stock 540. *Genetical Res.* **2**, 82–91.

197. GIBSON, I., and BEALE, G. H. (1962) The mechanism whereby the genes M_1 and M_2 in *Paramecium aurelia*, stock 540, control growth of mate-killer (mu) particles. *Genetical Res.* **3**, 24–50.

198. GIBSON, I., and BEALE, G. H. (1963) The action of ribonuclease and 8-azaguanine on mate-killer paramecia. *Genetical Res.* **4**, 42–54.

199. GIBSON, I., and BEALE, G. H. (1964) Infection into paramecia of metagons derived from other mate-killer paramecia. *Genetical Res.* **5**, 85–106.

200. GIBSON, I., and SONNEBORN, T. M. (1964) Killer particles and metagons of *Para-mecium* grown in *Didinium. Genetics* **50**, 249–50.

201. GIBSON, I., and SONNEBORN, T. M. (1964) Is the metagon an m-RNA in *Paramecium* and a virus in *Didinium*? *Proc. Nat. Acad. Sci., U.S.* **52**, 869–76.

202. GILLHAM, N. W. (1963) The nature of exceptions to the pattern of uniparental inheritance for high level streptomycin resistance in *Chlamydomonas reinhardi. Genetics* **48**, 431–40.

203. GILLHAM, N. W. (1965) Induction of chromosomal and nonchromosomal mutations in *Chlamydomonas reinhardi* with N-methyl-N'-nitro-N-nitrosoguanidine. *Genetics* **52**, 529–37.

203a. GILLHAM, N. W. (1965) Linkage and recombination between nonchromsomal mutations in *Chlamydomonas reinhardi. Proc. Nat. Acad. Sci., U.S.* **54**, 1560–7.

204. GILLHAM, N. W., and LEVINE, R. P. (1962) Studies on the origin of streptomycin resistant mutants in *Chlamydomonas reinhardi. Genetics* **47**, 1463–74.

205. GILMAN, L. C. (1939) Mating types in *Paramecium caudatum. Am. Naturalist* **73**, 445–50.

206. GILMAN, L. C. (1941) Mating types in diverse races of *Paramecium caudatum*. *Biol. Bull.* **80**, 384–402.
207. GILMAN, L. C. (1949) Intervarietal mating reactions in *Paramecium caudatum*. *Biol. Bull.* **97**, 239.
208. GILMAN, L. C. (1950) The position of Japanese varieties of *Paramecium caudatum* with respect to American varieties. *Biol. Bull.* **99**, 348–9.
209. GILMAN, L. C. (1954) Occurrence and distribution of mating type varieties in *Paramecium caudatum*. *J. Protozool.* **1** (Suppl.), 6.
210. GILMAN, L. C. (1956) Distribution of the varieties of *Paramecium caudatum*. *J. Protozool.* **3** (Suppl.), 4.
211. GILMAN, L. C. (1956) Size differences among twelve varieties of *Paramecium caudatum*. *J. Protozool.* **3** (Suppl.), 4.
211a. GOLDSTEIN, M. (1964) Speciation and mating behavior in *Eudorina*. *J. Protozool.* **11**, 317–44.
211b. GORMAN, D. S., and LEVINE, R. P. (1965) Cytochrome f and platocyanin: their sequence in the photosynthetic electron transport chain of *Chlamydomonas reinhardi*. *Proc. Nat. Acad. Sci., U.S.* **54**, 1665–9.
212. GOWANS, C. S. (1956) Genetics investigations on *Chlamydomonas eugametos*. Doctoral thesis, Stanford University, Stanford, Calif.
213. GOWANS, C. S. (1960) Some genetic investigations on *Chlamydomonas eugametos*. *Z. Vererb.* **91**, 63–73.
214. GRANICK, S. (1963) The plastids: their morphological and chemical differentiation. In *Cytodifferentiation and Macromolecular Synthesis*, ed. M. LOCKE, Academic Press, New York, pp. 144–74.
215. GREEN, D. E., and HECHTER, O. (1965) Assembly of membrane subunits. *Proc. Nat. Acad. Sci., U.S.* **53**, 318–25.
216. GREEN, P. B. (1964) Cinematic observations on the growth and divisions of chloroplasts in *Nitella*. *Am. J. Bot.* **51**, 334–42.
217. GREENBLATT, C. L., and SCHIFF, J. A. (1959) A pheophytin-like pigment in dark-adapted *Euglena gracilis*. *J. Protozool.* **6**, 23–28.
217a. GRELL, K. G. (1964) The protozoan nucleus. In *The Cell*, ed. J. BRACHET and A. MIRSKY, Academic Press, New York, vol. 6, 1–79.
218. GROSS, J. A., JAHN, T. L., and BERNSTEIN, E. (1955) Effect of antihistamines on the pigments of green protista. *J. Protozool.* **2**, 71–75.
219. GRUCHY, D. F. (1955) The breeding system and distribution of *Tetrahymena pyriformis*. *J. Protozool.* **2**, 178–85.
220. GUILLERMOND, A. (1941) *The Cytoplasm of the Plant Cell*, Chronica Botanica Co., Waltham, Mass.
220a. HAIRSTON, N. G. (1958) Observations on the ecology of paramecium with comments on the species problem. *Evolution* **12**, 440–450.
221. HAMILTON, L. D., and GETTNER, M. E. (1958) Fine structure of kappa in *Paramecium aurelia*. *J. Biophys. Biochem. Cytol.* **4**, 122–3.
222. HANSON, E. D. (1953) A new mutant kappa in variety 4, *Paramecium aurelia*. *Microbial Genetics Bull.* **7**, 14.
223. HANSON, E. D. (1954) Studies on kappa-like particles in sensitives of *Paramecium aurelia*, variety 4, *Genetics* **39**, 229–39.
224. HANSON, E. D. (1955) Inheritance and regeneration of cytoplasmic damage in *Paramecium aurelia*. *Proc. Nat. Acad. Sci., U.S.* **41**, 783–6.
225. HANSON, E. D. (1957) Some aspects of the quantitive study of cytoplasmic particles: mixed populations of kappa in *Paramecium aurelia*, variety 4. *J. Exptl. Zool.* **135**, 29–56.
226. HANSON, E. D. (1962) Morphogenesis and regeneration of oral structures in *Paramecium aurelia*. *J. Exptl. Zool.* **150**, 45–68.

227. HARTMANN, M. (1955) Sex problems in algae, fungi, and protozoa. *Am. Naturalist* **89**, 321–46.

228. HARTSHORNE, J. N. (1953) The function of the eyespot in *Chlamydomonas*. *New Phytologist* **52**, 292–7.

229. HASTINGS, P. J., LEVINE, E. E., COSBEY, E., HUDOCK, M. O., GILLHAM, N. W., SURZYCKI, S. J., LOPPES, R., and LEVINE, R. P. (1965) The linkage groups of *Chlamydomonas reinhardi*. *Microbial Genetics Bull.* **23**, 17–19.

230. HAWKINS, S. E. (1963) Some preliminary studies on the basis of cytoplasmic inheritance in amobae. *J. Protozool* **10** (Suppl.), 29.

231. HAWKINS, S. E., COLE, R. J., and DANIELLI, J. F. (1962) Preliminary studies on the basis of cytoplasmic inheritance in *Amoeba*. *Nature* **196**, 396.

232. HAWKINS, S. E., and DANIELLI, J. F. (1961) Investigations of free amino acid differences in amoebae. *Exptl. Cell Res.* **23**, 504–9.

233. HEARON, J. Z., and KIMBALL, R. F. (1955) Tests for a role of H_2O_2 in x-ray mutagenesis. I. Estimations of the concentration of H_2O_2 inside the nucleus. *Radiation Res.* **3**, 283–94.

234. HEATHERINGTON, S. (1934) The sterilization of protozoa. *Biol. Bull.* **67**, 315–21.

235. HECKMANN, K. (1961) Paarungstypen und ihre genetische Determination bei dem marinen ciliaten *Euplotes vannus* O. F. MÜLLER. *Naturwissenschaften* **48**, 438–9.

236. HECKMANN, K. (1963) Paarungssystem und genabhängige Paarungstyp-Differenzierungbei dem hypotrichen Ciliaten *Euplotes vannus* O. F. MÜLLER. *Arch. Protistenk.* **106**, 393–421.

237. HECKMANN, K. (1964) Experimentelle Untersuchungen an *Euplotes crassus*. I, Paarungssystem, Konjugation und Determination der Paarungstypen. *Z. Vererbungsl.* **95**, 114–24.

238. HECKMANN, K. (1965) Aspects of mating-type determination in ciliates. *2nd Intern. Conf. Protozool.*, *Excerpta Medica* **91**, 63–64.

239. HECKMANN, K., and SIEGEL, R. W. (1964) Evidence for the induction of mating-type substances by cell to cell contacts. *Exptl. Cell. Res.* **36**, 688–91.

240. HIWATASHI, K. (1949) Studies on the conjugation of *Paramecium caudatum*. I. Mating types and groups in the races obtained in Japan. *Sci.Repts.TôhokuUniv.*, *Biol.***18**,137–40.

241. HIWATASHI, K. (1951) Studies on the conjugation of *Paramecium caudatum*. IV. Conjugating behaviour of individuals of two mating types marked by a vital staining method. *Sci. Repts. Tôhoku Univ.*, *Biol.* **19**, 95–99.

242. HIWATASHI, K. (1958) Artificial induction of conjugation by EDTA in *Paramecium caudatum*. 29th Annual Meeting Zoological Society of Japan.

243. HIWATASHI, K. (1958) Inheritance of mating types in variety 12 of *Paramecium caudatum*. *Sci. Repts. Tôhoku Univ.*, *Biol.* ser. 4 **24**, 119–29.

244. HIWATASHI, K. (1959) Induction of conjugation by ethylenediamine tetraacetic acid (EDTA) in *Paramecium caudatum*. *Sci. Repts. Tôhoku Univ.*, *Biol.* ser. 4 **25**, 81–90.

245. HIWATASHI, K. (1960) Analyses of the change of mating type during vegetative reproduction in *Paramecium caudatum*. *Jap. J. Genetics* **35**, 213–21.

246. HIWATASHI, K. (1960) Locality of mating reactivity on the surface of *Paramecium*. *J. Protozool.* **7** (Suppl.), 20.

247. HIWATASHI, K. (1960) Inheritance of difference in the life feature of *Paramecium caudatum*, syngen 2. *Bull. Marine Biol. Sta. Asamushi, Tôhoku Univ.* **9**, 157–9.

248. HIWATASHI, K. (1961) Locality of mating reactivity on the surface of *Paramecium caudatum*. *Sci. Repts. Tôhoku Univ.*, *Biol.* ser. 4 **27**, 93–99.

249. HIWATASHI, K. (1963) Serotype inheritance in *Paramecium caudatum*. *Genetics* **48**, 892.

250. HIWATASHI, K. (1964) Mating type inheritance in *Paramecium caudatum* syngen 3. *Genetics* **50**, 255–6.

251. HIWATASHI, K. (1965) The effect of brei on the differentiation of mating type in *Paramecium caudatum*. *Genetics* **52**, 448.

252. HOARE, C. A. (1954) The loss of the kinetoplast in trypanosomes, with special reference to *Trypanosoma evansi*. *J. Protozool*. **1**, 28–33.
253. HOLLAENDER, A. (1960) *Radiation Protection and Recovery*, Pergamon Press, New York.
254. HOLLAENDER, A. (1961) Symposium on recovery of cells from injury. *J. Cell. Comp. Physiol*. **58** (Suppl. 1), 1–248.
255. HUDOCK, G. A., and LEVINE, R. P. (1964) Regulation of photosynthesis in *Chlamydomonas reinhardi*. *Plant Physiol*. **39**, 889–97.
256. HUDOCK, G. A., McLEOD, G. C., MORAVKOVA-KIELY, J., and LEVINE, R. P. (1964) The relation of oxygen evolution to chlorophyll and protein synthesis in a mutant strain of *Chlamydomonas reinhardi*. *Plant Physiol*. **39**, 898–903.
257. HUFNAGEL, L. (1965) Structural and chemical observations on pellicles isolated from paramecia. *J. Cell Biol*. **27**, 46A.
257a. HURST, D. D. (1957) The mode of mating type inheritance in *Tetrahymena pyriformis*, variety 2. *J. Protozool*. **4** (Suppl.), 17–18.
257b. IGARASHI, S. (1966) Temperature-sensitive mutation in *Paramecium aurelia*. I. Induction and inheritance. *Mutation Res*. **3**, 13–24.
257c. IGARASHI, S., and KIMBALL, R. F. (1964) Temperature sensitive mutation induced by x-rays in *Paramecium*. *Genetics* **50**, 258.
258. INOKI, S. (1952) A new experimental method and genetical interpretation on the antigenic variation in *Trypanosoma gambiense*. *Med. J. Osaka Univ*. **3**, 81–86.
259. INOKI, S. (1952) Studies on the immunological variations in *Trypanosoma gambiense*. *Med. J. Osaka Univ*. **3**, 357–71.
260. INOKI, S. (1956) Origin of the akinetoplastic strain of *Trypanosoma gambiense*. *Cytologia* Suppl., Proceedings of the International Genetics Symposia, Tokyo, pp. 550–4.
261. INOKI, S. (1960) Studies on antigenic variation in the Welcome strain of *Trypanosoma gambiense*. I. Improvements in technique. *Biken's J*. **3**, 215–22.
262. INOKI, S. (1960) Studies on antigenic variation in the Welcome strain of *Trypanosoma gambiense*. II. On the first relapse appearing in mice treated with human plasma. *Biken's J*. **3**, 223–8.
263. INOKI, S., KITAURA, T., KUROGOCHI, Y., OSAKI, H., and NAKABAYASI, T. (1952) Genetic studies on the antigenic variation in *Trypanosoma gambiense*. *Jap. J. Gen*. **27**, 85–92.
264. INOKI, S., and MATSUSHIRO, A. (1958) Antigenic variation in *Tetrahymena pyriformis*. *Med. J. Osaka Univ*. **8**, 763–70.
265. INOKI, S., and MATSUSHIRO, A. (1959) Relationship between kinetoplast elimination and para-rosaniline resistance in *Trypanosma gambiense*. *Biken's J*. **2**, 371–4.
266. INOKI, S., and MATSUSHIRO, A. (1960) Transformation of drug resistance in *Trypanosoma*. *Biken's J*. **3**, 101–6.
267. INOKI, S., NAKABAYASHI, T., FUKUKITA, S., and OSAKI, H. (1959) Studies on the immunological variation in *Trypanosoma gambiense*. IV. Further considerations on the screening method. *Biken's J*. **2**, 277–83.
268. INOKI, S., NAKABAYASHI, T., OSAKI, H., and FUKUKITA, S. (1957) Studies on the immunological variation in *Trypanosoma gambiense*. III. Process of the antigenic variation in mice. *Med. J. Osaka Univ*. **7**, 731–43.
269. INOKI, S., OSAKI, H., and MAKABAYASHI, T. (1956) Studies on the immunological variation in *Trypanosoma gambiense*. II. Verifications of the new variation system by Ehrlich's and *in vitro* methods. *Med. J. Osaka Univ*. **7**, 165–73.
270. INOKI, S., TANIUCHI, Y., MATSUSHIRO, A., and SAKAMOTO, H. (1960) Multiplication ability of the akinetoplastic form of *Trypanosoma evansi*. *Biken's J*. **3**, 123–8.
271. INOKI, S., TANIUCHI, Y., SAKAMOTO, H., ONO, T., and KUBO, R. (1961) Interspecific transformation of drug-resistance between *Trypanosoma gambiense* and *Trypanosoma evansi*. *Biken's J*. **4**, 111–9.

272. JACOB, F., and MONOD, J. (1961) On the regulation of gene activity. *Cold Spring Harbor Symp. Quant. Biol.* **26**, 193–209.

273. JACOB, F., and MONOD, J. (1963) Genetic repression, allosteric inhibition and cellular differentiation. In *Cytodifferentiation and Macromolecular Synthesis*, ed. M. LOCKE, Academic Press, New York, pp. 30–64.

274. JENNINGS, H. S. (1908) Heredity, variation and evolution in Protozoa. II. Heredity and variation in size and form in Paramecium, with studies of growth, environmental action and selection. *Proc. Am. Phil. Soc.* **47**, 393–546.

275. JENNINGS, H. S. (1929) Genetics of the protozoa. *Biblio. Genetica* **5**, 105–330.

276. JENNINGS, H. S. (1937) Formation, inheritance and variation in the teeth of *Difflugia corona*. A study in the morphogenetic activities of rhizopod protoplasm. *J. Exptl. Zool.* **77**, 287–336.

277. JENNINGS, H. S. (1938) Sex reaction types and their interrelations in *Paramecium bursaria*. *Proc. Nat. Acad. Sci., U.S.* **24**, 112–7.

278. JENNINGS, H. S. (1939) Genetics of *Paramecium bursaria*. I. Mating types and groups, their interrelations and distribution: mating behavior and self sterility. *Genetics* **24**, 202–33.

279. JENNINGS, H. S. (1941) Inheritance in Protozoa. In *Protozoa in Biological Research*, ed. G. N. CALKINS and F. M. SUMMERS, Columbia Univ. Press, N.Y., pp. 710–71.

280. JENNINGS, H. S. (1941) Genetics of *P. bursaria*. II. Self-differentiation and self-fertilization of clones. *Proc. Amer. Phil. Soc.* **85**, 25–48.

281. JENNINGS, H. S. (1942) Senescence and death in Protozoa and invertebrates. In *Problems of Aging*, 2nd ed., ed. E. W. COWDRY, Williams and Wilkins Co., Baltimore, pp. 29–49.

282. JENNINGS, H. S. (1942) Genetics of *Paramecium bursaria*. III. Inheritance of mating type, in cross and in clonal self-fertilization. *Genetics* **27**, 193–211.

283. JENNINGS, H. S. (1944) *Paramecium bursaria*: life history. I. Immaturity, maturity and age. *Biol. Bull.* **86**, 131–45.

284. JENNINGS, H. S., and OPITZ, P. (1944) Genetics of *Paramecium bursaria*. IV. A fourth variety from Russia. Lethal crosses with an American variety. *Genetics* **29**, 576–83.

285. JIROVEC, O. (1929) Studien über blepharoplastlose Trypanosomen. *Arch. f. Protistenk.* **68**, 187–208.

286. JOHNSON, W. H., and MILLER, C. A. (1957) The nitrogen requirements of *Paramecium multimicronucleatum*. *Physiol. Zool.* **30**, 106–13.

287. JOLLOS, V. (1913) Über die Bedeutung der Conjugation bei Infusorien. *Arch. f. Protistenk.* **30**, 328–34.

288. JOLLOS, V. (1914) Variabilität und Vererbung bei Mikroorganismen. *Zeitschr. f. Indukt. Abst. u. Vererb.* **12**, 14–35.

289. JOLLOS, V. (1921) Experimentelle Protistenstudien. I. Untersuchungen über Variabilität und Vererbung bei Infusorien. *Arch. f. Protistenk.* **43**, 1–222.

290. JOLLOS, V. (1924) Untersuchungen über Variabilität und Vererbung bei Arcellen. *Arch. f. Protistenk.* **49**, 307–74.

291. JOLLOS, V. (1934) Dauermodifikationen und Mutationen bei Protozoen. *Arch. f. Protistenk.* **83**, 197–219.

292. JONES, A. (1964) Description and genetic analysis of an antigen of *Paramecium aurelia*. Dissertation, University of Pennsylvania.

293. JONES, I. G. (1965) Studies on the characterization and structure of the immobilization antigens of *Paramecium aurelia*. *Biochem. J.* **96**, 17–23.

294. JONES, I. G. (1965) Immobilization antigen in heterozygous clones of *Paramecium aurelia*. *Nature* **207**, 769.

295. JONES, I. G., and BEALE, G. H. (1963) Chemical and immunological comparisons of allelic immobilization antigens in *Paramecium aurelia*. *Nature* **197**, 205–6.

296. JUDIN, A. L. (1965) The role of nucleus and cytoplasm in the inheritance of some characters in amoebae, *2nd Intern. Conf. Protozool.*, *Excerpta Medica*, **91**, 62–63.

297. JURAND, A., BEALE, G. H., and YOUNG, M. R. (1964) Studies on the macronucleus of *Paramecium aurelia*. II. Development of macronuclear anlagen. *J. Protozool.* **11**, 491–7.

298. KALF, G. F. (1964) Deoxyribonucleic acid in mitochondria and its role in protein synthesis. *Biochemistry* **3**, 1702–6.

299. KARAKASHIAN, M. W., and KARAKASHIAN, S. J. (1964) The inheritance of susceptibility to free-living algal infection in aposymbiotic *Paramecium bursaria*. *J. Protozool.* **11** (Suppl.), 19.

300. KARAKASHIAN, S. J. (1963) Growth of *Paramecium bursaria* as influenced by the presence of algal symbionts. *Physiol. Zool.* **36**, 52–68.

301. KARAKASHIAN, S. J., and KARAKASHIAN, M. W. (1965) Evolution and symbiosis in the genus *Chlorella* and related algae. *Evolution* **19**, 368–77.

301 a. KARAKASHIAN, S. J., and SIEGEL, R. W. (1965) A genetic approach to endocellular symbiosis. *Exptl. Parasit.* **17**, 103–22.

302. KATASHIMA, R. (1959) Mating types in *Euplotes eurystomus*. *J. Protozool.* **6**, 75–83.

303. KATES, J. R., and GOLDSTEIN, L. (1964) A comparison of the protein composition of three species of amoebae. *J. Protozool.* **11**, 30–35.

304. KATOH, S., and TAKAMIYA, A. (1961) A new leaf copper protein "plastocyanin" a natural Hill oxidant. *Nature* **189**, 665–6.

305. KAUFMANN, B. P., and McDONALD, M. R. (1956) Organization of the chromosome. *Cold Spring Harbor Symp. Quant. Biol.* **21**, 233–46.

306. KAUFMANN, B. P., and McDONALD, M. R. (1957) The nature of the changes effected in chromosomal materials by the chelating agent EDTA. *Proc. Nat. Acad. Sci.*, *U.S.* **43**, 262–70.

307. KIDDER, G. W., and DEWEY, V. C. (1951) The biochemistry of ciliates in pure culture. In *Protozoa*. vol. I, ed. A. LWOFF, Academic Press, New York, pp. 323–400.

308. KIMBALL, A. W., and HOUSEHOLDER, A. S. (1954) A stochastic model for the selection of macronuclear units in *Paramecium* growth. *Biometrics* **10** 361–74.

309. KIMBALL, R. F. (1939) Mating types in *Euplotes*. *Am. Naturalist* **73**, 451–6.

310. KIMBALL, R. F. (1939) Change of mating type during vegetative reproduction in *P. aurelia*. *J. Exptl. Zool.* **81**, 165–79.

311. KIMBALL, R. F. (1939) A delayed change of phenotype following a change of genotype in *Paramecium aurelia*. *Genetics* **24**, 49–58.

312. KIMBALL, R. F. (1941) Double animals and amicronucleate animals in *Euplotes patella* with particular reference to their conjugation. *J. Exptl. Zool.* **86**, 1–32.

313. KIMBALL, R. F. (1942) The nature and inheritance of mating types in *Euplotes patella*. *Genetics* **27**, 269–85.

314. KIMBALL, R. F. (1943) Mating types in the ciliate Protozoa. *Quart. Rev. Biol.* **18**, 30–45.

315. KIMBALL, R. F. (1947) The induction of inheritable modification in reaction to antiserum in *Paramecium aurelia*. *Genetics* **32**, 486–99.

316. KIMBALL, R. F. (1949) Inheritance of mutational changes induced by radiation in *Paramecium aurelia*. *Genetics* **34**, 412–24.

317. KIMBALL, R. F. (1949). The induction of mutations in *Paramecium aurelia* by beta radiation. *Genetics* **34**, 210–22.

318. KIMBALL, R. F. (1953) Three new mutants and the independent assortment of five genes in variety 1 of *Paramecium aurelia*. *Microbial Genetics Bull.* **8**, 10.

319. KIMBALL, R. F. (1955) The effects of radiation on Protozoa and the eggs of invertebrates and other insects. In *Radiation Biology*, ed. A. HOLLAENDER, McGraw Hill, New York, vol. II, pp. 285–331.

320. KIMBALL, R. F. (1955) The role of oxygen and peroxide in the production of radiation damage in *Paramecium*. *Ann. N.Y. Acad. Sci.* **59**, 638–47.

320a. KIMBALL, R. F. (1957) The effect of radiations on genetic mechanims of *Paramecium aurelia*. *J. Cell. Comp. Physiol.* **35** (Suppl. 1), 157–69.

321. KIMBALL, R. F. (1961) Postirradiation processes in the induction of recessive lethals by ionizing radiation. *J. Cell. Comp. Physiol.* **58** (Suppl.), 163–70.

322. KIMBALL, R. F. (1962) Chromosome duplication and mutation. In *Strahlenwirkung und Milieu*, ed. H. FRITZ-NIGGLI, Urban and Schwarzenberg, Munich and Berlin, pp. 116–25.

323. KIMBALL, R. F. (1963) Studies on radiation mutagenesis in microorganisms. *Proc. 11th Intern. Congr. Genetics, The Hague* **2**, 227–34.

324. KIMBALL, R. F. (1963) X-ray dose rate and dose fractionation studies on mutation in *Paramecium. Genetics* **48**, 581–96.

325. KIMBALL, R. F. (1963) The relation of repair to differential radiosensitivity in the production of mutations in *Paramecium*. In *Symposium on Repair from Genetic Radiation Damage and Differential Radiosensitivity of Germ Cells*, ed F. H. SOBELS, Pergamon Press, London, pp. 167–78.

326. KIMBALL, R. F. (1964) The distribution of x-ray induced mutations to chromosomal strands in *Paramecium aurelia. Mutation Res.* **1**, 129–38.

327. KIMBALL, R. F. (1964) Studies on reparable premutational lesions with alkylating agents. *Genetics* **50**, 262.

328. KIMBALL, R. F. (1964) Physiological genetics of the ciliates. In *Biochemistry and Physiology of Protozoa*, ed. S. H. HUTNER, Academic Press, New York, vol. III, pp. 243–75.

329. KIMBALL, R. F. (1965) Further studies on mutagenesis by triethylene melamine in *Paramecium aurelia. Genetics* **52**, 452.

329a. KIMBALL, R. F., and BARKA, T. (1959) Quantitative cytochemical studies on *Paramecium aurelia*. II. Feulgen microspectrophotometry of the macronucleus during exponential growth. *Exptl. Cell Res.* **17**, 173–82.

330. KIMBALL, R. F., and GAITHER, N. (1951) The influence of light upon the action of ultraviolet on *Paramecium aurelia. J. Cell. Comp. Physiol.* **37**, 211–33.

331. KIMBALL, R. F., and GAITHER, N. (1953) Influence of oxygen upon genetic and nongenetic effects of ionizing radiation on *Paramecium aurelia. Proc. Soc. Exptl. Biol. Med.* **82**, 471–7.

332. KIMBALL, R. F., and GAITHER, N. (1954) Lack of an effect of a high dose of x-rays on aging in *Paramecium aurelia*, variety 1. *Genetics* **39**, 977.

333. KIMBALL, R. F., and GAITHER, N. (1955) Behavior of nuclei at conjugation in *Paramecium aurelia*. I. Effect of incomplete chromosome sets and competition between complete and incomplete nuclei. *Genetics* **40**, 878–89.

334. KIMBALL, R. F., and GAITHER, N. (1956) Behavior of nuclei at conjugation in *Paramecium aurelia*. II. The effects of x-rays on diploid and haploid clones, with a discussion of dominant lethals. *Genetics* **41**, 715–28.

335. KIMBALL, R. F., GAITHER, N., and PERDUE, S. W. (1961) Metabolic repair of premutational damage in *Paramecium. Intern. J. Radiation Biol.* **3**, 133–47.

336. KIMBALL, R. F., GAITHER, N., and WILSON, S. M. (1957) Postirradiation modification of mutagenesis in *Paramecium* by streptomycin. *Genetics* **42**, 661–9.

337. KIMBALL, R. F., GAITHER, N., and WILSON, S. M. (1959) Recovery in stationary-phase paramecia from radiation effects leading to mutation. *Proc. Nat. Acad. Sci., U.S.* **45**, 833–9.

338. KIMBALL, R. F., HEARON, J. Z., and GAITHER, N. (1955) Tests for a role of H_2O_2 in x-ray mutagenesis. II. Attempts to induce mutations by peroxide. *Radiation Res.* **3**, 435–43.

339. KIMBALL, R. F., and PERDUE, S. W. (1962) Studies on the refractory period for the induction of recessive lethal mutation by x-rays in *Paramecium. Genetics* **47**, 1595–607.

340. KIMBALL, R. F., and VOGT-KÖHNE (1961) Quantitative cytochemical studies on *Paramecium aurelia*. IV. The effect of limited food and starvation on the macronucleus. *Exptl. Cell Res.* **23**, 479–87.

341. KIMURA, M. (1957) Some problems of stochastic processes in genetics. *Ann. Math. Stat.* **28**, 882–901.

342. KIRBY, JR., H. (1941) Organisms living on and in Protozoa. In *Protozoa in Biological Research*, ed. G. N. CALKINS and F. M. SUMMERS, Columbia University Press, New York, pp. 1009–1113.

343. KIRK, J. T. O. (1963) The deoxyribonucleic acid of broad bean chloroplasts. *Biochim. Biophys. Acta* **76**, 417–24.

344. KISLEV, N., SWIFT, H., and BOGORAD, L. (1965) Nucleic acids of chloroplasts and mitochondria in Swiss chard. *J. Cell Biol.* **25**, 327–44.

345. KOIZUMI, S. (1958) An analysis of the process of transformation of antigenic type induced by antiserum treatment in *Paramecium caudatum*, stock K_A6. *Sci. Repts. Tôhoku Univ., Biol.*, Ser. 4 **24**, 23–31.

346. KOIZUMI, S. (1960) Antigenic type transformation after selfing conjugation in *Paramecium caudatum*, stock K_A6. *Sci. Repts. Tôhoku Univ., Biol.*, Ser. 4 **26**, 297–307.

347. KOIZUMI, S. (1966) Serotypes and immobilization antigens in *Paramecium caudatum*. *J. Protozool.* **13**, 73–6.

347a. KOIZUMI, S., and PREER, J. R. JR. (1966) Transfer of cytoplasm by microinjection in *Paramecium aurelia*. *J. Protozool.*, **13** (Suppl.), 27.

348. KRASSNER, S. M. (1964) Comparative enzyme studies on *Leishmania*. 1st Intern. Congr. Parasit., Rome.

349. KRINSKY, N. I., and LEVINE, R. P. (1964) Carotenoids of wild type and mutant strains of the green alga, *Chlamydomonas reinhardi*. *Plant Physiol.* **39**, 680–7.

349a. KUNG, C. (1966) Aerobic respiration of kappa particles in *Paramecium aurelia* stock 51, *J. Protozool.* **13** (Suppl.), 11–12.

350. LANDMAN, O. E., and HALLE, S. (1963) Enzymically and physically induced inheritance changes in *Bacillus subtilis*. *J. Mol. Biol.* **7**, 721–38.

351. LANG, N. J. (1963) Electron-microscopic demonstration of plastids in *Polytoma*. *J. Protozool.* **10**, 333–9.

352. LARISON, L. L., and SIEGEL, R. W. (1961) Illegitimate mating in *Paramecium bursaria* and the basis for cell union. *J. Gen. Microbiol.* **26**, 499–508.

353. LEFF, J., MANDEL, M., EPSTEIN, H. T., and SCHIFF, J. A. (1963) DNA satellites from cells of green and aplastidic algae. *Biochem. Biophys. Res. Comm.* **13**, 126–30.

354. LEVINE, M. (1952) Diverse mate-killers; their interbreeding and genetic basis. *Genetics* **37**, 599.

355. LEVINE, M. (1953) The diverse mate-killers of *Paramecium aurelia*, variety 8: their interrelations and genetic basis. *Genetics* **38**, 561–78.

356. LEVINE, M., and HOWARD, J. L. (1955) Respiratory studies on mate-killers and sensitives of *Paramecium aurelia*, variety 8. *Science* **121**, 336–7.

357. LEVINE, R. P. (1955) Chromosome structure and the mechanism of crossing over. *Proc. Nat. Acad. Sci., U.S.* **41**, 727–30.

358. LEVINE, R. P. (1956) Chromosome organization and gene recombination. *Cold Spring Harbor Symp. Quant. Biol.* **21**, 247–56.

359. LEVINE, R. P. (1960) Genetic control of photosynthesis in *Chlamydomonas reinhardi*. *Proc. Nat. Acad. Sci., U.S.* **46**, 972–8.

360. LEVINE, R. P. (1960) A screening technique for photosynthetic mutants in unicellular algae. *Nature* **188**, 339–40.

361. LEVINE, R. P. (1963) The electron transport system of photosynthesis deduced from experiments with mutants of *Chlamydomonas reinhardi*. In *Photosynthesis Mechanisms in Green Plants*, Publ. 1145, Nat. Acad. Sci., Wash., pp. 158–73.

362. LEVINE, R. P., and EBERSOLD, W. T. (1958) Gene recombination in *Chlamydomonas reinhardi*. *Cold Spring Harbor Symp. Quant. Biol.* **23**, 101–9.

363. LEVINE, R. P., and EBERSOLD, W. T. (1958) The relation of calcium and magnesium to crossing over in *Chlamydomonas reinhardi*. *Z. Vererb.* **89**, 631–5.

364. LEVINE, R. P., and EBERSOLD, W. T. (1960) The genetics and cytology of *Chlamydomonas*. *Ann. Rev. Microbiol.* **14**, 197–216.

365. LEVINE, R. P., and FOLSOME, C. E. (1959) The nuclear cycle in *Clamydomonas reinhardi*. *Z. Vererb.* **90**, 215–22.

366. LEVINE, R. P., and PIETTE, L. H. (1962) An investigation of electron spin resonance in wild type *Chlamydomonas reinhardi* and mutant strains having impaired photosynthesis. *Biophys. J.* **2**, 369–79.

367. LEVINE, R. P., and SMILLIE, R. M. (1962) The pathway of triphosphopyridine nucleotide photoreduction in *Chlamydomonas reinhardi*. *Proc. Nat. Acad. Sci., U.S.* **48**, 417–21.

368. LEVINE, R. P., and SMILLIE, R. M. (1963) The photosynthetic electron transport chain of *Chlamydomonas reinhardi*. I. Triphosphopyridine nucleotide photoreduction in wild-type and mutant strains. *J. Biol. Chem.* **238**, 4052–7.

369. LEVINE, R. P., and TOGASAKI, R. K. (1965) A mutant strain of *Chlamydomonas reinhardi* lacking ribulose diphosphate carboxylase activity. *Proc. Nat. Acad. Sci., U.S.* **53**, 987–90.

370. LEVINE, R. P., and VOLKMANN, D. (1961) Mutants with impaired photosynthesis in *Chlamydomonas reinhardi*. *Biochem. Biophys. Res. Comm.* **6**, 264–9.

371. LEWIN, J. C. (1950) Obligate autotrophy in *Chlamydomonas moewusii* Gerloff. *Science* **112**, 652–3.

372. LEWIN, R. A. (1953) The genetics of *Chlamydomonas moewusii* Gerloff. *J. Genetics* **51**, 543–60.

373. LOEFER, K. B. (1936) Isolation and growth characteristics of the "zoochlorella" of *Paramecium bursaria*. *Am. Naturalist* **70**, 184–8.

374. LOEFER, J. B., and OWEN, R. D. (1961) Characterization and distribution of "H" serotypes in 25°C cultures of *Tetrahymena pyriformis*, variety 1. *J. Protozool.* **8**, 387–91.

375. LOEFER, J. B., OWEN, R. D., and CHRISTENSEN, E. (1958) Serological types among 31 strains of the ciliated protozoan, *Tetrahymena pyriformis*. *J. Protozool.* **5**, 209–17.

376. LORCH, I. J., and DANIELLI, J. F. (1953) Nuclear transplantation in Amoebae. I. Some species characters of *Amoeba proteus* and *Amoeba discoides*. *Quart. J. Micr. Sci.* **94**, 445–60.

377. LORCH, I. J., and DANIELLI, J. F. (1953) Nuclear transplantation in Amoebae. II. The immediate results of transfer of nuclei between *Amoeba proteus* and *Amoeba discoides*. *Quart. J. Micr. Sci.* **94**, 461–80.

378. LOURIE, E. M., and O'CONNOR, R. J. (1936) Trypanolysis *in vitro* by mouse immune serum. *Ann. Trop. Med. Parasit.* **30**, 365–88.

379. LOURIE, E. M., and O'CONNOR, R. J. (1937) A study of *Trypanosoma rhodesiense* relapse strains *in vitro*. *Ann. Trop. Med. Parasit.* **31**, 319–39.

380. LUCK, D. J. L. (1963) Genesis of mitochondria in *Neurospora crassa*. *Proc. Nat. Acad. Sci., U.S.* **49**, 233–40.

381. LUCK, D. J. L. (1965) Formation of mitochondria in *Neurospora crassa*. *Am. Naturalist* **99**, 241–53.

382. LUCK, D. J. L., and REICH, E. (1964) DNA in mitochondria of *Neurospora crassa*. *Proc. Nat. Acad. Sci., U.S.* **52**, 931–8.

383. LURIA, S. E., and DELBRUCK, M. (1943) Mutations of bacteria from virus sensitivity to virus resistance. *Genetics* **28**, 491–511.

384. LWOFF, A. (1950) *Problems of Morphogenesis in the Ciliates; the Kinetosomes in Development, Reproduction and Evolution*, John Wiley and Sons, New York.

385. LYMAN, H., EPSTEIN, H. T., and SCHIFF, J. A. (1961) Studies of chloroplast development in *Euglena*. I. Inactivation of green colony formation by ultraviolet light. *Biochim. Biophys. Acta* **50**, 301–9.

386. LYON, M. F. (1961) Gene action in the x-chromosome of the mouse. *Nature* **190**, 372–3.

387. LYON, M. F. (1962) Sex chromatin and gene action in the mammalian x-chromosome. *Am. J. Human Genetics* **14**, 135–48.

388. McCALLA, D. R. (1962) Chloroplasts of *Euglena gracilis* affected by furadantin. *Science* **137**, 225–6.

389. McCALLA, D. R. (1965) Effect of nitrofurans on the chloroplast system of *Euglena gracilis*. *J. Protozool.* **12**, 34–41.

390. McCALLA, D. R. (1965) Chloroplast mutagenesis: effect of N-methyl-N'-nitro-N-nitrosoguanidine and some other agents on *Euglena*. *Science* **148**, 497–9.

391. McDONALD, B. B. (1958) Quantitative aspects of deoxyribosenucleic acid (DNA) metabolism in an amicronucleate strain of Tetrahymena. *Biol. Bull.* **114**, 71–94.

391a. McDONALD, B. B. (1964) Exchange of cytoplasm during conjugation in *Tetrahymena*. *J. Protozool.* **11** (Suppl.), 11.

392. MacDOUGALL, M. S. (1929) Modifications in *Chilodon uncinatus* produced by ultraviolet radiation. *J. Exptl. Biol.* **54**, 95–109.

393. MacDOUGALL, M. S. (1931) Another mutation of *Chilodon uncinatus* produced by ultraviolet radiation with a description of its maturation processes. *J. Exptl. Zool.* **58**, 229–36.

394. MALY, R. (1958) Eine genetisch bedingte Störung der Zelltrennung beim *Paramecium aurelia* var. 4. Ein Beitrag zum Problem der Mutabilität plasmatischer Systeme. *Z. Vererbungslehre* **89**, 397–421.

395. MALY, R. (1960) Die Normalisierung genetisch bedingter Defekte der Zelltrennung bei *Paramecium aurelia* durch Sauerstoffmangel und Kohlenmonoxyd. *Z. Vererbungslehre* **91**, 226.

396. MALY, R. (1960) Die Wirkung eines Komplexbildners und von Metallionen auf die Ausprägung des *snaky-* und *monstra*-Charakters bei *Paramecium aurelia*. *Z. Vererbungslehre* **91**, 333–7.

397. MALY, R. (1961) Die Aufhebung eines Defektes der Zelltrennungen beim *snaky*-Stamm von *Paramecium aurelia* in Salzlösungen. *Z. Vererbungslehre* **92**, 462–4.

398. MALY, R. (1962) Die Analyse eines Teilprozesses der Zytokinese mit Hilfe einer Mutante von *Paramecium aurelia*. *Zool. Anz.*, *Verh. Deuts. Zool. Gesell. Wien.* **26** (Suppl.), 84–6.

399. MARGOLIN, P. (1956) An exception to mutual exclusion of the ciliary antigens in *Paramecium aurelia*. *Genetics* **41**, 685–99.

400. MARGOLIN, P. (1956) The ciliary antigens of stock 172, *Paramecium aurelia*, variety 4. *J. Exptl. Zool.* **133**, 345–87.

401. MARGOLIN, P., LOEFER, J. B., and OWEN, R. D. (1959) Immobilizing antigens of *Tetrahymena pyriformis*. *J. Protozool.* **6**, 207–15.

402. MARKERT, C. L. (1963) Epigenetic control of specific protein synthesis in differentiating cells. In *Cytodifferentiation and Macromolecular Synthesis*, ed. M. LOCKE, Academic Press, New York, pp. 65–84.

403. MAUPAS, E. (1888) Recherches expérimentales sur la multiplication des infusoires ciliés. *Arch. d. Zool. Exp. et Gén.* (2) **6**, 165–277.

404. MAUPAS, E. (1889) La rajeunissement karyogamique chez les ciliés. *Arch. d. Zool. Exp. et Gén.* (2) **7**, 149–517.

405. MAYR, E. (1963) *Animal Species and Evolution*, The Belknap Press of Harvard University Press, Cambridge, Mass.

406. MAZIA, D. (1954) The particulate organization of the chromosome. *Proc. Nat. Acad. Sci., U.S.* **40**, 521–7.

407. MEDAWAR, P. B. (1957) *The Uniqueness of the Individual*, Basic Books, Inc., New York.
408. MERESCHKOWSKI, C. (1905) Über Natur und Ursprung der Chromatophoren im Pflanzenreiche. *Biol. Centralblatt* **25**, 593–604.
409. METZ, C. B. (1947) Induction of "pseudo selfing" and meiosis in *Paramecium aurelia* by formalin killed animals of opposite mating type. *J. Exptl. Zool.* **105**, 115–40.
410. METZ, C. B. (1948) The nature and mode of action of the mating type substances. *Am. Naturalist* **82**, 85–95.
411. METZ, C. B. (1954) Mating substances and the physiology of fertilization in ciliates. In *Sex in Microorganisms*, ed. D. H. Wenrich, Symp. Am. Assoc. Adv. Sci., pp. 284–334
412. MICHAELIS, P. (1959) Cytoplasmic inheritance and the segregation of plasmagenes. *Proc. Xth Int. Cong. Genetics* **1**, 375–85.
413. MILLER, C. A., and VAN WAGTENDONK, W. J. (1956) The essential metabolites of a strain of *Paramecium aurelia* in axenic medium. *J. Gen. Microbiol.* **15**, 280–91.
414. MITCHISON, N. A. (1955) Evidence against micronuclear mutations as the sole basis for death at fertilization in aged, and in the progeny of ultra-violet irradiated, *Paramecium aurelia*. *Genetics* **40**, 61–75.
415. MIYAKE, A. (1956) Physiological analysis of the life cycle of the Protozoa. III Artificial induction of selfing conjugation by chemical agents in *P. caudatum*. *J. Inst. Polyt., Osaka*, Ser. D **7**, 14.
416. MIYAKE, A. (1958) Induction of conjugation by chemical agents in *P. caudatum*. *J. Inst. Polyt., Osaka*, Ser. D **9**, 251.
417. MIYAKE, A. (1960) Artificial induction of conjugation by chemical agents in *P. aurelia*, *P. micromultinucleatum*, *P. caudatum* and between them. *J. Protozool.* **7** (Suppl.), 15.
418. MIYAKE, A. (1961) Artificial induction of conjugation by chemical agents in *Paramecium* of the "*aurelia* group" and some of its applications to genetic work. *Am. Zoologist* **1**, 373–74.
419. MIYAKE, A. (1964) Induction of conjugation by cell-free preparations in *Paramecium multimicronucleatum*. *Science* **146**, 1583–5.
420. MOEWUS, F. (1938) Vererbung des Geschlechts bei *Chlamydomonas eugametos* und verwandten Arten. *Biol. Zentr.* **58**, 516–36.
421. MOEWUS, F. (1948) Über die Erblichkeit des Kopulationsverhaltens bei *Chlamydomonas*, *Z. Naturforsch.* **3** B, 279–90.
422. MORIBER, L. G., HERSHENOV, B., AARONSON, S., and BARSKY, B. (1963) Teratological chloroplast structures in *Euglena gracilis* permanently bleached by exogenous physical and chemical agents. *J. Protozool.* **10**, 80–6.
423. MOTT, M. R. (1963) Cytochemical localization of antigens of Paramecium by ferritin-conjugated antibody and by counterstaining the resultant absorbed globulin. *J. Roy. Microscop. Soc.* **81**, 159–62.
424. MOTT, M. R. (1963) Identification of the sites of the antigens of *Paramecium aurelia* by means of electron microscopy. *J. Protozool.* **10** (Suppl.), 31.
425. MOTT, M. R. (1965) Electron microscopy of the immobilization antigens of *Paramecium aurelia*. *2nd Intern. Conf. Protozool. Excerpta Medica* **91**, 250.
426. MOTTRAM, J. C. (1941) Abnormal paramecia produced by blastogenic agents and their bearing on the cancer problem. *Cancer Res.* **1**, 313–23.
427. MOTTRAM, J. C. (1942) *The Problem of Tumours*, H. K. LEWIS & Co., London.
428. MUELLER, J. A. (1961) Further studies on the nature of the "co-factor" required for kappa infection in *Paramecium aurelia*, syngen 4. *Am. Zoologist* **1**, 375.
429. MUELLER, J. A. (1962) Induced physiological and morphological changes in the B particle and R body from killer paramecia. *J. Protozool.* **9**, 26.
430. MUELLER, J. A. (1963) Separation of kappa particles with infective activity from those with killing activity and identification of the infective particles in *Paramecium aurelia*. *Exptl. Cell Res.* **30**, 492–508.

431. MUELLER, J. A. (1964) Paramecia develop immunity against kappa. *Am. Zoologist* **4**, 313–4.

432. MUELLER, J. A. (1965) Kappa-affected paramecia develop immunity. *J. Protozool.* **12**, 278–81.

432a. MUELLER, J. A. (1965) Vitally stained kappa in *Paramecium aurelia*. *J. Exptl. Zool.* **160**, 369–72.

433. MÜHLPFORDT, H. (1963) Über die Bedeutung und Feinstruktur des Blepharoplasten bei Parasitischen Flagellaten, I. Teil. *Z. Trop. Parasitol.* **14**, 357–98.

434. MÜHLPFORDT, H. (1963) Über die Bedeutung und Feinstruktur des Blepharoplasten bei Parasitischen Flagellaten, II, Teil. *Z. Trop. Parasitol.* **14**, 475–501.

435. MULLER, H. J., CARLSON, E., and SCHALET, A. (1961) Mutation by alteration of the already existing gene. *Genetics* **46**, 213–26.

436. NAKAMURA, K., and GOWANS, C. S. (1964) Nicotinic acid-excreting mutants in *Chlamydomonas*. *Nature* **202**, 826–7.

437. NAKAMURA, K., and GOWANS, C. S. (1964) Some genetic aspects of nicotinamide auxotrophs and mutants resistant to a nicotinamide antimetabolite in *Chlamydomonas eugametos*. *Genetics* **50**, 271.

438. NAKAMURA, K., and GOWANS, C. S. (1965) Genetic control of nicotinic acid metabolism in *Chlamydomonas eugametos*. *Genetics* **51**, 931–45.

439. NANNEY, D. L. (1953) Nucleo-cytoplasmic interaction during conjugation in *Tetrahymena*. *Biol. Bull.* **105**, 133–48.

440. NANNEY, D. L. (1953) Mating type determination in *Paramecium aurelia*, a model of nucleo-cytoplasmic interaction. *Proc. Nat. Acad. Sci., U.S.* **39**, 113–9.

441. NANNEY, D. L. (1954) X-ray studies on paramecins and kappas of variety 4 of *Paramecium aurelia*. *Physiol. Zool.* **27**, 79–89.

442. NANNEY, D. L. (1954) Mating type determination in *Paramecium aurelia*. A study in cellular heredity. In *Sex in Microorganisms*, American Association for the Advancement of Science, Wash., D.C., pp. 266–83.

443. NANNEY, D. L. (1956) Caryonidal inheritance and nuclear differentiation. *Am. Naturalist* **90**, 291–307.

444. NANNEY, D. L. (1957) Mating type inheritance at conjugation in variety 4 of *Paramecium aurelia*. *J. Protozool.* **4**, 89–95.

445. NANNEY, D. L. (1959) Genetic factors affecting mating type frequencies in variety 1 of *Tetrahymena pyriformis*. *Genetics* **44**, 1173–84.

445a. NANNEY, D. L. (1959) Vegetative mutants and clonal senility in *Tetrahymena*. *J. Protozool.* **6**, 171–7.

446. NANNEY, D. L. (1960) The relationship between the mating type and the H serotype systems in *Tetrahymena*. *Genetics* **45**, 1351–8.

447. NANNEY, D. L. (1962) Anomalous serotypes in *Tetrahymena*. *J. Protozool.* **9**, 485–7.

448. NANNEY, D. L. (1963) Aspects of mutual exclusion in *Tetrahymena*. In *Biological Organization at the Cellular and Super-Cellular Level*, ed. R. J. C. HARRIS, Academic Press, N.Y., pp. 91–109.

449. NANNEY, D. L. (1963) The inheritance of H-L serotype differences at conjugation in *Tetrahymena*. *J. Protozool.* **10**, 152–5.

450. NANNEY, D. L. (1963) Irregular genetic transmission in *Tetrahymena* crosses. *Genetics* **48**, 737–44.

451. NANNEY, D. L. (1963) Cytoplasmic inheritance in Protozoa. In *Methodology in Basic Genetics*, ed. W. J. BURDETTE, Holden-Day, San Francisco, pp. 355–80.

452. NANNEY, D. L. (1964) Macronuclear differentiation and subnuclear assortment in ciliates. In *Role of Chromosomes in Development*, ed. M. LOCKE, Academic Press, N.Y., pp. 253–73.

453. NANNEY, D. L., and ALLEN, S. L. (1959) Intranuclear coordination in *Tetrahymena*. *Physiol. Zool.* **32**, 221–9.

454. NANNEY, D. L., and CAUGHEY, P. A. (1953) Mating type determination in *Tetrahymena pyriformis*. *Proc. Nat. Acad. Sci.*, U.*S.* **39**, 1057–63.
455. NANNEY, D. L., and CAUGHEY, P. A. (1955) An unstable nuclear condition in *Tetrahymena pyriformis*. *Genetics* **40**, 388–98.
456. NANNEY, D. L., CAUGHEY, P. A., and TEFANKJIAN, A. (1955) The genetic control of mating type potentialities in *Tetrahymena pyriformis*. *Genetics* **40**, 668–80.
457. NANNEY, D. L., and DUBERT, J. M. (1960) The genetics of the H serotype system in variety 1 of *Tetrahymena pyriformis*. *Genetics* **45**, 1335–58.
458. NANNEY, D. L., and NAGEL, M. J. (1964) Nuclear misbehavior in an aberrant inbred *Tetrahymena*. *J. Protozool.* **11**, 465–73.
459. NANNEY, D. L., NAGEL, J., and TOUCHBERRY, R. W. (1964) The timing of H antigenic differentiation in *Tetrahymena*. *J. Exptl. Zool.* **155**, 25–42.
460. NANNEY, D. L., REEVE, S. J., NAGEL, J., and DePINTO, S. (1963) H serotype differentiation in *Tetrahymena*. *Genetics* **48**, 803–13.
461. NANNEY, D. L., and RUDZINSKA, M. A. (1960) Protozoa. In *The Cell*, ed. J. BRACHET and A. E. MIRSKY, Academic Press, N.Y., vol. IV, pp. 109–50.
462. NASS, M. M. K., and NASS, S. (1963) Intramitochondrial fibers with DNA characteristics. I. Fixation and electron staining reactions. *J. Cell Biol.* **19**, 593–608.
463. NASS, M. M. K., NASS, S., and AFZELIUS, B. A. (1965) The general occurrence of mitochondrial DNA *Exptl. Cell Res.* **37**, 516–39.
464. NASS, S., and NASS, M. M. K. (1963) Intramitochondrial fibers with DNA characteristics. II. Enzymatic and other hydrolytic treatments. *J. Cell Biol.* **19**, 613–29.
465. NASS, S., NASS, M. M. K., and HENNIX, U. (1965) Deoxyribonucleic acid in isolated rat-liver mitochondria. *Biochim. Biophys. Acta* **95**, 426–35.
466. NOBILI, R. (1959) The effects of aging and temperature on the expression of the gene *am* in variety 4, stock 51, of *Paramecium aurelia*. *J. Protozool.* **6** (Suppl.), 29.
467. NOBILI, R. (1960) The effect of macronuclear regeneration on vitality in *Paramecium aurelia*, syngen 4. *J. Protozool.* **7** (Suppl.), 15.
468. NOBILI, R. (1960) Kappa in amacronucleate *Paramecium aurelia*: its development and effect on survival time. *J. Protozool.* **7** (Suppl.), 15.
469. NOBILI, R. (1961) L'azione del gene *am* sull'apparato nucleare di *Paramecium aurelia* durante la riproduzione vegetativa e sessuale in relazione all'età del clone ed alla temperatura di allevamento degli animali. *Caryologia* **14**, 43–58.
470. NOBILI, R. (1961) Variazioni volumetriche del macronucleo e loro effetti nella riproduzione vegetativa in *Paramecium aurelia*. *Atti Soc. Toscane Sci. Natl. Pisa*, *B***67**, 217–32.
471. NOBILI, R. (1961) Effetti della rigenerazione del macronucleo sulla vitalita' di *Paramecium aurelia*, syngen 4. *Atti Assoc. Genetica Italiana* **6**, 75–86.
472. NOBILI, R. (1961) Alcune considerazioni sulla liberazione e sull'azione delle particelle kappa in individui amacronucleati di *Paramecium aurelia*, stock 51, syngen 4. *Atti Soc. Tosc. Sci. Nat.*, ser. B, pp. 158–72.
473. NOBILI, R. (1961) Il comportamento del kappa in esemplari amacronucleati di *Paramecium aurelia*, stock 51, syngen 4. *Boll. di Zool.* **28**, 579–96.
474. NOBILI, R. (1962) Il dimorfismo nucleare dei Ciliati: inerzia vegetativa del micronucleo. *Atti Acad. Naz. Lincei. Rend. Classe Sci. Fis. Mat. Nat'l Series VIII* **32**, 392–6.
475. NOBILI, R. (1962) Su un nuovo ceppo "killer" ad azione paralizzante di *Paramecium aurelia*, syngen 2. *Boll. di Zool.* **29**, 555–65.
476. NOBILI, R. (1963) Effects of antibiotics, base-and amino acid-analogues on mating reactivity of *Paramecium aurelia*. *J. Protozool.* **10** (Suppl.), 24.
477. NOBILI, R. (1964) On conjugation between *Euplotes vannus* O. F. Mueller and *Euplotes minuta* Yocum. *Caryologia* **17**, 393–7.
478. NOBILI, R. (1965) Mating types and their inheritance in *Euplotes minuta* Yocum (Ciliata, Hypotrichida). *Atti Ass. Genet. It., Pavia* **10**, 110–21.

478a. NOBILI, R. (1966) Mating types and mating type inheritance in *Euplotes minuta* Yocom (Ciliata, Hypotrichida). *J. Protozool.* **13**, 38–41.

479. NOBILI, R., and AGOSTINI, G. (1964) Coniugazione e reproduzione vegetativa di *Paramecium aurelia* sotto l'azione del 6-azauracile e della *p*-fluorofenilalanina. *Atti Ass. Genet. It.*, *Pavia* **9**, 72–86.

480. NOBILI, R., and DE ANGELIS, F. K. (1963) Effetti degli antibiotici sulla riproduzione di *Paramecium aurelia*. *Atti Ass. Genet. It.*, *Pavia* **8**, 45–57.

481. NOVICK, A., and WEINER, M. (1957) Enzyme as an all-or-none phenomenon. *Proc. Nat. Acad. Sci.*, *U.S.* **43**, 553–66.

482. OEHLER, R. (1922) Die Zellverbindung von *Paramecium bursaria* mit *Chlorella vulgaris* und anderen Algen. *Arb. Staatsinstitut Exper. Therapie* (*Frankfurt*) **15**, 3–19.

483. ORD, M. J., and DANIELLI, J. F. (1956) The site of damage in amoebae exposed to x-rays. *Quart. J. Micro. Sci.* **97**, 29–37.

484. ORIAS, E. (1960) The genetic control of two lethal traits in variety 1, *Tetrahymena pyriformis*. *J. Protozool.* **7**, 64–9.

485. ORIAS, E. (1963) Mating type determination in variety 8, *Tetrahymen pyriformis*. *Genetics* **48**, 1509–18.

486. OSAKI, H. (1959) Studies on the immunological variation in *Trypenosoma gambiense* (serotypes and the mode of relapse). *Biken's J.* **2**, 113–27.

486a. OSSIPOV, D. V. (1966) Analysis of hereditary mechanisms determining thermostability of *Paramecium caudatum*. *Genetica* **1**, 119–31.

486b. OUTKA, D. E. (1961) Conditions for mating and inheritance of mating type in variety 7 of *Tetrahymena pyriformis*. *J. Protozool.* **8**, 179–84.

487. PAPAZIAN, H. P. (1952) The analysis of tetrad data. *Genetics* **37**, 175–88.

488. PARSONS, J. A. (1964) Mitochondrial incorporation of tritiated thymidine in *Tetrahymena pyriformis* and a quantitative autoradiographic analysis relating to mitochondrial origin. *Am. Zoologist* **4**, 308.

489. PARSONS, J. A. (1964) The division of mitochondrial DNA in *Tetrahymena pyriformis*. *J. Cell Biol.* **23**, 70A.

490. PASCHER, A. (1916) Über die Kreuzung einzelliger, haploider Organismen: *Chlamydomonas*. *Ber. Deutsch. Bot. Ges.* **34**, 228–42.

491. PASCHER, A. (1918) Über die Beziehung der Reduktionssteilung zur Mendelschen Spaltung. *Ber. Deutsch. Bot. Ges.* **36**, 163–8.

492. PATAU, K. (1941) Eine statistische Bemerkung zu Moewus' Arbeit "Die Analyse von 42 erblichen Eigenschaften der *Chlamydomonas eugametos* Gruppe, III". *Z. induk. Abstammungs- u. Vererbungslehre* **79**, 317–9.

493. PERKINS, D. D. (1953) The detection of linkage in tetrad analysis. *Genetics* **38**, 187–97.

494. PHILIP, U., and HALDANE, J. B. S. (1939) Relative sexuality in unicellular algae. *Nature* **143**, 334.

495. PIEKARSKI, G. (1949) Blepharoplast und Trypaflavinwirkung bei *Trypanosoma brucei*. *Zentralbl. f. Bakt.* **153**, 109–15.

495a. PLAUT, W., and SAGAN, L. A. (1958) Incorporation of thymidine in the cytoplasm of *Amoeba proteus*. *J. Biophys. Biochem. Cytol.* **4**, 843–6.

496. PORTIER, P. (1918) *Les Symbiontes*, Masson, Paris.

497. POWERS, JR., E. L. (1943) The mating types of double animals in *Euplotes patella*. *Am. Midl. Nat.* **30**, 175–95.

498. POWERS, JR., E. L. (1948) Death after autogamy in *Paramecium aurelia* following exposure in solution to the radiactive isotopes P^{32} and $Sr^{89, 90}$, Y^{90}. *Genetics* **33**, 120–1.

499. POWERS, JR. E. L., and SHEFNER, D. (1948) Lethal changes induced by x-rays in *Paramecium aurelia*. *Genetics* **33**, 624–5.

500. PREER, JR., J. R. (1946) Some properties of a genetic cytoplasmic factor in *Paramecium*. *Proc. Nat. Acad. Sci.*, *U.S.* **32**, 247–53.

501. PREER, JR. J. R. (1948) A study of some properties of the cytoplasmic factor "kappa" in *P. aurelia*, variety 2. *Genetics* **33**, 349–404.

502. PREER, JR. J. R. (1948) Microscopic bodies in the cytoplasm of "killers" of *P. aurelia*, and evidence for the identification of these bodies, with the cytoplasmic factor "kappa". *Genetics* **33**, 625.

503. PREER, JR. J. R. (1950) Microscopically visible bodies in the cytoplasm of the "killer" strains of *P. aurelia*. *Genetics* **35**, 344–62.

504. PREER, JR. J. R. (1950) The role of the genes, cytoplasm and environment in the determination of resistance and sensitivity. *Yearbook Amer. Phil. Soc.* 1950, pp. 161–3.

505. PREER, JR., J. R. (1957) Genetics of the Protozoa. *Ann. Rev. Microbiol.* **11**, 419–38.

506. PREER, JR., J. R. (1957) A gene determining temperature sensitivity in *Paramecium*. *J. Genetics* **55**, 375–8.

507. PREER, JR., J. R. (1959) Nuclear and cytoplasmic differentiation in the Protozoa. In *Developmental Cytology*, ed. D. RUDNICK, Ronald Press, New York, pp. 3–20.

508. PREER, JR., J. R. (1959) Studies on the immobilization antigens of *Paramecium*. I. Assay methods. *J. Immunol.* **83**, 276–83.

509. PREER, JR., J. R. (1959) Studies on the immobilization antigens of *Paramecium*. II. Isolation. *J. Immunol.* **83**, 378–84.

510. PREER, JR., J. R. (1959) Studies on the immobilization antigens of *Paramecium*. III. Properties. *J. Immunol.* **83**, 385–91.

511. PREER, JR., J. R. (1959) Studies on the immobilization antigens of *Paramecium*. IV. Properties of the different antigens. *Genetics* **44**, 803–14.

512. PREER, JR., J. R., BRAY, M., and KOIZUMI, S. (1963) The role of cytoplasm and nucleus in the determination of serotype in *Paramecium*. *Proc. XIth Intern. Congr. Gen., The Hague* **1**, 189.

513. PREER, JR., J. R., HUFNAGEL, L. A., and PREER, L. B. (1966) Structure and behavior of "R" bodies from killer paramecia. *J. Ultrastructure Res.* **15**, 131–43.

514. PREER, JR., J. R., and PREER, L. B. (1959) Gel diffusion studies on the antigens of isolated cellular components of *Paramecium*. *J. Protozool.* **6**, 88–100.

515. PREER, L. B., and PREER, J. R. JR. (1964) Killing activity from lysed particles of *Paramecium*. *Genetical Res.* **5**, 230–9.

516. PREER, JR., J. R., SIEGEL, R. W., and STARK, P. S. (1953) The relationship between kappa and paramecin in *Paramecium aurelia*. *Proc. Nat. Acad. Sci., U.S.* **39**, 1228–33.

517. PREER, JR., J. R., and STARK, P. (1953) Cytological observations on the cytoplasmic factor "kappa" in *Paramecium aurelia*. *Exptl. Cell Res.* **5**, 478–91.

518. PRINGLE, C. R. (1956) Antigenic variation in *Paramecium*, variety 9. *Z. indukt. Abstam. u. Vererb.* **87**, 421–40.

519. PRINGSHEIM, E. G. (1915) Die Kulture von *Paramecium bursaria*. *Biol. Zentr.* **35**, 375.

520. PRINGSHEIM, E. G., and PRINGSHEIM, O. (1952) Experimental elimination of chromatophores and eyespot in *Euglena gracilis*. *New Phytologist* **51**, 65–76.

521. PRINGSHEIM, E. G., and PRINGSHEIM, O. (1958) Apoplastidy in *Euglena*. *Rev. Algol.* (New Ser.) **4**, 41.

522. PROVASOLI, L., HUTNER, S. H., and SCHATZ, A. (1948) Streptomycin-induced chlorophyll-less races of *Euglena*. *Proc. Soc. Exptl. Biol. Med.* **69**, 279–82.

523. RABINOWITZ, M., SINCLAIR, J., DeSALLE, L., HASELKORN, R., and SWIFT, H. H. (1965) Isolation of deoxyribonucleic acid from mitochondria of chick embryo heart and liver. *Proc. Nat. Acad. Sci., U.S.* **53**, 1126–33.

524. RANDALL, J., and DISBREY, C. (1965) Evidence for the presence of DNA at basal body site in *Tetrahymena pyriformis*. *Proc. Roy. Soc. B* **162**, 473–91.

525. RANDALL, G., WARR, J. R., HOPKINS, J. M., and McVITTE, A. (1964) A single-gene mutation of *Chlamydomonas reinhardi* affecting motility. *Nature* **203**, 912–4.

525a. Rao, M. V. N. (1958) Mating types in *Stylonychia pustulata*. *Current Science* **27**, 395.

526. Raper, J. R. (1952) Chemical regulation of sexual processes in the Thallophytes. *Botan. Rev.* **18**, 447–545.

527. Ray, Jr., C. (1956) Nuclear behavior in haploid clones of *Tetrahymena pyriformis*. *J. Protozool.* **3** (Suppl.), 3.

528. Ray, Jr., C. (1956) Meiosis and nuclear behavior in *Tetrahymena pyriformis*. *J. Protozool.* **3**, 88–96.

529. Ray, D. S., and Hanawalt, P. C. (1964) Properties of the satellite DNA associated with the chloroplasts of *Euglena gracilis*. *J. Mol. Biol.* **9**, 812–24.

530. Ray, D. S., and Hanawalt, P. C. (1965) Satellite DNA components in *Euglena gracilis* cells lacking chloroplasts. *J. Mol. Biol.* **11**, 760–8.

531. Reeve, E. C. R. (1962) Mathematical studies of mesosome distribution. *Genetical Res.* **3**, 47–50.

532. Reeve, E. C. R., and Ross, G. J. S. (1962) Mate-killer (mu) particles in *Paramecium aurelia:* the metagon division hypothesis. *Genetical Res.* **3**, 328–30.

533. Reeve, E. C. R., and Ross, G. J. S. (1963) Mate-killer (mu) particles in *Paramecium aurelia:* further mathematical models for metagon distribution. *Genetical Res.* **4**, 158–61.

534. Reich, E. (1964) Binding of actinomycin as a model for the complex-forming capacity of DNA. In *The Role of Chromosomes in Development*, ed. M. Locke, Academic Press, N.Y., pp. 73–81.

535. Reilly, M., and Lilly, D. M. (1963) A chemically defined medium for *Paramecium caudatum*. *J. Protozool.* **10** (Suppl.), 12.

536. Reisner, A. (1955) A method of obtaining specific serotype mutants in *Paramecium aurelia* stock 169, var. 4. *Genetics* **40**, 591–2.

537. Renner, O. (1958) Auch etwas über F. Moewus, *Forsythia* und *Chlamydomonas*. *Z. Naturforsch.* **13b**, 399–403.

538. Rhoades, M. M. (1943) Genic induction of an inherited cytoplasmic difference. *Proc. Nat. Acad. Sci., U.S.* **29**, 327–9.

539. Rhoades, M. M. (1955) Interaction of genic and non-genic hereditary units and the physiology of non-genic inheritance. In *Handbuch der Pflanzenphysiologie*, ed. W. Ruhland, Berlin, Vol. 1, pp. 19–57.

540. Rhoades, M. M. (1961) Meiosis. In *The Cell*, ed. J. Brachet and A. E. Mirsky, Academic Press, New York, Vol. 3, pp. 1–75.

541. Ringo, D. L. (1963) Electron microscopy of *Astasia longa*. *J. Protozool.* **10**, 167–73.

542. Ris, H., and Plaut, W. (1962) Ultrastructure of DNA-containing areas in the chloroplast of *Chlamydomonas*. *J. Cell Biol.* **13**, 383–92.

543. Robbins, W. J., Hervey, A., and Stebbins, M. E. (1953) *Euglena* and vitamin B_{12}. *Ann. N.Y. Acad. Sci.* **56**, 818–30.

544. Robertson, M. (1929) The action of acriflavine upon *Bodo caudatus*. *Parasitology,* **21**, 375–416.

545. Roman, H., and Jacob, F. (1958) A comparison of spontaneous and ultraviolet-induced allelic recombination with reference to the recombination of outside markers. *Cold Spring Harbor Symp. Quant. Biol.* **23**, 155–60.

546. Rössle, R. (1905) Spezifische Sera gegen Infusorien. *Arch. Hyg., Berl.* **54**, 1–31.

547. Rössle, R. (1909) Zur Immunität einzelliger Organismen. *Verh. dtsch. path. Ges.* **13**, 158–62.

548. Roth, L. E., and Daniels, E. W. (1961) Infective organisms in the cytoplasm of *Amoeba proteus J. Biophys. and Biochem. Cytol.* **9**, 317–23.

549. Rubin, B. A. (1948) Detection of the mutagenic effect of transmutation. *Genetics* **33**, 626–7.

550. RUDENBERG, F. H. (1962) Electron microscopic observations of kappa in *Paramecium aurelia*. *Texas Reports on Biology and Medicine* **20**, 105–12.

551. RUDZINSKA, M. M., D'ALESANDRO, P. A., and TRAGER, W. (1964) The fine structure of *Leishmania donovani* and the role of the kinetoplast in the leishmania leptomonad transformation. *J. Protozool.* **11**, 166–91.

552. RUPERT, C. S., GOODGAL, S. H., and HERRIOT, R. M. (1958) Photoreactivation *in vitro* of ultraviolet inactivated *Hemophilus influenzae* transforming factor. *J. Gen. Physiol.* **41**, 451–71.

553. RUSSELL, W. L. (1963) The effect of radiation dose rate and fractionation on mutation in mice. In *Repair from Genetic Radiation Damage*, ed. F. H. SOBELS, Pergamon Press, Oxford, pp. 205–17, 231–5.

554. RYAN, F. J. (1955) Attempt to reproduce some of Moewus' experiments on *Chlamydomonas* and *Polytoma*. *Science* **122**, 470.

555. SAGAN, L., BEN-SHAUL, Y., EPSTEIN, H. T., and SCHIFF, J. A. (1965) Studies of chloroplast development in *Euglena*, XI. Radioautographic localization of chloroplast DNA. *Plant Physiol.* **40**, 1257–60.

556. SAGER, R. (1954) Mendelian and non-Mendelian inheritance of streptomycin resistance in *Chlamydomonas reinhardi*. *Proc. Nat. Acad. Sci., U.S.* **40**, 356–63.

557. SAGER, R. (1955) Inheritance in the green alga *Chlamydomonas reinhardi*. *Genetics* **40**, 476–89.

558. SAGER, R. (1955) Non-Mendelian inheritance in *Chlamydomonas*. *Genetics* **40**, 594.

559. SAGER, R. (1960) Genetic systems in *Chlamydomonas*. *Science* **132**, 1459–65.

560. SAGER, R. (1961) Photosynthetic pigments in mutant strains of *Chlamydomonas*. *Carnegie Inst. Wash. Yearbook* **60**, 374–6.

561. SAGER, R. (1962) A nonmapable unit factor in *Chlamydomonas*. *Genetics* **47**, 982.

562. SAGER, R. (1962) Streptomycin as a mutagen for nonchromosomal genes. *Proc. Nat. Acad. Sci., U.S.* **48**, 2018–26.

563. SAGER, R. (1964) Studies of cell heredity with *Chlamydomonas*. In *Biochemistry and Physiology of Protozoa*, ed. S. H. HUTNER, Academic Press, N.Y., vol. III, pp. 297–318.

564. SAGER, R. (1964) Non-chromosomal genes in *Chlamydomonas*. *Proc. 11th Intern. Congr. Genetics, The Hague* (*Genetics Today*), pp. 579–89.

565. SAGER, R. (1964) Nonchromosomal heredity. *New Engl. J. Med.* **271**, 352–7.

566. SAGER, R. (1965) Mendelian and non-Mendelian heredity: a reappraisal. *Proc. Roy. Soc., London*, Mendel Centenary Symposium, in press.

567. SAGER, R. (1965) On non-chromosomal heredity in microorganisms. In *15th Symp. Soc. Genl. Microbiol.*, ed. M. R. POLLOCK and M. H. RICHMOND, Cambridge Univ. Press, Cambridge, pp. 324–42.

568. SAGER, R., and GRANICK, S. (1953) Nutritional studies with *Chlamydomonas reinhardi*. *Ann. N.Y. Acad. Sci.* **56**, 831–8.

569. SAGER, R., and ISHIDA, M. R. (1963) Chloroplast DNA in *Chlamydomonas*. *Proc. Nat. Acad. Sci., U.S.* **50**, 725–30.

570. SAGER, R., and RAMANIS, Z. (1963) The particulate nature of nonchromosomal genes in *Chlamydomonas*. *Proc. Nat. Acad. Sci., U.S.* **50**, 260–8.

571. SAGER, R., and RAMANIS, Z. (1964) Recombination of nonchromosomal genes in *Chlamydomonas*. *Genetics* **50**, 282.

572. SAGER, R., and RAMANIS, Z. (1965) Recombination of nonchromosomal genes in *Chlamydomonas*. *Proc. Nat. Acad. Sci., U.S.* **53**, 1053–61.

573. SAGER, R., and TSUBO, Y. (1961) Genetic analysis of streptomycin resistance and dependence in *Chlamydomonas*. *Z. Vererbungs.* **92**, 430–8.

574. SAGER, R., and TSUBO, Y. (1962) Mutagenic effects of streptomycin in *Chlamydomonas*. *Archiv. für Mikrobiol.* **42**, 159–75.

575. SAGER, R., and ZALOKAR, M. (1958) Pigments and photosynthesis in a carotenoid-deficient mutant of *Chlamydomonas*. *Nature* **182**, 98–100.

576. SATIR, B., and ROSENBAUM, J. L. (1965) The isolation and identification of kineto-some-rich fractions from *Tetrahymena pyriformis*. *J. Protozool.* **12**, 397–405.

577. SCHAECHTER, M., and DELAMATER, E. D. (1955) Mitosis in *Chlamydomonas*. *Am. J. Botany* **42**, 417–22.

578. SCHAEFFER, A. A. (1946) X-ray mutations in the giant multinuclear amoeba *Chaos chaos* Linn. *Anat. Rec.* **96**, 531.

579. SCHENSTED, I. V. (1958) Model of subnuclear segregation in the macronucleus of ciliates. *Am. Naturalist* **92**, 161–70.

580. SCHIFF, J. A., LYMAN, H., and EPSTEIN, H. T. (1961) Studies on chloroplast devel-opment in *Euglena*. II. Photoreversal of the U.V. inhibition of green colony formation. *Biochem. Biophys. Acta* **50**, 310–8.

581. SCHIFF, J. A., LYMAN, H., and EPSTEIN, H. T. (1961) Studies of chloroplast devel-opment in *Euglena*. III. Experimental separation of chloroplast development and chloroplast replication. *Biochem. Biophys. Acta* **51**, 340–6.

582. SCHNELLER, M. V. (1958) A new type of killing action in a stock of *Paramecium aurelia* from Panama. *Proc. Indiana Acad. Sci.* **67**, 302–3.

582a. SCHNELLER, M. V. (1962) Some notes on the rapid lysis type of killing found in *P. aurelia*. *Am. Zool.* **2**, 446.

583. SCHNELLER, M. V., SONNEBORN, T. M., and MUELLER, J. A. (1959) The genetic control of kappa-like particles in *Paramecium aurelia*. *Genetics* **44**, 533–4.

584. SCHWEIGER, H. G., and BERGER, S. (1964) DNA dependent RNA synthesis in chloro-plasts of *Acetabularia*. *Biochim. Biophys. Acta* **87**, 533–5.

585. SEAMAN, G. R. (1960) Large-scale isolation of kinetosomes from the ciliated proto-zoan *Tetrahymena pyriformis*. *Exptl. Cell Res.* **21**, 292–302.

585a. SEED, J. R. (1963) The characterization of antigens isolated from *Trypanosoma rhodesiense*. *J. Protozool.* **10**, 380–9.

585b. SHAW, R. F., and WILLIAMS, N. E. (1963) Physiological properties of *Tetrahymena vorax*. *J. Protozool.* **10**, 486–91.

586. SEED, J. R., SHAFER, S., FINGER, I., and HELLER, C. (1964) Immunogenetic analysis of proteins of *Paramecium*. VI. Additional evidence for the expression of several loci in animals of a single antigenic type. *Genetical Res.* **5**, 137–49.

587. SETLOW, J. K., BOLING, M. E., and BOLLUM, F. J. (1965) The chemical nature of photoreactivable lesions in DNA. *Proc. Nat. Acad. Sci., U.S.* **53**, 1430–6.

588. SETLOW, R., and DOYLE, B. (1956) The action of ultraviolet light on paramecin and the chemical nature of paramecin. *Biochim. Biophys. Acta* **22**, 15–20.

589. SETLOW, J. K., and SETLOW, R. B. (1963) Nature of the photoreactivable ultraviolet lesion in deoxyribonucleic acid. *Nature* **197**, 560–2.

589a. SHAW, R. F. (1960) Antigenic relations among stocks of *Tetrahymena vorax* and *Tetrahymena paravorax*. *J. Protozool.* **7** (Suppl.), 14.

590. SIEGEL, R. W. (1950) Determination and inheritance of a new type of killing action in *Paramecium aurelia*, variety 3. *Microbial Genetics Bull.* **3**, 12.

591. SIEGEL, R. W. (1952) The genetic analysis of mate-killing in *Paramecium aurelia*. *Genetics* **37**, 625–6.

592. SIEGEL, R. W. (1953) A genetic analysis of the mate-killer trait in *Paramecium aurelia*, variety 8. *Genetics* **38**, 550–60.

593. SIEGEL, R. W. (1954) Mate-killing in *Paramecium aurelia*, variety 8. *Physiol. Zool.* **27**, 89–100.

594. SIEGEL, R. W. (1956) Mating types in *Oxytricha* and the significance of mating type systems in ciliates. *Biol. Bull.* **110**, 352–7.

595. SIEGEL, R. W. (1957) An analysis of the transformation from immaturity to maturity in *Paramecium aurelia*. *Genetics* **42**, 394–5.

596. SIEGEL, R. W. (1958) An intrafertile colony of *Paramecium bursaria*. *Am. Nat.* **92**, 253–4.

597. SIEGEL, R. W. (1960) Hereditary endosymbiosis in *Paramecium bursaria*. *Exptl. Cell Res.* **19**, 239–52.

598. SIEGEL, R. W. (1961) Nuclear differentiation and transitional cellular phenotypes in the life cycle of *Paramecium*. *Exptl. Cell Res.* **24**, 6–20.

598a. SIEGEL, R. W. (1962) A study of selfing caryonides in *Paramecium aurelia*. *J. Protozool.* **9** (Suppl.), 28.

599. SIEGEL, R. W. (1963) New results on the genetics of mating types in *Paramecium bursaria*. *Genetical Res.* **4**, 132–42.

599a. SIEGEL, R. W. (1965) Hereditary factors controlling development in *Paramecium*. *Brookhaven Symp. in Biol.* **18**, 55–65.

599b. SIEGEL, R. W. (1965) Genic control of the life cycle in Ciliates. *2nd Intern. Conf. Protozool.*, *Excerpta Medica* **91**, 64–5.

600. SIEGEL, R. W., and COHEN, L. W. (1963) A temporal sequence for genic expression: cell differentiation in *Paramecium*. *Am. Zool.* **3**, 127–34.

600a. SIEGEL, R. W., and HECKMANN, K. (1966) Inheritance of autogamy and the killer trait in *Euplotes minuta*. *J. Protozool.* **13**, 34–8.

601. SIEGEL, R. W., and KARAKASHIAN, S. (1959) Dissociation and restoration of endocellular symbiosis in *Paramecium bursaria*. *Anat. Rec.* **134**, 639.

602. SIEGEL, R. W., and LARISON, L. L. (1960) Induced illegitimate mating in *Paramecium bursaria*. *Anat. Rec.* **136**, 383.

603. SIEGEL, R. W., and LARISON, L. L. (1960) The genic control of mating types in *Paramecium bursaria*. *Proc. Nat. Acad. Sci., U.S.* **46**, 344–9.

604. SIMONSEN, D. H., and VAN WAGTENDONK, W. J. (1949) Oxygen consumption of "killer" and "sensitive" stocks of *Paramecium aurelia*, variety 4. *Federation Proc.* **8**, 250–1.

605. SIMONSEN, D. H., and VAN WAGTENDONK, W. J. (1952) Respiratory studies on *Paramecium aurelia*, variety 4, killers and sensitives. *Biochim. Biophys. Acta* **9**, 515–27.

606. SIMONSEN, D. H., and VAN WAGTENDONK, W. J. (1956) The succinoxidase system of killer and sensitive stocks of *Paramecium aurelia*, variety 4. *J. Gen. Microbiol.* **15**, 39–46.

607. SIMPSON, L. (1965) The kinetoplast and transformation in *Leishmania*. *2nd Intern. Conf. Protozool.*, *Excerpta Medica* **91**, 41–2.

608. SKAAR, P. D. (1956) Past history and pattern of serotype transformation in *Paramecium aurelia*. *Exptl. Cell Res.* **10**, 646–56.

609. SMILLIE, R. M., and LEVINE, R. P. (1963) The photosynthetic electron transport chain of *Chlamydomonas reinhardi*. II. Components of the triphosphopyridine nucleotide reductive pathway in wild-type and mutant strains. *J. Biol. Chem.* **238**, 4058–62.

610. SMITH, G. M., and REGNERY, D. C. (1950) Inheritance of sexuality in *Chlamydomonas reinhardi*. *Proc. Nat. Acad. Sci., U.S.* **36**, 246–8.

611. SMITH, J. E. (1961) Purification of kappa particles of *Paramecium aurelia*, stock 51. *Amer. Zool.* **1**, 390.

612. SMITH-SONNEBORN, J. E., GREEN, L., and MARMUR, J. (1963) Deoxyribonucleic acid base composition of kappa and *Paramecium aurelia*, stock 51. *Nature* **197**, 385.

612a. SMITH-SONNEBORN, J. E., and VAN WAGTENDONK, W. J. (1964) Purification and chemical characterization of kappa of stock 51, *Paramecium aurelia*. *Exptl. Cell Res.* **33**, 50–9.

613. SOBELS, F. H. (1963) *Symposium on Repair from Genetic Radiation Damage and Differential Radiosensitivity in Germ Cells*. Pergamon Press, N.Y.

614. SOLDO, A. T. (1960) Cultivation of two strains of killer *Paramecium aurelia* in axenic medium. *Proc. Soc. Exptl. Biol. and Med.* **105**, 612–15.

615. SOLDO, A. T. (1963) Axenic culture of Paramecium—some observations on the growth behavior and nutritional requirements of a particle-bearing strain of *Paramecium aurelia* 299λ. *Ann. N.Y. Acad. Sci.* **108**, 380–8.

616. SONNEBORN, T. M. (1937) Sex, sex inheritance and sex determination in *P. aurelia*. *Proc. Nat. Acad. Sci.*, *U.S.* **23**, 378–95.

617. SONNEBORN, T. M. (1938) Mating types in *P. aurelia*: diverse conditions for mating in different stocks; occurrence, number and interrelations of the types. *Proc. Am. Phil. Soc.* **79**, 411–34.

618. SONNEBORN, T. M. (1938) Sexuality and genetics in *Paramecium aurelia*. *Yearbook Am. Phil. Soc.*, **1938**, pp. 220–2.

619. SONNEBORN, T. M. (1939) *P. aurelia*: mating types and groups; lethal interactions: determination and inheritance. *Am. Naturalist* **73**, 390–413.

620. SONNEBORN, T. M. (1940) The relation of macronuclear regeneration in *P. aurelia* to macronuclear structure, amitosis and genetic determination. *Anat. Rec.* **78**, 53–4.

621. SONNEBORN, T. M. (1942) A case of the inheritance of environmental effects and its explanation in *Paramecium*. *Proc. Ind. Acad. Sci.* **51**, 262–3.

622. SONNEBORN, T. M. (1942) Sex hormones in unicelluar organisms. *Cold Spring Harbor Symp. Quant. Biol.* **10**, 111–25.

623. SONNEBORN, T. M. (1943) Gene and cytoplasm. I. The determination and inheritance of the killer character in variety 4 of *P. aurelia*. II. The bearing of determination and inheritance of characters in *P. aurelia* on problems of cytoplasmic inheritance, pneumococcus transformations, mutations and development. *Proc. Nat. Acad. Sci.*, *U.S.* **29**, 329–43.

624. SONNEBORN, T. M. (1943) Acquired immunity to specific antibodies and its inheritance in *P. aurelia*. *Proc. Ind. Acad. Sci.* **52**, 190–1.

625. SONNEBORN, T. M. (1944) Exchange of cytoplasm at conjugation in *Paramecium aurelia*, variety 4. *Anat. Rec.* **89** (Suppl.), 49.

626. SONNEBORN, T. M. (1945) The dependence of the physiological action of a gene on a primer and the relation of primer to gene. *Am. Naturalist* **79**, 318–39.

627. SONNEBORN, T. M. (1946) Experimental control of the concentration of cytoplasmic genetic factors in *Paramecium*. *Cold Spring Harbor Symp. Quant. Biol.* **11**, 236–55.

628. SONNEBORN, T. M. (1946) Inert nuclei: inactivity of micronuclear genes in variety 4 of *Paramecium aurelia*. *Genetics* **31**, 231.

629. SONNEBORN, T. M. (1947) Recent advances in the genetics of *Paramecium* and *Euplotes*. *Adv. Genetics* **1**, 263–358.

630. SONNEBORN, T. M. (1947) Developmental mechanisms in *Paramecium*. *Growth Symp.* **11**, 291–307.

631. SONNEBORN, T. M. (1948) Symposium on plasmagenes, genes and characters in *P. aurelia*. *Am. Naturalist* **82**, 26–34.

632. SONNEBORN, T. M. (1948) Genes, cytoplasm, and environment in *Paramecium*. *Sci. Monthly* **67**, 154–60.

633. SONNEBORN, T. M. (1948) The determination of hereditary antigenic differences in genetically identical *Paramecium* cells. *Proc. Nat. Acad. Sci.*, *U.S.* **34**, 413–8.

634. SONNEBORN, T. M. (1949) Ciliated protozoa: cytogenetics, genetics, and evolution. *Ann. Rev. Microbiol.* **3**, 55–80.

635. SONNEBORN, T. M. (1950) Methods in the general biology and genetics of *P. aurelia*. *J. Exptl. Zool.* **113**, 87–143.

636. SONNEBORN, T. M. (1950) The cytoplasm in heredity. *Heredity* **4**, 11–36.

637. SONNEBORN, T. M. (1951) The role of the genes in cytoplasmic inheritance. In *Genetics in the Twentieth Century*, ed. L. C. Dunn, MacMillan, N.Y., pp. 291–314.

638. SONNEBORN, T. M. (1951) Some current problems of genetics in the light of investigations on *Chlamydomonas* and *Paramecium*. *Cold Spring Harbor Symp. Quant. Biol.* **16**, 483–503.

639. SONNEBORN, T. M. (1953) Environmental control of the duration of phenomic or cytoplasmic lag in *Paramecium aurelia*. *Microbial Genetics Bull.* **7**, 23.

640. SONNEBORN, T. M. (1954) Gene-controlled, aberrant nuclear behavior in *Paramecium aurelia*. *Microbial Genetics Bull.* **11**, 24–25.

641. SONNEBORN, T. M. (1954) Is the gene K active in the micronucleus of *Paramecium aurelia*? *Microbial Genetics Bull.* **11**, 25–26.

642. SONNEBORN, T. M. (1954) Patterns of nucleocytoplasmic integration in *Paramecium*. *Caryologia* **6** (Suppl.), 307–25.

643. SONNEBORN, T. M. (1954) The relation of autogamy to senescence and rejuvenescence in *Paramecium aurelia*. *J. Protozool.* **1**, 38–53.

644. SONNEBORN, T. M. (1956) An exceptional autogamous clone in variety 4 of *Paramecium aurelia* and its interpretation. *J. Protozool.* **3** (Suppl.), 8–9.

645. SONNEBORN, T. M. (1956) The distribution of killers among the varieties of *Paramecium aurelia*. *Anat. Rec.* **125**, 567–8.

646. SONNEBORN, T. M. (1957) Breeding systems, reproductive methods, and species problems in Protozoa. In *The Species Problem*, ed. E. MAYR, Am. Assoc. Adv. Sci. Publ. **50**, 155–324.

647. SONNEBORN, T. M. (1957) Diurnal change of mating type in *Paramecium*. *Anat. Rec.* **128**, 626.

648. SONNEBORN, T. M. (1958) Classification of syngens of the *Paramecium aurelia—multimicronucleatum* complex. *J. Protozool.* **5** (Suppl.), 17–18.

649. SONNEBORN, T. M. (1959) Kappa and related particles in *Paramecium*. *Adv. in Virus Res.* **6**, 229–356.

649a. SONNEBORN, T. M. (1960) The gene and cell differentiation. *Proc. Nat. Acad. Sci., U.S.* **46**, 149–65.

650. SONNEBORN, T. M. (1963) Does preformed cell structure play an essential role in cell heredity? In The *Nature of Biological Diversity*, ed. J. M. ALLEN, McGraw-Hill, New York, pp. 165–221.

651. SONNEBORN, T. M. (1963) Sex in *Suctoria*: mating types in *Tokophrya infusionum*. *J. Protozool.* **10** (Suppl.), 25.

652. SONNEBORN, T. M. (1964) The differentiation of cells. *Proc. Nat. Acad. Sci., U.S.* **51**, 915–29.

653. SONNEBORN, T. M. (1965) The metagon: RNA and cytoplasmic inheritance. *Am. Naturalist* **99**, 279–307.

654. SONNEBORN, T. M., and BALBINDER, E. (1953) The effect of temperature on the expression of allelic genes for serotypes in a heterozygote of *Paramecium aurelia*. *Microbial Genetics Bull.* **7**, 24–25.

655. SONNEBORN, T. M., and BARNETT, A. (1958) The mating type system in syngen 2 of *Paramecium multimicronucleatum*. *J. Protozool.* **5** (Suppl.), 18.

656. SONNEBORN, T. M., and DIPPELL, R. V. (1946) Mating reactions and conjugation between varieties of *P. aurelia* in relation to conceptions of mating type and variety. *Physiol. Zool.* **19**, 1–18.

657. SONNEBORN, T. M., and DIPPELL, R. V. (1960) The genetic basis of the difference between single and double *Paramecium aurelia*. *J. Protozool.* **7** (Suppl.), 26.

658. SONNEBORN, T. M., and DIPPELL, R. V. (1961) The limit of multiplicity of cortical organelle systems in *P. aurelia*, syngen 4. *Am. Zool.* **1**, 390.

659. SONNEBORN, T. M., and DIPPELL, R. V. (1961) Self-reproducing differences in the cortical organization in *Paramecium aurelia*, syngen 4. *Genetics* **46**, 900.

660. SONNEBORN, T. M., and DIPPELL, R. V. (1961) The modes of replication of cortical organization in *Paramecium aurelia*, syngen 4. *Genetics* **46**, 899–900.

661. SONNEBORN, T. M., and DIPPELL, R. V. (1962) Two new evidences of cortical autonomy in syngen 4 of *Paramecium aurelia*. *J. Protozool.* **9** (Suppl.), 28.

662. SONNEBORN, T. M., DIPPELL, R. V., and JACOBSON, W. E. (1947) Some properties of kappa (killer cytoplasmic factor) and of paramecin (killer substance) in *Paramecium aurelia*, variety 4. *Genetics* **32**, 106.

663. SONNEBORN, T. M., DIPPELL, R. V., SCHNELLER, M. V., and TALLAN, I. (1953) The explanation of "anomalous" inheritance following exposure to ultraviolet in variety 4 of *Paramecium aurelia. Microbial Genetics Bull.* **7**, 25–26.

664. SONNEBORN, T. M., GIBSON, I., and SCHNELLER, M. V. (1964) Killer particles and metagons of *Paramecium* grown in *Didinium. Science* **144**, 567–8.

665. SONNEBORN, T. M., JACOBSON, W. E., and DIPPELL, R. V. (1946) Paramecin 51, an antibiotic produced by *Paramecium aurelia:* amounts released from killers and taken up by sensitives; conditions protecting sensitives. *Anat. Rec.* **96**, 514–5.

666. SONNEBORN, T. M., and MUELLER, J. A. (1959) What is the infective agent in breis of killer paramecia? *Science* **130**, 1423.

667. SONNEBORN, T. M., MUELLER, J. A., and SCHNELLER, M. V. (1959) The classes of kappa-like particles in *Paramecium aurelia. Anat Rec.* **134**, 642.

668. SONNEBORN, T. M., OGASAWARA, F., and BALBINDER, E. (1953) The temperature sequence of the antigenic types in variety 4 of *Paramecium aurelia* in relation to the stability and transformations of antigenic types. *Microbial Genetics Bull.* **7**, 27.

669. SONNEBORN, T. M., and SCHNELLER, M. (1950) Transformations of serotype A, stock 51, var. 4, *Paramecium aurelia,* induced by ultraviolet light. *Microbial Genetics Bull.* **3**, 15.

670. SONNEBORN, T. M., and SCHNELLER, M. V. (1955) Genetic consequences of ageing in variety 4 of *Paramecium aurelia. Rec. Genetics Soc. Am.* **24**, 596.

671. SONNEBORN, T. M., SCHNELLER, M. V., and CRAIG, M. F. (1956) The basis of variation in phenotype of gene-controlled traits in heterozygotes of *Paramecium aurelia. J. Protozool.* **3** (Suppl.), 8.

672. SONNEBORN, T. M., and SONNEBORN, D. R. (1958) Some effects of light on the rhythm of mating type changes in stock 232-6 of syngen 2 of *P. multimicronucleatum. Anat. Rec.* **131**, 601.

673. SONNEBORN, T. M., TALLAN, I., BALBINDER, E., OGASAWARA, F., and RUDNYANSKY, B. (1953) The independent inheritance of 5 genes in variety 4 of *Paramecium aurelia. Microbial Genetics Bull.* **7**, 27–28.

674. SONNEBORN, T. M., and WHALLON, J. (1950) Transformation of serotype A, stock 51 variety 4, *Paramecium aurelia. Microbial Genetics Bull.* **3**, 15.

675. STEERS, E. (1961) Electrophoretic analysis of immobilization antigens of *Paramecium aurelia. Science* **133**, 2010–11.

676. STEERS, E. (1962) A comparison of the tryptic peptides obtained from immobilization antigens of *Paramecium aurelia. Proc. Nat. Acad. Sci., U.S.* **48**, 867–74.

677. STEERS, E. (1965) Amino acid composition and quaternary structure of an immobilizing antigen from *Paramecium aurelia. Biochemistry* **4**, 1896–901.

678. STEFFENSEN, D. (1953) Induction of chromosome breakage at meiosis by a magnesium deficiency in *Tradescantia. Proc. Nat. Acad. Sci., U.S.* **39**, 613–20.

679. STEFFENSEN, D. (1955) Breakage of chromosomes in *Tradescantia* with a calcium deficiency. *Proc. Nat. Acad. Sci., U.S.* **41**, 155–60.

680. STEFFENSEN, D. (1957) Effects of various cation imbalances on the frequency of x-ray induced chromosomal aberrations in *Tradescantia. Genetics* **42**, 239–52.

681. STEFFENSEN, D., ANDERSON, L., and KASE, S. (1956) Crossing over studies with *Drosophila* and maize. *Genetics* **41**, 663.

682. STEIN, J. R. (1958) A morphologic and genetic study of *Gonium pectorale. Am. J. Bot.* **45**, 664–72.

682a. STEIN, J. R. (1965) Sexual populations of *Gonium pectorale* (Volvocales). *Am. J. Bot.* **52**, 379–88.

683. STEINERT, M. (1960) Mitochondria associated with the kinetonucleus of *Trypanosoma mega. J. Biochem. Biophys. Cytol.* **8**, 542–6.

684. STOCK, C. C., JACOBSON, W. E., and WILLIAMSON, M. (1951) An influence of 2, 6—diaminopurine upon the content of kappa in *Paramecium aurelia*, variety 4. *Proc. Soc. Exptl. Biol. Med.* **78**, 874–6.

685. SUEOKA, N. (1960) Mitotic replication of deoxyribonucleic acid in *Chlamydomonas reinhardi*. *Proc. Nat. Acad. Sci., U.S.* **46**, 83–91.

686. SUYAMA, Y. (1966) Mitochondrial DNA from *Tetrahymena pyriformis*. *Bacteriol. Proc.*, p. 33.

687. SUYAMA, J., and BONNER, W. D. (1965) Isolation and characterization of mitochondrial DNA. Abstract presented at the annual meetings of Northeastern Section for American Society of Plant Physiologists, p. 6.

688. SUYAMA, Y., and BONNER, W. D. (1966) DNA from plant mitochondria. *Plant Physiol.* **41**, 383–8.

689. SUYAMA, Y., and PREER, JR., J. R. (1965) Mitochondrial DNA from Protozoa. *Genetics* **52**, 1051–8.

690. SUYAMA, Y., PREER, JR., J. R., and BONNER, W. D. (1965) Mitochondrial DNA and its density distribution. *Plant Physiol.* **40** (Suppl.), 14.

691. SWIFT, H. (1963) Cytochemical studies on nuclear fine structure. *Exptl. Cell Res.* **9** (Suppl.), 54–67.

692. SWIFT, H. (1965) Nucleic acids of mitochondria and chloroplasts. *Am. Naturalist* **99**, 201–27.

693. SWIFT, H., ADAMS, B. J., and LARSEN, K. (1964) Electron microscope cytochemistry of *Drosophila* salivary glands and Tetrahymena. *J. Roy. Micros. Soc.* **83**, 161–7.

694. TAKAYANAGI, T., and HAYASHI, S. (1964) Cytological and cytogenetical studies on *Paramecium polycaryum*. V. Lethal interactions in certain stocks. *J. Protozool.* **11**, 128–32.

695. TALIAFERRO, W. H. (1930) *The Immunology of Parasitic Infections*, John Bale Sons and Danielsson Ltd., London.

696. TALLAN, I. (1959) Factors involved in infection by the kappa particles in *Paramecium aurelia*, syngen 4. *Physiol. Zool.* **32**, 78–89.

697. TALLAN, I. (1961) A cofactor required by kappa in the infection of *Paramecium aurelia* and its possible action. *Physiol. Zool.* **34**, 1–13.

698. TARTAR, V. (1961) *The Biology of Stentor*, Pergamon Press, New York.

699. TAUB, S. R. (1958) Nucleo-cytoplasmic interactions in mating type determination in variety 7 of *Paramecium aurelia*. *J. Protozool.* **5** (Suppl.), 18.

700. TAUB, S. R. (1959) The genetics of mating type determination in syngen 7, *Paramecium aurelia*, *Genetics* **44**, 541–2.

701. TAUB, S. R. (1962) The effect of nuclear genes on nuclear differentiation in syngen 7, *Paramecium aurelia*. *Genetics* **47**, 990–1.

702. TAUB, S. R. (1963) The genetic control of mating type differentiation in *Paramecium*. *Genetics* **48**, 815–34.

703. TEWARI, K. K., JAYARAMAN, J., and MAHLER, H. R. (1965) Separation and characterization of mitochondrial DNA from yeast. *Biochem. Biophys. Res. Comm.* **21**, 141–8.

704. THIMANN, K. V. (1940) Sexual substances in the algae. *Chronica Botanica* **6**, 31–32.

705. THOMPSON, P. E. (1962) Asynapsis and mutability in *Drosophila melanogaster*. *Genetics* **47**, 337–49.

706. TRAGER, W. (1957) Nutrition of a hemoflagellate (*Leishmania tarentolae*) having an interchangeable requirement for choline or pyridoxal. *J. Protozool.* **4**, 269–76.

707. TRAGER, W. (1965) The kinetoplast and differentiation in certain parasitic protozoa. *Am. Naturalist* **99**, 255–66.

708. TRAGER, W., and RUZINSKA, M. A. (1964) The riboflavin requirement and the effects of acriflavin on the fine structure of the kinetoplast of *Leishmania tarentolae*. *J. Protozool.* **11**, 133–45.

709. VAN WAGTENDONK, W. J. (1948) The action of enzymes on paramecin. *J. Biol. Chem.* **173**, 691–704.

710. VAN WAGTENDONK, W. J. (1948) The killing substance paramecin: chemical nature. *Am. Naturalist* **82**, 60–68.

711. VAN WAGTENDONK, W. J. (1951) Antigenic transformations in *P. aurelia*, variety 4, stock 51, under the influence of trypsin and chymotrypsin. *Exptl. Cell Res.* **2**, 615–29.

712. VAN WAGTENDONK, W. J., CLARK, J. A. D., and GODOY, G. A. (1963) The biological status of lambda and related particles in *Paramecium aurelia*. *Proc. Nat. Acad. Sci., U.S.* **50**, 835–8.

713. VAN WAGTENDONK, W. J., CONNER, R. L., MILLER, C. A., and RAO, M. R. R. (1953) Growth requirements of *Paramecium aurelia* variety 4, stock 51.7 sensitives and killers in axenic medium. *Ann. N.Y. Acad. Sci.* **56**, 929–37.

714. VAN WAGTENDONK, W. J., ZILL, L. P., and SIMONSON, D. H. (1950) Chemical and physiological studies on paramecin and kappa. *Proc. Ind. Acad. Sci.* **60**, 64–66.

715. VAN WISSELINGH, C. (1920) Über Variabilität und Erblichkeit. *Z. Induk. Abstam. u. Vererb.* **22**, 65–126.

716. VICKERMAN, K. (1965) Mitochondrial behavior in the life-cycles of the African trypanosomes. 2nd Intern. Conf. Protozool., *Excerpta Med. Found.* **91**, 146.

716a. VIVIER, E., SCHREVEL-DEBERSEE, G., and OGER, C. (1964) Observations sur les variétés et types sexuels de *Paramecium caudatum;* hérédité et changement de type sexuel. *Arch. Zool. Exp. Gén., Protistologica* **104** (Notes et Revue), 49–67.

717. WAGNER, R. P., and MITCHELL, H. K. (1964) *Genetics and Metabolism*, 2nd ed., Wiley, New York.

718. WALLIN, I. E. (1927) *Symbionticism and the Origin of Species*, Williams and Wilkins, Baltimore.

719. WEAVER, E. C., and BISHOP, N. I. (1963) Photosynthetic mutants separate electron paramagnetic resonance signals of *Scenedesmus*. *Science* **140**, 1095–7.

720. WEISS, P. (1962) From cell to molecule. In *The Molecular Control of Cellular Activity*, ed. J. M. ALLEN, McGraw-Hill, New York, pp. 1–72.

720a. WELLS, C. (1961) Evidence for micronuclear function during vegetative growth and reproduction in the ciliate, *Tetrahymena pyriformis*. *J. Protozool.* **8**, 284–90.

721. WERBITZKI, P. W. (1910) Ueber blepharoblastlose Trypanosomen. *Centralbl. f. Bakt., I. Abt. Orig.* **53**, 303–15.

722. WETHERELL, D. F., and KRAUSS, R. W. (1957) X-ray-induced mutations in *Chlamydomonas eugametos*. *Am. J. Botany* **44**, 609–19.

723. WHITEHOUSE, H. L. K. (1942) Crossing-over in *Neurospora*. *New Phytologist* **41**, 23–62.

724. WHITEHOUSE, H. L. K. (1949) Multiple-allelomorph heterothallism in the fungi. *New Phytologist* **48**, 212–44.

725. WHITEHOUSE, H. L. K. (1957) Mapping chromosome centromeres from tetratype frequencies. *J. Genetics* **55**, 348–60.

726. WHITING, A. R. (1950) Absence of mutagenic action of x-rayed cytoplasm in *Habrobracon*. *Proc. Nat. Acad. Sci., U.S.* **36**, 368–72.

727. WHITING, A. R. (1960) Protection and recovery of the cell from radiation damage. In *Radiation, Protection and Recovery*, ed. A. HOLLAENDER, Pergamon Press, New York, pp. 117–56.

728. WICHTERMAN, R. (1939). Cytogamy: a new sexual process in joined pairs of *Paramecium caudatum*. *Nature* **144**, 123–4.

729. WICHTERMAN, R. (1941) Studies on zoochlorellae-free *Paramecium bursaria*. *Biol. Bull.* **81**, 304–5.

730. WICHTERMAN, R. (1948) The biological effects of x-rays on mating types and conjugation of *Paramecium bursaria*. *Biol. Bull.* **94**, 113–27.

731. WICHTERMAN, R. (1953) *The Biology of Paramecium*, Blakiston, New York.

732. WIDMAYER, D. J. (1965) A nonkiller resistant kappa and its bearing on the interpretation of kappa in *Paramecium aurelia*. *Genetics* **51**, 613–23.

733. WILLE, JR., J. J. (1964) Abnormal morphogenesis and altered cellular localization of DNA-like RNA in *Paramecium aurelia*. *Genetics* **50**, 294–5.

733a. WILLIAMS, N. E. (1961) Polymorphism in *Tetrahymena vorax*. *J. Protozool*. **8**, 403–10.

734. WILLIAMSON, M., JACOBSON, W. E., and STOCK, C. C. (1952) Testing of chemicals for inhibition of the killer action of *Paramecium aurelia*. *J. Biol. Chem*. **197**, 763–70.

735. WINTERSBERGER, E. (1964) DNA-abhängige RNA-Synthese in Rattenleber-Mitochondrien. *Z. Physiol. Chem*. **336**, 285–8.

735a. WOOD, H. K. (1953) Some factors affecting delayed separation of conjugants in *Paramecium aurelia*. Doctoral dissertation, Indiana Univ., Bloomington, Ind.

735b. WOODARD, J., GELBER, B., and SWIFT, H. (1961) Nucleoprotein changes during the mitotic cycle in *Paramecium aurelia*. *Exptl. Cell Res*. **23**, 258–64.

735c. WOODARD, J., WOODARD, M., and GELBER, B. (1964) Cytochemical studies of conjugation in *Paramecium aurelia*. *J. Cell Biol*. **23**, 125A.

736. WULFF, D. L., and RUPERT, C. S. (1962) Disappearance of thymine photodimer in ultraviolet irradiated DNA upon treatment with a photoreactivating enzyme from baker's yeast. *Biochem. Biophys. Res. Comm*. **7**, 237–40.

737. YEUNG, K. K. (1965) Maintenance of kappa particles in cells recently deprived of gene *K* (stock 51, syngen 4) of *Paramecium aurelia*. *Genetical Res*. **6**, 411–8.

738. YPHANTIS, D. A. (1960) Rapid determination of molecular weights of peptides and proteins. *Ann. N.Y. Acad. Sci*. **88**, 586–601.

739. YPHANTIS, D. A. (1964) Equilibrium ultracentrifugation of dilute solutions. *Biochemistry* **3**, 297–317.

740. ZAHALSKY, A. C., HUTNER, S. H., KEANE, M., and BURGER, R. M. (1962) Bleaching *Euglena gracilis* with antihistamines and streptomycin-type antibiotics. *Arch. Mikrobiol*. **42**, 46–55.

FIBRILLAR SYSTEMS IN PROTOZOA

Dorothy R. Pitelka

Cancer Research Genetics Laboratory, University of California, Berkeley

CONTENTS

I. INTRODUCTION

When nineteenth-century microscopists first described intracellular structures in protozoa they were inclined to assume, explicitly or implicitly, that these were directly analogous to organelles or even organs in metazoa. Further and more critical examination led to an almost complete about-face: the protozoan level of organization came to be visualized as so different from cellular organization in metazoa that few analogies could or needed to be sought. The vagaries of protozoan morphology seemed limitless; the more bizarre this morphology appeared, the more eloquently it bespoke the uniqueness of the protozoan constitution.

As long as the wave-length of light set an absolute lower limit on the size of structures that could be seen, interest in protozoan anatomy was largely confined to protozoologists. Brilliant and perceptive studies yielded important insights into phylogeny and morphogenesis within the eucellular protists and showed how versatile protoplasmic construction could be. But especially among zoologists—who had not, and still have not, been able to trace metazoan origins in the protozoa—few were willing to accept protozoa as useful models, either as cells or as organisms.

The fibrillar structures that figure so conspicuously in protozoan morphology were especially, and properly, suspect. It simply was not possible to prove, for example, that silver-staining elements in ciliates represented or did not represent the same thing as silver-staining elements in nerve tissue, or that the myonemes of protozoa were or were not true counterparts of muscle fibrils, and no amount of inspired speculation could substitute for the evidence that was technically inaccessible.

When C. V. Taylor, in 1941,[242] wrote his comprehensive review of fibrillar systems in ciliates, he noted, among his general conclusions, that the myriad fibers described could not all be the same thing, structurally or functionally; that some of them might prove to be directly comparable to fibers reported in ciliated cells of metazoa; and that in most cases, despite abundant circumstantial evidence and some experimentation, their functions had not been demonstrated. He urged biologists looking at both protozoa and metazoa (pp. 260–1) to search out and emphasize "not merely differences but also, and more fundamentally, similarities, in both the structural and functional processes of protoplasmic differentiation", pointing out reasonably that "fibrillar differentiation is one of the most likely kinds of protoplasmic differentiation that might be expected". And he called for the application of critical observational methods "perhaps such as that of the recently developed electron microscope" *together* with stringent experimental techniques.

Since Taylor wrote, electron microscopy has dramatically demonstrated that cytoplasmic organelles of equivalent structure are present in all eucells, including protozoa, and has engendered a field of comparative cytology that cuts gleefully across phylogenetic barriers in search of functional correlates. Membranous and particulate components were the first to be recognized as ubiquitous, but within the last five years it has become evident that fibrillar differentiation is indeed one of the universal kinds of protoplasmic differentiation. Discrete fibrils are found in almost all types of cells; protozoa do not have a monopoly on any kind of fibrillar unit. If the experimental approaches for which Taylor pled have not, with few exceptions, been applied to cytoplasmic fibrils this is partly because there has not yet been time—morphology has to be got out of the way first. But the appropriateness of protozoa as experimental models is no longer in question.

The uniqueness of the protozoa lies not in the possession of any peculiar protoplasmic components but in the architectural complexity and precision with which ordinary components are arranged in a self-sufficient, infinitely reproducible cell body. In the flagellates and ciliates at least, any attempt to explore the bases of this complexity and precision leads inevitably to a consideration of their fibrillar systems, which seem either to set or intimately to reflect the specific architectural pattern.

It is possible now to look at protozoan fibrillar systems from the viewpoints of both protozoologist and cell biologist, knowing—as Taylor could not know 25 years ago—that the two views differ only in emphasis. Such is the intent of this review. Although fibrillar structures of compelling interest are present in all classes of protozoa, only the flagellates and ciliates will be examined here, since these groups seem to me to offer the best opportunities for a comparative survey.

II. TYPES OF CYTOPLASMIC FIBRILS

Development of a definitive terminology for cytoplasmic fibrils must await the accumulation of considerably more information about properties other than appearance. For descriptive convenience, common terms will be employed in the following ways: A *fiber* is visible as such in the light microscope. It may be composed of one (rarely) or more *fibrils* identifiable by electron microscopy. Such fibrils, as several protozoologists have pointed out,[88, 156, 173, 178, 190] can generally be grouped in three morphologic categories: *striated root fibrils, tubular fibrils* (or *microtubules*), and fine *filaments*. The three categories together are not all-inclusive nor are they on present evidence mutually exclusive. In this Section II, the morphology of representative fibrils of the three categories, found in a wide variety of cell types, will be described. Omitted from my discussion are all intranuclear fibrils and the sparse, DNA-containing filaments identifiable in such cytoplasmic organelles as mitochondria and chloroplasts.

10*

A. Striated Root Fibrils

In their most characteristic form these are discrete, dense fibrils of variable diameter, usually tapering, showing distinct cross-banding, and attached at one end to a kinetosome. The cross-banding is frequently complex, with a major pattern repeated about every 60 mμ, but a wide range of spacings has been reported. Striated root fibrils are found in some ciliates, some flagellates, some spermatozoa and zoospores of higher algae and fungi, and many metazoan ciliated and flagellated cells.[64, 229] They are not confined to motile cilia, being found commonly in photoreceptor[47] and other cells in which immobile cilia serve a purely sensory function.

Suitable thin sections of striated root fibrils commonly show that they are made up of many longitudinal filaments. It is not clear whether the fibril banding in most instances reflects a repeating macromolecular pattern of filaments in register, as in collagen fibrils, or represents material added to the filament bundle at regular intervals. The former possibility is more likely for most of the large, "conventional" root fibrils, which reveal an apparently intrinsic striation whatever the plane of section.

In addition to these discrete root fibrils, many kinetosomes bear short, blunt, lateral projections known as "basal feet"[75] that appear either homogeneous or roughly banded. Sakaguchi[216] has recently pictured "pericentriolar filamentous bodies" extending from interphase centrioles of various non-ciliated cells in mammals. They are relatively short, confined to the Golgi regions of the cells, and consist of bundles of very fine filaments with dense striations at 70-mμ intervals. The broadest (about 150 mμ), proximal segment of the body shows a narrow stripe about midway in each major interval; the narrower, intermediate portion has several stripes in each major interval; and the slender distal portion exhibits the major striation only. The relative lengths of the three segments vary, as do the angle and site of attachment to the centriole; there may be one or several bodies per centriole, and each may branch. Sakaguchi suggests that many of the striated, kinetosome-based structures described in other cells may be differentially developed homologues of his filamentous bodies; striated root fibrils could be long intermediate segments, basal feet might represent proximal segments and so on. Sakaguchi's idea is attractive and would be more so if his fibrils could be shown to have a wide distribution in unspecialized cells.

B. Microtubules

Fibrils appearing as hollow cylinders with reported diameters of 15 to 30 mμ were recognized in certain specialized organelles almost as soon as thin-sectioning methods for electron microscopy were developed. These organelles included cilia of metazoa[65] and protozoa,[226] sheath elements of spermatozoa,[23] centrioles and mitotic spindles,[98] and the contractile axostyle of a flagellate.[89] By 1958, Roth[205] was able to point to the presence of intracytoplasmic microtubules in a considerable number of ciliates and flagellates. Since then, their existence as a common protoplasmic component in protistan, animal, and plant cells, both with and without relation to a kinetosome or centriole, has been established beyond doubt.[12, 25, 41, 66, 121, 173, 218, 227, 228]

Early workers were careful to acknowledge that the hollow appearance of microtubules might be an illusion, but recent examination of isolated fibrils demonstrates that electron-opaque solutions may enter the lumen, at least under the conditions of isolation. Microtubules isolated from flagella by André and Thiéry[6] and Pease,[168] from the mitotic apparatus by Sakai, Solari, Kiefer and Mazia,[217] and from erythrocytes by Gall[72] are made up of ten to fourteen (counting is difficult; the number could be the same in all) slender, longitudinal filaments. High-resolution cross-sections of microtubules in plant cells by Ledbetter and Porter[121] reveal thirteen filaments, embedded in a matrix, making up the tubule wall. The filaments may be interpreted as rows of globular units, each about 35 Å in diameter;[217] banding often seen in microtubules perhaps reflects a transverse or oblique alignment of the globular units of adjacent filaments. In all instances microtubules appear to have considerable rigidity, running straight or nearly so in their cellular loci as well as after isolation.

Microtubules from different sources may differ strikingly in properties other than their individual appearance. For example, they are intimately joined as doublets in the peripheral fibrils of the ciliary axoneme and as triplets in the kinetosome and centriole, but not elsewhere as a rule; they are differentially sensitive to fixing agents, the fibrils of cilia and of protozoan cytoplasmic systems being well preserved with ordinary osmium fixatives whereas spindle fibrils and many cytoplasmic fibrils seem to require special conditions for fixation. Thus there seems no reason to suppose a priori that all microtubules are the same kind of thing, and it has been surprising to find such close correspondence in the morphology at macromolecular dimensions of three rather different sorts of tubular fibrils.

An important property of some microtubules is their tendency to be linked in an orderly manner either to one another or to adjacent membranes. Usually, fine bridges are apparent in electron micrographs, indicating physical interconnection; these may bind the fibrils in two-dimensional ribbons or in three-dimensional bundles showing, typically, hexagonal packing. Fibrils linked in this way maintain a constant center-to-center spacing, usually of more than 35 mμ. In other words they are not in actual contact like the doublets and triplets of flagella. Orderly assemblages of linked microtubules are very characteristic of most flagellates and all ciliates. Similar, although usually less precise, arrays occur in some metazoan cells, but the most common cytoplasmic microtubules, and the microtubules composing spindle fibers, generally do not show interconnections or parallel spacing over long distances.

C. Filaments

A fine filamentous component dispersed through the cytoplasmic matrix is of common occurrence;[259, 260] more than one kind of fibrous protein is to be expected. The filaments we are concerned with, whether or not they are the same as these, are recognizable as fibrillar entities when they are grouped in bundles or sheets having non-random distributions characteristic of certain cell types or states. Individual filaments are reported as 4 to 10 mμ in diameter; they are more or less sinuous and of indeterminate length, and show at best only a rough common orientation within the aggregate. They have been reported variously as being beaded, banded, helical, or tubular, but further examination at very high resolution is necessary for confirmation.

Familiar fibrillar structures in metazoan cells answering this description include neurofilaments, tonofilaments, filaments of the terminal web of some epithelia, smooth muscle filaments, and probably many others. Whether these have anything in common is not known. It is obvious that the filaments composing striated and tubular fibrils also might be included in this category. Furthermore, there are in protozoa many examples of massive bodies or dense connectives that seem to have a filamentous substructure. In short, no restrictive morphological definition of this class of fibrils is possible.

How to present, with anything resembling lucidity, the mass of descriptive data on protozoan fibrils is a knotty problem. The following three sections (III, IV, V) of this chapter will recount the structure and distribution of fibrils first in phytoflagellates, then in zooflagellates, and finally in ciliates. For each of these groups, fibrils will be described in sequence according to the three categories just outlined. Section VI will gather the limited experimental evidence and discuss possible functional interpretations of the accumulated data. This treatment will result in a brutal dismemberment of individual organisms and even organelles, but as a means of comparing fibril systems and tracing possible homologies I have found it a lesser evil than a series of organismal descriptions. The reader who wishes to put a cell together again will have to consult the original references cited, see Taylor's review[242] for a light-microscopic picture of many species, or turn, for general morphological accounts, to any current textbook of protozoology. Considerations of fibrillar systems in relation to other aspects of protozoan ultrastructure or function may be found in several earlier reviews.[9, 53, 93, 150, 173, 178, 229, 245] The higher taxonomic designations used here are those recommended by the Committee on Taxonomy of the Society of Protozoologists.[104]

III. PHYTOFLAGELLATES

A. Striated Root Fibrils

What may be the most primitive form of striated root fibril is found in relatively simple chrysomonad flagellates such as *Chromulina psammobia* (Fig. 1), studied by Rouiller and Fauré-Fremiet.[210] Here a slender, obliquely striated (at 43 mμ) fibril is attached laterally to one of the two kinetosomes and passes inward to and along one side of the cone-shaped apex of the nucleus. In *Synura caroliniana*[127] and *Paraphysomonas vestita*,[134] two or more similar, banded fibrils leave one or both kinetosomes and pass to and around the nucleus, branching to enclose it in a fibrous cage. In all three cases the banded fibrils lie close to the nuclear membrane but show no structural attachment to it. Such a fibril or bundle running from kinetosome to nucleus is a classic example of a *rhizoplast*.[53] In these flagellates it is also an example of a *parabasal fibril*, since the Golgi complex occupies a constant position alongside it.

Rhizoplasts and parabasal fibers are recognized and defined by light microscopy according to their position; their widespread occurrence in flagellates argues for a fundamental significance in a fibrous linkage of kinetosomes with nuclei and/or Golgi bodies. Mitosis follows kinetosome duplication, and new parabasal (Golgi) bodies appear at the distal ends of fibers growing out from new or old kinetosomes. But present electron-

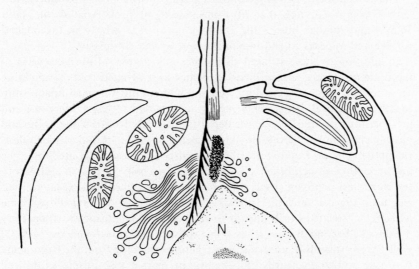

Fig. 1. Drawing of the anterior end of *Chromulina psammobia*, showing an obliquely striated rhizoplast attached laterally to the kinetosome of the free flagellum and descending to pass along one side of the apex of the nucleus (N). The Golgi body (G) occupies a constant position near the rhizoplast. Redrawn from Rouiller and Fauré-Fremiet.[210]

microscopic evidence does not prove that these fibrils are always of similar ultrastructure. Thus a pair of fibrils serving simultaneously as rhizoplasts and parabasal fibrils is shown in the chrysomonad *Hydrurus foetidus* by Joyon.[109] Here the two fibrils are said to attach laterally to the base of a kinetosome, on opposite sides, and to run for some distance along opposite sides of the nuclear apex, with one Golgi complex adjacent to each. The fibrils in this case are slender and sinuous and show no striation in the available micrographs.

Rhizoplasts are encountered sporadically among several genera of green flagellates tentatively placed in a new class, Prasinophyceae, by Manton and her colleagues.[52, 138, 167] In *Micromonas squamata*,[137] a fibril showing some indication of striation runs from the side of the single, laterally inserted kinetosome anteriad, to end on the adjacent nuclear surface. *Pedinomonas minor*[52] has four flagellar roots composed of microtubules (see Section III, B); one of these is accompanied by a striated fiber that passes for some distance along the nuclear surface. *Heteromastix rotunda*[139] possesses one rhizoplast and *Prasinocladus marinus*[167] and species of *Platymonas*[138] have two. Each consists of a massive bundle of fine filaments showing distinct cross-bands at extraordinarily long intervals of 250 to 500 mμ. In all three genera, the rhizoplast runs along the surface of the nucleus, which is flattened against it, and on past the nucleus to end either at the cell surface or at the posterior chloroplast surface.

The rhizoplast of the cryptomonad flagellate *Chilomonas paramecium*[1, 109] is composed, like that of *Pedinomonas*, of both striated (at about 70 mμ) and tubular fibrils; the complex occupies a groove in the nuclear surface and appears to end free in the postnuclear cytoplasm.

In addition to these striated rhizoplasts and parabasal fibrils, several of the same or closely related phytoflagellates have striated roots terminating on other cell organelles or simply ending without any detected relationship to other structures. Thus *Pedinomonas tuberculata*[137] has at least one and possibly four striated root fibrils departing laterally from a kinetosome and passing close under the cell membrane, between the latter and a chloroplast. In motile cells of *Halosphaera*[136] several conspicuously striated roots lie just under the cell membrane. *Chilomonas paramecium*[109] has, in addition to the rhizoplast complex, a second, heavier, striated fibril passing laterally to end near the cell surface. In *Prasinocladus marinus*[167] and *Prymnesium parvum*[132] striated fibrils appear to interconnect kinetosomes, apparently not passing beyond them as roots. Some species of *Chrysochromulina*[133, 166] have fibrous strands of uncertain substructure extending from the haptonema base (see p. 329) to nearby chloroplasts or from a kinetosome to the cell surface.

Among the euglenoid flagellates, striated root fibrils are reported only for *Entosiphon sulcatum*, where Mignot[143, 144] describes a fibril with a striation of 60–70 mμ that links the two flagellum-bearing kinetosomes and passes back to the anterior end of the siphon. His micrographs illustrate only the part of this banded fibril running between the bases of the kinetosomes. The striation is complex, with several sub-bands of varying widths separating heavy major striae; longitudinal filamentous subunits are evident.

Oddly enough, none of the true volvocid flagellates has revealed striated flagellar roots in studies conducted to date, but Joyon[109] reports composite root fibrils in *Haematococcus* and *Stephanasphaera*, one component being massive, dense material. In the zoospores or spermatozoids of the multi-cellular green algae *Stigeoclonium*[131] and *Oedogonium*[100, 101] fibrils with striations of 15 to 33 mμ appear as one component of the compound flagellar

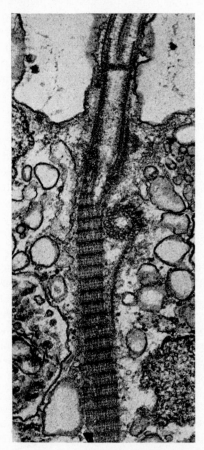

FIG. 2. Part of a flagellated cell from the scyphistoma of the coelenterate *Aurelia aurita*. The heavy, striated root fibril attaches to dense material around the base of the kinetosome and extends deep into the cell. A second kinetosome/centriole is cut in cross section on the right; a strand from it appears to join or accompany the main striated fibril. × 44,500. From J. A. Westfall, unpublished.

roots. In addition there is in both gamete and zoospore of *Oedogonium* a complex striated ring linking all of the kinetosomes in an anterior circle.

Some fungal zoospores also have striated flagellar roots. In *Blastocladiella*[70] three banded fibrils radiate from the kinetosome base, passing through canals in an encircling mitochondrion to the cell periphery. *Monoblepharella*[70] has an extraordinary flat ring, like a washer, surrounding the kinetosome; in cross-section it has the compound striated structure of a root fibril, as though it were composed of a complete circle of fused root fibrils.

In most of the instances described above the attachment of the striated root fibril to the kinetosome appears to be intimate, the fibrous material appearing external to two or three neighboring triplet microtubules at the proximal (basal) end of the kinetosome. Since high-resolution micrographs of favorable section planes are rare, the nature of the attachment cannot be specified; the angle of departure of the fibril appears to vary widely.

The striated root fibrils of most metazoa bear a closer resemblance to those of the flagellates than to those of ciliates (but see p. 314). In many instances[64, 75, 120] the triplet microtubules of the metazoan kinetosome are embedded in dense material at their bases; the attachment of the striated root typically is at this proximal level and may appear continuous with the dense substance, either external to the kinetosome cylinder or just below it. The fibril usually is directed downward into the cell, running toward and often past the nucleus. Where a pair of kinetosomes (or centrioles) is present, one bearing the flagellum and the other located nearby and at an angle to it, the striated root fibril (Fig. 2) often receives components from both kinetosomes.[252]

B. Microtubules

The microtubules of the flagellum and kinetosome are, of course, always present in flagellates and ciliates, but these are not our primary concern here; they have been described in innumerable papers and in great detail[229, 178] and another redescription is hardly necessary. (Neither will I have space in this chapter to consider such structures as mastigonemes or paraxial rods, associated with the external parts of flagella.) Cytoplasmic microtubules are found, either associated with or independent of kinetosomes, in many phytoflagellates and perhaps will prove to be present in all of them.

In the chrysomonads *Hydrurus foetidus, Dinobryon divergens*,[109] and *Prymnesium parvum*,[135] bands of microtubules depart from the kinetosome bases and run peripherally. In *Pedinomonas minor*,[52] four precisely arrayed bands of microtubules diverge from the single kinetosome in alternate ribbons of two and three tubules and run the length of the cell immediately under the surface membrane. *Heteromastix rotunda*, like *Pedinomonas* assigned to the class Prasinophyceae,[139] has two bands, one composed of two and one of seven microtubules; both pass outward from the kinetosomes to the cell surface.

In addition to the conventional flagellar apparatus and associated fibrils, some chrysomonads possess haptonemata, extensively studied by Manton and her colleagues. They are short to very long extensions from the cell, usually arising between the two flagella. Each is composed of three concentric membranes (of which the outermost is continuous with the cell membrane and the inner two delimit an enclosed cylindrical space) and an inner group of six to eight microtubules. In some species the haptonema is spring-like, extending as a long thread or retracting into a tight coil; it typically has an adhesive surface and functions in attachment of the cell to objects in the environment. Within the cell, the microtubules of the haptonema continue into the cytoplasm, where they are visible in cross-sections[130] first as seven, then as eight and finally, near the base, as nine microtubules arranged in three rows and interconnected by bridges.

Tubular fibrils have been demonstrated in the volvocid flagellates only by Joyon,[110] as parts of peripherally-directed flagellar roots in *Haematococcus* and *Stephanasphaera*. They occur as regular components of the root-fibril complexes of *Stigeocloneum*[131] and *Oedogonium*[100, 101] and in the spermatozoid of a fern,[128] as well as in spermatozoids of a number of brown algae[129] and in zoospores of some aquatic fungi.[69, 70]

The cryptomonad flagellates *Chilomonas paramecium*[1, 109] and *Cyathomonas truncata*[145] have rather complex microtubular organelles. In both, a ribbon of microtubules originating at the side of one kinetosome passes up to the cell surface. In *Chilomonas* it appears to end in the region of the contractile vacuole; in *Cyathomonas* it makes a quarter circuit of the anterior end of the cell and then plunges deep into the cell along one side of a long, vacuolated canal called the infundibulum. Both species also have medially directed rhizoplasts consisting at least in part of tubular fibrils. In *Cyathomonas* these arise as a ribbon at one side of a kinetosome, but in *Chilomonas* they appear to emanate from inside the lumen of the kinetosome.

Euglenoid flagellates have extensive and orderly arrays of tubular fibrils underlying the complex pellicle, and composing internal pharyngeal rods in some genera. The pellicle system has been pictured by many authors (see Ref. 173, for earlier papers) and most recently has been studied in elegant detail in *Euglena spirogyra* by Leedale[122, 123] and in nineteen species of euglenoids by Mignot.[143, 144, 146] Leedale demonstrates that the moderately flexible pellicle of *E. spirogyra* consists of a number of longitudinal strips of homogeneous or fine filamentous material articulating with one another laterally by a sort of tongue-in-groove arrangement, the whole system being covered externally by a continuous unit membrane. Each rather heavy strip is arched and sculptured in a complex fashion, and is prolonged beneath its neighbor by flanges and teeth. Microtubules appear in constant positions paralleling the two edges of each strip.

Mignot's comparative survey reduces the rather conflicting observations of previous authors, on different genera, to a common, exquisitely orderly

10a*

plan. The degree of rigidity of the cell body in different genera and species is related both to the thickness of the pellicular strips—which lose their suppleness as their thickness increases—and to the development of filamentous trusses joining adjacent strips and limiting their free articulation. Species showing most pronounced euglenoid movement (conventionally, and confusingly, known as metaboly) have the thinnest pellicular supporting material and the most freely movable interstrip joints, while in rigid species the pellicular strips may actually be fused. In all cases, microtubules are present, varying widely in number but disposed in similar fashions accom-

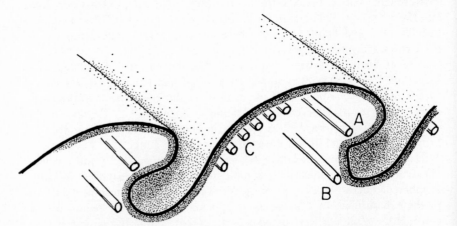

Fig. 3. Diagram showing the groups of microtubules associated with pellicle strips in a typical euglenoid flagellate; the complex shape of the interlocking strips themselves is not shown. A, B, and C microtubules appear in characteristic positions as explained in the text. Redrawn from Mignot.[146]

panying each strip. One or a few tubules, called A fibrils by Mignot,[146] lie adjacent to the line of articulation between neighboring strips in most genera (Fig. 3). Typically a single B fibril runs nearby, under the groove of each strip. And a number of C microtubules ranging from one to eighty lies beneath one slope of the groove. The number of microtubules is not related to the suppleness of the body, the smallest number being found in *Euglena acus*, which is flexible but does not exhibit euglenoid movement, and the largest in the completely rigid *Calycimonas*.

Pellicular structure within the deeply invaginated anterior reservoir is of particular interest and has been considerably clarified by Mignot's work.[146] Pellicle strips at the anterior end of the cell recurve to enter the neck of the reservoir. (Apparently it is at this level that duplication of pellicular entities begins prior to cell division;[146, 232, 233] new pellicle strips appear as baby ridges within the grooves of preexisting strips.) Farther down the reservoir neck the strips diminish in number, decrease in thickness, and ultimately disappear, leaving only the cell membrane lining the reservoir proper. The course of the microtubules is best traced from the bottom of the reservoir upward. Small groups of microtubules arise in association with the kinetosomes of the two flagella and pass upward under the reservoir membrane, taking two different directions. One group assumes a steep spiral course immediately beneath the membrane and, with the appearance of additional fibrils, becomes the A and B fibrils of the emerging pellicle strips. The second group, also augmented somewhere along the way by many new fibrils, follows a very flat helical path peripheral to the first group. As a result, sections through the neck of the reservoir always appear to include longitudinal and circular microtubule series. The peripheral group surrounds the reservoir neck up to its opening on the cell surface and then disperses to become the C-fibril bands of the fully developed pellicle strips. The number of strips on the body surface increases equatorially and diminishes again near the posterior pole.

Both *Peranema trichophorum* and *Entosiphon sulcatum* possess characteristic rodlike organelles lacking any observed connection with kinetosomes but associated with an ingestion apparatus. In *Peranema* there are two rods fused anteriorly, plus a system of articulating fibers outlining the cytostome and visible in the light microscope. When the organism feeds, the rods, which themselves are rigid, are moved about energetically. The comparable organelle in *Entosiphon* is an inverted hollow cone called the siphon; it appears rigid and its role in feeding activities is uncertain. Unlike *Peranema*, *Entosiphon* maintains a constant cell shape and does not ingest large organisms. The rod organelles in both organisms[143, 206] are composed of hexagonally packed microtubules, each unit linked to its six neighbors by fine bridges. At the margins of the bundle a dense matrix embeds some of the tubules. The articulating cytostomal fibers of *Peranema*, logically suspected of functioning to move the rod organelle, appear in Roth's early micrographs as sheets of fibrous or homogeneous material of uncertain structure. In *Entosiphon*, small packets of three to five microtubules may be found between the three broad rods that make up the rigid cone.

C. Filaments

A miscellany of ill-defined structures constitutes the phytoflagellates' only contribution to this category. That many rhizoplasts are made up of longitudinally oriented filaments, with or without transverse striation, has already been noted. More or less condensed meshworks of filamentous material perhaps make up the pellicle strips of euglenoids. A peculiar arrangement of dense material that may or may not be fibrillar in structure seems to be characteristic of the volvocid flagellates, some of which have not revealed flagellar roots. In *Chlamydomonas*,[83] *Chlorogonium*,[96] *Polytoma*,[119] and *Volvox* and *Stephanosphaera*[109] such material appears in a discrete band or cone linking the kinetosomes at one or more levels, or forms cup-shaped masses around their bases. Lang's pictures[119] suggest that the band arching between the two kinetosomes of *Polytoma* may be striated. Somewhat similar bridges between the two kinetosomes appear in cryptomonad flagellates;[1, 109, 145] additional dense material may take the form of a peculiar crescent-shaped band linked to one or both kinetosomes.

D. Summary

One gains the impression that the phytoflagellates are not particular about what kind of root fibrils they have, as long as there is something attaching to the flagellar base. Thus among chrysomonads there have been reported striated rhizoplasts, unstriated rhizoplasts, peripherally directed fibrils of uncertain substructure, and peripheral microtubules; among the cryptomonads, a rhizoplast composed of both striated and tubular fibrils, plus additional striated roots, plus peripherally directed microtubules, plus bands of dense material. The volvocids examined to date have enigmatic configurations of dense material plus, in some instances, peripherally directed microtubules. The prasinophycid flagellates have extraordinarily complex fibrillar systems incorporating striated filament bundles, some of which are rhizoplasts, and orderly sets of microtubules that run peripherally. The euglenids have highly developed peripheral microtubule systems with only a few elements connected to kinetosomes, and in one case a striated root.

The confusion here is certainly ours and not the flagellates'. Problems of preservation, especially of marine species, have been formidable; many of the studies cited were performed when techniques of embedment and micrography were primitive; most of the observations of fibrils were made incidentally, by authors primarily interested in other aspects of cell structure and therefore not impelled to apply the highest resolving power of the microscope to fibril structure and attachment. In attempting to summarize the facts, therefore, I may be imposing distinctions that do not exist and overlooking others. A few tentative generalizations may nonetheless be permissible.

1. Most of the fibrils recognizable as rhizoplasts and parabasal fibers of light microscopy appear to be striated. A range of appearances is seen, from a bundle of filaments with sparse banding to a compact fibril with compound striation.

2. There is no consistent morphological difference between root fibrils that attach to nucleus or parabasal body and those that are equally intimately associated with chloroplasts, mitochondria, or plasma membrane, or with no particular organelle at all. The organellar attachment may in many instances be transient, dependent on life-cycle stage.

3. Most of the kinetosome-based microtubules pass outward to run under the cell surface (but there are clearly others extending deep into the cytoplasm). These peripherally directed microtubules are the only kinds of fibrils that have been reported in all phytoflagellate orders thus far examined.

plexes. Apparently at least one fibril is attached to each kinetosome, and certainly some of these are striated. Among them are a slender, conventional parabasal fibril extending posteriad, with the large, elongate Golgi membranes oriented along it, and the much heavier costa passing posteriad just below the line of adhesion of the trailing flagellum. In all instances the costa and parabasal fibril have a complex striation, well shown in Joyon's Plate 37b,[109] consisting of dense and light bands each subdivided into two or more stripes. The major interval is measured at 50–75 mμ by different authors. At least one of the fibrils emerging from the kinetosome cluster inserts at the anterior end of the axostyle.

Fragmentary observations on other flagellates of the order Trichomonadida demonstrate a typical parabasal fibril in *Foaina*[89] and in *Devescovina striata* and *Calonympha* sp.[156] In *Devescovina*, Noirot-Timothée[156] finds an unstriated rod in the position of a costa. This undoubtedly represents the cresta, distinguishable from a costa by its behavior during cell division.[117]

The very complex hypermastigid flagellate genus *Trichonympha* has a parabasal apparatus including scores of well-developed, elongate Golgi bodies, each with a parabasal fibril running longitudinally along its nuclear face.[82, 92, 179] The fibrils originate far anteriad, in contact with a complex centrosomal region whose ultrastructure is incompletely known. The fibrils are flat, striated ribbons and for the first part of their course are radially arranged to compose the compact wall of the rigid, conical, rostral tube. As long as they are part of the tube, the striations of all of the parabasal fibrils, and possibly of an intervening matrix, are in register. When the tube ends, the individual fibrils thicken, separate, and for some distance follow sinuous courses near the rows of postrostral kinetosomes. Then, part way down the flagellated zone, they turn inward toward the nucleus and acquire their Golgi bodies. The interval of parabasal-fibril striation may vary within a single fibril, from as little as 27 mμ within the rostral tube to as great as 55 mμ posterior to it.

Gibbons and Grimstone[82] find in the hypermastigid genus *Holomastigotoides* a zigzag fibril accompanying the rows of kinetosomes and making contact regularly with each kinetosome near its upper end. The fibril is composed of a compact bundle of filaments with sparse but regular crossbands, one in each interkinetosomal interval; its origin is not reported.

B. Microtubules

The tubular fibrils of zooflagellates appear in two recurrent configurations: regularly arranged tubules immediately beneath the pellicle, some but not all of them arising at the bases of kinetosomes; and extensive ribbons, sheets, or bundles composing the conspicuous axostyle, usually not directly attached to any kinetosome.

In the ameboflagellates *Naegleria*[224] and *Tetramitus*,[8] microtubules are clearly associated with kinetosomes. In *Naegleria* a compact, curving ribbon, called the spur, consisting of half a dozen or so microtubules in a rather dense matrix, arises at the base of each of the two kinetosomes and passes toward the cell surface. Other microtubules diverge individually from the kinetosomes. In *Tetramitus* (Fig. 5) similar spurs depart from two of the four kinetosomes. These fibrils pass under the cell membrane on the ventral surface, some of them apparently converging in a deep depression leading to the invaginated gullet. Microtubules diverging individually or in small clusters from the anterior end of the striated root may also contribute to the pellicular system, while others issuing from its posterior end seem to enter directly the fibril system surrounding the gullet.

Schuster[225] finds that the solitary myxameba of the slime molds *Didymium nigripes* and *Physarum cinereum* possesses a pair of centrioles with attached microtubule complexes. Some microtubules, possibly representing persistent spindle fibrils, diverge randomly into the surrounding Golgi region while others form an organized ribbon of linked fibrils. When the myxameba transforms into a flagellate, the centrioles move to the cell surface and sprout flagella at the extreme anterior apex of the now polarized cell. The microtubule ribbons from both kinetosomes, resembling the spur of *Naegleria* or *Tetramitus*, extend posteriad under the cell membrane as the "flagellum-cone", terminating near or on the posterior end of the polarized nucleus.

All trypanosome flagellates examined have a system of pellicular microtubules, parallel and equidistant, forming a single layer just beneath the cell membrane.[5, 111, 215, 247] In some micrographs bridges between adjacent fibrils are apparent. Anderson and Ellis[5] show clearly that some (only about four) of these microtubules recurve under the membrane of the reservoir and penetrate the cytoplasm to make contact with the base of the flagellum-bearing kinetosome. In the related bodonid flagellates, *Cryptobia helicis*[191, 192] and *Bodo saltans*,[172, 173] similar microtubules, some of which arise at the kinetosomes (Fig. 8), lie beneath the cell membrane, forming a trypanosome-like system over the whole surface in *Cryptobia* but restricted to anterior spiral tracts in *Bodo*. Microtubules of the peripheral system descend into the cytoplasm in a slender cluster alongside a deep invagination of the cell membrane that may serve as a cytostome in at least one trypanosome, *T. mega*,[237] and in *Bodo* (Fig. 9).

An extraordinary development of microtubular structures among flagellates is found in *Giardia*. Cheissin[30] reports and Friend[68] confirms that the enigmatic "median body", occupying a central position posterior to and between the two nuclei, is an oval aggregate of slightly curved, roughly parallel microtubules. The long intracytoplasmic paths of the flagellar axonemes, noted above (p. 295) have no known parallel among protozoa, although intracellular axonemes are routine in some metazoan sperm.[227]

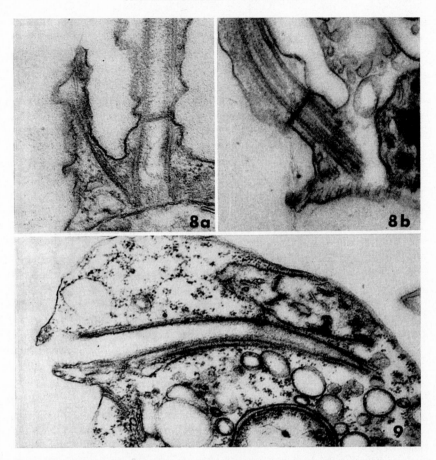

FIG. 8a and b. Longitudinal sections through the kinetosomes and bases of the two flagella of *Bodo saltans*. In Fig. 8a a ribbon of microtubules, cut longitudinally, diverges from the kinetosome base into a cytoplasmic lip bordering the flagellar depression; in Fig. 8b the microtubules under the cell membrane in the cytoplasmic lip are cut obliquely. × 45,000.

FIG. 9. Longitudinal section of the "cytostome" of *Bodo saltans*. Microtubules run the length of the open canal and are visible also in the lower lip. × 33,000. Figure 8 and 9 from Pitelka[172] (and unpublished).

Ribbons of microtubules, similar to those of the median body and presumably extending from its ventral surface, accompany the axonemes of the pair of caudal flagella. Associated with the peripheral doublets of the other axonemes are unusual, tiny (8–9 mμ in diameter) microtubules (Fig. 6). The sucking disc, occupying some two-thirds of the ventral surface of the cell and surrounded by the crystalline flange, consists of a sheet of longitudinally oriented, linked microtubules, spaced about 20 mμ apart and about 20 mμ under the cell membrane; from each microtubule a fibrous ribbon extends dorsad into the cytoplasm, as described on page 298 (Fig. 6).

Axostyles are characteristic of zooflagellates in several orders, and in most of them are fairly stiff rods or tapering cylinders, occupying the major axis of the cell and incompletely enclosing the nucleus and a cytoplasmic zone that may contain characteristic inclusions. These conventional axostyles will be described shortly. The oxymonad flagellates appear to be unique in the possession of axostyles that are capable of active, undulatory movement.

In *Pyrsonympha*, examined by Grassé,[89] and in *Oxymonas* and *Saccinobaculus*, studied by Grimstone and Cleveland,[95] the contractile axostyle is an elongate pile of slightly curved sheets of longitudinally oriented microtubules. The sheets differ in number among species and among individuals from three or four up to seventy or more, and the number of fibrils per sheet ranges from two or three in very narrow sheets on one side of the pile up to 150 in large axostyles. The sheets may be close-packed (about 30 mμ apart) and parallel, or slightly separated by irregular spaces. Within a sheet the individual microtubules are spaced at about 40 mμ, center-to-center, and are linked by fine bridges; filamentous links to adjacent sheets are also detectable where the arrangement of sheets is compact.

Walls of the axostyles of the trichomonad flagellates (*Trichomonas*,[94, 109, 151, 161] *Tritrichomonas*,[3, 4] *Foaina*,[89] *Mixotricha*,[34] *Devescovina* and *Calonympha*[156] and of some hypermastigid flagellates (*Lophomonas*,[10, 11] *Joenia*,[89] *Holomastigotoides*[82]), although differing in detail, all consist of ribbons or sheets of parallel microtubules. There may be numerous, rather narrow ribbons overlapping serially to form a perforate cylinder, as in the calyx of *Lophomonas*; a single continuous sheet forming a closed or incomplete cylinder; or one or more extensive sheets rolled up to form a multi-layered cylinder.

In *Trichonympha*,[179] two or possibly three concentric sheets of microtubules lie immediately beneath the cell membrane covering the turgid, hemispherical rostral cap. These perhaps resemble the pellicular microtubule systems of simpler zooflagellates more closely than anything else yet reported from the higher Zoomastigophorea. Anderson[2] has reported unpatterned, wandering microtubules in the cytoplasm of *Tritrichomonas* examined after glutaraldehyde-osmium fixation.

C. Filaments

Organized systems of fine filaments of the sort that will be encountered frequently in the ciliates are extremely rare among flagellates. Perhaps the only clear example is a well-defined, roughly hexagonal meshwork demonstrated by Cleveland and Grimstone[34] in the trichomonad flagellate *Mixotricha*. The filaments are about 10 mμ in diameter and show a beading or banding with a 7-mμ period. They are somewhat sinuous and run in interweaving tracts. The meshwork lies just below the surface membrane, and its pattern is regularly related to the disposition of small surface papillae, to each of which one bacterium and one or more spirochaetes are attached in a consistent, polarized fashion.

Apart from this ciliate-like system, zooflagellates present the same assortment of vaguely filamentous structures as do phytoflagellates. Where kinetosomes are numerous and close-packed, very fine filaments in consistent patterns may connect specific triplet fibrils of adjacent ones, as shown by Gibbons and Grimstone.[82] Occasionally, as in *Lophomonas*,[10] more massive fibrous strands interconnect adjacent kinetosomes at one or more levels. *Pyrsonympha*[89] has a peculiar, dense paraxostyle adjacent to its microtubular axostyle.

D. Summary

It is perhaps only technical accident that makes the structure and distribution of fibril systems seem better defined in even the simpler zooflagellates than in the phytoflagellates. The predominantly symbiotic zooflagellates are characterized by increasing levels of architectural elaboration, involving multiplication of flagellar units and of associated intracytoplasmic structures. That most of the latter are fibrillar was known by light microscopists long ago, and most of them are clearly characterized at the electron-microscope level now.

The ameboflagellates—the simplest of the zooflagellate series for which details of fibrillar ultrastructure are known—already display large, discrete, striated root fibrils and ordered systems of peripheral microtubules, resembling the cryptomonads or euglenids more than any other phytoflagellate groups. Unwilling to relinquish either the ameboid or the flagellate mode of life, these organisms must produce new kinetosomes and complete new fibril systems with each ameba-to-flagellate transformation. The assumption of distinct morphological polarity and defined cell shape accompanies this change, and invites morphogenetic analysis. The slime mold myxameba already has the centrioles and the anlage of the peripheral microtubule system that will characterize the flagellate, but plasmodial phases of the life cycle lack these structures;[225] they presumably are formed *de novo* in germinating spores.

Reminiscent both of the euglenids and of *Tetramitus* is the system of peripheral microtubules (some kinetosome-based) of the trypanosomes and bodonids; the similarity of the "cytostome" in *Bodo* and some trypanosomes to the *Tetramitus* gullet and also to the *Cyathomonas* infundibulum is particularly striking. No kinetoplastid flagellates are known to have conspicuous striated root fibrils.

The higher Zoomastigophorea have a repertoire of peculiar organelles whose origins are not readily traced except in very general terms. The costa and parabasal fibril resemble the striated flagellar roots of the ameboflagellates.

The microtubular axostyles of the oxymonads appear to be fundamentally different from those of the trichomonads and hypermastigids. Peripheral microtubules have been seen to date only in the rostrum of *Trichonympha*. Different sorts of filamentous connections provide physical attachment of close-packed kinetosomes to one another in different groups.

The inadequacy of sampling and variations in technique again limit the credibility of any generalizations and the following are merely suggestive.

1. The striated root fibril is a common product of the kinetosome region (light microscopists have amply documented its outgrowth from kinetosome or centrosome during morphogenesis). In most, but not all, cases it connects the morphogenetic center with something else (Golgi bodies, axostyle, or nucleus). Yet its terminus is not inserted in the something else, like a stem in a pear, but rather runs alongside it.

2. Microtubules clearly do not have to be directly connected with the kinetosome region, but in most cases there is an indirect connection of sorts—a delegation from the microtubule complement or else an intervening striated fibril. The kinetosome-based microtubules usually pass peripherally.

3. Whereas striated fibrils often make contact (*Naegleria, Trichonympha*) with two or more kinetosomes, individuals or clusters of microtubules generally are intimately related with no more than one.

4. In no case has direct continuity between microtubules of the kinetosome itself and any other intracytoplasmic fibril been demonstrated.

E. Fibrils in the Superclass Opalinata

These curious protozoa seem to be ciliated flagellates; they have some of the life-cycle and cytologic characteristics of flagellates but are equipped with a uniform ciliature displaying the kind of beating activity characteristic of ciliate cilia.[165] Ultrastructural evidence[154, 170, 251, 262] has not dispelled the mystery of their phylogenetic affinities; their fibril systems thus are best considered apart from either the zooflagellate or the ciliate sections.

Cilia are arranged in longitudinal rows (kineties), as in ciliates, over the flattened body. Where all the rows from the two sides approach the anterior margin, there is an elongate field of close-packed kinetosomes, called the falx (Fig. 10). Between the kineties, the cell surface is thrown into numerous, slender, longitudinal folds, within each of which is a ribbon of linked microtubules. Recent work by Wessenberg[251] demonstrates that at least some of the microtubules of each ribbon originate at the kinetosomes of the falx.

Two slender fibrous bands depart from the left anterior margin[251] of each kinetosome of the longitudinal rows and, converging, pass anteriad toward the next kinetosome. The structure of the bands is not clear, although they show evidences of cross striation in longitudinal section. Falcular kinetosomes lack these bands, but have one or two engimatic, short, fibrous projections instead.

FIG. 10. Tangential section at the anterior end of *Opalina virguloidea*. The falx, consisting of about four rows of rather close-set cilia, runs down the right-hand side of the picture. From it, rows of somatic cilia and the intervening narrow cytoplasmic folds diverge to the right and left. Ribbons of microtubules, not identifiable as such at this low magnification, occupy the cytoplasmic folds and, anteriorly, enter the superficial cytoplasm of the falx as seen here on the right. In deeper sections of this series, these microtubule ribbons can be seen to attach laterally to falcular kinetosomes.
× 21,000. From H. Wessenberg, unpublished.

A slender tract of fine, roughly parallel filaments accompanies each kinety just to the left of the kinetosomes and their fibrous interconnections. Similar tracts pass transversely beneath the pellicular folds, forming a regular, rectangular lattice. A meshwork of filaments surrounds the kinetosomes of the falx.

V. CILIATES

A. Morphology of the Ciliate Cortex

In the exquisite and baffling intricacy of their fibrillar organization, the ciliates make all other cells look simple. The variety of designs is too rich for comfort. Every kind of cytoplasmic fibril encountered in other cells appears to have been exploited by the ciliates, in a range of permutations and combinations that at first glance—and too often at second and third glances as well—seems dictated by mere whimsy. Nonetheless, there emerge from this bewildering profusion certain identifiable patterns that recur in the most remotely related groups. Since the ciliates comprise a coherent, probably monophyletic subphylum, since a high order of fibrillar differentiation seems to be a necessary part of their organization, and since they are, above all, versatile and competent cells, an analysis of these recurrent patterns should be highly instructive, and perhaps more meaningful than scrutiny of simpler cell types in which homologies may be harder to trace. This is precisely what Taylor[242] was attempting in 1941; the present survey repeats his effort in the contemporary context of ultrastructure.

Most of the conspicuous morphological organization of the ciliate body is confined to a cortical layer about two microns deep and to invaginations of this cortex that form the feeding apparatus and other cell orifices. Ectoplasmic sculpturing, multiple pellicular membranes, rows of kinetosomes, and fibrillar structures are intimately interrelated in this cortex. Specimens stained for light microscopy, especially by silver-impregnation techniques, often show linear patterns that electron microscopy[50, 171] has demonstrated to be configurations of membranes rather than of fibrils. Before confronting the true fibrillar systems, it is necessary to look at the cortex and pellicle of a representative ciliate in order to identify the non-fibrillar silverline system and other cortical elements. Paramecium[50, 176, 226, 238] is a suitable example.

Ehret and Powers[50] conceived of the cortex of Paramecium as a layer of repeating units called ciliary corpuscles; their concept has proved a most useful one, with application to ciliates in general. Each corpuscle is a rectangular to hexagonal area, bordered by pronounced ridges in the ectoplasm and centered around one or a pair (depending on species and body region) of kinetosomes. The kinetosomes, and therefore the corpuscles, are aligned in approximately longitudinal rows over the body surface. Such a kinetosome row, which grows by elongation with insertion of new kinetosomes and is usually cut in two at cell fission, is a *kinety*. In *Paramecium*, trichocysts.

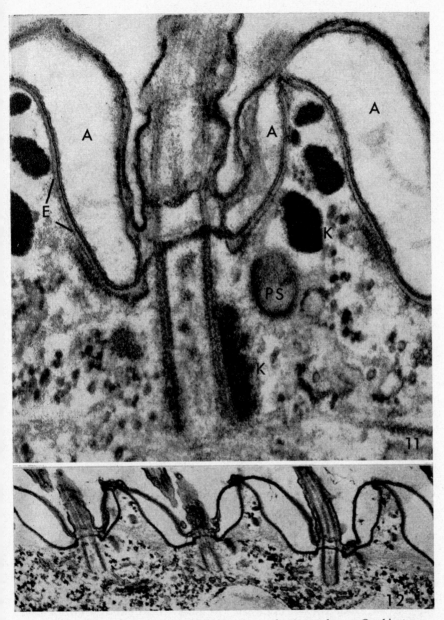

Fig. 11. Cross-section into the cortex of *Paramecium multimicronucleatum*. One kinetosome is cut longitudinally, with the base of its cilium. Note the 3-ply unit membrane covering the cell surface and cilium and, directly beneath it on either side of the cilium, alveolar spaces (A) limited by unit membranes. Beneath and generally parallel to the innermost alveolar membrane is the thin granular layer of epiplasm (E). At the right of the base of the kinetosome is the broad attachment of the kinetodesmal fibril (K); other kinetodesmal fibrils are cut in cross section in the ectoplasmic ridge to the right of the kinetosome. A tangential section of the base of a parasomal sac (PS) is seen at the right of the kinetosome. × 70,000.

Fig. 12. Cross-section of the cortex at lower magnification, including three kinetosomes and the alveoli and ectoplasmic ridges between them. Cross-sectioned kinetodesmal fibriles are visible in the ectoplasmic ridges, and filaments of the infraciliary system run across the base of each ridge. × 21,000. Figures 11 and 12 from Pitelka.[176]

located in the transverse ectoplasmic ridges between corpuscles, alternate with kinetosomes or kinetosome pairs along each kinety.

The entire cell surface, including the surfaces of cilia and all body openings, is covered by a continuous unit membrane, which is the cell membrane proper. Immediately beneath this is a mosaic of membrane-limited alveoli (Figs. 11, 12). It is along the margins of the alveoli that silver tends to deposit, yielding a lattice-like overall pattern in stained specimens. One pair of more or less inflated alveoli occupies each ectoplasmic depression. The members of the pair abut closely along the longitudinal midline of each ciliary corpuscle, their membranes being indented centrally to permit emergence of the cilia between them. The contiguous membranes thus form a shallow, double septum bisecting each corpuscle longitudinally, and this line of contiguity, repeated in consecutive corpuscles along the kinety, appears in silver-impregnated specimens as a meridional line connecting silver-stained kinetosomes and trichocysts like beads on a string. At the margins of the corpuscles, neighboring alveoli may be distinct, their membrane limits coinciding with the ectoplasmic ridges, or they may be confluent over the crests. Just to the right of each cilium or pair, a slender, finger-like invagination of the cell membrane, called the *parasomal sac*, projects down through the alveolar membranes and cavity, to end blindly in the superficial ectoplasm.

Directly beneath and generally parallel to the inner alveolar membrane is a thin, condensed cytoplasmic layer called by Fauré-Fremiet[55] the *epiplasm*. It has a fine granular or filamentous substructure and averages about 10 to 15 mμ in thickness. The epiplasm continues uninterrupted across the minute gap between adjacent alveoli; around the upper end of each kinetosome it thickens to form a ring, and then appears to merge with the terminal plate closing off the top of the kinetosome lumen. It also forms a thickened ring around each parasomal sac, but at the bottom of the sac is thin or absent. Thus the epiplasmic layer forms an almost—but not quite—complete boundary separating the body of the cytoplasm from the pellicular membrane system and cilia. Kinetosomal microtubules penetrate the epiplasm and so do the parasomal sacs.

Most ciliates have similar mosaics over the general body surface and at least parts of the buccal cavity, probably coinciding with the silverline pattern reported for the species. There appear to be some exceptions, however.

In *Stentor*, Randall and Jackson[196] showed pellicular alveoli in parts of the buccal region but not elsewhere; in more recent electron micrographs of *Spirostomum* and *Blepharisma*[40, 67, 113] alveoli are clearly lacking from the areas shown. According to Villeneuve-Brachon[248] these three heterotrich genera do not have silverline systems. No alveoli have been seen in the entodiniomorph ciliates although silverline networks are present.[155] Published electron micrographs of some holotrichs (e.g., *Didinium*[266]) do not show conventional alveoli. The conditions of successful fixation for electron microscopy are not the same for all ciliates, and surface membranes may be particularly vulnerable to osmotic or other damage. Furthermore, alveoli may in some species be very flat, without detectable lumina, in well-fixed cells. Determination of their presence or absence, and correlation of alveolar with silverline patterns, therefore require particular attention to them. They may be present in some species for which they have not been reported; however the evidence now suggests that the alveolar mosaic is a very common but not invariable component of the ciliate pellicle and defines most silverline lattices.

Parasomal sacs similarly have been identified in many but not all ciliates. They are conspicuous at least in tetrahymenids, astomes, an apostome, peritrichs, hypotrichs, and suctoria (see references cited below for members of these groups). Their position with relation to the kinetosome differs in different ciliates; in peritrichs and suctorians they are distributed on non-ciliated surfaces. An epiplasmic layer also is commonly present, although often unrecognized. It may appear as an additional pellicular membrane in micrographs that do not resolve unit-membrane structure. In such ciliates as *Blepharisma* (Fig. 24), where pellicular alveoli are absent, a discontinuous, membrane-like layer lacking the three-ply construction of the unit membrane probably represents epiplasm. In some peritrichs the epiplasm is quite thick,[58] and in at least one, *Trichodinopsis*,[63] it is locally elaborated to form skeletal plates on the adhesive disc.

A counterpart of the ciliary corpuscle may be identified as the repeating unit of the cortex in most species in which reduction and specialization of somatic ciliature have not modified it beyond recognition. It consists of one or a pair of kinetosomes and a surrounding territory definable by a specific allotment of membranous and fibrillar elements. The ectoplasm may or may not be sculptured in corresponding units. Alveolar membranes (when present) always divide each corpuscle along its kinetal axis, but may not coincide with its margins.

B. Fibril Systems of the Body Surface

Striated, microtubular, and filamentous fibril patterns are interwoven in characteristic ways in the ciliate's somatic cortex, and in different ways in the oral apparatus. The latter—an intricate construction even among gymnostomes—is dedicated to the common function of ingestion. Homologies among different groups in somatic infraciliature and in mouth parts may become apparent when the two regions are treated separately in the following sections. Finally, two important, highly specialized ciliate taxa will be discussed individually, since the limited information available for them does not readily permit comparison with other ciliates.

1. STRIATED FIBRILS

A fiber closely paralleling each somatic kinety on its right side was recognized first in apostome ciliates by Chatton and Lwoff,[29] who subse-

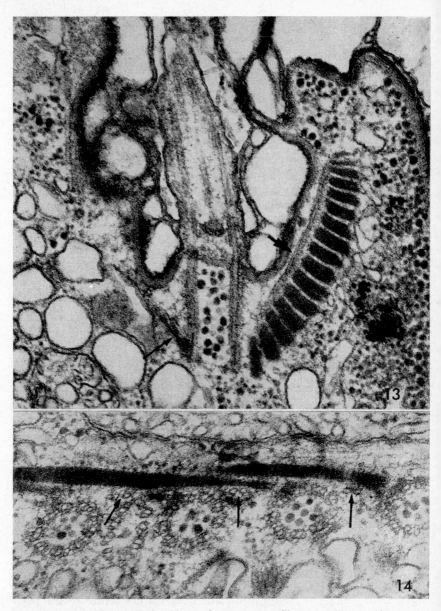

Fig. 13. Cross-section through a kinety of an apostome ciliate, showing one kinetosome and cilium base cut longitudinally. At the right of the kinetosome is the cross-sectioned kinetodesmos, consisting of a pile of sixteen individual, dense fibrils. Immediately above it are microtubules of the right radial ribbon (heavy arrow). From the left side of the kinetosome base, other microtubules (thin arrow) pass upward toward the left. × 75,000.

Fig. 14. Longitudinal section of one kinety of the apostome, anterior direction to the left. Kinetosomes are cut in cross-section; second from the left is an elliptical section of a new, non-ciliated kinetosome. A striated kinetodesmal fibril is attached to the ciliate's right, anterior margin of each ciliated kinetosome and passes to the right and anteriad. A right radial ribbon of two microtubules (arrows) is cut in cross section just posterior and to the right of each ciliated kinetosome. × 75,000. Figures 13 and 14 from Bradbury and Pitelka[17] (and unpublished).

quently identified similar fibers in other ciliates and expressed their relationship to the kinety in the rule of desmodexy.[28] The fiber, called the *kinetodesmos*, when present is always at the right of the kinety if the observer stands inside the cell and keeps turning around to face the surface; when a cell's anterior pole is viewed from above, the kinetodesma are clockwise from the kineties. Kinetodesma usually are not argentophilic.

The first detailed electron-microscope study of an apostome ciliate has recently been reported by Bradbury[15] and Bradbury and Pitelka.[17] The organism, found on the California coast, represents a new genus. The prominent kinetodesmos (Figs. 13, 14) consists of a pile of overlapping, tapering, striated fibrils, each one arising from the right anterior margin of the base of a kinetosome and passing slightly to the right and anteriad to join the bottom of the pile. At any one point there may be seven to eighteen fibrils in the stack; it follows that each fibril continues anteriad past six to seventeen kinetosomes of the compact kinety before tapering to an end at the top of the pile. The period of the fibrils is about 16 mμ.

Kinetodesma unmistakably similar in structure and orientation to those of the apostome were seen in members of the order Hymenostomatida in some of the earliest electron-microscope studies of ciliates.[141, 142, 226] An isolated kinetodesmal fibril of *Paramecium multimicronucleatum*, shown in Fig. 15, reveals complex striation with a major interval of 30 to 35 mμ. Its broad attachment to the right anterior quadrant of the base of the kinetosome is shown in Figs. 11 and 19. Where kinetosomes of *Paramecium* are paired, the kinetodesmal fibril always arises from the posterior member of the pair; thus there is one kinetodesmal fibril per ciliary corpuscle. The kinetodesmal bundle runs in the ectoplasmic crest to the right of each kinety; it is looser than in the apostome and includes usually five or six fibrils.[50, 141, 176, 226, 238] Individual fibrils are probably at least as long

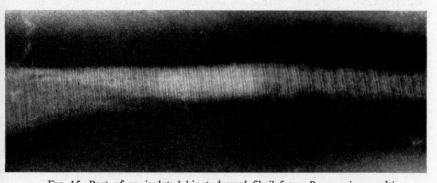

FIG. 15. Part of an isolated kinetodesmal fibril from *Paramecium multimicronucleatum*, negatively stained with phosphotungstic acid. The complex striation of the fibril (major interval about 30 mμ) is apparent; the fibril becomes broader near its origin out of the field to the left. × 90,000. From Pitelka.[176]

as in the apostome, however, since the distance between fibril-bearing kinetosomes is considerably greater in *Paramecium*. In *Tetrahymena, Colpidium, Glaucoma,* and *Ophryoglena*,[31, 142, 171, 200] the structure and kinetosomal attachment of the kinetodesmal fibrils are like those of *Paramecium* but the individual fibrils are much shorter, reaching only one or two interkinetosomal intervals anteriad.

An interesting modification of the kinetodesmal system appears in the astome ciliate *Metaradiophrya gigas* studied by de Puytorac.[182, 184] Individual fibrils, with an interval of about 20 mμ, arise at the right anterior margins of kinetosomes and extend anteriad, forming, in the posterior portion of the body, kinetodesmal bundles of seven to fifteen fibrils like those of *Paramecium*. More anteriorly, fibrils arising from successive kinetosomes along each row begin to fuse with one another to form a solid kinetodesmal rod of increasing diameter. These rods are visible in living cells as refractile fibers, anisotropic, and identifiable cytochemically as protein. Near the anterior pole the rods articulate with a heavy, hooked holdfast composed of similar dense material but in cross-section displaying a crystalline pattern of intersecting bands, the intervals being about 20 mμ.

In a related astome, *Mesnilella trispiculata*, de Puytorac[187] finds that only a few of the many kinetodesmal bundles fuse to form one heavy and one to four slender, striated (at 12 to 21 mμ for the kinetodesmal fibrils and small fused spicules, 65 mμ for the single heavy spicule) fibers extending for half or more of the length of the very long, vermiform cell. In two other astomes (*Haptophrya gigantea*,[186] *Anaplophrya commune*[185]) belonging to different families, skeletal rods are lacking and kinetodesma are composed of overlapping, striated fibrils. For all three of these genera, de Puytorac in his published reports concluded that kinetodesmal fibrils were attached to the right *posterior* margins of the kinetosomes and passed posteriad to join their respective bundles, instead of anteriad as in *Metaradiophrya*, Bradbury's apostome, and the hymenostomes.

A significant question is posed by de Puytorac's micrographs of all three astomes in which the unconventional, posterior-directed orientation of kinetodesmal fibrils is reported. It has been noted repeatedly[76, 82, 178] that in those instances in which the precise orientation of a section relative to cell polarity is ascertainable, there is a consistent relationship between the kinetosome's asymmetry and its polarity: the inward skewing of triplets in the cross-sectioned kinetosomal cylinder is clockwise when viewed distally from the base of the kinetosome. Because of the technical requirements that must be met in order reliably to identify three-dimensional orientations in sections, only a few proven cases are known. Among these are *Paramecium*, the tetrahymenids, and Bradbury's apostome, where the anterior course of the kinetodesmal fibrils has been established in large pellicle fragments or sections including identifiable organelles such as buccal structures,[15, 141, 142, 171] and kinetodesmal attachment therefore is a reliable landmark. Viewed from the interior of the cell, a basal cross-section of a kinetosome with its kinetodesmal fiber attachment always has the precise pattern of asymmetry diagrammed in Fig. 16a.

De Puytorac's publications include high-resolution micrographs of *Anaplophrya* (Ref. 185, Fig. 6), *Haptophrya* (Ref. 186, pl. III, Fig. 9) and *Mesnilella* (Ref. 187, pl. III, Fig. c) in which it is possible to see, in the same fields, kinetodesmal fibril attachment and the skewing direction in cross-sectioned kinetosomes. Skewing is clockwise in every case and the relative orientation of kinetodesmal fibril attachment is exactly as shown for *Paramecium*. This leaves open three alternative interpretations. First, as diagrammed in Fig. 16b, the polarity of the kinetosome in the three astomes may be inverse relative to other established examples: the three published micrographs showing clockwise kinetosome skewing may be views from the

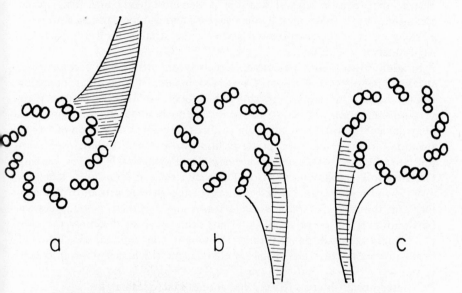

FIG. 16a. Diagram of a cross-sectioned kinetosome of *Paramecium*, looking outward from the base of the kinetosome. Triplet fibrils are skewed inward in a clockwise direction and the kinetodesmal fibril is attached to three triplets and proceeds to the right and anteriad.

FIG. 16b. A cross-sectioned kinetosome of *Mesnilella* as it would appear from the base of the kinetosome *if* the kinetodesmal fibril is attached at the right posterior margin of the kinetosome. The kinetosomal triplets must in this case be skewed inward in a counterclockwise direction, the inverse of the asymmetry-polarity relationship demonstrated in all authenticated examples.

FIG. 16c. A cross-sectioned kinetosome of *Mesnilella* as it would appear from the base of the kinetosome if the asymmetry-polarity relationship is the same as in other known cases; the kinetodesmal-fibril attachment must then be on the left *if* the fibril proceeds posteriad.

outside looking in. This is the only circumstance under which the orientation of kinetodesmal fibrils in these pictures can be to the right and posteriad, as reported. Second, kinetosome polarity may be the same here as in *Paramecium* and elsewhere, but the fibril orientation may be to the left and posteriad (Fig. 16c), in violation of the rule of desmodexy. Third—and most appealing—the relationship may be exactly the same as in *Paramecium* (Fig. 16a), the kinetodesmal fibrils actually being directed anteriad as in de Puytorac's *Metaradiophrya*, and not posteriad. At the time his papers were published, a posterior course did not appear exceptional, since posteriorly directed fibrils in *Stentor* were interpreted as homologues of kinetodesmal fibrils of *Paramecium*. However, for reasons that will become apparent on page 320, this homology is unlikely. Recently, de Puytorac (personal communication) has reexamined his original micrographs and agrees that the third alternative interpretation suggested above is the most likely one. This would mean that in the apostomes, hymenostomes, and astomes, which have what we may call classic kinetodesmal systems, the striated fibril always has a right-anterior orientation.

In addition to these well-defined, precisely oriented, easily recognizable, striated kinetodesma, structures observed incidentally in other holotrich ciliates have been tentatively called kinetodesmal fibrils although their precise orientation and substructure remain to be determined. Yagiu and Shigenaka[266] illustrate slender, short fibrils with some indication of 14-mμ striation, arising in an appropriate position with respect to kinetosomes of the ciliary girdles of *Didinium nasutum*. De Puytorac[188] makes passing reference to kinetodesmal fibrils in *Prorodon viridis*, and Grain[88] similarly notes them in *Isotricha*. Fauré-Fremiet[55] suggests that a tract of fine filaments in the cortex of *Paranassula brunnea* may represent a kinetodesmal fibril; however, in several of his published prints of cortical sections (notably pl. 5, Fig. 14), small, dense profiles resembling conventional kinetodesmal fibrils in cross-section are visible in ectoplasmic ridges neighboring ciliary rows.

Striated fibrils (interval 16 mμ) that are not kinetodesmal, but suggestively resemble the root fibrils of some flagellates and metazoan ciliated cells, occur in two mobiline peritrich ciliates, *Trichodina urinicola* and *Trichodinopsis paradoxa*[63] (Fig. 17). They are limited to certain kinetosome rows of the complex aboral girdles of locomotor cilia, and they pass toward the center of the adhesive disc, ending in contact with skeletal plates of the disc in *Trichodina* or passing between the plates and ending against the epiplasm of the aboral surface in *Trichodinopsis*. Their attachments to kinetosomes are of three types: direct insertion against the outer surface of the kinetosome, accompanied by a small dense granule; similar direct insertion but with a small striated body resembling a basal foot; and indirect insertion (of more than one fibril per kinetosome) at the ends of fibrous strands which are, in turn, attached to the inner surfaces of the kinetosomal triplets.

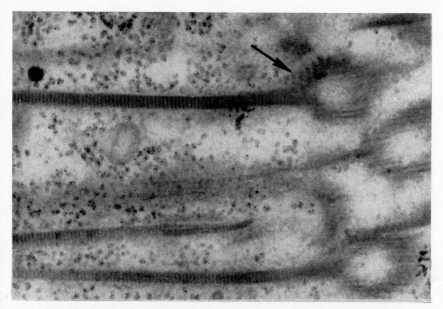

FIG. 17. Group of obliquely-sectioned kinetosomes of the superior girdle of locomotor cilia of the peritrich *Trichodinopsis paradoxa*. Striated root fibrils, attached obliquely at the kinetosome bases, extend down toward the center of the adhesive disc. At their point of attachment is a small, striated body (arrow) resembling a basal foot. × 78,000. From Favard, Carasso and Fauré-Fremiet.[63]

In the free-living sessiline peritrich *Opisthonecta henneguyi*, Bradbury[16] and Rosenberg and Grim[202] find striated fibrils running beneath the marginal kinetosomes of the trochal band, a ciliary girdle homologous to the more elaborate locomotor girdles of the mobiline peritrichs. The attachment of the fibrils to kinetosomes has not been observed, but the authors regard them as counterparts of the ciliary roots demonstrated by Favard, Fauré-Fremiet, and Carasso.[63]

Striated fibrils of a very different sort are found in the stalks of many sessiline peritrichs.[58, 194] These are constituents of the elastic, supporting element of contractile or non-contractile stalks and are extracellular, secreted structures produced by the aboral scopula and clearly related in organization to the modified scopular cilia. Although not strictly relevant to our discussion, they demonstrate that the organization of the ciliary axoneme can be reflected in fibrillar structures not connected with the kinetosome and lying entirely *outside* the ciliary membrane. Thus in *Epistylis*[58] the striated material appears first as nine slender fibrils closely appressed against the membrane around the base of each cilium. Distally the fibrils thicken progressively, and beyond the limits of the short cilia they outline cylindrical canals filling the body of the stalk. The striation

11*

of the fibrils is complex, with a major interval of about 22 mμ, and longitudinal filamentous organization is indicated. Cytochemical observations on the stalks of several peritrich genera by Randall and Hopkins[194] indicate that the stalk substance is primarily protein and possibly related to the keratin group of proteins.

No typical striated fibrils have been reported from any ciliates of the subclasses Suctoria (whose ciliated forms have not been studied) or Spirotrichia. Noirot-Timothée[155] suggests that short, slender fibrils of uncertain structure attached asymmetrically to kinetosomes of some entodiniomorphs may be kinetodesmal fibrils. The more recent micrographs of Roth and Shigenaka[208] show a rather elaborate network of dense fibrillar material in this region, including components that might be kinetodesmal. Very characteristic of the adoral ciliary band of these entodiniomorphs[20, 155, 208] is a heavy, banded rod below and directly linking the bases of obliquely aligned kinetosomes. The basal rod is composed of very dense material with a lighter segment in each interval between kinetosomes.

A system of tangentially oriented, striated root fibrils, surprisingly similar to those of hymenostomes, has been observed in the ciliated cells of a dicyemid mesozoan by Bresciani and Fenchel.[18] The fibrils are perpendicular to the axes of the kinetosomes, are attached asymmetrically and, according to the authors, pass posteriad, overlapping only for a short distance the next posterior kinetosome and its fibril. No other cell type, outside of the ciliates, has clearly revealed this sort of tangential root-fibril pattern. Striated ciliary roots in the endostyle of an ascidian, pictured by Olsson,[160] run parallel to the cell surface, gathering at a fibrillar terminal bar in the lateral cell membrane. The single published micrograph suggests that they are attached to dense material below the kinetosome bases and then curve laterally; it does not indicate whether they assemble in orderly rows.

2. MICROTUBULES

Probably all ciliates have systems of tubular fibrils associated with kinetosomes, and many have additional microtubular arrays that are not kinetosome-based, as well as wandering, unpatterned endoplasmic microtubules.

The following classes of organized microtubule arrays may be recognized tentatively: (1) ribbons of microtubules arising at the bases of somatic and some buccal kinetosomes and passing upward to run beneath and attached to pellicular membranes; (2) bands of microtubules beneath and parallel to pellicular membranes but not known to arise in association with kinetosomes; (3) annular and radial microtubules around the pore of the contractile vacuole; (4) ribbons or sheets of microtubules subtending the cell membrane in the region of the cytostome, probably extensions of (1); and (5) nemadesma, usually if not always in the buccal region, frequently attached to kinetosomes, consisting of close-packed bundles of long microtubules.

All of these have been recognized at least sporadically in widely divergent ciliate groups. The first three classes will be considered now.

a. Peripheral, kinetosome-based microtubules

The microtubule ribbons associated with somatic kinetosomes of *Paramecium*[176] and of several tetrahymenids[171] have been studied most thoroughly and can provide detailed models for this discussion. As previously noted, cilia arise in pairs over most of the body surface of *Paramecium multimicronucleatum*. The posterior kinetosome of each pair bears the kinetodesmal fibril, attached to the three triplets of its right, anterior margin. If the most anterior of these triplets is assigned the number 1 and the remainder numbered in the clockwise direction (when the cross section is

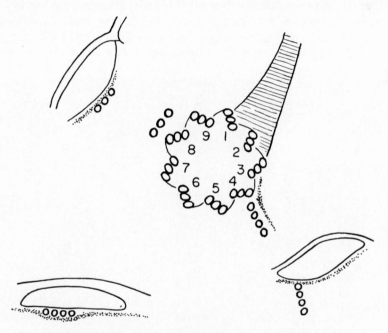

FIG. 18. Diagrams of a somatic kinetosome and microtubules in *Paramecium* or *Tetrahymena*. A cross-sectioned kinetosome, viewed from the base, is shown with its triplet fibrils numbered as described in the text. The striated kinetodesmal fibril attaches to triplets 1–3; the right, radial microtubule ribbon originates next to triplet 4, and the left, tangential ribbon originates next to triplets 8 and 9. The right, radial ribbon passes to the cytoplasmic surface and is attached by one edge only to the epiplasm beneath the pellicular alveolus, as shown at right. The left, tangential ribbon also passes to the cytoplasmic surface but remains parallel to the epiplasm, as shown at upper left. At the lower left is a cross-sectional view of longitudinal pellicular microtubules of the sort occurring in *Tetrahymena*; these are not kinetosome-based and they lie *between* the innermost alveolar membrane and the epiplasm.

viewed from the base outward), then the kinetodesmal fibril attaches to triplets 1 to 3 (Figs. 18, 19). Adjacent to the proximal extremity of triplet 4 is the innermost member of a radially oriented ribbon of four or five microtubules, linked in a row by fine bridges. This ribbon diverges from the kinetosome as it passes upward, coming to lie under the pellicle to the right of and posterior to the cilium. Only one edge of the ribbon—the same microtubule that arose closest to the kinetosome—is attached to the epiplasm (Figs. 18, 19). In *P. multimicronucleatum*, this *right, radial ribbon* ends near the top of the ectoplasmic crest marking the right, posterior boundary of the ciliary corpuscle.

At the left anterior margin of every kinetosome (both members of each pair), forming a tangent to triplets 8 and 9 at their proximal ends, a ribbon of three or four microtubules appears; it likewise diverges from the kinetosome, passing upward to the epiplasm. This *left, tangential ribbon* lies immediately beneath and parallel to the epiplasmic layer (Figs. 18, 19); it runs to the left and slightly anteriad (if it originated at a single kinetosome or

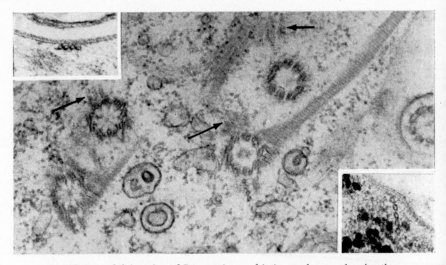

FIG. 19. Superficial section of *Paramecium multimicronucleatum*, showing the fibril arrangements diagrammed in Fig. 18. Two pairs of kinetosomes are seen in cross section, anterior direction toward the upper right. The broad attachment of the kinetodesmal fibril to the base of the posterior kinetosome of each pair identifies the orientation of the section. The right, radial ribbon is cut in good cross section at the right, posterior margin of the posterior kinetosome of each pair. A right, radial ribbon sectioned in position beneath the pellicle, attached by one edge to the epiplasm, is seen in the lower inset. The left, tangential ribbons are cut obliquely in this section. Three of the four are identifiable (arrows); the fourth kinetosome is sectioned below the point of origin of the left ribbon. One left, tangential ribbon in position under the pellicle is shown in the upper inset. × 53,000. Insets × 60,000. From Pitelka[176] (and unpublished).

the anterior one of a pair) or slightly posteriad (if from the posterior kineto-some of a pair) to end in the nearest ectoplasmic ridge.

The tetrahymenid ciliates[171] have identical microtubule ribbons. Kineto-somes are not paired in the species examined, and each one bears one right, radial ribbon and one left, tangential ribbon, each of which extends only as far as the limits of its kinetosome's territory (Fig. 20).

When first described by Pitelka,[171] these were called, respectively, the postciliary and transverse fibrils. Because their paths of divergence from the kinetosome differ in different ciliates, not always being posterior and trans-

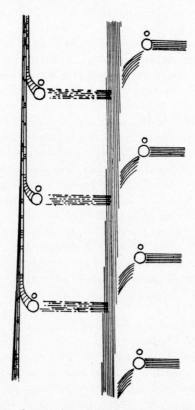

FIG. 20. Diagram of part of two kineties of *Tetrahymena* or *Colpidium*, viewed from above, anterior direction toward the top of the page, ciliate's right to the viewer's left. Kinetosomes are shown as open circles, parasomal sacs as smaller circles anterior to the kinetosomes. Kinety at left is shown with attached kinetodesmal fibrils, overlapping to form a bundle at the ciliate's right. Kinety at right is shown with attached right radial and left tangential microtubule ribbons; at the ciliate's right of this kinety is the longitudinal pellicular ribbon of overlapping microtubules; the ends of the next adjacent series of left tangential ribbons are indicated in broken lines.
From Pitelka.[171]

verse, their orientation at their point of origin seems, at least for the purposes of this survey, to offer a more reliable basis for identifying them.

These microtubules, because of their divergent courses, are recognized only with difficulty in most micrographs of thin sections, but some of them are likely to be detectable in almost any plane, and a rare tangential section (Fig. 21) near the cell surface may show traces of all of them, recurring consistently in each ciliary corpuscle. Whereas the ectoplasmic sculpturing of *Paramecium* makes the mapping of any cortical section almost diagrammatically clear, other ciliates are less cooperative and their fibril systems are much more difficult to trace. Nonetheless, there are numerous examples of microtubule patterns that appear to be directly comparable to those just described.

In Bradbury's apostome, each cilium-bearing kinetosome of the unspecialized kineties has its kinetodesmal fibril attached to triplets 1 to 3, a right radial ribbon arising next to triplet 4 and consisting usually of only two or three microtubules, and a left tangential ribbon composed of four or five microtubules, whose precise relationship to the kinetosomal triplets has not been seen clearly (Figs. 13, 14). Distances between kineties are relatively great. The left tangential ribbon runs leftward under the pellicle. We have traced it in some instances at least as far as the downward slope of the groove within which the next kinety lies, but have been unable to identify its terminus. The right radial ribbon passes to the right, between pellicle and kinetodesmos (Fig. 13), at least to the top of this same slope, so that there may be some overlap of left and right ribbons from adjacent kineties (actual fusion seems unlikely but cannot be eliminated on present evidence). Thus in the young life-cycle stages examined (tomite and protomite) from this apostome, where the kinetosomes are crowded close together in each kinety, the orientation of the microtubule ribbons is predominantly transverse, and the ciliary "corpuscle" or territory is very much broader than long.

The heterotrich ciliates have conspicuous fibers at the right of the somatic kineties, satisfying the Chatton-Lwoff definition of kinetodesma (Fig. 22). Early electron micrographs of *Stentor*[59, 196] demonstrated that these were composed of microtubules that arose at kinetosomes and passed to the right and posteriad. Recent micrographs] of *Spirostomum*[40, 67] and of *Blepharisma*[113] make it evident that the microtubule ribbons are more elaborate equivalents of the right radial ribbons of the hymenostomes. As indicated in Kennedy's micrographs reproduced in Fig. 23, an orderly ribbon of about nine microtubules, flanked by strands of very dense material, arises from the right, posterior margin of the posterior kinetosome of each pair (this kinetosome in *Blepharisma undulans* does not bear a cilium, but in other heterotrichs it may). In the absence of an anterior kinetodesmal marker, it is not possible to number the triplets with assurance that the numbering corresponds to that used for *Paramecium*, but if the anteriormost triplet is

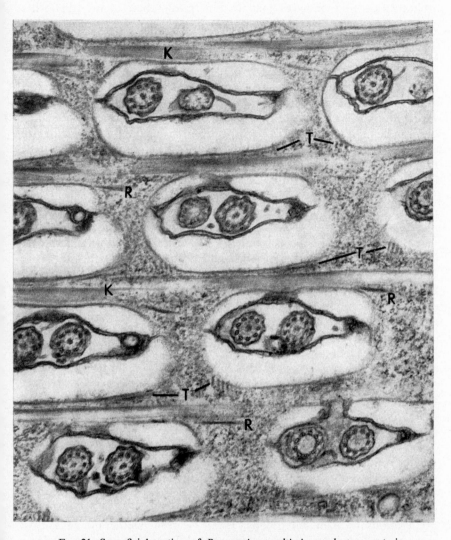

FIG. 21. Superficial section of *Paramecium multimicronucleatum*, anterior direction to the left, ciliate's right toward the top of the page. The paired cilia are sectioned near their bases and are flanked by the membranes and cavities of the paired pellicular alveoli. Kinetodesmal fibrils (K) appear in this micrograph as lightly-stained bands running across the page in ectoplasmic ridges between ciliary rows. In the ectoplasm of each kinetosomal territory, one right radial (R) and two left tangential (T) microtubule ribbons can be identified. Because they run at different angles to the section plane, they are variously cut in cross, oblique and near-longitudinal section. × 33,000. From Pitelka and Child.[178]

arbitrarily called 1, it seems that the innermost tubule of the ribbon lies closest to triplet 4. This ribbon passes upward, to the right and posteriad, joining a stack of microtubule ribbons or sheets composing the kinetodesmos (Fig. 24). Each ribbon extends for a considerable distance posteriad, overlapping similar ribbons from several, more posterior kinetosomes. The left edge of each ribbon in the kinetodesmos lies close, and in some instances seems to adhere, to the inner surface of the pellicle. The number of ribbons varies with body region and with species, from three or four to more than twenty. The number of fibrils per ribbon in the bundle is large enough to suggest that microtubules from more than one kinetosome may contribute to a single ribbon in the kinetodesmos. In all cases, the microtubules are laterally linked by bridges within each layer but not linked at all between layers.

At the left anterior margin of the base of the anterior kinetosome of each pair, curving slightly around triplets 8 and 9, is a row of four to six (*Blepharisma undulans*) or about nine (*Spirostomum ambiguum*) microtubules that passes up toward the pellicle (Fig. 23). Another fibril originates near the anterior margin of the posterior kinetosome of each pair and passes directly to the right to terminate apparently near or in contact with the kinetodesmos. The structure of this fibril is not clear; it is very slender and dense and shows an oblique banding in some micrographs (Fig. 23) that could indicate a homology with the anterior, striated kinetodesmal fibrils of the hymenostomes.

All of these features—the dense anterior fibril and the left tangential ribbon as well as the more conspicuous right radial ribbons with their accompanying dense strands—are observable in micrographs of *Stentor* (Ref. 196, Figs. 19 and 23; and 262, Fig. 28) and *Condylostoma* (Ref. 261, Figs. 3–5) as well as in *Spirostomum* and *Blepharisma*. *Bursaria*[231] has at least a similar microtubular kinetodesmal bundle.

A fibril bundle astonishingly similar to the heterotrich microtubular kinetodesmos is found in association with specialized rows of cilia on the non-retractile proboscis of the rhabdophorine gymnostome, *Dileptus anser*.[45] Two kineties, each consisting of paired kinetosomes, run down the ventral surface of the proboscis; midway between them is a fiber visible in stained preparations by light microscopy. In an electron micrograph of a cross section, the fiber is evident as a stack of slightly curving lamellae, made up of fibrils that are probably microtubules. A single longitudinal section (Fig. 6 in Ref. 45) is shown, in which clues to right-left and antero-posterior orientation are lacking. Fibrils from kinetosomes in a row on one side of the picture arch over to join the bundle of overlapping fibrils resembling the heterotrich kinetodesmos. Approaching the same bundle from the other side is a similar series of arching fibrils from indistinctly visible kinetosomes of another kinety. Dumont believes that these also enter the fibril bundle, fracturing the rule of desmodexy. Superficially, the picture suggests bilateral symmetry; but the fibrils approaching from the kinety on the observer's

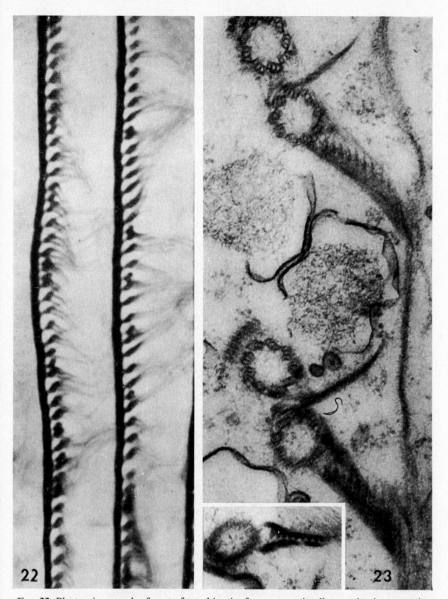

FIG. 22. Photomicrograph of part of two kineties from a protein-silver-stained preparation of *Condylostoma* sp., viewed from outside the cell, anterior direction toward the top of the page, ciliate's right to viewer's eft. The heavy kinetodesmos lies at the ciliate's right of the row of paired kinetosomes; from each pair a fiber extends to the right and posteriad to join the kinetodesmos. From M. Tuffrau, unpublished.

FIG. 23. Two pairs of cross-sectioned kinetosomes from one kinety of *Blepharisma undulans*, viewed from inside the cell, anterior direction toward the top, ciliate's right at viewer's right. A right, radial microtubule ribbon leaves the posterior member of each kinetosome pair and passes to the right and posteriad; the kinetodesmal bundle is more superficial and does not appear in this plane. A left, tangential ribbon is visible adjacent to the anterior kinetosome of each pair. A slender, dense, vaguely banded fibril extends from between the two kinetosomes of each pair toward the right and anteriad. Inset shows the microtubules of the right radial ribbon cut in cross section and flanked by strands of dense material. × 77,500; inset × 57,000. From Kennedy.[113]

left stop abruptly just short of the bundle in the plane of the micrograph; they are not contributing fibrils to the group visible in this picture. Further examination of *Dileptus* is needed; the origin and substructure of the fibrils are not resolved in the published micrographs.

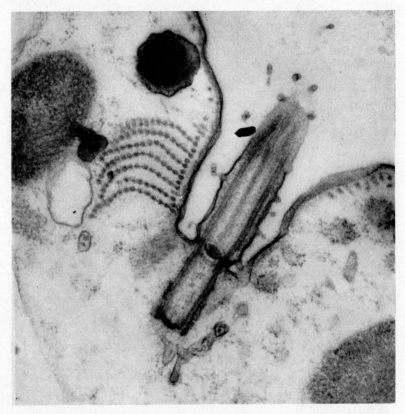

Fig. 24. Cross-section into the cortex of *Blepharisma undulans*, showing one kinetosome and cilium base cut longitudinally. At the ciliate's right (viewer's left) of the kinetosome is a cross-sectioned kinetodesmos. At the left and right of the groove in which the cilium stands, just beneath the cell membrane, are subpellicular microtubules. × 47,000. From Kennedy.[113]

Good examples of kinetosome-based microtubule ribbons are available among the trichostomes. Grain[88] demonstrates in the somatic kineties of *Isotricha* and *Paraisotricha* left tangential ribbons of about six microtubules associated with triplets 7 to 9 in my enumerating system, and apparently two or even three narrow ribbons arising at the right posterior margin of the kinetosome. The left tangential ribbons pass leftward under the pellicle into the ectoplasmic ridge separating adjacent kineties, while the right-hand ribbons pass up to the pellicle, to the right and posteriad.

De Puytorac[187, 190] reports the occurrence of leftward-directed or right-posterior microtubule ribbons in several of his astomes and in the gymnostome *Prorodon viridis*,[188] and Fauré-Fremiet[55] states that posterior fibrils are present in *Paranassula brunnea*. In some astomes, de Puytorac[182, 186] finds bundles of microtubules associated with the striated skeletal elements; their origin and extent are not clear.

Radial and tangential microtubule ribbons also occur in some specialized ciliary zones. Some of these contribute in characteristic ways to the ciliate mouth parts and will be discussed below, but in some instances their arrangement differs little from that of the somatic region. Daniel and Mattern[40] illustrate for *Spirostomum* and Kennedy[113] for *Blepharisma* radial ribbons arising at the kinetosomes of the most posterior of three rows composing each peristomial membranelle, and tangential ribbons originating at the kinetosomes of the most anterior (Figs. 39, 40). Both pass upward and under the membrane on opposite sides of the slender ectoplasmic fold that separates adjacent membranelles. Thus each fold carries a series of ribbons contributed by the anterior kinetosome row of the membranelle posterior to it and another series contributed by the posterior row of the membranelle anterior to it. Roth and Shigenaka,[208] studying entodiniomorph ciliates, show tangential microtubule ribbons originating at the bases of kinetosomes of the adoral cilia and passing upward into adjacent microvilli. Bretschneider[21] illustrates similar tangential ribbons at the kinetosomes of the specialized paralabial organ, but believes that the ribbons in this case pass downward into the underlying cytoplasm.

In the gymnostome *Didinium nasutum*, cilia are confined to two girdles, one surrounding the base of the proboscis and one approximately equatorial. Yagiu and Shigenaka[266] describe two ribbons of five to seven microtubules emerging from dense material around the base of each kinetosome and passing peripherally. Their text-fig. 2 shows one ribbon radially disposed at its origin and the other tangentially with respect to the kinetosome cylinder. The authors believe that both ribbons extend anteriad to run under and parallel to the pellicle on opposite sides of the ciliary row.

Favard, Carasso, and Fauré-Fremiet[63] show microtubules arising singly or in twos and threes around kinetosomes of the specialized ciliary girdles of mobiline peritrichs; their course is unknown.

b. *Microtubules not kinetosome-based.*

In many ciliates the single or multiple pellicular membranes are locally or generally associated with microtubules not identifiable with the radial or tangential ribbons. Pitelka[171] demonstrated in *Tetrahymena*, *Colpidium*, and *Glaucoma* bands of overlapping microtubules running longitudinally beneath and parallel to the pellicular membranes, to the right of each kinety and above the kinetodesmos. Tokuyasu and Scherbaum[244] have made the very interesting observation that these longitudinal fibrils clearly lie *between* the epiplasmic layer and the inner alveolar membrane (Fig. 18), whereas the kinetosome-based microtubule ribbons adhere to the inner surface of the epiplasm. The related hymenostome *Ophryoglena*[200] has very steep, slender ectoplasmic crests running longitudinally between kineties; each crest contains twelve to twenty microtubules in a single row of unknown origin and extent. The epiplasmic layer is not identifiable in the pictures shown. Favard, Carasso, and Fauré-Fremiet[63] illustrate in the peritrich *Trichodina* a single row of microtubules, linked by bridges, which again lies between the pellicular alveoli and the epiplasm on one side of a fold separating adjacent ciliary girdles of the basal disc.

Prorodon viridis[188] has peculiar, membrane-limited, longitudinal canals lying parallel to the kineties; these are partly surrounded by sheets of twenty to forty-five longitudinal microtubules. Some of the subpellicular microtubules of the gymnostome *Didinium nasutum* illustrated by Yagiu and Shigenaka[266] are thought by the authors to originate at kinetosomes of the ciliary girdles, as noted above. Described as distinct from these and hence unrelated to any kinetosomes are wider microtubule ribbons oriented normal to the pellicle both on the proboscis and on the non-ciliated body surface.

In at least some of the heterotrich ciliates,[67, 113, 231, 265] subpellicular microtubules run longitudinally in the ridges between kineties, lying close to and below the presumed epiplasmic layer as shown in Fig. 24 of *Blepharisma*. The origin of these is unknown. Entodiniomorph ciliates examined by Noirot-Timothée[155] and Bretschneider[19] have, on the non-ciliated body surface, a complex pellicle composed of a limiting unit membrane and several non-membranous layers. One of these consists of parallel small bundles of microtubules, each bundle containing two orderly rows of two to four tubules. Packets of microtubules resembling these, but of unknown origin, contribute to the wall of the esophagus and endoplasmic sac.[88] In the paralabial organ, steep folds alternate with rows of modified cilia. Roth and Shigenaka[208] show that the surface of each fold is limited by a unit membrane, beneath which is a narrow layer of dense material (epiplasm?) and under this, on each side of the fold, a layer of linked microtubules running parallel to the length of the fold.

In only a few instances, such as *Tetrahymena*,[171] where fibril distribution could be studied in isolated pellicle strips, is it clear that these microtubules are not continuous with any of the kinetosome-based systems. Their position between pellicular membranes and epiplasm may be significant in this case; more information is needed for most of the other examples.

c. *Microtubules associated with contractile vacuoles*

The association of microtubules with the discharge pore of the ciliate contractile vacuole was first demonstrated in 1958 by Rudzinska[213] for the suctorian *Tokophrya*, and subsequently in astomes by de Puytorac[183,

[184, 185] and in *Paramecium* by Schneider.[222] In all cases the exit pore is a permanently open invagination of the pellicle, closed off from the contractile vacuole by two unit membranes (the cell membrane and the vacuole membrane). The exit canal is surrounded by annular microtubules and by a cone of microtubules radiating from its wall to the adjacent vacuole membrane (Fig. 25). Similar arrangements have since been demonstrated in *Tetrahymena* by Elliott and Bak,[51] in *Ophryoglena* by Roque, de Puytorac, and Savoie,[200] in *Ichthyophthirius* by Mosevich,[148] and in several peritrichs by Carasso, Fauré-Fremiet, and Favard.[26] Although kinetosomes are always present in the vicinity of the pore, no connection has been noted.

Of particular interest is an extensive association of microtubules with the membranes of both reservoir and contributing vacuoles of *Paramecium* and *Ichthyophthirius*. Apparently a similar arrangement occurs in *Paraisotricha*.[46] According to Schneider's[222] detailed analysis, single microtubules appear first around the expanded inner (near the main vacuole)

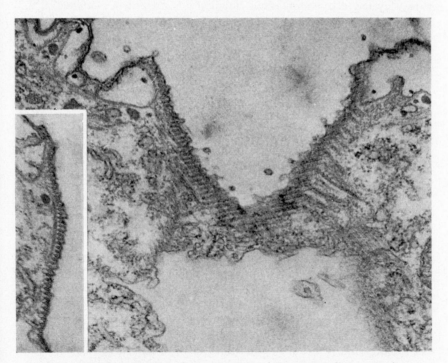

FIG. 25. Oblique section of the exit pore of the contractile vacuole in *Paramecium multimicronucleatum*, showing annular microtubules around the membrane of the pore and radial microtubules extending inward toward the membrane of the partially inflated reservoir vacuole. Inset shows the annular microtubules in cross section, from another section in a series through the same pore. × 44,000. From Pitelka, unpublished.

ends of the radial contributing canals and continue, gathering into bands, around the narrow tubes that open into the central reservoir vacuole; they then pass, in bands of 10 to 40, along the peripheral (nearest the cell surface) wall of the reservoir vacuole and converge at the exit pore.

3. FILAMENTS

Filaments often make up a complete or perforate layer separating ectoplasm from endoplasm in ciliates. Such a boundary is particularly clearly shown in de Puytorac's[187]micrographs of the astome *Mesnilella*. It consists of an outer layer of transversely oriented filament bundles and an inner layer of longitudinal ones; in both the filaments are roughly parallel and slightly undulating. The whole forms a fine-meshed criss-cross lattice. Similar ecto-endoplasmic boundaries are present in other astomes studied by de Puytorac and in a number of trichostomes,[88, 153] where extensions from the boundary layers may form a karyophore suspending the nucleus or may surround digestive or ingestive structures. Among gymnostomes, a two-layered ecto-endoplasmic boundary is present in *Didinium*.[266] It appears as a coherent fabric, penetrated by microtubule bundles (nemadesma) from kinetosomes of the ciliary girdles. *Paranassula*[55] has a network of filament tracts near the bases of somatic kinetosomes; *Prorodon*[188] has a layer of filaments at the bases of ectoplasmic crests, rather more peripheral than the ecto-endoplasmic boundary.

In *Paramecium*, a roughly hexagonal fibrous network at the level of the kinetosome bases was recognized in light-microscope preparations by G. von Gelei[73, 162, 164, 165] and has been called the infraciliary lattice. Electron micrographs show it to be made up of anastomosing tracts of filaments (Fig. 26); kinetosomes generally appear within the interstices of the lattice.[176, 226] Although it is located predominantly at what may be considered the ecto-endoplasmic boundary, the system sends branches profusely through the ectoplasm. These may appear beneath or in the ectoplasmic crests, and small bundles of them insert firmly at the margins of alveoli in isolated pellicle strips. *Frontonia* is reported to have a similar infraciliary lattice, but in *Ophryoglena*[200] a discrete filament network is located more peripherally, enmeshing the distal ends of the kinetosomes and running under the ectoplasmic crests.

A system similar in many ways to the infraciliary lattice of *Paramecium* is found in the contractile heterotrich, *Spirostomum*.[67, 265] In the fixed, contracted organisms the network appears at a level below the somatic basal bodies and is a rather loose, thick layer of filaments with no evident common orientation. Cisternae of endoplasmic reticulum frequently but not consistently parallel its edges. *Condylostoma*[264] has a similar network, but the non-contractile *Blepharisma* apparently lacks it.[113]

In *Stentor*, Randall and Jackson[196] and Fauré-Fremiet and Rouiller[59,60] demonstrated what appears now to be a highly developed variant of the

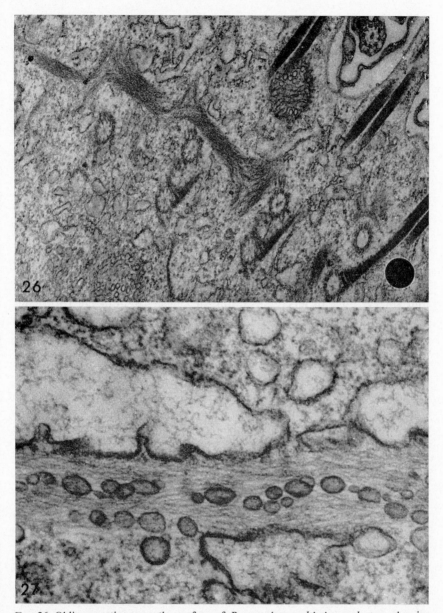

FIG. 26. Oblique section near the surface of *Paramecium multimicronucleatum*, showing several filament bundles of the infraciliary lattice running in the cytoplasm separating kinetosome pairs. × 30,000. From Pitelka.[176]

FIG. 27. Part of a longitudinal body myoneme of the peritrich *Epistylis anastatica*, showing the roughly oriented filaments composing the myoneme, sacs of endoplasmic reticulum incompletely surrounding it, and small membranous vesicles within the bundle. × 50,000. From Fauré-Fremiet, Favard and Carasso.[58]

Spirostomum filament system. One long, heavy bundle, tapering anteriorly, lies beneath and to one side of each somatic kinety; neighboring bundles are connected sporadically by branches, and small diverticula seem to wander off into the cytoplasm. The component filaments appear short and only vaguely oriented in a longitudinal direction. In at least some micrographs,[60] one edge of the filament bundle approaches the overlying infraciliature, but a cortical attachment has not been described. A consistent feature of the bundles is the presence, all along the surfaces and occasionally within the filament mass, of sacs and canals of endoplasmic reticulum. The filament bundles are conspicuously straight in overall contour even in strongly contracted cells.

A filament bundle of apparently identical morphology constitutes the myoneme of the contractile stalk of the vorticellid peritrichs.[60, 62, 194, 236] The constituent filaments again show, in the fixed specimens, a heterogeneous orientation but with their long axes roughly approximating the long axis of the myoneme. Membranous canaliculi or small vesicles permeate the mass, and larger sacs, often with ribosomes on their cytoplasmic surfaces, incompletely surround the bundle. The stalk myoneme is directly continuous with smaller bundles diverging within the cell body. Both the vorticellids and peritrichs with non-contractile stalks or none are capable of contracting the cell body. Myonemes serving to retract the peristome and to constrict its encircling protoplasmic lip are recognizable in all of them and always show the structure illustrated in Fig. 27.

Favard, Carasso, and Fauré-Fremiet[63] demonstrate in the complex, mobiline peritrichs *Trichodina* and *Trichodinopsis* tracts of filaments of similar appearance and dimensions but lacking the accompanying membranous reticulum, which regularly link individual plates or rods of the elaborate, articulating skeleton, or pass from skeletal plates to the subjacent epiplasm. These are considered to be elastic ligaments without contractile properties. Bradbury[16] finds in *Opisthonecta* massive filamentous material linking kinetosomes of the trochal band with heavy rods that she tentatively identifies as homologues of trichodinid skeletal elements.

In the entodiniomorph ciliates there is also, according to Noirot-Timothée,[156] a distinction between tracts or sheets of filaments festooned with endoplasmic reticulum and those lacking it. The latter include an innermost layer of the pellicle complex and, apparently continuous with this layer, a loose, perforate fabric surrounding the endoplasmic sac, as well as abundant tracts passing in various directions among different body parts.[155] Membrane-associated filament tracts constitute heavy fibers surrounding the retractable adoral ciliary zone and presumed sphincters near the cytoproct.

In any of the ciliates in which two kinetosomes occupy a single territory these are usually connected basally by a delicate filamentous bridge that may show cross-banding.

4. SUMMARY

On balance, the morphology of ciliate peripheral fibril systems is somewhat more comprehensible than seemed likely only a few years ago. Undeniably, the very effort to comprehend introduces a prejudice—one does not like always to admit defeat when matching wits with the ciliates.

The origin of peripherally directed microtubules at the proximal margins of somatic kinetosomes is of widespread occurrence and may turn out to be universal when enough examples are seen at high resolution. At least among trichostomes, hymenostomes, apostomes, and heterotrichs, the most thoroughly analysed examples conform to an identified pattern: one or more radially oriented microtubule ribbons at the right, posterior margin of the kinetosome and/or one tangentially oriented ribbon at its left; both ribbons may be slightly curved. Surely these alternative orientations cannot be without significance. The radially oriented ribbon tends to stay that way through its subsequent course, in the sense that only one of its edges adheres to the sub-pellicular epiplasm (Fig. 18). The tangentially oriented ribbon tends to remain so disposed that its whole width is parallel to the epiplasmic layer (Fig. 18). The right radial ribbon is often, if not always, accompanied at its origin by one or two strands of dense material; the tangential ribbon usually is not.

It would be gratifying to find comparable, recurrent designs in the association of microtubules with flagellate kinetosomes, but appropriate pictures of the latter at sufficiently high resolution are so rare that it is not possible to draw parallels. The "spur" of microtubules flanked by dense material that originates at kinetosomes of *Naegleria* and *Tetramitus* (Fig. 5) is somewhat suggestive of a ciliate radial ribbon.

The subpellicular microtubules that lack any demonstrated kinetosome connection appear sporadically; whether a position external to the epiplasm is significant remains to be seen. It is evident that microtubules may border membranes within the cell as well as at the surface (e.g., around the canals of *Prorodon*, around the contractile vacuoles of many species), and whether these have any connection with the other systems is not known.

The spotty distribution of "good" striated kinetodesmal fibrils is somewhat puzzling; they are too conspicuous to be overlooked in all of the hymenostomes, astomes, and apostomes studied but may be rudimentary in other groups and perhaps totally lacking in some. Unlike the striated roots of flagellates and metazoa, they never connect the kinetosome with any other cell organelle; kinetodesmal fibrils regularly accompany each other but nothing else. The only apparent counterpart of the flagellar striated root fibril is seen in the peritrichs, where the roots terminate at skeletal or pellicular structures.

The filament systems that proliferate within or just beneath the ectoplasm in many ciliates are sufficiently similar in appearance and general distribution to support the suggestion that they are homologous. If so, then the presence or absence of accompanying membranous reticulum may determine whether or not they are overtly contractile (see discussion of function on pp. 363–4). In many species where they constitute a widespread webbing, it has been difficult to detect any consistent and precise correspondence between their arrangement and that of kinetosomes, but this disorder may be illusory. In *Metaradiophrya*, for example, de Puytorac[182, 184] found that the ecto-endoplasmic boundary layer was composed of orderly filament bundles associated with kinetosomes in geometrically defined arrays.

Some general conclusions seem justified regarding the morphology of somatic fibrillar systems in ciliates with relatively uniformly ciliated body surfaces.

1. The ciliary corpuscle, or what may now be better termed the *kinetosomal territory*, contains a specific array of cytoplasmic fibrils diverging from the single or paired kinetosomes. The attachment of these fibrils at the base of the kinetosome follows a precise pattern, conferring or reflecting the pronounced asymmetry and polarity that are fundamental properties of each territory. Each fibril is of characteristically limited length, and some in each territory are approximately coextensive with the limits of the territory in one or more directions.

2. The microscopically visible kinetodesmos is common but apparently not universal. It consists of striated fibrils or ribbons of tubular fibrils issuing from individual kinetosomes along a kinety and overlapping serially along the latter's *right* side (rule of desmodexy). If the term *kinetodesmos* is used in the sense of the original Chatton-Lwoff definition, then not all kinetodesmal fibrils are homologues.

3. Tracts of fine filaments of indeterminate length and imprecise orientation may interconnect kinetosomes at differing levels or may be interspersed among them; their apportionment relative to kinetosomal territories is usually obscure.

4. Apart from the filament tracts, there is no fibril system that provides *direct* connections between kinetosomes of any two territories in the unspecialized body ciliature.

5. In no case has direct continuity between microtubules of the kinetosome itself and any other intracytoplasmic fibril been demonstrated.

C. Fibril Systems of the Oral Region

1. The Buccal Apparatus of Paramecium and Tetrahymena

Although the absence or presence and degree of development of specialized buccal ciliary organelles constitute primary taxonomic characters distinguishing subclasses and orders, there appears on present evidence to be no ciliate (except the mouthless astomes and suctorians) that does not have

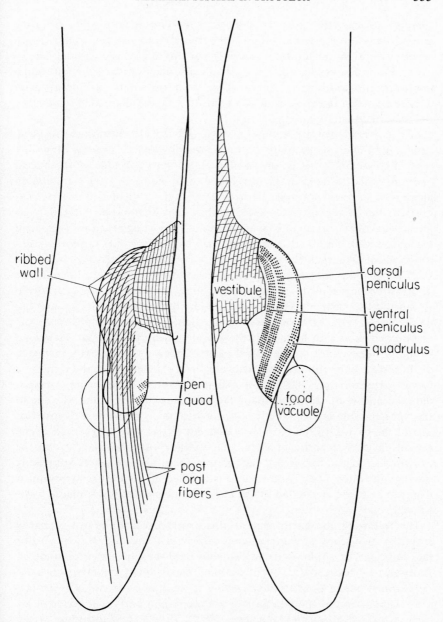

FIG. 28. The buccal apparatus of *Paramecium*. Left drawing shows the buccal wall viewed from the right side, right drawing shows the view from the left. Explanation in text. Redrawn from Gelei.[74]

complex fibrillar structures in the more or less conspicuously modified zone around the true cytostome. Many of the fibrils are identifiable as derivatives of the perioral infraciliature, whether or not this is confined within a buccal cavity. *Paramecium* once again provides a convenient model for an introduction to ciliate mouth parts. Although by no means simple, its buccal cavity is more compact and less formidably contorted by spiralling than some other well-described ciliate mouths.

For an overall view of the major features of buccal organization, a drawing from a light-microscope study of *P. caudatum* by Gelei[74] serves admirably (Fig. 28). Not shown is a row of cilia along the right edge of the buccal overture; this is the endoral membrane, a homologue of the undulating membrane of tetrahymenids. Otherwise the right wall of the cavity is not ciliated, but bears instead oblique sculpturings that Gelei referred to as pharyngeal fibers but that Ehret and Powers[49] more appropriately renamed the ribbed wall. On the left and dorsal walls of the cavity are three longitudinal bands of cilia, each composed of four rows, called (from left to right) the ventral peniculus, dorsal peniculus, and quadrulus. These are homologues of the three membranelles of the tetrahymenids. Cilia are compactly arranged within the two peniculi, but the rows of the quadrulus separate somewhat on the dorsal wall. All three bands spiral slightly as they pass posteriad; the ventral peniculus ends first, while the dorsal peniculus and quadrulus extend to the posterior limit of the buccal cavity. Gelei noted correctly that each of the four ciliary rows of the quadrulus is accompanied on the right by a row of parasomal sacs (his *Nebenkerne*, not shown in the drawing), whereas only three rows of sacs accompany the two peniculi, one to the left, one to the right and one between the two. The cytostome is at the dorsal, posterior end of the cavity. In the cytoplasm adjacent to the ribbed right wall of the buccal cavity is a series of fibers that extend posteriad well beyond the cytostome and end free in the endoplasm. These postoral fibers are readily seen in life; when a new food vacuole is pinched off behind the cytostome it seems to be guided posteriad by the fibers, which are flexibly displaced by its passage.

The following account of buccal ultrastructure will be drawn primarily from my own study of *Paramecium multimicronucleatum*.[174, 175, 177] For the most part it confirms details already published in a careful study of *P. aurelia* by Schneider,[223] but examination of interrupted sequences of serial transverse sections through the buccal cavities of several cells permits some redefinition of spatial relations among mouth parts. The terminology used is that of Ehret and colleagues,[48, 49, 50] who first identified at the electron-microscope level the major elements of buccal structure in *P. bursaria*.

Cilia of the endoral membrane arise from only the outer row (farther from the buccal cavity) of a staggered double row of kinetosomes (Fig. 29). The latter are embedded in an extensive, intricate network of very fine filaments, dotted

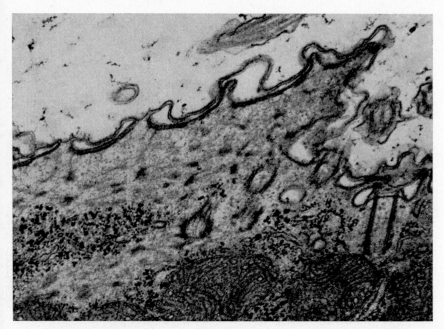

FIG. 29. Oblique section of the endoral membrane and right lip of the buccal cavity of *Paramecium multimicronucleatum*. Two staggered rows of kinetosomes are present in the endoral membrane, only one row being ciliated. At the far right is a somatic kinetosome, commonly non-ciliated in this area. A distinct ectoplasmic ridge separates the endoral membrane from the ribbed right wall of the buccal cavity. The filamentous reticulum is evident below the ribbed wall and the endoral membrane. × 30,000. From Pitelka, unpublished.

with small, dense nodes, which embraces the entire buccal cavity except for a dorsal zone comprising the cytostome and its lips. This network (*Stützfasernetz* of Schneider) will be called the *filamentous reticulum*. Schneider demonstrates that in certain areas, particularly under the anterior ends of the peniculi and quadrulus and again near the posterior end of the cavity, the nodes and filaments of the reticulum are organized in a regular, semicrystalline fashion (Fig. 30); elsewhere the filaments radiate more haphazardly from scattered or clustered nodes (Fig. 31). Both filaments and nodes appear to make contact with kinetosomes of the endoral membrane, peniculi, and quadrulus. No other fibrils have been detected in association with kinetosomes of the endoral membrane.

Extending dorsally and posteriad (Fig. 32) from the endoral membrane is the non-ciliated ribbed wall. It consists of obliquely oriented, sharp ridges in the ectoplasm, separated by long, narrow alveoli of the pellicular mosaic (Fig. 33). The epiplasm is limited to the grooves between ridges, and appears to connect with filaments of the underlying reticulum. In some but not all

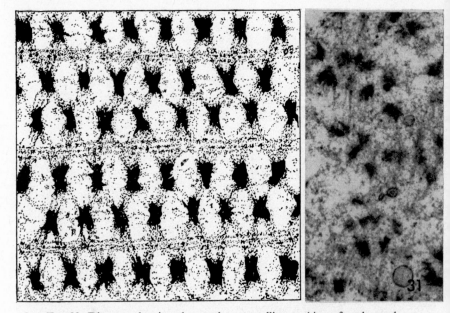

FIG. 30. Diagram showing the regular, crystalline packing of nodes and intervening material in parts of the filamentous reticulum of *Paramecium aurelia*. Drawn from an electron micrograph by Schneider.[223]

FIG. 31. Electron micrograph of the filamentous reticulum, more randomly organized here, from *P. multimicronucleatum*. × 36,000. From Pitelka, unpublished.

of my micrographs of the upper ribbed wall, one or two microtubules of unknown origin and extent are found near the crests of the ribs. At the extreme anterior end of the buccal cavity the ribbed wall, without further elaboration, arches dorsally to meet the quadrulus. More posteriorly, the cytostomal area intrudes between them and two new differentiations make their appearance. Arrayed under the dorsal half of the ribbed wall are bundles of hexagonally packed microtubules (Fig. 33). As these proceed posteriad, the bundles (nemadesma) increase in size and gather beneath the dorsalmost one or two ribs of the wall. I have been unable to identify the anterior origin of these nemadesma; they do not appear to be associated with the kinetosomes of the endoral membrane—which are the only kinetosomes in the neighborhood—and, contrary to Schneider's suggestion, definitely are not related to microtubule ribbons shortly to be described on the left wall. Posteriorly, the nemadesma extend free in the cytoplasm well past the cytostome and food vacuole as the microscopically visible postoral fibers of Gelei.

The second new differentiation associated with the ribbed wall is a peculiar groove (Fig. 33) that, beginning fairly far forward and extending posteriad

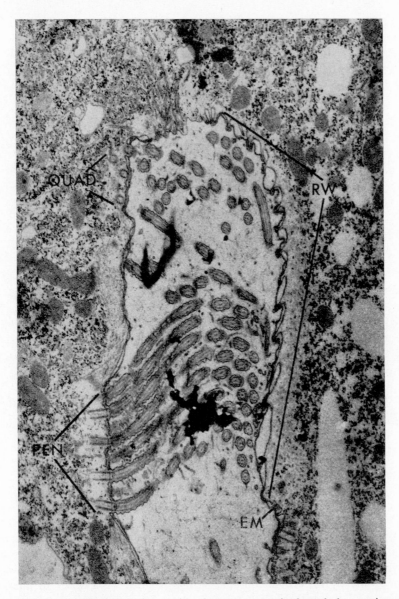

Fig. 32. Low-magnification section cutting almost transversely through the anterior and of the buccal cavity of *Paramecium multimicronucleatum*. The ventral opening of the buccal cavity to the outside is at the bottom of the picture; the ciliate's right is at the viewer's right. Beginning at the lower right and proceeding counterclockwise around the buccal wall one sees some non-ciliated somatic kinetosomes, the endoral membrane (EM, no kinetosomes included in this section), the ribbed wall (RW) extending dorsally to the right and left lips (not labeled) of the cytostome (the cytostomal surface itself begins just posterior to this level and is not present in the section), the four ciliary rows of the quadrulus (QUAD), a non-ciliated expanse of the left wall, and the eight ciliary rows of the two peniculi (PEN). Pellicular alveoli and filamentous reticulum are present along all parts of the buccal wall except the cytostomal lips. Two large, dense, dirt particles obscure some of the cilia within the buccal cavity. × 12,000. From Pitelka, unpublished.

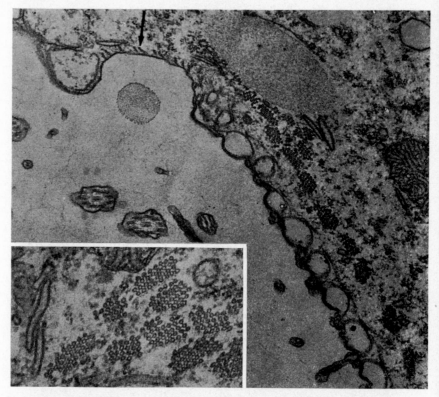

FIG. 33. Dorsal end of the ribbed wall and the right lip of the cystosome of *Paramecium multimicronucleatum*. Below the pellicular alveoli of the ribbed wall are the clusters of microtubules (shown at higher magnification in the inset) making up the postoral fibers. The right lip of the cytostome is a groove lined by the cell membrane only, subtended by narrow ribbons of microtubules (arrow). × 32,000; inset × 62,000. From Pitelka, unpublished.

around the whole length of the cytostome, marks the dorsal edge of the ribbed wall and constitutes the right lip of the cytostomal area. Pellicular alveoli and epiplasm end at the last ridge of the ribbed wall; the groove is lined only by the cell membrane, here subtended by a series of narrow ribbons of two or three microtubules, whose origin is unknown. Dorsal to this grooved right lip, the cytostomal area—actually an elongate, triangular zone—consists of a highly convoluted, ameboid cytoplasmic surface limited only by the unit cell membrane (Fig. 34).

The left lip of the cytostome is clearly marked by a band of irregular, low, sawtooth ridges (both structurally and spatially distinct from the ribbed wall). Each ridge is subtended (Figs. 35, 36) by one broad ribbon of ten to fifteen microtubules, usually accompanied by a narrow ribbon of two or three. The cytoplasm of the sawtooth band is limited only by the unit cell membrane. Throughout the extent of the band, small, membrane-limited vesicles in the shape of flat or curved discs are abundant in the cytoplasm. Ridges fade out on the cytostomal side of the band and at the same level their microtubule ribbons veer off into the endoplasm. The ribbons may be

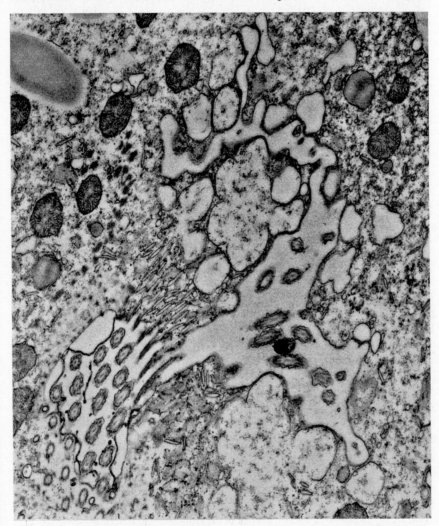

Fig. 34. Section through the extreme posterior end of the buccal cavity and cytostome of *Paramecium multimicronucleatum*. The cilia and kinetosomes of the quadrulus and tangentially-sectioned ridges of the sawtooth band (left cytostomal lip) are seen in the lower left; the cytostomal area is an irregular, ameboid cytoplasmic surface occupying most of the right half of the picture; some buccal cilia are sectioned in the lumen. In the upper left center, postoral fibers cut in cross section are evident as small, dense patches. × 13,000. From Pitelka, unpublished.

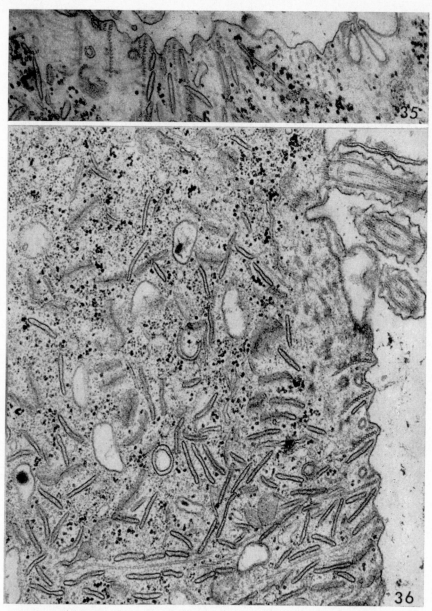

FIG. 35. Section of the left and right lips of the cytostome, cut at approximately the same anterior level as shown in Fig. 32. The left lip, or sawtooth band, is ridged and carries broad and narrow ribbons of microtubules and characteristic disc-shaped vesicles. The right lip is at this level an irregular groove with many narrow microtubule ribbons. Both lips are bounded by the unit cell membrane only. × 30,000.

FIG. 36. Section of the left end of the sawtooth band and the nearest row of cilia of the quadrulus. Pellicular alveoli and filamentous reticulum extend only as far as the first ridges of the sawtooth band. Microtubule ribbons near the bottom of the picture descend into the endoplasm; characteristic vesicles are abundant. × 30,000. Figures 35 and 36 from Pitelka, unpublished.

found, always accompanied by strings or clusters of disc-shaped vesicles, deep in the endoplasm anywhere around and posterior to the cytostomal area. Ridges and microtubules that disappear in this fashion from the cytostomal side of the left lip are continuously replaced by new ones on the side adjacent to the quadrulus. The microtubules appear to arise as radial ribbons from kinetosomes of the nearest row of the quadrulus. The filamentous reticulum underlying the quadrulus reaches as far as the leftmost ridge of the sawtooth band, where its nodes and filaments are aligned, as shown by Schneider, with the first ribbon of microtubules.

Except for the separation between rows of the quadrulus, the infraciliature of the three ciliated bands is similar. Right radial ribbons of microtubules arise at the bases of kinetosomes of only the right-hand row in all three. According to present evidence, ribbons from the ventral peniculus end shortly; those of the dorsal peniculus extend in orderly fashion below the pellicular mosaic toward the quadrulus without reaching it, and those of the quadrulus extend, as just described, into the sawtooth left lip of the cytostome and then posteriad into the endoplasm. Additional fibrous links among penicular kinetosomes, extending in several directions and at two different levels, have been clearly shown by Schneider; some of these resemble filaments of the surrounding reticulum.

The opening from vestibule into the buccal cavity is ventral, between ventral peniculus and endoral membrane. Posterior to the buccal overture, this wall is a smooth expanse of pellicle with large alveoli and underlying filamentous reticulum.

The relatively shallow buccal cavity of *Tetrahymena*, as might be expected, resembles that of *Paramecium* in most respects. Preliminary examination by Miller and Stone[147] and a more detailed study by Nilsson and Williams,[152] based on analysis of whole, isolated mouths as well as of sections, demonstrate the close correspondence of undulating membrane with endoral membrane, and of the three membranelles with the peniculi and quadrulus. The right wall of the buccal cavity is a non-ciliated ribbed wall (called oral ribs by both sets of authors) and beneath it is a filamentous reticulum. Radial ribbons of microtubules arise from the right row of kinetosomes of at least membranelles I and II. According to Nilsson and Williams these "membranellar connectives" attach to the nearest row of kinetosomes of the next adjacent membranelle—a connection not observed in *Paramecium*. Additional connectives linking membranelles with the undulating membrane region appear in whole mounts, but their substructure has not been demonstrated in sections. The ribs of the ribbed wall contain what appear in whole mounts to be coarse fibers; in sections they are identified as ribbons of microtubules. Nilsson and Williams find that each rib originates near a kinetosome of the non-ciliated row of the undulating membrane, and they show tubular fibrils—apparently right radial ribbons—arising at the bases of kinetosomes of this row and continuing into the oral ribs. As in *Paramecium*, the ribbed wall is characterized by distinct pellicular alveoli occupying the depressions between ribs.

Instead of the multiple postoral fibers of *Paramecium*, there is a single large nemadesmos running past the cytostome into the posterior endoplasm. It is made up, according to Nilsson and Williams, of assembled microtubules from the ribbed wall, plus others coming from the third membranelle. The cytostome is an identifiable aperture, bounded on the right side by converging oral ribs and on the left by a valve-like flap of cytoplasm. Behind the cytostome an open cytopharynx trails off alongside the postoral fiber. It is lined in part by pellicle, complete with alveoli, and in part by just the unit cell membrane. This patch of membrane without underlying alveoli extends anteriad past the cytostome in a long strip separating ribbed wall on the right from the pellicle of the left wall, but is not known to be associated with microtubule ribbons like the cytostomal lips in a comparable position in *Paramecium*.

While the published micrographs of sectioned *Tetrahymena* are considerably less informative than those of *Paramecium*, whole-mount preparations of the tetrahymenid buccal cavity demonstrate the existence of effective interconnections among ciliary organelles; further examination of their nature in sectioned material is needed. Structure of the cytostomal area seems to be quite different in the two genera. The demonstration of microtubules originating at undulating-membrane kinetosomes, continuing along the oral ribs and converging to form part of the postoral fiber is significant; such evidence is lacking for *Paramecium*. The possibility that microtubules from the third membranelle (homologues of microtubule ribbons of the sawtooth band in *Paramecium*?) may contribute to the postoral fiber of *Tetrahymena* suggests another interesting divergence from the pattern in *Paramecium*.

Of the buccal structures seen here, the filamentous reticulum, the nemadesma, the right radial ribbons of the infraciliature, the left cytostomal lip with its microtubule ribbons, and endoral-membrane-ribbed-wall may be recognized as common ciliate mouth parts, each recurring in at least two or more orders.

2. THE FILAMENTOUS RETICULUM

The filamentous reticulum was first recognized by Rouiller and Fauré-Fremiet[209] in the peritrich *Campanella umbellaria*, where it forms a long, coiled, microscopically visible fiber accompanying the spiralling funnel of the infundibulum (invaginated part of the peritrich buccal cavity leading to the cytostome). Called by the authors the reticulate fiber and believed to provide elastic, skeletal support for the infundibular wall, its homologue has since been found in other peritrichs (*Epistylis*,[58] *Vorticella*,[195] *Termitophrya*,[157] *Opisthonecta*[16, 202]). As in *Paramecium* it shows an orderly, hexagonal to rectangular pattern in some areas an is more random in others, its filaments and nodes being linked to neighboring kinetosomes in a

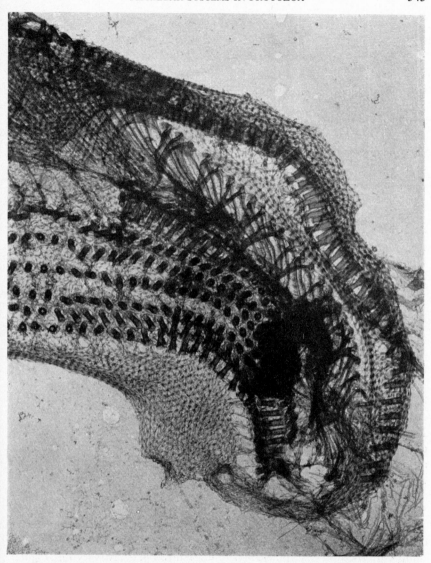

FIG. 37. Buccal apparatus isolated from the peritrich *Opisthonecta henneguyi*. The buccal wall, opened out and lying almost flat (upper edge folded over) is enmeshed in and perhaps held together by a very extensive, distinct, filamentous reticulum. Multiple rows of cylindrical kinetosomes constituting the polykineties of the buccal cavity are seen entering the picture from the left center and curving posteriad. Kinetosomes of the haplokinety form a long row at the folded, upper right edge of the fragment. Between polykinety and haplokinety lie the infundibular crests, extending diagonally backward; at the upper ends of the crests are peculiar, bristle-like cytoplasmic extensions, here lying over the crests but pointing leftward. The cytostome, not identifiable here, would be at the left, lower extremity of the fragment. × 9000. From L. E. Rosenberg and J. N. Grim, unpublished.

regular manner. Also as in *Paramecium* it forms, at least in some species, an extensive layer surrounding much of the buccal cavity (Fig. 37).

A filamentous reticulum has been identified in only a few other holotrichs. Bradbury[15] finds in her apostome a rather discrete, reticulate fiber with a concentration of longitudinally oriented filaments and microtubules at the periphery of a vaguely patterned network containing nodes. It appears next to one of the short kineties of the ventral surface of the cell and passes to the roof of the rosette. The latter is, in the non-feeding stages examined, a flat, closed, ciliated, cylindrical chamber lined by pellicle from which radial septa, carrying microtubules, extend into the lumen.

Among heterotrichs, a filamentous reticulum is reported in *Nyctotherus*, where King, Beams, Tahmisian, and Devine[115] found a long peristomial band, with typical filaments and nodes, intimately associated via filamentous connections with kinetosomes of the peristomial membranelles. The band continues, past the membranelles, beneath the non-ciliated surface of the buccal cavity. Micrographs of *Bursaria*[231] show what appears to be a filamentous reticulum beneath peristomial membranelles.

Both in ciliates that have a distinct filamentous reticulum and in those that lack it, the kinetosomes making up a membranelle or other compound organelle are typically linked by filamentous strands or masses, often forming orderly patterns at one or two specific levels of the kinetosome, and these strands contribute to the filamentous reticulum if one is present (for example, the adoral infraciliature of *Opisthonecta*[6]). Kennedy[113] reports that some of the fibrous interconnections in *Blepharisma* membranelles arise as direct branches of peripheral kinetosomal microtubules, which however show no diminution beyond the branching point. His micrographs (e.g., Ref. 113, Fig. 21) suggest to me rather that the interconnecting filaments arise from denser material closely adherent to the peripheral kinetosomal fibrils at basal and equatorial levels, and not from the microtubules themselves. The point needs confirmation.

3. NEMADESMA

Nemadesma are among the most intriguing and apparently versatile of the ciliate mouth parts. They consist, according to Fauré-Fremiet's[53] definition, of an ensemble of parallel microtubules showing, in cross section, regular rectangular or hexagonal packing. In the many instances in which nemadesma can be recognized and studied by light microscopy they are stiff and elastic, are movable but not contractile, and react as proteins to cytochemical tests.

Gymnostome ciliates are uniformly characterized by the presence of skeletal rods in the region of the cytopharynx. In the suborder Rhabdophorina[37] the rods outline a cytopharyngeal tube that is highly expansible to accomodate ingestion of prey. Cyrtophorine gymnostomes—all herbivores—usually have a cytopharyngeal basket wherein fusion of rods prohibits marked distension. In both suborders the rods are nemadesma. The cylinder circumscribed by the nemadesma is in at least its lower regions filled with cytoplasm enclosing characteristic vesicles (the phagoplasm of Fauré-Fremiet[54]); the upper ends of the rods commonly surround a more or less invaginated area of the cell surface, furnished with microtubule ribbons and limited by a single unit membrane. Although compound ciliary organelles are lacking from the oral region, infraciliature neighboring the cytopharynx usually differs from that of somatic regions. Probably the nemadesma ordinarily originate at the bases of oral kinetosomes[54, 88] but proof is available for only a few examples.

The number, size, shape, and distribution of gymnostome nemadesma differ considerably among genera. There may be two or more concentric circles of rods of different size and shape. Rhabdophorine gymnostomes examined include *Coleps*,[211] *Prorodon*,[188, 211] *Holophrya*,[189] *Plagiocampa*,[57] *Dileptus*,[45, 54] *Alloiozona* and *Didesmis*,[87, 88] and *Didinium*.[266] Of these *Didinium* is unique in that some of the nemadesma appear to arise far anteriad on the non-ciliated proboscis, as microtubule ribbons at first subtending the pellicle. They pass medially into the endoplasm and then posteriad, becoming rearranged as nemadesma somewhere in this course. Other nemadesma, presumably distinct from those in the proboscis, descend from kinetosomes of the ciliary girdles, through the ecto-endoplasmic filament layer, into the endoplasm.

In all of the other gymnostomes examined the nemadesma arise somewhere near the circumoral kinetosomes. Often there is dense, fibrous material capping the nemadesmos or linking it to a kinetosome. Only Grain[88] has shown, for *Alloiozona*, a high-resolution micrograph of the kinetosome-nemadesmos attachment; microtubules originate at a disc-shaped density overlapping the bottom of the kinetosome (Fig. 38). In *Holophrya*,[189] nemadesma are linked in pairs anteriorly by conspicuous tracts of protein material showing complex banding; no association with kinetosomes is apparent. In many rhabdophorines, explosive trichocysts are also present around the cytopharynx. The term "trichite" has been used both for trichocysts and for nemadesma and, through this confusion, has for the present lost its usefulness.

The dense, fibrous material associated with anterior ends of some rhabdophorine nemadesma appears to be elaborated and extended as a ring joining all of the rods anteriorly in the cyrtophorine genus *Paranassula*[55] or as prominent teeth in *Chlamydodon*.[112] In *Nassula*,[211] a peripheral sheath made up of more loosely organized microtubules unites the nemadesma in a continuous cylinder. Fauré-Fremiet[55] reports that in *Paranassula*, nemadesma cut in longitudinal section show, astonishingly, a regular, compound striation markedly similar to that of striated kinetodesmal fibrils.

The few trichostome ciliates examined also have nemadesma. Grain[88] shows them descending from the vestibular infraciliature of *Isotricha* and cites their presence in *Dasytricha*; their kinetodesmal attachment apparently

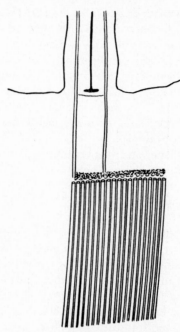

FIG. 38. Drawing showing the attachment of an oral nemadesmos of the gymnostome *Alloiozona* to the base of a kinetosome. Drawn from an electron micrograph by Grain.[88]

is similar to that illustrated for *Alloiozona*. In addition to these oral nemadesma, Grain finds in *Paraisotricha* and the gymnostome *Alloiozona* nemadesma issuing from kinetosomes of specialized cilia adjacent to a discrete cytoplasmic zone containing peculiar concretions; the nemadesma enter or surround the concretion zone. Fauré-Fremiet and André[56] describe typical pharyngeal nemadesma in *Tillina*.

Among the hymenostome ciliates, nemadesma descend directly from vestibular[200] and buccal[268] kinetosomes of *Ophryoglena*, and reportedly from membranellar kinetosomes in *Frontonia*.[53, 114, 199, 211, 267] As already noted, their origin in *Paramecium* is unknown (but is *not* from membranelles) and in *Tetrahymena* appears to be compound, involving the undulating membrane and third membranelle.

Nemadesma have not been reported from peritrich ciliates. But in the spirotrichs they appear in abundance and in a variety of patterns. The heterotrichs *Stentor*,[196] *Condylostoma*,[263, 264] *Spirostomum*,[40, 265] and *Blepharisma*[113] have similar nemadesmal systems associated with peristomial membranelles. The micrographs by Daniel and Mattern[40] and Kennedy[113] show clearly that in *Spirostomum* and *Blepharisma* nine to eleven microtubules originate from a dense disc at the bottom of each membranellar kinetosome in two, usually unequal rows (Figs. 39, 40). Those from the three kinetosome rows of each membranelle converge, fan-like, to form a single large nemadesmos showing hexagonal packing in cross section. The nemadesma descend for many micra into the endoplasm around and behind the cytostome and, probably in all cases, bifurcate to meet their neighbors in a continuous zigzag fiber. At least in *Blepharisma* nemadesma also descend to join this fiber from kinetosomes of the undulating membrane. *Nyctotherus*[115] has nemadesma issuing from at least some of the membranellar kinetosomes, but their subsequent path has not been traced.

In the entodiniomorph ciliates examined by Bretschneider,[19, 20, 21] Noirot-Timothée,[155] and Roth and Shigenaka[208] cilia are restricted to one or two coiled bands in the oral region. As noted above (p. 316), kinetosomes rest on heavy, banded rods, whose texture resembles the thin, dense discs found at the bases of specialized kinetosomes in some other ciliates (e.g. *Alloiozona*, Fig. 38). From the lower surface of the rod, exactly opposite the base of each kinetosome but usually at an angle to it, arises a retrociliary fiber which is a nemadesmos. Anywhere from a dozen to a hundred or more hexagonally packed microtubules compose a single nemadesmos. The bundles are numerous and pass in many different directions, sometimes accumulating in clusters. It is possible that some of them, diminished to around half a dozen fibrils, become the packets in the wall of the esophagus mentioned earlier (p. 326).

4. CYTOPHARYNGEAL MICROTUBULE RIBBONS AND THE RIBBED WALL

Ribbons of microtubules associated particularly with the cytopharynx have been identified in a number of ciliates. Randall and Jackson[196] first illustrated them below an unidentified part of the oral cavity wall in *Stentor*, and Noirot-Timothée[155] and Grain[88] have called attention to their widespread occurrence. Several common characteristics distinguish them: (1) the ribbons lie normal to the cell membrane; (2) the cell is limited in this area by a single unit membrane—alveoli that may be present elsewhere in the buccal cavity or oral zone are absent here; and (3) peculiar small vesicles, often with a heavy or double membrane, are found in the cytoplasm of this region.

The ciliate cytostome is defined by Corliss[36] as a two-dimensional aperture, typically permanently open, between the buccal cavity (if present) or the body surface and the cytopharynx. The cytopharynx is in turn (Ref. 36, p. 268) "The non-ciliated passageway . . . leading from the cytostome into the inner cytoplasm of the organism" and often supported by fibers. "In most ciliates, during feeding, food vacuoles are formed at the [innermost] end of the cytopharynx. . . ."

Cytostome and cytopharynx often appear in the light microscope as well-defined structures, but they may be harder to distinguish at the electron-microscope level. Thus in *Paramecium multimicronucleatum*, food vacuoles appear to be formed by ameboid action within the naked, convoluted zone

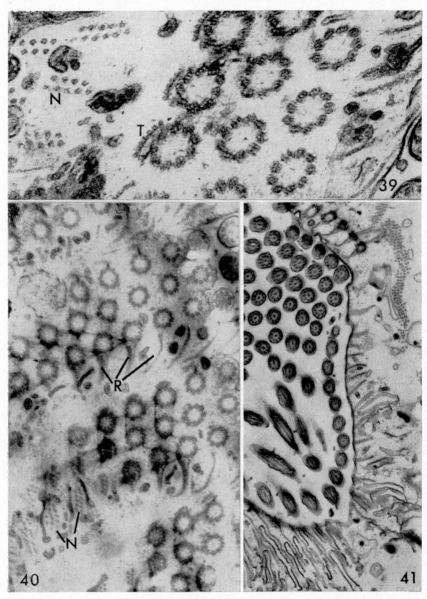

FIG. 39–41

at the postero-dorsal surface of the buccal cavity; buccal ciliation extends to the posterior limit of the cavity, and what has been identified as a cyto-pharynx may be the cytoplasm-filled zone bordered by postoral fibers, along which food vacuoles pass immediately after their formation. Where electron microscopists have identified a permanent, non-ciliated passage satisfying the definition of a cytopharynx it displays—except in *Tetrahymena*—the three characteristics distinguishing the zone of microtubule ribbons. It seems resonable to call the latter *cytopharyngeal ribbons*, while recognizing that in ciliates with specialized oral ciliature the ribbons may traverse some length of the buccal or vestibular wall before passing the cytostome.

Grain's micrograph (Ref. 88, Fig. 8) of the *Alloiozona* cytopharynx shows what may be a typical picture for gymnostomes: a cylindrical, membrane-limited cytopharynx with radiating microtubule ribbons, situated in the center of a vesicle-packed zone, which in turn is surrounded by the tiers of nemadesma forming the pharyngeal basket. The cytopharyngeal ribbons are reported to arise in pairs from kinetosomes of the anteriormost cilia surround-ing the apical cytostome. Other gymnostomes for which cytopharyngeal rib-bons are reported are *Didesmis*,[88] *Prorodon*,[188] *Holophrya*,[189] and pro-bably *Coleps*[211] and *Chlamydodon*.[112] According to de Puytorac,[189] the cytopharyngeal ribbons of *Holophrya* arise at the anterior ends of the nemadesma, without any direct kinetosomal connection. In *Didinium*, prey is ingested through the non-ciliated apical proboscis, which may be retracted and greatly distended in the process. Yagiu and Shigenaka[266] illustrate microtubule ribbons arising in pairs under the cell membrane near the anterior end of the proboscis; one ribbon of each pair passes centripetally to become reorganized as a nemadesmos while the other remains peripheral, subtending the surface membrane like a cytopharyngeal ribbon and continu-ing posteriad into the ciliated zone. Other microtubules run in bands imme-diately below and parallel to the cell membrane; if my interpretation of the

FIG. 39. Cross-sectioned kinetosomes of part of one membranelle of the heterotrich *Blepharisma undulans*. At the extreme left are several groups of cross-sectioned micro-tubules composing a nemadesmos (N) of the next adjacent membranelle; they will converge deeper in the endoplasm. At the left of each kinetosome of the leftmost row in this picture is a tangential row (T) of microtubules. × 59,000.

FIG. 40. A low-magnification view of a section cutting parts of several membranelles; the section passes from a superficial level on the right into the deeper cytoplasm on the left. Nemadesmal microtubules (N) descending from the kinetosome bases are visible at lower left. Radial ribbons (R) of microtubules extend from the lowermost row of kine-tosomes of each membranelle in this picture and pass upward into the ectoplasmic folds between membranelles, on the right. Fibrous interconnections among kinetosomes of each membranelle are apparent. × 25,000.

FIG. 41. Section through the cytopharyngeal region of the buccal cavity, showing mem-branellar kinetosomes and nemadesma at upper right, cytopharyngeal ribbons and characteristic, elongate vesicles surrounding the part of the cavity at center and bottom of the picture. × 14,000. Figure 39–41 from Kennedy.[113]

authors' description is correct these are extensions of kinetosome-based ribbons from the ciliary girdles. If the whole proboscis is considered to represent an expanded, everted cytopharynx, then the anterior ciliary girdle is perioral, and the fibril arrangement may be not fundamentally different from that in other gymnostomes.

According to Grain,[86, 88] the cytopharyngeal ribbons of the trichostome *Paraisotricha* arise from kinetosomes of specialized vestibular kineties; other trichostomes with similar ribbons reported by the same author[88] are *Isotricha* and *Dasytricha*, and Fauré-Fremiet and André[56] describe what seem to be the same thing in *Tillina*.

In the hymenostomes, conventional cytopharyngeal ribbons have been seen only in *Paramecium*, where they characterize the sawtooth band (Figs. 35, 36). Rows of microtubules that may represent cytopharyngeal ribbons in *Ophryoglena*[200] occur in an orderly cylinder surrounding an endoplasmic zone filled with small vesicles behind the cytostome, and apparently arise as distinct radial ribbons from membranellar kinetosomes. All of the hymenostomes examined have ribbed walls extending posteriad from the endoral-undulating membrane; only in *Tetrahymena* do the ribs, with accompanying pellicular alveoli, continue into the cytopharynx.

In all peritrichs studied, a characteristically differentiated zone of infundibular crests shows clear homology both to the ribbed wall and to the region of cytopharyngeal ribbons. *Epistylis*,[58] *Vorticella* and *Zoothamnium*,[26] *Opisthonecta*[16, 202] and *Telotrochidium* (= *Opisthonecta*) and *Termitophrya*[158] have distinct surface ridges or crests arising near the kinetosomes of the infundibular portion of the haplokinety. The latter consists of two staggered rows of kinetosomes, only one row being ciliated, exactly like the endoral-undulating membrane of hymenostomes.[16, 158] In position and general contour, the infundibular crests therefore resemble the ribs of the hymenostome right buccal wall. However, the infundibular crests are limited by a unit membrane only,[58] lacking the pellicular alveoli that characterize the ribbed wall, and they carry microtubule ribbons that continue posteriad, with the crests, into the cytopharynx. Characteristic, membrane-limited vesicles appear around the cytopharynx in the usual fashion. The apparent identity in peritrichs of ribbed wall and zone of cytopharyngeal ribbons is in marked contrast to the situation in *Paramecium*, where serial sectioning proves the two to be quite distinct. Ultrastructural evidence generally supports the idea that peritrichs are most closely related to hymenostomes and further study of both tetrahymenids and peritrichs should be rewarding.

Cytopharyngeal ribbons appear commonly in spirotrich ciliates (Fig. 41), usually associated with characteristic vesicles, but in no case has the extent of the area involved been traced. They are illustrated in the heterotrichs *Stentor*,[196] *Spirostomum*,[40] and *Blepharisma*,[113] and in entodiniomorphs.[88, 155]

In brief, cytopharyngeal ribbons of microtubules appear more commonly than any of the other ciliate mouth parts among species examined to date. Their origin from the right radial ribbons of specific membranellar kineto-somes is reasonably clearly indicated in *Paramecium*, and a corresponding origin in some other ciliates might be inferred from the available hints. For most examples, clues to their origin and extent are lacking. Whether they are always restricted, throughout their length, to parts of the buccal wall lacking pellicular alveoli is an open question.

5. SUMMARY

Only *Paramecium*, the all-purpose ciliate, has provided sufficient details of the ins and outs of oral fibrillar structures to yield a reasonably clear picture of their architecture, and even here some critical pieces of evidence are painfully lacking. To obtain sufficient sequences of oriented serial sections through the enormous cavern that is a typical ciliate mouth, and to reconstruct the three-dimensional geometry of its spiralling contours require an expenditure of effort that only the most confirmed ciliate addict could enjoy. Knowing details for one ciliate may clarify interpretations of similar structures in others.

Already it is perfectly evident that definable mouth parts exist and are widely if variously distributed among ciliate taxa—whether or not these mouth parts have been correctly identified here, even as a first approxima-tion. The assembled evidence furnishes a series of clues for their recognition, and a jumble of questions that will have to be answered for numbers of species before a comprehensive view of the structure and function of the ingestive apparatus and its adaptive variants can emerge. The justification of the effort lies in the fact that fibrillar units that are not unique to the ciliate mouth, nor to the ciliates, nor to the protozoa, are most ingeniously engi-neered to promote the essential function of food intake.

In addition to the tentative listing of mouth parts offered in the preceding pages and diagrammed in Fig. 42, some general observations may be pertinent.

1. The filamentous reticulum is a reasonably well-defined mouth part, its fibrillar subunit perhaps related to that of the filament systems of the body surface. Its nodes are often applied against adjacent kinetosomes, where they are indistinguishable from the ill-defined "dense material" so often associated with sites of attachment of all kinds of fibrils at somatic as well as oral kineto-somes. The reticulum within a single cell may show varying degrees of conden-sation from a loose, random dispersion to orderly, crystalline packing.

2. Nemadesma, where their origins are at all clear, most frequently arise as rows of microtubules passing centripetally from the bases of perioral kinetosomes. Cytopharyngeal ribbons, by contrast, most frequently appear to be extensions of peripherally-directed radial ribbons comparable to thosa of somatic kinetosomes. This distinction will perhaps not prove to be e

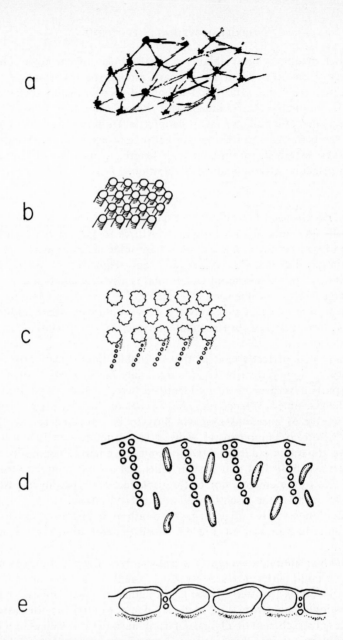

FIG. 42. Diagram showing the mouth parts recognized among ciliates. *a*—The filamentous reticulum, here shown with randomly arranged nodes and interconnecting filaments. *b*—Shallow three-dimensional view of a nemadesmos, with linked microtubules packed hexagonally. *c*—Membranellar (or other perioral) kinetosomes with right, radial ribbons extending from the kinetosome row along one edge. *d*—Cytopharyngeal ribbons subtending the limiting unit membrane. These often originate as the radial ribbons shown in *c*. Between the ribbons are characteristic cytopharyngeal vesicles. *e*—Ribbed wall, with pellicular alveoli and epiplasm, and occasional microtubules. Diagrams are not drawn to scale.

general rule; apparent exceptions such as the oral nemadesmos of *Tetrahymena* need to be investigated.

3. Conventional, striated root fibrils have not been demonstrated in buccal infraciliature, but highly organized filament bundles, such as those in parts of the filamentous reticulum of *Paramecium* (Fig. 30) and the polykinety of *Opisthonecta*,[16] may show banding.

4. Within membranelles or other compound ciliary organelles, kinetosomes are directly and liberally interconnected by dense material, delicate filaments, or tracts of filaments (but not microtubules), often occurring at equatorial and basal levels of the kinetosome wall. Direct fibrous connections between membranelles have been reported but need confirmation.

5. In no case has direct continuity between microtubules of the kinetosome itself and any other intracytoplasmic fibril been unequivocally demonstrated.

D. Fibril Systems in the Order Hypotrichida

Information on the ultrastructure of hypotrich fibrillar systems is available only for the genus *Euplotes*, studied by Roth,[203, 204] Gliddon,[84, 85] and Wise.[255, 256] The choice of genus is fortunate, since *Euplotes* has long been a favorite experimental organism, and also unfortunate inasmuch as it represents an evolutionary extreme of specialization-by-reduction among the hypotrichs. With more primitive genera completely unrepresented, it is scarcely possible now to relate the ultrastructural picture of *Euplotes* to those of other ciliates.

An idea of the varieties of hypotrich fiber systems—apparently variations on a common theme—as well as of the overall distribution of fibers in *Euplotes* comes from light-microscope studies.[242] Tuffrau[246] has recently surveyed a number of genera, using an elegant protein-silver technique that reveals intracellular fibers but not the superficial silverline network (Gliddon[85] has shown that the latter corresponds to a mosaic of pellicular alveoli). Tuffrau finds two main kinds of fibers associated with cirri of the ventral cell surface and with peristomial membranelles: ciliary roots that penetrate more or less deeply into the endoplasm and tangential fibers that remain subpellicular. Their distribution forms complex patterns in more primitive, abundantly ciliated hypotrichs. In highly evolved forms with a reduced number of cirri the fibrillar system is also reduced to a few elements.

Most pertinent here are the roots that diverge from the basal plates of cirri. Those from the large transverse (called anal by many authors) cirri of *Euplotes* are conspicuous, long, heavy fibers (Fig. 43) that pass anteriad well beneath the cell surface and converge near the anterior end of the band of peristomial membranelles; opinion still differs[85, 246] as to whether actual connection exists. These are the fibers that have been subjected to surgical manipulation in experimental studies of coordination to be discussed in Section VI. In other genera such as *Stylonychia* the same heavy anal fibers are present but extend only a short distance anteriad, ending

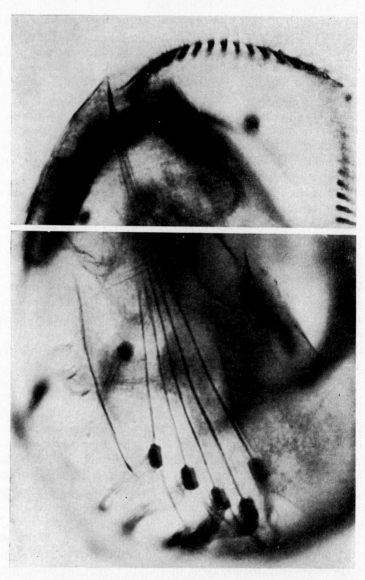

FIG. 43. Photomicrographs of a protein-silver-stained whole mount of the hypotrich *Euplotes eurystomus*. Lower part shows the rectangular basal plates of the five transverse (anal) cirri, with the heavy anal fibers extending anteriad. Upper part is a different optical plane of the same organism, showing the anterior convergence of the anal fibers near but apparently not in contact with the end of the row of adoral membranelles. From M. Tuffrau, unpublished.

free in the cytoplasm. Similar, more slender fibers depart from other cirri in all genera and also end shortly. Tuffrau's tangential fibers often have a disposition suggesting that of kinetodesma; those associated with the cirri of *Euplotes* appear to pass posteriad.

The three electron-microscope studies of *Euplotes* are in general agreement, the later work adding new detail to Roth's early observations. Kinetosomes are close-packed in orderly rows within cirri and membranelles, and are liberally interconnected by strands of dense, fibrous material at two discrete levels, one basal and one about midway up the kinetosome (Fig. 44). It is presumably this firm, heavy, double-layered webbing that accounts for the appearance of a distinct, rectangular basal plate beneath each cirrus in light-microscope preparations (Fig. 43). It seems on present evidence that *all* the fiber systems of *Euplotes* are composed of microtubules; this makes their topography particularly difficult to follow in thin sections. Microtubules depart singly or in small clusters from the kinetosomes of membranelles and diverge in no discernible pattern (Fig. 45); they may interconnect adjacent membranelles or perhaps simply intermesh in the surrounding cytoplasm. No special alignments of fibrils along the membranelle band have been described.

From each cirrus, bundles of parallel microtubules pass in at least two directions (Fig. 44). Inserted on the dense interkinetosomal material at both base and equator, the microtubules originate in small ribbons or clusters. Figures 44 and 46 show, in addition to bundles passing in the plane of the section, what I interpret to be a wide radial microtubule ribbon cut in cross section, arising at the base of each kinetosome along one edge of the cirrus. The appearance of this ribbon, flanked by strands of dense material, is reminiscent of the origin of the heterotrich kinetodesmal microtubule ribbon (see Fig. 23, inset), or perhaps of the origin of nemadesmal fibrils from oral kinetosomes in some species (Fig. 38). It is not known whether the ribbon—if it is a ribbon—is directed peripherally or centripetally. Less orderly microtubules depart in various directions, including straight down into the endoplasm, from the basal and equatorial densities around all cirral kinetosomes, as shown in Fig. 47.

Which of these groupings of microtubules converge to form the heavy anal fibers is not apparent. But there is no doubt that the fiber is a rather large cluster of parallel microtubules showing—surprisingly—no orderly packing in cross section but instead being linked by bridges in a seemingly random fashion (Fig. 48). According to Gliddon[85] the several root fibers from each of the other cirri—all composed of clustered microtubules—pass more or less gradually up toward the pellicle, ending at or near a granular layer (presumably epiplasm) that parallels the inner alveolar membrane of the general body surface.

Wise[255] finds extensive, curving sheets of linked, parallel microtubules in the cytoplasm; their association with other organelles and body regions is

12a*

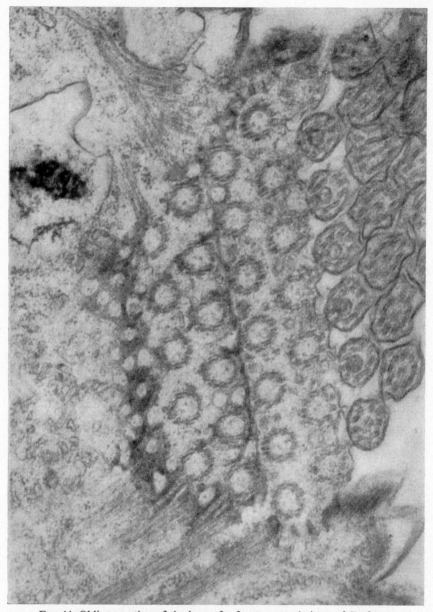

FIG. 44. Oblique section of the base of a fronto-ventral cirrus of *Euplotes eurystomus*, showing microtubule bundles extending toward the lower left and the upper left of the picture from peripheral kinetosomes. Kinetosomes of the lowermost row also bear microtubule ribbons shown in another specimen in Fig. 46. Kinetosomes of the cirrus are abundantly interconnected by webs of dense material at basal and equatorial levels. × 50,000. From R. Gliddon, unpublished.

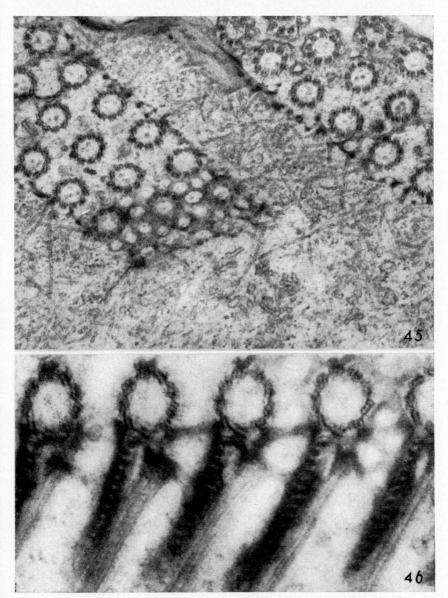

Fig. 45. Oblique section at the base of two adjacent membranelles of *Euplotes*, showing dense interconnections among kinetosomes at basal and equatorial levels, and microtubules radiating in all directions from kinetosomes or associated dense material. × 48,000. From R. Gliddon, unpublished.

Fig. 46. Cross-section through kinetosomes along a row at one edge of a cirrus. Microtubule bundles originate at dense discs at one side of each kinetosome; radial ribbons of microtubules accompanied by strands of dense material arise nearby. × 81,000. From B. N. Wise, unpublished.

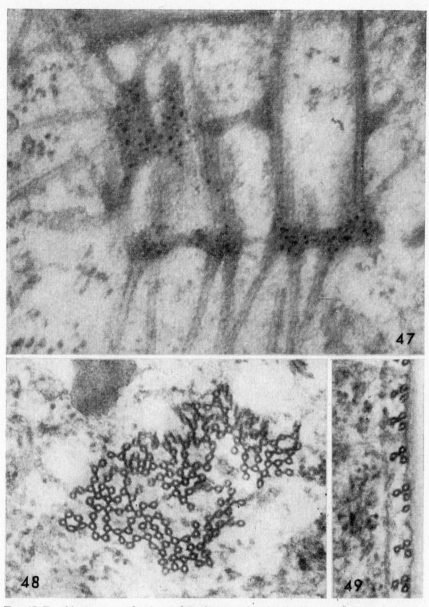

FIG. 47. Two kinetosomes of a cirrus of *Euplotes*, cut longitudinally to show dense material at basal and equatorial levels and origin of diverging microtubules in this material. × 108,000.

FIG. 48. Cross-section of an anal fiber, showing component microtubules linked in irregular arrangements × 108,000.

FIG. 49. Transverse section into the cortex, showing longitudinal microtubules neatly arranged in packets of three (four in one case) just beneath the surface membranes (not distinct in this plane). Transverse microtubules running in the plane of the micrograph may be seen just below; other microtubules pass in various directions. × 81,000.

Figures 47–49 from B. N. Wise, unpublished.

unknown, and they resemble no other fibril configuration in ciliates, with the possible exception of cytopharyngeal ribbons.

Two layers of oriented microtubules lie immediately beneath the epiplasm. In the outer one the fibrils are longitudinal and are neatly arranged in packets of three (Fig. 49); beneath this is a single sheet of transversely oriented microtubules. Additional individual microtubules passing in any direction through the ectoplasm are common.

Despite the rather clear distinction in Tuffrau's light micrographs between deeper-lying ciliary roots and superficial tangential fibers, electron microscopy does not yet permit identification of the latter. They could be bundles similar to the roots (which are actually just subcortical), oriented in different directions. Continuation of correlated light- and electron-microscope studies is needed.

E. Fibril Systems in the Subclass Suctoria

Only adult, non-ciliated stages of suctorians have been examined in any detail in the electron microscope, and the focus of interest has been the tentacles, which presumably have no homologue in other ciliates. Rudzinska's[214] recent scrutiny of the tentacles in *Tokophrya infusionum* reveals a remarkable fibrillar system extending from deep within the cytoplasm of the cell body out to the knobbed tip of the tentacle. As indicated in Fig. 50, seven bundles, each containing seven microtubules in two rows, outline a cylinder within the cylindrical tentacle. Functionally, this separates the tentacle into two channels: a peripheral one through which cytoplasmic particles from the suctorian move out to the terminal knob (presumably carrying enzymes that assist in paralysis and lysis of the prey organism), and a central one through which prey cytoplasm moves into the body of the predator. The tentacles shorten and broaden during feeding, and the fibrillar tube then appears somewhat stretched to accomodate the flow of food. In the terminal knob there is an apical invagination of the cell membrane, a new fibril is added to each bundle of seven, and apparently the outer row of each bundle curves outward under the membrane of the apex to continue down the periphery of the knob. Feeding tentacles of *Ephelota plana*[212] and of *Discophrya piriformis*[181] have similar microtubular tubes within them, but the intriguing 7-times-7 arrangement is not found. Rouiller, Fauré-Fremiet, and Gauchery[212] show a tube containing many microtubules in *Ephelota*, with radial bands of microtubules extending into its lumen, and Pottage[181] describes twenty-five to thirty fibrils arranged in ten groups of two or three each in *Discophrya*.

Ephelota is unusual in possessing both feeding tentacles of the type just described and prehensile tentacles of radically different construction. The latter are band-shaped and divided internally by septa into as many as seven longitudinal compartments. Within each compartment is an irregular axial bundle of filaments. In these early electron micrographs, the filaments seem coarser, longer, straighter, and more parallel than those of the filament systems of other ciliates. The prehensile tentacles are capable of flexing and contracting, but only slowly.

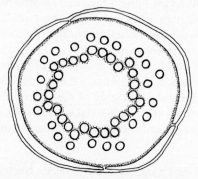

Fɪɢ. 50. Diagram of a cross-sectioned tentacle of the suctorian *Tokophrya*, showing the pellicular membranes externally and the cylinder of microtubules within the tentacle. The microtubules are in seven bundles of seven, the inner rows of four each overlapping slightly in this non-feeding example. A single extra microtubule is present on the right. Drawn from an electron micrograph by Rudzinska.[214]

VI. THE QUESTION OF FUNCTION

Four general kinds of functions have been attributed to protozoan fibrillar systems by innumerable investigators during the last hundred years: (1) Contraction; that is, active changes in the length of a fiber to accomplish observable movement of a cell or its parts; cilia and myonemes are obviously contractile organelles. (2) Mechanical support, rigid or elastic. (3) Coordination; the cooperative activity of ciliate cilia and myonemes often has been assumed to require the transmission of nerve-like impulses along intracellular fibers. (4) Morphogenesis; this includes both a role in the induction of specific organelles and active participation in morphogenetic movements.

These four functions are not mutually exclusive. A single fibril could play more than one role, and the mechanisms of motility involved in active contraction and in morphogenetic movements need not be totally dissimilar. More than one morphologic kind of fiber has been implicated in speculations about each of the functions. The available evidence, such as it is, can perhaps be summarized more easily under functional headings than morphological ones.

A. Contraction

Cilia and their movement are currently the object of intense investigation in many laboratories, with results that promise to be of first significance to understanding the mechanisms of protoplasmic contraction. They have not yet, however, answered definitively the questions of which elements of the ciliary axoneme are contractile, or whether change of length is brought about by shortening of fibrillar elements or by sliding of adjacent fibrils past one another in the manner of the Hanson–Huxley model of muscle contraction. Physical and chemical analyses of cilia isolated from *Tetrahymena* reveal that at least two major protein components are present, one of which is found in the peripheral fibrils and another, an adenosine triphosphatase protein called dynein, in the arms that project from these fibrils.[77, 78, 79, 80] According to Gibbons,[77, 80] the peripheral–fibril protein resembles actin in some of its properties, but the ATPase appears to have more in common with the ATPase of the mitotic apparatus than with myosin and to bear a close resemblance to myxomyosin extracted from slime molds. In other words, close parallelism with the contractile apparatus of muscle—itself not fully understood—seems unlikely[24, 38, 219, 221, 250] (see Refs. 178, 229 for earlier literature). Gibbons suggests (Ref. 77, p. 1009) "That the longitudinal elements which contract are the outer fibers and that the contractions result from the interaction of the arms with two adjacent outer fibers."

Further discussion of the chemical nature of ciliary proteins and the mechanisms of motility would be beyond the scope of this review. The development over the last decade of methods of isolation and analysis of cilia and the mitotic apparatus is undoubtedly the most promising achievement in the area of investigation of protoplasmic fibrils; other fibrillar structures—so spectacularly available in the protozoa—should be accessible to the same or similar techniques.

Although the doublet microtubules of the ciliary axoneme are strongly implicated as contractile elements, this still cannot be their only function, since identical doublets (often lacking arms) are present in nonmotile sensory cilia. The nature of ciliary movement demands the presence of elements that resist compression, and most current hypotheses attribute this supportive function, as well as contractility, to the microtubules.

Evidence in favor of contractile function for other microtubular fibrils is circumstantial. Perhaps the strongest comes from the observations of Grassé[89] and Grimstone and Cleveland[95] on the axostyles of oxymonad flagellates. These observers agree that the axostyle is actively undulatory; their electron micrographs demonstrate that it is made up of packed, linked microtubules (p. 3/2) in a structureless, low-density matrix. If the bridges linking neighbouring microtubules correspond to the ATPase-bearing arms on the ciliary doublets, then the two systems may have the same contractile equipment. Bridges of similar appearance, however, are present in microtubule organelles that are not themselves contractile, such as the pharyngeal nemadesma of euglenids or gymnostomes.

Schneider[222] offers a plausible argument in favor of a contractile function for microtubules associated with the contractile vacuole and its exit pore in *Paramecium* and other ciliates. The pulsating reservoir vacuoles of most ciliates and flagellates are formed, or at least filled, by coalescence of smaller, evanescent vacuoles that appear within the surrounding permanent, membranous sponge (where active segregation of water occurs; see Refs. 26, 61, 173). In *Paramecium* and some others the main reservoir vacuole is fed by permanent contributing vacuoles which are in turn surrounded by the membranous sponge. Fluid accumulates in and distends the radial vacuoles of *Paramecium* while the reservoir vacuole remains collapsed; all of the inflated radial vacuoles then empty abruptly via narrow injector canals into the reservoir, which fills as they collapse and in turn expels its contents through the permanent discharge pore at the body surface.

The sytem requires the build-up and release of hydrostatic pressure in a one-way sequence of structures; back-flow has to be prevented, and the injector canals are particularly significant, since they separate compartments that fill alternately. The question is whether the microtubules (p. 327) that course along the membranes of radial vacuoles and their injector canals, along the peripheral side of the main vacuole, and around the discharge pore are effective agents in this process and whether they have to be contractile. Recent observations on *Amoeba*[108]—which has no microtubules associated with the vacuolar membrane—and on *Ichthyophthirius*[148]— which has them—indicate that the membrane of the main vacuole collapses into folds at systole and does not contract, and the same is probably true of *Paramecium*. The ciliate discharge pore appears to be a permanently open structure, not a contractile one, yet it is around the pore that the heaviest concentration of microtubules is found. The collapse of the main vacuole logically could result from a buildup of hydrostatic pressure causing rupture of the double membrane closing off the exit pore. But why does not the fluid, in *Paramecium*, return to the collapsed radial vacuoles via the injector canals, which permitted its passage only a moment earlier? Evidently the injector canals must operate either as sphincters or as valves, being able to resist back-flow from the reservoir vacuole at a pressure sufficient to rupture the exit-pore membrane. Perhaps active contraction is not necessary; elasticity with a critical stretching threshold or else a mechanical valve action might suffice. The situation needs another close examination.

A case has often been made in favor of a contractile function for the peripheral microtubules of euglenids and trypanosomes. Mignot[146] has demonstrated, however, that the motility of the euglenid cell body is not related to the number of microtubules (p. 292). His observations and those of Leedale[122] support the conclusion that euglenid contortions result from ameboid movement confined within a plastic pellicle.

It is not so easy to dismiss the possibility that microtubules participate in the rapid undulatory movements of trypanosomes, and seems even less so in the case of many animal spermatozoa.[33, 126, 169, 198, 227] The presence of microtubules as the *only* observed fibrillar component in sites or at times suggesting a close association with directed protoplasmic movement has also been reported in sporozoa, especially gregarines,[249] and in heliozoans,[105, 118, 243] and radiolarians[103] among the protozoa (see Ref. 173 for other examples), and in several other kinds of plant and animal cells.[25, 121] Although the protozoan mitotic apparatus displays many individual eccentricities, its fibrous component has in all cases studied proved to be microtubular (*e.g.*, *Prymnesium*,[132] *Astasia*,[14] *Barbulanympha*, [173] and in both macronuclei and micronuclei of ciliates,[27, 85, 88, 207]). It is at least interesting to note that the microtubules most reasonably suspected of a role in protoplasmic movement include almost all of the different morphological types and groupings seen in fixed cells—doublet microtubules in the cilium, close-packed, linked microtubules in the oxymonad axostyle, membrane-linked tubules in the trypanosome, and loosely grouped, unlinked, not-quite-parallel microtubules of the mitotic apparatus. Biochemical and biophysical analyses of more of these are badly needed; it should be relatively easy, for example, to obtain useful quantities of isolated trypanosome pellicles.

Attention to a filamentous component of cytoplasm as a possible site of contractility has been sporadic. Over the years, Wohlfarth-Bottermann has repeatedly demonstrated filaments in the cytoplasm of amebae[257, 258] and slime molds;[259, 260] in the amebae he suggests that they make up a contractile gel-reticulum, whereas in actively streaming *Physarum* he finds similar filaments aggregated in distinct tracts. His observations on *Physarum* have recently been confirmed by McManus and Roth,[140] who found similar structures in other genera as well, and by Porter, Kawakami, and Ledbetter; [180] Nachmias[149] has seen comparable tracts in *Chaos*. Variations in filament thickness and orientation under different conditions were found by Nachmias and by McManus and Roth. The latter even found microtubules in some cases and suggested that all of these appearances reflected differences either in fixation or in physiological condition of the same fibrillar elements. Recently, Cloney[35] has found filament bundles in contracting epithelium of a metamorphosing tunicate.

Identity of the filament bundle of the contractile vorticellid stalk with the myoneme can scarcely be questioned, and the arrangement of similar bundles in the peritrich cell body and in the contractile heterotrich *Stentor* is consistent with the assumption that all of these organelles are specialized for rapid and fairly powerful contraction. Many workers have pointed out the general similarity of the roughly oriented filaments to those of vertebrate smooth muscle, and the resemblance of the membranous reticulum that consistently accompanies the myoneme to sarcoplasmic reticulum. As is postulated for muscle, the membranes could transmit excitation to all parts of the fiber, or deliver metabolites necessary for rapid contraction, or both.

Although investigation of the mechanism of contractility, including the possible participation of filaments, in ameboid locomotion is currently very active, almost no attempt has been made to apply experimental methods to ciliate myonemes since Hoffmann-Berling[102] demonstrated that glycerine-extracted, vorticellid stalk myonemes would contract and relax rhythmically if bathed in an appropriate solution containing adenosine triphosphate. This same property—rhythmic alternation of form in a constant medium—is shown by glycerine-extracted cilia[81, 178] but not by muscle.

Since *Spirostomum* is quite rapidly contractile, its more dispersed filament network must be very nearly as effective as the compact myonemes of *Stentor*. The similar disposition of filament tracts (but without accompanying membranes) in *Paramecium* and many other ciliates that are not notably contractile suggests the possibility that networks of contractile proteins could contribute tonus and elasticity to the cortex in most ciliates, but would become powerfully and repetitively contractile only when present in sufficient mass or supplied with whatever it is that the membrane reticulum provides. Even *Paramecium* may respond to electric stimuli with a pronounced ectoplasmic contraction.[39]

Since vorticellids can be cultivated in quantity and have their stalk myonemes well separated from active cilia, they would seem to furnish ideal material for analysis; not least of the questions to be asked is how different are the properties of the filamentous myoneme from those of the predominantly microtubular cilia under similar conditions of treatment.

B. Mechanical Support

Any fibrous protein contributes to the structural integrity of the protoplasm containing it, whether or not the fibril has any other function. It has been suggested just above that a more or less thick, perforate fabric of roughly oriented filaments may enhance the elastic firmness of the ciliate ectoplasmic gel. Microtubules from all sources appear to have considerable rigidity when isolated and it is reasonable to suppose that the long, parallel fibrils attached to the inner surface of the pellicle and gullet in so many flagellates and ciliates provide some support, whatever else they may or may not do. The microtubules associated with the contractile-vacuole exit pore seem logically to be supportive, and perhaps a sufficient function for the whole system along the vacuole and pore walls is to restrain the pulsating radial vacuoles (where these are permanent structures) from wandering or being swept away from their attachment to the main vacuole, and to keep the latter tied in position next to the exit pore. The vagrant contractile vacuole of free-living amebae has, presumably, no permanent exit, and no associated tubular fibrils.

Microtubular organelles that quite clearly are skeletal include most of the nemadesma of flagellates (e.g., the pharyngeal rods of euglenoids) and ciliates (the pharyngeal rods of gymnostomes, the postoral fibers of *Paramecium*, the membranellar nemadesma of heterotrichs). In many instances these structures can be seen in living cells to move passively, but not to contract; they typically surround, at a distance, the cytostomal area, where the formation of food vacuoles distorts cell shape at least locally. If the nemadesma buttress the cytopharyngeal region, the microtubule ribbons perhaps give some mechanical stability to the delicate cytoplasmic surface of the opening itself. Their function, however, must in some manner also be related to that of the enigmatic vesicles almost always found associated with them. The suggestion that they might serve as sphincters to close off the forming food vacuole is unappealing, since their orientation is longitudinal with respect to the cytopharyngeal canal, rather than circular; furthermore they commonly end free in the endoplasm, in which case their postulated contraction could have little mechanical effect.

The filamentous reticulum is probably instrumental in maintaining the rather complex shape of the buccal cavity.[209] Any ciliate that "strudels" (there is no equivalent in English of this delightfully descriptive German verb), that is, creates by the activity of its oral ciliature a strong vortex toward and within the buccal cavity, must require some substantial skeletal reinforcement of its buccal wall. In at least several instances, the position of the filamentous reticulum qualifies it for this role.

Striated root fibrils have commonly been supposed to provide anchorage and support.[64, 178] It is clear that an actively beating flagellum or cilium has to be rooted in or on a substance with enough tensile strength to counterbalance the force exerted during the beat. Any fibrillar structures attached to the shallow kinetosome must inevitably be affected by this force; the fibrils will absorb, dissipate, or transmit the mechanical effect depending upon their rigidity or elasticity and upon their insertion, or lack of it, on other structures.

The capacity of striated roots to connect other organelles to the kinetosome has been noted above; its possible morphogenetic significance will be discussed shortly. Electron micrographs show the connection to be one of close apposition, often over considerable distances, of the striated root and the surface of the organelle (or organelles, since the same striated fibril may serve several different ones). This apposition may, however, effect a firm physical attachment, apparent as such when the intracellular organelles are visibly displaced or distorted in rhythm with movements of the flagellum-bearing apex of the cell. There must be good physiological reasons why mitochondria or Golgi elements or chloroplast or nucleus or axostyle have to be tethered in some flagellates near the flagellar pole; these reasons do not concern us now. The striated (or nonstriated) root fibril, perhaps developed as a flagellar anchor, may be pressed into ancillary service as a tether for whatever organelles need to be restrained in space, or may be hyperdeveloped as an elastic cytoskeleton as in the case of the trichomonad costa.

That the "secondary" functions of striated roots may supercede, or may have preceded in evolution, the supposed primary one of mechanical support is indicated by the presence of heavy root fibrils on nonmotile, sensory cilia in many metazoa,[47] and is implied by Sakaguchi's[216] evidence that banded rootlets are common adjuncts of some non-ciliated centrioles. It is also true that some active flagella, such as those in the posterior flagellated zone of *Trichonympha*[82, 179] or those of trypanosomes, either lack root fibrils altogether or have fibrils too tenuous to be of much mechanical significance. It may be worth noting that such rootless flagella often have very long kinetosomes or are confined basally within a deep groove or invagination of the cell surface; either arrangement could provide the necessary basal stability to balance the force of beat.

If a major role of the striated root is to counterbalance the force of the ciliary beat, does it then follow that the position of the roots in ciliates must correspond with the direction in which this force is most frequently imparted to the cilium base? It has been elegantly demonstrated by Párducz[165] that in *Paramecium* and many other holotrichs, the effective stroke of the body cilia during normal forward locomotion is directed backwards and to the right (in Párducz's usage, meaning to the *viewer's* right when he looks at the ciliate surface; this is the *ciliate's* left, according to the protocol used in describing ciliate topography in Section V of this chapter). This means that the stroke is directed about 180° away from the point of attachment of the striated kinetodesmal fibril, and this fibril would thus bear the brunt of the counterforce, suggesting that the answer to the question is yes. To complicate matters, however, some of the kineties on the oral surface of *Paramecium* have a pronounced asymmetric curvature, and all accompanying fibrils of course are oriented accordingly. As shown in Fig. 51, kineties converging from the two sides of the mouth toward the preoral suture meet at approximately right angles; their kinetodesmal fibrils, passing anteriad, similarly meet, and even cross over one another,[176] at right angles. On both sides of the oral suture, cilia beat posteriad and toward the viewer's right during normal forward swimming, or, at least during feeding,[91] even toward the viewer's left, in the direction of the mouth. The normal, preferred, direction of beat is therefore not related in any consistent way to the orientation and site of attachment of the striated kinetodesmal fibrils, and anterior to the mouth the beating plane forms an angle of about 90° with the kinetodesmal fibril.

This inconsistency—which may be even more pronounced in other ciliates—does not mean that the striated fibril cannot provide any internal resistance to the beating force, but it does mean that the disposition of the fibril is not necessarily dictated by the predominant direction of that force. There must be some other explanation for the prevalence of desmodexy. In the opalinids, where the fibrils asymmetrically accompanying the kinety are at its left (that is, *not* displaying desmodexy, p. 304), the normal beating direction of the cilia[165] nevertheless is identical with that in *Paramecium*. And in heterotrichs, where the kinetodesmos is composed of microtubules passing to the right and posteriad from the kinetosomes, the normal ciliary beating direction is also posteriad.

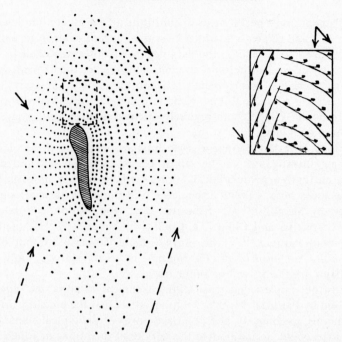

FIG. 51. Diagrams to show the arrangement of kineties in the area around the mouth in *Paramecium*. Kineties, shown as rows of kinetosomes in the diagram on the left, are strongly curved around the ciliate's left (viewer's right) side of the mouth, less strongly curved on the right. On both sides, kinetosomes of adjadent kineties are aligned in false secondary rows radiating from the mouth. The predominant direction of ciliary beating during normal forward locomotion is indicated by the short, solid arrows. The square outlined by dotted lines is reproduced at a mote magnified scale at the right. Kinetosomes and accompanying kinetodesmal fibrils are shown, to illustrate the angle at which kineties meet along the preoral suture. Ciliary beating direction is again shown by short, solid arrows: some cilia of the preoral area may beat toward the mouth. The long, broken arrows on the left-hand figure indicate the direction in which metachronal waves progress along the body surface; the wave crests are perpendicular to these arrows. The direction of wave passage does not change as the waves pass over this area of pronounced kinety curvature. Further explanation in text.

C. Coordination

Although based on limited experimental evidence, the idea that fibril systems can function as protoneurons to coordinate the motor activities of ciliates has been and remains deeply entrenched in protozoological and biological literature. Light microscopists saw stainable "fibers" linking the kinetosomes of the body surface in orderly networks, including both longitudinal and lateral connectives. The most superficial of these are the silverline "fibers", now known to be configurations of pellicular membranes and not fibers at all. The deeper-lying infraciliary lattice, composed of tracts of fine filaments, is so pervasive as to constitute an almost continuous micro-webbing in some ciliates—in which case the concept of neuroid pathways might be hard to defend— and has not been observed at all in others (e.g., *Tetrahymena*). Furthermore in contractile ciliates the filament systems are clearly identified as myonemes, as reported above. The truly fibrillar candidates for the function of coordination, then, are the striated roots and the microtubule systems, both precisely oriented in every kinetosomal territory along each kinety.

Exploiting a variety of ingenious techniques, including those of neurophysiology, investigators of the motor responses of ciliates and ciliated tissue are currently accumulating an impressive body of data, too voluminous to be reviewed here. Recent discussions of pertinent evidence have been published by Sleigh,[229, 230] Kinosita, Dryl, and Naitoh,[116] Jahn and Bovee,[107] Pitelka and Child,[178] Child,[32] Grebecki,[91] Dryl and Grebecki[44] and Párducz.[165] The overwhelming consensus is that fibrillar pathways *are not involved* in coordination of ciliary activity. Only a few of the major arguments will be summarized.

Perhaps the simplest and most telling argument of all is one repeatedly emphasized by Párducz[163, 164, 165] to the effect that the precisely oriented, discontinuous, asymmetric, and polarized fibrils of the typical ciliate cortex cannot conceivably accommodate the variety of directions in which waves of coordinated ciliary activity may be observed to progress. In *Paramecium* (which is by far the most extensively studied ciliate) metachronal waves during normal swimming move forward from the posterior end of the body, their crests forming left-wound spirals over the cell surface. Their direction of progression is indicated by the long broken arrows in Fig. 51. This means that over much of the body surface, cilia of any kinety beat in metachronal sequence—not inconsistent with the idea that excitatory impulses could be transmitted at finite speed along the kinety. However, in the area of most pronounced kinety curvature (Fig. 51) anterior to the buccal cavity the waves of coordinated activity *do not bend* with the kineties but, instead, continue to pass obliquely anteriad, with the result that wave crests here are parallel to kineties and the direction of wave travel is perpendicular to kineties. In other words, the cilia of any one of the curved kineties in this zone are beating in unison, and this is quite incompatible with the image of an excitatory impulse moving along the kinety. Moreover, in responding to stimuli of various sorts and degrees, the ciliature of *Paramecium* shows metachronal waves passing in any direction, or radiating from any spot on the body surface. To explain the propagation of the excited state on the basis of longitudinal, transverse and oblique passage of impulses along and between existing fibrils requires so many improbable assumptions that it quickly becomes unpalatable.

The bulk of current research on ciliary activity is focussed on the same factors that govern the transmission of excitation in other types of cell.

Since experimental alterations of transmembrane potential and of environ-mental factors affecting it do elicit ciliary responses mimicking those ob-servable in natural activity, there seems to be no reason to seek an esoteric explanation for coordination in ciliates. Ciliate structure displays no unique elements, and it should logically not be necessary to assume unique basic mechanisms of behavior. For ciliated cells in general, it is probable that membrane transmission of a stimulus, together with mechanical effects (viscous drag) operating through the medium, and behavioral characters (autonomous beat and preferred direction) built into each cilium will suffice to explain the varieties of coordinated activity and response.

There still remains, however, the experimental study by Taylor[241] that for more than 40 years has kept open the possibility of coordination of specialized ciliary organelles by fibrils.[22] In a series of well-designed and well-controlled microsurgical experiments, he demonstrated that severing the heavy anal fibers of *Euplotes* (which pass from anal cirri to the neighbor-hood of the adoral membranelle band; p. 353) resulted in loss of coordination between the membranelle band and the anal cirri. Taylor's experiments have recently been repeated by Okajima in Kinosita's laboratory and by Gliddon in Sleigh's laboratory. The two workers have obtained results that appear, in preliminary reports, to be diametrically opposed, Gliddon[84] confirming Taylor's findings and Okajima and Kinosita[159] reporting con-tinuing coordinated activity after cutting the anal fibers. It is not possible now to reconcile the conflicting evidence, although full publication of both reports may reveal variations in technique or in the amount of damage done to or around the site of the operation.

More importantly, a disruption of coordination of anal cirri and membra-nelles following careful destruction of the proper fibers does not necessarily mean that the anal fibers are acting like nerves; nor, as Sleigh has pointed out,[230] are observations made on the anal fibers of *Euplotes* generalizable to other cells. It has been noted above (p. 353) that only *Euplotes* among the hypotrichs has fibers reaching far enough to be suspected of making the connection between anal cirri and membranelles; other hypotrichs seem to have much shorter ones. Similar microtubule bundles depart from other cirri of *Euplotes* but do not connect with other motor organelles and have not been implicated in coordination. Bělař[13] and Jacobson[106] have argued that cutting important skeletal fibers could result in the dis-ruptive effect on coordination observed by Taylor. Gliddon sought to test this hypothesis by using a radio frequency cautery, which destroys the fiber but leaves the damaged ends mechanically connected by a firm clot, and found the same interruption in coordination as followed cutting the fibers.

Certainly it would be astonishing if the anal fibers alone among micro-tubular structures, in *Euplotes* alone among ciliates, were capable of con-ducting a coordinating impulse. Machemer[125] has recently made a study of locomotor behavior in the hypotrich *Stylonychia* and concludes that it corresponds, on a more complex level, to that described by Párducz[165] for *Paramecium* and presumably depends on the same mechanisms.

One of the problems in research on ciliary coordination has been the difficulty of direct observation of beating cilia. Most of the detailed descriptive studies of living specimens have been concerned not with individual cilia but with cirri and membranelles. A question relatively neglected is: whatever the nature of the processes at the cell surface effecting metachronal coordination, how do the many cilia (up to 120 clustered in a cirrus of *Euplotes*, forty or more in two or three long rows composing a membranelle of *Euplotes* or *Stentor*) of a compound organelle manage to beat in perfect synchrony? No mechanism of firm adhesion among the component cilia has been found; delicate membrane microvilli occur in cilia of compound organelles and might have some effect if they intertwine, but similar membrane extensions often are present on somatic cilia and may in any case be artefacts.[176] It may at least be worth noting that in somatic ciliature beating metachronally, the kinetosome-based fibrils all diverge from the kinetosome, overlapping but not connecting with each other, suggesting that the internal mechanical effect of the ciliary beat is dissipated into the surrounding cytoplasm. By contrast, within membranelles or cirri, kinetosomes not only are close-packed but also are liberally interconnected by fibrous material, often in basal and equatorial webs; this would have the effect of transmitting any mechanical stress throughout the basal structure of the compound organelle. Under these circumstances, synchrony of beat might be very strongly favored by mechanical influences both externally and in the cell cortex.

D. Morphogenesis

1. THE ROLE OF THE KINETOSOME

The role of the kinetosome/centriole as a morphogenetic center is too well documented to need defense.[117, 124] At the light-microscope level, many kinds of structures—mostly fibrous—visibly "grow out from" it in cycles synchronized with cell division. Electron microscopy has yet to demonstrate whether this growth is an induction of the synthesis and polymerization *in situ* of new fibrous and membranous materials, or merely an attraction of preexisting components to the kinetosome site; probably both processes take place. Both ribosomes and mitochondria commonly are abundant in the neighborhood of kinetosomes, so that equipment for protein synthesis and energy transfer is available. The one thing that seems certain is that only the peripheral fibrils of the flagellum itself are produced by direct outgrowth of the microtubules of the kinetosome/centriole; everything else takes form near to rather than from the kinetosomal fibrils.

However the kinetosome acts in inducing fibril development, it clearly has specific instructions as to when, where, and what kind to induce. Manton[132] has shown that before mitosis begins in *Prymnesium* many new microtubules appear, at least some of them diverging from the quartet of parent and daughter kinetosomes. This of course is approved, cyclic, centriolar behavior, although the kinetosomes do not appear as poles of the spindle once the latter is identifiable. Some of the kinetosome-based fibrous structures of a trichomonad flagellate are replaced when the cell divides and others are retained, while new ones develop to complete the allotment for both daughters;[117] this delicate maneuvering in time and space requires an impressive sort of savoir-faire on the part of the kinetosome cluster. In *Paramecium*, the anterior kinetosome of a pair bears only a left, tangential, microtubule ribbon, whereas the posterior one has a left, tangential ribbon and in addition a right, radial ribbon and a kinetodesmal fibril, each associated with specific triplet fibrils of the kinetosome, each arising at a specific compass point. An early sign of impending cell division is the multiplication of kinetosomes in territories adjacent to the presumptive fission line, beginning at the left of the buccal overture and progressing leftward around the cell. Within each kinetosomal territory affected, a new kinetosome appears anterior to each old one.[42] Ehret and de Haller (Refs. 48, Fig. 48, 178) and Dippell[42] have shown that at this time kinetodesmal fibrils are present on two or three, if not all four, of the kinetosomes in the territory. Evidently a striated fibril is organized at this time by at least the anterior member of the old kinetosome pair, which heretofore has lacked one. If the daughter kinetosomes also bear them now, they presumably will lose them after the two pairs have moved apart.

First efforts to determine the nature of the information carried by the kinetosome have been for the most part equivocal. Randall and Disbrey[193] have presented light-microscopic evidence of the association of DNA—about 1 per cent of nuclear DNA—with kinetosomes in synchronized *Tetrahymena*, detectable only during an interval prior to fission. Efforts to isolate and purify kinetosomes (again of *Tetrahymena*, the amenable ciliate) have yielded fractions[7, 99, 220] that contain fairly high proportions of kinetodesmal fibrils and associated pellicle, so that chemical analyses are of uncertain significance. The mechanism of kinetosome formation, like that of fibril induction, is still unknown.

Morphologically, the appearance of new kinetosomes is variable. They are reported to arise very close to,[17, 42, 132] remote from,[48, 90] or in the absence of [224, 225] preexisting ones; daughter centrioles commonly are annular,[71] newly formed kinetosomes in Bradbury's apostome[17] are long, and elliptical in cross section, but in *Stentor*[197] are reported to be almost spherical; during an epidemic of cilium production in mouse embryo tracheal cells,[43] kinetosome formation involves intermediate or inductive bodies that are granular or filamentous and do not all resemble kinetosomes.

2. THE ROLE OF CYTOPLASMIC FIBRILS

The movement of one kinetosome pair away from the parent territory in *Paramecium* is a simple example of the sorts of morphogenetic movements that occur routinely during protozoan reproduction. Morphogenesis in ciliates may be a prolonged and elaborate ritual, during which oral structures, in particular, migrate or are carried by allometric growth over long distances.

Consider how important accurate replication of surface architecture is to a ciliate. The organism depends for feeding, locomotion, and mating upon the activity of its ciliature. The kinds of motor effects produced by the cilia—and therefore the gamut of motor responses open to a given species—depend in turn on the number, length and spacing of its cilia;[97] the topography of the ciliated surface thus is inseparable from the locomotor and feeding habits of the ciliate. This topography therefore must be assiduously maintained not only through the ordinary hazards of living but also through the biologically extraordinary hazards of reproduction of a highly differentiated cell.

The enormous literature on morphogenetic processes in protozoa is comprehensively reviewed by Tartar.[240] We are concerned here not with the manifold broad problems of morphogenesis but merely with the question of how fibrillar structures might be involved in local morphogenetic events. In view of the conspicuous polarity and asymmetry of the ciliate cell, of the extent to which preexisting cortical patterns—even abnormal ones—determine new patterns, and of the existence of longitudinal and circumferential gradients,[234, 235, 239] one can hardly doubt that the geometric precision of fibril arrangement within each kinetosomal territory is a significant part of the picture. If each kinetosome or kinetosome pair is endowed with the authority to establish and maintain the morphologic and functional contours of its own territory, how might fibrils be employed? Do the kinetodesma determine the direction of movement of separating kinetosome pairs? Might the local microtubule ribbons play a role, perhaps by some sort of feedback system, in measuring the shape of a kinetosomal territory relative to neighboring ones?

That the onset of fibrillogenesis in the buccal apparatus of *Tetrahymena* may be an indispensable event in the program leading to nuclear and cell division is suggested by the results of extensive experiments done by many workers in Zeuthen's laboratory. Analysis of the differential susceptibility of stages in the cell cycle to division delay induced by heat or other treatments has led the group to postulate the existence of one or a class of "divison proteins". The hypothesis suggests that synthesis of these specific proteins is halted and already-synthesized pools destroyed as a result of administration of heat shock; the cell cannot proceed to divide in the absence of the division proteins and this can account for many observed phenomena in heat-shock-synchronized cultures.[269] It is known that total cellular protein, by contrast, increases markedly during the synchronizing treatment. Recently, Williams and Zeuthen[254] have found that the sequence of visible events in oral fibrillogenesis in treated cells closely parallels the behavior of the postulated division proteins, so closely in fact that the authors propose that the protein precursors of oral fibrils represent one if not the main species of division protein. The predominant fibrils of the oral apparatus are microtubules, and microtubules also are present in the mitotic spindle (the *Tetrahymena* strains used in most of the experiments are amicronucleate, but spindle-like bundles are seen in dividing macronuclei of many ciliates), and in the kinetosomal territories of the presumptive fission line. The implication is that microtubule growth in one or all of these sites is essential if development is to proceed. That more than just morphogenetic movement may be involved is suggested by the results of an autoradiographic study by Williams and Zeuthen.[253] Tritiated amino acids were found both to enter and to leave the mature oral apparatus of prefission cells; this might mean either that its proteins are degraded and renewed, or that formed proteins may move away for use elsewhere in the cell, to be replaced by newly synthesized ones. With the potentialities of electron-microscope autoradiographic techniques, this sort of approach is a most promising one.

VII. EPILOGUE

There is a significant parallelism between the sorts of general conclusions one can draw today from a survey of information on cytoplasmic fibrils and those that Taylor[242] reached from his review of ciliate fiber systems 25 years ago (see p. 282). The explosive development of biophysical and biochemical techniques in that interval has opened wonderful new landscapes to view; the factual details with which we have to deal are so different from those accessible to Taylor that a quick comparison of the descriptive sections of his chapter and this one would scarcely suggest that we are talking about the same things. But we have, in a sense, come full circle. Once more we are approaching the limits of validity of purely morphological observation. Once again we have to concede that the functions of the structures we can see are largely unknown.

The potent differences between the outlooks of 1941 and the present are at least two. One is the certain conviction now that no organism is an island, that the most improbable act by the most esoteric creature may, when examined, provide the best possible illustration of a ubiquitous biological phenomenon. The other is that the techniques required to answer the most urgent questions are at hand now and have barely begun to be exploited.

Ultrastructural evidence suggests that all of the kinds of cytoplasmic fibrils are made up of aggregates of very slender filaments. This is hardly surprising; the number of morphological aspects that a fibrous protein polymer can assume is limited, and it remains to be seen whether electron microscopy can distinguish among species of fibrous proteins. Continuing biochemical analysis of isolated protein units will provide answers to questions at one end of the scale. The modes of aggregation of such units into filament bundles, into tubular arrays of varying sizes and degrees of packing order, into all of the other visible modifications of fibrous structure will have to be investigated both in the test tube and in the cell. Morpho-genetic studies are among the most difficult to undertake by the static methods of electron microscopy, but techniques of ultrastructural autoradiography and cytochemistry, with rigorous light-microscopic control, make them feasible. All of these approaches, and many others, are open.

The powerful artifices of modern molecular biology tend to convey the biologist who employs them farther and farther from the living organism. His major technical problems derive from the necessity to eliminate from his experimental system those parts of the organism and those phases of its activity that are irrelevant to the question he has posed. Granting the ultimate truth that no part and no phase are ever quite irrelevant to any other, molecular biologists may be grateful for the existence of protistan organisms where in all parts and phases are incorporated in a single cell. Despite the blatant fractionation inflicted on protozoan cells in the fore-going pages, it must be very obvious that their fibrillar systems—although crying out for study by methods of molecular biology—will be understand-able only as integral parts of living organisms.

ACKNOWLEDGMENTS

For their generosity in making available to me micrographs for reproduc-tion—many of them previously unpublished—or manuscripts and personal observations, I am deeply indebted to the following colleagues: W. Bala-muth, P. C. Bradbury, N. Carasso, E. R. Dirksen, E. Fauré-Fremiet, P. Fa-vard, D. S. Friend, M. S. Fuller, R. Gliddon, J. N. Grim, J. R. Kennedy, Jr., D. Mazia, J. R. Nilsson, P. de Puytorac, R. Reichle, L. E. Rosenberg, M. Tuffrau, H. Wessenberg, J. A. Westfall, N. E. Williams, B. N. Wise and E. Zeuthen. Permission to reprint illustrations has been granted by publishers of the following journals: *Journal of Cell Biology* (Rockefeller University Press) for Figs. 6 and 7; *Journal de Microscopie* (C.N.R.S., Paris) for Figs. 17 and 27; *Journal of Protozoology* (Society of Protozoologists) for Figs. 20, 23, 24, 39, 40, and 41. My own research has been supported in part by U.S. Public Health Service Grant CA-07015. In addition I am most grateful to Mrs. Emily Reid for expert preparation of diagrams, to John Underhill for meticulous photographic work, to Mrs. Jacquelynne Vittori for able secretarial help, and to Miss Vickie Brauer for assistance in in-numerable ways.

REFERENCES

1. ANDERSON, E. (1962) A cytological study of *Chilomonas paramecium* with particular reference to the so-called trichocysts. *J. Protozool.* **9**, 380–95.
2. ANDERSON, E. (1964) Cytoplasmic microtubules and specialized micropinocytotic regions of the plasmalemma of *Tritrichomonas muris*. *J. Protozool.* **11** (Suppl.), 28.
3. ANDERSON, E., and BEAMS, H. W. (1959) The cytology of *Tritrichomonas* as revealed by the electron microscope. *J. Morphol.* **104**, 205–35.
4. ANDERSON, E., and BEAMS, H. W. (1961) The ultrastructure of *Tritrichomonas* with special reference to the blepharoplast complex. *J. Protozool.* **8**, 71–75.
5. ANDERSON, W. A., and ELLIS, R. A. (1965) Ultrastructure of *Trypanosoma lewisi*. Flagellum, microtubules and the kinetoplast. *J. Protozool.* **12**, 483–99.
6. ANDRÉ, J., and THIÉRY, J. P. (1963) Mise en évidence d'une sous-structure fibrillaire dans les filaments axonématiques des flagelles. *J. Microscopie* **2**, 71–80.
7. ARGETSINGER, J. (1965) The isolation of ciliary basal bodies (kinetosomes) from *Tetrahymena pyriformis*. *J. Cell Biol.* **24**, 154–6.
8. BALAMUTH, W., and BRADBURY, P. C. (1966) Unpublished work.
9. BEAMS, H. W., and ANDERSON, E. (1961) Fine structure of protozoa. *Ann. Rev. Microbiol.* **15**, 47–68.
10. BEAMS, H. W., KING, R. L., TAHMISIAN, T. N., and DEVINE, R. (1960) Electron microscope studies on *Lophomonas striata* with special reference to the nature and position of the striations. *J. Protozool.* **7**, 91–101.
11. BEAMS, H. W., TAHMISIAN, T. N., ANDERSON, E., and WRIGHT, W. (1961) Studies on the fine structure of *Lophomonas blattarum* with special reference to the so-called parabasal apparatus. *J. Ultrastruct. Res.* **5**, 166–83.
12. BEHNKE, O. (1964) A preliminary report on "microtubules" in undifferentiated and differentiated vertebrate cells. *J. Ultrastruct. Res.* **11**, 139–46.
13. BĚLAŘ, K. (1921) Protozoenstudien III. *Arch. Protistenk.* **43**, 431–62.
14. BLUM, J. J., SOMMER, J. R., and KAHN, V. (1965) Some biochemical, cytological and morphogenetic comparisons between *Astasia longa* and a bleached *Euglena gracilis*. *J. Protozool.* **12**, 202–9.
15. BRADBURY, P. C. (1965) Doctoral dissertation, University of California, Berkeley.
16. BRADBURY, P. C. (1965) The infraciliature and argyrome of *Opisthonecta henneguyi* Fauré-Fremiet. *J. Protozool.* **12**, 345–63.
17. BRADBURY, P. C., and PITELKA, D. R. (1965) Observations on kinetosome formation in an apostome ciliate. *J. Microscopie*, **4**, 805–10.
18. BRESCIANI, J., and FENCHEL, T. (1965) Studies on dicyemid Mesozoa. I. The fine structure of the adult (the nematogen and rhombogen stage). *Vidensk. Medd. Dansk. Naturh. Foren.* **128**, 85–92.
19. BRETSCHNEIDER, L. H. (1959) Die submikroskopische Struktur der Pellikula von *Epidinium ecaudatum*. (Ophryoscolecidae), *Proc. Koninkl. Nederl. Akad. Wetensch.* (Ser. C) **62**, 542–55.
20. BRETSCHNEIDER, L. H. (1960) Elektronenmikroskopische Untersuchung des Peristomapparates einiger Ophryoscoleciden. *Proc. Koninkl. Nederl. Akad. Wetensch.* (Ser. C) **63**, 291–317.
21. BRETSCHNEIDER, L. H. (1962) Das Paralabialorgan der Ophryoscoleciden. *Proc. Koninkl. Nederl. Acad. Wetensch.* (Ser. C) **65**, 523–37.
22. BULLOCK, T. H., and HORRIDGE, G. A. (1965) *Structure and Function in the Nervous Systems of Invertebrates*, Vol. 1, FREEMAN, San Francisco.
23. BURGOS, M. H., and FAWCETT, D. W. (1955) Studies on the fine structure of the mammalian testis. I. Differentiation of the spermatids in the cat. *J. Biophys. Biochem. Cytol.* **1**, 287–300.

24. BURNASHEVA, S. A. (1965) Isolation of the contractile proteins from cilia of *Tetrahymena pyriformis* and a study of their properties. In *Progress in Protozoology*, Internat. Congr. Ser. 91, Excerpta Medica Foundation, London, pp. 239–40.

25. BYERS, B., and PORTER, K. R. (1964) Oriented microtubules in elongating cells of the developing lens rudiment after induction. *Proc. Nat. Acad. Sci.* 52, 1091–8.

26. CARASSO, N., FAURÉ-FREMIET, E., and FAVARD, P. (1962) Ultrastructure de l'appareil excréteur chez quelques ciliés péritriches. *J. Microscopie* 1, 455–68.

27. CARASSO, N., and FAVARD, P. (1965) Microtubules fusoriaux dans les micro-et macronucleus de ciliés péritriches en division. *J. Microscopie* 4, 395–402.

28. CHATTON, E., and LWOFF, A. (1935) La constitution primitive de la strie ciliaire des infusoires. La desmodéxie. *C.R. Soc. Biol.* 118, 1068–72.

29. CHATTON, E., and LWOFF, A. (1935) Les ciliés apostomes. I. Aperçu historique et général; étude monographique des genres et des espèces. *Arch. Zool. Exptl. Gén.* 77, 1–453.

30. CHEISSIN, E. M. (1964) Ultrastructure of *Lamblia duodenalis*. I. Body surface, sucking disc and median bodies. *J. Protozool.* 11, 91–98.

31. CHEISSIN, E. M., and MOSEWICH, T. N. (1962) An electron microscope study of *Colpidium colpoda* (Ciliata, Holotricha). *Arch. Protistenk.* 106, 181–200.

32. CHILD, F. M. (1965) Ciliary coordination in glycerinated mussel gills. In *Progress in Protozoology*, Internat. Congr. Ser. 91, Excerpta Medica Foundation, London, p. 110.

33. CHRISTENSEN, K. (1961) Fine structure of an unusual spermatozoan in the flatworm *Plagiostomum*. *Biol. Bull.* 121, 416.

34. CLEVELAND, L. R., and GRIMSTONE, A. V. (1964) The fine structure of the flagellate *Mixotricha paradoxa* and its associated microorganisms. *Proc. Roy. Soc. B.* 59, 668–86.

35. CLONEY, R. A. (1965) Cytoplasmic filaments in contractile epidermal cells. *J. Cell Biol.* 27, 19 A–20 A.

36. CORLISS, J. O. (1959) An illustrated key to the higher groups of the ciliated protozoa with definition of terms. *J. Protozool.* 6, 265–81.

37. CORLISS, J. O (1961) *The Ciliate Protozoa*, Pergamon Press, London.

38. CULBERTSON, J. R., and BANERJEE, S. P. (1965) Biochemistry of cilia isolated from *Tetrahymena*. In *Progress in Protozoology*, Internat. Congr. Ser. 91, Excerpta Medica Foundation, London, p. 240.

39. CZARSKA, L. (1965) Cytoplasmic streaming in *Paramecium caudatum* exposed to electric field. *Acta Protozool.* 3, 269–74.

40. DANIEL, W. H., and MATTERN, C. F. T. (1965) Some observations on the structure of the peristomial membranelle of *Spirostomum ambiguum*. *J. Protozool.* 12, 14–27.

41. DE-THÉ, GUY (1964) Cytoplasmic microtubules in different animal cells. *J. Cell Biol.* 23, 265–76.

42. DIPPELL, R. V. (1965) Reproduction of surface structure in *Paramecium*. In *Progress in Protozoology*, Internat. Congr. Ser. 91, Excerpta Medica Foundation, London, p. 65.

43. DIRKSON, E. R., and CROCKER, T. T. (1966) Replication of basal bodies in mammalian respiratory epithelium; an electron microscopic study. *J. Microscopie* (in press).

44. DRYL, S., and GREBECKI, A. (1965) Recent advances in research on the excitability of ciliates. In *Progress in Protozoology*, Internat. Congr. Ser. 91, Excerpta Medica Foundation, London, pp. 104–5.

45. DUMONT, J. N. (1961) Observations on the fine structure of the ciliate *Dileptus anser*. *J. Protozool.* 8, 392–402.

46. DUMONT, J. N., and ANDERSON, E. (1964) The unique structure of the contractile vacuole of a parasitic protozoan (*Paraisotricha* sp.) from the caecum of the horse. *J. Protozool.* 11 (Suppl.), 30.

47. EAKIN, R. M. (1963) Lines of evolution in photoreceptors. In *General Physiology of Cell Specialization*, ed. D. MAZIA and A. TYLER, McGraw-Hill, New York, pp. 393–425.

48. EHRET, C. F., and DE HALLER, G. (1963) Origin, development and maturation of organelles and organelle systems of the cell surface in *Paramecium. J. Ultrastruct. Res.*, Suppl. 6, 1–42.

49. EHRET, C. F., and POWERS, E. L. (1957) The organization of gullet organelles in *Paramecium bursaria. J. Protozool.* 4, 55–59.

50. EHRET, C. F., and POWERS, E. L. (1959) The cell surface of *Paramecium. Internat. Rev. Cytol.* 8, 97–133.

51. ELLIOTT, A. E., and BAK, I. J. (1964) The contractile vacuole and related structures in *Tetrahymena pyriformis. J. Protozool.* 11, 250–61.

52. ETTL, H., and MANTON, I. (1964) Die fernere Struktur von *Pedinomonas minor* Korschikoff. *Nova Hedwegia* 8, 421–51.

53. FAURÉ-FREMIET, E. (1961) Cils vibratiles et flagelles. *Biol. Revs.* 36, 464–536.

54. FAURÉ-FREMIET, E. (1961) Le cytoplasme stomo-pharyngien des ciliés cyrtophores. *C.R. Acad. Sci.* 253, 357–62.

55. FAURÉ-FREMIET, E. (1962) Le genre *Paranassula* Kahl (Ciliata Cyrtophorina). *Cahiers Biol. Mar.* 3, 61–77.

56. FAURÉ-FREMIET, E., and ANDRÉ, J. (1964) Étude au microscope éléctronique de *Tillina praestans* (Cilié Trichostomatida). *J. Protozool.* 11 (Suppl.), 46.

57. FAURÉ-FREMIET, E., and ANDRÉ, J. (1965) L'organisation du cilié gymnostome *Plagiocampa ovata* Gelei. *Arch. Zool. Exptl. Gén.* 105, 360–7.

58. FAURÉ-FREMIET, E., FAVARD, P., and CARASSO, N. (1962) Étude au microscope éléctronique des ultrastructures d'*Epistylis anastatica* (cilié péritriche). *J. Microscopie* 1, 287–312.

59. FAURÉ-FREMIET, E., and ROUILLER, C. (1958) Myonémes et cinétodesmes chez les ciliés du genre *Stentor. Bull. Microscop. Appl.* 8, 117–9.

60. FAURÉ-FREMIET, E., and ROUILLER, C. (1958) Réseau canaliculaire dans les myonémes endoplasmique de quelques ciliés. *C.R. Acad. Sci.* 246, 2039–42.

61. FAURÉ-FREMIET, E., and ROUILLER, C. (1959) Le cortex de la vacuole contractile et son ultrastructure chez les ciliés. *J. Protozool.* 6, 29–37.

62. FAURÉ-FREMIET, E., ROUILLER, C., and GAUCHERY, M. (1956) Les structures myoides chez les ciliés. Étude au microscope éléctronique. *Arch. Anat. Microscop. Morphol. Exptl.* 45, 139–61.

63. FAVARD, P., CARASSO, N., and FAURÉ-FREMIET, E. (1963) Ultrastructure de l'appareil adhésif des urcéolaires (ciliés péritriches). *J. Microscopie* 2, 337–68.

64. FAWCETT, D. W. (1961) Cilia and Flagella. In *The Cell*, Vol. II, ed. J. BRACHET and A. E. MIRSKY, Academic Press, New York, pp. 217–98.

65. FAWCETT, D. W., and PORTER, K. R. (1954) A study of the fine structure of ciliated epithelia. *J. Morphol.* 94, 221–82.

66. FAWCETT, D. W., and WITEBSKY, F. (1964) Observations on the ultrastructure of nucleated erythrocytes and thrombocytes, with particular reference to the structural basis of their discoidal shape. *Z. Zellforsch.* 62, 785–806.

67. FINLEY, H. E., BROWN, C. A., and DANIEL, W. A. (1964) Electron microscopy of the ectoplasm and infraciliature of *Spirostomum ambiguum. J. Protozool.* 11, 264–80.

68. FRIEND, D. S. (1966) The fine structure of *Giardia muris. J. Cell. Biol.* 29, 317–22.

69. FULLER, M. S., and REICHLE, R. (1965) The zoospore and early development of *Rhizidiomyces apophysatus. Mycologia* 57, 946–61.

70. FULLER, M. S., and REICHLE, R. (1966) Unpublished work.

71. GALL, J. G. (1961) Centriole replication. A study of spermatogenesis in the snail *Viviparus. J. Biophys. Biochem. Cytol.* 10, 163–94.

72. GALL, J. G. (1965) Fine structure of microtubules. *J. Cell Biol.* 27, 32A.

73. GELEI, G. von (1937) Ein neues Fibrillensystem im Ectoplasma von *Paramecium. Arch. Protistenk.* 89, 133–62.

74. GELEI, J. von (1934) Der feinere Bau des Cytopharynx von *Paramecium* und seine systematische Bedeutung. *Arch. Protistenk.* **82**, 331–62.
75. GIBBONS, I. R. (1961) The relationship between the fine structure and direction of beat in gill cilia of a lamellibranch mollusc. *J. Biophys. Biochem. Cytol.* **11**, 179–205.
76. GIBBONS, I. R. (1961) Structural asymmetry in cilia and flagella. *Nature* **190**, 1128–9.
77. GIBBONS, I. R. (1963) Studies on the protein components of cilia from *Tetrahymena pyriformis. Proc. Nat. Acad. Sci.* **50**, 1002–10.
78. GIBBONS, I. R. (1965) Dynein: a protein with adenosine triphosphatase activity from cilia. *Science* **149**, 424–6.
79. GIBBONS, I. R. (1965) An effect of adenosine triphosphate on the light scattered by suspensions of cilia. *J. Cell Biol.* **26**, 707–12.
80. GIBBONS, I. R. (1965) Proteins associated with movement in cilia. *J. Cell Biol.* **27**, 33A–34A.
81. GIBBONS, I. R. (1965) Reactivation of glycerinated cilia from *Tetrahymena pyriformis. J. Cell Biol.* **25**, 400–2.
82. GIBBONS, I. R., and GRIMSTONE, A. V. (1960) On flagellar structure in certain flagellates. *J. Biophys. Biochem. Cytol.* **7**, 697–716.
83. GIBBS, S. P., LEWIN, R. A., and PHILPOTT, D. E. (1958) The fine structure of the flagellar apparatus of *Chlamydomonas moewusii. Exptl. Cell Res.* **15**, 619–22.
84. GLIDDON, R. (1965) Ciliary activity and coordination in *Euplotes eurystomus.* In *Progress in Protozoology*, Internat. Congr. Ser. 91, Excerpta Medica Foundation, London, p. 216.
85. GLIDDON, R. (1966) Unpublished work.
86. GRAIN, J. (1963) Sur l'ultrastructure du vestibule de *Paraisotricha colpoidea* Fiorentini, cilié trichostome de l'intestin du cheval. *C.R. Acad. Sci.* **257**, 2534–7.
87. GRAIN, J. (1964) Ultrastructure de l'appareil buccal du cilié *Alloiozona trizona* Hsung. *C.R. Acad. Sci.* **258**, 331–3.
88. GRAIN, J. (1965) Premiéres observations sur les systémes fibrillaires chez quelques ciliés des ruminants et des équidés. *Arch. Zool. Exptl. Gén.* **105**, 185–92.
89. GRASSÉ, P. P. (1956) L'ultrastructure de *Pyrsonympha vertens* (Zooflagellata Pyrsonymphina): les flagelles et coaptation avec le corps, l'axostyle contractile, le paraxostyle, le cytoplasme. *Arch. Biol.* **67**, 595–611.
90. GRASSÉ, P. P. (1961) Le reproduction par induction du blépharoplaste et du flagelle de *Trypanosoma equiperdum* (flagellé protomonadine). *C.R. Acad. Sci.* **252**, 3917–21.
91. GREBECKI, A. (1965) Gradient stomato-caudal d'excitabilité des ciliés. *Acta Protozool.* **3**, 79–101.
92. GRIMSTONE, A. V. (1959) Cytoplasmic membranes and the nuclear membrane in the flagellate *Trichonympha. J. Biophys. Biochem. Cytol.* **6**, 369–78.
93. GRIMSTONE, A. V. (1961) Fine structure and morphogenesis in protozoa. *Biol. Revs.* **36**, 97–150.
94. GRIMSTONE, A. V. (1965) Observations on fine structure of flagellates. In *Progress in Protozoology*, Internat. Congr. Ser. 91, Excerpta Medica Foundation, London, p. 87.
95. GRIMSTONE, A. V., and CLEVELAND, L. R. (1965) The fine structure and function of the contractile axostyles of certain flagellates. *J. Cell Biol.* **24**, 387–400.
96. HALLER, G., DE, and ROUILLER, C. (1961) La structure fine de *Chlorogonium elongatum.* I. Étude systématique au microscope électronique. *J. Protozool.* **8**, 452–62.
97. HARRIS, J. E. (1961) The mechanics of ciliary movement. In *The Cell and the Organism*, eds. J. A. RAMSAY and V. B. WIGGLESWORTH, Cambridge Univ. Press, pp. 22–36.
98. HARVEN, E. DE, and BERNHARD, W. (1956) Étude au microscope électronique de l'ultrastructure du centriole chez les vertebrés. *Z. Zellforsch.* **45**, 378–98.
99. HOFFMAN, E. J. (1965) The nucleic acids of basal bodies isolated from *Tetrahymena pyriformis. J. Cell Biol.* **25**, 217–28.

100. HOFFMAN, L. R., and MANTON, I. (1962) Observations on the fine structure of the zoospore of *Oedogonium cardiacum* with special reference to the flagellar apparatus. *J. Exptl. Bot.* **13**, 443–9.

101. HOFFMAN, L. R., and MANTON, I. (1963) Observations on the fine structure of *Oedogonium*. II. The spermatozoid of *O. cardiacum*. *Amer. J. Bot.* **50**, 455–63.

102. HOFFMANN-BERLING, H. (1958) Der Mechanismus eines neuen Kontraktionszyklus. *Biochim. Biophys. Acta* **27**, 247–55.

103. HOLLANDE, A., CACHON, J., and CACHON-ENJUMET, M. (1965) L'infrastructure des axopodes chez les Radiolaires Sphaerellaires périaxoplastidiés. *C.R. Acad. Sci.* **261**, 1388–91.

104. HONIGBERG, B. M., and COMMITTEE (1964) A revised classification of the Phylum Protozoa. *J. Protozool.* **11**, 7–20.

105. HOVASSE, R. (1965) Ultrastructure comparée des axopodes chez les héliozoaires des genres *Actinosphaerium*, *Actinophrys* et *Radiophrys*. *Protistologica* **1**, 81–88.

106. JACOBSON, I. (1931) Fibrilläre Differenzierungen bei Ciliaten. *Arch. Protistenk.* **75**, 31–100.

107. JAHN, T. L., and BOVEE, E. C. (1964) Protoplasmic movements and locomotion of protozoa. In *Biochemistry and Physiology of Protozoa*, Vol. III, ed. S. H. HUTNER, Academic Press, New York, pp. 62–130.

108. JAHN, T. L., RINALDI, R. A., and WIGG, D. (1964) The water expulsion of *Amoebaproteus*. *J. Protozool.* **11** (suppl.), 32.

109. JOYON, L. (1963) Contribution a l'étude cytologique de quelques protozoaires. flagellés. *Ann. Fac. Sci. Univ. Clermont*, **22**, 1–96.

110. JOYON, L. (1965) Compléments à la connaissance ultrastructurale des genres *Haematococcus pluvialis* Flotow et *Stephanosphaera pluvialis* Cohn. *Ann. Fac. Sci. Univ. Clermont* **26**, 57–69.

111. JUDGE, D. M., and ANDERSON, H. S. (1964) Ultrastructure of *Trypanosoma lewisi*. *J. Parasitol.* **50**, 757–62.

112. KANEDA, M. (1962) Fine structure of the oral apparatus of the gymnostome ciliate *Chlamydodon pedarius*. *J. Protozool.* **9**, 188–95.

113. KENNEDY, J. R., JR. (1965) The morphology of *Blepharisma undulans* Stein. *J. Protozool.* **12**, 542–61.

114. KENNEDY, J. R., JR. (1965) Fine structure of the oral region of *Frontonia lucas*. In *Progress in Protozoology*, Internat. Congr. Ser. 91, Excerpta Medica Foundation, London, p. 217.

115. KING, R. L., BEAMS, H. W., TAHMISIAN, T. N., and DEVINE, R. L. (1961) The ciliature and infraciliature of *Nyctotherus ovalis* Leidy. *J. Protozool.* **8**, 98–111.

116. KINOSITA, H., DRYL, S., and NAITOH, Y. (1964) Relation between the magnitude of membrane potential and ciliary activity in *Paramecium*. *J. Fac. Sci. Univ. Tokyo* **10**, 303–9.

117. KIRBY, H. (1944) Some observations on cytology and morphogenesis in flagellate protozoa. *J. Morphol.* **75**, 361–421.

118. KITCHING, J. A. (1964) The axopods of the sun animalcule *Actinophrys sol* (Heliozoa). In *Primitive Motile Systems in Cell Biology*, ed. R. D. ALLEN and N. KAMIYA, Academic Press, New York, pp. 445–55.

119. LANG, N. J. (1963) An additional ultrastructural component of flagella. *J. Cell Biol.* **19**, 631–4.

120. LANSING, A. I., and LAMY, F. (1961) Fine structure of the cilia of rotifers. *J. Biophys. Biochem. Cytol.* **9**, 799–812.

121. LEDBETTER, M. C., and PORTER, K. R. (1964) Morphology of microtubules of plant cells. *Science* **144**, 872–4.

122. LEEDALE, G. F. (1964) Pellicle structure in *Euglena*. *Brit. Phycol. Bull.* **2**, 291–306.

13*

123. LEEDALE, G. F., MEEUSE, B. J. D., and PRINGSHEIM, E. G. (1965) Structure and physiology of *Euglena spirogyra*. *Arch. Mikrobiol.* **50**, 68–102.
124. LWOFF, A. (1950) *Problems of Morphogenesis in Ciliates*, John Wiley & Sons, New York.
125. MACHEMER, H. (1965) Analyse kurzzeitlicher Bewegungserscheinungen des Ciliaten *Stylonychia mytilus* Ehrenberg. *Arch. Protistenk.* **108**, 153–90.
126. MAKIELSKI, S. K. (1965) Flagellar structure in the spermatozoa of *Sciara coprophila*. *J. Cell Biol.* **27**, 62A.
127. MANTON, I. (1955) Observations with the electron microscope on *Synura caroliniana* Whitford. *Proc. Leeds Philos. Soc.* **6**, 306–16.
128. MANTON, I. (1959) Observations on the microanatomy of the spermatozoid of the bracken fern (*Pteridium aquilinum*). *J. Biophys. Biochem. Cytol.* **6**, 413–8.
129. MANTON, I. (1964) A contribution towards understanding of "the primitive fucoid". *New Phytol.* **63**, 244–54.
130. MANTON, I. (1964) Further observations on the fine structure of the haptonema in *Prymnesium parvum. Arch. Mikrobiol.* **49**, 315–30.
131. MANTON, I. (1964) Observations on the fine structure of the zoospore and young germling of *Stigeoclonium. J. Exptl. Bot.* **15**, 399–411.
132. MANTON, I. (1964) Observations with the electron microscope on the division cycle in the flagellate *Prymnesium parvum* Carter. *J. Roy. Microscop. Soc.* **83**, 317–25.
133. MANTON, I., and LEEDALE, G. F. (1961) Further observations on the fine structure of *Chrysochromulina ericina* Parke and Manton. *J. Mar. Biol. Assoc. U.K.* **41**, 145–55.
134. MANTON, I., and LEEDALE, G. F. (1961) Observations on the fine structure of *Paraphysomonas vestita*, with special reference to the Golgi apparatus and the origin of scales. *Phycologia* **1**, 37–57.
135. MANTON, I. and LEEDALE, G. F. (1963) Observations on the fine structure of *Prymnesium parvum* Carter. *Arch. Mikrobiol.* **45**, 285–303.
136. MANTON, I., OATES, K., and PARKE, M. (1963) Observations on the fine structure of the *Pyraminonas* stage of *Halosphaera* and preliminary observations on three species of *Pyramimonas. J. Mar. Biol. Assoc. U.K.* **43**, 225–38.
137. MANTON, I., and PARKE, M. (1960) Further observations on small green flagellates with special reference to possible relatives of *Chromulina pusilla* Butcher. *J. Mar. Biol. Assoc. U.K.* **39**, 275–98.
138. MANTON, I., and PARKE, M. (1965) Observations on the fine structure of two species of *Platymonas* with special reference to flagellar scales and mode of origin of the theca. *J. Mar. Biol. Assoc. U.K.* **45**, 743–54.
139. MANTON, I., RAYNS, D. G., ETTL, H., and PARKE, M. (1965) Further observations on green flagellates with scaly flagella: the genus *Heteromastix* Korshikov. *J. Mar. Biol. Assoc. U.K.* **45**, 241–55.
140. MCMANUS, M. A., and ROTH, L. E. (1965) Fibrillar differentiation in myxomycete plasmodia. *J. Cell Biol.* **25**, 305–18.
141. METZ, C. B., PITELKA, D. R., and WESTFALL, J. A. (1953) The fibrillar systems of ciliates as revealed by the electron microscope. I. *Paramecium. Biol. Bull.* **104**, 408–25.
142. METZ, C. B., and WESTFALL, J. A. (1954) The fibrillar systems of ciliates as revealed by the electron microscope. II. *Tetrahymena. Biol. Bull.* **107**, 106–22.
143. MIGNOT, J. P. (1963) Quelques particularités de l'ultrastructure d'*Entosiphon sulcatum* (Duj.) Stein; flagellé euglénien. *C.R. Acad. Sci.* **257**, 2530–3.
144. MIGNOT, J. P. (1964) Observations complémentaires sur la structure des flagelles d'*Entosiphon sulcatum* (Duj.) Stein, flagellé euglénien. *C.R. Acad. Sci.* **258**, 3360–3.
145. MIGNOT, J. P. (1965) Étude ultrastructurale de *Cyathomonas truncata* From. (flagellé cryptomonadine). *J. Microscopie* **4**, 239–52.
146. MIGNOT, J. P. (1965) Ultrastructure des Eugléniens. I. Étude de la cuticule chez différentes espèces. *Protistologica* **1**, 5–15.

147. MILLER, O. L., and STONE, G. E. (1963) Fine structure of the oral area of *Tetra-hymena patula. J. Protozool.* **10**, 280–8.

148. MOSEVICH, T. N. (1965) Electron microscopic study of the structure of the contractile vacuole in the ciliate *Ichthyophthirius multifilus* (Fouquet). *Acta Protozool.* **3**, 61–67.

149. NACHMIAS, V. T. (1964) Fibrillar structures in the cytoplasm of *Chaos chaos. J. Cell Biol.* **23**, 183–8.

150. NANNEY, D. L., and RUDZINSKA, M. A. (1960) Protozoa. In *The Cell*, Vol. IV, ed. J. BRACHET and A. E. MIRSKY, Academic Press, New York, pp. 109–50.

151. NIELSEN, M. H., and LUDVIK, J. (1964) On the ultrastructure of *Trichomonas vaginalis*. In *Electron Microscopy*, Vol. B, ed. M. TITLBACH, Proc. 3rd Eur. Regional Conf. Prague, pp. 181–2.

152. NILSSON, J. R., and WILLIAMS, N. E. (1966) An electron microscope study of the oral apparatus of *Tetrahymena pyriformis. C. R. Trav. Lab. Carlsberg* **35**, 119–41.

153. NOIROT-TIMOTHÉE, C. (1958) L'ultrastructure de la limite ectoplasme-endoplasme et des fibres formant le caryophore chez les ciliés du genre *Isotricha* Stein (holotriches trichostomes). *C.R. Acad. Sci.* **247**, 692–5.

154. NOIROT-TIMOTHÉE, C. (1959) Recherches sur l'ultrastructure d'*Opalina ranarum. Ann. Sci. Nat. Zool.* (Sér. 12), **1**, 265–81.

155. NOIROT-TIMOTHÉE, C. (1960) Étude d'une famille de ciliés: les Ophyryoscolecidae. Structures et ultrastructures. *Ann. Sci. Nat. Zool.* (Sér. 12) **2**, 527–718.

156. NOIROT-TIMOTHÉE, C. (1963) Les fibres des protozoaires. Ultrastructure comparée. In *Progress in Protozoology*, Proc. 1st Internat. Conf. Protozool., Prague, 1961. Czech. Acad. Sci., pp. 393–5.

157. NOIROT-TIMOTHÉE, C. (1965) The oral ciliature of *Termitophrya* (Ciliata, Peritricha). In *Progress in Protozoology*, Internat. Congr. Ser. 91, Excerpta Medica Foundation, London, pp. 223–4.

158. NOIROT-TIMOTHÉE, C., and LOM, J. (1965) L'ultrastructure de l'haplocinétie des ciliés péritriches. Comparaison avec la membrane ondulante des hyménostomes. *Protistologica* **1**, 33–41.

159. OKAJIMA, A., and KINOSITA, H. (1965) Cinematographic analysis of ciliary coordination in *Euplotes*. In *Progress in Protozoology*, Internat. Congr. Ser. 91, Excerpta Medica Foundation, London, p. 228.

160. OLSSON, R. (1962) The relationship between ciliary rootlets and other cell structures. *J. Cell Biol.* **15**, 596–9.

161. OSADA, M. (1962) Electron microscopic studies on protozoa. II. Studies on *Trichomonas muris. Keio J. Med.* **11**, 227–52.

162. PÁRDUCZ, B. (1958) Das interziliäre Fasernsystem in seiner Beziehung zu gewissen Fibrillenkomplexen der Infusorien. *Acta Biol. Acad. Sci. Hung.* **8**, 191–218.

163. PÁRDUCZ, B. (1958) Reizphysiologische Untersuchungen an Ziliaten. VII. Das Problem der vorbestimmten Leitungsbahnen. *Acta Biol. Acad. Sci. Hung.* **8**, 219–51.

164. PÁRDUCZ, B. (1962) On a new concept of cortical organization in *Paramecium. Acta Biol. Acad. Sci. Hung.* **13**, 299–322.

165. PÁRDUCZ, B. (1966) Ciliary movement and coordination in ciliates. *Internat. Rev. Cytol.* **21**, 91–128.

166. PARKE, M., LUND, J. W. G., and MANTON, I. (1962) Observations on the biology and fine structure of the type species of *Chrysochromulina* (*C. parva* Lackey) in the English Lake District. *Arch. Mikrobiol.* **42**, 333–52.

167. PARKE, M., and MANTON, I. (1965) Preliminary observations on the fine structure of *Prasinocladus marinus. J. Mar. Biol. Assoc. U.K.* **45**, 525–36.

168. PEASE, D. C. (1963) The ultrastructure of flagellar fibrils. *J. Cell Biol.* **18**, 313–26.

169. PHILLIPS, D. H. (1965) Fine structure of the motile apparatus in the non-flagellated sperm of *Sciara copophrila* (Diptera). *J. Cell Biol.* **27**, 77 A.

170. PITELKA, D. R. (1956) An electron microscope study of cortical structures of *Opalina obtrigonoidea*. *J. Biophys. Biochem. Cytol.* **2**, 423–32.

171. PITELKA, D. R. (1961) Fine structure of the silverline and fibrillar systems of three tetrahymenid ciliates. *J. Protozool.* **8**, 75–89.

172. PITELKA, D. R. (1961) Observations on the kinetoplast-mitochondrion and the cytostome of *Bodo*. *Exptl. Cell Res.* **25**, 87–93.

173. PITELKA, D. R. (1963) *Electron-Microscopic Structure of Protozoa*, Pergamon Press, Oxford.

174. PITELKA, D. R. (1963) Fine structure of the buccal apparatus in *Paramecium*. *Proc. XVIth Internat. Congr. Zool., Washington*, **2**, 293.

175. PITELKA, D. R. (1964) The morphology of the cytostomal area in *Paramecium*. *J. Protozool.* **11** (suppl.), 14–5.

176. PITELKA, D. R. (1965) New observations on cortical ultrastructure in *Paramecium*. *J. Microscopie* **4**, 373–94.

177. PITELKA, D. R. (1966) Unpublished work.

178. PITELKA, D. R., and CHILD, F. M. (1964) The locomotor apparatus of ciliates and flagellates: relations between structure and function. In *Biochemistry and Physiology of Protozoa*, Vol. III, ed. S. H. HUTNER, Academic Press, New York pp. 131–98.

179. PITELKA, D. R., and SCHOOLEY, C. N. (1958) The fine structure of the flagellar apparatus in *Trichonympha*. *J. Morphol.* **102**, 199–246.

180. PORTER, K. R., KAWAKAMI, N., and LEDBETTER, M. C. (1965) Structural basis of streaming in *Physarum polycephalum*. *J. Cell Biol.* **27**, 78 *A*.

181. POTTAGE, R. H. (1959) Electron microscopy of the adults and migrants of the suctorian ciliate *Discophrya piriformis*. *Proc. XVth Internat. Congr. Zool. London*, pp. 472–3.

182. PUYTORAC, P. DE (1959) Le cytosquelette et les systèmes fibrillaires du cilié *Metaradiophrya gigas* de Puytorac, d'aprés étude au microscope électronique. *Arch. Anat. Microsc. Morphol. Exptl.* **48**, 49–62.

183. PUYTORAC, P. DE (1960) Observations en microscope électronique de l'appareil vacuolaire pulsatile chez quelques ciliés astomes. *Arch. Anat. Microscop. Morphol. Exptl.* **49**, 241–56.

184. PUYTORAC, P. DE (1961) Complément à l'étude de l'ultrastructure des ciliés du genre *Metaradiophrya* Heid. 1935. *Arch. Anat. Microscop. Morphol. Exptl.* **50**, 35–58.

185. PUYTORAC, P. DE (1961) Observations sur l'ultrastructure d'*Anoplophrya commune* de Puyt., cilié parasite du ver *Eophila savignyi* (G. et H.). *C.R. Soc. Biol.* **155**, 783–6.

186. PUYTORAC, P. DE (1963) Contribution à l'étude des ciliés astomes Haptophryidae Cépéde, 1903 (cytologie, ultrastructure, taxinomie). *Ann. Sci. Nat., Zool.* (Sér. 12), **5**, 173–90.

187. PUYTORAC, P. DE (1963) Observations sur l'ultrastructure du cilié astome; *Mesnilella trispiculata* K. *J. Microscopie* **2**, 189–96.

188. PUYTORAC, P. DE (1964) Quelques aspects de l'ultrastructure du Cilié: *Prorodon viridis* Ehrbg. Kahl. *Acta Protozool.* **2**, 147–52.

189. PUYTORAC, P. DE (1965) Sur l'ultrastructure du complexe cytostome-cytopharynx chez le cilié *Holophrya vesiculosa* Kahl. *C.R. Soc. Biol.* **159**, 661–3.

190. PUYTORAC, P. DE (1965) Ultrastructures fibrillaires et ultrastructures squelettiques cytoplasmique chez les ciliés. In *Progress in Protozoology*, Internat. Congr. Ser. 91, Excerpta Medica Foundation, London, pp. 88–90.

191. PYNE, C. K. (1959) L'ultrastructure de *Cryptobia helicis* (flagellé, Fam. Bodonidae). *C.R. Acad. Sci.* **248**, 1410–3.

192. PYNE, C. K. (1960) L'ultrastructure de l'appareil basal des flagelles chez *Crytobia helicis* (flagellé, Bodonidae). *C.R. Acad. Sci.* **250**, 1912.

193. RANDALL, J., and DISBREY, C. (1965) Evidence for the presence of DNA at basal body sites in *Tetrahymena pyriformis*. *Proc. Roy. Soc. B* **162**, 473–91.

194. RANDALL, J. T., and HOPKINS, J. M. (1962) On the stalks of certain peritrichs. *Phil. Trans. Roy. Soc. Lond. B* **245**, 59–79.

195. RANDALL, J., HOPKINS, J. M., EADIE, J. M., and BUTCHER, R. W. (1963) Studies of cilia, basal bodies and some related organelles. I. Observations on fine structure. *Proc. Linn. Soc. Lond.* **174**, 31–36.

196. RANDALL, J. T., and JACKSON, S. F. (1958) Fine structure and function in *Stentor polymorphus. J. Biophys. Biochem. Cytol.* **4**, 807–30.

197. RANDALL, J., WATSON, M. R., SILVESTER, N. R., ALEXANDER, J. B., and HOPKINS, J. M. (1963) Studies of cilia, basal bodies and some related organelles. II. Genesis and macromolecular properties. *Proc. Linn. Soc. Lond.* **174**, 37–40.

198. ROBISON, W. G., JR. (1965) Ultrastructure and motility of a syncytial sperm bundle in an armored scale insect. *J. Cell Biol.* **27**, 86A.

199. ROQUE, M. (1961) Recherches sur les hyménostomes péniculiens. *Bull. Biol. Fr. Belg.* **95**, 431–519.

200. ROQUE, M., DE PUYTORAC, P., and SAVOIE, R. (1965) *Ophryoglena bacterocaryon* sp. n., cilié holotriche péniculien. (Cytologie, ultrastructure, cycle). *Arch. Zool. Exptl. Gén.* **105**, 309–94.

201. ROSENBERG, L. E., and GRIM, J. N. (1965) Additional ultrastructural observations on *Telotrochidium henneguyi* (syn. *Opisthonecta*). In *Progress in Protozoology*. Internat. Congr. Ser. 91, Excerpta Medica Foundation, London, p. 222.

202. ROSENBERG, L. E., and GRIM, J. N. (1966) Unpublished work.

203. ROTH, L. E. (1956) Aspects of ciliary fine structure in *Euplotes patella. J. Biophys. Biochem. Cytol.* **2** (suppl.), 235–42.

204. ROTH, L. E., (1957) An electron microscope study of the cytology of the protozoan *Euplotes patella. J. Biophys. Biochem. Cytol.* **3**, 985–1000.

205. ROTH, L. E. (1958) A filamentous component of protozoan fibrillar systems. *J. Ultrastruct. Res.* **1**, 223–34.

206. ROTH, L. E. (1959) An electron-microscope study of the cytology of the protozoan *Peranema trichophorum. J. Protozool.* **6**, 107–116.

207. ROTH, L. E. (1964) Motile systems with continuous filaments. In *Primitive Motile Systems in Cell Biology*, ed. R. D. ALLEN and N. KAMIYA, Academic Press, New York, pp. 527–46.

208. ROTH, L. E., and SHIGENAKA, Y. (1964) The structure and formation of cilia and filaments in rumen protozoa. *J. Cell Biol.* **20**, 249–70.

209. ROUILLER, C., and FAURÉ-FREMIET, E. (1957) Ultrastructure réticulée d'une fibre squelettique chez un cilié. *J. Ultrastruct. Res.* **1**, 1–13.

210. ROUILLER, C., and FAURÉ-FREMIET, E. (1958) Structure fine d'une flagellé chrysomonadien: *Chromulina psammobia. Exptl. Cell Res.* **14**, 47–67.

211. ROUILLER, C., FAURÉ-FREMIET, E., and GAUCHERY, R. M. (1956) The pharyngeal protein fibers of the ciliates. *Proc. Stockholm Conf. on Electron Microscopy*, pp. 216–8.

212. ROUILLER, C., FAURÉ-FREMIET, E., and GAUCHERY, M. (1956) Les tentacules d'*Ephelota*; étude au microscope électronique. *J. Protozool.* **3**, 194–200.

213. RUDZINSKA, M. A. (1958) An electron microscope study of the contractile vacuole in *Tokophrya infusionum. J. Biophys. Biochem. Cytol.* **4**, 195–202.

214. RUDZINSKA, M. A. (1965) The fine structure and function of the tentacle in *Tokophrya infusionum. J. Cell Biol.* **25**, 459–77.

215. RUDZINSKA, M. A., D'ALESANDRO, P. A., and TRAGER, W. (1964) The fine structure of *Leishmania donovani* and the role of the kinetoplast in the leishmania-leptomonad transformation. *J. Protozool.* **11**, 166–91.

216. SAKAGUCHI, H. (1965) Pericentriolar filamentous bodies. *J. Ultrastruct. Res.* **12**, 13–21.

217. SAKAI, H., SOLARI, A. J., KIEFER, B., and MAZIA, D. (1966) The molecular subunit of the microtubules of the mitotic apparatus and its identification. In prep.

218. SANDBORN, E., KOEN, P. F., McNABB, J. D., and MOORE, G. (1964) Cytoplasmic microtubules in mammalian cells. *J. Ultrastruct. Res.* **11**, 123–38.
219. SATIR, P. (1965) Studies on cilia. II. Examination of the distal region of the ciliary shaft and the role of the filaments in motility. *J. Cell Biol.* **26**, 805–34.
220. SATIR, B., and ROSENBAUM, J. L. (1965) The isolation and identification of kineto-some-rich fractions from *Tetrahymena pyriformis*. *J. Protozool.* **12**, 397–405.
221. SATIR, P., and SATIR, B. (1964) A model for ninefold symmetry in α keratin and cilia. *J. Theoret. Biol.* **7**, 123–8.
222. SCHNEIDER, L. (1960) Elektronenmikroskopische Untersuchungen über das Nephri-dialsystem von *Paramecium*. *J. Protozool.* **7**, 75–90.
223. SCHNEIDER, L. (1964) Elektronenmikroskopische Untersuchungen an den Ernäh-rungsorganellen von *Paramecium*. I. Der Cytopharynx. *Z. Zellforsch.* **62**, 198–224.
224. SCHUSTER, F. L. (1963) An electron-microscope study of the amebo-flagellate, *Naegleria gruberi* (Schardinger). I. The ameboid and flagellate stages. *J. Protozool.* **10**, 297–313.
225. SCHUSTER, F. L. (1965) Ultrastructure and morphogenesis of solitary stages of true slime molds. *Protistologica* **1**, 49–62.
226. SEDAR, A. W., and PORTER, K. R. (1955) The fine structure of cortical components of *Paramecium multimicronucleatum*. *J. Biophys. Biochem. Cytol.* **1**, 583–604.
227. SILVEIRA, M., and PORTER, K. R. (1964) The spermatozoids of flatworms and their microtubular systems. *Protoplasma* **59**, 240–65.
228. SLAUTTERBACK, D. B. (1963) Cytoplasmic microtubules. I. *Hydra*. *J. Cell Biol.* **18**, 367–88.
229. SLEIGH, M. A. (1962) *The Biology of Cilia and Flagella*, Pergamon Press, Oxford.
230. SLEIGH, M. A. (1965) Ciliary coordination in protozoa. In *Progress in Protozoology*, Internat. Congr. Ser. 91, Excerpta Medica Foundation, London, pp. 110–1.
231. SNIGIREVSKAYA, E. S. (1964) An electron microscope study of fibrillar formations of *Bursaria truncatella* (Heterotricha). In *Electronnaia i Fluorestsentnaia Mikroskopiia Kletki*, Akademia Nauk SSSR, Nauchnyi Sovet po Problemem Tsitologii, pp. 43–49.
232. SOMMER, J. R. (1965) The ultrastructure of the pellicle complex of *Euglena gracilis*. *J. Cell Biol.* **24**, 253–8.
233. SOMMER, J. R., and BLUM, J. J. (1964) Pellicular changes during division in *Astasia longa*. *Exptl. Cell Res.* **35**, 423–5.
234. SONNEBORN, T. M. (1963) Does preformed cell structure play an essential role in cell heredity? In *The Nature of Biological Diversity*, ed. J. M. ALLEN. McGraw-Hill, New York, pp. 165–221.
235. SONNEBORN, T. M. (1964) The differentiation of cells. *Proc. Nat. Acad. Sci.* **51**, 915–29.
236. SOTELO, J. R., and TRUJILLO-CENOZ, O. (1959) The fine structure of an elementary contractile system. *J. Biophys. Biochem. Cytol.* **6**, 126–8.
237. STEINERT, M., and NOVIKOFF, A. B. (1960) The existence of a cytostome and the occurrence of pinocytosis in the trypanosome (*Trypanosoma mega*). *J. Biophys. Biochem. Cytol.* **8**, 563–70.
238. STEWART, J. M., and MUIR, A. R. (1963) The fine structure of the cortical layers in *Paramecium aurelia*. *Quart. J. Microscop. Sci.* **104**, 129–34.
239. TARTAR, V. (1961) *The Biology of Stentor*. Pergamon Press, London.
240. TARTAR, V. (1966) Morphogenesis in Protozoa. In *Research in Protozoology*, Vol. 2, ed. T. T. CHEN, Pergamon Press, Oxford (in press).
241. TAYLOR, C. V. (1920) Demonstration of the function of the neuromotor apparatus in *Euplotes* by the method of microdissection. *Univ. Calif. Publ. Zool.* **19**, 403–70
242. TAYLOR, C. V. (1941) Fibrillar systems in ciliates. In *Protozoa in Biological Research*, ed. G. N. CALKINS and F. M. SUMMERS, Columbia Univ. Press, New York, pp. 191–270.
243. TILNEY, L. G. (1965) Microtubules in the heliozoan *Actinosphaerium nucleofilum* and their relation to axopod formation and motion. *J. Cell Biol.* **27**, 107 A.

244. TOKUYASU, K., and SCHERBAUM, O. H. (1965) Ultrastructure of mucocysts and pellicle of Tetrahymena pyriformis. J. Cell Biol. 27, 67–82.

245. TRAGER, W. (1964) The cytoplasm of protozoa. In The Cell, Vol. 6, ed. J. BRACHET and A. E. MIRSKÝ, Academic Press, New York, pp. 81–138.

246. TUFFRAU, M. (1965) Les différenciations fibrillaires d'origine cinétosomienne chez les ciliés hypotriches. Arch Zool. Exptl. Gén. 105, 83–96.

247. VICKERMAN, K. (1962) The mechanism of cyclical development in trypanosomes of the Trypanosoma brucei sub-group: an hypothesis based on ultrastructural observations. Trans. Roy. Soc. Trop. Med. Hyg. 56, 487–95.

248. VILLENEUVE-BRACHON, S. (1940) Recherches sur les ciliés hétérotriches. Arch Zool. Exptl. Gén. 82, 1–180.

249. VIVIER, E., and SCHREVEL, J. (1964) Étude, au microscope électronique, d'une grégarine du genre Selinidium, parasite de Sabellaria alveolata L. J. Microscopie 3, 651–70.

250. WATSON, M. R., HÝNES, R. D., and WARR, J. R. (1965) Electrophoresis of the ciliary protein of Tetrahymena pyriformis. In Progress in Protozoology, Internat. Congr. Ser. 91. Excerpta Medical Foundation, London, p. 238.

251. WESSENBERG, H. (1966) Observations on cortical ultrastructure in Opalina. J. Microscopie, 5, 471–92.

252. WESTFALL, J. A. (1965) Nematocysts of the sea anemone Metridium. Amer. Zool. 5, 377–93.

253. WILLIAMS, N. E., and ZEUTHEN, E. (1965) An autoradiographic study of oral structures in synchronized Tetrahymena. In Progress in Protozoology, Internat. Congr. Ser. 91, Excerpta Medica Foundation, London, p. 232.

254. WILLIAMS, N. E., and ZEUTHEN, E. (1966) The development of oral fibers in relation to oral morphogenesis and induced division synchrony in Tetrahymena. C.R. Trav. Lab. Carlsberg, 35, 101–20.

255. WISE, B. N. (1965) Fine structure of Euplotes: Filaments, vesicles and kinetosomes. J. Cell Biol. 27, 113A–114A.

256. WISE, B. N. (1966) Unpublished work.

257. WOHLFARTH-BOTTERMANN, K. E. (1960) Protistenstudien X. Licht- und elektronenmikroskopische Untersuchungen an der Amöbe Hyalodiscus simplex n. sp. Protoplasma 52, 58–107.

258. WOHLFARTH-BOTTERMANN, K. E. (1961) Cytologische Studien VII. Strukturaspekte der Grundsubstanz des Cytoplasmas nach Einwirkung verschiedener Fixierungsmittel. Protoplasma 53, 259–90.

259. WOHLFARTH-BOTTERMANN, K. E. (1964) Cell structures and their significance for ameboid movement. Internat. Rev. Cytol. 16, 61–131.

260. WOHLFARTH-BOTTERMANN, K. E. (1964) Differentiations of the ground cytoplasm and their significance for the generation of the motive force of ameboid movement. In Primitive Motile Systems in Cell Biology, ed. R. D. ALLEN and N. KAMIYA, Academic Press, New York, pp. 79–108.

261. YAGIU, R., and SHIGENAKA, Y. (1959) Electron microscopical observation of Condylostoma spatiosum Ozaki & Yagui, in ultra-thin section. IV. The fibrils between the basal granule and the longitudinal fibrillar bundle. Zool. Mag. 68, 414–8 (in Japanese).

262. YAGIU, R., and SHIGENAKA, Y. (1960) Electron-microscopical studies of the fibrillar system in the protozoan ciliates. Jap. J. Exptl. Morphol. 14, 1–52 (in Japanese).

263. YAGIU, R., and SHIGENAKA, Y. (1960) Electron microscopical observations of Condylostoma spatiosum Ozaki & Yagui in ultra-thin section. VIII. The fibrils connecting the pre-oral membranelle. Zool. Mag. 69, 325–31 (in Japanese).

264. YAGIU, R., and SHIGENAKA, Y. (1963) An electron microscope study of the fibrillar system of two heterotrichous ciliates, Condylostoma spatiosum and Spirostomum ambiguum. In Progress in Protozoology, Proc. 1st Internat. Conf. Protozool., Prague, 1961, pp. 411–3.

265. YAGIU, R., and SHIGENAKA, Y. (1963) Electron microscopy of the longitudinal fibrillar bundle and the contractile fibrillar system in *Spirostomum ambiguum*. *J. Protozool.* **10**, 364–9.
266. YAGIU, R., and SHIGENAKA, Y. (1965) Electron microscopy of the ectoplasm and the proboscis in *Didinium*. *J. Protozool.* **12**, 363–81.
267. YUSA, A. (1964) Fine structure of some cortical fibrillar systems in *Frontonia vesiculosa*. *J. Protozool.* **11** (suppl.), 36–7.
268. YUSA, A. (1965) Fine structure of some buccal and cortical fibrillar systems in *Ophryoglena flava* with special reference to the so-called "uhrglaskörper". In *Progress in Protozoology*, Internat. Congr. Ser. 91, Excerpta Medica Foundation, London, pp. 213–4.
269. ZEUTHEN, E. (1964) The temperature-induced division synchrony in *Tetrahymena*. In *Synchrony in Cell Division and Growth*, ed. E. ZEUTHEN, Interscience Publishers, New York, pp. 99–158.

The following list of references, added at the time of reading of the page proofs of this chapter, consists of papers published since the preparation of the manuscript was completed; references to these papers have not been inserted in the text and their content is not covered in the chapter. The list is intended to include all pertinent recent publications on ultrastructure of ciliates and flagellates, and a sampling of relevant reports on fibrillar structures in other organisms (30. January 1967).

1. ANDERSON, E., and DUMONT, J. N. (1966) A comparative study of the concrement vacuole of certain endocommensal ciliates-a so-called mechanoreceptor. *J. Ultrastruct. Res.* **15**, 414–50.
2. ANDERSON, W. A., WEISSMAN, A., and ELLIS, R. A. (1967) Cytodifferentiation during spermiogenesis in *Lumbricus terrestris*. *J. Cell Biol.* **32**, 11–26.
3. BATISSE, A. (1966) L'ultrastructure des tentacles suceurs d'*Ephelota gemmipara* Hertwig. *C. R. Acad. Sci.* **262**, 771–4.
4. BATISSE, A. (1965) Les appendices préhenseurs d'*Ephelota gemmipara* Hertwig. *C. R. Acad. Sci.* **261**, 5629–32.
5. BIKLE, D., TILNEY, L. G., and PORTER, K. R. (1966) Microtubules and pigment migration in the melanophores of *Fundulus heteroclitus* L. *Protoplasma* **61**, 322–45.
6. BOISSON, C., MATTEI, X., and BOISSON, M. E. (1965) Le flagelle de *Trypanosoma gambiense* étudié au microscope électronique. *C. R. Soc. Biol.* **159**, 228–30.
7. BRADBURY, P. C. (1966) The fine structure of the mature tomite of *Hyalophysa chattoni*. *J. Protozool.* **13**, 591–607.
8. CHEISSIN, E. M. (1965) Ultrastructure of *Lamblia duodenalis* II. The locomotory apparatus, axial rod and other organelles. *Arch. Protistenk.* **108**, 8–18.
9. CRAWLEY, J. C. W. (1966) Fine structure and cytoplasmic streaming in *Physarum polycephalum*. *J. Roy. Microscop. Soc.* **85**, 313–22.
10. CULBERTSON, J. R. (1966) Physical and chemical properties of cilia isolated from *Tetrahymena pyriformis*. *J. Protozool.* **13**, 397–405.
11. DEMBITZER, H. M., and HIRSHFIELD, H. I. (1966) Some new cytological observations in the heterotrichous ciliate, *Blepharisma*. *J. Cell Biol.* **30**, 201–7.
12. DINGLE, A. D., and FULTON, C. (1966) Development of the flagellar apparatus of *Naegleria*. *J. Cell Biol.* **31**, 43–54.
13. ELLIOT, A. M., and CLEMMONS, G. L. (1966) An ultrastructural study of ingestion and digestion in *Tetrahymena pyriformis*. *J. Protozool.* **13**, 311–23.
14. FAVARD, P., and CARASSO, N. (1965) Mise en évidence d'un reticulum endoplasmique dans le spasmonéme de ciliés péritriches. *J. Microscopie* **4**, 567–72.
15. GONATAS, N. K. and ROBBINS, E. (1965) The homology of spindle tubules and neurotubules in the chick embryo retina. *Protoplasma* **58**, 377–91.

16. GRAIN, J. (1966) Étude cytologique de quelques ciliés holotriches endocommensaux des ruminants et des equidés. Thèses, Fac. Sci. Univ. Clermont-Ferrand C.N.R.S. 141 pp.

17. GRIM, J. N. (1966) Isolated ciliary structures of *Euplotes patella*. *Exptl. Cell Res.* **41**, 206–10.

18. GRIMSTONE, A. V. (1966) Structure and function in Protozoa. *Ann. Rev. Microbiol.* **20**, 131–50.

19. GRIMSTONE, A. V., and GIBBONS, I. R. (1966) The fine structure of thecentriol arapparatus and associated structures in the complex flagellates *Trichonympha* and *Pseudotrichonympha*. *Phil. Trans. Roy. Soc. London* B **250**, 215–42.

20. GRIMSTONE, A. V., and KLUG, A. (1966) Observations on the substructure of flagellar fibres. *J. Cell Sci.* **1**, 353–62.

21. ITERSON, W. VAN, HOENIGER, J. F. M., and ZANTEN, E. N. VAN (1967) A "microtubule" in a bacterium. *J. Cell Biol.* **32**, 1–10.

22. JONES, A. R., and JAHN, T. L. (1965) Effect of hexamethonium chloride on the ciliary and contractile systems of the ciliate *Spirostomum*. *J. Protozool.* **12**, 340–2.

23. JOYON, L., and LOM, J. (1966) Sur l'ultrastructure de *Costia necatrix* Leclercq (zooflagellé); place systématique de ce protiste. *C. R. Acad. Sci.* **262**, 660–3.

24. JURAND, A., and BOMFORD, R. (1965) The fine structure of the parasitic suctorian *Podophrya parameciorum*. *J. Microscopie* **4**, 509–22.

25. KIEFER, B., SAKAI, H., Solari, A. J. and MAZIA, D. (1966) The molecular unit of the microtubules of the mitotic apparatus. *J., Molec. Biol.* 75–80.

26. LEMBI, C. A., and LANG, N. J. (1965) Electron microscopy of *Carteria* and *Chlamydomonas*. *Amer. J. Bot.* **52**, 464–77.

27. MANTON, I. (1966) Observations on scale production in *Prymnesium parvum*. *J. Cell Sci.* **1**, 375–80.

28. MANTON, I., and STOSCH, H. A. von (1966) Observations on the fine structure of the male gamete of the marine centric diatom *Lithodesmium undulatum*. *J. Roy. Microscop. Soc.* **85**, 119–134.

29. MIZUKAMI, I., and GALL, J. (1966) Centriole replication. II. Sperm formation in the fern, *Marsilea*, and the cycad. *Zamia*. *J. Cell Biol.* **29**, 97–112.

30. NACHMIAS, V. T. (1966) Further studies by electron microscopy on fibrils from *Chaos chaos*. *J. Cell Biol.* **31**, 154A.

31. NAGAI, R., and REBHUN, L. I. (1966) Cytoplasmic microfilaments in streaming *Nitella* cells. *J. Ultrastruc. Res.* **14**, 571–89.

32. NIELSEN, M. H., LUDVIK, J., and NIELSEN, R. (1966) On the ultrastructure of *Trichomonas vaginalis* Donné. *J. Microscopie* **5**, 229–50.

33. OKIJIMA, A., and KINOSITA, H. (1966) Ciliary activity and coordination in *Euplotes eurystomus*. I. Effect of microdissection of neuromotor fibers. *Comp. Biochem. Physiol.* **19**, 115–31.

34. OKTEM, N. (1966) Observations sur l'ultrastructure de *Nyctotherus cordiformis* Stein, cilié parasite de batraciens. *C. R. Soc. Biol.* **159**, 1974–6.

35. PHILLIPS, D. M. (1966) Substructure of flagellar tubules. *J. Cell Biol.* **31**, 635–38.

36. PRELLE, A. (1965) Some ultrastructural aspects of the ciliate *Leptopharynx costatus* Mermod. *Prostistologica* **1**, 23–8.

37. PUYTORAC, P. DE, and GRAIN, J. (1965) Structure and ultrastructure of *Balantidium zenopi*, sp. nov., trichostome ciliate, parasite in *Xenopus fraseri* Boul. *Protistologica* **1**, 29–36.

38. RHEA, R. P. (1966) Electron microscopic observations on the slime mold *Physarum polycephalum* with specific reference to fibrillar structures. *J. Ultrastruc. Res.* **15**, 349–79.

39. ROBISON, W. G., JR. (1966) Microtubules in relation to the motility of a sperm syncytium in an armored scale insect. *J. Cell Biol.* **29**, 251–66.

40. RUDZINSKA, M. A., JACKSON, G. J., and TUFFRAU, M. (1966) The fine structure of *Colpoda maupasi* with special emphasis on food vacuoles. *J. Protozool.* **13**, 440–59.
41. SAKAI, H. (1966) Studies on sufhydryl groups during cell division of sea-urchin eggs. VIII. Some properties of mitotic apparatus proteins. *Biochim. Biophys. Acta* **112**, 132–6.
42. SIMPSON, C. F., and WHITE, F. H. (1964) Structure of *Trichomonas foetus* as revealed by electron microscopy. *Amer. J. Vet. Res.* **25**, 815–24.
43. TILNEY, L. G., HIRAMOTO, Y., and MARSLAND, D. (1966) Studies on the microtubules in heliozoa. III. A pressure analysis of the role of these structures in the formation and maintenance of the axopodia of *Actinosphaerium nucleofilum* (Barrett). *J. CellBiol.* **29**, 77–95.
44. TILNEY, L. G., and PORTER, K. R. (1965) Studies on microtubules in Heliozoa. I. The fine structure of *Actinosphaerium nucleofilum* (Barrett), with particular reference to the axial rod structure. *Protoplasma* **60**, 317–34.

METABOLISM AND PATHOGENIC MECHANISMS OF PARASITIC PROTOZOA

J. D. FULTON

National Institute for Medical Research, Mill Hill, London N.W. 7

CONTENTS

INTRODUCTION

Protozoa form one of the several large groups of organisms which, like bacteria and viruses, give rise to infectious diseases. Throughout the ages epidemics of cholera, plague, smallpox, yellow fever, and other diseases occurred but have now been brought under control. In tropical and subtropical climates, however, protozoan diseases still exact a heavy toll of human and domestic animal life and imperil social and economic welfare. Some of these diseases like amoebiasis and malaria are cosmopolitan in character. Malaria is undoubtedly the most destructive of human ills; new infections are estimated at 200 million or more per year with 2 million deaths. In India, China, and more recently in East Africa, leishmaniasis presents a serious threat to human life and welfare. Trypanosomiasis, both human and animal, has cast a blight over enormous areas in Africa and South America. Within recent years, a high mortality of sheep in New Zealand has been ascribed to toxoplasmosis; and to judge by the results of surveys, man himself is infected throughout the world. In backward lands these diseases sometimes prove disastrous, resulting in ill health followed by reduced production of food and other commodities, so that the inhabitants are impoverished and cut off from civilizing influences; the association of pestilence and famine is a common experience in human history. The etiology of these protozoal ills is now well understood, and in some cases the means to limit or eradicate them is at hand but have not always been applied with vigour. A promising aspect has been the eradication of malaria in some areas by residual insecticides. Such methods are however not applicable to all the above infections. Protection against protozoal diseases by vaccination with dead or avirulent organisms has not been applied to man but has proved successful in *Babesia* and *Anaplasma* infections in cattle.

As compared to bacteria the means by which protozoa exert their harmful effects is less well understood and research into the pathogenic mechanism involved less persistently investigated. While the main objective of biochemical investigation on parasitic protozoa has in some cases been the elucidation of their pathogenic mechanisms, progress has been restricted

The following abbreviations have been used in this article: ATP, adenosine triphosphate. DPN, diphosphopyridine nucleotide (now named NAD, nicotinamide adenine dinucleotide). DPNH, reduced form of DPN (now NADH$_2$). TPN, triphosphopyridine nucleotide (now named NADP nicotinamide adenine dinucleotide phosphate).† TPNH, reduced form of TPN (now NADPH$_2$). NPN, non protein nitrogen. PAB, p-aminobenzoic acid. TCA, tricarboxylic acid cycle or Krebs' cycle. RNA, ribonucleic acid. DNA, deoxyribonucleic acid. EMP scheme of glycolysis, Embden–Meyerhof–Parnas scheme.
Report of the Commission on Enzymes of the International Union of Biochemistry.

and success limited, largely because most protozoa are not easily cultured under axenic conditions and are not available in necessary amounts for study under suitable conditions. The introduction of techniques from other disciplines, such as paper chromatography and electrophoresis from chemistry, and others from physics, immunology and genetics, has done much to restore the balance in favour of the experimenter.

The efficient parasite lives in harmony with its host. The relationship may be a delicate one, as indicated by its marked specificity in choice of host and even site of invasion. Now more frequently recognized are zoonoses in which infection is transferred from an animal host to man or in the reverse direction by means of a vector. Lack of specificity in choice of host is also met as in toxoplasmosis. The effects on the host depend on a number of factors: age, sex, diet, genetic, and mechanical (as in the plugging of brain capillaries in malignant tertian malaria). Hypersensitivity, once produced in the host, may be important; also the site of infection, and any toxic substances produced. The number and virulence of the invading parasites likewise plays a part.

The phylum Protozoa comprises members with such varied and complex life cycles that class relationships are often not immediately apparent, and may not in fact exist. Although open to criticism the simple classification here used is satisfactory for the present purpose. The phylum has been divided into four classes given in the sequence in which they will be discussed. Different genera and species comprising a class will be discussed in the appropriate sections, under the title of the disease which they cause.

CLASSIFICATION

Phylum Protozoa

CLASS I. RHIZOPODA
        Amoebiasis

CLASS II. MASTIGOPHORA (FLAGELLATA)
        Trypanosomiasis
        Leishmaniasis
        Trichomoniasis

CLASS III. SPOROZOA
        Malaria
        Babesiosis (Piroplasmosis)
        Toxoplasmosis
        Sarcosporidiosis
        Coccidiosis

CLASS IV. CILIATA
        Balantidiosis

I. RHIZOPODA

Amoebiasis

Only one Rhizopod is pathogenic to man, *Entamoeba histolytica*, the pathogen of amoebiasis in man and of a symptomless infection in certain Old World monkeys. The disease in man is cosmopolitan and is acquired by swallowing infected material. The normal site of infection is the large intestine but secondary infections may occur in other tissues such as liver, brain, lung, and skin. Most infections are chronic and symptomless but may be acute and accompanied by dysentery. The parasite occurs in a motile trophozoite stage and in a cystic stage. Multiplication is by simple fission. Two races of different size are recognized, a non-pathogenic smaller, of mean diameter 7 μ, and a larger, of mean diameter 13 μ, a potential tissue invader, its members differing in virulence and invasive power. Among protozoa pathogenic to man, *E. histolytica* appeared for years to be practically unique in its requirement of other microorganisms for growth in culture; metabolic and physiological studies on it were bedevilled until recently by failure in culturing it axenically. Now this appears to have been accomplished, and we may look for progress in these fields.

Culture Experiments

Much information on the nutritional needs of *Entamoeba histolytica* has been obtained through culture experiments. Descriptions of those which gradually led to its axenic culture follow in approximately chronological order. Success was first obtained[45] in a diphasic medium of Locke-egg-serum (LES) consisting of coagulated egg with an overlay of Locke's solution plus human serum, maintained at 37°, a medium successful in the culture of other intestinal organisms. Later, human serum was replaced by crystalline egg albumin (LEA medium). Subcultures were made by transfer to fresh medium of a drop of sediment from the bottom of the culture tube. The method was applied to cultivation of *E. histolytica*[115] and other entozoic amoebae of man and monkeys, and it was found that better growth was obtained by the addition of solid rice-starch, which the amoebae ingested. With this medium all stages in the life cycle, including encystment and excystment, of *E. histolytica* and other species, can be obtained *in vitro*. Without giving much thought to the nutritional needs of the organism many authors have suggested modified versions of the above media.

In all the earlier experiments, culture of the amoeba was carried out in the presence of a mixed bacterial flora; it soon became obvious that a simplification of this flora was desirable. Bacteria-free material was obtained from the liver abscesses of cats experimentally infected with *E. histolytica*[95] and added to several media each containing one species of bacterium, thus establishing monoxenic cultures. Mercuric chloride was used to free cysts from bacteria, and the cleaned cysts used to initiate fresh cultures. Many other chemical agents have subsequently been so employed. Meleney and col-leagues[272] sterilized cysts in this way, and found[390] that no excystment occurred in the absence of living bacteria unless reducing agents such as cysteine or thioglycollate were added or oxygen tension was reduced. Rees[323] obtained cysts by microisolation and washed them in sterile solution to free them from bacteria. The method has had a wide application in the prepara-tion of monoxenic cultures with which to test the ability of a single species of bacterium to promote multiplication of amoebae. In this way the influence of twenty-six species of bacteria from widely different taxonomic groups was studied;[92] even wider investigations in this field have been made[51] by testing 65 bacterial types for ability to support growth of *E. histolytica*, but a study of the biochemical characters of these organisms did not lead to a better basis for growth. The method was also used to study excystment in microcultures in absence of bacteria.[325] Monoxenic cultures have also proved of value in chemotherapeutic tests *in vitro*, especially when employing an essentially liquid culture medium like that of Hansen.[180] Such culture is also of value in preparation of antigen material, and in growth studies, although growth is slower and metabolism is reduced. Further, it has provided a lead to the final goal of axenic culture. A novel type of monoxenic culture was prepared by Phillips[312] who eliminated bacteria with anti-biotics or by micro isolation of cysts, and replaced them by *Trypanosoma cruzi*, (with dead trypanosomes growth of amoebae succeeded only in microcultures). Others[294] carried out a series of experiments on the growth of *E. histolytica* cultures with *T. cruzi* heated at different temperatures. Their results suggest that possibly the entamoeba requires a heat-labile *T. cruzi*-respiratory enzyme. The original author[313] found that other related species of the genus *Trypanosoma* could not replace *T. cruzi* nor could three species of *Leishmania* or *Trichomonas*. One advantage of this type of culture is that *T. cruzi* can be eliminated by heat more readily than bacteria, and proteins and enzymes are not damaged. Also these trypanosomes resist antibiotics and amoebicides, so this type of culture is of value in chemotherapeutic tests. It is of interest that encystment does not occur in presence of *T. cruzi*. The dependence of *E. histolytica* on *T. cruzi* metabolism has been studied.[314] When metabolic activity of the trypanosome was completely inhibited, no growth of amoebae occurred or when amoebae and trypanosomes were separated by a semi-permeable membrane. These studies were extended[307] using other haemoflagellates, and best growth was attained in presence of *T. cruzi*. Phillips[315] has described further studies with the amoeba-try-panosome cultures and the improvements effected over a period of 10 years, but the exact role of the trypanosomes is still unknown.

An advance in culture technique was also made by Jacobs[196] in an attempt to grow amoebae in absence of live bacteria. For this purpose he freed amoebae in monoxenic cultures with *Clostridium perfringens* from bacteria by means of penicillin to which they are very sensitive. He then inoculated with amoebae a suitable medium containing *Escherichia coli* killed by heat and was able to subculture them over a period of some months. However some doubt has been cast on whether viable bacteria were not actually present.

Other authors[364, 365] were able to grow *E. histolytica* in sterile minced chick embryo, while Reeves and colleagues employed sterile chick embryo tissue juice for the same purpose.[327] Diamond[113] was unable to accept the claims of earlier authors that *E. histolytica* has been grown in absence of bacteria, protozoa, fungi, or intact metazoan cells. He presents evidence of his own success in growing the parasite axenically in culture over a period of months. The medium he used was diphasic and the liquid portion contained cell-free extract of chick embryo which appears to be essential for growth.

Although practical applications of the method have as yet been restricted, the problem of axenic culture appears to have been solved. It will now be easier to study the nutritional needs of the organism. The preparation of a simple culture medium for nutritional and other studies on *E. histolytica* has been described.[31, 302] This medium has the advantage of not supporting growth of *Blastocystis* with which many faecal samples are contaminated. Unsuccessful attempts to prepare an essentially synthetic medium were made;[181] the medium provided good growth but was very complex and contained buffered saline with trace minerals, amino acids, vitamins of the B group, nucleic acid, cholesterol and rice starch. Attempts to improve simple media by addition of proteins of low molecular weight have been unsuccessful. The presence of complex materials such as liver extract, egg, blood, serum, peptone, agar, vitamins, sugars and filtrates of dead as well as of live bacteria, used until recently, has hampered nutritional and physiological studies. Even the simplified media in which *E. histolytica* can be cultured *in vitro* provide only restricted information on the nutritional needs of the parasite. Nevertheless a few defined substances are regarded as essential for amoebic growth.

Siddiqui[378] sought to throw light on the variable biological characters of *Entamoebae* species, not morphologically distinguishable, by studying their temperature tolerance in culture. He used a classical strain of *E. histolytica*, the Laredo strain of this parasite, which is atypical, as well as *E. moshkovskii*, a free living form found in sewage and *E. invadens* from a grass snake. The survival rate of the different forms was observed at different temperatures. Optimal temperatures were determined as well as thermal death points. Some amoebae were induced to grow at what was originally an abnormal temperature. Growth at the higher temperatures was not correlated with size of trophozoites. The Laredo strain was regarded as a mutant of a normal strain of *E. histolytica*. It has been accepted that anaerobiosis is a growth requirement for *E. histolytica* and that CO_2 may be a growth factor. Because of the low oxygen tension and high CO_2 tension which occurs in the human large intestine, similar conditions for growth in culture and for isolation of this organism were adopted by Nelson and Jones[303] by using a CO_2–bicarbonate buffer system in their medium. It consisted of Hanks BSS, 1.4 per cent sodium bicarbonate solution, horse serum, and rice powder. Growth and encystment of strains in culture followed a pattern corresponding to that *in vivo* and the basic characters of the strains were not altered by prolonged cultivation. The ready and vigorous growth response of strains indicated that the physiological needs of the organism were being supplied. It is sometimes necessary to prepare large amounts of *E. histolytica* for serological or biochemical studies and Reeves and Ward[328] have therefore used the modified Shaffer-Frye medium[326] in thin layers under purified nitrogen. The chamber in which the organisms were grown was provided with a vessel containing 30 per cent sodium hydroxide to absorb volatile acid products of metabolism. The quantity of bacterial cells added was of importance in controlling the yield of amoebae. The authors were able to obtain 2–4 ml packed amoeba containing 100 mgm or more dried weight of organisms per ml from each litre of medium. The harvest appeared to be 20 times as great as that usually obtained in tubes and the method should prove of advantage in studies on this organism.

   E. histolytica has been cultured[229] in a three-amino acid medium to which serum and cells of *Bacteroides symbiosus* had been added. When iron salts were omitted from the medium the amoeba did not survive more than two or three transfers. It appeared that growth and multiplication was closely correlated, in first transfers, with the iron content of the original medium which was present mostly in the ferrous form. In support of the data that iron was a growth requirement for *E. histolytica* evidence was obtained that the antiamoebic activity of 7-iodo-8-hydroxy quinoline-5-sulfonic acid was due to the iron-binding property of this substance.

CARBOHYDRATES

   Rice starch was first used in culture[115] to improve amoebic growth; some hold that rice is a source of carbohydrate, as suggested by glycogen storage within the parasite following its use, while others maintain that it also provides protein. Analysis of rice starch and rice powder used in cultivation of *E. histolytica* showed that a number of substances are present, including carbohydrates, lipids, fatty acids, and protein, as well as vitamins.[276] The fact that sugar is broken down under anaerobic conditions suggests that a glycolytic system is functioning. Incubation of washed trophozoites with uniformly labelled ^{14}C-glucose was used to measure the amount of labelled glycogen and CO_2 produced and it appeared that the amoebae used extracellular glucose.[39] Interesting reports on carbohydrate metabolism were given,[221, 222] from which it appeared that CO_2 and H_2S are formed by either intact or lysed *E. histolytica* in presence of sugars under anaerobic conditions if cystine is also present; also that glucose is phosphorylated and pyruvate formed and decarboxylated. Other hexoses or sucrose

could replace glucose. A pathway of biological oxidation was evident in
E. histolytica in which dehydrogenase activity and sulphur-reducing enzyme
systems take part. Bragg and Reeves[52] have studied the pathway of
glucose dissimilation by the Laredo strain of *E. histolytica* which grows at
a lower temperature than normal strains of this parasite and is reported to
ferment glucose to CO_2, H_2, acetic acid, and ethanol as main products,
plus a small amount of lactic acid. All enzymes of the EMP pathway were
demonstrated; proof rested on the degree of labelling of the carbon dioxide
produced from glucose-^{14}C, labelled in various ways and by step-wise
degradation of the acetic acid derived from glucose-1-^{14}C. Earlier work[119,
186] indicated that carbohydrate was broken down by *E. histolytica*, partly
by the Entner–Doudoroff pathway and partly by the EMP pathway, in
agreement with the finding of aldolase in the parasite.[277] H_2S was also
produced in small amount. It was suggested[366] that rice flour added to
cultures may be acted on by bacteria to provide intermediate breakdown
products beneficial or essential to the multiplication of amoebae. It can
however be dispensed with when *T. cruzi* is present.

LIPIDS

The suggestion[391] that cholesterol acted as a growth factor has received
some support. It has been recognized that it may also act by absorbing
harmful fatty acids produced during culture. It appeared[171] that it could
replace serum in liver infusion medium. Others[81] have studied the influence
of added cholesterol and dihydrocholesterol upon the multiplication of nine
strains of *E. histolytica* in a particular medium. Dihydrocholesterol was
found to inhibit growth of eight of these strains, whereas cholesterol inhibited
growth of six and had no observed effect on the remainder. Results did not
suggest that the growth-inhibitory effect of dihydrocholesterol was due to
interference with cholesterol metabolism. A variety of other steroids was
found to repress growth of one strain of the organism. The authors discuss
a possible relationship between sensitivity to dihydrocholesterol and amoebic
pathogenicity.

The lipid needs of *E. histolytica* in culture are usually supplied by the crude
material present in the medium, and cholesterol has been widely studied in
this way. The need of the organism for steroid has been confirmed[230] and
information provided on the most suitable type. For this purpose the horse
serum used in a modified Shaffer-Frye culture medium was replaced by a
trace of rabbit *Bacteroides symbiosus* antiserum, so that there was a deficiency in sterol-containing lipids. The medium was supplemented by human
and horse serum and growth promoting activity appeared to reside in the
neutral lipid fraction. It was further traced to the fraction containing free
cholesterol, whereas the cholesterol ester fraction was inactive. Cholesterol
fulfilled all lipid requirements and only sub-optimal growth was obtained
with β-sitosterol, whereas other related compounds were inactive.

PROTEINS

The formation of ulcers has often been ascribed to the need of E. *histolytica* for proteins or their breakdown products such as peptones and amino acids. In this connection, Snyder and Meleney[391] drew attention to the need of blood serum in culture media. Since the accompanying bacteria grew in its absence, the need for serum was probably referable directly to the amoebae. Others have suggested, as a result of their extensive cytochemical studies,[321] that the chromatoid bodies, sometimes observable in amoebic cysts, function as a store for proteins. However the chemical composition of these bodies is not known; it should provide an interesting study for the biochemist.

PHYSICO-CHEMICAL FACTORS

Tonicity and pH are also of importance in cultures of E. *histolytica* and it was pointed out[195] that control of oxidation-reduction potential in culture media, in absence of bacteria, had not till then been given consideration, while other authors indicated[391] the importance of anaerobiosis. It is not clear whether harm is done directly to the amoeba by oxygen or through oxidation of some essential factor required by the parasite. In this connection studies[59, 60] have indicated the diffusion of reducing and nitrogenous substances from coagulated egg medium and the effect thereby exerted on growth.

There was evidence of small-scale spontaneous oxidation in stored medium. The findings were in agreement with the theory that some component of egg-white which aided growth of E. *histolytica* may be rendered inactive by oxidation. Some investigators provided[83, 197] much useful data on the best conditions of oxidation-reduction potential for growth in culture and their relationship to excystation and encystation. In the absence of bacteria, chemical agents such as cysteine, thioglycollate and reductone may be used as agents for providing low oxidation-reduction potential.

NUTRITIONAL NEEDS

Although excessive growth of bacteria may prove harmful in culture, it is clear that these organisms supply metabolites and other factors to the amoebae which engulf them. They may also supply enzymes for utilization of available food. In this connection Nakamura,[291] following his earlier investigations on heated T. *cruzi* as a nutritional source, supplied E. *histolytica* in culture with succinic dehydrogenase from rabbit heart, to replace that supplied by T. *cruzi*. He was able to subculture on ten occasions by this means; but the mechanism of action of the enzyme was not elucidated. Subsequent studies[292, 295] on the nutritional needs of the parasite have suggested that DPN, ATP and ribose-5-phosphate supplied factors usually provided by bacteria, and the need for vitamins and co-enzymes as well as their function have been discussed. Nakamura and colleagues[293, 298] have also studied the effect of a wide range of antimetabolites on growth of *E. histolytica* and sometimes obtained an inhibition of growth which could be reversed by the appropriate substance. In continuation of studies on growth requirements of *E. histolytica*[475] the presence of altered structures in accompanying bacteria in culture which they term "round bodies" have been described and appeared to result from treatment with penicillin. The conclusion was reached that they promoted growth of amoebae and were thought to be bacterial protoplasts with a high content of RNA.

PATHOGENESIS

The part played by bacteria in the pathogenesis of amoebic infection has been clearly indicated by Phillips and colleagues.[317] Cultures of *E. histolytica* grown with *T. cruzi* were inoculated intracaecally in three groups of young guinea pigs: germ-free animals, animals with one intestinal bacterium, and animals with the usual mixed intestinal flora. The amoeba did not establish itself in the germ-free hosts. In animals with one bacterium, except those harbouring a streptobacillus, and also in those with mixed flora, the incidence of infection was above 90 per cent. It was thought that although *E. histolytica* is the specific organism of intestinal amoebiasis, other microorganisms play a part in the development of the disease. In their absence the amoebae appeared to be harmless inhabitants of the intestine. Phillips[316] carried out further studies in this field and found that a lesion sometimes developed when inoculation of *E. histolytica* in association with *T. cruzi* was accompanied by trauma of the caecal wall at the site of inoculation or when reducing agents such as cysteine or thioglycollate were added to the mixture. Amoebae were able to survive in germ-free tissue, but when very active specially cultured amoebae were used for inoculation, amoebic lesions resulted in the germ-free host. The parasites when transferred from one germ-free host to another were more effective in producing lesions than those from culture. Tissue infections resulted but there was absence of propagation in the germ-free intestine, and death rarely occurred in these germ-free animals. Attention has been drawn[363] to the variation in character of different strains of *E. histolytica*, including size, ability to grow in culture, and to produce disease in animals. The authors also investigated the lytic power of some strains for the red blood cells of different animal species, which in the past was attributed to the presence of endotoxins. It was recognized that there was some selectivity in the lytic properties of various strains of the parasite for the erythrocytes of these species. Others[350] investigated the changes in electrophoretic properties of serum proteins in amoebic liver disease and observed a fall in total protein with concomitant rise in gamma globulin. The serum cholinesterase level has been used as a test of liver function in amoebiasis[367] and found to be much lower in those infected than in normal individuals. When the liver was also involved the esterase level fell further than when only intestinal amoebiasis was present.

The precipitins, known to be present for many years in cat serum during experimental *E. histolytica* infection have now been more fully investigated in the case of human patients.[19] The pattern of precipitation in agar gel with serum from infected human patients was described. At least ten lines of precipitation were present in those with symptomatic infections, in contrast to the fewer lines described by earlier authors, and the reaction appeared to be specific in character. The quality of the amoebic antigen used was of paramount importance. It is known that polymorphonuclear leucocytes attack *E. histolytica* when the latter are damaged by agents such as heat. Experiments have now been carried out to find whether normal amoebae produce a factor which inhibits leucocytes.[199] The results led to the belief that *E. histolytica* had a toxic effect on leucocytes of the eight animal species tested. Rapid and extensive lysis of leucocyte cytoplasmic granules took place possibly as a result of release of enzymes from lysosomes within them which can digest structural elements. The amoebae presumably produce these results through their enzymes but these do not appear to be proteolytic in nature. The factors which govern the pathogenicity of *E. histolytica* are still not clear especially as it has been found that the enzyme patterns of pathogenic and non-pathogenic types are similar. The above authors believe that their observations may assist in the understanding of pathogenicity and virulence in this parasite. Neal[301] has investigated the influence of ency-station on the invasiveness of *E. histolytica*. A virulent strain was passed through three excystment-encystment cycles. The virulence of the three substrains was then determined by the degree of caecal ulceration produced in experimentally infected rats. There was no change in virulence after encystation. There was however some evidence that periodic encystation may preserve invasiveness. The effect of cholesterol on growth and virulence of *E. histolytica* was investigated[369] as it was not clear from previous work whether the influence exerted by this steroid was merely on growth and nutrition of the organism. The author used a strain of parasite non-infective for rats; any change in virulence or pathogenicity could therefore be con-veniently studied. There appeared to be no correlation between size of cysts and trophozoites and virulence. Marked ulceration occurred in rats when cholesterol was added to the growth medium or when this material was included in the host diet. It was concluded that cholesterol exerted a marked increase in virulence which persisted for long periods. The exact mechanism of its production, whether direct or indirect, is still not clear. Hussein[191, 192] investigated the pathogenicity in man and animals of *E. histolytica* from the point of view of cyst size, since it is well recognized that large and small forms exist. He found that each race bred true without alteration in size or character. Acute amoebiasis occurred only in infections due to the large race. Biagi *et al.*[41, 42] have studied the effect of cholesterol on the patho-genicity of *E. histolytica* in guinea-pig infections and came to the conclusion that it increased invasiveness for intestinal mucosa and caused production

of hepatic abcesses. The presence of large amounts of cholesterol in the
intestine was correlated with larger lesions in the caecum and amoebic
abscess of the liver was encountered almost exclusively in animals whose
blood cholesterol was raised.

ENZYMES

Various authors have studied the enzymes present in amoebae. Hyaluronidase was found[50] in material cultured from the freshly isolated liver
of hamsters but disappeared on continued culture, suggesting that it may
appear only in vivo. Due possibly to differences in technique among the
several authors the presence of this enzyme has been as often denied as
confirmed. By three different methods its presence was repeatedly confirmed[200] in E. histolytica from human infections. By an ingenious method
amylase was demonstrated in cultures containing soluble starch;[179] it was
also found by others and quantitative determinations of its activity were
made.[29] Evidence has been provided[182, 324] that the amoeba also contains a protease and the important observation was made that one strain
could digest human and animal intestinal epithelium. Further studies of the
action of this enzyme on a number of natural and synthetic substrates were
also made.[201, 202] The authors concluded that whether pathogenic or not,
E. histolytica possessed peptic and tryptic, but not chymotryptic, powers.
Neal[300] reported that a high proteolytic activity did not appear to be
necessary for invasion of the intestinal wall by amoebae. Nakamura and
Edwards,[296, 297] in a series of enzyme studies, have detected gelatinase
and casease in the amoeba and list a large number of enzymes reported
present by other authors. Among them is acid phosphatase demonstrated
cytochemically.[79] While alkaline phosphatase, amylase, aldolase and lactic
dehydrogenase were also reported to be present.[277]

Summary

In spite of the profusion of data available on the cultural and biochemical
characters of E. histolytica it is still difficult to draw sound conclusions about
its nutritional needs and its metabolism. The reason for this is partly that,
until recently, the complex of E. histolytica and bacteria was being studied,
and the biochemical contribution of each organism could not be accurately
assessed. A beginning has however been made in studying the part played
by the associated organisms; a concentrated study on the comparative
biochemistry of those organisms which support growth, as well as those
which do not, should yield information of value. Early success in cultivation
with the complex media then employed was probably a reflection of the
amoeba's poor synthetic capabilities which as a phagotroph it is able to
offset. Fundamental information is gradually being built up and if the new
medium of axenic cultivation can be simplified and defined, success in

nutritional and metabolic studies is assured. Complete analysis of the enzyme systems present in the parasite, in which progress has recently been made, will also become feasible. Former difficulties in obtaining sufficient material for study have in part been offset by the use of more refined techniques and apparatus. Biochemists are being increasingly attracted to this potentially fruitful field of protozoan studies.

The fundamental factors in the pathogenesis of amoebiasis are still far from clear. The study of the amoebic enzymes should be helpful in describing how tissues are invaded, although ulcer formation and tissue destruction are no longer attributed entirely to the histolytic action of the amoeba. However it is probably true that the invasive characteristics of the organism are in part due to the presence of hyaluronidase. The digestion of intestinal epithelial tissues by proteolytic enzymes present in the amoeba, as already described, is also highly significant, and the part played by bacteria is likewise accepted as a contributory factor in the pathogenseis of the disease.

II. MASTIGOPHORA (FLAGELLATA)

Trypanosomiasis

Trypanosomes parasitize a wide range of vertebrate hosts including fish, amphibians, reptiles, birds, and mammals. They were seen in fish in the first half of the 19th century. Gruby accorded them generic status in 1843. Interest in them was revived in 1878 when Lewis saw them in the blood of rats in India and in 1880 when Evans found that they were the parasite of surra, a disease of horses and camels in India and elsewhere. In 1894 Bruce recognized their role in the serious cattle disease then known in Zululand as nagana. Human trypanosomiasis was first recognized at Bathurst on the Gambia River where in May 1901 Forde found trypanosomes in the blood of a European, later named by Dutton *Trypanosoma gambiense*. In 1902 Castellani found trypanosomes in human blood in Uganda and showed that they were also present in the cerebrospinal fluid of sleeping sickness patients.

In 1910 *Trypanosoma rhodesiense*, described by Stephens and Fantham as a new species, was found in a much more acute infection. Human and animal trypanosomiases are diseases of considerable antiquity and have exercised a baleful influence on African history. During a 1902–5 epidemic in Uganda 200,000 people, equivalent to two-thirds of the population, died in the province of Busoga. The disease in man is now under control but eradication has not been effected; today the disease is of greater economic importance in cattle than in man. In Africa trypanosomiasis is transmitted mainly by tsetse flies, of which more than twenty species are known; it has denied vast areas to domestic animals as well as cutting off the human inhabitants from civilizing influences. The method of trypanosome development in the tsetse fly varies with the species of trypanosome. Infection is also carried to animals by other biting flies, such as Tabanids. *T. equiperdum* is the parasite in the disease of horses known as dourine; it is transmitted during coitus. *T. lewisi* is carried by the rat flea and infects rats when its vector is ingested. The scourges in East and West Africa by infections of *T. rhodesience* and *T. gambiense* respectively are paralleled by those in Brazil where Chagas in 1909 first reported the presence of *T. cruzi*. This trypanosome is carried by reduviid bugs and is transmitted through faecal contamination at the biting site; multiplication of the leishmania form takes place in the tissues of the mammalian host and the cycle is continued in blood and lymph by trypanosome forms as in the case of the African species.

Trypanosomes were the first parasitic protozoa to be used for physiological research; the literature on the subject is now considerable. The phenomenon of drug resistance in microorganisms was first observed in trypanosomes by Ehrlich and colleagues early in this century and has led to much investigation and speculation; and many species of trypanosomes, in both man and animals, have been used in metabolic studies.

Hoare[187] has suggested a classification of trypanosomes of medical and veterinary importance based on phylogenetic considerations and supported by similarities in physiological characters. This classification is briefly outlined in Table 1 and includes nearly all the species for which metabolic data are given below.

It is of great interest that von Brand and colleagues[57, 61] have suggested that mammalian trypanosomes may be divided into groups according to the effect of cyanide on their aerobic respiration. The oxygen uptake of the blood forms of the *lewisi* subgroup is markedly suppressed by 0.001 m cyanide, that of the *evansi* and *brucei* subgroups is unaffected or even stimulated by the same concentration, and that of the congolense group is affected to an intermediate degree. The cyanide insensitive trypanosomes also use glucose much faster than the sensitive. In their studies on the influence of -SH inhibitors on the blood stream form of some trypanosomes, the same authors[62] reported that the *lewisi* group was less sensitive to these inhibitors than the *brucei* group, the reverse of what had previously been found for cyanide. The division agree fairly well with those[187] based on differences in life cycle and morphology. These points will be discussed later when some of the metabolic experiments on which the results were based have been recorded.

Metabolic Studies

Respiratory and Carbohydrate Metabolism

Attention has been drawn[299] to the dark purple colour of blood infected with trypanosomes of the *brucei-evansi* groups, resulting from deficient oxygenation of haemoglobin during the later stages of infection in some animals. There was no compensatory increase in carbon dioxide. Fenny-vessy and Reiner[127] measured the oxygen consumption and carbon dioxide production of the blood stream form of *T. equiperdum* and found them

TABLE 1. CLASSIFICATION AND CHARACTERS OF TRYPANOSOMES STUDIED, BASED ON HOARE (1957)

| | Lewisi group | | Vivax group | Congolense group | Brucei group | | | | |
| | | | | | Brucei sub-group | | Evansi sub-group | | |
	T. lewisi	T. cruzi	T. vivax	T. congolense	T. gambiense	T. rhodesiense	T. evansi	T. equinum	T. equiperdum
Mammalian hosts	Rats	Man, dog, cat, armadillo, opossum	Bovines, sheep, goat, antelope	Bovines, equines, pig, sheep, goat, dog	Man	Man, antelope	Bovines equines, camel, dog	Equines	Equines
Insect host or vector	Fleas	Triatomid bugs	Tsetse flies	Tsetse flies	Tsetse flies	Tsetse flies	Tabanid flies	Tabanid flies	None
Distribution	Cosmopolitan	America	Tropical Africa	Tropical Africa	Tropical Africa	Tropical East Africa	Cosmopolitan	S. America	Europe, Africa, Asia

Table I is reproduced with permission of the Editor of *Experimental Parasitology* from an article by Fulton and Spooner, 1959 **8**, 137.

unaffected by cyanide. Others[329] made quantitative studies on the relationships between oxygen consumption, glucose utilization, and acid production, which Fennyvessy[126] showed to occur with sugar breakdown. Christophers and Fulton[93] carried out extensive experiments on the respiratory metabolism of normal and arsenic-resistant strains of *T. rhodesiense*, which behaved very similarly apart from the reaction to arsenicals, and found the metabolism unaffected by cyanide. Numerous experimenters have shown that oxygen is rapidly consumed by blood-stream forms and much more slowly by the corresponding culture forms. The respiratory quotient varies from group to group, being low in the pathogenic African forms and high in the *T. lewisi* group, and in developmental stages. Experiments will be described later in which the behaviour of the blood stream and culture forms of *T. rhodesiense* and *T. gambiense* were compared directly. The composition and physical characteristics of the medium in which trypanosomes respire are of importance. The addition of certain sugars, plasma or serum, certain amino acids, and buffering agents has proved beneficial. The importance of glucose for *T. lewisi* was first shown by Biot et al.[43] Kudicke and Evers[220] found that many of the common hexoses, with the exception of galactose, aided survival; glycerol also proved a good substrate. Later authors[466] found the enormous amount of glucose metabolized by the pathogenic African trypanosomes to be in the order of 50 to 100 per cent of their dry weight per hour. Moulder[287] showed that young forms of *T. lewisi*, which later reproduce, use less oxygen than older dividing forms, but more sugar. Glucose also aided the development of trypanosomes in culture.[176] Sugar consumption is higher in the *evansi-brucei* group than in the *lewisi* group. There does not appear to be a carbohydrate reserve within these parasites; they soon disintegrate and die if glucose is not present. In the case of *T. cruzi*, however, this is not the case and little or no carbohydrate substrate appears to be used by it. Some indication of the nature of enzymes present in the various groups, as judged by the effect of cyanide and other reagents, will be discussed more fully in connection with particular investigations. It has been established that the enzyme systems of the blood-stream African pathogenic trypanosomes differ from those of the culture forms corresponding to the proventricular form in the tsetse fly, as we shall see later. In this connection the presence or absence of heavy-metal respiratory catalysts, such as the cytochromes, has marked implications from the phylogenetic point of view. The loss of enzymes on adoption of a parasitic existence has been discussed by a number of workers.[218] Thus the culture forms of trypanosomes, which correspond to developmental stages in the insect vector, are regarded as more primitive than and ancestral to the blood stream forms.

Desowitz[109] investigated the effect of anti-serum on the respiratory rate of *Trypanosoma vivax*, and found that oxygen consumption was reduced and lysis of the parasites was apparent. The method was claimed to provide a rapid and simple method for determining antibody titres during the immune response to trypanosomiasis. Subsequent authors[263] observed that sera from patients infected with *T. gambiense* inhibited the respiration of trypanosomes *in vitro* whereas that from normal individuals did not. The effect of ageing and of complement on the reaction was also studied.

It was found[357] that 2-deoxy-*d*-glucose inhibited the fermentation of mannose, glucose, fructose and glycerol by *T. gambiense*. Glucose fermentation was similarly inhibited in *T. rhodesiense*. The evidence suggested that the substance inhibited metabolism at two sites in the Embden–Meyerhof–Parnas pathway of glycolysis. The inhibition of glycerol utilization was much more sensitive to reversion by glucose than that of the others. A second analogue of glucose, namely glucosamine, which resembles 2-deoxy-*d*-glucose structurally, was also capable of inhibiting glycerol utilization but had no apparent effect on the fermentation of glucose. The structure of these inhibitors were shown to be highly specific. The possibility that 2-deoxy-*d*-glucose inhibits the transport of substrates across the cell wall was discussed. Baernstein[27] has written a most useful review on electron transport mechanisms in parasitic protozoa, including trypanosomes. He is of the opinion that problems of cultivation and harvesting in a sufficiently pure state must be attempted before satisfactory results can be obtained. Some progress in this direction has been made in recent years.

Intermediate Carbohydrate Metabolism

Glucose is the carbohydrate most readily available to trypanosomes in the mammalian host. The degradation products produced in its breakdown indicate that oxidation is generally incomplete. The process of breakdown proceeds farthest along the glycolytic chain in the *lewisi* group and less far in the *brucei-evansi* group. Some studies on the breakdown of sugar are described below in approximately chronological order, indicating the nature of the enzymes present, including those of phosphorylative type.

Although it was shown by earlier workers that glucose was decomposed aerobically and anaerobically by trypanosomes, little was known about the steps involved till Reiner, and others[329] described experiments with *T. equiperdum* and *T. lewisi*. They found that the former breaks down sugar anaerobically by forming 1 mol pyruvate and 1 mol glycerol from each molecule of glucose. The same reaction occurred as a first step aerobically and was followed by oxidation of the glycerol to pyruvic acid and water; a little lactic acid and CO_2 were also formed. *T. lewisi* decomposed glucose anaerobically by forming 1 mol succinic acid and 1 mol glycol. On oxidation of the latter the final products were succinic, acetic and formic acids, along with CO_2 and ethyl alcohol. No proof of the occurrence of phosphorylating reactions was obtained. It was reported[154] that glucose was broken down aerobically to succinic, pyruvic, lactic, acetic, and formic acids along with glycerol, ethyl alcohol, and CO_2 by the blood stream form of *T. rhodesiense*, but quantitative data were not provided. Previously it was shown[346] that in washed suspensions of *T. lewisi*, aerobic and anaerobic glycolysis was activated by carbon dioxide; they characterized chemically the end products of glucose breakdown. Chen and Geiling[91] described the transformation of glucose into fructose 1,6-diphosphate by lysed *T. equiperdum*, followed by splitting of the latter and the coupled oxidation-reduction of 3-phosphoglyceraldehyde into the corresponding acid, with formation of pyruvic acid, thus proving that a phosphorylative mechanism is involved. Studies of the intermediate steps in the breakdown of glucose by *T. evansi*[261] gave further evidence that glycolysis proceeds by the classical chain of phosphorylating reactions. Harvey[183] used *T. hippicum* (*T. evansi*) in similar studies to find whether biochemical differences exist between parent strain and its arsenic-fast variant. Glucose and glycerol were oxidized quantitatively to pyruvic acid; anaerobically, glycerol was also formed. The breakdown occurred by the normal EMP pathway and many of the enzymes involved were specifically analysed. A number of dehydrogenases were present but the presence of cytochrome oxidase or of succinic, malic, or lactic dehydrogenase could not be demonstrated. Little catalase was present and no evidence of a tricarboxylic acid cycle. Moulder[286, 287] studied the oxidative metabolism of *T. lewisi* in phosphate-saline, paying attention to the possible effects of antibodies on metabolic processes. It was found that a number of sugar and other substrates were broken down in the absence of CO_2. The high rate of oxidation of glutamine and glutamate is of interest. Changes in the nature of glucose metabolism by *T. lewisi* in the rat, described earlier, were related chronologically to the appearance of the enzyme ablastin which prevents reproduction. Ablastin appears to bring about these changes by inhibition of oxidative assimilation in such a way as to stop cell division and growth. There was no evidence of a TCA cycle and neither pyruvate, succinate, fumarate or α-ketoglutarate were oxidized to a significant degree. Further studies on the metabolism of *T. lewisi*[343] showed that aerobic metabolism depended on a complete cytochrome system and inhibition was light-reversible in the case of carbon monoxide. Cyanide strongly inhibited respiration, while sensitivity to arsenite was much lower than in the members of the brucei group. Lactic and succinic dehydrogenases, cozymase, and a complete succinoxidase system were present. The main breakdown product of glucose was succinic acid, accompanied by lactic and small amounts of pyruvic and acetic acids. This author[345] compared the manner of breakdown of glucose in 11 species of trypanosome, both aerobically and anaerobically. Cyanide sensitivity was studied and spectroscopic examinations for cytochromes carried out. The blood stream form of *T. congolense* had been relatively little studied until Agosin and von Brand[8] identified the main metabolic end products from glucose and established quantitative relationships between the amount of substrate utilized and metabolites produced. They found that O_2 was consumed nearly as fast as by the brucei forms but glucose was used at a lower rate. The RQ was high and the products, acetic, pyruvic, and traces of succinic acid with CO_2, accounted for nearly all the glucose used. Observations on the metabolism of the culture form of the same species were first carried out by von Brand and Tobie.[63] These forms correspond to the non-infective stages occurring in the tsetse fly host. Like the blood stream form the culture form was sensitive to cyanide and the sulphydryl inhibitors iodoacetamide and arsenite, but only to a slight extent to the Krebs' cycle inhibitors fluoroacetate and malonate. The RQ was about 0.9; aerobically, glucose was broken down mainly to pyruvate and acetate, with small amounts of lactate, succinate, and glycerol. Anaerobically, the chief products were pyruvate acetate and succinate and also a little glycerol. A comparison of the carbon balances of other culture trypanosomes so far studied clearly showed that both qualitative and quantitative differences existed. The possibility of characterizing groups of culture flagellates by their metabolic patterns, as with the bloodstream forms, has not yet been achieved. The need had long been felt for further comparative studies on the blood-stream and culture forms of other trypanosomes. Such studies were carried out by von Brand and colleagues[65] with *T. gambiense*; they showed that profound qualitative and quantitative differences exist among these forms. By the blood-stream form, glucose was almost quantitatively degraded to pyruvate, but the culture form gave little pyruvate, with large amounts of succinic and acetic acids as well as C_1, C_3, C_4, and C_5 volatile acids and some lactic acid. The respiratory quotient of the culture form was about unity, and very low, less than 0.1, in the blood stream form, which consumed more oxygen. The need for study of the infective forms occurring in the tsetse fly was stressed by the authors. Ryley[346] carried out an investigation on the comparative metabolism of the bloodstream and culture forms of *T. rhodesiense*. This trypanosome undergoes marked changes in habitat and morphology during its life cycle. In the bloodstream it is polymorphic varying from long slender forms through intermediate to stumpy forms containing volutin granules. Changes in shape occur in the tsetse fly from the long thin forms in the mid-gut through crithidial forms to short metacyclic forms in the salivary glands, the infective forms for the mammalian host. The author describes biochemical differences and similarities found in an old monomorphic, syringe-passaged strain in rats, all being long and slender, and a cultured form of the same species maintained at 24°C. The motility and respiration of both forms depended on an extracellular supply of substrate. These trypanosomes showed intense motility and little translatory movement; this is of interest in connection with the synthesis of acetyl choline by this organism.[71] But acetyl choline may have functions other than contributing to motility; it was absent in another, less active protozoan, *P. gallinaceum*. Both forms of the trypanosome were able to oxidize glycerol, glucose, fructose and mannose; culture forms were also able to use some Krebs' cycle intermediates such as a-keto-glutarate, succinate, malate, and fumarate. As with other culture forms the respiratory quotient was high. Glucose was oxidized mainly to CO_2 and water, accompanied by small amounts of acetic and succinic acids. Anaero-bically, succinate was preponderately formed and CO_2 was assimilated. In the blood stream form the RQ was low and pyruvic acid the main end product, under anaerobic conditions accompanied by glycerol. Cell-free preparations of both forms contained phosphorylating enzymes and a number of dehydrogenases. Fumarase and aconitase were also present. Pyruvic oxidase was present in culture forms but absent in blood-stream forms. Grant and Fulton[166] used ^{14}C labelled glucose to study the meta-bolic pathways involved in the formation of pyruvate by the parent strain, some drug resistant variants, and a recently isolated human strain of the same species. Their experiments also showed that pyruvate is a main product of glucose breakdown by *T. rhodesiense in vitro*. For this purpose [U-^{14}C]-, [1-^{14}C]- and [3-4-^{14}C] glucose and [Na^{14}C]-bicarbonate were used, as well as [2-^{14}C] acetate. The distribution of isotope in pyruvate formed by the incubation of *T. rhodesiense* with specifically ^{14}C-labelled glucose was in agreement with the Embden–Meyerhof–Parnas (EMP) scheme.

Only minor amounts of glucose were used for cell synthesis or evolved as $^{14}CO_2$. Under anaerobic conditions equal amounts of pyruvate and glycerol were formed. The oxidative pathway of glucose utilization in which C_1 of glucose is evolved as CO_2 does not appear to be used to any extent. The incorporation of ^{14}C from [U-^{14}C] glucose in succinate and cell carbon indicates that a small amount of pyruvate is metabolized by the trypano-some. The similar radioactivities of alanine and aspartate in trypanosome protein from U-^{14}C glucose suggested a direct synthesis of oxalacetate from pyruvate and CO_2, from which succinate, labelled in the carboxyl group, was formed. The negligible radioactivity in fatty acids and protein-bound glutamic acid from U-^{14}C glucose or pyruvate, and respiratory CO_2 from the [2-^{14}C] acetate, indicated a negligible formation or utilization of acetate by reactions of the TCA cycle. The very high blood-pyruvate level was correlated with the degree of infection and suggests that this substance is the main *in vivo* end product, as indicated by earlier chemical data and also that more was formed than the host could metabolize. Its further metabolism was studied by comparing radioactivities of metabolites after incubation of trypanosomes with [U-^{14}C] glucose, [2-^{14}C] acetate or with $NaH^{14}CO_3$. It appeared that succinate was formed through fixation of CO_2 leading to oxalacetate from pyruvate followed by reduction. The resistant variants of the parent and the recently isolated strain behaved similarly. In their studies on terminal respiration in mammalian trypanosomes, Fulton and Spoon-er[152] used specific methods with seventeen species including some culture forms as well as blood-stream forms, to find whether the presence or absence of a cytochrome system is correlated with the biological classification of these organism. At least two different types of respiratory enzyme systems were observed, as indicated by a difference in cyanide sensitivity; they occurred not only in blood stream forms of different species but in blood-stream and culture forms of the same species. The scheme outlined by Hoare[187] did not wholly agree with the chemical results. The sensitivity to cyanide of the blood-stream form of *T. congolense*[62] and of *T. vivax*[110] was not confirmed when the white cells were completely removed. Results with azide were rather variable and depended to a considerable extent on the pH of the medium. Neither of these substances is a specific inhibitor of the cytochrome system. The use of carbon monoxide and the reversal of its action by light confirmed that a heavy metal-catalysed respiratory system does operate in cyanide sensitive trypanosomes, shown by spectroscopic methods to contain cytochromes a and b. The culture form of *T. gambiense* was shown for the first time to contain these bands and similar bands are now known to be present in corresponding forms of *T. rhodesiense*. The culture form of *T. lewisi* but not that of *T. cruzi* also showed the cytochrome *c* band. The respiration of the latter was inhibited to some degree by carbon monoxide in the dark but reversal by light was not apparent. There was no evidence of a similar system in the other groups shown in Table 1. Even where cytochromes were demonstrated the presence of a cytochrome oxidase was not confirmed, possibly due to the presence of a succinic dehydrogenase which kept cytochrome *c* reduced. It is also possible that trypanosome cytochrome oxidases do not oxidize mammalian cytochrome *c*, or only at a very slow rate. It was not clear whether the transition from a cytochrome to a non-cytochrome pathway, occurring during the development of African trypanosomes, took place in the mammalian host or in the insect at the infective stage. To settle this point a study of insect salivary gland forms seems necessary; this would prove technically very difficult. A study of the transition in the reverse direction when the blood stream forms are reverting to insect forms in culture would however be feasible. Vickerman[431] has expressed some views on this matter which will be discussed later. The respiration of all the species studied was very sensitive to peroxide; this suggests that they do not contain catalase. The inhibition was probably not due to interaction with thiol groups of trypanosome enzymes, since other thiol inhibitors such as iodoacetamide and arsenite affect only brucei-group trypanosomes. Homogenates of *T. rhodesiense* oxidized reduced diphosphopyridine nucleotides (DPNH) by a system in which cytochrome was absent. Although *T. rhodesiense* can survive for some hours anaerobically the possibility of exploiting this pathway for chemotherapeutic purposes was considered since it differs from the condition in the mammalian host. While a cytochrome system was observed in the insect and blood-stream forms of the *lewisi* group, no evidence for a similar system was found in the latter forms of the vivax, congolense or brucei-groups. The presence and nature of cytochrome in the different species of pathogenic trypansomes is import-

14*

ant both theoretically and practically for chemotherapy as well as for phylogeny. As Moulder has pointed out, a new and efficient respiratory system has replaced the cytochrome system, if we judge by the high QO_2 of the African trypanosomes, and is able to function more rapidly than the systems present in the ancestral forms, the monogenetic insect flagellates. While this has created some difficulties regarding the views on evolution of the mammalian trypanosomes, the presence of an efficient oxidase system points to a highly advantageous special adaption to the parasitic existence. Grant and Sergent[167] have investigated the hydrogen transport systems in cell free extracts of *T. rhodesiense* in which cytochromes are absent but a high rate of respiration is present. They have described the properties of what they term a L-α-glycerophosphate oxidase, and its role in respiration; its action does not appear to be mediated by pyridine nucleotides. The substrate specificity and marked activity of this oxidase indicated that it could account for almost all the *in vitro* respiratory activity of the parasite. The latter, like a number of other tissues, contains a cytoplasmic diphospho-pyridine nucleotide (DPN)-linked α-glycerophosphate dehydrogenase and a particulate α-glycerophosphate oxidase system which reacts with oxygen. The L-α-glycerophosphate oxidase system in trypanosomes differed from that of mammalian origin, however, in that its reaction with oxygen was not mediated by a cytochrome system. They believe that the reactions catalysed by the two components are coupled and constitute a hydrogen transport systen for oxidation of reduced diphosphospyridine nucleotide (DPNH). This is effected by indirect hydrogen transfer to the respiratory chain via L-α-glycerophosphate. Grant and others[169] investigated further the nature and distribution of respiratory enzymes and enzyme systems present in subcellular fractions of blood-stream and culture forms of trypanosomes, and showed that they occurred in particulate sub-cellular fractions. The L-α-glycerophosphate oxidase present in blood-stream forms of the brucei group was insensitive to cyanide. In contrast, succinoxidase and α-glycero-phosphate oxidase activities in the corresponding culture forms and in blood stream forms of *T. lewisi* were inhibited by cyanide. A difference in the type of oxidase and the magnitude of dehydrogenase in the blood and culture form of *T. rhodesiense* was noted. This doubtless reflects the change in temperature and oxygen tension on passing from a warmblooded to an insect host. The oxidase system described above was then found by Grant and Sergent[168] to catalyse the oxidation of L-α-glycerophosphate to di-hydroxyacetone phosphate in presence of certain electron acceptors. It was termed an anaerobic L-α-glycerophosphate dehydrogenase and its activity was inhibited by certain thiol group reagents. It appeared that a thiol group essential for the activity of the intact oxidase is located in the dehydrogenase component. Anderson et al.[13] concluded from ultramicroscope studies on *T. equiperdum* that no mitochondria were present in this organism. Vicker-man,[431] however, in studying by similar methods the members of the brucei group during cyclical development, reported that both the blood-stream and culture form of *T. rhodesiense* contained a mitochondrial system, much more developed in the latter. He believes that mitochondria are produced at a specific time in the life cycle of the trypanosome, namely on transition from mammalian blood-stream to insect mid-gut forms. The ultrastructure changes during development were correlated with respiratory metabolic studies. Besides the absence of cytochrome pigments the blood forms lack the ability to use the Krebs' cycle intermediates possessed by the culture forms. Terminal respiration of the former is mediated as described above by a L-α-glycerophosphate oxidase-L-α-glycerophosphate dehydrogenase system. The absence of cytochromes and Krebs' cycle enzymes, which occur in higher cells, is significant, for in the latter they occur in different situations in the mitochondria. In the tsetse fly glucose concentration and oxygen tension is reduced and the trypansome adapts itself by producing more mitochondria accompanied by a change in the respiratory pathway. The actual mechanism of production of these particles is not known. It is known, however, that cytochrome synthesis in other microorganisms takes place as the result of the lowering of oxygen tension. According to Vickerman, cytochrome synthesis in trypanosomes may be equated with mitochondrial production. The interesting observation is made that trypanosomes like *T. evansi*, which do not develop in the tsetse gut, as well as syringe-passaged forms, have little use for the kinetoplast, which is intimately associated with mitochondrial production, and may dispense with it and assume the akinetoplastic form. His view is that mitochondrial regression may occur when trypanosomes reach the metacyclic stage (the infective stage for mammals) in the tsetse fly, and may even be a requisite for infection.

Fat Metabolism

Although it was known from early in the century that some trypanosomes contained extractable lipids no experimental evidence has been provided on the nature of fat metabolism in these organisms. Kligler and Olitzki,[215] on studying the antigenic composition of *T. evansi*, extracted this parasite with different solvents and found that nearly 60 per cent of the cell weight is lipoidal in nature; they believed that the antigenic peculiarities of the trypanosome were ascribable to the presence of the lipids. Krijgsman,[218] in his extensive researches on the same organism, found that lipase was absent. It was moreover reported[286] that *T. lewisi* cannot metabolize formate or acetate. In the blood of rats with the virulent *T. equiperdum* infection, Linton[237, 238] found an increase in lipoidal phosphorus and lecithin, but in the non-pathogenic infection with *T. lewisi*, normal values. Cholesterol levels in blood remained unaffected even at the acute stages of infection. Moraczewski and Kelsey[278] used ^{32}P to study metabolism of phosphorus compounds in their investigation on the distribution of phospholipid and phosphoprotein fractions in *T. equiperdum*. Many other reports of a similar nature have appeared without adding fundamentally to our knowledge. Ikejiani[193] also carried out experiments in rats with the pathogenic *T. equiperdum* and non-pathogenic *T. lewisi*, to find whether differences in chemical composition, including lipids, explained their varied response to chemotherapeutic agents. It was indicated[58] that the culture form of *T. cruzi* contained more lipid than carbohydrate. Grant and Fulton[166] described the incorporation of isotopic glycerol derived from [U-^{14}C] glucose into trypansome lipids. The utilization of [2-^{14}C] acetate for lipid fatty acids indicates that fatty acid and triglyceride synthesis took place under these conditions *in vitro*.

A study was made[462] of the ingestion by *T. lewisi* and *T. equiperdum* of oil previously stained with Sudan IV in an attempt to clarify the physiology of fat absorption by this genus. An arsenical incorporated in the dyed material proved an effective trypanocidal agent when given orally. Similar studies[461] with a fluorescing agent, acridine orange, dispersed in cod liver oil, indicated that combination occurred between the acridine and cytoplasmic components of *T. lewisi*. The method offered a means of studying the passage of lipids into cells. Lipids of *T. brucei* have also been studied[163] when it was found that they accounted for 12 to 19 per cent of the dry weight of the parasite. Similar products appeared to be present in *T. vivax*.

Protein Metabolism

Because of their rapid rate of division it is clear that some trypanosomes must synthesize protein at a very high rate. There is, however, no experimental evidence that they can synthesize the smaller building blocks like amino acids from the simplest substances such as ammonia and available carbon sources. It follows that amino acids or peptides are either supplied by the host in plasma or other body tissues or as a result of the enzyme activity of the parasite on the host tissues. Krijgsman[218] in his studies on *T. evansi* showed that many of the necessary enzymes were present in the trypanosome. He identified the proteinase cathepsin, capable of splitting casein and peptone but not serum proteins. A number of peptidases were also present including carboxy- and amino-polypeptides, also a dipeptidase, but urease and aminases were absent, as well as pepsin- and trypsin-like enzymes. From immunological studies the specificity of trypanosome protein is accepted although studies on the chemical composition, including that of component amino acids, has not yielded clear indications of this specificity. Williamson and Desowitz[453] described some properties of protein fractions separable from homogenates of various species by electrophoretic and paper chromatographic methods. Intracellular amino acids were demonstrable in all the organisms, and alanine was present in considerable amount. In nine different species a close similarity existed in amino acid composition. It is now known that transamination reactions are of importance as a source of amino acids. Yet on the whole the protein metabolism of trypanosomes has been neglected. It was early recognised that addition of protein or amino acids to the suspension medium for trypanosomes was important for their continued activity. When respiratory methods were used, however, it was not always clear whether the latter increased oxygen uptake as the result of autoxidation or by serving as a metabolic substrate. The minute amount of plasma sometime present was believed to exercise its effect by supplying co-factors when glucose was present.[454]

Williamson and colleagues have investigated trypanosomal proteins more exhaustively by potentiometric and base titration and by electrophoretic methods.[68, 451, 452] Results are discussed in relation to the cytoplasmic composition of other types of cell, to microsomal nucleoprotein as a locus of drug action, and to the antigenic constitution of the parasite. Chemical and physical techniques have been employed to show that variant-specific antigens consist of two groups of unconjugated soluble proteins, a major 4S group and a minor 1S group. Gel diffusion studies showed that cellsap contained the highest concentration of antigens. Absorption experiments suggested that the agglutination and trypanocidal activity of anti-trypanosome immune serum is associated with 4S antigens.

Moulder[286] showed that *T. lewisi* oxidized glutamate and glutamine rapidly in absence of glucose, asparagine only slowly and dl-alanine not at all. It is also believed that trypanosomes can derive energy from protein by oxidative deamination reactions, although it was found that in cultures of *T. rhodesiense* and *T. gambiense* only traces of ammonia were produced.[413] An association between protein synthesis and sugar metabolism was shown.[166] On incubation of the blood-stream form of *T. rhodesiense* with [U-^{14}C] glucose it appeared that glutamic acid in the trypanosome protein remained essentially unlabelled whereas high radioactivity was found in alanine and aspartic acid and significant activity in serine and glycine. However, in massive trypanosome blood infections, it is unlikely that cell protein synthesis occurs to a significant extent as a result of breakdown of glucose. The high pyruvate content of blood in this infection, following incomplete catabolism of glucose by the parasite, may through decarboxylation and transamination reactions have contributed to protein synthesis. The high content of free alanine, already noted in this parasite, may have arisen by this reaction. The recent demonstration[73] of alanine as the chief constituent of the free amino acids of the tsetse may be relevant to trypanosome metabolism in this vector. Active transamination in cyclically transmitted *T. vivax* of cattle has been described.[404] Serum glutamic–oxalacetic transaminase (SGOT) and serum glutamic–pyruvic transaminase (SGPT) were followed throughout the period of infection; the latter was raised during parasitaemia but there was no exact correlation between the degree of parasitaemia and transaminase activity although the latter fell when parasites disappeared. High levels of both transaminases have been found in homogenates of living trypanosomes. Lippi and Sebastiani[239] reported a progressive rise in SGOT and SGPT during the course of experimental *T. brucei* infections in guinea pigs, believed to result from lesions in liver, heart, adrenals, and nervous tissue. The general nature of the changes taking place in the composition of blood serum during protozoal infection has been widely studied but does not appear to have yielded much information of fundamental importance. Schueler[353] during an investigation on drug-resistance in trypanosomes suggested that the appearance of resistance involved a shift in the iso-electric point of some of the protein constituents of trypanosome cell protein. Others[156] have investigated the blood serum fractions of guinea pig and man at different stages of infection with African trypanosomes by the classical method of Tiselius and by micro-electro-phoretic techniques, with similar results. The chief effect noted in the guinea pig was an increase of γ-globulin at the expense of α-globulin. At the early stage of the disease in man albumin was markedly decreased and γ-globulin increased; in the later stages there was a return to more normal values suggesting that the early changes were non-specific. Lysenko[249] analyzed the proteins of sera from rats infected with *T. lewisi* following treatment with salicylate, using the micro-Kjeldahl and electrophoretic methods. He found that the level of total protein and of γ-globulin fractions was higher in the untreated rats, which showed ablastic activity. It was concluded that salicylate treatment prevented ablastin formation, which when present was in the γ-globulin fraction. Olberg[306] separated the proteins of mice and guinea pigs infected with *T. brucei* into 7–10 fractions by paper-electrophoresis. The chief alteration observed was lowered albumin content, not specific for the disease.

Recent Studies on Culture Forms

The methods previously in use for the culture of pathogenic African trypanosomes did not promote the development of the infective metacyclic forms found in the tsetse fly. Trager[424] was able to overcome this difficulty by growing *T. vivax*, *T. brucei* and *T. congolense* in tsetse fly tissue culture. For this purpose the salivary glands and alimentary tract of a newly emerged fly and late pupa of *Glossina palpalis*, obtained aseptically, were grown in hanging drop cultures to which a minute drop of blood or trypanosome concentrate from an infected animal was added. The most interesting result was obtained with *T. vivax* which normally develops in the tsetse fly pro-boscis. When the cultures, usually maintained around 30°C, were raised to 38° and injected into a sheep, infection resulted. A method is therefore now available for obtaining these metacyclic forms *in vitro* and it should thus be possible to study the factors responsible for infectivity of trypanosomes. The relatively light infections which occurred in sheep after injection of these culture forms has also suggested to the author the possibility of immuniza-tion against this parasite by the use of attenuated cultures. Another series of related researches of this nature is of great interest. It is well known that strains of trypanosomes which have been passaged for a long time by syringe cannot be cultured or transmitted cyclically by the tsetse fly. Gordon and Miller[165] observed that tsetse flies artificially fed on culture forms of *T. rhodesiense* appeared to develop gut infections more readily than flies fed on infected mammalian hosts. In their early experiments *Glossina morsitans* was allowed to feed through a guinea pig skin membrane on a culture from a human patient which had been subcultured more than thirty times, and a patent salivary gland infection developed. One fly fed 27 days previously showed typical metacyclic forms. A guinea pig on which a number of flies similarly treated had fed had typical polymorphic forms in a peripheral blood film 9 days later. This method has therefore great possibilities for providing research workers with the infective metacyclic forms.

An important paper dealing with all aspects of trypanosomiasis which illustrates the urgent need for research in this field has been presented.[241] In dealing with the parasite, methods of preservation at low temperature, measurement of infectivity of value in chemotherapeutical studies, immunity, and susceptibility of various hosts were described as well as methods of culture. The production of metacyclic forms for setting up cyclically transmitted infections in the laboratory was also discussed. Studies on the vector including its physiological characters have provided data of value for application to the problems of breeding in the laboratory. By cytochemical methods Lehmann[231] made some limited studies of enzymes in blood stream and cultural forms of trypanosomes. Whereas it had been reported that trehalose, a disaccharide which occurs in the tsetse fly, could restore infectivity to cultural forms of *T. rhodesiense*, the present author could not confirm these findings. He observed acid phosphatase in bloodstream forms of *T. rhodesiense*, *T. congolense* and *T. brucei* but not in *T. gambiense*. An interesting observation was that the infectivity of a culture of *T. rhodesiense* disappeared at nearly the same time as the acid phosphatase content diminished, but a causal relationship between them was not established. A comprehensive review on the use of avian embryos and tissue culture methods in the study of parasitic protozoa has been made by Pipkin *et al.*[318, 319] while the nutrition and physiology of the *Trypanosomatidae* has been well described.[174]

Trypanosoma cruzi

Since the characters, mode of transmission, and metabolic activities of *T. cruzi* differ widely from those of the African trypanosomes, it is given special consideration here; it possesses an added interest in the reports of a number of authors that injection of extracts of the organism have proved curative for certain types of malignant tumour. Unfortunately these results have not been substantiated nor has the claim that the trypanosome contain endotoxins. The organism does however provide growth promoting substances for *Entamoeba histolytica* cultures.[312]

T. cruzi gives rise to South American trypanosomiasis or Chagas's disease which is not amenable to chemotherapeutic treatment. Transmission to man is by reduviid bugs, by the contaminative method; the faeces of the transmitting agent containing metacyclic trypanosomes infect the wound caused by the insect bite. No dividing forms are found in the peripheral blood and multiplication occurs in organs and tissues, especially the heart muscle. Within a host cell the trypanosome assumes the leishmanial form, and after repeated divisions the leptomonad and subsequently the crithidial form, which again invades the blood stream and becomes a trypanosome.

It was first noted[53] that the blood stream form, in contrast to African pathogenic trypanosomes, uses very little sugar. Oxygen is consumed and CO_2 produced and the RQ is about 1.0. The organism is cyanide-sensitive and while cytochromes a and b are detectable spectroscopically, cytochrome c appears to be absent, as first noted.[30] These authors failed to obtain inhibition of respiration by carbon monoxide. The cytochromes presented other peculiarities. There is considerable similarity between the behaviour of the blood stream and culture forms. Unlike the other trypanosomes described, a supply of extra-cellular hexose is not required for motility. The culture form possesses an endogenous respiration and the polysaccharide present is not glycogen but is composed of galactose rather than glucose units.[58] In spite of the clinical importance of the disease there is relatively little known of the intermediary metabolism of the blood stream form of the parasite. The culture form has been more often studied and appears to have a phosphorylating type of glycolysis which may not correspond exactly with the classical Embden–Meyerhof–Parnas scheme. The main products of sugar degradation are succinic, accompanied by acetic and lactic acids and in some cases formic and pyruvic acids, depending on the age of the culture. In contrast to the brucei group of trypanosomes *T. cruzi* can degrade glucose beyond the pyruvic acid stage. Available data suggest that the TCA cycle may also be involved, since it was shown[56] that certain intermediates of this cycle are consumed. Aldolase was the first enzyme of the glycolytic chain identified.[28] Unlike the corresponding enzyme from yeast it proved independent of metal activators. Certain enzymes of the TCA cycle have also been identified, for example the TPN-linked iso-citric dehydrogenase,[10] as well as a typical succinic dehydrogenase.[9] It is therefore puzzling that succinic acid should be present in culture. Baernstein[22, 23] found that an active malic dehydrogenase was present which was linked to cytochrome and fumarate reduction, possibly through flavoproteins. Fumarase was also present. The detection of aldolase, isomerase, and triose-phosphate dehydrogenase in homogenates of *T. cruzi* provided further evidence for the presence of a conventional glycolytic system. However α-glycerophosphate was not detected nor lactic dehydrogenase, although pyruvate occurs in culture. Their absence was possibly due to the method of preparation of homogenates by sonic vibration in $NaHCO_3$. Fumaric dehydrogenase and transaminases were also present but not aconitase, which is characteristic of the Krebs' cycle. The failure of carbon monoxide to inhibit oxidase suggested that the oxidase of *T. cruzi* differs from the cytochrome c oxidase of other organisms. These TCA-cycle enzymes are missing in the brucei group of trypanosomes. In absence of sugar von Brand et al.[64] observed an increase in ammonia nitrogen in cultures of *T. cruzi*, indicating that nitrogenous materials were being metabolized. It was of interest therefore to learn[36] of the presence of transaminases in this organism whereby glutamic acid was formed from α-ketoglutarate and alanine from pyruvate in presence of a number of amino acids, and also provided evidence relating to amino acid metabolism. Halevy[177] carried out comparative studies of lipid metabolism in *Trypanosomidae* including *T. cruzi*, and showed that steroid was synthesized by this species. Sterols were present in free form and contained more glycerides than some related species; less radiocarbon was incorporated from labelled substrates. Boné and Parent[46] have put forward evidence that serum present in culture media provides stearic acid which they believe is an essential growth factor for *T. cruzi*. The synthetic capabilities of *T. cruzi* have been indicated by a study of its nutritional requirements. Haematin and ascorbic acid have long been accepted as growth factors[246] but many gaps in our knowledge of the biochemistry and physiology of *T. cruzi* remain. Fernandes and Castellani[128] have studied nucleotide and polynucleotide synthesis in this organism by means of radioactive glycine and adenine, the former to study *de novo* synthesis of purines and the latter to study the behaviour of preformed substrates. The adenine was incorporated at a high rate indicating that the preformed purine pathway was preferred. Glycine was incorporated with acid-soluble adenine nucleotides and with protein but at a slow rate. These authors[129] confirmed the use of free purines as precursors for synthesis of nucleotides, by studying the effect of purine analogues on *T. cruzi* in culture. Both 6-mercaptopurine and certain adenine antagonists showed a marked inhibitory effect. In further studies, Silva and colleagues[379] observed the effect of the amino nucleoside of stylomycin on *T. cruzi* in tissue culture and found that it produced a marked effect on intracellular leishmania forms. This effect could not be counteracted by adenine, adenosine, desoxyadenosine, or the metabolites which may take part in the *de novo* synthetic pathway to purine nucleotides. The same authors[130] found the above aminonucleoside saved the lives of infected mice and appeared to change the acute disease into a chronic form. Analogues of the aminonucleoside inhibited the incorporation of adenine into the nucleic acid purines of *T. cruzi*.[80] Rey and Fernandes[330] studied the *in vitro* synthesis of pyrimidine nucleotides in *T. cruzi* and showed that orotic acid can be incorporated into soluble nucleotide and nucleic acid pyrimidines. Uracil was a good precursor of pyrimidine nucleotides.

Zeledón[469-473] carried out a series of studies on four species of haemoflagellates from culture, including *Endotrypanum schaudinni* and *T. cruzi*.

14 a*

Respiration was measured in the presence of various substrates, and the author believed that a complete tricarboxylic acid cycle of metabolism was involved. Transamination reactions were observed. The effect of pH changes and of inhibitors suggested the importance of -SH enzymes and also those with a heavy metal catalyst. Shaw et al.[370] also studied intermediary carbohydrate metabolism in the same two organisms, as well as others, using autoradiographic techniques with [14 C]-glucose as substrate. The main route of glucose breakdown was by the Embden–Meyerhof–Parnas reaction and evidence of a Krebs' tricarboxylic cycle was also obtained. These experiments are of interest because they included *E. schaudinni* which has been little studied from the physiological aspect since its discovery more than 50 years ago.

Physiological Lesions in Trypanosome Infections

The mechanism by which trypanosomes damage their hosts is still far from clear in spite of the considerable amount of work devoted to this problem, mostly in infections with pathogenic African trypanosomes. Three opposing views have been put forward: (1) that a toxin was responsible, although this has never been proved; (2) that exhaustion of blood sugar and glycogen reserves occurred, also unproved; (3) that internal asphyxia occurred. This latter view was put forward[214] and it was thought the increased metabolism of sugar during infection caused a rise in lactic acid in blood and thereby lowered the oxygen carrying power of haemoglobin, leading to interference with oxidation processes. Yorke[465] drew attention to the presence of auto- and iso-agglutinins in the blood of man and animals suffereing from trypanosomiasis. Others[15] believed that agglutination of *T. equiperdum* in the heart and lungs of infected rats prevented proper aeration of blood. Scheff and Rabati[352] studied the oxygen consumption of normal and trypanosome-infected mice and concluded that the host tissues were rendered anoxic as a result of oxygen consumption by the parasite. Von Brand[54] studied the gaseous exchanges in *T. equiperdum*- and *evansi*-infected rats. His results did not confirm those of some earlier authors, since the increase in the oxygen consumption of the hosts was significant only towards the end of fatal infections, as a result of parasite respiration, and was not sufficient to asphyxiate the hosts. Other authors have ascribed disturbance of liver function and failure to lay down glycogen to the consumption of blood sugar by large numbers of parasites, but this cannot be the real explanation, since such disturbances occur when parasites are few. It will be remembered also that *T. cruzi*, which is pathogenic, consumes very little sugar, but does invade muscle cells, especially those of the heart. The effect of infection on nitrogen metabolism has been widely studied. French [137-141] in his investigations on animal trypanosomiasis has reported a disturbance of nitrogen metabolism resulting in increased excretion. There was also a change in mineral metabolism and a lowering of albumin/globulin ratios of plasma proteins, but only inconstant changes in the total level of proteins. In sleeping sickness the protein content of the CSF is increased. Non-protein nitrogen was increased at the time of crisis, but blood urea was not altered. Disturbances in fat metabolism have already been noted and fatty changes in host organs may be produced. Zwemer and Culbertson[476] found a notable increase in serum potassium during *T. equiperdum*-infection of rats, probably arising from red cells or tissues. They believed the increase was an important factor in the cause of death. Other effects of parasitism on the host depend on a number of factors indicated earlier. Protozoa may also cause allergic conditions. From the biochemical point of view relatively little is known of the relationship between the physiological activities of the parasites and the reaction of host tissues.

The toxic manifestations which occur in humans infected with *T. rhodesiense* and *T. gambiense* have been described.[203, 337] Although jaundice was not common there was a parenchymatous disorder of the liver, indicated by an increase in serum bilirubin in early cases but not necessarily in late cases. The bromsulphthalein test was abnormal in the early acute febrile case. There were also abnormalities in urinary pigment, excess urobilinogen being present in a large proportion of cases accompanied by bilirubinuria and frequently by seroflocculation abnormalities. Abnormal hippuric acid synthesis also occurred. Serum protein changes were detected by electrophoresis and the pathogenesis of these changes was discussed. In early acute cases a reduction in total protein and serum albumin occurs before any rise in γ-globulin, but increase of the latter may be considerable in the chronic stage. Biochemical changes in human serum have also been discussed[122] at various stages in the course of *T. gambiense* infection, including those of protein, pigments, cholesterol, and other substances. Results have been compared with those obtaining in *T. rhodesiense* infection and the authors believe serum changes could serve as a basis for distinguishing the species of parasite present. The effect of treatment on the changes is also discussed and much information, adequately documented, is provided. Gray[170] measured the serum transaminase levels in African sheep and cattle infected with *T. vivax*. Glutamic-pyruvate transaminase (GPT) and glutamic-oxalacetic transaminase (GOT) levels were determined before and after infection. The GPT level was unaltered during the prepatent period but increased in amount in proportion to the number of trypanosomes present in the blood; after treatment it became normal. The rise in GOT level in serum was smaller than in GPT. Homogenates of *T. vivax* contained large amounts of these substances compared with normal serum and it is possible that the increases observed during infection were the result of destruction of the trypanosomes themselves and not due to their pathological effects on the host tissues. Infections with *T. lewisi* in rats have proved of considerable interest to parasitologists particularly in regard to immunity due to the presence of an antibody named ablastin, which inhibits reproduction of the trypanosome and reduces glucose utilization, from which one end product is lactic acid. D'Alesandro and Sherman[104] have therefore sought to determine whether changes occur in lactic dehydrogenase in this parasite associated with the presence of antibody. Three times as much enzyme was present in the parasites during the early reproducing phase of infection when consumption of glucose was high as in the nonreproducing phase, but no qualitative changes in the enzyme were detected in the later phases. Enzyme activity was not inhibited by ablastic serum and it therefore appears that ablastin affects the enzyme level of the parasite indirectly. Although lactic dehydrogenase levels in plasma tend to exceed normal values during infection and in pathological processes, in infection with *T. lewisi* the enzyme content was below normal and later rose to its original value. The metabolism of liver lipids during infection with *T. brucei* by the guinea pig has been described.[136] As a result of alteration in metabolism young infected animals gained less weight than is usual and older animals lost weight. The liver weight relative to body weight was increased in all experimental animals, as a result of increase in neutral fat, cholesterol, phosphatides, and water in that organ. On the other hand the content of fat-free dry matter, glycogen, and proteins decreased. It was shown[253] that metabolic and pathogenic differences were detectable in the Tulahuen and Peruvian strains of *T. cruzi* by studying their metabolism of [^{14}C]-glucose uniformly labelled as well as that of glucose labelled in positions 1, 2, and 6. Most radioactivity was incorporated into organic acids and CO_2 and some into protein, but at different rates in the two strains. These strains used the pentose phosphate pathway of glucose breakdown at different rates and this fact was considered to be related in some way to pathogenicity.

Summary

The intensive studies reported here on the metabolism of trypanosomes suggests that as a result of parasitic adaptation they have lost a number of enzyme systems. This is especially true of the blood stream forms of the vivax, congolense, and brucei groups which no longer possess the cytochrome type of terminal respiratory pathway found in monogenetic trypanosomes, the blood stream forms of the lewisi group, and the insect stages of all groups, and as a result of this loss are no longer cyanide sensitive. It is somewhat difficult to interpret these facts in the light of current thought about the evolution of mammalian trypanosomes, which are believed to have evolved from monogenetic flagellates. These blood-stream forms, which have no oxidizable reserves and are dependent for respiration and motility on added substrates, oxidize sugars incompletely and produce very little CO_2. They possess some proteolytic enzymes but protein and fat metabolism have been relatively little studied. Trypanosomes contrast markedly with malarial parasites which appear to possess all the enzyme systems of the vertebrate hosts. A restricted amount of information has been derived from cultural studies of trypanosomes, but culture has never been possible in a defined medium in absence of blood. In all media the African trypanosomes develop only to the stage occurring in the insect gut and are therefore non-infective for vertebrates. The completion of their life cycle *in vitro* has been a major problem awaiting solution until the recent studies described above were made. It is of interest that *T. lewisi* and *T. cruzi*, which undergo normal development in insects, give rise to the infective stage in culture, at least over a period of time. They require haematin, ascorbic acid, and serum for successful culture. By the use of modern techniques such as electrophoresis, chromatography, and infrared and ultraviolet spectroscopy, considerable progress in studies on the composition and enzyme systems of the different species has resulted. Points of attack on enzyme systems present in African trypanosomes, by chemotherapeutic agents such as arsenicals, have been determined. Thus phenylarsenoxide in presence of incubates of *T. evansi* is known to interfere with the activity of hexokinase, a sulphydryl enzyme, which phosphorylates glucose in presence of ATP. *T. cruzi* and *T. lewisi* which do not respond to arsenicals are also less sensitive to sulphydryl inhibitors. The problem of host–parasite relationship in trypanosome infections requires much further study for the development of a rational chemotherapy. A solution of the problem of drug resistance, which is of the utmost practical importance, is also awaited; in cases it has resulted from diminished uptake of drug, possibly due to alteration in the character of parasite protein. At other times different metabolic pathways have been developed by the resistant forms. Sometimes alteration in genetic characters is the basis of these changes. The physiological investigations described have been of considerable value in clarifying problems of phylogeny and taxonomy.

Leishmaniasis

Three diseases, clinically distinct, are all called leishmaniasis: Kala-azar or visceral leishmaniasis, Oriental sore or cutaneous leishmaniasis, and South American or muco-cutaneous leishmaniasis (espundia). The organisms giving rise to these three conditions cannot be distinguished morphologically or culturally. Kala-azar occurs widely in Europe, Asia and Africa and is transmitted by *Phlebotomus* (sandfly) species. Infection by means of nasal and other secretions is also recognized. The disease is of generalized character and frequently fatal with wide involvement of the reticulo-endothelial system and gross enlargement of liver and spleen. The cutaneous form known as Oriental sore in the Old World is confined to the skin and is common in the Middle East. When spread to muccous membranes, the disease is known as espundia and occurs widely in South and Tropical America. It is convenient to accept the existence of only two species of parasite, namely *Leishmania donovani* the agent of the visceral form of the disease and *L. tropica* the agent of the cutaneous and muco-cutaneous forms. Of the latter a number of subspecies occur; (1) *L. braziliensis*, the agent of the muco-cutaneous form, characterized by chronic destructive lesions and few recoveries, (2) *L. peruviana*, the agent of a benign infection known as uta in Peru, similar to the "pian bois" of Panama and Guiana, (3) *L. mexicana*, the agent of chiclero's ulcer in Mexico, Guatemala, and British Honduras, which especially affects the ear, and (4) *L. diffusa*, reponsible for a particular form of infection in Venezuela. Besides the varied clinical manifestations, differences in immunological behaviour are recognized. The basis for the choice of different sites of infection is not understood but may reflect an alteration in virulence of the parasites. The parasites are easily cultured in media containing blood, and the leishmania forms, characteristically present in tissues, assume the flagellated, highly motile, leptomonad characters which are present in insects and are infective to mammals. Both forms divide by binary fission.

Culture and Nutritional Studies

The early difficulties met in attempts to maintain parasitic protozoa continuously in pure culture proved a bar to progress in metabolic studies. *Leishmania* are among those which have been cultured with greatest ease; they require blood or serum in the medium. Lwoff[247] has indicated the importance of haematin and ascorbic acid as growth factors. There is also something present in serum which is essential, probably not protein, since euglobulin, pseudoglobulin, albumin, and combinations of these substances were excluded as the factor concerned.[362] Haemoglobin or washed erythrocytes did not contain it. The substance is dialysable and survived a temperature of 70°C but not one of 100°C, and it was not p-aminobenzoic acid, pyridoxine, nicotinic acid, or thiamine, but possibly was cholesterol or fatty acid. Cholesterol has been found present in all species of protozoa examined, and sterols sometimes appear to be necessary as growth factors. The evolutionary significance of sterols has been discussed by a number of workers.[100] The greatest diversity among the principal components of a sterol occurs in the most primitive forms. With the progress of evolution cholesterol assumes more importance, and is the principal sterol of vertebrates. Little is known, however, about the steroid metabolism of protozoa. Serum, besides supplying some factor, may also play a part as a detoxifying agent for products of metabolism, as demonstrated in cultures of *Haemophilus pertussis*. Trager[419] investigated the development of *Leishmania donovani in vitro* at 37°C. The leptomonad form occurs in the lumen of the alimentary tract of sandflies, while the non-motile ovoid form, the leishmania, occurs in the reticulo-endothelial cells of the vertebrate host. The flagellate form readily develops at temperatures of 22–30°C in blood medium, and normally will not survive at 37°C. The leishmania form which grows at 37°C has been obtained in culture only within surviving host cells. The author, during attempts at extracellular cultivation of the intracellular stage, has observed at 37°C a limited development of a form which is considered as intermediate both morphologically and physiologically between the leishmania and leptomonad form. It was obtained when free leishmania forms from the spleens of infected hamsters were added to a medium of human red cell extract and human serum. The aflagellate forms resembled leishmania but were larger in size, multiplied for a few days, and gradually died off. Leptomonads from cultures at 28°C survived under the above conditions for only a few days. Human serum was replaceable by hamster serum but not by that of rabbit. Nicotinamide added to the medium prevented development of the intermediate forms and caused death of leptomonads. It appeared from the morphological variations in the parasite that the special nutritional requirement of the intracellular forms had not been met. Trager[421] also studied the nutrition of a haemoflagellate *L. tarentolae* which parasitizes lizards. The leptomonads were grown in a defined medium containing inorganic salts, glucose, haemin, seventeen amino acids, purines and pyrimidines, and a mixture of vitamins of the B group. Addition of plasma improved growth, while cholesterol and lecithin, in absence of plasma, had growth-stimulating effects. The growth requirements of the flagellate forms were further defined. Partial deficiency of choline resulted in loss of the flagellum.

Krassner[217] using Trager's medium, has studied the effect of temperature on growth and nutritional needs of *L. tarentolae* from lizards, and found that the highest temperature for satisfactory growth was around 28°C. The extracellular cultivation of leishmania forms of *L. donovani*, *L. tropica*, and *L. braziliensis* in a cell free medium by gradual adaptation of leptomonad cultures to progressively increased incubation temperatures has been studied.[11] The medium was diphasic and consisted of a blood agar base overlaid with physiological salt solution. After acclimatization at 28°C and then at 32°C the leptomonads underwent transformation to leishmaniae and continued to multiply. The authors concluded that leishmaniae are not necessarily intracellular parasites. It should now be possible to pursue fruitful physiological studies on the leishmanial forms, which was previously done by Fulton and Joyner[148] with similar forms isolated from infected hamster tissues. It has been shown that infected liver and spleen of hamsters may remain infective at —79°C over a period of months.[283]

Metabolic Studies

Our knowledge of the biochemistry of *Leishmania* is fragmentary in spite of the fact that ample material for study has been available following the introduction of modern techniques of chemistry and allied subjects. It appears that biochemists are not fully aware of the rewards which these investigations could bring. A detailed study of the different species might also provide an explanation for the different clinical manifestations seen in the various infections. It is clear from culture experiments described above that the adaptation of insect flagellates to life in warm blooded hosts involves nutritional and metabolic changes. It has been suggested that a necessary basis for metabolic studies is a knowledge of the chemical composition of parasites. Limited experiments by chemical methods were carried out[361] on the antigens of culture forms of L. tropica. This organism possesses a polysaccharide antigen, and a protein antigen. The non-immune patient was not allergic to either antigen, while those with Oriental sore were allergic to the polysaccharide type.

The first accurate measurements of gas exchanges in L. tropica were made by Soule.[392] This author showed that O_2 was consumed and CO_2 formed. The parasite appeared to be an obligate aerobe; in fact all leishmaniae are aerobic fermenters. An atmosphere of N_2 or H_2 inhibited growth, and injury to the parasite was also caused by partial pressures of CO_2 above 30 per cent. The respiratory quotient approached unity. Further studies were made on L. tropica[348] by developing a solid and liquid medium for continuous maintenance of the strain, and for production of material sufficient for metabolic studies. The authors observed that carbohydrate exerted a sparing action on the protein of the medium. The organism possessed marked proteolytic powers which increased in the absence of dextrose, indicating that the latter was important as a source of energy. Omission of carbohydrate was follwed by decreased production of volatile acids and an increase in ammonia, amino nitrogen and rise in pH of the medium.

The utilization of protein was indicated by the increase in split-products derived from it. Aerobic conditions were found necessary for survival of the parasite. It appeared, as earlier workers had observed, that haemoglobin, or part of its molecule, was necessary for growth. It has been suggested that under aerobic conditions hemin is required for synthesis of enzymes such as catalase, peroxidase, and cytochromes. Ammonia is the most important end product of leishmania nitrogenous metabolism. In the above experiments there was no indication of the production of urea, uric acid, or creatinine. The production of acids in culture had previously been shown to occur by indirect methods. Salle[347] carried out similar experiments with L. donovani. In absence of glucose there was a marked increase in ammonia nitrogen of the medium. The organism, like L. tropica, appeared to prefer carbohydrate to protein as a source of energy. Chang and Negherbon[85] observed differences in the rate of growth of three species of leishmania in culture. The maximum temperature for growth was around 30°C. Each species was differently affected by temperature and it was concluded that their physiological characters differed. Chang[84] made observations on biochemical activities and respiration on the same three species in culture. During growth succinic, lactic, pyruvic, and a small amount of formic acid as well as of carbon dioxide were formed. Death appeared to take place when the sugar of the medium was exhausted. Eh values remained constant over two weeks and no reducing systems were set free. The best growth occurred around an Eh value of 330 mV. Glucose and fructose were utilized but not maltose or lactose and none of the sugars was completely oxidized. Quantitative studies were made on acid production in cultures of *L. donovani*[103] and the results suggested that metabolic activity altered with the age of the culture. It now became clear that metabolic studies on the leishmania form of the parasite were desirable for comparative purposes and to aid in understanding the pathogenic effects exerted on the reticulo-endothelial host cells. Adler and Ashbel[4] made some observations on the metabolism of spermophil and golden hamster spleen tissue infected with *L. donovani* and *L. infantum* and of spleen tissue of hamsters infected with *L. tropica*. They had previously observed that the flagellate stage of all the human leishmanias under both anaerobic and aerobic conditions gave rise to considerable glycolysis. Experiments were also made on Leishman-Donovan bodies of *L. donovani* and *L. infantum*. The infected liver and spleen gave rise to aerobic glycolysis and thus differed from normal tissue. The glycolysis and oxygen consumption were proportional to the degree of infection of these tissues. The Leishman-Donovan bodies freed from tissues produced no appreciable aerobic glycolysis and in this way differed from the flagellate stage. Fulton and Joyner[148] carried out an extended series of observations on the metabolism of the flagellate and leishmania stages of *L. donovani*. The Leishman-Donovan bodies were obtained in quantity from infected hamster spleens and kept in a simple liquid medium at 25°C. This medium proved suitable for primary culture from infected tissues and also allowed a truer estimation of the changes in pH and of the rate of growth than is possible with diphasic media. The effect of respiratory inhibitors on both forms of the parasite was also studied. It was confirmed that flagellate forms depended to a considerable extent on glucose and other carbohydrate for continued respiratory activity but could not utilize glycerol. The chief metabolic product formed was succinic acid, while CO_2 was also formed; the respiratory quotient remained constant during the experiment. The presence of -SH groups in the parasite was demonstrated. The leishmania forms were less active metabolically but retained infectivity during the experiment. They consumed oxygen and produced CO_2. Glucose was utilized more slowly than by the flagellate forms and the parasites were less dependent on it; they continued to respire in phosphate buffer for some hours in its absence, and this fact suggested that on liberation from tissues they possessed anoxidisable substrate. The influence of leishmania infections on blood sugar levels in man has not been widely studied.. The level was not materially altered during infection of dogs with *L. donovani*.[403] Cyanide, azide and iodoacetate inhibited the oxygen uptake of flagellates and LD forms to a varying extent. Leishmanicidal drugs caused inhibition of respiration in both forms of the parasite. Von Brand and Johnson[57] in a comparative study of the effect of cyanide on the respiration and motility of the leptomonad forms of *L. tropica*, *L. donovani*, and *L. braziliensis* found that strong and apparently irreversible inhibition occurred at certain concentrations. Von Brand and Agosin[56] observed that the rate of endogenous respiration of leptomonad forms of *Leishmania* in culture was increased by intermediates of the Krebs' cycle, and that pyruvate, α-ketoglutarate, and fumarate were utilized. The inhibitory action of malonate on respiration was prevented by excess succinate and the authors therefore concluded that the Krebs' cycle was probably operative. Some of the information given regarding carbohydrates utilized, products formed in culture, the value of respiratory quotient and rate of oxygen consumption, as well as the effect of some inhibitors of oxygen consumption and other useful data have been summarized.[55] The effect of carbohydrates and related substances and of some amino-compounds on respiration of *L. enriettii* was tested by Zeledón.[469, 470] He found that not only glucose, but fructose, mannose, and raffinose were stimulatory, galactose and maltose less so, while a number of other sugars produced no effect. *L. enriettii* was incapable of oxidising asparagine, glutamine, glutamic acid, aspartic acid, or alanine but could oxidise glucosamine. Respiratory studies on Krebs' cycle intermediates were carried out at pH 7.2 and 5.0. At the lower pH greater stimulation was produced than by glucose. The results suggested to the author a complete or partial TCA cycle of metabolism, but more rigid criteria are desirable. Chatterjee and Ghosh[87] found that sucrose was oxidized by *L. donovani* and that respiration in its presence resembled that when glucose was used as substrate. The authors claimed that a sucrose-splitting enzyme was present in cell-free extracts, which produced glucose and fructose from the disaccharide. The temperature of inactivation, co-factor requirement, Km value and pH optima were studied. They[88] also studied the aerobic and anaerobic metabolism of resting-cell suspensions of this organism in the presence and absence of extracellular substrates. In contrast to the findings of some other authors, they noted that cultured organisms had a high endogenous metabolism. For 30–60 minutes respiratory activity and motility continued in absence of added substrates. A polysaccharide was obtained from the organisms, composed of glucose, galactose and arabinose units. The optimum pH for respiratory activity lay between pH 7 and 8. The effect of ionic concentration and of metabolic inhibitors was studied with results similar to those of earlier authors. A number of sugars and the amino-acids *dl*-glutamate, *dl*-aspartate, *l*-glutamine and *l*-asparagine served as substrates for oxidative metabolism. As others had found, succinic acid was the main product of aerobic and anaerobic metabolism; the formation of malic acid was also observed. There was no Pasteur effect. The same authors[89] described the fixation of CO_2 associated with glucose metabolism. When glucose was replaced by glycerol, ribose, or pyruvate, no measurable amount of CO_2 fixation occurred. Dinitrophenol, α,α^1-dipyridyl and 8-hydroxyquinolines markedly inhibited glucose utilization as well as CO_2 assimilation. The high rate of CO_2 assimilation is considered by the authors to be complementary to the very active transaminase system previously found by them to be present in the organism. Studies on lipid metabolism have been largely neglected. Halevy[177] made comparative determinations of the composition and metabolism of lipids of certain *Trypanosomidae* including *L. tropica*. By adding to the cultures sodium acetate 1-^{14}C, a precursor of steroids and various fatty acids, there was little difference in the sterol content, free or esterified, among the different species, and most sterol was present in the free state. In *L. tropica* the incorporation of radio carbon with sterol and sterol esters occurred slowly, whereas incorporation with glycerol took place at the highest rate. The author is of the opinion that studies on lipid metabolism might help to distinguish biochemically the various species of trypanosomidae; parasitic species like *L. tropica* of vertebrates synthesize less sterol and contain more glycerol than other forms parasitizing invertebrates. The discovery that *Trypanosomidae* contain sterols other than cholesterol shows that the synthetic capabilities of these organisms differs from that of their vertebrate hosts. Sterols in *Trypanosomidae* were found by the author to be mostly free, in contrast to sterols present in serum which are mainly esterified. It was reported[58] that *T. cruzi* contained considerably more lipids than carbohydrates, and a large part of the unsaponifiable fraction was composed of cholesterol.

During investigations on the amino-acid requirements of *L. donovani*, Chatterjee, and Ghosh[86] studied transaminase activity in cell-free extracts by incubating extracts of the organism with α-ketoglutarate or pyruvate and corresponding-NH$_2$ group donors like amino acids, amino-acid amides, and glucosamine, adenine, etc., so that the formation of glutamate or alanine was observed. With α-ketoglutarate the highest transaminase activities occurred with amino-acids different from those which were most active with pyruvate. Among the amino-acid amide transaminases both glutamine and asparagine transaminase systems were very active in the cell-free extracts, which suggests that glutamine and asparagine might play a significant part in the amino-acid metabolism of the protozoon. Among the purines and pyrimidines only adenine, guanine, and cytosine could transaminate with pyruvate in the extracts but not with α-ketoglutarate. The authors suggest that this indicates in this protozoon a new mechanism of formation and interconversion of purines and pyrimidines. A pyridoxal or pyridoxamine phosphate requirement could not be demonstrated. A strong hexokinase activity was detected in cell-free extracts of *L. donovani* which was most marked with glucose, fructose, mannose, and *d*-glucosamine.[90] The activity of the enzyme did not appear to be markedly dependent on functional-SH groups.

Voller *et al.*[432] studied the effects of a trivalent and pentavalent antimonial on the *in vitro* metabolism of radioactive glucose by the culture forms of *L. tropica*.

The leptomonad forms from culture were used in presence of [1,4-^{14}C]-succinate and [^{14}C]-glucose with or without addition of the drugs at a temperature of 28°C for 3 hours. Chromatographic techniques were used to separate the metabolic products. Succinate was metabolized to only a slight extent but glucose was actively metabolized. Activity was detected in association with metabolites of the glycolytic and Krebs' cycles and in transamination products. The drugs suppressed utilization of glucose but not of succinate. Similar experiments were carried out[254] using *L. enriettii* following their earlier work of a similar nature on *T. cruzi*. Glucose uniformly labelled with ^{14}C and labelled also in positions 1, 2, and 6 was used. It was found that active carbon was incorporated into CO_2, protein, and into organic acid products of volatile character more than into non-volatile types. The authors concluded that the main pathways of glucose metabolism were those of glycolysis (EMP) and the Krebs' cycle. The pentose phosphate pathway was only of minor importance.

Diet and Infection

Actor[2] made an extended study of the effect of protein and vitamin deficiencies on leishmaniasis in mice maintained on purified diets. Deoxypyridoxine, a pyridoxine analogue, caused an increase in parasitaemia and the effect was reversed by pyridoxine. Pyridoxine deficiency late in the infection had an adverse effect on acquired resistance, possibly due to interference with antibody production through reduced amino-acid metabolism. However, in view of the marked physiological changes in the host following vitamin and protein deficiency, factors other than protective antibodies may be involved. Pantothenate had a dual effect; administration of the analogue pantoyltaurine, or deficiency of pantothenate was followed early in the infection by a decrease in parasite numbers, followed later by an increase. Protein-free diet led to significantly higher parasite counts, an effect reversed by an adequate diet. It had been shown[336] that deficient diet led to early emaciation and death, whereas excess protein in the diet favoured survival. A relationship between diet and *Leishmania* infections known to exist for malaria was thus established. It was however found that infection in golden hamsters was not influenced by a milk diet.[144]

Serum Protein Changes

The progress of human kala-azar is accompanied by marked changes in the serum proteins. This subject has been widely investigated in recent years by electrophoretic methods. Observations of this nature on American military personnel suffering from kala azar[284] indicated an increase in the globulin fraction of serum and a decrease in albumin content. The positive formol gel test, which is not diagnostic, was associated with hyperglobulinaemia and hypoalbuminaemia. Ada and Fulton[3] followed the changes in the serum protein pattern of golden hamsters infected with *L. donovani*. By treating the host with an antimonial drug so that the parasites disappeared, the abnormal pattern of serum proteins, accompanied by increases in phospholipids, cholesterol, and neutral fat, was changed to normal. The changes were therefore ascribed to the activities of *L. donovani* and not to associated renal conditions and the presence of amyloidosis. Similar experiments were carried out on chinchillas and rabbits infected with *L. donovani*.[402] The total protein was not greatly altered but the usual decrease in albumin and complementary increase in globulins occurred. The degree to which the different fractions were altered was different in the two species. These changes are discussed in relation to the pathogenesis of the disease. Rossan[339] used eight different animals infected with the same parasite and confirmed earlier results. Response in the susceptible animals (cotton rat, golden hamster, Chinese hamster, chinchilla, mouse, and gerbil) was remarkably similar. The guinea pig and rabbit, with low susceptibility to *L. donovani*, showed little or no change in their serum components, only the α-globulins increased during the course of infection.

Fraga de Azevedo[135] discussed the biology of *L. donovani* in relation to pathogenicity and epidemiology of the disease. Host–parasite relationships were also dealt with and the pathological effects associated with invasion of the reticulo-endothelial system which is accompanied by serum protein and other changes in the blood. Serological reactions also came under review. An explanation of the anaemia which occurs in patients with visceral leishmaniasis has been sought.[262] The various theories on its pathogenesis are discussed at length. There is a marked increase in blood volume in some cases and the occurrence of hypochlorhydria with lowered iron absorption and the presence of increased iron in the serum. The authors also showed that there was an increase in serum glutamic-oxalacetic transaminase. Zuckerman[474] has tentatively suggested that the increased haemolysis of red cells may arise from an auto-immune reaction accompanied by increase in bilirubin and urobilin in presence of normal red cell fragility.

Effect of Drugs

Attention has been drawn to the inhibitory effect of drugs on respiration and other metabolic processes of *L. donovani*. The morphological changes in trypanosomes and malaria parasites produced by treatment of the infected host with drugs has attracted attention. Mayer[264] gives a brief account of the blepharoplastless forms of *L. donovani* which appeared in the liver of hamsters on treatment with synthalin. In recent years the effect of antibiotics and other new drugs on the parasite has been reported. Others[78] showed that amphotericin B, fungizone, fumagillin, nystatin, antimony dimercaptosuccinate, and xerosin were effective against *L. donovani* infection of the mouse and hamster. *L. braziliensis* gives rise to muco-cutaneous leishmaniasis, an infection of chronic character which sometimes does not respond to any form of therapy. Furtado et al.[155] found that amphotericin B was highly effective against the organism *in vitro*. The mode of action of nystatin on *L. donovani in vitro* was studied.[160] It inhibited aerobic and anaerobic metabolism, possibly due to accompanying cell disintegration. Endogeneous and exogenous metabolism in presence of various substrates was inhibited most effectively under aerobic conditions. No effect could be detected against recognized enzyme systems. The authors consider that the physical effects of the drug on the parasite were important and probably broke down vital cellular structures. The drug was used with success in treatment of a patient suffering from post-kala azar dermal leishmaniasis.

Summary

The above makes clear the incompleteness of our knowledge of the bio-chemical properties of *Leishmania*. Further studies on the nutritional requirements of parasitic species are essential to the discovery of a defined medium which will permit the investigation of intermediary metabolism. Although carbohydrate metabolism has been studied to the almost complete exclusion of lipid and protein metabolism, even now it is not clear whether a complete glycolytic (EMP) cycle is functional in *Leishmania* or whether a Krebs' (TCA) cycle is involved. Enzyme studies have been sadly neglected. This is a pity from the point of view of chemotherapy, for the fact that similar enzymes may be present in host and parasite does not preclude the use of a selective inhibitor for certain metabolic pathways in the parasite. It has been shown[257] that although the respective enzymes may catalyse the same reactions in host and parasite they may react differently to inhibitors. Thus sera from roosters immunized against lactic dehydrogenase from rabbit muscle inhibited that particular enzyme but not a similar enzyme isolated from schistosomes. Presumably the reverse effect would have been obtained by suitable procedures. It may be claimed that leishmaniasis can be kept under control by known drugs. This happy result has not followed from theoretical consideration but from trial and error. This is not surprising when we consider how little attention has been paid to the metabolic characters of the intracellular forms. The use of antimetabolites as chemotherapeutic agents has met with some success in laboratory studies but apparently not in practice. Biochemical studies on the leptomonad forms have been numer-ous but have yielded little of interest to chemotherapy. The different clinical pictures presented by the various species of parasite suggest that a difference in physiological characters exists. A study of the reason for these differences, which involves a change in host-parasite relationships, should be most rewarding. Although the nature of metabolic disturbances occurring during infection have been frequently described little or nothing is known about the intimate mechanisms by which parasites produce damage or death in the mammalian host.

Trichomoniasis

The Trichomonads are spindle or pear-shaped organisms with three to five anterior flagella and an undulating membrane. They are for the most part parasitic; only a few free-living forms are known. Three genera, *Tri-*

trichomonas, *Trichomonas*, and *Pentatrichomonas*, characterized by the number of flagella are recognized by some authors. They have a wide range of hosts, including warm and cold-blooded vertebrates such as fish, frogs, reptiles, birds, and mammals as well as invertebrates. Wenrich[446] has described three species which infect man, namely *Trichomonas tenax* of the mouth, *T. hominis* of the intestine, and *T. vaginalis* of the genital tract. According to this author, species differentiation is justified by differences in morphology, physiology, and cultural characters, and by mode of transmission and site of infection. In man, pathogenicity is low, the most troublesome species being *T. vaginalis*. This parasite is cosmopolitan in character and occurs primarily in the vagina and urethral glands, but does not appear to invade the uterus. It is claimed that there is a higher morbidity rate in childbirth when this organism is present. In males it occurs in the urethra and prostate; infection can occur during coitus. Antibiotics have proved of value in treatment, tetracyclines and streptomycin being preferred to penicillin. The organism was early grown in bacteria-free culture[6, 426-428] and later much more conveniently with the aid of penicillin.[208] As a result, numerous studies on the nutrition, metabolism, physiology, and chemotherapy of the parasite have now been reported. *T. foetus*, a pathogen of cattle, is also cosmopolitan. It occurs commonly in the mucous membrane of the vagina and also invades the uterus causing infertility, abortion, and stillbirths. It is spread by coitus from preputial infection of bulls—a truly venereal disease of cattle. In 1928 Riedmüller first showed it to be a specific cause of abortion, and initiated a long series of researches. A bacteria-free culture was obtained[459] and since then its biochemical, physiological, and immunochemical characters have been widely studied. The purification of cultures by means of antibiotics has been described.[279] *T. gallinae* of pigeons, doves, and other birds infects the upper alimentary tract and at times the liver and pancreas; it may cause a high mortality. It is easy to isolate on Locke's solution-egg-serum (LES medium) and was first cultured by Bos.[47] *T. gallinarum* of the lower alimentary tract severely affects young turkeys, often with fatal results, especially when liver and caeca are involved.

NUTRITIONAL STUDIES

In general, trichomonads can be cultured only on complex media preferably at low oxygen tensions. Each synthetic medium devised has required addition of complex organic materials such as ribonucleic acid, serum proteins, liver, vitamins, etc. The different species can multiply over the wide temperature range of 25–42°C and the generation time is approximately 5–7 hours. The other physicochemical factors affecting growth such as pH and oxidation-reduction potential have been carefully investigated.

Since *T. vaginalis* was first isolated in pure culture,[426] numerous nutritional studies on this organism have been made. Some authors[207] grew the organism on a basic medium consisting mainly of cysteine, peptone, liver infusion, and maltose, with addition of unheated blood serum (CPLM); later they replaced the liver infusion with growth factors including ascorbic acid, glutamic acid, choline chloride, folic acid, and xanthopterin.[208] This medium gave satisfactory growth and proved of value as a starting point for studying the unknown but necessary components present in blood serum. Sprince and Kupferberg,[399, 400] in a general study on nutrition of protozoa, described a simplified medium, based on that above, for the investigation of these unknown factors and as a starting point for studying the growth requirements and maintenance of this parasitic flagellate. The modifications of the CPLM medium replaced Difco peptone by trypticase, a pancreatic digest of casein devoid of carbohydrate, and replaced the liver infusion by a mixture of B vitamins, purines, pyrimidines, and some other components. Although easier to prepare and better defined chemically, growth was not so good as in the original medium. The authors found that the added human blood serum could be separated into two fractions, one ether soluble and another ether insoluble, both of which were necessary for sustained growth of T. vaginalis. Linoleic acid was one of the active components of the ether soluble fraction and serum albumin was an active component of the other fraction. Replacement of serum with linoleic acid plus serum albumin was ineffective. These authors[224] then produced a simplified medium containing trypticase, cysteine, maltose, agar, distilled water, and human serum, known as STS medium (simplified trypticase serum medium), and established the need of T. vaginalis for pantothenic acid as an essential metabolite, and for phosphate. This demonstration that T. vaginalis requires pantothenic acid led to the study of the inhibitory effects of pantothenic analogues.[206] The inhibitory effect of several of these compounds was shown in vitro. A phenyl pantothenone analogue was found to be competitively antagonized by Ca pantothenate. T. foetus and T. gallinae were also sensitive to this compound. In human patients, however, and in monkeys, the infection was not eradicated. The failure to treat vaginitis successfully is possibly explained by the competitive inhibition resulting from the pantothenic levels present in blood. Johnson[209] in an introduction to the study of growth factors observed that ascorbic acid, glutamic acid, and choline had a stimulating effect on cell multiplication, and that liver infusion was replaceable by folic acid, nicotinamide, and human serum. The use of the STS medium allowed ascorbic acid to be dispensed with; a suitable redox potential was maintained by cysteine. He had already shown[205] that T. vaginalis grew best at a pH between 5.5 and 6.0 and that the organism was a facultative anaerobe. Oxygen exerted a depressing effect on the population in culture while anaerobic conditions favoured population growth. Trussell and Johnson[427] studied the fermentation of thirty-two carbohydrates and related compounds in pure cultures and showed that glucose and its polymers maltose, soluble starch, dextrin, and glycogen were readily utilized, while fructose and galactose were used to a lesser extent. In an attempt to replace 'trypticase' in the complete medium described,[397] it was observed that pancreatic extracts were very effective in stimulating growth of T. vaginalis. The substance responsible for growth appeared to differ from other known growth factors, and was designated factor "S". It is thermostable, water soluble, and dialysable. The lipocaic fraction (Lilly) was the most active preparation tested, being effective at a concentration of 25γ per millilitre of medium. Neither crystalline B_{12}, amino acids of fortified casein hydrolysate, streptogenin from insulin, nor the lipotropic substances methionine and choline could replace the active material from the pancreas. It seemed that the activity of pancreas extract might be due to the nucleic acids or their derivatives. A detailed study of the effect of these substances on growth of the organism was therefore made.[398] It was found that ribonucleic acid (RNA) but not deoxyribonucleic acid (DNA) could partially replace "trypticase" or lipocaic fraction (Lilly) in a modification of the Sprince-Kupferberg medium for maintenance of T. vaginalis in continued culture. Alkaline or enzymatic hydrolysis of RNA did not destroy these properties whereas acid hydrolysis did. Hydrolytic derivatives of DNA did not stimulate growth. Sustained growth was obtained with the monoribonucleotides adenylic, guanilic, uridylic, and cytidylic acids or their bases, but not by the corresponding ribonucleosides adenosine, guanosine, uridine, and cytidine. The authors therefore considered that T. vaginalis can convert the free purine and pyrimidine bases, but not the nucleosides, to the monoribonucleotides essential for growth. The inhibitory effect of certain nucleotides was not apparent in a medium rich in peptides or amino acids, but only when the content of these substances was low. They appear to inhibit growth by competing with peptides and amino acids for phosphate.

When T. foetus was first isolated in pure culture,[459] it grew on egg medium with added blood or in broth with horse serum. Riedmüller[331] showed that serum from particular sources contained a thermostable factor capable of withstanding a temperature of 90°C for 1 hour, and could not be replaced by washed or haemolysed red cells. The addition of certain hexoses and polysaccharides but not pentoses improved growth, and the acidity of the culture medium increased. Growth was better under anaerobic conditions. Cailleau[74] also conducted experiments on the nutritional needs of different strains of this parasite. The utilization of sugars and polyalcohols was studied, and also the effect of many types of serum on parasite growth. She concluded, from changes observed in the medium, that nitrogen metabolism was minimal, with very small changes in protein and non-protein nitrogen and the absence of ammonia production. Proteolytic enzymes were not detected. This author[75] also came to the conclusion that cholesterol and ascorbic acid are growth factors for T. foetus. Some doubt has however been subsequently cast on these observations. Weiss and Ball[439] made the first detailed study of protein nutrition of T. foetus, using a complete amino acid medium and bacteria-free cultures to find whether the nitrogenous needs of the parasite resembled those of other organisms. The effects of partially digested protein on the growth rate of the organism were specially studied. Each amino acid was removed in turn from the medium and the authors concluded that thirteen of them were essential for growth. Once these necessary amino acids had been determined, the growth response to proteins, including casein, lactalbumin, and wheat germ protein, as well as their products of digestion by pepsin, trypsin, and papain, were studied in the presence of glucose and vitamins. Serum also contained a factor which improved all the media tested. With whole protein, growth was relatively poor; on digestion, growth improved till 50 per cent soluble nitrogen was present. The requirements of *T. foetus* for an unsaturated fatty acid was shown;[349] and the author has claimed that serum can be replaced in cultures of *T. foetus* by Tween 80 (a possible source of oleic acid) and cholesterol. Choline plus potassium glycerophosphate enhanced growth in the presence of these two substances, and a method for ensuring adequate suspension of cholesterol is described. Lwoff[247] agrees that there are factors in blood serum apparently necessary for *Trichomonas* growth and considers that serum may contain a toxic factor and a growth factor at the same time, depending on its source. She points out that serum contains lipases in different amounts according to its origin, human serum having a low content, horse serum a high. By setting acids free, serum could be rendered unsuitable for *Trichomonas* growth. Thus the toxic action can be abolished by heating with consequent enzyme destruction. It is also worthwhile to consider the action of catalase present in some sera, which can destroy hydrogen peroxide formed at high oxygen tensions. It is still impossible to use a synthetic culture medium for *T. vaginalis* or *T. foetus*; they require blood serum. The semi-synthetic media contain a wide range of substances like vitamins and amino acids whose individual contributions to growth are generally unknown. A detailed study of the lipophilic growth factors for *T. foetus* has been made.[464] The relative value of water soluble and ether soluble fractions of bovine serum, as well as certain unsaturated fatty acids and cholesterol, were investigated. The authors found that a dependent growth factor was present in the water soluble fraction, the action of which can be complemented by the addition of lipophilic serum components. The possibility of substituting the ether soluble fraction by cholesterol or fatty acids alone or in combination showed that in absence of cholesterols, oleic acid exhibited the greatest effect. This effect was antagonized when cholesterol was present. Linoleic and linolenic acid were toxic to *T. foetus* in absence of cholesterol but in its presence were beneficial when present within certain limits. This effect may be explained by the fact that lipids including cholesterol can "detoxify" fatty acids, which is equivalent therefore to growth enhancement, at least in certain bacterial cultures. Some of the contradictory views of the part played by cholesterol and linoleic acid as

growth factors have been resolved; it is now apparent that in cultures of
T. foetus the activity of fatty acids depends on other factors in the medium.
Linoleic and linolenic acid have a stimulatory effect in presence of cholesterol, while unsaturated fatty acids with one double bond exert a stimulatory
effect in the absence as well as in the presence of cholesterol. The antagonism
between cholesterol and fatty acids becomes apparent only when they are
present in certain concentrations. The authors regard cholesterol as a growth
factor for *T. foetus*.

T. gallinae is easy to culture on Locke's solution-egg-serum medium, as
used for *Entamoeba histolytica*.[47] Diamond[112] made a comparative study
of twenty-eight media of mono- and diphasic type for culture of this organism
with normally associated bacteria, for use in surveys. The best were Ringer-
Loeffler serum, saline-Loeffler serum, and saline-serum, pigeon serum being
the most satisfactory. The review on *T. gallinae*[401] covers history, nomenclature, morphology, cultivation, biochemistry, host-parasite relationships,
and other aspects. The importance of the early work of Cailleau on growth
factors for *T. gallinae* is indicated.

As previously noted,[206] certain compounds toxic to *T. vaginalis, T.
foetus* and *T. gallinae* were antagonized by Ca pantothenate and this vitamin
and its analogues acted in competitive fashion. Jones and Smith[210] reviewed
the requirements of *T. gallinae* for pantothenate and for other vitamins of
the B group. In the medium which they used, known chemical agents
replaced peptone and liver infusion. By removing vitamins in turn from the
basal medium a reduction in growth took place indicating that nicotinamide,
Ca pantothenate, choline chloride, and pyridoxamine were essential for *T.
gallinae*. Although pantothenate is an integral part of coenzyme A, which is
associated with carbohydrate metabolism, so important for trichomonads,
its absence exercised less effect on growth than absence of the others. Folic
acid, biotin, and pyridoxine also appeared to be necessary for growth but
exerted their effect in subcultures later than the four others.

Since the growth of trichomonads in a synthetic medium has not yet been
attained, the requirements for unidentified growth factors, and saturated and
unsaturated fatty acids, have been studied[377] in the case of *T. gallinae* and
T. gallinarum. These authors used a synthetic medium containing fifty-seven
compounds, including cholesterol. It was shown that three factors were
required for growth, and for fermentation of maltose. One known as R was
present in proteins associated with ribonucleic acid and in some other
proteins. A second factor T was present in trypticase and in the above
proteins but in smaller amount, and is believed to be a peptide containing
proline. A third factor S found in serum was replaceable by a saturated and
an unsaturated fatty acid active only in combination. Saturated fatty acids
with 14 to 18 C atoms proved to be a specific requirement at certain concentrations in presence of oleic acid, a fact not previously recognized. Also
unsaturated acids with 18 to 22 carbon atoms, including those essential for

higher animals, were active in the same range of concentration when palmitic acid was used as supplement. At the highest dosage the unsaturated forms were toxic. Surface active agents containing mixtures of fatty acids could replace serum, which itself contained a fourth factor. The same supplements were effective growth promoters for *T. gallinarum* and *T. foetus* in another synthetic medium. The identity of the factors with those described by other workers has not been definitely established. It does appear from this work that albumin supplies essential nutrients for trichomonads and does not act merely as a detoxifying agent. It may also act as a lipid-transporting agent. The authors point out that when a completely synthetic medium is devised for growth of trichomonads, these organisms should prove useful in the study of the intermediate metabolism of the sterols and fatty acids. Lund and Shorb[242] carried out further researches on the steroid needs of trichomonads in a more defined medium. For a strain of *T. gallinae* in a trypticase medium lacking ribonucleic acid, it was found that cholesterol and a number of other steroids could act as replacements. The precursors of cholesterol such as acetate and mevalonic acid, with or without liver extract, and squalene, could not replace cholesterol itself, nor could fat-soluble vitamins, carotene, vitamins D_2 or D_3, vitamin K_3, or vitamin E. They believe that their work largely confirms that of Cailleau described earlier. It is important that the steroids used in these experiments should be chemically pure.

The advantages of maintaining trichomonads in axenic culture for a study of physiological and biological characteristics is obvious, but although this has been readily accomplished with most species, it proved difficult in the case of the oral flagellate of man, *T. tenax*. Diamond[114] has now been successful by using a medium of nutrient broth supplemented with horse serum and a cell-free extract of chick embryo. All the axenic cultures obtained had been previously grown in association with *T. cruzi*; those accompanied by bacteria could not be grown in this way.

The effect of nutrients on cell composition has not been widely studied. The lipid biochemistry of *Trichomonads* has been concerned mainly with the nutritional needs of the organism. Thus Etinger and Halevy[120] have tried to obtain some basic data on the lipid biochemistry of *T. vaginalis*. They have also sought to show to what degree the lipid composition of the organism is affected by the presence in the medium of sera from different animals, which is the usual source of essential lipid nutrients. By using axenic cultures it was shown that the sterol of *T. vaginalis* was cholesterol. It appeared to be absorbed directly from the medium since synthesis of this sterol from ^{14}C labelled sodium acetate did not occur. Similar results were obtained with calf, horse, and human serum. Comparable findings had been reported for *T. foetus*[178] and it appeared that this parasite absorbed cholesterol unchanged. Shorb[375] has suggested that parasitic and free living protozoa may be differentiated by their ability to synthesize lipid, a property which trichomonads appear to lack, as a result of acquiring essential lipids from their hosts.

METABOLISM

T. gallinae

The first metabolic study on a trichomonad was carried out[450] with *T. hepatica* (*T. gallinae*). They investigated its aerobic carbohydrate metabolism, the use of various substrates of the Krebs' cycle, oxygen consumption, and the action of inhibitors, as well as the optimal oxygen tension for respiratory studies. Their results resembled those obtained later for *T. foetus*[406] described below. The organism appeared to lack a Krebs' cycle. Cyanide and azide did not inhibit oxygen consumption whereas methylene blue and dinitrophenol did. Optimal respiration occurred at a tension of 5–10 per cent oxygen. A brief report on the free amino acids in this parasite as determined by two-dimensional paper chromatography techniques was given[433] and comparable results were obtained with the same parasite.[407]

T. vaginalis

Following the isolation of pure cultures of *T. vaginalis*,[427] the authors studied the fermentation by this organism of thirty-two compounds including mono, di, and poly-saccharides, alcohols, glucosides, and inositol. They observed the effect of these substances on population growth and the resulting shift in pH of the medium. Under the conditions they employed only glucose and its polymers maltose, soluble starch, glycogen, and dextrin were utilized to any considerable extent. Fructose and galactose had only a slight effect on growth. The absence of activity of lactose was striking. Their results seemed to differ somewhat from those obtained[74] with *T. foetus*. Ninomyia and Suzuoki[304] investigated the metabolism of this organism in pure culture at 37°C. The parasites collected by gentle centrifugation were used for manometric experiments in a medium of liver extract containing 1 per cent peptone, 20 per cent bovine serum, 1 per cent maltose, 0.1 per cent cysteine, and 0.5 per cent NaCl, under aerobic and anaerobic conditions. The optimal pH for these studies was found to be 5.6, and the optimal range of salt concentration 0.1–0.2 M NaCl. The rate of respiration was affected by O_2 tension; when high, respiration was inhibited to some extent, possibly due to formation of hydrogen peroxide. It proceeded best in an atmosphere of 5 per cent O_2 and 95 per cent N_2 in presence of glucose. Maltose and glucose were rapidly oxidized and lactate and pyruvate at about half their rate. Succinate, citrate, dl-alanine, formate, acetate, butyrate, glutamate, and gluconate were not metabolized. Inhibition of respiration was marked with -SH reagents and fluoride, but cyanide, azide, malonate, and arsenate did not inhibit. Hydrogen peroxide was an effective inhibitor, and catalase activity of the organism was not detected. Under anaerobic conditions a gas believed to be hydrogen, as well as carbon dioxide, was evolved. The behaviour of *T. vaginalis* with respect to inhibition by -SH compounds and its insensitivity to cyanide and malonate resembles that of *T. foetus* described later, except that the latter showed catalase activity. Presumptive evidence was also given for the presence of triosephosphate dehydrogenase. Since in a nutritional sense *T. vaginalis* appears to be the more exacting of the two organisms the authors have suggested that in evolution to a parasitic existence, *T. foetus* is probably intermediate between *T. vaginalis* and a free living ancestor. Studies on the carbohydrate metabolism and respiration of the same parasite were made,[225] and it was found that the major product from glucose was lactic acid. Quantitative data on gaseous exchanges were given, and oxygen consumption was found to be less than in the case of *T. foetus*. The value of RQ varied with the conditions of experiment. The production of gas other than CO_2, in significant amounts, was not demonstrated. Wellerson *et al.*[441] more fully investigated CO_2 production during growth of *T. vaginalis* and by use of ^{14}C-labelled bicarbonate, demonstrated CO_2 fixation and showed that it occurred mostly outside the cell. The labelled carbon occurred only in the carboxyl group of lactic acid. The presence of certain enzymes generally associated with the hexosemonophosphate shunt was also noted. The first studies of intermediary metabolism were made.[456] It was demonstrated that two enzymes associated with phosphorylative glycolysis, namely hexokinase and aldolase, were present in *T. vaginalis*, and the author assumed that their presence was an indication of the breakdown of glucose in a manner similar to that occurring in yeast and vertebrate tissue. This was the first demonstration that a parasitic flagellate living outside the blood stream of warm blooded vertebrates possesses such a mechanism. Read[322] carried out some comparative studies on the physiology of the trichomonads, *T. vaginalis*, *T. gallinae*, and *T. foetus*. Carbohydrate was found to be required for growth *in vitro* and probably *in vivo* and was therefore of importance in physiological studies. Small differences were noted in the sugars used by the different species. Gaseous fermentation by *T. vaginalis* and *T. foetus* was inhibited by fluoride, iodoacetate, dinitrophenol and other agents, but not by arsenate or arsenite. Wirtschafter and Jahn[457] made some interesting observations on the metabolism of *T. vaginalis* with special reference to the glycolytic pathway; its presence was confirmed by enzymatic and chemical methods and phosphoglucomutase, α-glycerophosphate dehydrogenase, and lactic dehydrogenase were demonstrated. Eleven phosphorylated intermediates in the cycle were also identified by the use of chromatographic methods on homogenates of the harvested organism. Having provided evidence for the presence of the EMP pathway in the breakdown of glucose by *T. vaginalis*, the oxidative metabolism of this organism was studied.[458] Although in many aerobic organisms the Krebs' (TCA) cycle takes part in the oxidation of pyruvate to CO_2 and water, accompanied by the esterification of phosphate in an energy-rich form, it has been demonstrated relatively seldom in parasitic protozoa. For example, in the studies[304] quoted above, the rate of oxidation of lactate and pyruvate was shown to be slow compared with that for glucose, and the utilization of Krebs' cycle intermediates was not observed. The authors consider the circumstances unusual since pyruvate and malate were oxidized aerobically in absence of the ability of the organism to utilize other intermediates of the Krebs' cycle. Attempts to inhibit oxidation of pyruvate with blocking agents such as malonate, arsenite, parapyruvate, and fluoroacetate were not successful. Isotopic experiments with 2-^{14}C pyruvate indicated that some unknown compounds, not Krebs' cycle intermediates, incorporated ^{14}C. It was not possible to demonstrate the presence of the cycle by isolation or inhibition of enzymes or by tracer studies. Wellerson and Kupferberg,[442] by using cell-free extracts of T. vaginalis, have confirmed the results of the above studies and showed that all the enzymes of the EMP cycle were operative. The absence of phosphorylase in presence of a high glycogen content in the cell suggested that another route for breakdown of glucose may function in T. vaginalis. The presence of an active TPN-linked "malic enzyme" was demonstrated although no functional citric acid cycle has been recognized in this organism. The studies described[223] on terminal respiration in T. vaginalis led to somewhat different conclusions. It was shown that actively growing cultures metabolize glucose U-^{14}C, succinate 2,- 3-^{14}C to $^{14}CO_2$, and amino acids which are then incorporated with protein. Radioactivity was present in all the 15 amino acids obtained by hydrolysis of parasite protein from cells grown in presence of U-^{14}C glucose; this led the authors to believe that a TCA cycle might be operative. Cell free systems which could carry out the reactions of this cycle were however not obtained. The indirect evidence that a Krebs' cycle may be operative has raised a number of questions which require study; the complex nutritional needs of the parasite are such that little synthetic activity by the cycle would be necessary. The terminal acceptor in the electron chain has not yet been determined and cytochromes appear to be absent. Pyridine nucleotides and flavoproteins have been demonstrated in which electron transport is linked to oxygen[440] and malic acid is an important metabolic product. The relative impermeability of the cell membrane has been invoked to explain the negligible effect on growth and respiration of Krebs' cycle intermediates. Baernstein[24, 25, 26] showed in turn that an aldolase, specially activated by cobaltous ions, a lactic dehydrogenase which is DPN-linked, and a very active malic dehydrogenase also DPN and l(-)-malate linked, were present in homogenates of T. vaginalis. Smith and Spriggs[389] carried out a chromatographic analysis of the free amino acids of T. vaginalis, the presence of lysine, aspartic acid, alanine, valine, and leucine was verified, while arginine and glutamic acid were tentatively identified.

Michaels and Treick[274-5] studied the action on this organism of some 3- and 5-nitropyridines and pyrimidines, which inhibit growth in vitro and in vivo and are detoxified on reduction. When inhibitory concentrations were present there was a decrease in rates of synthesis of DNA, RNA, and protein which paralleled the rate of multiplication. There was also accumulation of polysaccharide when maltose, but not when glucose, was present; polysaccharide appeared to differ structurally from the glycogen normally stored. The balance of enzymes usually present was disturbed by the inhibitors which appeared to affect an energy-yielding mechanism. The demonstration of phosphogluconate dehydrogenase and "malic enzyme" in addition to other enzymes known to be present suggested the existence of alternate pathways of sugar breakdown. In spite of the presence of active succinic and malic dehydrogenases, the existence of a Krebs' cycle was not confirmed. They also made *T. vaginalis* resistant to the above compounds *in vitro* and resistance persisted *in vivo*. Cross resistance was present indicating a similar site of action for both types of drug. On acquiring resistance, generation time was increased and the population density was lowered. Adler, Back and Sadovsky[5] made the parasite resistant to a number of drugs *in vitro* including stilbamidine and colchicine.

T. foetus

Reference has been made to the earlier studies of Cailleau and Riedmü ller on the utilization of carbohydrate by *T. foetus* which gives rise to a fall in pH of the culture medium. Stewart[405] drew attention to the presence of glycogen within *T. foetus* in cultures and that its amount was related to the amount of sugar consumed. Death of the organism *in vitro* was associated with decrease in the number of organisms with high glycogen content, but not to deficiency or exhaustion of carbohydrates or serum in the medium.

In a study of the immunological components of *T. foetus*, a specific substance and a glycogen-like polysaccharide were isolated from dried cells in a yield of 5–10 per cent.[124] The specific substance when purified contained the same dominant serological specificity as the intact protozoa. A serologically inactive polysaccharide, which appeared to be glycogen was also obtained. Manners and Ryley[256] investigated the nature of the intracellular polysaccharide in *T. foetus* and *T. gallinae* synthesized during growth to the extent of 10–30 per cent of the dry weight of the cell. After isolation and purification the material was subjected to detailed structural analysis. The results obtained indicated that branched α-1 : 4-glucosans were present which resembled glycogen but were not identical with animal glycogens. They also differ in some respects from other known protozoal polysaccharides and from each other in the degree of branching. This fact may indicate a difference in the enzyme systems responsible for their synthesis. The "glycogens" from *T. foetus* and *T. gallinae* were found to have unit chain lengths of fifteen and nine glucose residues respectively. Quantitative studies on the utilization of glucose were made [14] in bacteria-free cultures suspended in nutrient broth and saline; they noted that a gas other than CO_2 was formed which burned explosively on admixture with air. With less than

0.1 per cent glucose in the medium, good growth was not obtained and the rate of its consumption was not uniform throughout growth. Suzuoki and Suzuoki[406] studied its carbohydrate metabolism for the first time with organisms obtained by gentle centrifugation of cultures followed by washing and supension in buffered saline. Manometric measurements were made of O_2 uptake, CO_2 production and of anaerobic acid formation. The optimum salt concentration was 0.19–0.26 M NaCl and the optimal pH range lay between 7.0 and 7.6. In these conditions endogenous respiration continued for some hours. The effect of twenty-seven substrates on respiration was observed. Only glucose, maltose, sucrose, fructose, mannose, and galactose increased O_2 uptake over endogenous uptake while other substrates including pyruvate and lactate supported respiration poorly. There was no inhibition of respiration by cyanide, azide, hydroxylamine, or malonate but iodoacetate and fluoride, which affect the reactions of the EMP glycolytic cycle, were markedly inhibitory. The bands of cytochrome b were observed spectroscopically but the a and c bands and those of cytochrome oxidase were absent. Catalase and peroxidase were present in the organism. It is of interest that Riedmüller,[331] who was the first to study the metabolism of this organism by manometric methods, found that respiration was insensitive to 95 per cent carbon monoxide. He too could not detect any cytochrome pigments, catalase, or peroxidase in the parasite. During anaerobic breakdown of glucose, H_2 and CO_2 were evolved and large amounts of acid, 70 per cent of which was succinic, were produced; lactic and pyruvic acids were formed only in small amount. Aerobic acid production paralleled utilization of glucose and in this case 83 per cent of the acids consisted of succinic acid with less than 10 per cent of lactic and pyruvic acids. During cultivation, hydrogen and possibly methane was detected. The authors concluded that the carbohydrate metabolism of T. foetus was rather like that of pathogenic African trypanosomes and that this fact might provide a clue in the search for drugs effective against trichomonads. However in T. foetus carbohydrate metabolism proceeds much further than pyruvate, which is the main product from trypanosomes, and as noted, succinic and other acids are formed. The evolution of hydrogen and methane is likewise not characteristic of trypanosome metabolism. Ryley[344] concentrated attention on the glycogen reserves of the parasite as the centre of catabolic activities. In cell-free preparations a number of enzymes were demonstrated. Experiments were carried out in Ringer–phosphate or Ringer–bicarbonate solution at 37°C. It was clear that the energy metabolism of the organism is intimately associated with the intracellular glycogen which is synthesized during growth, aided by other carbohydrates available outside the cell. Under aerobic and anaerobic conditions breakdown to succinic, acetic, CO_2, and hydrogen occurred. Addition of glucose, fructose, galactose, and lactose to the medium caused increased production of acids as well as of intracellular glycogen. The author points out that different strains do not behave

15*

exactly alike metabolically. No cytochrome bands were detected in thick suspensions of *T. foetus*, and cellular respiration was therefore mediated by other systems. Cytochrome oxidase appeared to be absent. The value of QO_2 was about 176 and was increased by addition of a number of sugars. Catalase activity was observed. Arsenate and azide stimulated endogenous respiration but abolished motility, whereas aerobic respiration was inhibited by iodoacetate only. In absence of added sugar glycogen disappeared from inside the cell under aerobic or anaerobic conditions. The enzymes amylase, maltase, phosphorylase, hexokinase, phosphoglucomutase, ketoisomerase, aldolase, and a triosephosphate oxidizing system were present in cell free extracts, and provide good evidence for an EMP glycolytic cycle. Doran[116, 117, 118] compared the metabolism of *T. foetus* with that of trichomonads from the nasal cavity and caecum of swine by manometric methods, under standardized aerobic and anaerobic conditions. Quantitative and qualitative differences were observed in each species regarding sugars metabolized and the effect they had on respiration. The main qualitative difference noted was that *T. foetus* did not metabolize raffinose or lactose. The action of inhibitors was also studied. In all three forms under anaerobic conditions gas formation was increased by addition of lactate and pyruvate. Acids were formed by all species during metabolism. An atmosphere of oxygen inhibited glucose utilization and stimulated endogenous respiration. The results differed to some extent from those of earlier workers regarding the optimal physico-chemical conditions for the organism or rate at which sugars were metabolized and this fact may be due to the difference in experimental conditions and in the strains used. All three trichomonads studied behaved alike as regards pH and salinity, absence of a Krebs' cycle, presence of catalase, inhibition by iodoacetate and arsenite and absence of inhibition by cyanide, azide, hydroxylamine, 2,4-dinitrophenol, and malonate, aerobic acid formation, and gas production. In spite of the fact that caecal trichomonads from pigs can parasitize the nasal cavity of the same host and reproductive tract of bovines, the author believes that lack of stimulation by pyruvate and lactate and effect of inhibitory agents as well as certain morphological characters are indicative of valid differences between the caecal form and the two other forms. Differences between *T. foetus* and the nasal form were less obvious. More detailed studies showed that the metabolism of the caecal trichomonad resembled most that of *T. suis* although its behaviour differed in minor respects. In further studies by the same author, acid production, the effect of inhibitors, and substrate utilization by four strains of *T. foetus* was determined. Minor differences in their metabolic characters were found. The production of lactic acid accounted for 30–50 per cent of the total acids formed and was much higher than recorded by other observers. The writer finally concluded that the nasal strain was a highly adapted strain of *T. foetus*. Biochemical and physiological studies were made[235] on three species of trichomonads, *T. foetus*, *Pentatrichomonas gallinarum*, and a nasal and a caecal form of *T. suis*. They included investigations on meta-bolism of carbohydrate, relation between population and pH, substrate utilization and production of acid and gas, as well as on enzyme activity, carried out in an attempt to clarify the taxonomic status of these organisms. Thioglycollate broth with 1 per cent ox serum was used as culture medium The main product of the three species, amounting to 50 per cent of the total acid production, was succinic acid; the caecal strain produced more lactic acid, and some pyruvic acid was found in all cultures. The largest amount of acid was produced by the nasal strain. Some differences occurred in the nature and amount of carbohydrate utilized and these affected the respira-tory responses. Certain enzymes associated with the EMP glycolytic cycle were present in all four forms, and two of them showed malic dehydrogenase activity. Formic dehydrogenase activity was marked in all four and presump-tive evidence for a hydrogenlyase system was present in two. Formic hydro-genlyase has been identified as the resultant of two enzymes, (1) formic dehydrogenase which breaks down formic acid to $2H^+ + 2e$ and (2) hydro-genase which converts these products to gaseous H_2. The status of these two enzymes is however still not clear, for some organisms produce H_2 in their absence while other organisms have both enzymes and do not produce gas. All the organisms behaved as facultative anaerobes but were active under aerobic conditions. The results obtained were essentially in agreement with those of earlier workers. Although pyruvate and malate were used aerob-ically there was no definite proof of the presence of a Krebs' cycle. The possibility of a hexosemonophosphate shunt was suggested by the detection of glucose-6-phosphate dehydrogenase activity. The nature of the terminal respiration systems present was not determined. Comparison and evaluation of separate reports on metabolism of trichomonads is rendered difficult by discrepancies in results which arise from age of the culture, medium used, pH and buffer composition, number of parasites present per vessel, and other factors. Until these discrepancies are resolved, progress in the study of the physiology of these organisms will be retarded.

There is little information available on the free amino acids of *Trichomo-nads*. The total amino acid content of *T. foetus*, *T. suis*, *T. gallinae*, and of other species was determined by means of paper electrophoretic tech-niques.[271] It was not possible to distinguish one species from another by this means. The amounts of the various acids were determined in hydrolysates by column chromatography and showed some variation. Aspartic and glutamic acid were present in greatest amounts in all species, whereas histidine was in smallest amount. Johnson[204] first determined the free amino acids present in *T. foetus* by chromatographic methods. This was done in order to obtain information on the nitrogen sources available to this parasite, and as a guide to the nature of its protein metabolism. Some eighteen to nineteen amino acids were recognized. It was found that blood serum, an essential ingredient of the medium, contained most of the amino acids present. The accurate determination of amino acid sources by withdrawal techniques could therefore not be applied. There was close correlation between the amino acids present in the medium and in the organism, thus leaving the question of the nature of the essential amino acids unsolved.

The methods of preserving human pathogenic protozoa without loss of virulence were studied.[438] They concluded that the method of storage by freezing is simple and allows maintenance of strains with the least possible effort. They had no success in preserving *T. vaginalis* and only a limited success with *T. hominis*. McEntegart[265] studied further the maintenance of stock strains of trichomonads at low temperatures, and had considerable success when slow freezing to −79°C was carried out in presence of 10 per cent glycerol. Even without glycerol *T. gallinae* was preserved at this temperature for four months. *T. vaginalis* remained viable for four months and *T. hominis* for 6 months. *T. foetus* could not, however, be preserved under these conditions. Joyner[211] made the interesting observation that when an egg-yolk-citrate diluent with 10 per cent glycerol was used *T. foetus* could be eliminated from infected bull semen by subjecting it to a freezing process similar to that used for preservation of spermatozoa; he confirmed this fact. Levine and Marquardt[232] used the cysteine–peptone–liver infusion–maltose (CPLM) medium with 5–10 per cent glycerol and found that *T. foetus* survived under these conditions at −79°C. Other authors have confirmed this fact with different media; the experimental conditions are obviously important. Fitzgerald and Levine[131] have continued their studies on the effect of storage temperatures and other factors on the survival of this organism in the presence of glycerol.

Virulence and Pathogenicity

The effect of cultivation on the virulence of *T. vaginalis* for mice when injected intraperitoneally has been studied.[236] After two to three months maintenance *in vitro* loss of virulence was marked; when frozen at −43°C for short periods virulence, like viability, was finally lost. It has been reported that *T. foetus* survived much better at −95°C than at −28°C. A relation between growth rate and virulence has been established in some instances. Honigberg[188] pointed out that *T. gallinae* varies in virulence for normal and experimental hosts and established that *T. vaginalis* is composed of truly pathogenic strains. He is of the opinion that virulence is an expression of physiological characters inherent in both strains. Treatment of an avirulent strain of *T. gallinae* with a cell-free preparation from a virulent strain enhanced the virulence of the former, judged by the size of the lesions produced in mice.[189] The prevention of the transformation by deoxyribonuclease suggests that the transformation was brought about by the genetic agent deoxyribonucleic acid (DNA) of the virulent strain. The results were somewhat equivocal because of the large variations in the size of the lesions encountered. Mandel and Honigberg[255] have also isolated and characterized DNA from the same two parasites and found it to have a high content of adenine and thymine. It was suitable for use in transformation experiments for which unimpaired biological activity is essential.

Shorb[376] has dealt very fully with the physiology of trichomonads and with factors which affect pathogenicity. It is known that differences in pathogenicity exist among strains of the same species. A number of authors have sought an explanation in biochemical differences. Asami and Nakamura[18] accept *T. vaginalis* as a true pathogen and describe some experiments on inoculation of the human vagina with bacteria-free parasites of this species and the changes in glycogen of the mucosa which followed. They suggest that consumption of this glycogen facilitated bacterial invasion and the ensuing vaginitis. Although some strains of *T. vaginalis* have shown differences in biochemical activity towards various sugars no relationship between these differences and pathogenicity was established. Differences in pathogenicity for cells have been widely studied in tissue culture. The presence of enzymes which may be associated with pathogenicity have been described by Watkins and colleagues[434, 435, 436] and in other publications. They drew attention to the presence of enzymes in *T. foetus* which brought about the serological inactivation of blood-group substances but this property was absent in *T. vaginalis*. The enzyme of *T. foetus* causing inactivation of the H receptor on human erythrocytes could, for example, be differentiated from that acting on the M receptor.

In his review on the electron transport mechanisms in parasitic protozoa Baernstein[27] has drawn attention to the limited use of oxygen by trichomonads, their insensitivity to cyanide and azide, and the possible occurrence of cytochrome b in *T. foetus*. Hydrogen peroxide is produced by some species; from it the organisms are protected by catalase in the cells. The hydrogen gas produced by some strains is believed to be associated with electron transport mechanisms. Being largely anaerobic in character trichomonads depend on dehydrogenase-coupled reactions involving pyridine and flavoproteins which give rise to reduced compounds. The degradation of sugars in the first stages is mainly by glycolytic reactions, possibly via the pentose shunt. Some components of the citric acid cycle have been recognized and call for further study. The mechanism of H_2 evolution is also worthy of further investigation in the presence of chemically defined media. Biochemical studies of this nature have already contributed something to our knowledge of the pathogenicity of these organisms.

Summary

Physiological and biochemical investigations on *Trichomonas* have been pursued with vigour in the last few years. By comparative studies of this kind the problem of species identity will in time be solved and host-parasite relationships clarified. However, if outstanding fundamental questions are to be answered, emphasis must continue to be placed on the importanc of acquiring basic knowledge of these organisms. It is probably true that energy producing reactions have been more intensively studied than those of endergonic nature, concerned with reproduction and growth. Thus nitrogen metabolism has received less attention than carbohydrate metabolism, although in the case of *T. foetus* the latter has been fairly intensively studied. It was found that for this organism the essential amino acids corresponded to those required by higher animals. The specific location of the three different species of *Trichomonas* in the mouth, gut, and genital tract of man have not yet been described in biochemical terms. Progress in the study of optimal culture techniques has yielded good dividends and new knowledge of the nutritional needs of the parasites has been gained. The discovery of the ideal defined medium in which all components are known is still a goal for the future. Success in this field would provide considerable aid in solving the problems of chemotherapy. The preservation of strains by freezing methods is in itself an advance which is likely to aid in attracting more workers to this particular field. The physiological pathology of the various infections has not so far been sufficiently studied.

III. SPOROZOA

All sporozoa are parasitic and have a complicated life cycle, in some cases including spore formation. Their taxonomic relationships are by no means clear.

Malaria

All malarial parasites are included within the genus *Plasmodium*. Infections occur in mammals including man, apes, monkeys, and rodents as well as in reptiles and birds, and most forms have been used in laboratory studies. Those in other primates sometimes bear a strong resemblance to the human forms and are also carried by anopheline mosquitoes in distinction to the bird parasites whose vectors are Culicines. There are four species of plasmodia which infect man and he can also be infected with certain monkey parasites. The complex life cycle involves development in vertebrate and invertebrate hosts. When a human is bitten by an infected mosquito, sporozoites develop in the skin at the site for a time, then pass via the blood to internal organs and tissues where an extraerythrocytic cycle occurs, especially in the liver. Some days later, after schizogony in that organ, the red corpuscles are invaded by parasites which there undergo schizogony during a developmental cycle of 24 to 72 hours, according to the species. Pigment called haemozoin is formed by the parasite within the red cell. On completion of schizogony the red cell ruptures and approximately twelve to thirty merozoites are set free; these now enter fresh red cells to continue the erythrocytic cycle. At this time fever and chills occur. A small percentage of merozoites give rise to male and female gametocytes which on being taken up by mosquitoes undergo syngamy in the insect gut. Oocysts develop in the gut wall, and finally sporozoites reach the mosquito salivary glands. Human infection results when the mosquito feeds; in this way the cycle is repeated.

Plasmodia have provided material for extensive researches by the biochemist; because of the difficulty in obtaining material at other stages of development, erythrocytic forms have been almost invariably used in these studies. In this respect, our knowledge is somewhat limited for immunological properties and the effect of drugs[194] make clear the differences in metabolic behaviour among the various stages of development in the mosquito the exo-erythrocytic and erythrocytic forms, as well as among the different species. The most widely used parasites in laboratory studies have been *Plasmodium knowlesi* and *P. cynomolgi* of monkeys, both of which can infect man, *P. gallinaceum* of the domestic fowl, *P. lophurae* of ducks, and *P. relictum* and *P. cathemerium* of canaries. Since the discovery of *P. berghei* and the related *P. vinckei* of rodents some 20 years ago they too have been widely employed in malarial studies. The intracellular nature of several malaria parasites has been established by electron microscope studies and their fine structure determined.[134, 146, 340, 341]

Early Metabolic Studies

Metabolic studies were initiated by Christophers and Fulton[93] with *P. knowlesi*, the pathogen of heavy synchronous infections in the rhesus monkey. By differential centrifugation the invaded red cells were separated as a brown layer above non-invaded cells, highly uniform, almost free from leucocytes, and with only a small percentage of normal cells. Respiration measurements were carried out in conventional apparatus at 37°C and the material had undiminished infectivity after some hours. Parasites freed from red cells by saponin were also used in this way,[94] but survived less well than those within red cells, and respiratory activity was diminished. The main results were that parasites utilized oxygen at a steady rate over a period of hours in absence of added substrate, and CO_2 was produced in approximately the same amount. Added glucose increased the respiration of washed cells and disappeared but glycogen was not synthesized. Haemoglobin of the invaded erythrocyte was reduced in amount and rapidly de-oxygenated by the parasite. Formation of acid comparable to that produced by trypanosomes was not apparent in well-buffered suspensions, and non-protein nitrogen was increased. Experiments on respiratory inhibition by drugs were also carried out under similar conditions,[145] in the hope that antimalarial activity might be assessed by this method. When carried out under standard conditions results were repeatable and inhibition of respiration paralleled in some degree therapeutic effect, in so far as antimalarial drugs were effective inhibitors; but good correlation was not always obtained. Cyanide was a potent inhibitor which suggested that *P. knowlesi* possessed a heavy-metal respiratory enzyme. With free parasites, Fulton[143] observed that only glucose, fructose, mannose, maltose, and glycerol, out of a large selection of sugars tested, were oxidized by this parasite. The blood sugar of heavily infected monkeys was reduced and liver glycogen was depleted. These results were confirmed and extended[252] by using three species of monkey plasmodia and two avian species. The authors noted that respiration increased with the size of the parasite and concluded that glucose was one important source of energy. Coggeshall and Maier[98] also studied the possibility of assaying anti-malarial drugs by comparing the effect on respiration *in vitro* with therapeutic effect *in vivo* but found little correlation between the two. Wendel[444] found however that the *in vivo* and *in vitro* activity of 69 out of a series of 76 hydroxynaphthoquinones were in agreement. Velick[430] used the highly synchronous infection of *P. cathemerium* in canaries and observed that oxygen consumption increased with the size of the parasite and was accelerated during nuclear division, associated with an increase in respiratory quotient. Various authors expressed the view that fundamental problems in malaria could be solved by a better understanding of the metabolic characters of the parasites. It seemed possible also to explain the action of drugs on this basis and thereby provide aid in the search for chemotherapeutic agents. In the same way nutritional factors might also be revealed and the goal of cultivation *in vitro* would then prove feasible. With the advent of World War II, there was a marked stimulus to study these problems, and the researches involved will now be described.

Carbohydrate Metabolism

The early experiments[37, 38] indicated the importance of glucose for malaria parasites. This substance is apparently not stored but is rapidly oxidized and, as we shall see, provides energy for synthetic activities. This energy is stored partly in the high-energy phosphate bonds of ATP. Extensive studies on the respiration and carbohydrate metabolism of *P. knowlesi* were also made[443, 445] and showed that about half the glucose present was converted to lactate and pyruvate with subsequent partial oxidation of these substances. Anaerobiosis was found to stimulate glycolysis by infected cells and lactate proved as good a substrate for respiration as glucose. The method of glucose oxidation by fowl cells invaded by *P. gallinaceum* was studied in detail.[380] These workers showed that glucose was broken down in quantitative fashion anaerobically to lactate and suggested that a phosphorylating glycolysis, characteristic of certain mammalian tissues, was operative. Under aerobic conditions the lactate and pyruvate formed were largely oxidized to CO_2 and water, and respiration in presence of these substrates was as active as with glucose. When based on the surface area of the parasites the rate of anaerobic utilization of glucose was about 100 times that of normal red cells. Some later authors used parasites free from red cells or cell-free extracts of parasites to study carbohydrate metabolism. This was necessary because of permeability factors which prevent the polar substances such as phosphorylated sugars or tri-carboxylic acids from penetrating the red cell membrane to reach the parasite. Similar results were obtained[396] for the same parasite freed from red cell material by haemolytic serum. The free parasites also utilized succinate, malate, fumarate, oxalacetate, cis-aconitate, and α-ketoglutarate. These free parasites oxidized pyruvate at maximum rate only in presence of dicarboxylic acids such as succinate, thiamine, or diphosphothiamine, DPN, TPN, ATP, and manganous ions. Substrates were oxidized by these free parasites at about half the rate of parasitized red cells, and some acetate was formed from pyruvate. The oxidation of the latter was inhibited by malonate and succinate accumulated. It was concluded that the oxidation of pyruvate took place by the TCA cycle of Krebs. Bovarnick and colleagues[48, 49] found that washed *P. lophurae*, freed from red cells by saponin, resumed oxygen uptake only slowly on addition of glucose but more quickly with lactate, pyruvate, succinate, and fumarate. It was concluded that the longer induction period in oxidation of glucose by substrate-depleted cells was due to the need for phosphorylation of this substance before it is utilized. Shortening of the induction period can be effected by increased ATP formation which is derived from energy-producing oxidative processes in the cell. By the use of cell-free extracts of *P. gallinaceum*, it was shown[394, 395] that glucose was converted to lactate by a phosphorylating glycolysis. These preparations contained enzymes catalyzing this reaction by ATP, the splitting of fructose 1 : 6-diphosphate to form 3-phosphoglyceraldehyde and the dismutation between the latter and pyruvate. From the results described it appears that glucose is oxidized by the same pathways in all three parasites. Comparison[158, 266] of the glucose and lactate used over the same period by fixed numbers of the human malaria parasites *P. falciparum* and *P. vivax* and two monkey parasites *P. knowlesi* and *P. cynomolgi* indicates that *P. vivax* consumed about five to six times as much as *P. cynomolgi*. Intermediate values were obtained for the other two parasites.

Much of the energy of the glycolytic reaction is locked up in the pyruvate produced before it takes part in the Krebs' cycle in which much ATP is produced. Nevertheless the energy available from glycolysis is not negligible in view of the large amounts of lactate formed from glucose. The work on culturing *P. knowlesi* at low oxygen tension has indicated that energy obtained from glycolysis is probably utilized for the synthetic activities of the parasite.[17]

The incorporation of radioactivity from [^{14}C]-glucose and [1 : 4-^{14}C]-succinate into the soluble metabolic intermediates of *P. berghei* freed from red cells, and into normal and parasitized mouse blood cells was studied.[70] The free parasites used glucose at a low rate and gave rise mainly to lactate. Parasitized cells showed an increased rate of glycolysis and oxidative reactions. Incorporation of radioactivity from labelled succinate occurred only in trace amounts.

Nitrogen Metabolism

During the cycle of development of the erythrocytic invader, which in the forms studied takes 24 to 48 hours, there is a 10- to 30-fold increase in number and comparable increase in size with a consequent heavy demand on its synthetic capabilities. Evidence from studies on other protozoa suggests that plasmodia probably require pre-formed amino acids for building blocks. Since in the red cell they occur to only a limited extent, red cell or serum proteins, or free amino acids in serum, presented themselves as probably sources. It was first suggested[69] that part of the nitrogen requirement of the parasite is satisfied by the breakdown of haemoglobin of the invaded cell whose globin is utilized and whose heme portion is rejected as pigment. It was shown[93] that in invaded cells haemoglobin does in fact disappear over a period of some hours' incubation, accompanied by other changes in nitrogen components. Confirmation of the loss of haemoglobin was given[44] in human and monkey malaria by means of staining techniques. Ball and colleagues[34] followed by quantitative methods the almost complete conversion of haemoglobin to haematin by *P. knowlesi*, both *in vitro* and *in vivo*. There was no spectroscopic evidence of the formation of any intermediate in this conversion and quantitative data indicated that all pigment was retained by the parasite, suggesting that haemoglobin breakdown probably occurred after being taken in by it. Morrison and Jeskey[280, 281] showed that characteristic parasite protein is obtained from red cell protein and they also made quantitative observations on the breakdown of haemoglobin. An enzyme has not yet been isolated from malaria parasites which will break down haemoglobin to haematin and globin. Following the observations[289] that cell-free extracts of *P. gallinaceum* hydrolysed horse or chicken haemoglobin at a slow rate or not at all, but split denatured globin at a much faster rate, the breakdown of haemoglobin by extracts of *P. knowlesi* could not be demonstrated.[34] It has been shown[101] that cell-free extracts of *P. berghei* also hydrolysed globin and denatured haemoglobin to liberate free amino acids. Red cells invaded by these two parasites do, however, form large quantities of amino acids and their haemoglobin origin has been suggested by the work of the authors quoted as well as by that described.[172] It appears that the utilization of amino acids for synthesis by the parasite involves oxidative reactions.[289] The authors found that *P. gallinaceum* within chick cells produced large amounts of amino nitrogen in air when glucose was present, but more ammonia when glucose was absent. Under anaerobic conditions little amino nitrogen was produced. The normal course of events is the utilization of amino acids for protein synthesis, their source is believed to be largely the globin of the host red cell. The studies of McKee and Geiman[267, 268] on the part played by amino acids in the nutrition of *P. knowlesi* showed that *dl*-methionine was the only one which had to be added to culture medium containing plasma to induce growth and multiplication. Their observations led them to conclude that the parasite used the protein of the host red cell. They also showed that *dl*-methionine or PAB given to monkeys in which *P. knowlesi* infection was controlled by fasting cancelled this control. Further, parasite growth was inhibited by two analogues of methionine, methoxinine and ethionine, and their action was inhibited by increased methionine. Fulton and Grant[147] provided confirmatory evidence of the importance of methionine by showing that *P. knowlesi* grown in ^{35}S-labelled erythrocytes *in vivo* obtained about 80 per cent of its methionine requirements from the red-cell globin, the remainder presumably being obtained from serum. The conversion of ^{35}S-methionine to ^{35}S-cystine by the parasite was shown to occur *in vitro*, thus providing an extra source of cystine sulphur. The uptake of dl-^{35}S-methionine by invaded erythrocytes in culture was much greater than that for similarly labelled cysteine. Monkey haemoglobin was found to contain respectively 6.0 and 2.4 times the amount of these substances present in the protein of a mature parasite. As other authors have suggested, the extracellular supply of methionine supplements the supply from haemoglobin, insufficient for the provision of cystine and the building up of parasite protein. The parasites apparently can not use that present in serum protein. Groman[172] also investigated the mechanisms by which the malaria parasite converts the nitrogenous supplies of the invaded erythrocyte into parasite protoplasm by observing under different experimental conditions *in vivo* and *in vitro*, the changes which occur in nitrogenous fractions of chicken erythrocytes invaded by *P. gallinaceum*. He observed a relation between aerobic oxidative metabolism and nitrogen metabolism to which attention had already been drawn, and which threw some light on the host–parasite relationship.[289] The evidence obtained indicated that the parasite is supplied with nitrogen mainly by breakdown of haemoglobin. From this work it seemed that *P. gallinaceum* destroyed only about one quarter the amount of this substance broken down by *P. knowlesi*. Data from *in vivo* and *in vitro* experiments indicated a quantitative similarity in the changes in NPN and amino nitrogen which occurred, and in the rate at which pigment was formed. The earlier views[69] have therefore received much experimental confirmation. With regard to the nature of the pigment, Sinton and Ghosh [381, 382] gave a wide review of the literature and also carried out a long series of investigations on *P. knowlesi* pigment which established it as haematin. Similar investigations[150, 335] established that the same pigment was formed by *P. gallinaceum* and also by *P. berghei*. Deegan and Maegraith[107, 108] have, however, provided evidence that the pigment in certain human and simian malarias does not exist free as haematin but in combination with a nitrogenous compound. They base their view partly on the fact that free haematin is inhibitory to succinic dehydrogenase which was shown to be active in parasite metabolism.[396] The occurrence of pigment within the parasite, which posed some problems on permeability, has been simply explained by the electron microscope studies[340, 341] on *P. lophurae* and *P. berghei*. It now appears that the malarial parasite is phagotrophic and engulfs particles of the host cell haemoglobin, which is then digested within food vacuoles. Moulder[288] has pointed out how these results may also help to explain the relation between sickle cell anaemia and resistance to malaria. Thus in sickle cells the haemoglobin is abnormal with reduced solubility and increased viscosity of its solutions. Because of these properties this abnormal haemoglobin could interfere with phagotrophy by the parasites and thereby reduce susceptibility to infection.

It is known that the red cells of American negro males are deficient in glucose-6-phosphate dehydrogenase activity and may undergo severe haemolysis on treatment with 8-ammoquinolines and other drugs. The deficiency trait was shown[12] to occur in East Africans and its occurrence paralleled that of the sickle cell trait in the same region. It was suggested that the enzyme deficiency, like the latter trait, may put the bearers at a selective advantage in malarious regions, since the conditions for growth and multiplication of the malaria parasite are less favourable. This view has been partly verified in the case of children who suffer from the deficiency and have lower parasitaemias than others. Sherman[371] had found by kinetic, electrophoretic, and other methods that the lactic dehydrogenase of *P. lophurae* infecting duck red cells differed qualitatively from the analogous enzyme in the host erythrocyte, being about three times as active and appeared to possess a physiological advantage over the host cell enzyme under the conditions prevailing in the red cell. This author[372] has investigated other enzymes from the point of view of host–parasite relationships. Since glucose-6-phosphate dehydrogenase is involved in maintenance of a reduced glutathione level in the red cell necessary for *in vitro* cultivation, and glutathione contributes to the cysteine requirements of plasmodia, the activity of the enzyme and the level of reduced glutathione were assayed in *P. lophurae* infections of ducks in which the parasite has a preference for mature erythrocytes. Similar experiments were carried out with *P. berghei* infections in mice in which reticulocytes are preferentially invaded. There was no increase in enzyme activity in either infection as a result of parasitization. In both infections enzyme deficiency did not become apparent till an 80 per cent level of parasitaemia was approached. A linear relationship between enzyme level and parasitaemia was not apparent. The instability of red cell enzyme content was possibly due to phagotrophy by parasites which destroy haemoglobin and other cytoplasmic components including enzymes. In duck erythrocytes, which contain an abnormal amount of reduced glutathione compared with erythrocytes of other species, there was no glutathione instability over a wide range of parasitaemia. In *P. knowlesi* infections the parasite has been reported to cause an increase in dehydrogenase activity which was regarded as favourable for its development by stabilizing conditions in the host cell. The studies on *P. lophurae* and *P. berghei*, both virulent parasites which invade different types of red cells, indicate a stable host-parasite complex. The enzymic advantage indicated for lactic dehydrogenase above did not apply to glucose-6-phosphate dehydrogenase. Sherman and Hull[373, 374] studied the pigment and proteins of *P. lophurae*. Unlike that of simian and human malarias the pigment is of low solubility in buffers and required the addition of urea. On the basis of spectral and electrophoretic studies it appeared to be a protein-porphyrin complex closely resembling methaemoglobin but distinct from haematin. It thus differed from other malarial pigments and the nature of its association with proteins was not clear. Soluble parasite proteins constituted about 50 per cent of the total volume of the parasite and appeared to be homogeneous. While they resembled haemoglobin in some respects they were nevertheless distinct from it.

Chickens were found to have two distinct haemoglobins which when present in their respective amounts could affect the growth of malarial parasites. Analysis before, during, and after infection with *P. lophurae* showed the presence of an α-component, constituting 25 per cent of the total, which moved more rapidly during electrophoresis than a second β-component. No detectable breakdown of red cell haemoglobin occurred outside the parasite and host synthesis of haemoglobins continued in much the same proportions as in uninfected birds in spite of marked anaemia and reticulocytosis.

During the development of chloroquine resistance in *P. berghei* Peters[310] observed certain morphological differences in the normal and resistant strains. Pigment was absent in the latter strain and when resistance was lost pigment formation was resumed. Peters *et al.*[311] have now shown that phagotrophy occurs in normal and resistant parasites and that the resistant forms do not form typical grains of haemozoin. It was suggested that the underlying mechanism preventing their formation may be the inability of the parasites to render haematin insoluble through absence of combination with some basic substance. Earlier observations on the same parasite[99] had suggested that ferrihaemic acid, a possible intermediary product arising during the breakdown of haemoglobin by the malarial parasite, might be produced in abnormal amounts by certain strains of this parasite. The possibility that this porphyrin formed an insoluble complex with chloroquine, or other drugs to which the parasites would become tolerant, was put forward to explain the development of chloroquine resistance. The absence of pigment or its presence in decreased amounts in resistant parasites would lend support for this view and an inverse relationship between drug formation and pigment formation would obtain. This is in agreement with the findings[310, 412] in which similar observations regarding drug resistance and absence of pigment were made. The findings received further confirmation.[198] In addition this author was also of the opinion that quinine and chloroquine resistant strains of *P. berghei* were less virulent for mice, but this property was not shared by a pyrimethamine-resistant strain. Schueler and Cantrell[354] in studying the antagonism of the antimalarial action of chloroquine by ferrihaemate had put forward a hypothesis on the mechanism of chloroquine resistance which is similar to that suggested above.

Baernstein[27] has reviewed the electron transport mechanisms in plasmodia. These parasites possess oxidases which are sensitive to inhibitory agents such as cyanide, azide and carbon monoxide and this fact suggests that a cytochrome oxidase is present. Only a limited number of species have been studied in detail either within the red cell or freed from it by saponin or immune serum, and all appear to conform to a general pattern. No pure enzymes have so far been isolated. The inhibition of oxygen uptake by naphthoquinones, which in other organisms act on cytochrome reductase, suggests that intermediate carriers may be present.

Nucleic Acids

Since the synthesis of protein is closely linked with nucleic acid metabolism it is convenient to record here what is known about nucleic acids in malaria parasites. Investigations in this subject have been somewhat limited. Chen[91a] studied the structure of nuclei in *Plasmodium elongatum* using the Feulgen technique. Deane[106] also applied the Feulgen staining method to nuclear studies in *P. vivax* and *P. knowlesi* and found DNA in both parasites, the merozoites stained most intensely and the DNA increased markedly as the parasites developed. Ball *et al.*[34] followed the changes in nucleic acid phosphorus of *P. knowlesi* parasites and calculated that each parasitized red cell contained approximately ten to twenty times as much nucleic acid phosphorus as the normal red cell, whether grown *in vitro* or *in vivo*. The results of Lewert[233, 234] also indicated that there was a marked ribonucleic acid metabolism in *P. gallinaceum*, as in almost all organisms studied, the nucleus containing DNA and the cytoplasm RNA. DNA is present in large amounts in avian erythrocytes but absent or nearly so in mammalian erythrocytes. The breakdown of the nuclear DNA of the invaded erythrocyte provides material for parasite anabolism. The same author also studied changes in these acids and in protein in invaded cells by ultra violet absorption methods. Whitfield[447, 448] has used *P. berghei* in researches on these cellular constituents which were found in much larger amounts in the invaded erythrocytes, the amount of RNA about twice that of DNA. By calculation he arrived at the amount of each substance present per parasite; he also determined the nature of the purine and pyrimidine components. From the quantitative aspects, his results were somewhat difficult to interpret because of the large numbers of reticulocytes which were present and which also contain nucleic acids. The same author[449] also studied the distribution of radioactive phosphorus in *P. berghei* and found it highest in the lipid fraction, varying at different periods during infection.

Lipids

Only a few investigaions have been carried out and have dealt almost exclusively with *P. knowlesi*. Morrison and Jeskey[280] isolated the free parasites and analysed them after removal of haemoglobin. They found the average percentage content of dried material was pigment, 10–11 per cent; lipid, 28–29 per cent; and protein, 61 per cent. The extracted lipids were solid at room temperature and rather viscous at 37°C. The non-saponifiable portion amounted to 16–32 per cent of the total and the chief component was cholesterol. Of the fatty acids less than 0.3 per cent was present in volatile form while 36 per cent was stearic acid and the remainder was an 18-C unsaturated acid, possibly oleic. The alteration in composition of the invaded erythrocyte indicated that lipids increased by more than 500 per cent during parasite development. Ball *et al.*[34] also showed that an increase in fatty acids and phospholipid phosphorus took place under the same conditions. A crystalline haemolytic substance was isolated from normal blood[228] and was thought at first to be a lysolecithin. This was disproved[227] and finally it was characterized as an unsaturated monocarboxylic fatty acid with one double bond, whose haemolytic properties were specifically inhibited by antimalarials, but potentiated by haematin. It was present in greatly increased amounts during *P. knowlesi* infections, both free and within red cells. The suggestion was made that the malaria parasites produce it, or are responsible for its appearance, and that it aids in metabolizing the contents of the red cell and helps in the release of merozoites.

This acid has been identified by Morton and Todd[282] as *cis*-vaccenic acid (*cis*-heptadec-10-ene-1-carboxylic acid) and confirmed by synthesis.

Cultivation

Knowledge of the biochemistry of erythrocytic stages of malaria parasites has benefited from experiments on cultivation. Exo-erythrocytic forms of plasmodia and sporozoites have also been cultured in living cells such as bone marrow or chick embryo but the results obtained have not supplied much information on the growth factors involved.

Attention has already been drawn to the early cultivation investigations,[37, 38] but no real advances were made till Trager[414] began his *in vitro* studies on the survival of the avian parasite *P. lophurae*. The first aim was to discover the conditions in which development would occur, rather than to maintain parasites alive for long periods; it was already known[96] that *P. knowlesi* and *P. inui* could be preserved in the frozen state for more than two months, and that the best criterion for survival was by inoculation to fresh hosts. At a temperature around 40°C survival *in vitro* was favoured by a balanced salt solution with high potassium content, by aeration at moderate oxygen tension, and by choosing a suitable density of parasites. Frequent replacement of the medium was essential, and concentrated duck red cell extract had a favourable effect, also plasma, serum, or chick embryo extract, in presence of glucose and glutathione. Yeast and liver extract was also beneficial. As judged by ex-flagellation of male gametocytes a small number of parasites survived for 5 days, and by infectivity test, up to 6 days. Trager[415] then found that addition of Ca pantothenate accompanied by better aeration and gentle agitation with more frequent addition of fresh red cells extended the survival time to 16 days. Multiplication took place for the first few days but was exceeded by the death rate. Somewhat similar results had been obtained[102] with *P. circumflexum*, which developed for three or four generations and proved infective after 13 days. Trager[416] benefited by the studies of other workers in this field, described later, and observed that the omission of vitamins from his medium was deleterious to development. Alteration in the concentration of added biotin over a wide range did not affect multiplication; the parasites increased in numbers 2- to 3-fold over a 2-day culture period and could be subcultured. They were actively multiplying after eight days. This author[423] reported the enhanced folic and folinic acid content of erythrocytes parasitized by plasmodia and the much smaller amount in free plasmodia. Previous evidence has supported the view that folic acid and related compounds play an important role in the metabolism of these parasites. It appeared that the metabolism of the host cell was increased with regard to these two substances as a result of the presence of the parasites rather than that the latter were responsible for their synthesis. He[425] studied the effect of drugs on the levels of folic and folinic acids of erythrocytes parasitized with *P. lophurae* in the case of both a normal and a sulphadiazine-resistant strain. The results indicated that the synthetic mechanism was present in the host cells and not in the parasite. The author was of the opinion that resistance to these two drugs may depend on a reduced need for the products of a reaction which these drugs inhibit. Studies of a similar nature were made[258] on the survival in the "Harvard" medium of four species of avian malaria, *P. gallinaceum*, *P. lophurae*, *P. cathemerium*, and *P. relictum*. The parasites in culture were observed in stained smears and their viability judged by inoculation into fresh birds. The medium was not very satisfactory but even without multiplication, viability continued in some cases for 63 hours. Glenn and Manwell[162] considered that in some cases folic acid and vitamin B_{12} and liver coenzyme concentrate aided growth. Spandorf and Manwell[393] using the above medium supplemented by certain factors had some success in culturing *P. circumflexum* but not *P. vaughani*, although viability was maintained for some days. Nydegger and Manwell[305] maintained *P. hexamerium* in the "Harvard" medium suitably supplemented with malate and pyruvate for 96 hours, and on subculturing at 72-hour intervals the period of continuous culture was extended to nine days.

Because of pressing war needs, efforts were begun at Harvard to uncover some vital link in the metabolism or growth requirements of malaria parasites which might lead to the synthesis of more efficient antimalarials. It appeared that this objective could best be served by *in vitro* cultivation studies, so that metabolism of malaria parasites and the effect of drugs on them could be studied in absence of host influences. Researches of outstanding interest among many others were reported.[33, 34, 269] The parasite found most suitable was *P. knowlesi* of monkeys but others including human forms were also studied. Earlier metabolic and respiratory studies were reviewed and the chemical and physical needs of normal and parasitized erythrocytes determined. From analytical data on the blood of the monkey host a non-defined complex culture medium was devised.[33] It contained cellular elements of blood, inorganic salts, sugar, proteose peptone, amino acids, vitamins, purines, and pyrimidines, as well as serum, or 1 per cent crystalline serum albumin. It was not possible to decide which components were essential for growth, although the absence of proteose peptone was detrimental to growth and multiplication. The chief growth component furnished by the peptone appeared to be *p*-aminobenzoic acid (PAB); later it replaced proteose peptone in the medium. PAB is one of the precursors of the B vitamin folic acid, of great importance in biosynthetic reactions, which cannot be synthesized by higher animals from PAB. In view of the early observations on inhibition of multiplication in *P. knowlesi* by sulphonamides, and reversal of this action by PAB itself, it has been suggested that the malaria parasite synthesizes folic acid from PAB and other components. The medium was maintained at pH 7.45 and the apparatus was kept gently rocked at a temperature of 38.5°C. Two types of techniques were used. The first, termed the rocker-dilution (RD), in which one part of whole blood and three parts of diluting medium were present, was equipped with gas inlet and outlet tubes and a slow current of 5 per cent CO_2 and 95 per cent air was passed over the contents. A second technique was termed the rocker-perfusion (RP); in one type, blood, isolated by a cellophane membrane, was bathed in nutrient fluid, in another type larger volumes of blood were used and a cellophane tube containing nutrient medium was passed through the culture material. The apparatus was rocked as before and the same mixture of gases was present. The first type (RD) was most suitable when nutrients and metabolic substances were retained or drugs were added, and the rate of change had to be determined. In the second type, the rocker-perfusion apparatus (RP), waste products were removed at maximum rate; it proved useful for long term cultures since the contents were kept in an approximately physiological state, and it was also valuable for a study of nutritional needs. Cytological examination was regularly made. In a series of 235 culture experiments the increase in parasite numbers varied from 2- to 11-fold with an average 4-fold increase during the life cycle of 24 hours; it compared favourably with the course of events *in vivo*. The cultured blood remained infective for fresh hosts during seven generations. With successful culture it became possible to study the changes taking place in infected cells *in vitro* as well as *in vivo*. It became evident that a high oxygen tension was harmful to the parasites and that they can obtain a considerable portion of their energy from the anaerobic breakdown of sugar. One difference between the parasites growing *in vitro* and *in vivo* was that the former consumed less oxygen. The pattern of phosphorus metabolism was also different. The nutritional need for PAB, glucose, and methionine was established. In many ways the carbohydrate metabolism in different species of malaria parasites followed the same pattern. Discussed earlier in this paper are the increase of metabolism with size, the nature of the glycolytic processes and other metabolic characteristics including phosphorus turnover, formation of lipids and of nucleic and fatty acids, as well as pigment formation from haemoglobin. The influence of host diet on infection has been widely studied. The importance of the amino acid methionine and *p*-aminobenzoic acid for growth and multiplication *in vivo*, in agreement with the results of culture experiments has been confirmed.[159] Ascorbic acid is also important *in vivo* but apparently not *in vitro*, and this fact may indicate that its effect is exerted through the host. The work described[415, 416] has already been mentioned in connection with certain vitamins. Seeler and Ott[358, 359, 360] have confirmed the fact that in chickens infected with *P. lophurae* the multiplication rate increases with increased biotin deficiency. Similar effects were encountered in folic acid deficiency.[338] Brooke[67] studied the effect of dietary deficiencies in canaries, pigeons, and ducks infected with a variety of malaria parasites. In general the effect of the experimental diets was to cause a more severe primary attack, a greater tendency to relapse, and reduced resistance to superinfection. The earlier work of Passmore and Sommerville[309] did not detect any difference in monkeys maintained on deficient diets from those fed normally as far as malaria infection was concerned; the course and severity of primary malarial attacks were not affected by the nutritional state of the monkeys. Animal nutrition studies in which infected blood was obtained from a host made deficient in a particular factor have provided useful material for *in vitro* studies with a medium deficient in that factor.

It is clear that many of the nutritional needs of the parasite would be determined if cultivation outside red cells were attained. Many *Sporozoa* are obligate intracellular parasites, and some have been grown in tissue culture but none extracellularly *in vitro*. Trager[417] was the first to undertake the culture of extra-cellular malaria parasites. He obtained considerable development of *P. lophurae* in a complex medium containing extract of duck erythrocytes into which the parasites had been directly liberated from the host cell by means of specific antiserum. Later evidence indicated that the extract supplied not only haemoglobin as a source of nitrogen but growth factors as well. The addition of ATP, DPN, and pyruvic acid was specially beneficial and allowed 100 per cent survival for about two days; the free forms continued development during the first two days of cultivation, but degeneration then proceeded till very few normal parasites were present on the fifth day, as shown by staining. This author[418] showed that the addition of *l*-malic acid and coenzyme A concentrates improved the complex medium still further; it had been indicated by other authors that addition of succinate and fumarate aided respiration. He[420] then suggested that *P. lophurae* was unable to synthesize coenzyme A, which may be supplied by the host erythrocyte. The coenzyme A content of normal and infected erythrocytes was therefore determined, and in the normal cells found to be about double that in the invaded cells. The effect of this enzyme was uninfluenced by the addition of free pantothenic acid (part of its molecule); the enzyme appears to be mobilized in presence of the parasite rather than to be synthesized by it. Coenzyme A plays a part in supplying energy by the oxidation of glucose via the Krebs' cycle and in the synthesis of many cell constituents by the provision of 2-carbon units through the activity of its acetyl derivative. This substance is therefore of the utmost metabolic importance. Trager[422] further found that extracellular survival of *P. lophurae* on the fourth day of cultivation was favourably influenced by addition to the medium of folinic acid at a level of 5 μg per ml; also that *P. falciparum* developed better in a medium with a high content of this substance. Glenn and Manwell[162] in their studies on the cultivation of avian parasites noted that folic acid, and also vitamin B_{12} and liver coenzyme concentrate, favoured the development of *P. hexamerium* in duck red cells. The results obtained by extracellular cultivation even in absence of actual increase in numbers should advance considerably our knowledge of the requirements of malaria parasites. Thus it appears that methionine, PAB, glucose, pantothenate, etc. supplement materials already present in the red cell which furnishes the correct milieu for growth while the parasite itself supplies the necessary enzymes. These studies have also been helpful in other ways. Thus a number of workers have noted that free parasites convert glucose to lactate at the normal rate but oxidize pyruvate much more slowly, and also, unlike invaded erythrocytes, give rise to acetate which is not further metabolized. This series of events receives at least a partial explanation on the hypothesis of Trager that malaria parasites cannot themselves synthesize coenzyme A. Free parasites are also much more permeable than ordinary cells to highly polar substances such as the tricarboxylic acids of the Krebs' cycle, coenzyme A, ATP, and pyridine nucleotides, all of which lead to increased length of survival. The need for polar cofactors, which they cannot make for themselves, thus becomes clear.

Pipkin and Jensen[318, 319] have fully described the use of avian embryos and of tissue culture in the study of malarial parasites. The advantages of the former method for cultivation over the use of adult experimental animals is clearly indicated in the study of individual species of plasmodia. The employment of tissue cultures of various kinds in the investigation of different stages of parasite development has advantages for the malariologist and can be applied in studying the effect of drugs. Indications of the probable sequence of events *in vivo* after culture are also given.

Effect of Drugs on Parasite Metabolism

Many short term studies have been made on the effect of antimalarial drugs on parasite metabolism using *in vitro* techniques with isolated parasites, or a combination of *in vitro* and *in vivo* techniques. In the latter the host was treated with the agent under test and blood was collected at the desired interval after treatment and its chemical and morphological changes studied. By the *in vitro* method the effect of host is eliminated and the inhibited metabolic systems could sometimes be ascertained and the question whether the drug acts *per se* answered. The *in vivo* technique on the other hand gives information on whether degradation was taking place with possible formation of an active metabolite. During culture techniques metabolic changes due to drugs have also been accurately observed. The fact that atabrine (quinacrine) and quinine were effective inhibitors of respiration of certain malaria parasites at comparable concentrations both *in vitro* and *in vivo* suggested that these two drugs act directly on the parasite. Since inhibition of a parasite requires a certain concentration of drug at a particular site, many experiments were carried out on the distribution of antimalarials among the different blood constituents. Shannon et al.[368] laid the pharmacological basis for the use of atabrine in malaria, showing that a high percentage of this substance was bound by blood proteins. Similar experiments were performed with quinine and its distribution was studied in normal and parasitized blood.[82] The authors found that drug concentration in invaded erythrocytes was much higher than in serum. It soon emerged that certain drugs had a specific action on different stages of development of the parasite. Thus Fairley[123] found that the action of paludrine was fundamentally different from the action of atabrine and quinine; it is a complete prophylactic in *P. falciparum* malaria and in both *P. vivax* and *P. falciparum* infections a powerful schizonticide which produces its effects on the early schizont and prevents nuclear division, and thus the formation of merozoites.

The effect of antimalarials on enyzme systems of erythrocytic forms has also been widely studied, but isolation of a pure enzyme from malaria parasites has not been accomplished. Lipase activity was shown to be inhibited by substances related to quinine and by synthetic antimalarials.[142] Other antimalarials with quinoline or acridine structure were shown[184] to act in the same way. Wright and Sabine[463] found that atabrine inhibited the flavoprotein enzyme d-amino acid oxidase, while Haas[175] reported that low concentrations of the drug inhibited cytochrome reductase, and also a flavo-protein and glucose-6-phosphate dehydrogenase. Cytochrome oxidase was inhibited to a lesser degree, while TPN and cytochrome c were unaffected. Hellerman and colleagues[185] were of the opinion that this substance interfered with flavoprotein because of its ability to combine with the enzyme proteins, a property shared by other substances, and not because of structural relationship to the flavin coenzymes. Speck and Evans[394, 395] observed that hexokinase in *P. gallinaceum* extracts was inhibited by quinacrine. Evans[121] has also pointed out that in spite of the similarity in biochemical behaviour among the species of plasmodia, no explanation is yet forthcoming of species specificity in infections, nor of the highly specific environmental needs of each phase of development. All the enzymes in malaria parasites appear to resemble those in other cells. There is some evidence however that differences exist between enzyme systems of parasites and their analogues in other cells, especially in sensitivity to antimalarial drugs. This finding helps to explain the differential effects of drugs on parasite and host.

During quinine therapy serum concentrations occur around 0.00001 M. Most results on inhibition of respiration have been obtained *in vitro* with concentrations 100 to 1000 times as great. Silverman *et al.*[380] found inhibition of aerobic and anaerobic conversion of glucose to lactate by *P. gallinaceum* using the higher concentrations. Quinine appears to interfere with some step in the oxidation of pyruvate to CO_2 and water, and it was found[395] that the enzymes hexokinase and lactic dehydrogenases were inhibited by a similar concentration.

The eradication by sulphanilamide of *P. knowlesi* infection in monkeys and its inhibition of parasite respiration reported by Coggeshall,[97] suggests that its effect on malaria parasites may be similar to its effect on bacteria. This was confirmed when it was shown[260] that PAB, an essential growth factor for some malarial parasites, had a definite antagonistic effect on the action of sulphonamides against *P. lophurae*. In culture experiments also, sulphadiazine inhibited parasite growth and its inhibition was prevented by PAB.

Wendel,[444] as previously indicated, studied the effects of a series of alkylated 3-hydroxy-1 : 4-naphthaquinones on the respiration and carbohydrate metabolism of *P. knowlesi* and *P. lophurae*, against which they were therapeutically effective although with little action in human malaria. The metabolic fate of these drugs was studied in the different hosts in an attempt to find whether the results depended on true species specificity or on the method of degradation by the host. The many factors involved made it difficult to reach general conclusions.

When dealing with the effect of drugs on malaria parasites it is worth remembering the observation[415] that pantothenate is a growth factor for *P. lophurae*, which led to the investigations of analogues of pantothenate as antimalarials. Mead *et al.*[270] showed that d-pantoyltaurine was active against avian malaria. The activity of pantothenone against *P. gallinaceum*[259] was antagonized by pantothenic acid. It has been suggested that paludrine was synthesized as a result of considerations of this nature. McKee and Geiman[268] showed that methoxinine and ethionine, which are analogues of methionine, antagonized methionine activity in cultures of *P. knowlesi*, and were in turn inhibited by excess methionine. Many other results of a similar nature have been reported.

These results with antimalarial drugs indicate that their action is anti-enzymic and competitive, and can be reversed by coenzymes or essential metabolites. Plausible explanations of their selective action have yet to be discovered. The phenomenon of drug resistance has likewise not received an adequate explanation. When the effect of antimalarial drugs on parasite metabolism was investigated originally,[145] it was hoped that a speedy method of evaluating therapeutic effect might be evolved. Although the early hopes were not fulfilled, subsequent cultivation studies by other authors have led us to believe that an understanding of the activity of certain agents against the various developmental stages and various species of the parasite will be realised. Apart from the study of analogues it can only be claimed that on rare occasions have effective antimalarials been synthesized as a result of a 'rational approach'. Advances in chemotherapy have, on the other hand, shown a marked reliance on the empirical approach. It would be unrealistic to minimise the clarity of thought and ingenuity which have been expended on this approach. Probably too, it will never be known how many metabolic leads have proved unfruitful. The general consensus is that the antimetabolite approach has been disappointing except perhaps in the employment of agents which block the utilization of compounds of specific importance to parasites. For that reason we can not afford to neglect nutritional and metabolic studies. Energy production is one important aspect of metabolism, and more than one writer has suggested that a study of differences in energy metabolism aimed at interfering selectively with microbial energy production might also form a sound basis for chemo-therapeutic studies. Efforts to interfere with anabolic processes of parasites might prove equally fruitful. In the case of intracellular parasitism, as exemplified by malaria, competition between host cell and invading organism for essential growth factors has also to be considered. The inability of the parasite to grow outside the cell suggests a need for transitory intermediate metabolites which are only found within the host cell.

Physiological Pathology

Widespread changes of a physiological character occur in the host as a result of malaria infection, and have been reviewed.[149] Studies outlined earlier have indicated also that the nutritional state of the host affects the rate of parasite growth and multiplication. Changes in blood constituents of a quantitative and qualitative character as a result of the malfunction of organs and glands also occur. The part played by vitamins has proved of considerable importance for *in vivo* and *in vitro* studies. A characteristic feature of the malaria attack is the paroxysm and at that time the level of protein pigments, potassium, and other inorganic ions of the blood may be markedly disturbed, as well as that of sugar, cholesterol and lecithin, accompanied by physico-chemical changes. The mechanism of these alterations is not always clear. The presence of a toxin has not yet been established.

Circulatory disturbances giving rise to tissue anoxia and many other sequelae including centrilobular necrosis of the liver are recognized. A similar mechanism is believed to play a part in carbon tetrachloride poisoning.[16, 76]

Isolated mitochondria from normal and drug-treated animals have been used to study pharmacological effects of drugs. For example, carbon tetrachloride interferes with the enzymic activity of mitochondria, often followed by fatty degeneration and necrosis. Oxidative phosphorylation by mitochondria is disorganized by other agents, such as stilboestrol, and thyroxine has an uncoupling action on oxidative phosphorylation by liver mitochondria. Riley and Deegan[332] studied the results of malaria infection on host liver mitochondria, apparently the first study of mitochondrial metabolism in liver damage induced by plasmodia. These authors considered whether similar processes to those described above might be operative, contributing to the liver damage in malaria. An attempt was made to determine the nature and extent of biochemical changes occurring in liver mitochondria of mice during *P. berghei* infection. They found some resemblance to the damage mentioned above: a lowered oxidative capacity associated with lowered P : 0 ratio; an inability to carry out DPN-linked oxidations, partly reversed by this agent; increase in ATP-ase activity; and depression of that stimulated by DPN, along with others not specific for malaria. It was noteworthy that anaemic mice and those suffering from anorexia had similar symptoms but to a less marked degree. The studies were pursued further[334] using a strain of the same parasite with a more acute infection and shorter periods of anaemia and anorexia. The evidence obtained suggested that changes in oxidative phosphorylation resulted from structural changes in mitochondria rather than from interference with specific enzymes. This agreed with earlier results[333] concerning a factor in serum from infected monkeys which interferes with mitochondrial function. Respiratory and phosphorylating mechanisms were inhibited, possibly by loss of co-factors from mitochondria accompanied by structural damage; but this could not be claimed as specific for malaria since the effects resembled those caused by carbon tetrachloride. Tissue damage may or may not be caused for similar reasons *in vivo*. With the new strain of *P. berghei* causing more acute infections the results obtained were the same as in earlier experiments. The authors believe that the effect was not exerted on the respiratory enzymes *per se*, but resulted from disturbance of the organized structure of mitochondria. Anorexia due to infection probably contributed to the results obtained. The pattern of fatty acid changes in the liver suggested that malaria was exerting a specific effect. Dehydrogenase and cytochrome oxidase activities remained unchanged in infected mice. Further experiments of similar nature to those described above were made[251] with monkeys infected with *P. knowlesi*, in which the physiology and infective pattern of the disease resembles that in man. As judged by *in vitro* experiments, mitochondrial function in monkeys dying of malaria did not exhibit severe disturbance but only a slight degree of structural damage, with a slight lowering of dehydrogenase activity. Whether those changes in mitochondria observed *in vitro* reflected the course of events *in vivo* is not clear. Circulatory disturbances possibly upset mitochondrial function. The relationship of the degree of mitochondrial damage in mice and monkeys to histological lesions was quite different in the two animals and suggests that species differences exercise some control on the nature of the lesions. Some monkeys even when moribund as a result of infection could be revived by nor-adrenaline. However if a limited amount of liver damage was accompanied by other stresses and strains, it could on occasions prove fatal. There are a number of factors, sometimes related, which are responsible for the pathogenic effects of malaria. Mercado and von Brand[273] and Devakul and Maegraith[111] have shown that cortico-steroids exercise an important influence on glycogen and fat changes in the liver in this disease, and they are known to vary widely in tissues during the course of infection. Frequently a lipid depletion has been observed in the adrenal cortex of infected rats. Adrenal dysfunction is regarded as one of the reasons for reduced glycogen synthesis in infected rats.

Tella and Maegraith[408, 409] have described some of the physiopathological changes occurring in virulent malarial and *Babesia* infections of laboratory animals. They presented a number of features common to both infections including destruction of non-parasitized as well as of parasitized red blood cells. No haemolysin was detected and the mechanism of haemolysis was unexplained. The authors refer to a stable lytic factor in tissues which is inhibited by normal serum; during blackwater fever this inhibition is overcome. Some minor differences in individual protein fractions of blood were observed but no constant pattern was apparent. The circulation in malaria was studied[383, 384] by portal angiography, using the virulent *P. knowlesi* infections in rhesus monkeys, in order to find a basis for the disease processes which occur in the malignant tertian form with which it has some properties in common. Arterial, venous, and portal pressures were recorded. The authors concluded that anoxia was responsible for much tissue damage, due to vaso-constriction of sympathetic origin, and the latter was discussed in relation to the nature of the shock produced.

Zuckerman[474] has attempted to explain the damage suffered by host cells in certain protozoal diseases including malaria, piroplasmosis, leishmaniasis, and trypanosomiasis by invoking auto-immune and other processes. All are diseases of the blood and tissues in which parasites, even in certain trypanosome infections such as that due to *Endotrypanum schaudinni*, occur within cells of the host which thus can be easily affected. The evidence she presented for the occurrence of auto-immune reactions in these diseases was, in her own words, "fragmentary", but acted as a good stimulant to thought Kuvin *et al.*[226] described the clinical and physiological responses in man following sporozoite infection with two different species of parasites. They made extensive observations on parasitaemia, cell counts, haemoglobin content, and survival time of chromium-tagged red cells, accompanied by others on serum iron and protein alterations, albumin/globulin ratios, and on the serum transaminases present, as well as many other determinations. They concluded that the host's reaction to malaria was diffuse, and many possible lines for the further study of the disease were indicated. Others using electrophoretic methods[1] have described the alteration in serum proteins and of 19 S antibody production during the course of malaria in man. The chief finding was an increase in occurrence of 2 M macroglobulins accompanied by appearance of malarial antibodies. The belief that malaria had a selective effect in maintaining high rates of glucose-6-phosphate dehydrogenase (G-6-PD) deficiency has been put forward by some authors.[132, 285] Others found no support for the view that deficiency of this enzyme protects against malaria[219] on studying 519 male children in Thailand. It was found[133] that the changes in content of the above enzyme and in 6-phosphogluconate dehydrogenase occurred in monkeys after infection with *P. knowlesi*. Only infected cells showed an increase and it was not present in red cells of mice infected with *P. berghei*. The free parasites lacked this activity. Reasons for the intracellular character of the parasites and for possible protection afforded against malaria by the G-6-PD deficiency were put forward. Powell and Brewer[320] have tested the hypothesis that G-6-PD deficiency, an inherited disorder affecting the red cell, influences infection in man with malignant tertian malaria. Studies were made in non-immune subjects, some with enzyme deficiency. No evidence was obtained to support the view that the deficient group enjoyed a biological advantage against this infection.

Summary

Cultural and biochemical studies on the malarial parasite have been prompted by a number of considerations, not least the need for new and more potent antimalarial drugs. It seemed possible that some critical factor in metabolism or nutrition of parasites might provide useful leads to the desired end. For practical reasons only the erythrocytic form of the parasite has been used in these studies, for which a wide range of organisms from man, monkey, birds, and later rodents, was available. These species showed a remarkable uniformity in reaction; no basis for species specificity is known. The preparations used consisted of invaded erythrocytes or parasites freed from the erythrocytes by various means, and suspended in an appropriate medium. Cell-free extracts of parasites have also been used. Comprehensive studies on enzymes involved in respiration and on protein and carbohydrate metabolism have been carried out. Inhibition and other studies have indicated that heavy metal catalysts of cytochrome type as well as flavoproteins and dehydrogenase systems involving DPN and TPN are involved in the respiratory mechanism. Information concerning nitrogen metabolism is limited but proteinases have been described in cell-free extracts. Hydrolysis and metabolism of erythrocyte protein takes place whereby haematin is set free and globin is utilized. A number of carbohydrates besides glucose can be used as substrates by the parasite. From the latter, lactic acid is formed by a process of phosphorylating glycolysis, followed by its partial oxidation to CO_2 and water by a mechanism similar to the TCA cycle. Although the enzymes present perform similar functions to those present in other organisms they are not necessarily identical and none has yet been isolated in a pure state. Differences in sensitivity to antimalarial drugs between the enzymes present in malarial parasites and the corresponding enzymes in other tissues have been recorded. It is possible that the differential activity of chemotherapeutic agents on host and parasite may be explained in this way. The study of phases of development of the parasite other than that occurring in the erythrocyte is highly desirable. Great progress has been made in studies on the nutritional needs of these parasites. The simplest medium in which growth and multiplication took place was an isotonic salt solution containing glucose + PAB. However, maximum growth required a much more complex medium containing salts, glucose, PAB, vitamins, purines and pyrimidines, and certain other organic components contributed by serum and red blood corpuscles. During growth of invaded erythrocytes total phosphorus, phospholipid, nucleic acid, fatty acids, and flavin adenine dinucleotides were increased several-fold. Studies on the mode of action of chemotherapeutic agents against the different enzyme systems were intensively pursued. The successful culture of the malaria parasite, in or outside the erythrocyte, in a simple defined medium on a large scale, would do much to simplify the problems of metabolism which this parasite poses.

Babesiosis

The parasites of the genus *Babesia* (formerly Piroplasma) occur within the red corpuscles of certain domestic animals as non-pigmented forms. Exoerythrocytic forms such as occur in malaria have not been described. They cause a high mortality especially in cattle, horses, and dogs throughout the world. About twenty species have been named but only a few are parasites of domestic animals. These forms within red corpuscles are pear shaped and divide into groups of two or four. They are transmitted by ticks. The life history, even of important species, is incompletely known, and along with classification presents a great challenge to the protozoologist. The disease, often referred to as piroplasmosis, results in destruction of red corpuscles, and the haemoglobin which appears in the urine gives rise to the name "red-water fever". *Babesia bigemina*, the parasite of Texas fever, once a scourge of cattle in the United States of America, has now been eliminated; the disease was of historical importance in immunological and transmission studies. Practically nothing is known of the biochemistry of these parasites or of the parasites of the genus *Theileria* which differ from the babesias in that schizogony takes place in the reticuloendothelial cells of the host. The forms which occur in the red corpuscles are considered gametocytes which infect the tick vector. An important species is *T. parva* which gives rise to East Coast Fever in Africa and elsewhere, with resultant very high mortality. *Theileria* does not respond as well to chemotherapeutic agents as *Babesia* does. Another related genus, *Anaplasma*, also undergoes schizogony in red corpuscles; the two infections are frequently found associated with *Babesia* in cattle. Anaplasmosis is an infective and transmissible disease which at times assumes epidemic proportions and has proved a threat to cattle rearing in North America. The taxonomic position of the genus is unsettled. The occurrence of piroplasmosis in man was reported for the first time from Yugoslavia.[386] The patient had his spleen removed some years earlier and subsequently lived on a tick-infested farm where the cattle suffered from piroplasmosis. Garnham and Bray[157] studied the susceptibility of the higher primates to piroplasms. The chimpanzee and rhesus monkey behaved like man to infection with *B. divergens* or *B. bovis*. The intact animal was resistant but on splenectomy acquired a fulminating infection accompanied by haemoglobinuria. The authors suggested that latent piroplasmosis may exist widely in man under the above conditions. They were unable to infect splenectomized primates with *Theileria parva*.[66]

Some of the physiological and pathological processes occurring in *B. canis* infection of puppies, which frequently proves fatal have been investigated.[250] It was found that in severe and fatal cases the clinical condition showed little relation to the degree of parasitaemia. The plasma often brought about lysis of parasitized as well as of normal cells, because of some change occurring in it. The subject was investigated by injecting intravenously red cells from a normal donor labelled with ^{32}P or ^{59}Fe, into an infected animal. Whereas normal plasma inhibited mechanical lysis, that from infected animals exacerbated it. The mechanisms of lysis remain obscure. Independent of the degree of parasitaemia, the dissociation curves of oxyhaemoglobin of dogs, as determined *in vitro*, remained normal. The suggestion was made that the tissues themselves during infection may fail to accept oxygen, possibly due to interference with cytochrome systems. No abnormal pigments such as methaemoglobin or methaemalbumin occurred in the blood but oxyhaemoglobin and methaemoglobin were frequently observed in the urine. The concentration of Na and K ions in blood, unlike the conditions in malaria, were hardly altered, and the chloride balance remained undisturbed. There was seldom a marked fall in total proteins of blood, but there was a reversal of the albumin/globulin ratio. Blood sugar values generally remained unchanged, but liver glycogen was depleted. Blood urea usually increased during infection, indicating that kidney function was impaired, while liver dysfunction was evidenced by jaundice and bilirubinuria. In general the changes in the host organs resembled those found in malaria and indicated their nonspecific character. The authors measured the respiratory activity of *B. canis* within red cells and in the free state following haemolysis of the host cell by saponin. It seemed from the results that *B. canis* was not a serious competitor with the host cells for oxygen. Parasitaemia was found to be affected by the nutritional state of the host, and inhibition of infection resulted from a milk diet. It is probable that some of the biochemical changes in plasma were due to variation in activity of the adrenals. As in malaria, *l*-nor-adrenaline exerted a dramatic though temporary effect during the stage of shock by restoring blood pressure and circulation; the animals recovered consciousness. There were analogies between the physiological and pathological responses to *B. canis* infections but it was concluded that the latter processes are non-specific and occur in other acute medical states. The factors bringing them about may be soluble physiologically active substances of simple structure which arise from the parasite, from host tissues, or from their interaction. Tella and Maegraith[408, 409] have investigated further the physiological changes occurring in primary acute blood-transmitted *Babesia* infections in puppies. They were of the opinion that bradykinin might be involved in the vascular haemolysis. Observations were also made on total and individual serum-protein levels before and after infection following the use of standard inocula of parasites. Some minor differences were noted in the behaviour of individual protein fractions. There was, for example, some lowering of total serum protein levels as infection became severe, accompanied by the usual fall in albumin levels and reversal of albumin-globulin ratios. No consistent pattern was observed in this infection or in malaria. Intracellular phagotrophy in *B. rodhaini* infections in mice was studied with the electron microscope.[342] The parasites are intra-erythrocytic and feed on the host erythrocyte as do malaria parasites, engulfing large portions by means of the invagination of plasma membranes with the resultant formation of food vacuoles. Typical mitochondria were not observed. Digestion of haemoglobin appeared to be complete since no pigment was detectable. Zuckerman[474] has discussed the cause of blood loss in piroplasmosis which is believed to be greater than can be accounted for by the degree of parasitaemia in cattle and dogs. The anaemia generally persists after disappearance of parasites; direct injury to old cells can be excluded as a cause. Marked phagocytic activity with engulfment of red cells has been observed but the red cell fragility remains little affected. Barratt and Yorke[35] and Thompson[411] have observed, however, that red cell destruction is correlated with parasitaemia; this differs from the conditions in blackwater fever in which parasites are very scanty. The question of the occurrence of auto-immune reactions appears to be still *sub-judice*.

Beveridge[40] has observed that drug shock may occur in mice infected with *B. rodhaini*, possibly as a result of substances arising from destroyed parasites. The production of a toxin has not been demonstrated. A preliminary study of the pharmacologically active substances present in the blood and urine of animals infected with *B. rodhaini* and other pathogenic organisms was made.[164] The possible liberation of histamine from infected animals was considered. The immediate cause of death in protozoal infections is generally obscure. The results showed that the blood and urine of infected animals contained substances which are active on smooth muscle and are not affected by atropine, eserine, or lysergic acid diethylamide. They were stable when boiled with HCl but not with alkali, extractable with hot ethanol, readily dialysed, and destroyed by papain or chymotrypsin. They thus appeared to have the properties of peptides, but they were not isolated. It was suggested that they had their origin in the action of parasitic enzymes on plasma proteins, or possibly were of the nature of kinins released from plasma globulins. Active substances also appeared in urine when intravascular haemolysis was produced by drugs or incompatible cellular material, and in trypanosome- or virus-infected animals, as well as in other infectious diseases. Modern biochemical investigations on the three genera *Babesia*, *Theileria* and *Anaplasma* should provide a fruitful field of study and make notable contributions to comparative biochemistry.

Toxoplasmosis

Toxoplasma was first described in 1908 by Splendore in Brazil and in the same year by Nicolle and Manceaux in North Africa, in a small rodent of that area—the gondi. These two authors therefore gave it the name *Toxoplasma gondii*. Until 1939 the interest in the parasite was chiefly zoological, but in that year Wolf, Cowen, and Paige described infection in infants with symptoms of encephalomyelitis. The host range of the parasite is wide covering nearly all warm blooded animals including man and some birds. The infection has a cosmopolitan distribution and appears to be more prevalent in warm moist regions than in hot or cold dry regions. Its incidence has been determined by serological surveys. The disease is regarded as a zoonosis but the mode of spread is unknown except that prenatal infections occur in man and animals. The lack of host restriction suggests that there is only one valid species of parasite. It is an obligate intracellular parasite and occurs in many types of cells including those of tissues of the reticuloendothelial system and in white cells of the blood as well as in epithelial cells. During acute infections free proliferative forms are found, crescentic or arc shaped, one end being thicker than the other, with a vesicular nucleus and measuring approximabely 2–4 μ by 4 to 7 μ. They are spasmodically motile. Multiplication occurs by binary fission or by budding. In chronic infections they occur in cyst-like agglomerations in which all traces of the host cell disappear. This form may remain dormant in the host over a period of years, especially in brain tissue, and proves infective on reinoculation to fresh animals. The proliferative forms are much less resistant than the cysts to the external environment. A number of serological tests have been devised including specific staining procedures by means of fluorescent antibody. The most successful chemotherapeutic treatment consists in administration of sulphonamides along with the antimalarial drug pyrimethamine.

Metabolic Studies

In spite of the wide-spread nature of the disease the only metabolic studies on the organism reported so far are those of Fulton and Spooner.[151, 153] These authors were able to obtain pure suspensions of parasites, free from other cells, from the peritoneal exudates of cotton rats infected three days earlier from a donor animal. The pooled exudate from a number of animals was passed through gauze to remove gross particles and then centrifuged. The supernatant was rejected and the cellular material was resuspended in phosphate buffered saline at pH 7.4 by shaking gently with glass beads, a procedure which also liberated parasites from white cells. The ruptured white cells readily agglutinated and were removed. The suspension was passed through a sintered glass filter of pore size 25–30 μ by gentle suction. By this means practically all white cells were removed and after centrifugation parasites were re-suspended in a suitable volume of buffered saline and any red corpuscles present were either agglutinated by anti-serum or haemolysed by addition of complement. Red corpuscle ghosts could be removed because of their relatively rapid sedimentation. The parasites, now free from other cells (Fig. 1), were recovered by centrifugation and suspended in a medium appropriate to the problem being studied.

In manometric studies an average of 4.9×10^8 parasites were used per flask. The mean value of QO_2 was 30, and the RQ varied from 0.83 to 1.14. Respiration continued at a steady rate in suspensions in glucose-saline for some hours and was influenced only to a small extent by the addition of serum. There was no endogenous respiration of intact parasites. The effect of a large number of substrates on respiration indicated that a number of simple sugars and glutamine were readily metabolized. Pyruvate supported respiration to a limited extent but lactate or certain intermediates of the Krebs' cycle failed to do so. Glycogen, which occurs in the host cells in which T. gondii multiplies, stimulated respiration to some extent. The only phosphorylated sugar metabolized by intact cells was glucose-6-phosphate, but a number of others which take part in the glycolytic cycle were oxidized when the cells were homogenized and suggested that permeability factors had interfered with their utilization in the first instance. Hexokinase was demonstrated in these homogenates, and also DPNH oxidase. Besides carbon dioxide the products of glucose metabolism were lactic and acetic acids and another acid of low R_F value not identified. The CO_2 and lactate formed accounted for 80 per cent of the glucose used. By gas chromatography the presence of traces of propionic, butyric, and valeric acids was also demonstrated in the medium. Under anaerobic conditions the production of lactic acid was increased. Arsenite, iodoacetate, p-chloromercuribenzoate, mapharside and cyanide markedly inhibited parasite respiration, but the sulpha drugs, active chemotherapeutically, did not. The inhibition of respiration by cyanide suggested that cytochrome oxidase was present and this fact was confirmed by observing inhibition of respiration by carbon monoxide and its reversal by light. By using the spectrophotometric techniques,[213] the cytochromes a, b, and c were readily detected. Catalase was also shown to be present and prevented the inhibitory action of hydrogen peroxide on respiration, which is so marked in the case of trypanosomes. The effect of various sera on respiration was next studied since it had been reported[125] that fresh sera of rabbit, guinea pig, rat, monkey, sheep, cow, horse, and dog, are lethal to *T. gondii*, whereas sera of man and mouse are innocuous. Results on respiration were not so clear cut however, although some respiratory reduction by sera with high antibody titoe was observed, in some cases accompanied by agglutination of parasites to a marked degree. It seemed possible that the presence of antibodies in human serum would be detectable by respiratory experiments of this nature. This was found to be the case but there was no obvious correlation between the results of these tests and those of the dye test. It was established in these experiments that *T. gondii* obtains part of its energy by means of phosphorylating glycolysis. The fact that isolated parasites were used may have disturbed some relationship between host and parasite existing *in vivo* and so affected the overall picture of metabolism. The pure suspension of parasites used provided a useful antigen for a direct agglutination and complement fixation test. By using such an antigen comparison of results of serological tests from different laboratories now becomes possible.

The first immunochemical studies on *T. gondii* were made by Hook and Faber.[190] These authors considered that antigens responsible for particular antibodies concerned in serological tests such as that of complement fixation and dye test might be separable from the intact parasite. They made attempts to fractionate the organism into protein and carbohydrate components and to determine their antigenic activity *in vitro* and *in vivo*. For this purpose toxoplasms were harvested from the peritoneal exudate of infected mice and subjected to sonic vibration, followed by removal of debris by centrifugation. A protein fraction was obtained by ammonium sulphate fractionation. Extraction of protein-free carbohydrate was attempted with trichloracetic acid and was followed by cold ethanol fractionation. From these studies it appeared that antigenicity in both the dye test and complement fixation test was related to protein; the carbohydrate material showed no antigenic activity. Lunde and Jacobs[243] also concluded that the antigen involved in the haemagglutination test for *Toxoplasma* was of protein nature.

Pande and colleagues[308] also carried out immunochemical studies on *T. gondii*. By fractional precipitation with iso-propanol, followed by deproteinization, they separated a soluble carbohydrate fraction from pure suspensions of the parasite lysed with water. The fraction appeared to be homogeneous as judged by electrophoretic and ultracentrifugation techniques. Its immunological homogeneity was demonstrated by gel-diffusion methods. It sensitized sheep red corpuscles to agglutination and had a number of other interesting properties. This polysaccharide was however a poor antigen, unable to immunize mice against artificial infection with *T. gondii*, and the corresponding antisera did not protect mice. Also, no serological cross-reactivity was found between the polysaccharide antisera and carbohydrates of known polysaccharide composition and linkage.

Weinman and Klatchko[437] described the occurence of a toxin in the peritoneal fluid of mice infected with the RH strain of *T. gondii* and gave it the name toxotoxin; when given intravenously in a dose of 0.1 to 0.5 ml, it frequently caused rapid death. Intraperitoneal inoculation of five such lethal doses were however tolerated by mice. The exact source and nature of the substance causing death have not been determined. It is relatively stable to heat and tolerated heating at 56° for 30 min or a short time at 100°, but was inactivated by autoclaving. It can be stored when frozen and dried in the frozen state and then reconstituted. Treatment with certain physical and chemical agents left it unaffected, but it was destroyed by trypsin and may therefore be of protein nature. Activity was not lost on dialysis. The investigation was continued by Woodworth and Weinman[460] who observed that toxicity was markedly increased by heating at 56°C, and that the property resided in the globulin fraction of the exudate. Toxic material was not formed in cultures on embryonated hens eggs. The authors did not think that viscosity or other physical properties of the exudate was responsible for toxicity; the potency of the exudate was correlated with the number of parasites present in the exudate. The role of the substance in pathogenesis of the disease was doubtful. Preliminary experiments by the writer have led him to the conclusion that the substance or substances responsible for the death of mice have none of the attributes of a true toxin as generally understood. A substance pharmacologically similar to the diethylamide of *d*-lysergic acid was reported present in the peritoneal exudate of toxoplasma-infected mice.[429]

Lunde and Jacobs[244, 245] drew attention to the toxicity of *Toxoplasma* lysates for rabbits when given intravenously. Extracts of the organism in a volume corresponding to 100 micrograms protein given in this way was followed by death in rabbits within 24 hours; a few hours after inoculation, a state of prostration, listlessness, sometimes accompanied by diarrhoea, occurred. More rapid deaths were caused by increased dosage of the extracts. Pathological lesions were not characteristic but when present were found mainly in the intestinal tract, and included leucocytic exudations in the ileum as well as distension due to gas. The same amount of extract material given intraperitoneally gave rise to no untoward symptoms. It appeared that previous infection with different strains of *Toxoplasma* protected in varying degree. Immunization with extract failed to protect rabbits against a lethal dose of this material. Toxicity of extracts was destroyed by heating at 56°C for 35 min. Guinea pigs, mice, and chickens, unlike the rabbit, were unaffected. The authors comment that the toxic substance behaves like that from *Eimeria* and *Sarcocystis* to which reference has been made in the appropriate chapter, but differs from toxotoxin described above.

Pathogenesis

While the pathogenesis of *T. gondii* infections has not yet been studied from the biochemical point of view, it may in future be possible to relate biochemical lesions to pathogenicity. It has been pointed out by other writers however that it is not always in these aspects of metabolism that pathogenic organisms differ from saprophytes. In fact the metabolic characters of some organisms of these two types differ only in minor ways, and it has therefore been suggested that it is the character of the infective agent which allows it to invade and thrive at a particular site *in vivo* which counts in pathogenic behaviour. The question to be answered, as Dubos has suggested, is not why pathogens are possessed of certain characters but why saprophytes do not survive equally well under the same conditions. In his view only the complexities of *in vivo* environment can explain the phenomenon of pathogenicity. It therefore becomes necessary to study these factors under appropriate conditions. In a number of protozoal infections including toxoplasmosis, the elaboration of a toxin by the organism has been put forward as its pathogenicity factor. In no instance however has such a substance been isolated, or its administration been followed by the characteristics of the disease. One plant "toxin", has a low molecular weight with a structure similar to that of an essential metabolite of the invaded cell. It therefore acts as an antimetabolite and gives rise to a deficiency disease. Animal toxins are frequently of high molecular weight with the character of proteins, but could also be antimetabolites. Although in malaria and in certain virus infections changes in nucleic acid, carbohydrate, and protein metabolism of the infected cell have been reported, the relationship of these changes to the pathogenic process has not always been clear. For example, when a sensitive tissue like brain is infected, the result may be disproportionately magnified.

Enzyme Studies

The serum of women 20–40 years of age, clinically suspected of *Toxoplasma* infection, was examined for glutamic-oxalacetic and glutamic-pyruvic transaminase activity.[385] The values were mostly above normal but a causal relationship between the raised values and toxoplasmosis was not definitely established. Capella and Kaufman[77] studied the enzyme histochemistry of *Toxoplasma gondii*. By the use of tetrazolium stains respiratory enzymes within the parasites were examined. The presence of lactate, glucose-6-phosphate, and glycerophosphate dehydrogenases were demonstrated, as well as certain Krebs' cycle enzymes. They appeared to be located

16*

in mitochondria of both proliferative and cystic forms of the parasite. It seemed to the authors that lack of ability on the part of *Toxoplasma* to survive extracellularly could not be ascribed to the absence of energy-producing mechanisms. Lycke *et al.*[248] have described some experiments on the enhancement by hyaluronidase and lysozyme of the penetration by *Toxoplasma gondii* into cultured host cells. It was found that the former enzyme in 0.01 mg amounts and the latter in 1 mgm amount per ml suspension of *T. gondii* increased infectivity of mono-layer cultures of the HeLa cells. This effect seemed to result directly from the activity of these enzymes and was lost if cells were washed before inoculation. There was evidence of a

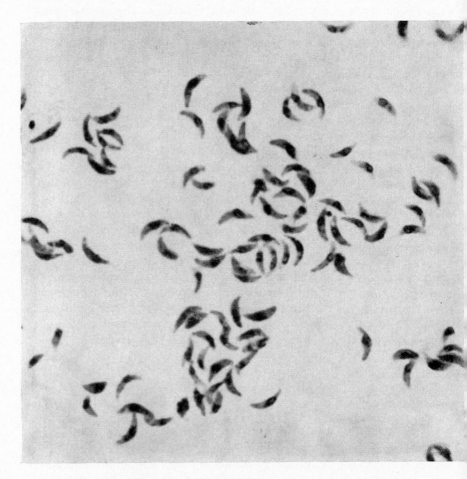

FIG. 1. Pure suspension of *Toxoplasma gondii* used for metabolic and serological studies. Reproduced with permission of the Editor of *Experimental Parasitology* from an article by Fulton and Spooner, 1960, **9**, 293.

penetration-promoting factor in lysed parasites which was enhanced by lysozyme; complement was not required to demonstrate it. Other enzymes failed to show a similar effect. The authors believe that the active substance was enzymic in nature.

Sarcosporidiosis

The genus *Sarcocystis* was established in 1882; only the cyst stage occurring in cardiac and skeletal muscle is well known. It is a cosmopolitan parasite of uncertain relation and undetermined taxonomic position and occurs more frequently in herbivores; it commonly infects pigs, cattle, sheep, horses, birds, and reptiles, and rarely man. Its pathogenicity is low. The flesh of animals may be rendered unsightly by the large masses which it forms. The cysts are thick walled with inner trabeculae and contain innumerable spores. The individual spores resemble *Toxoplasma* but both ends are rounded. The motile stage is somewhat larger, measuring $2 \times 10 \mu$, has a vesicular nucleus, and contains glycogen granules. Sarcosporidia were first seen by Miescher in 1843 in the muscles of mice. The method of transmission is doubtful, but animals can be infected by consuming contaminated material or by receiving inoculations of this material. No metabolic experiments have been carried out with these organisms.

The presence of a toxic substance in sarcosporidia is however well substantiated, and is one of the few instances recorded for parasitic protozoa. The occurrence of this toxic substance was reported by Pfeiffer in 1891. He showed that aqueous or glycerol extracts of the parasites killed rabbits, and the active principle was later named sarcocystin. It has been the subject of many subsequent researches. Other animals appear to be little affected by the same treatment. On receiving small amounts of saline extract of macerated parasites intravenously, intraperitoneally, or intradermally, rabbits become lethargic, with distended abdomen, and severe diarrhoea. The temperature rises and paralysis and death follow in a matter of hours. Serum from rabbits immunized with the toxic preparation neutralizes the toxin when allowed to act *in vitro* but is less effective when used *in vivo*. The chemical nature of the active substance is not known but it is dialysable, ultrafiltrable and heat labile, and therefore differs in some ways from the corresponding substances occurring in toxoplasmosis and coccidiosis. Sato[351] observed that the sarcosporidiotoxin from parasites of buffaloes was destroyed by CO_2 and acids but was stable to alkalis. He believed that the toxic principle acted on adrenals, liver, intestinal walls, and heart of the host. When absorbed by these tissues the toxicity of the saline extract was much reduced. He found that the immune serum from rabbits effectively neutralized the toxin *in vitro*. Lubyanetskii[240] also studied the toxins of sarcosporidia obtained from sheep and goats in feeding experiments. Mice, rats, and guinea pigs were sensitive to the toxic substance when injected, but dogs, goats, and calves did not react when fed contaminated material.

Awad[20] has carried out a number of investigations on this infection and provided new facts about the characteristics of sarcocystin. In his hands it was only lethal for rabbits, and immune serum was effective *in vivo* as well as *in vitro*.

Attention has been drawn above to the close resemblance between *Toxoplasma* and *Sarcocystis*. Mühlpfordt[290] used the Sabin–Feldman dye test in trying to differentiate the two types of infection. He concluded that the test could be used in the diagnosis of *Sarcocystis* infection, but was unable to differentiate between the two. Awad[21] used *Sarcocystis tenella* spores as a substitute for toxoplasms in the dye test for diagnosing infection with either organism. His results indicated that *S. tenella* spores could be used for diagnosis of both infections. The validity of these findings has however been subsequently disputed.

Coccidiosis

Coccidia include an important group of parasitic protozoa which affect man to a very limited extent but cause extensive epidemics in rabbits, poultry, and cattle, with resultant serious economic loss. The distribution is world wide, and involves no vector, direct infection by oocysts occurring through food and water. Diagnosis is made by finding oocysts in faeces. In man and animals the genera involved are *Isospora* and *Eimeria*, respectively. Infection occurs chiefly in the mucosa and sub-mucosa of the alimentary tract, in kidney tubules, and in the epithelium of the bile duct. The pathogenic effect varies with the species and severity of infection. Light infections may be symptomless, but in severe attacks extensive destruction of epithelium and marked haemorrhage may occur. The course of infection in man is as follows. After ingestion of ripe oocysts, sporozoites escape from the sporocyst in the upper small intestine and initiate infection in the mucosa lower down. They become schizonts, and from them merozoites are formed. The latter escape from the initial host cells and infect other cells to continue asexual multiplication. Some merozoites become gametocytes and develop to gametes. Immature oocysts develop from the zygote, are voided in the faeces and there sporulate. Local immunity develops, and there is a wide range of drugs available for prophylaxis and treatment. *In vitro*, development of the stages which occur within the host is not satisfactory.

Metabolic Studies

Joyner[212] has described some metabolic relationships between host and parasite, mainly with reference to the genus *Eimeria* of domestic poultry, in which six species are commonly found. Their location in the alimentary tract varies from the upper small intestine to the caecum, and the pathogenic stages are the schizonts or gametocytes. The degree of penetration of mucosa varies and the effects include inflammation, oedema, loss of weight, emaciation, haemorrhage, anemia, and death. In association with infection are alterations in blood-sugar values and liver content of glycogen. Muscle contraction of crop and caecum become less efficient, indicating that the metabolic functions of the host are affected. Alteration in diet exerted an influence on parasitaemia, the severity being reduced; mortality was largey avoided when diet was restricted to milk. A diet deficient in PAB likewise caused a lowering of parasitaemia. Baldwin and others[32] found that haemorrhage was controlled by vitamin K in the diet of *Eimeria tenella*-infected chicks with resultant lowering of mortality. Davies[105] reported that in avian coccidiosis the vitamin A reserves were lowered; this appeared to be of special interest since the conversion of carotene to vitamin A occurs in the intestine of chicks and of mammals. It has moreover been shown that cod liver oil in adequate amounts aids recovery from coccidiosis, possibly due to its vitamin A content. The therapeutic effectiveness of sulphonamides, as with other organisms, arises from competition with PAB; the cocci-diostatic action of the drugs can also be reversed by PAB. The requirements of chicks for the latter appear to be low, and they are relatively insensitive to drug-induced deficiencies of this substance. It was of interest that the action of pyrimethamine, concerned with the conversion of folic to folinic acid, should potentiate the activity of sulphonamides. This occurs, it is thought, because both drugs act against substances in the same metabolic chain which are concerned with nucleic acid synthesis. A requirement of *E. tenella* for thiamine has been suggested because of the coccidiostatic activity of certain thiamine antagonists. However, the structurally related thiamine antagonist pyrimethamine was not active in this sense and emphasizes the complexity of the host-parasite relationship.

Wilson and Fairbairn[455] have investigated the biochemistry of sporulation in oocysts of *E. acervulina*, which occurs outside the host where only gaseous exchanges with the environment occur. The oocysts were collected at the time of the first massive discharge into the intestine and isolated by centrifugal flotation in media of high density. Sporoblastic oocysts were obtained in maximal number by incubation for 10 hours at 30°C, sporulation being regarded as complete after 20 hours. Exact determination of the number of sporoblasts present was difficult as was also the time at which each sporoblast converted to a sporocyst containing two infective sporozoites. In spite of the cell division in the fresh oocysts, respiration within 68 hours gradually fell to less than one third of its value and then more slowly to still lower levels. The initial value of QO_2 was 9.5 and R.Q. 1.12. The latter value also fell over the period mentioned, probably due to alteration in the nature of the substrate being oxidized. Inhibition of sporulation by 10^{-3} M cyanide was complete over a period of 21 hours, and the action was reversible. Under anaerobic conditions sporulation did not occur. A carbohydrate characterized chemically as glycogen was present and decreased in amount during sporulation; cytochemical observations by others have confirmed this fact. Lipids were not metabolized during the first 10 hours of sporulation, but later supplanted carbohydrate as an energy source. When sporoblast formation was complete, oocyst metabolism became based on fat oxidation. It appeared that only small amounts of protein or amino acids were metabolised during sporoblast formation. Some differences in behaviour of other species of *Eimeria* are discussed by the authors.

Up to the time that Smith and Herrick[387] measured the metabolic rate of *E. tenella* and of the tissues parasitized by it, research on the organism had been concerned with the more practical questions of specificity, prevention, and resistance to environmental factors. They obtained sporulated and unsporulated oocysts from the caeca of infected chickens and freed them from host tissue. These oocysts are the products of second generation merozoites which are released on the 5th day following infection. A wide variation in the metabolic rate of oocysts produced by different groups of chickens was observed but remained unexplained. Respiration was measured in phosphate buffered saline at various pH values. Respiration of infected caecal tissue was also measured and compared with that of normal tissue. The parasitized tissue was found to consume more oxygen than that unparasitized. The respiration of unsporulated oocysts was 10 to 20 times that of sporulated forms. The effect of pH on respiration was negligible, and showed no variation between the range pH 1.2. to 8.8. Gill and Ray[161] demonstrated the presence of glycogen in the second asexual stages and in male gametocytes, as well as in gametes of *E. tenella*. The amount present in sporozoites was very small. The glycogen content appeared to be related to the physiological activity of the parasite. The authors have also described the presence of mucopolysaccharides and commented on the significance of phosphatases in *E. tenella*. The influence of parasites on physiological oxidations and on enzymes in parasitized tissues has been studied but little. An important enzyme concerned with the breakdown of pyruvate to CO_2 and water, via the Krebs' cycle, is succinic dehydrogenase. Smith and McShan[388] studied the effect of *Eimeria stiedae* infection on the succinic dehydrogenase activity of the liver tissue of rabbits. The host was infected with sporulated oocysts and after 5, 10, 15, and 20 days the succinic dehydrogenase activity was determined. It was greatest at 10 and 15 days after infection although infection was heaviest after 21 days. Thus during the earlier stages of the parasite life cycle, when schizogony and gametogony were taking place, the succinic dehydrogenase of infected liver increased, and at the oocyst stage proved physiologically less active. It was thought that the increased activity may protect the host against infection.

Toxin Production

It had previously been suggested that the diverse sytemic effects observed in coccidiosis might be due to the presence of a toxic substance, released by, or through the activity of, the parasite concerned. Burns[72] therefore sought for such a substance in *E. tenella* infections, while also investigating immunity by attempted preparation of coccidial antibodies in rabbits with extracts from the caecal contents and oocysts of infected chicks. Small amounts of these extracts given intravenously or intraperitoneally to rabbits killed the animals in 16 to 24 hours. After extraction of the infected tissues toxic substances were found in the material precipitated by 40–50 per cent saturation with ammonium sulphate. Further purification was effected in saline solution by adsorption on tricalcium phosphate and by dialysis. A purified preparation of oocysts was obtained by procedures involving digestion with pepsin. The oocysts were homogenized in saline, and the extract was used for injection into rabbits. These animals showed marked respiratory distress, prostration, and sometimes convulsions before dying within 24 hours, on receiving extractions from either of the two sources. Unmacerated oocysts did not cause death. Chickens unlike rabbits remained unaffected by inoculations. Attempts were made to prepare toxin neutralizing antibodies in rabbits and chicks, by graded inoculations. Serum from recovered chicks was also tested. Only the serum of rabbits so treated neutralized the toxic substance, and this fact tended to complicate conclusions regarding the antigenic nature of the toxin. Its purification is a necessary step for further progress in these studies. Whether an endo- or exo-toxin is involved was not determined and the significance of the substance in the syndrome of coccidiosis is still unknown. None of the symptoms characteristic of the disease were produced by it. The possibility that the response in rabbits is of an anaphylactic nature appears unlikely because of its delayed character. As well as failing to produce toxin-neutralizing antibodies, chickens were not protected from further coccidial infection by these toxic extracts. The material known as toxotoxin which occurs in the peritoneal exudate of mice infected with toxoplasma and causes death on intraperitoneal inoculation, appears to differ in action from the toxin of *E. tenella*, in so far as death occurs very rapidly with the former. It is of interest too that the material associated with *E. tenella* did not affect rats, guinea pigs, hamsters, or mice, just as it failed to affect chickens.

IV. CILIATA

Balantidiasis

Balantidium coli is a rare parasite of the human large intestine and occurs more often in pigs, monkeys, and other animals. It is a large organism some 50–80 μ long and 35–50 μ in breadth and the only parasitic ciliate of man, in whom it may cause diarrhoea and ulceration although it appears to be harmless in the pig. Treatment with aureomycin and terramycin has proved effective.

The organism has frequently been cultured in association with bacteria. Simple methods of purification have been described.[216] Very few studies have however been carried out on the metabolism of this organism. Agosin and von Brand[7] investigated its respiratory characteristics. The organisms were separated as far as possible from the accompanying mixed bacterial flora, whose growth was restricted by addition of streptomycin and penicillin. Determinations of oxygen consumption were made at 28° and 37°C under controlled conditions. Although they normally live in an anaerobic environment, the parasites consumed considerable quantities of oxygen and motility was unimpaired under the experimental conditions. In his experiments on the cultivation of *B. coli*, Schumaker[355] found that the organisms were resistant to high oxygen tensions in spite of being facultative anaerobes. The above authors found that inhibitors were more effective under anaerobic conditions. The organisms engulfed starch grains and stored glycogen. The data obtained were not conclusive for the presence of a tricarboxylic acid cycle. The RQ was slightly above 1.0 and true respiratory carbon dioxide was formed anaerobically, but the acids formed were not characterised. Aerobic respiration was cyanide sensitive, and the inhibition produced was reversible. The effect of iodoacetamide, sodium arsenite, and a naphthoquinone, regarded as sulphydryl glycolytic inhibitors, was marked, but *dl*-glyceraldehyde inhibited to only a limited extent. Malonate and fluoracetate were also active inhibitors of respiration. Tempelis and Lysenko[410] have shown that *B. coli* exhibits some hyaluronidase activity, and this fact may explain some of the clinical features of infection. The organisms were grown in presence of bacteria with addition of penicillin and streptomycin to restrict bacterial growth. For the detection of hyaluronidase activity, use was made of the streptococcus decapsulation test and the mucin clot prevention test. The tests used were not enirely satisfactory for the purpose in view. The authors suggest that once *B. coli* has penetrated the intestinal mucosa by mechanical means, hyaluronidase may help in extending the resulting lesion.

Axenic culture of *Balantidium coli* has been described by Gurski *et al.*[173] Cultures of the organism accompanied by bacteria have been made from pig and man by Zaman[467, 468] in diphasic medium maintained at 37°C for use in the immobilization and fluorescent antibody test, since neither test is affected by bacterial or other extraneous antigens present in these cultures. Antiserum was prepared by subcutaneous inoculation of rabbits with the washed parasites and was heated at 56°C for 20 minutes before use since otherwise lysis rapidly took place. Cross reactions occurred in the immobilization test with five pig strains but not with a human strain. The rate of immobilization was proportional to the concentration of serum and morphological changes occurred in the immobilized forms with appearance of precipitates at different parts of the parasite surface. The highest immobilizing titre was 1 : 64. The use of living cells gave rise to a highly specific fluorescent staining reaction, whereas after fixation staining was less specific. Use is being made of both tests to study antigenic differences in various species of *Balantidium*.

REFERENCES

1. ABELE, D. C., TOBIE, J. E., HILL, G. J., CONTACOS, P. G., and EVANS, C. B. (1965) Alterations in serum proteins and 19S antibody production during the course of induced malarial infections in man. *Amer. J. Trop. Med. Hyg.* **14**, 191.
2. ACTOR, P. (1960) Protein and vitamin intake and visceral leishmaniasis in the mouse. *Exptl. Parasitol.* **10**, 1.
3. ADA, G., and FULTON, J. D. (1948) Electrophoretic studies on the serum of golden hamsters infected with *Leishmania donovani*. *Brit. J. Exper. Path.* **29**, 524.
4. ADLER, S., and ASHBEL, R. (1940) A note on the metabolism of tissues infected with *Leishmania donovani*, *L. infantum* and *L. tropica*. *Ann. Trop. Med. Parasit.* **34**, 207.
5. ADLER, S., BACK, A., and SADOVSKY, A. (1952) Acquired resistance to colchicine in a strain of *Trichomonas vaginalis*. *Nature, Lond.* **170**, 930.
6. ADLER, S., and PULVERTAFT, R. J. V. (1944) The use of penicillin for obtaining bacteria-free cultures of *Trichomonas vaginalis* Donné 1837. *Ann. Trop. Med. Parasit.* **38**, 188.
7. AGOSIN, M., and von BRAND, T. (1953) Studies on the respiratory metabolism of *Balantidium coli*. *J. Infect. Dis.* **93**, 101.
8. AGOSIN, M., and von BRAND, T. (1954) Studies on the carbohydrate metabolism of *Trypanosoma congolense*. *Exptl. Parasitol.* **3**, 517.
9. AGOSIN, M., and von BRAND, T. (1955) Characterization and intracellular distribution of succinic dehydrogenase of *Trypanosoma cruzi*. *Exptl. Parasitol.* **4**, 548.
10. AGOSIN, M., and WEINBACH, E. C. (1956) Partial purification and characterization of the iso-citric dehydrogenase from *Trypanosoma cruzi*. *Biochem. Biophys. Acta* **21**, 117.
11. AKLILU, L., and SCHILLER, E. L. (1964) Extracellular cultivation of the Leishmanial bodies of species belonging to the Protozoan genus *Leishmania*, *Exptl. Parasitol.* **15**, 503.
12. ALLISON, A. C. (1960) Glucose-6-phosphate dehydrogenase deficiency in red blood cells of East Africans. *Nature, Lond.* **186**, 531.
13. ANDERSON, E., SAXE, L. H., and BEAMS, H. W. (1956) Electron microscope observations of *Trypanosoma equiperdum*, *J. Parasitology* **42**, 11.
14. ANDREWS, J., and von BRAND, T. (1938) Quantitative studies on glucose consumption by *Trichomonas foetus*. *Amer. J. Hyg.* **28**, 138.
15. ANDREWS, J., JOHNSON, C. M., and DORMAL, V. J. (1930) Lethal factors in experimental infections of *Trypanosoma equiperdum* in rats. *Amer. J. Hyg.* **12**, 381.
16. ANDREWS, W. H. H., and MAEGRAITH, B. G. (1948) The pathogenesis of the liver lesions due to the administration of carbon tetrachloride. *Ann. Trop. Med. Parasit.* **42**, 95.
17. ANFINSEN, C. B., GEIMAN, Q. M., McKEE, R. W., ORMSBEE, R. A., and BALL, E. G. (1946) Studies on malarial parasites. VIII. Factors affecting the growth of *Plasmodium knowlesi* in vitro. *J. Exper. Med.* **84**, 607.
18. ASAMI, K., and NAKAMURA, M. (1955) Experimental inoculation of bacteria-free *Trichomonas vaginalis* into human vaginae and its effect on the glycogen content of vaginal epithelia. *Amer. J. Trop. Med. Hyg.* **4**, 254.
19. ATCHLEY, F. O., AUERNHEIMER, A. H., and WASLEY, M. A. (1963) Precipitate patterns in agar gel with sera from human amoebiasis and *Entamoeba histolytica* antigen. *J. Parasitology* **49**, 313.

20. AWAD, F. I. (1954a) Ph. D. Thesis. London University. Studies on Sarcosporidiosis with particular reference to serological reactions.

21. AWAD, F. I. (1954b). A new dye-test for Toxoplasma and Sarcocystis infections by use of *Sarcocystis tenella* spores. *Trans. Roy. Soc. Trop. Med. Hyg.* **48**, 337.

22. BAERNSTEIN, H. D. (1953a) The enzyme systems of the culture form of *Trypanosoma cruzi*. *Ann. New York Acad. Sci.* **56**, 982.

23. BAERNSTEIN, H. D. (1953b). Malic dehydrogenase and related enzymes in the culture form of *Trypanosoma cruzi*. *Exptl. Parasitol.* **4**, 380.

24. BAERNSTEIN, H. D. (1955) Aldolase in *Trichomonas vaginalis*, *Exptl. Parasitol.* **4**, 323.

25. BAERNSTEIN, H. D. (1959) Lactic dehydrogenase in *Trichomonas vaginalis*. *J. Parasitology* **45**, 491.

26. BAERNSTEIN, H. D. (1961) Malic dehydrogenase in *Trichomonas vaginalis*. *J. Parasitology* **47**, 491.

27. BAERNSTEIN, H. D. (1963) A review of electron transport mechanisms in parasitic protozoa. *J. Parasitology* **49**, 12.

28. BAERNSTEIN, H. D., and REES, C. W. (1952) Aldolase in the culture form of *Trypanosoma cruzi*. *Exptl. Parasitol.* **1**, 215.

29. BAERNSTEIN, H. D., REES, C. W., and REARDON, L. V. (1954) Symbiosis in cultures of *Endamoeba histolytica* and single species of bacteria. *Amer. J. Trop. Med. Hyg.* **3**, 839.

30. BAERNSTEIN, H. D., and TOBIE, E. J. (1951) Cytochrome system of *Trypanosoma cruzi*. *Fed. Proc.* **10**, 159.

31. BALAMUTH, W., and SANDZA, J. G. (1944) Simple standardized culture medium for physiological studies on *Entamoeba histolytica*. *Proc. Soc. Exp. Biol. (Med.)* **57**, 161.

32. BALDWIN, F. M., WISWELL, O. B., and JANKIEWICZ, H. A. (1941) Haemorrhage control in *Eimeria tenella* infected chicks when protected by antihaemorrhagic factor, vitamin K. *Proc. Soc. Exp. Biol. Med.* **48**, 278.

33. BALL, E. G., ANFINSEN, C. B., GEIMAN, Q. M., McKEE, R. W., and ORMSBEE, R. A. (1945) *In vitro* growth and multiplication of the malaria parasite, *Plasmodium knowlesi*. *Science* **101**, 542.

34. BALL, E. G., McKEE, R. W., ANFINSEN, C. B., CRUZ, W. O., and GEIMAN, Q. M. (1948) Studies on malarial parasites. IX. Chemical and metabolic changes during growth and multiplication *in vivo* and *in vitro*. *J. Biol. Chem.* **175**, 547.

35. BARRATT, J. O. W., and YORKE, W. (1909). Über den Mechanismus der Entstehung der Haemoglobinurie bei Infektion mit *Piroplasma canis*. *Z. Immunitäts Forsch. Exp. Therap.* **4**, 313.

36. BASH-LEWINSON, D., and GROSSWICZ, H. (1957) Transaminases of *Trypanosoma cruzi*. *Bull. Research Council, Israel*, **6E**, 91.

37. BASS, C. C. (1912) Successful cultivation of malarial plasmodia. *J. Amer. Med. Assoc.* **59**, 936.

38. BASS, C. C., and JOHNS, F. M. (1912) The cultivation of malarial plasmodia (*Plasmodium vivax* and *Plasmodium falciparum*) in vitro. *J. Exper. Med.* **16**, 567.

39. BECKER, C. E., and GEIMAN, Q. M. (1955) Utilization of glucose by two strains of *Entamoeba histolytica*. *Exptl. Parasitol.* **4**, 493.

40. BEVERIDGE, E. (1953) *Babesia rodhaini*: a useful organism for the testing of drugs designed for the treatment of piroplasmosis. *Ann. Trop. Med. Parasit.* **47**, 134.

41. BIAGI, F., ROBLEDO, E., SERVIN, H., and MARTUSCELLI, A. (1962) The effect of cholesterol on the pathogenicity of *Entamoeba histolytica*. *Amer. J. Trop. Med. Hyg.* **11**, 333.

42. BIAGI, F., ROBLEDO, E., SERVIN, H., and MARVAN, G. (1963) Influence of some steroides in the experimental production of amoebic hepatic abscess. *Amer. I. Trop. Med. Hyg.* **12**, 318.

43. BIOT, C., BIOT, R., and RICHARD, G. (1911) Influence du glucose sur la vitalité du Trypanosoma lewisi in vitro. C.R. Soc. Biol. 71, 368.

44. BLACK, R. H. (1947) The consumption of haemoglobin by malaria parasites. Ann. Trop. Med. Parasit. 41, 215.

45. BOECK, W. C., and DRBOHLAV, J. (1925) The cultivation of Endamoeba histolytica. Amer. J. Hyg. 5, 371.

46. BONÉ, G. I., and PARENT, G. (1963) Stearic acid an essential growth factor for Trypanosoma cruzi. J. Gen. Microbiol. 31, 261.

47. BOS, A. (1932) Ueber Trichomoniasis bei Tauben. I. Die Kultur von Trichomonas columbae und ihre Bedeutung für die Diagnose der Trichomoniasis. Zent. Bakt. Parasitkde. I. Abt. Orig. 126, 550.

48. BOVARNICK, N. R., LINDSAY, A., and HELLERMAN, L. (1946a) Metabolism of the malarial parasite, with reference particularly to the action of antimalarial agents. I. Preparation and properties of Plasmodium lophurae separated from the red cells of duck blood by means of saponin. J. Biol. Chem. 163, 523.

49. BOVARNICK, N. R., LINDSAY, A., and HELLERMAN, L. (1946b) Metabolism of the malarial parasite, with reference particularly to the action of antimalarial agents. II. Atabrine (quinacrine) inhibition of glucose oxidation in parasites initially depleted of substrate. Reversal by adenylic acid. J. Biol. Chem. 163, 535.

50. BRADIN, J. L. (1953) Studies on the production of hyaluronidase by Endamoeba histolytica. Exptl.. Parasitol. 2, 230.

51. BRADNER, W. T. (1953) A study of the physiology of bacteria which support the growth of Endamoeba histolytica in vitro. J. Parasitology 39, 326.

52. BRAGG, P. D., and REEVES, R. E. (1962) Pathways of glucose dissimilation in the Laredo strain of Entamoeba histolytica. Exptl. Parasitol. 12, 393.

53. VON BRAND, T. (1933) Studien über die Kohlehydratstoffwechsel parasitischer Protozoen. II. Der Zuckerstoffwechsel der Trypanosomen. Zeit. Vergl. Physiol. 19, 587.

54. VON BRAND, T. (1952) The gaseous exchanges of Trypanosome-infected rats. Exptl. Parasitol. 1, 60.

55. VON BRAND, T. (1952) Chemical Physiology of Endoparasitic Animals. Acad. Press Inc., New York.

56. VON BRAND, T., and AGOSIN, M. (1955) The utilization of Krebs cycle intermediates by the culture forms of Trypanosoma cruzi and L. tropica. J. Infect. Dis. 97, 274.

57. VON BRAND, T., and JOHNSON, E. M. (1947) A comparative study of the effect of cyanide on the respiration of some Trypanosomidae. J. Cell. Compar. Physiol. 29, 33.

58. VON BRAND, T., McMAHON, P., TOBIE, E. J., THOMPSON, M. J., and MOSETTIG, E. (1959) Chemical composition of the culture form of Trypanosoma cruzi. Exptl. Parasitol. 8, 171.

59. VON BRAND, T., REES, C. W., JACOBS, L., and REARDON, L. V. (1943) Studies on reducing substances and gas formation in cultures of Endamoeba histolytica and a single species of symbiotic bacteria. Amer. J. Hyg. 37, 310.

60. VON BRAND, T., REES, C. W., REARDON, L. V., and SIMPSON, W. F. (1946) Chemical studies on egg-white medium for the cultivation of Endamoeba histolytica. J. Parasitology 32, 190.

61. VON BRAND, T., and TOBIE, E. J. (1948a) Further observations on the influence of cyanide on some trypanosomes. J. Cell Comp. Physiol. 31, 49.

62. VON BRAND, T., and TOBIE, E. J. (1948b) Influence of SH-inhibitors on the oxygen consumption of the blood stream form of some trypanosomes. J. Parasitology 34, Suppl. 19.

63. VON BRAND, T., and TOBIE, E. J. (1959) Observations on the metabolism of the culture form of Trypanosoma congolense. J. Parasitology 45, 204.

64. VON BRAND, T., TOBIE, E. J., KISSLING, R. E., and ADAMS, G. (1949) Physiological and pathological observations on four strains of Trypanosoma cruzi. J. Infect. Dis. 85, 5.

65. VON BRAND, T., WEINBACH, E., and TOBIE, E. J. (1955) Comparative studies on the metabolism of the culture form and bloodstream form of *Trypanosoma gambiense*. *J. Cell Compar. Physiol.* **55**, 421.

66. BRAY, R. S., and GARNHAM, P. C. C. (1961) Failure to infect splenectomized primates with *Theileria parva*. *J. Parasitology* **47**, 538.

67. BROOKE, M. M. (1945) Effect of dietary changes upon avian malaria. *Am. J. Hyg.* **41**, 81.

68. BROWN, K. N., and WILLIAMSON, J. (1964). The Chemical composition of trypanosomes IV. Location of fractions in subcellular fractions of *Trypanosoma rhodesiense*. *Exptl. Parasitol.* **15**, 69.

69. BROWN, W. H. (1911) Malarial pigment (so-called melanin) its nature and mode of production. *J. Exper. Med.* **13**, 290.

70. BRYANT, C., VOLLER, A., and SMITH, M. J. A. (1964) The incorporation of radioactivity from (^{14}C)-glucose into the soluble metabolic intermediates of malaria parasites. *Amer. J. Trop. Med. Hyg.* **13**, 515.

71. BÜLBRING, E., LOURIE, E. M., and PARDOE, U. (1949) The presence of acetylcholine in *Trypanosoma rhodesiense* and its absence from *Plasmodium gallinaceum*. *Brit. J. Pharmac. Chemother.* **4**, 290.

72. BURNS, W. C. (1959) The lethal effects of *Eimeria tenella* extracts on rabbits. *J. Parasitol.* **45**, 38.

73. BURSELL, E. (1960) Free amino acids of the tsetse fly (*Glossina*). *Nature, Lond.* **187**, 778.

74. CAILLEAU, R. (1937) La nutrition des flagellés tétramidités. Les stérols, facteurs de croissance pour les trichomonades. *Ann. Inst. Pasteur* **59**, 137.

75. CAILLEAU, R. (1938) Le cholestérol et l'acide ascorbique— facteurs de croissance pour le flagellé tétramitidé *Trichomonas foetus* Riedmüller. *C.R. Soc. Biol.* **127**, 861.

76. CALVERT, D. N., and BRODY, T. M. (1960) Role of the sympathetic nervous system in CCl_4 hepatotoxicity. *Amer. J. Physiol.* **198**, 669.

77. CAPELLA, J. A., and KAUFMAN, H. E. (1964) Enzyme histochemistry of *Toxoplasma gondii*. *Amer. J. Trop. Med. Hyg.* **13**, 664.

78. CAPPUCCINO, E. F., and STAUBER, L. A. (1959) Some compounds active against experimental visceral Leishmaniasis. *Proc. Soc. Exp. Biol.* (*Med.*) **101**, 742.

79. CARRERA, G. M. (1950) Acid phosphatase activity in the intestinal wall in experimental amebic colitis. *Proc. Soc. Exp. Biol.* (*Med.*) **73**, 682.

80. CASTELLANI, O., and FERNANDES, J. F. (1962) Nucleotide and polynucleotide synthesis in *Trypanosoma cruzi*. VI. *In vitro* effects of analogs of the aminonucleoside of Stylomycin. *Exptl. Parasitol.* **12**, 52.

81. CEDILLOS, R. A., REEVES, R. E., and SWARTZWELDER, J. C. (1961) Influence of added cholesterol and dehydrocholesterol upon the multiplication of *Entamoeba histolytica* in MS-F medium. *Exptl. Parasitol.* **11**, 305.

82. CEITHAML, J., and EVANS, E. A. (1946) The biochemistry of the malaria parasite. VII. *In vitro* studies on the distribution of quinine between blood cells and their suspending medium. *Arch. Biochem.* **10**, 397.

83. CHANG, S. L. (1946) Studies on *Entamoeba histolytica*. IV. The relation of oxidation reduction potentials to the growth, encystation and excystation of *E. histolytica* in culture. *Parasitology* **37**, 101.

84. CHANG, S. L. (1948) Studies on haemoflagellates. IV. Observations concerning some biochemical activities in culture and respiration of three species of *Leishmanias* and *Trypanosoma cruzi*. *J. Infect. Dis.* **82**, 109.

85. CHANG, S. L., and NEGHERBON, W. O. (1947) Studies on haemoflagellates. II. A study of the growth rates of *Leishmania donovani*, *L. brasiliensis*, *L. tropica* and *Trypanosoma cruzi* in culture. *J. Infect. Dis.* **80**, 172.

86. CHATTERJEE, A. N., and GHOSH, J. J. (1957) Transaminases of *Leishmania donovani* the causative organism of kala azar. *Nature, Lond.* **180**, 1425.

87. CHATTERJEE, A. N., and GHOSH, J. J. (1958) Metabolism of sucrose by *Leishmania donovani*. *Ann. Biochem. Exp. Med. Calcutta* **18**, 69.

88. CHATTERJEE, A. N., and GHOSH, J. J. (1959) Studies on the metabolism of *Leishmania donovani* the causative organism of kala azar. *Ann. Biochem. Exp. Med. Calcutta* **19**, 37.

89. CHATTERJEE, A. N., and GHOSH, J. J. (1960) Carbon dioxide assimilation by *Leishmania donovani*. *Nature, Lond.* **185**, 322.

90. CHATTERJEE, A. M., and RAY, J. J. (1958) Hexokinase activity in cell-free extracts of *Leishmania donovani*. *Nature, Lond.* **182**, 109.

91. CHEN, G., and GEILING, E. M. K. (1946) Glycolysis in *Trypanosoma equiperdum*. *Proc. Soc. Exp. Biol. (Med.)* **63**, 486.

91a. CHEN, T. T. (1944) The nuclei in avian malaria parasites. I. The structure of nuclei in *Plasmodium elongatum* with some consideration on technique. *Amer. J. Hygiene* **40**, 26–34.

92. CHINN, B. D., JACOBS, L., REARDON, L. V., and REES, C. W. (1942) The influence of the bacterial flora on the cultivation of *Endamoeba histolytica*. *Amer. J. Trop. Med.* **22**, 137.

93. CHRISTOPHERS, S. R., and FULTON, J. D. (1938) Observations on the respiratory metabolism of malaria parasites and trypanosomes. *Ann. Trop. Med. Parasit.* **32**, 43.

94. CHRISTOPHERS, S. R., and FULTON, J. D. (1939) Experiments with isolated malaria parasites (*Plasmodium knowlesi*) free from red cells. *Ann. Trop. Med. Parasit.* **33**, 161.

95. CLEVELAND, L. R., and SANDERS, E. P. (1930) The production of bacteria-free amoebic abscesses in the liver of cats and observations on the amoebae in various media with and without bacteria. *Science* **72**, 149.

96. COGGESHALL, L. T. (1939) Preservation of viable malaria parasites in the frozen state. *Proc. Soc. Exp. Biol. (Med.)* **42**, 499.

97. COGGESHALL, L. T. (1940) The selective action of sulfanilamide on the parasites of experimental malaria in monkeys *in vivo* and *in vitro*. *J. Exper. Med.* **71**, 13.

98. COGGESHALL, L. T., and MAIER, J. (1941) Determination of the activity of various drugs against the malaria parasite. *J. Infect. Dis.* **69**, 108.

99. COHEN, S. N., PHIFER, K. O., and YIELDING, K. L. (1964) Complex formation between chloroquine and ferrihaemic acid *in vitro*, and its effect on the antimalarial action of chloroquine. *Nature, Lond.* **202**, 805.

100. COOK, R. P. (1958) Ed. *Chemistry, Biochemistry and Pathology*. Academic Press Inc., New York.

101. COOK, L., GRANT, P. T., and KERMACK, W. O. (1961) Proteolytic enzymes of the erythrocytic forms of rodent and simian species of malarial plasmodia. *Exptl. Parasitol.* **11**, 372.

102. COULSTON, F. (1941) Cultivation experiments with the avian malaria *Plasmodium circumflexum*. *J. Parasitology* **27**, Suppl. 38.

103. CROWTHER, S., FULTON, J. D., and JOYNER, L. P. (1954) The metabolism of *Leishmania donovani* in culture. *Biochem. J.* **56**, 182.

104. D'ALESANDRO, P., and SHERMAN, J. W. (1964) Changes in lactic dehydrogenase levels of *Trypanosoma lewisi* associated with appearance of ablastic immunity. *Exptl. Parasitol.* **15**, 430.

105. DAVIES, A. W. (1952) Lowered liver vitamin A reserves in avian coccidiosis. *Nature, Lond.* **170**, 849.

106. DEANE, H. W. (1945) Studies on malarial parasites. II. The staining of two primate parasites by the Feulgen technique. *J. Cell. Compar. Physiol.* **26**, 139.

107. DEEGAN, T., and MAEGRAITH, B. G. (1956a) Studies on the nature of malarial pigment (Haemozoin). I. The pigment of the Simian species, *Plasmodium knowlesi* and *P. cynomolgi*. *Ann. Trop. Med. Parasit.* **50**, 194.

108. DEEGAN, T., and MAEGRAITH, B. G. (1956b). Studies on the nature of malarial pigment (Haemozoin). II. The pigment of the human species, *Plasmodium falciparum* and *P. malariae. Ann. Trop. Med. Parasit.* **50**, 212.

109. DESOWITZ, R. S. (1956a) Effect of antibody on the respiratory rate of *Trypanosoma vivax. Nature, Lond.* **177**, 132.

110. DESOWITZ, R. S. (1956b) Observations on the metabolism of *Trypanosoma vivax. Exptl. Parasitol.* **5**, 250.

111. DEVAKUL, K., and MAEGRAITH, B. G. (1958) Blood sugar and tissue glycogen in infections in *Macaca mulatta* with the Nuri strain of *Plasmodium knowlesi. Ann. Trop. Med. Parasit.* **52**, 366.

112. DIAMOND, L. S. (1954) A comparative study of 28 culture media for *Trichomonas gallinae. Exptl. Parasitol.* **3**, 251.

113. DIAMOND, L. S. (1961) Axenic cultivation of *Entamoeba histolytica. Science* **134**, 336.

114. DIAMOND, L. S. (1962) Axenic cultivation of *Trichomonas tenax*, the oral flagellate of man. *J. Protozool.* **9**, 442.

115. DOBELL, C., and LAIDLAW, P. P. (1926) The action of ipecacuanha alkaloids on *Entamoeba histolytica* and some other entozoic amoebae in culture. *Parasitology* **18**, 206.

116. DORAN, D. J. (1957). Studies on Trichomonads. I. The metabolism of *Tritrichomonas foetus* and Trichomonads from the nasal cavity and caecum of swine. *J. Protozool.* **4**, 182.

117. DORAN, D. J. (1958) Studies on Trichomonads. II. The metabolism of a *Trichomonas batrachorum*-type flagellate from the caecum of swine. *J. Protozool.* **5**, 89.

118. DORAN, D. J. (1959) Studies on Trichomonads. III. Inhibitors, acid production, and substrate utilization by 4 strains of *Tritrichomonas foetus. J. Protozool.* **6**, 177.

119. ENTNER, N. (1958) On the pathway of carbohydrate metabolism in *Entamoeba histolytica. J. Parasitology* **44**, 638.

120. ETINGER, H., and HALEVY, S. (1964) Lipid biochemistry of *Trichomonas vaginalis. Ann. Trop. Med. Parasit.* **58**, 409.

121. EVANS, E. A. (1946) Enzyme systems operating within the malaria parasite. *Fed. Proc.* **5**, 390.

122. EVENS, F., NIEMEGEERS, C., and CHARLES, P. (1963) Maladie du sommeil à *T. gambiense*. Étude de quelques réactions biochimiques du sérum humain. *Acad. Roy. des Sci. d'Outre-Mer. Classe des Sci. Naturelles & Méd.* (n.s.) **14**, 177 pp.

123. FAIRLEY, N. H. (1946) Researches on paludrine (M. 4888) in malaria. An experimental investigation undertaken by the L.H.Q. Medical Research Unit (A.I.F.), Cairns, Australia. *Trans. Roy. Soc. Trop. Med. Hyg.* **40**, 105.

124. FEINBERG, J. G., and MORGAN, W. T. J. (1953) The isolation of a specific substance and a glycogen-like polysaccharide from *Trichomonas foetus* (Var. Manley). *Brit. J. Exp. Path.* **34**, 104.

125. FELDMAN, H. (1956) The relationship of *Toxoplasma* antibody antibody activator to the serum-properdin system. *Ann. N.Y. Acad. Sci.* **66**, 263.

126. FENNYVESSY, B. VON (1926) Über die Bedeutung des Stoffwechsels der Parasiten für das Wirtstier bei der Trypanosomen Infektion. *Biochem. Zeit.* **173**, 289.

127. FENNYVESSY, B. VON and REINER. L. (1924) Untersuchungen über den respiratorischen Stoffwechsel der Trypanosomen. *Ztschr. Hyg. Infekt.-Krankh.* **102**, 109.

128. FERNANDES, J. F., and CASTELLANI, O. (1958) Nucleotide and polynucleotide synthesis in *Trypanosoma cruzi*. I. Precursors of purine compounds. *Exptl. Parasitol.* **7**, 224.

129. FERNANDES, J. F., and CASTELLANI, O. (1959) Nucleotide and polynucleotide synthesis in *Trypanosoma cruzi*. II. *In vitro* effect of Tioguanine and of the aminonucleoside of Stylomycin. *Exptl. Parasitol.* **8**, 480.

130. FERNANDES, J. F., PEREIRA, J. P. M., and SILVA, L. H. P. (1959) Nucleotide and polynucleotide synthesis in *Trypanosoma cruzi*. IV. Effect of an aminonucleoside of Stylomycin on mouse infections. *Exptl. Parasitol*. **8**, 496.

131. FITZGERALD, P. R., and LEVINE, N. D. (1961) Effect of storage temperature, equilibration time and buffers on survival of *Tritrichomonas foetus* in the presence of glycerol at freezing temperatures. *J. Protozool*. **8**, 21.

132. PLATZ, G., and SRINGAM, S. (1963) Malaria and glucose-6-phosphate dehydrogenase deficiency in Thailand. *Lancet*, ii, 1248.

133. FLETCHER, K. A., and MAEGRAITH, B. G. (1962) Glucose-6-phosphate and 6-phosphogluconate dehydrogenase activities in erythrocytes of monkeys infected with *Plasmodium knowlesi*. *Nature, Lond*. **196**, 1316.

134. FLEWETT, T. H., and FULTON, J. D. (1959) The relationship of *Babesia rodhaini* to the host erythrocyte. *Ann. Trop. Med. Parasit*. **53**, 501.

135. FRAGA DE AZEVEDO, J. (1962) Biologia da *Leishmania donovani* em relação com a sua accao patogenica e a epidemiologia do Kala-azar. *Rev. Iberica de Parasitologia* **22**, 48 pp. (*TDB* 1963, vol. 60, 625).

136. FREI, W. (1964) Der Stoffwechsel bei der Trypanosomeninfektion des Meerschweinschens mit besonderer Berücksichtigung der Leberlipide. *Acta Tropica Basle* **21**, 264.

137. FRENCH, M. H. (1938) Studies in animal trypanosomiases. I. Nitrogen and mineral metabolic disturbances induced by *Trypanosoma congolense* and *Trypanosoma brucei*. *J. Comp. Path. Therap*. **51**, 23.

138. FRENCH, M. H. (1938) II. Disturbances produced in the plasma proteins by *Trypanosoma congolense* and *Trypanosoma brucei*. *J. Comp. Path. Therap*. **51**, 36.

139. FRENCH, M. H. (1938) III. The effects of *Trypanosoma congolense* and *Trypanosoma brucei* on blood urea. *J. Comp. Path. Therap*. **51**, 42.

140. FRENCH, M. H. (1938) IV. The effect of *Trypanosoma congolense* and *Trypanosoma brucei* on some inorganic blood constituents. *J. Comp. Path. Therap*. **51**, 119.

141. FRENCH, M. H. (1938) V. Some disturbances of the host's carbohydrate metabolism induced by *Trypanosoma congolense* and *Trypanosoma brucei*. *J. Comp. Path. Therap*. **51**, 269.

142. FULTON, J. D. (1936) Studies in the chemotherapy of malaria. The inhibitory action of antimalarial drugs on blood lipases. *Ann. Trop. Med. Parasit*. **30**, 491.

143. FULTON, J. D. (1939) Experiments on the utilization of sugars by malarial parasites (*Plasmodium knowlesi*). *Ann. Trop. Med. Parasit*. **33**, 217.

144. FULTON, J. D. (1954) Protozoal infections and diet. *Lancet* **1**, 162.

145. FULTON, J. D., and CHRISTOPHERS, S. R. (1938) The inhibitive effect of drugs upon oxygen uptake by trypanosomes (*Trypanosoma rhodesiense*) and malaria parasites (*Plasmodium knowlesi*). *Ann. Trop. Med. Parasit*. **32**, 77.

146. FULTON, J. D., and FLEWETT, T. H. (1956) The relation of *Plasmodium berghei* and *Plasmodium knowlesi* to their respective red cell hosts. *Trans. Roy. Soc. Trop. Med. Hyg*. **50**, 150.

147. FULTON, J. D., and GRANT, P. T. (1956) The sulphur requirements of the erythrocytic form of *Plasmodium knowlesi*. *Biochem. J*. **63**, 274.

148. FULTON, J. D., and JOYNER, L. P. (1949) Studies on Protozoa. I. The metabolism of Leishman-Donovan bodies and flagellates of *Leishmania donovani*. *Trans. Roy. Soc. Trop. Med. Hyg*. **43**, 273.

149. FULTON, J. D., and MAEGRAITH, B. G. (1949) The physiologic pathology of malaria In Boyd's *Malariology*. W. B. SAUNDERS Co. Philadephia and London, pp. 904–34.

150. FULTON, J. D., and RIMINGTON, C. (1953) The pigment of the malaria parasite *Plasmodium berghei*. *J. Gen. Microbiol*. **8**, 157.

151. FULTON, J. D., and SPOONER, D. F. (1957) Preliminary observations on the metabolism of *Toxoplasma gondii*. *Trans. Roy. Soc. Trop. Med. Hyg*. **51**, 123.

152. FULTON, J. D., and SPOONER, D. F. (1959) Terminal respiration in certain mammalian trypanosomes. *Exptl. Parasitol.* **8**, 137.

153. FULTON, J. D., and SPOONER, D. F. (1960) Metabolic studies on *Toxoplasma gondii*. *Exptl. Parasitol.* **9**, 293.

154. FULTON, J. D., and STEVENS, T. S. (1945) The glucose metabolism *in vitro* of *Trypanosoma rhodesiense*. *Biochem. J.* **39**, 317.

155. FURTADO, T. A., CISALPINO, E. O., and SANTOS, U. M. (1960) *In vitro* studies of the effect of amphotericin B on *Leishmania braziliensis*. *Antibiotics and Chemotherapy* **10**, 692.

156. GANZIN, M., REBEYROTTE, P., MACHEBOEUF, M., and MONTEZIN, G. (1952) Étude par électrophorèse des fractions protéiques du sérum sanguin d'hommes et de cobayes infectés par des trypanosomes. *Bull. Soc. Path. Exot.* **45**, 518.

157. GARNHAM, P. C. C., and BRAY, R. S. (1959) The susceptibility of the higher primates to piroplasms. *J. Protozool.* **6**, 352.

158. GEIMAN, Q. M. (1948) Cultivation and metabolism of malarial parasites. *Proc. 4th Int. Cong. Trop. Med. Malaria* **1**, 618.

159. GEIMAN, Q. M., and MCKEE, R. W. (1948) Malarial parasites and their mode of life. *Science Monthly* **67**, 217.

160. GHOSH, B. K., and CHATTERJEE, A. N. (1961) Action of an antifungal antibiotic nystatin, on the protozoa *Leishmania donovani*. Part I. Studies on the metabolism of *Leishmania donovani*. *Ann. Biochem. Exptl. Med. Calcutta* **21**, 307.

161. GILL, B. S., and RAY, H. N. (1954) Glycogen and its probable significance in *Eimeria tenella* Raillet and Lucet 1891. *Ind. J. Vet. Sci.* **24**, 223.

162. GLENN, S., and MANWELL, R. D. (1956) Further studies on cultivation of avian malaria parasites: effects of heterologous sera and added metabolites on growth and reproduction *in vitro*. *Exptl. Parasitol.* **5**, 22.

163. GODFREY, D. G. (1961) *West African Institute for Trypanosiasis Research Ann. Rep.* 1961, Ed. K. C. WILLETT.

164. GOODWIN, L. G., and RICHARDS, W. H. G. (1960) Pharmacologically active peptides in the blood and urine of animals infected with *Babesia rodhaini* and other pathogenic organisms. *Brit. J. Pharmac. Chemother.* **15**, 152.

165. GORDON, R. M., and MILLER, J. K. (1961) Cyclical infections of *Glossina morsitans* with culture forms of *Trypanosoma rhodesiense*. *Nature, Lond.* **191**, 1317.

166. GRANT, P. T., and FULTON, J. D. (1957) The catabolism of glucose by strains of *Trypanosoma rhodesiense*. *Biochem. J.* **66**, 242.

167. GRANT, P. T., and SERGENT, J. R. (1960) Properties of L-a-glycerophosphate oxidase and its role in the respiration of *Trypanosoma rhodesiense*. *Biochem. J.* **76**, 229.

168. GRANT, P. T., and SERGENT, J. R. (1961) L-a-glycerophosphate dehydrogenase, a component of an oxidase system in *Trypanosoma rhodesiense*. *Biochem. J.* **81**, 206.

169. GRANT, P. T., SERGENT, J. R., and RYLEY, J. F. (1961) Respiratory systems in the Trypanosomidae. *Biochem. J.* **81**, 200.

170. GRAY, A. R. (1963) Serum transaminase levels in cattle and sheep infected with *Trypanosoma vivax*. *Expt. Parasitol.* **14**, 374.

171. GRIFFIN, A. M., and MCCARTEN, W. G. (1949) Sterols and fatty acids in the nutrition of entozoic amoebae in cultures. *Proc. Soc. Exp. Biol (Med.)* **72**, 645.

172. GROMAN, N. B. (1951) Dynamic aspects of the nitrogen metabolism of *Plasmodium gallinaceum in vivo* and *in vitro*. *J. Infect Dis.* **88**, 126.

173. GURSKI, D. R., LEE, J. J., and PIERCE, S. (1961) Isolation of *Balantidium* sp. from the blue-tongued skink (*Tiliqua nigrolutea*) in axenic culture. *J. Protozool.* Supplement **8**, 11.

174. GUTTMAN, H. N., and WALLACE, F. G. (1965) *Nutrition and Physiology of Trypanosomatidae. Biochemistry and Physiology of Protozoa.* Vol. III. Ed. S.A. Hutner, Academic Press, New York and London.

175. HAAS, E. (1944) The effect of atabrine and quinine on isolated respiratory enzymes. *J. Biol. Chem.* **155**, 321.

176. HAGEMEISTER, W. (1914) Über die Züchtung pathogener Trypanosomen auf künstlichen Nährböden. *Ztschr. Hyg. Infektkrankh.* **77**, 227.

177. HALEVY, S. (1962) Comparative studies of lipid metabolism of Trypanosomidae. I. *Trypanosoma cruzi; Leishmania tropica* and related species. *Bull. Res. Council of Israel*, 10E, No. 2, 65.

178. HALEVY, S. (1963) Lipid composition and metabolism of *Trichomonas foetus*. *Proc. Soc. Exp. Biol. Med.* **113**, 47.

179. HALLMAN, F. A., and DELAMATER, J. N. (1953) Demonstration of amylolytic activity in cultures of *Endamoeba histolytica*. *Exptl. Parasitol.* **2**, 170.

180. HANSEN, E. L. (1950) A liquid medium composed of dehydrated ingredients for culture of *Endamoeba histolytica* associated with a single bacterium. *J. Lab. Clin. Med.* **35**, 308.

181. HANSEN, E. L., and ANDERSON, H. H. (1948) An essentially synthetic liquid medium for *Entamoeba histolytica*. *Parasitology* **39**, 69.

182. HARINASUTA, C., and MAEGRAITH, B. G. (1958) The demonstration of proteolytic enzyme activity of *Entamoeba histolytica* by the use of photographic gelatin film. *Ann. Trop. Med. Parasit.* **52**, 508.

183. HARVEY, S. C. (1949) The carbohydrate metabolism of *Trypanosoma hippicum*. *J. Biol. Chem.* **179**, 435.

184. HELLERMAN, L., BOVARNICK, M. R., and PORTER, C. C. (1946) Metabolism of the malarial parasite: action of antimalarial agents upon separated *Plasmodium lophurae* and upon certain isolated enzyme systems. *Fed. Proc.* **5**, 400.

185. HELLERMAN, L., LINDSAY, A., and BOVARNICK, M. R. (1946) Flavoenzyme catalysis; Inhibition of *d*-amino acid oxidase by competition with flavin-adenine-dinucleotide of atabrine (quinacrine), quinine and certain other compounds. *J. Biol. Chem.* **163**, 553.

186. HILKER, D. M., and WHITE, A. G. C. (1959) Some aspects of the carbohydrate metabolism of *Entamoeba histolytica*. *Exptl. Parasitol.* **8**, 539.

187. HOARE, C. A. (1957) The classification of Trypanosomes of veterinary and medical importance. *Vet. Reviews and Annotations* **3**, 1.

188. HONIGBERG, B. M. (1961) Comparative pathogenicity of *Trichomonas vaginalis* and *Trichomonas gallinae* to mice. I. Gross pathology, quantitative evaluation of virulence and some factors affecting pathogenicity. *J. Parasitology* **47**, 545.

189. HONIGBERG, B. M., and READ, C. P. (1960) Virulence transformation of a trichomonad protozoan. *Science* **131**, 352.

190. HOOK, W. H., and FABER, J. E. (1957) Fractionation studies on the antigenic nature of *Toxoplasma gondii*. *Exptl. Parasitol.* **6**, 449.

191. HUSSEIN, Z. H. (1961) The pathogenicity of *Entamoeba histolytica* I. The mean cyst diameter in large and small race infections. *Trans. Roy. Soc. Trop. Med. Hyg.* **55**, 265.

192. HUSSEIN, Z. H. (1963) II. Amoebic culture. *Trans. Roy. Soc. Trop. Med. Hyg.* **57**, 101.

193. IKEJIANI, O. (1947) The antigenic composition and the effect of various extracts of *Trypanosoma equiperdum* and *Trypanosoma lewisi* on the leucocyte picture in experimental trypanosomiasis. *Amer. J. Hyg.* **45**, 144.

194. INGRAM, K. L., OTKEN, L. B., and JUMPER, J. R. (1961) Staining of malarial parasites by the fluorescent antibody technique. *Proc. Soc. Exp. Biol. (Med.)* **106**, 52.

195. JACOBS, L. (1941) Oxidation-reduction potentials in relation to the cultivation of *Entamoeba histolytica*. *J. Parasitology* **27**, Suppl. 31.

196. JACOBS, L. (1947) The elimination of viable bacteria from cultures of *Entamoeba histolytica* and the subsequent maintenance of such cultures. *Amer. J. Hyg.* **46**, 172.

197. JACOBS, L. (1950) Oxidation-reduction potentials in the cultivation of *Entamoeba histolytica. Amer. J. Trop. Med.* **30**, 803.

198. JACOBS, R. L. (1965) Selection of strains of *Plasmodium berghei* resistant to quinine, chloroquine and pyrimethamine (Research Notes). *J. Parasitology* **51**, 481.

199. JARUMILINTA, R., and KRADOLFER, F. (1964) The toxic effect of *Entamoeba histolytica* on leucoctyes *Ann. Trop. Med. Parasit.* **58**, 375.

200. JARUMILINTA, R., and MAEGRAITH, B. G. (1960) Hyaluronidase activity in stock cultures of *Entamoeba histolytica. Ann. Trop. Med. Parasit.* **54**, 118.

201. JARUMILINTA, R., and MAEGRAITH, B. G. (1961a) The patterns of some proteolytic enzymes of *Entamoeba histolytica* and *Acanthamoeba* sp. I. The action of *E. histolytica* and *Acanthamoeba* sp. on protein substrates. *Ann. Trop. Med. Parasit.* **55**, 505.

202. JARUMILINTA, R., and MAEGRAITH, B. G. (1961b) The patterns of some proteolytic enzymes of *Entamoeba histolytica* and *Acanthamoeba* sp. II. The action of *Entamoeba histolytica* and *Acanthamoeba* sp. on various synthetic substrates. *Ann. Trop. Med. Parasit.* **55**, 518.

203. JENKINS, A. R., and ROBERTSON, D. H. H. (1959) Hepatic dysfunction in human trypanosomiasis. II. Serum proteins in *Trypanosoma rhodesiense* infections and observations on the alterations found after treatment and during convalescence. *Trans. Roy. Soc. Trop. Med. Hyg.* **53**, 524.

204. JOHNSON, A. E. (1962) The free amino acids in *Trichomonas foetus. Exptl. Parasitol.* **12**, 168.

205. JOHNSON, G. (1942) Physiology of pure cultures of *Trichomonas* vaginalis. IV. Effect of hydrogen ion concentration and oxygen tension on population. *J. Parasitol.* **28**, 369.

206. JOHNSON, G., and KUPFERBERG, A. B. (1948) Chemotherapy of bacteria-free *Trichomonas vaginalis*. III. Action of analogues of pantothenic acid. *Proc. Soc. Exp. Biol. (Med.)* **67**, 390.

207. JOHNSON, G., and TRUSSELL, R. E. (1943) Experimental basis for the chemotherapy of *Trichomonas vaginalis* infections. I. *Proc. Soc. Exp. Biol. (Med.)* **54**, 245.

208. JOHNSON, G., TRUSSELL, R. E., and JAHN, F. (1945) Isolation of *T. vaginalis* with penicillin. *Science* **102**, 126.

209. JOHNSON, J. G. (1947) The physiology of bacteria-free *Trichomonas vaginalis. J. Parasitol.* **33**, 189.

210. JONES, I., and SMITH, B. F. (1959) Certain B-complex vitamins as growth promoting factors for *Trichomonas gallinae. Exptl. Parasitol.* **8**, 509.

211. JOYNER, L. P. (1954) The elimination of *Trichomonas foetus* from infected semen by storage in the presence of glycerol. *Vet. Record,* **66**, 727.

212. JOYNER, L. P. (1963) Some metabolic relationships between host and parasite with particular reference to the Eimeriae of domestic poultry. *Proc. Nutrition Soc.* **22**, 26.

213. KEILIN, D., and HARTREE, E. F. (1949) Effect of low temperature on the absorption spectra of haemoproteins, with observations on the absorption spectra of oxygen. *Nature, Lond.* **164**, 254.

214. KLIGLER, I. J., GEIGER, H., and COMAROFF, R. (1929) Susceptibility and resistance to trypanosome infections. VII. Cause of injury and death in trypanosome infected rats. *Ann. Trop. Med. Parasit.* **23**, 325.

215. KLIGLER, I. J., and OLITZKI, L. (1936) The antigenic composition of *Trypanosoma evansi. Ann. Trop. Med. Parasit.* **30**, 287.

216. KRASCHENINNIKOW, S., and TIESLER, E. (1959) Simple methods for purifying *Balantidia. J. Protozool.* **6**, 309.

217. KRASSNER, S. M. (1965) Effect of temperature on growth and nutritional requirements of *Leishmania tarentolae* in a defined medium. *J. Protozool.* **12**, 73.

218. KRIJGSMAN, B. J. (1936) Vergleichend physiologische Untersuchungen über den Stoffwechsel von *Trypanosoma evansi* im Zusammenhang mit der Anpassung an das Wirtstier. *Z. Vergl. Physiologie* **23**, 663.

219. KRUATRACHUE, M., CHAROENLARP, P., CHONGSUPHAJAISIDDHI, T., and HARINASUTA, C. (1962) Erythrocyte glucose-6-phosphate dehydrogenase and malaria in Thailand. *Lancet*, ii, 1183.

220. KUDICKE, R., and EVERS, E. (1924) Über den Einfluß von Zuckerarten und Alkoholen der Zuckerreihe auf die Beweglichkeit der Trypanosomen *in vitro*. *Ztschr. Hyg. Infekt. Krankh.* **101**, 317.

221. KUN, E., BRADIN, J. L., and DECHARY, J. M. (1955) Effect of metabolic inhibitors on production of CO_2 and H_2S by *Endamoeba histolytica*. *Proc. Soc. Exp. Biol. (N.Y.)* **89**, 604.

222. KUN, E., BRADIN, J. L., and DECHARY, J. M. (1956) Correlation between CO_2 and H_2 production by *Endamoeba histolytica*. *Biochim. Biophys. Acta* **19**, 153.

223. KUNITAKE, G., STITT, C., and SALTMAN, P. (1962) Terminal respiration in *Trichomonas vaginalis*. *J. Protozool.* **9**, 371.

224. KUPFERBERG, A. B., JOHNSON, G., and SPRINCE, H. (1948) Nutritional requirements of *Trichomonas vaginalis*. *Proc. Soc. Exp. Biol. (Med.)* **67**, 304.

225. KUPFERBERG, A. B., SINGHER, H. O., LAMPSON, G., LEVY, L., and ROMANO, A. H. (1953–4) Studies on the metabolism of *Trichomonas vaginalis*. *Ann. N.Y. Acad. Sci.* **56**, 1006.

226. KUVIN, S. F., BEY, H. K., STOHLMAN, F. JR., CONTACOS, P. G., and COATNEY, G. R. (1962) Clinical and physiological responses in sporozoite-induced B strain *Plasmodium cynomolgi* and *Plasmodium vivax* infections in normal volunteers. *Trans. Roy. Soc. Trop. Med. Hyg.* **56**, 371.

227. LASER, H. (1948) Haemolytic system in the blood of malaria-infected monkeys. *Nature, Lond.* **161**, 560.

228. LASER, H., and FRIEDMANN, E. (1945) Crystalline haemolytic substance from normal blood. *Nature, Lond.* **156**, 507.

229. LATOUR, N. G., and REEVES, R. E. (1965) An iron requirement for growth of *Entamoeba histolytica* in culture, and the antiamebal activity of *Entamoeba histolytica* in culture, and the antiamebal activity of 7-iodo-8-hydroxy-quinoline-5-sulfonic acid. *Exptl. Parasitol.* **17**, 203.

230. LATOUR, N. G., REEVES, R. E., and GUIDRY, M. A. (1965) Steroid requirements of *Entamoeba histolytica*. *Exptl. Parasitol.* **16**, 18.

231. LEHMANN, D. L. (1965) Enzyme content and its possible relation to infectivity of African trypanosomes. *Trans. Roy. Soc. Trop. Med. Hyg.* **59**, 297.

232. LEVINE, N. D., and MARQUARDT, W. C. (1955) The effect of glycerol and related compounds on survival of *Tritrichomonas foetus* at freezing temperatures. *J. Protozool.* **2**, 100.

233. LEWERT, R. M. (1952a) Nucleic acids in Plasmodia and the phosphorus partition of cells infected with *Plasmodium gallinaceum*. *J. Infect. Dis.* **91**, 125.

234. LEWERT, R. M. (1952b) Changes in nucleic acids and protein in nucleated erythrocytes infected with *Plasmodium gallinaceum* as shown by ultraviolet absorption measures. *J. Infect. Dis.* **91**, 180.

235. LINDBLOM, G. P. (1961) Carbohydrate metabolism of trichomonads: Growth, respiration and enzyme activity in four species. *J. Protozool.* **8**, 139.

236. LINDGREN, R. D., and IVEY, M. H. (1964) The effect of cultivation and freezing on the virulence of *Trichomonas vaginalis* for mice. *J. Parasitol.* **50**, 226.

237. LINTON, R. W. (1930a) The blood chemistry of an acute trypanosome infection. *J. Exptl. Med.* **52**, 103.

238. LINTON, R. W. (1930b) A comparison of the chemical alteration in the blood of rats infected with pathogenic and non-pathogenic trypanosomes. *J. Exptl. Med.* **52**, 695.

239. LIPPI, M., and SEBASTIANI, A. (1958) Attivita glutamicaossalacetica e glutammico-pyruvica del siero nella tripanosomiasi sperimentale della cavia da *Trypanosoma brucei*. *Archivio italiano di scienze mediche tropicale e di parassitologia* **39**, 145.

240. LUBYANETSKII, S. A. (1960) Toxins of sarcosporidia. From *Vet. Bull.* 1962, **32**, No. 3, Abstract 754.
241. LUMSDEN, W. H. R. (1964) Changing patterns of trypanosomiasis research in East Africa. *Trans. Roy. Soc. Trop. Med. Hyg.* **58**, 97.
242. LUND, P. G., and SHORB, M. S. (1962) Steroid requirements of *Trichomonads. J. Protozool.* **9**, 151.
243. LUNDE, M. N., and JACOBS, L. (1959) Characteristics of the toxoplasma haemagglutination test antigen. *J. Immunol.* **82**, 146.
244. LUNDE, M. N., and JACOBS, L. (1962) Toxicity of Toxoplasma Lysates on intravenous injection into rabbits. *J. Parasitology* **48**, No. 2, Section 2, 37.
245. LUNDE, M. N., and JACOBS, L. (1964) Properties of Toxoplasma lysates toxic to rabbits on intravenous injection. *J. Parasitol.* **50**, 49.
246. LWOFF, M. (1938) Physiologie Microbienne—L'hématine et l'acide ascorbique, facteurs de croissance pour le Flagellé *Schizotrypanum cruzi. Compt. Rend. Acad. Sci.* **206**, 540.
247. LWOFF, M. (1951) The nutrition of parasitic flagellates. In *Biochemistry and Physiology of Protozoa*, ed. A. LWOFF. Acad Press, Inc., New York.
248. LYCKE, E., LUND, E., and STANNEGARD, O. (1965) Enhancement by lysozyme and hyaluronidase of the penetration by *Toxoplasma gondii* into cultured host cells. *Brit. J. Exp. Path.* **46**, 189.
249. LYSENKO, M. G. (1951) Concerning salicylate inhibition of ablastic activity in *Trypanosoma lewisi* infection. *J. Parasitol.* **37**, 535.
250. MAEGRAITH, B., GILLES, H. M., and DEVAKUL, K. (1957) Pathological process in *Babesia canis* infections. *Ztschr. Tropenmed. Parasit.* **8**, 485.
251. MAEGRAITH, B. G., RILEY, M. V., and DEEGAN, T. (1962) Changes in the metabolism of liver mitochondria of monkeys infected with *Plasmodium knowlesi* and their importance in the pathogenesis of malaria. *Ann. Trop. Med. Parasit.* **56**, 483.
252. MAIER, J., and COGGESHALL, L. T. (1941) Respiration of malaria plasmodia. *J. Infect. Dis.* **69**, 87.
253. MANCILLA, R., and NAQUIRA, C. (1964) Comparative metabolism of C^{14} glucose in two strains of *Trypanosoma cruzi. J. Protozool.* **11**, 509.
254. MANCILLA, R., MAQUIRA, C., and LANAS, C. (1965) Metabolism of glucose labelled with carbon-14 in *Leishmania enriettii. Nature Lond.* **206**, 27.
255. MANDEL, M., and HONIGBERG, B. M. (1964) Isolation and characterization of deoxyribonucleic acid, of two species of *Trichomonas* Donné. *J. Protozool.* **11**, 114.
256. MANNERS, D. J., and RYLEY, J. F. (1955) Studies on the metabolism of Protozoa. 6. The glycogens of the parasitic flagellates *Trichomonas foetus* and *Trichomonas gallinae. Biochem. J.* **59**, 369.
257. MANSOUR, T. E., BUEDING, E., and STAVITSKY, A. B. (1954) The effect of a specific antiserum on the activities of lactic dehydrogenase of mammalian muscle and of *Schistosoma mansoni. Brit. J. Pharmacol.* **9**, 182.
258. MANWELL, R. D., and BRODY, G. (1950) Survival and growth of four species of avian *Plasmodia* on the Harvard Culture Medium. *J. National Malaria Soc.* **9**, 132.
259. MARSHALL, E. K. (1946) Chemotherapy of malaria. 1941–5. *Fed. Proc.* **5**, 298.
260. MARSHALL, E. K., LITCHFIELD, J. T., and WHITE, H. J. (1942) Sulfonamide therapy of malaria in ducks. *J. Pharmac. Exp. Ther.* **75**, 89.
261. MARSHALL, P. B. (1948) The glucose metabolism of *Trypanosoma evansi* and the action of trypanocides. *Brit. J. Pharmacol.* **3**, 8.
262. MARTINS, J. M., DE ALENCAR, J. E., and MAGALHÃES, V. B. (1965) The anaemia of kala-azar. *Rev. Inst. Med. Trop. São Paulo* **7**, 47.
263. MASSEYEFF, R., and GOMBERT, J. (1963) Inhibition de la respiration de trypanosomes par le sérum de malades atteints de trypanosomiase Africaine à *T. gambiense. Ann. Inst. Pasteur* **104**, 115.

264. MAYER, M. (1940) Über morphologische Veränderung an Blutparasiten durch Einwirkung chemotherapeutischer Substanzen. Die Wirkung von Synthalin (Dekamethylene-Diguanid) auf Trypanosomen und Leishmanien. *Arquivos do Inst. Biol. Buenos Aires* 11, 229.

265. McENTEGART, M. G. (1954) The maintenance of stock strains of Trichomonads by freezing. *J. Hygiene* 52, 545.

266. McKEE, R. W. (1951) *Parasitic Infections in Man*, pp. 130–49. Ed. MOST, H. Colombia Univ. Press, New York.

267. McKEE, R. W., and GEIMAN, Q. M. (1947) Observations on the action of ascorbic acid in adrenal cortical function. *Fed. Proc.* 6, 276.

268. McKEE, R. W., and GEIMAN, Q. M. (1948) Methionine in the growth of the malarial parasite, *Plasmodium knowlesi*. *Fed. Proc.* 7, 172.

269. McKEE, R. W., ORMSBEE, R. A., ANFINSEN, C. B., GEIMAN, Q. M., and BALL, E. G. (1946) Studies on malarial parasites. VI. The chemistry and metabolism of normal and parasitized (*P. knowlesi*) monkey blood. *J. Exp. Med.* 84, 569.

270. MEAD, J. F., RAPPORT, M. M., SENEAR, A. E., MAYNARD, J. T., and KOEPFLI, J. B. (1946) The synthesis of potential antimalarials. Derivatives of pantoyltaurine. *J. Biol. Chem.* 163, 465.

271. MEHRA, K. N., LEVINE, N. D., and REBER, E. F. (1960) The amino acid composition of Trichomonad protozoa. *J. Protozool.* 7, Suppl. 12.

272. MELENEY, H. E., FRYE, W. W., LEATHERS, W. S., and SNYDER, T. L. (1940) The sterilization of the cysts of *Endamoeba histolytica*, with preliminary observations on subsequent excystation. *Proc. 3rd Internat. Congr. Microbiol.* p. 410.

273. MERCADO, T. I., and VON BRAND, T. (1957) The influence of some steroids on glycogenesis in the liver of rats infected with *Plasmodium berghei*. *Amer. J. Hyg.* 66, 20.

274. MICHAELS, R. M., and TREICK, R. W. (1962) The mode of action of certain 3- and 5-nitropyridines and pyrimidines. III. Biochemical lesions in *Trichomonas vaginalis*. *Exptl. Parasitol.* 12, 401.

275. MICHAELS, R. M., and TREICK, R. W. (1963) The mode of action of certain 3- and 5-nitropyridines and pyrimidines. IV. Development of drug resistance by *Trichomonas vaginalis*. *J. Protozool.* 10, 208.

276. MICHAELSON, J. B., DeLAMATER, J. N., and TALPIS, L. (1953) Comparison of starches used in the culture of *Endamoeba histolytica*. *Amer. J. Trop. Med. Hyg.* 2, 219.

277. MIGNANI, E., and BICKEL, J. (1961) Studi sulla biologia di *E. histolytica*. V. Osservazioni sull' attività enzimatica di stipiti di *E. histolytica* in coltura. *Riv. Parasit.* 22, 157.

278. MORACZEWSKI, S. A., and KELSEY, F. E. (1948) Distribution and rate of metabolism of phosphorus compounds in *Trypanosoma equiperdum*. *J. Infect. Dis.* 82, 45.

279. MORGAN, B. B. (1946) *Bovine Trichomoniasis*. Burgess Publishing Co. Minneapolis. Minnesota.

280. MORRISON, D. B., and JESKEY, H. A. (1947) The pigment, lipids and proteins of the malaria parasite (*P. knowlesi*). *Fed. Proc.* 6, 279.

281. MORRISON, D. B., and JESKEY, H. A. (1948) Alterations in some constituents of monkey erythrocyte infected with *Plasmodium knowlesi* as related to pigment formation. *J. Nat. Malaria Soc.* 7, 259.

282. MORTON, I. D., and TODD, A. R. (1950) The haemolytic acid present in horse brain. I. Purification and identification as *cis*-octadec-11-enoic acid. *Biochem. J.* 47, 327.

283. MOST, H., ALGER, N., and YOELI, M. (1964) Preservation of *Leishmania donovani* by low temperature freezing. *Nature, Lond.* 201, 735.

284. MOST, H., and LAVIETES, P. H. (1947) Kala azar in military personnel. Report of 30 cases. *Medicine* 26, 221.

285. MOTULSKY, A. G. (1964) Cultivation of plasmodia and immunology of malaria. *Amer. J. Trop. Med. Hyg.* 13, 145.

286. MOULDER, J. W. (1948a) The oxidative metabolism of *Trypanosoma lewisi* in a phosphate saline medium. *J. Infect. Dis.* **83**, 33.
287. MOULDER, J. W. (1948b) Changes in the glucose metabolism of *Trypanosoma lewisi* during the course of infection in the rat. *J. Infect. Dis.* **83**, 42.
288. MOULDER, J. W. (1962) *The Biochemistry of Intracellular* Parasitism. Univ. of Chicago Press.
289. MOULDER, J. W., and EVANS, E. A. (1946) The biochemistry of the malaria parasite. VI. Studies on the nitrogen metabolism of the malaria parasite. *J. Biol. Chem.* **164**, 145.
290. MÜHLPFORDT, H. (1951) Das Verhalten Sarcosporidieninfizierter Tiere im Sero-Farbtest auf Toxoplasmose nach Sabin-Feldman *Z. Tropenmed. Parasit.* **3**, 205.
291. NAKAMURA, M. (1952) Substitution of an enzyme preparation for *Trypanosoma cruzi* in cultures of *Endamoeba histolytica. Kitasato Arch. Exp. Med.* **25**, 43.
292. NAKAMURA, M. (1955) Growth factors for *Entamoeba histolytica. Proc. Soc. Exp. Biol. (Med.)* **89**, 680.
293. NAKAMURA, M. (1961) Effect of antimetabolites on the growth of *Entamoeba histolytica.* IV. Folic acid analogues. *Exp. Cell Res.* **25**, 648.
294. NAKAMURA, M., and ANDERSON, H. H. (1951) Effect of heat-treatment on the respiration of *Trypanosoma cruzi* used for the cultivation of *Entamoeba histolytica. Amer. J. Trop. Med.* **31**, 438.
295. NAKAMURA, M., and BAKER, E. E. (1956) Nutritional requirements of *Endameoba histolytica. Amer. J. Hyg.* **64**, 12.
296. NAKAMURA, M., and EDWARDS, P. R. (1959a) Enzymes of *Entamoeba histolytica.* I. Gelatinase. *Proc. Soc. Exp. Biol. (Med.)* **100**, 403.
297. NAKAMURA, M., and EDWARDS, P. R. (1959b) Casease in *Entamoeba histolytica. Nature, Lond.* **183**, 397.
298. NAKAMURA, M., and JONSSON, S. (1957) The effect of antimetabolites on the growth of *Endamoeba histolytica.* I. Purine and pyrimidine analogs. *Arch. Biochem. Biophys.* **66**, 183.
299. NAUSS, R. W., and YORKE, W. (1911) Reducing action of trypanosomes on haemoglobin. *Ann. Trop. Med. Parasit.* **5**, 199.
300. NEAL, R. A. (1960) Enzymic proteolysis by *Entamoeba histolytica;* biochemical characteristics and relationship with invasiveness. *Parasitology* **50**, 531.
301. NEAL, R. A. (1965) Influence of encystation on invasiveness of *Entamoeba histolytica. Exper. Parasitol.* **16**, 369.
302. NELSON, E. C. (1947) Alcoholic extract medium for the diagnosis and cultivation of *Endamoeba histolytica. Amer. J. Trop. Med.* **27**, 545.
303. NELSON, E. C., and JONES, M. M. (1964) Cultivation of *Entamoeba histolytica* in carbon dioxide–bicarbonate buffer system media. *Amer. J. Trop. Med. Hyg.* **13**, 667.
304. NINOMYIA, H., and SUZUOKI, Z. (1952) The metabolism of *Trichomonas vaginalis* with comparative aspects of Trichomonads. *J. Biochem. Tokyo* **39**, 321.
305. NYDEGGER, L., and MANWELL, R. D. (1962) Cultivation requirements of the avian malaria parasite *Plasmodium hexamerium. J. Parasitology* **48**, 142.
306. OLBERG, H. (1955) Die papierchromatographische Analyse von Mäusen-Seren *Naturwissenschaften* **42**, 211.
307. PAN, C. T. (1960) Studies on the monoxenic cultivation of *Entamoeba histolytica* with hemoflagellates. *J. Infect. Dis.* **106**, 284.
308. PANDE, P. G., SHUKLA, R. R., and SEKARIAH, P. C. (1961) A heteroglycan from *Toxoplasma gondii. Nature, Lond.* **190**, 644.
309. PASSMORE, R., and SOMMERVILLE, T. (1940) An investigation of the effect of diet on the course of experimental malaria in monkeys. *J. Malaria Inst. of India* **3**, 447.
310. PETERS, W. (1964) Pigment formation and nuclear division in chloroquine-resistant malaria parasites (*Plasmodium berghei* Vincke & Lips (1948) *Nature, Lond.* **203**, 1290.

311. PETERS, W., FLETCHER, K. A., and STÄUBLI, W. (1965) Phagotrophy and pigment formation in a chloroquine-resistant strain of *Plasmodium berghei* Vincke & Lips (1948). *Ann. Trop. Med. Parasit.* **59**, 126.

312. PHILLIPS, B. P. (1950) Cultivation of *Endamoeba histolytica* with *Trypanosoma cruzi*. *Science* **111**, 8.

313. PHILLIPS, B. P. (1951) Comparative effects of certain species of trypanosomidae on the growth of *Endamoeba histolytica* in the absence of bacteria. *Amer. J. Trop. Med.* **31**, 290.

314. PHILLIPS, B. P. (1953) The effects of various treatment procedures on the metabolism of *Trypanosoma cruzi* and on its ability to support growth of *Endamoeba histolytica*. *Amer. J, Trop. Med. Hyg.* **2**, 47.

315. PHILLIPS, B. P. (1962) Further studies with ameba-trypanosome cultures. *Amer. J. Trop. Med. Hyg.* **11**, 6.

316. PHILLIPS, B. P. (1964) Studies on the ameba-bacteria relationship in amebiasis. III. Induced amebic lesions in the germ-free guinea-pig. *Amer. J. Trop. Med. Hyg.* **14**, 391.

317. PHILLIPS, B. P., WOLFE, P. A., REES, C. W., GORDON, H. A., WRIGHT, W. H., and REYNIERS, J. A. (1955) Studies on the ameba-bacteria relationship in amebiasis. Comparative results of the intracecal inoculation of germ free, monocontaminated and conventional guinea pigs with *Entamoeba histolytica*. *Amer. J. Trop. Med. Hyg.* **4**, 675.

318. PIPKIN, A. C. (1960) Avian embryos and tissue culture in the study of parasitic protozoa. II. Protozoa other than Plasmodium. *Expt. Parasitol.* **9**, 167.

319. PIPKIN, A. C., and JENSEN, D. V. (1958) Avian embryos and tissue culture in the study of parasitic protozoa. I. Malarial parasites. *Exptl. Parasitol.* **7**, 491.

320. POWELL, R. D., and BREWER, G. J. (1965) Glucose-6-phosphate-dehydrogenase deficiency and falciparum malaria. *Amer. J. Trop. Med. Hyg.* **14**, 358.

321. RAY, H. N, and SEN GUPTA, P. C. (1954) A cytochemical study of *Entamoeba histolytica.*- *J. Indian Med. Ass.* **23**, 529.

322. READ, C. P. (1957) Comparative studies on the physiology of Trichomonad Protozoa. *J. Parasitol.* **43**, 385.

323. REES, C. W. (1942) The construction of a micromanipulator for the isolation of protozoa. *Amer. J. Trop. Med.* **22**, 487.

324. REES, C. W., BAERNSTEIN, H. D., REARDON, L. V., and PHILLIPS, L. (1953) Some interactions *in vitro* of *Endamoeba histolytica* and single species of microbial symbionts *Amer. J. Trop. Med. Hyg.* **2**, 1002.

325. REES, C. W. REARDON, L. V. and BARTGIS, I. L. (1950) The excystation of *Entamoeba histolytica* without bacteria in microcultures. *Parasitology* **40**, 338.

326. REEVES, R. E., MELENEY, H. E., and FRYE, W. W. (1957a) Bacteria-free cultures of *Entamoeba histolytica* with chick embryo tissue juice. *Z. Tropenmed. Parasit.* **8**, 213.

327. REEVES, R. E., MELENEY, H. E., and FRYE, W. W. (1957b) A modified Shaffer-Frye technique for the cultivation of *Entamoeba histolytica* and some observations on its carbohydrate requirements. *Amer. J. Hyg.* **66**, 56.

328. REEVES, R. E., and WARD, A. B. (1965) Large lot cultivation of *Entamoeba histolytica*. *J. Parasitology* **51**, 321.

329. REINER, L., SMYTHE, C. V., and PEDLOW, J. T. (1936) On the glucose metabolism of trypanosomes. *J. Biol. Chem.* **113**, 75.

330. REY, L., and FERNANDES, J. F. (1962) Nucleotide and polynucleotide synthesis in *Trypanosoma cruzi*. VII. Precursors of the pyrimidine nucleotides. *Exptl. Parasitol.* **12**, 55.

331. RIEDMÜLLER, L. (1936) Beitrag zum kulturellen Verhalten von *Trichomonas foetus* *Zent. Bakt.*, Abt. 1, Orig. **137**, 428.

332. RILEY, M. V., and DEEGAN, T. (1960) The effect of *Plasmodium berghei* malaria on mouse-liver mitochondria. *Biochem. J.* **76**, 41.

333. RILEY, M. V., and MAEGRAITH, B. G. (1961) A factor in the serum of malaria-infected animals capable of inhibiting the *in vitro* oxidative metabolism of normal liver mitochondria. *Ann. Trop. Med. Parasit.* **55**, 489.

334. RILEY, M. V., and MAIGRAITH, B. G. (1962) Changes in the metabolism of liver mito-chondria of mice infected with rapid acute *Plasmodium berghei* malaria. *Ann. Trop. Med. Parasit.* **56**, 473.

335. RIMINGTON, C., and FULTON, J. D. (1947) The pigment of the malarial parasites *Plasmodium knowlesi* and *Plasmodium gallinaceum*. *Biochem. J.* **41**, 619.

336. RITTERSON, A. L., and STAUBER, L. A. (1949) Protein intake and Leishmaniasis in the hamster. *Proc. Soc. Exp. Biol. Med.* **70**, 47.

337. ROBERTSON, D. H. H., and JENKINS, A. R. (1959) Hepatic dysfunction in human trypanosomiasis. I. Abnormalities of excretory function, seroflocculation phenomena and other tests of hepatic function with observations on the alterations of these tests during treatment and convalescence. *Trans. Roy. Soc. Trop. Med. Hyg.* **53**, 511.

338. ROOS, A., HEGSTED, D. M., and STARE, F. J. (1946) Nutritional studies with the duck. IV. The effect of vitamin deficiencies on the course of *P. lophurae* infection in the duck and the chick. *J. Nutrition* **32**, 473.

339. ROSSAN, R. N. (1960) Serum proteins of animals infected with *Leishmania donovani*, with special reference to electrophoretic patterns. *Exptl. Parasitol.* **9**, 302.

340. RUDZINSKA, M. A., and TRAGER, W. (1957) Intracellular phagotrophy by malaria parasites: an electron microscope study of *Plasmodium lophurae*. *J. Protozool.* **4**, 190.

341. RUDZINSKA, M. A., and TRAGER, W. (1959) Phagotrophy and two new structures in the malaria parasite *Plasmodium berghei*. *J. Biophys. Biochem. Cytol.* **6**, 103.

342. RUDZINSKA, M. A., and TRAGER, W. (1962) Intracellular phagotrophy in *Babesia rodhaini* as revealed by electron microscopy. *J. Protozool.* **9**, 279.

343. RYLEY, J. F. (1951) Metabolism of the parasitic flagellate *Trypanosoma lewisi*. *Biochem. J.* **49**, 577.

344. RYLEY, J. F. (1955) Studies on the metabolism of the Protozoa. 5. Metabolism of the parasitic flagellate, *Trichomonas foetus*. *Biochem. J.* **59**, 361.

345. RYLEY, J. F. (1956) Studies on the metabolism of the Protozoa. 7. Comparative carbohydrate metabolism of eleven species of trypanosome. *Biochem. J.* **62**, 215.

346. RYLEY, J. F. (1962) Studies on the metabolism of the Protozoa. 9. Comparative metabolism of blood stream and culture forms of *Trypanosoma rhodesiense*. *Biochem. J.* **85**, 211.

347. SALLE, A. J. (1931) The metabolism of protozoa. III. The metabolism of *Leishmania donovani*. *J. Infect. Dis.* **49**, 481.

348. SALLE, A. J., and SCHMIDT, C. L. A. (1928) The metabolism of *Leishmania tropica*. *J. Infect. Dis.* **43**, 378.

349. SANDERS, M. (1957) Replacement of serum for *in vitro* cultivation of *Trichomonas foetus*. *J. Protozool.* **4**, 118.

350. SANTHANAGOPALAN, T., VERMA, N. P. S., CHATTERJEE, A. K., and PAL, S. K. (1964) Electrophoretic patterns of serum proteins in amoebic liver disease. *Indian. J. Path. Bact.* **7**, 102–6.

351. SATO, S. (1926) On the toxic action of Sarcosporidiotoxin and its serological study. *Japan Med. World* **6**, 62. [*Tropical Diseases Bulletin* 1927, **24**, 399].

352. SCHEFF, G., and RABATI, F. (1938) Über die Einwirkung von Dinitrophenol auf den Energieumsatz und Sauerstoffverbrauch normaler und infizierter Mäuse. *Biochem. Ztschr.* **298**, 101.

353. SCHUELER, F. W. (1947) The mechanism of drug resistance in trypanosomes. II. A method for the differential staining of normal and drug-resistant trypanosomes and its possible relation to the mechanics of drug resistance. *J. Infect. Dis.* **81**, 139.

354. SCHUELER, F. W., and CANTRELL, W. F. (1964) Antagonism of the antimalarial action of chloroquine by ferrihemate and an hypothesis of the mechanism of chloroquine resistance. *J. Pharmac Exp. Ther.* **143**, 278.

355. SCHUMAKER, E. (1931) The cultivation of *Balantidium coli. Amer. J. Hyg.* **13**, 281.

356. SEARLE, D. S., and REINER, L. (1941) The role of carbon dioxide in the glucose metabolism of *T. lewisi. J. Biol. Chem.* **141**, 563.

357. SEED, J. R., BAQUERO, M. A., and DUDA, J. F. (1965) Inhibition of hexose and glycerol utilization by 2-deoxy-d-glucose in *Trypanosoma gambiense* and *Trypanosoma rhodesiense. Exptl. Parasitol.* **16**, 363.

358. SEELER, A. O., and OTT, W. H. (1944) Effect of riboflavin deficiency on the course of *Plasmodium lophurae* infection in chicks. *J. Infect. Dis.* **75**, 175.

359. SEELER, A. O., and OTT, W. H. (1945) Studies on nutrition and avian malaria. III. Deficiency of "folic acid" and other unidentified factors. *J. Infect. Dis.* **77**, 82.

360. SEELER, A. O., and OTT, W. H. (1946) Effect of deficiencies in vitamins and in protein on avian malaria. *J. Nat. Malaria Soc. Tennessee* **5**, 123. (*Tropical Diseases Bulletin* 1947 **44**, 185).

361. SENEKJIE, H. A. (1941) On the polysaccharide of *Leishmania tropica. Amer. J. Hyg.* **34**, 63.

362. SENEKJIE, H. A., and LEWIS, R. A. (1945) An enquiry into the growth factors of certain blood and tissue flagellates. *Amer. J. Trop. Med.* **25**, 345.

363. SHAFFER, J. G., and IRALU, V. (1963) The selective ability of strains of *Entamoeba histolytica* to hemolyse red blood cells. *Amer. J. Trop. Med. Hyg.* **12**, 315.

364. SHAFFER, J. G., and SIENKIEWICZ, H. S. (1952) Propagation of a strain of *Endamoeba histolytica* in tissue-bearing culture. *Science* **116**, 306.

365. SHAFFER, J. G., SIENKIEWICZ, H. S., and WASHINGTON, J. E. (1953) The propagation of *Endamoeba histolytica* in tissue bearing culture without accompanying bacteria or other microorganisms. *Amer. J. Hyg.* **57**, 366.

366. SHAFFER, J. G., WALTON, J. G., and FRYE, W. W. (1948) Studies on the growth requirements of *Endamoeba histolytica*. II. Preliminary observations on the cultivation of *E. histolytica* in a modified thioglycollate medium. *Amer. J. Hyg.* **47**, 222.

367. SHAKIR, M. H., SAIF, M., and ABDEL-FATTAH, F. (1964) The serum cholinesterase levels in amoebiasis. *J. Egyptian Med. Ass.* **47**, 307.

368. SHANNON, J. A., EARLE, D. P., BRODIE, B. B., TAGGART, J. V., and BERLINER, R. W. (1944) The pharmacological basis for the rational use of atabrine in the treatment of malaria. *J. Pharmac. Exp. Ther.* **81**, 307.

369. SHARMA, R. (1959) Effect of cholesterol on the growth and virulence of *Entamoeba histolytica. Trans. Roy. Soc. Trop. Med. Hyg.* **53**, 278.

370. SHAW, J. J., VOLLER, A., and BRYANT, C. (1964) Intermediary carbohydrate metabolism of four species of Trypanosomatidae. *Ann. Trop. Med. Parasit.* **58**, 17.

371. SHERMAN, I. W. (1961) Molecular heterogeneity of lactic dehydrogenase in avian malaria. (*Plasmodium lophurae). J. Exptl. Med.* **114**, 1049.

372. SHERMAN, I. W. (1965) Glucose-6-phosphate dehydrogenase and reduced glutathione in malaria-infected erythrocytes. (*Plasmodium lophurae* and *P. berghei). J. Protozool.* **12**, 394.

373. SHERMAN, I. W., and HULL, R. W. (1960a) The pigment (hemozoin) and proteins of the avian malaria parasite *Plasmodium lophurae. J. Protozool.* **7**, 409.

374. SHERMAN, I. W., and HULL, R. W. (1960b) Observations on the host haemoglobin during *Plasmodium lophurae* infections in chicks. *J. Parasitology* **46**, 765.

375. SHORB, M. S. (1963) The lipid composition of *Tetrahymena pyriformis* and *Trichomonas gallinae. Progress in Protozoology*, p. 153. Ed. Academic Press. New York and London.

376. SHORB, M. S. (1964) The physiology of Trichomonads. *Biochemistry* and *Physiology of Protozoa*, p. 384. Ed. S. H. HUTNER, Academic Press, New York and London.

377. SHORB, M. S., and LUND, P. G. (1959) Requirements of Trichomonads for unidentified growth factors, saturated and unsaturated fatty acids. *J. Protozool.* **6,** 122.

378. SIDDIQUI, W. A. (1963) Comparative studies of effect of temperature on three species of Entamoeba. *J. Protozool.* **10,** 480.

379. SILVA, L. H. P., YONEDA, S., and FERNANDES, J. F. (1959) Nucleotide and polynucleotide synthesis in Trypanosoma cruzi. III. Effect of the aminonucleoside of Stylomycin on the parasite in tissue culture. *Exptl. Parasitol.* **8,** 486.

380. SILVERMAN, M., CEITHAML, J., TALIAFERRO, L. G., and EVANS, E. A. (1944) In vitro metabolism of Plasmodium gallinaceum. *J. Infect Dis.* **75,** 212.

381. SINTON, J. A., and GHOSH, B. N. (1934a) Studies of malarial pigment (haemozoin). Part I. Investigation of the action of solvents on haemozoin and the spectroscopical appearances observed in the solutions. *Rec. Malar. Survey India* **4,** 15.

382. SINTON, J. A., and GHOSH, B. N. (1934b) Studies of malarial pigment (haemozoin). Part III. Further researches into the action of solvents, and the results of observations on the action of oxidising and reducing agents on optical properties, and on crystallisation. *Rec. Malar. Survey India* **4,** 205.

383. SKIRROW, M. B., MAEGRAITH, B. G., and CHONGSUPHAJAISIDDHI, T. (1964a) The circulation in malaria. I. Portal angiography in the normal rabbit and monkey (*Macaca mulatta*). *Ann. Trop. Med. Parasit.* **58,** 491.

384. SKIRROW, M. B., CHONGSUPHAJAISIDDHI, T., and MAEGRAITH, B. G. (1964b) II. Portal angiography in monkeys (*Macaca mulatta*) infected with Plasmodium knowlesi and in shock following manipulation of the gut. *Ann. Trop. Med. Parasit.* **58,** 502.

385. SKORCZYNSKI, M., GLOWIŃSKI, M., LIMAŃSKI, M., and KUCHARCZYK, W. (1962) Transaminaseaktivität im Blutserum toxoplasmoseverdächtiger Frauen. *Angewandte Parasit.* **3,** 46.

386. SKRABALO, Z., and DEANOVIC, Z. (1957) Piroplasmosis in man. *Doc. Med. Geograph. Trop.* **9,** 11.

387. SMITH, B. F., and HERRICK, C. A. (1944) The respiration of the protozoan parasite, Eimeria tenella. *J. Parasitology* **30,** 295.

388. SMITH, B. F., and MCSHAN, W. H. (1949) The effect of the protozoan parasite Eimeria stiedae on the succinic dehydrogenase activity of liver tissue of rabbits. *Ann. N.Y. Acad. Sci.* **52,** 496.

389. SMITH, B. F., and SPRIGGS, A. S. (1959) Chromatographic analysis of the free amino acids in Trichomonas vaginalis. *J. Protozool.* **6,** Suppl. 31.

390. SNYDER, T. L., and MELENEY, H. E. (1941) The excystation of Endamoeba histolytica in bacteriologically sterile media. *Amer. J. Trop. Med.* **21,** 63.

391. SNYDER, T. L., and MELENEY, H. E. (1943) Anaerobiosis and cholesterol as growth requirements of Endamoeba histolytica. *J. Parasitology* **29,** 278.

392. SOULE, M. H. (1925) Microbic respiration. III. The respiration of Trypanosoma lewisi and Leishmania tropica. *J. Infect. Dis.* **36,** 245.

393. SPANDORF, A., and MANWELL, R. D. (1960) In vitro growth of Plasmodium circumflexum and P. vaughani. *Exptl. Parasitol.* **10,** 287.

394. SPECK, J. F., and EVANS, E. A. (1945a) The biochemistry of the malaria parasite. II. Glycolysis in cell-free preparations of the malaria parasite. *J. Biol. Chem.* **159,** 71.

395. SPECK, J. F., and EVANS, E. A. (1945b) The biochemistry of the malarial parasite. III. The effects of quinine and atabrine on glycolysis. *J. Biol. Chem.* **159,** 83.

396. SPECK, J. F., MOULDER, J. W., and EVANS, E. A. (1946) The biochemistry of the malaria parasite. V. Mechanism of pyruvate oxidation in the malaria parasite. *J. Biol. Chem.* **164,** 119.

397. SPRINCE, H., GILMORE, E. L., and LOWY, R. S. (1949) An unidentified factor in pancreas, essential for the sustained growth of Trichomonas vaginalis. *Arch. Biochem.* **22,** 483.

398. SPRINCE, H., GOLDBERG, R., KUCKER, G., and LOWY, R. S. (1953–4) The effect of ribonucleic acid and its nitrogenous constituents on the growth of *Trichomonas vaginalis. Ann. N.Y. Acad. Sci.* **56**, 1016.

399. SPRINCE, H., and KUPFERBERG, A. B. (1947a) The nutrition of Protozoa. I. A simplified medium for the investigation of unknown factors in blood serum essential for the sustained growth of *Trichomonas vaginalis. J. Bact.* **53**, 435.

400. SPRINCE, H., and KUPFERBERG, A. B. (1947b) The nutrition of Protozoa. II. The separation of human blood serum into two fractions, both essential for the sustained growth of *Trichomonas vaginalis. J. Bact.* **53**, 441.

401. STABLER, R. M. (1954) *Trichomonas gallinae:* a Review. *Expt. Parasitol.* **3**, 368.

402. STAUBER, L. A., OCHS, J. Q., and COY, N. H. (1954) Electrophoretic patterns of the serum proteins of chinchillas and hamsters infected with *Leishmania donovani. Exptl. Parasitol.* **3**, 325.

403. STEIN, L., and WERTHEIMER, E. (1942) A new fraction of a cold susceptible protein in blood of dogs infected with kala-azar. *Ann. Trop. Med. Parasit.* **36**, 17.

404. STEPHEN, L. E., and GRAY, A. R. (1960) The trypanocidal activity of nucleosidin against *Trypanosoma vivax* in West African Zebu cattle. *J. Parasitology* **46**, 509.

405. STEWART, H. M. (1938) Glycogen content of a flagellate of cattle *Trichomonas foetus. Amer. J. Hyg.* **28**, 80.

406. SUZUOKI, Z., and SUZUOKI, T. (1951) Carbohydrate metabolism of *Trichomonas foetus. J. Biochem. Tokyo* **38**, 237.

407. SWENSON, P. A. (1960) The amino acid pool of *Trichomonas gallinae. J. Protozool.* **7**, Suppl. 26.

408. TELLA, H., and MAEGRAITH, B. G. (1965a) Physiopathological changes in primary acute blood-transmitted malaria and *Babesia* infections. I. Observations on parasites and blood-cells in rhesus monkeys, mice, rats and puppies. *Ann. Trop. Med. Parasit.* **59**, 135.

409. TELLA, H., and MAEGRAITH, B. G. (1965b) II. A comparative study of serum-protein levels in infected rhesus monkeys, mice and puppies. *Ann. Trop. Med. Parasit.* **59**, 153.

410. TEMPELIS, C. H., and LYSENKO, M. G. (1957) The production of hyaluronidase by *Balantidium coli. Exptl. Parasitol.* **6**, 31.

411. THOMPSON, J. G. (1924) Researches on blackwater fever in Southern Rhodesia. *Res. Mem. London School Hyg. Trop. Med.* No. 6, 1–149.

412. THOMPSON, P. E., BAYLES, A., OLSZEWSKI, B., and WAITZ, J. A. (1965) Quinine-resistant *Plasmodium berghei* in mice. *Science* **148**, 1240.

413. TOBIE, E. J., VON BRAND, T., MEHLMAN, B. (1950) Cultural and physiological observations on *Trypanosoma rhodesiense* and *Trypanosoma gambiense. J. Parasitology* **36**, 48.

414. TRAGER, W. (1941) Studies on conditions affecting the survival *in vitro* of a malarial parasite (*Plasmodium lophurae*). *J. Exptl. Med.* **74**, 441.

415. TRAGER, W. (1943) Further studies on the survival and development *in vitro* of a malarial parasite. *J. Exptl. Med.* **77**, 411.

416. TRAGER, W. (1947) The development of the malaria parasite *Plasmodium lophurae* in red blood cell suspensions *in vitro. J. Parasitology* **33**, 345.

417. TRAGER, W. (1950) Studies on the extracellular cultivation of an intracellular parasite (avian malaria). I. Development of the organisms in erythrocyte extracts, and the favouring effect of adenosinetriphosphate. *J. Exptl. Med.* **92**, 349.

418. TRAGER, W. (1952) Studies on the extracellular cultivation of an intracellular parasite (avian malaria). II. The effects of malate and of coenzyme A concentrates. *J. Exptl. Med.* **96**, 465.

419. TRAGER, W. (1953) The development of *Leishmania donovani* in vitro at 37°C. Effects of the kind of serum. *J. Exptl. Med.* **97**, 177.

420. TRAGER, W. (1954) Coenzyme A and the malarial parasite *Plasmodium lophurae*. *J. Protozool*. **1**, 231.
421. TRAGER, W. (1957) Nutrition of a haemoflagellate (*Leishmania tarentolae*), having an interchangeable requirement for choline or pyridoxal. *J. Protozool*. **4**, 269.
422. TRAGER, W. (1958) Folinic acid and non-dialyzable materials in the nutrition of malaria parasites. *J. Exptl. Med.*. **108**, 753.
423. TRAGER, W. (1959a) The enhanced folic and folinic acid contents of erythrocytes infected with malaria parasites. *Exptl. Parasitol*. **8**, 265.
424. TRAGER, W. (1959b) Development of *Trypanosoma vivax* to the infective stage in tsetse fly tissue culture. *Nature, Lond*. **184**, B.A. 30.
425. TRAGER, W. (1961) Effect of drugs on the folic and folinic acid contents of erythrocytes infected with malaria parasites. *Exptl. Parasitol*. **11**, 298.
426. TRUSSELL, R. E. (1939) Experimental and clinical *Trichomonas vaginitis*. *J. Iowa Med. Soc*. **30**, 66.
427. TRUSSELL, R. E., and JOHNSON, G. (1941) Physiology of pure cultures of *Trichomonas vaginalis*. III. Fermentation of carbohydrates and related compounds. *Proc. Soc. Exp. Biol. (Med.)* **47**, 176.
428. TRUSSELL, R. E., and PLASS, E. D. (1940) The pathogenicity and physiology of pure culture of *Trichomonas vaginalis*. *Amer. J. Obst. Gynaec*. **40**, 883.
429. VARELA, G., VAZQUEZ, A., and TORROELLA, J. (1956) Probable existencia de la dietil-amida del ácido D-lisergico en la infection par *Toxoplasma gondii*. *Rev. Inst. Salub. Enferm. Trop*. **16**, 29. (*Tropical Diseases Bulletin* 1957, vol. 54, 1359).
430. VELICK, S. F. (1942) The respiratory metabolism of the malaria parasite, *P. cathemerium*, during its developmental cycle. *Amer. J. Hyg*. **35**, 152.
431. VICKERMAN, K. (1962) The mechanism of cyclical development in trypanosomes of the *Trypanosoma brucei* sub-group: an hypothesis based on ultrastructural observations. *Trans. Roy. Soc. Trop. Med. Hyg*. **56**, 487.
432. VOLLER, A., SHAW, J. J., and BRYANT, C. (1963) The effect of two antimony drugs on the *in vitro* metabolism of radioactive glucose by culture forms of *Leishmania tropica* (Wright, 1903). *Ann. Trop. Med. and Parasit*. **57**, 404.
433. WARREN, L. G., and ALLEN, K. W. (1959) Glutamic decarboxylase and free amino acids in *Trichomonas gallinae*. *J. Protozool*. **6**, Suppl. 20.
434. WATKINS, W. M. (1953) The serological inactivation of the human blood-group substances by an enzyme preparation obtained from *Trichomonas foetus*. *Biochem. J*. **54**, xxxiii.
435. WATKINS, W. M., LARNITZ, M. L., and KABAT, E. A. (1962) Development of H activity by human blood-group B substance treated with coffee-bean α-galactosidase, *Nature, Lond*. **195**, 1204.
436. WATKINS, W. M., and MORGAN, W. T. (1954) Inactivation of the H receptors on human erythrocytes by an enzyme obtained from *Trichomonas foetus*. *Brit. J. Exptl. Path*. **35**, 181.
437. WEINMAN, D., and KLATCHKO, H. J. (1949–50) Description of toxin in Toxoplasmosis. *Yale J. Biol. Med*. **22**, 323.
438. WEINMAN, D., and MCALLISTER, J. (1947) Prolonged storage of human pathogenic protozoa with conservation of virulence. *Amer. J. Hyg*. **45**, 102.
439. WEISS, E. D., and BALL, G. H. (1947) Nutritional requirements of *Tritrichomonas foetus* with special reference to partially digested proteins. *Proc. Soc. Exp. Biol. (Med.)* **65**, 278.
440. WELLERSON, R., DOSCHER, G. E., and KUPFERBERG, A. B. (1959) Metabolic studies on *Trichomonas vaginalis*. *Ann. N.Y. Acad. Sci*. **83**, 253.
441. WELLERSON, R., DOSCHER, G. E., and KUPFERBERG, A. B. (1960) Carbon dioxide fixation in *Trichomonas vaginalis*. *Biochem. J*. **75**, 562.

442. WELLERSON, R., and KUPFERBERG, A. B. (1962) On glycolysis in *Trichomonas vaginalis. J. Protozool.* **9**, 418.

443. WENDEL, W. B. (1943) Respiratory and carbohydrate metabolism of malaria parasites (*Plasmodium knowlesi*). *J. Biol. Chem.* **148**, 21.

444. WENDEL, W. B. (1946) The influence of naphthoquinones upon the respiratory and carbohydrate metabolism of malarial parasites. *Fed. Proc.* **5**, 406.

445. WENDEL, W. B., and KIMBALL, S. (1942) Formation of lactic acid and pyruvic acid in blood containing *Plasmodium knowlesi. J. Biol. Chem.* **145**, 343.

446. WENRICH, D. H. (1947) The species of *Trichomonas* in man. *J. Parasitology* **33**, 177.

447. WHITFIELD, P. R. (1952) Nucleic acids in erythrocytic stages of a malaria parasite. *Nature, Lond.* **169**, 751.

448. WHITFIELD, P. R. (1953a) Studies on the nucleic acids of the malaria parasite, *Plasmodium berghei* (Vincke & Lips). *Aust. J. Biol. Sci.* **6**, 234.

449. WHITFIELD, P. R. (1953b) The uptake of radioactive phosphorus by erythrocytic stages of *Plasmodium berghei. Aust. J. Biol. Sci.* **6**, 591.

450. WILLEMS, R., MASSART, L., and PEETERS, G. (1942) Über den Kohlenhydratstoffwechsel von *Trichomonas heptica. Naturwissenschaften* **30**, 169.

451. WILLIAMSON, J. (1963) The chemical composition of trypanosomes. II. Cytoplasmic constitutents and drug resistance. *Exptl. Parasitol.* **13**, 348.

452. WILLIAMSON, J., and BROWN, K. N. (1964) The chemical composition of trypanosomes III. Antigenic composition of *Brucei* trypanosomes. *Exptl. Parasitol.* **15**, 44.

453. WILLIAMSON, J., and DESOWITZ, R. S. (1961) The chemical composition of trypanosomes. I. Protein, amino acid and sugar analysis. *Exptl. Parasitol.* **11**, 161.

454. WILLIAMSON, J., and ROLLO, I. M. (1952) Stimulating effect of amino acids on the survival at 37°C of *Trypanosoma rhodesiense* in a serum-free synthetic medium. *Nature, Lond.* **170**, 376.

455. WILSON, P. A. G., and FAIRBAIRN, D. (1961) Biochemistry of sporulation in oocysts of *Eimeria acervulina. J. Protozool.* **8**, 410.

456. WIRTSCHAFTER, S. K. (1954) Evidence for the existence of the enzymes hexokinase and aldolase in the protozoan parasite *Trichomonas vaginalis. J. Parasitology* **40**, 360.

457. WIRTSCHAFTER, S. K., and JAHN, T. L. (1956) The metabolism of *Trichomonas vaginalis.* The glycolytic pathway. *J. Protozool.* **3**, 83.

458. WIRTSCHAFTER, S. K., SALTMAN, P., and JAHN, T. L. (1956) The metabolism of *Trichomonas vaginalis.* The oxidative pathway. *J. Protozool.* **3**, 86.

459. WITTE, J. (1933) Bakterienfreie Züchtung von Trichomonaden aus dem Uterus des Rindes in einfachen Nährböden. *Zent. f. Bakt. I. Abt. Orig.* **128**, 188.

460. WOODWORTH, H. C., and WEINMAN, D. (1960) II. Studies on the toxin of toxoplasma (toxotoxin). *J. Infect. Dis.* **107**, 318.

461. WOTTON, R. M., and BECKER, D. A. (1963) The ingestion of particulate lipid containing a fluorochrome dye, acridine orange, by *Trypanosoma lewisi. Parasitology* **53**, 163.

462. WOTTON, R. M., and HALSEY, W. R. (1957) The ingestion of particulate fat from the blood by *Trypanosoma lewisi* and *Trypanosoma equiperdum. Parasitology* **47**, 427.

463. WRIGHT, C. I., and SABINE, J. C. (1944) The effect of atabrine on the oxygen consumption of tissues. *J. Biol. Chem.* **155**, 315.

464. WYSS, W., KRADOLFER, F., and MEIER, R. (1960) Lipophilic growth factors for *Trichomonas. Exptl. Parasitol.* **10**, 66.

465. YORKE, W. (1910) Auto-agglutination of red blood cells in Trypanosomiasis. *Proc. Roy. Soc. B* **83**, 238.

466. YORKE, W., ADAMS, A. R. D., and MURGATROYD, F. (1929) Studies in chemotherapy. A method for maintaining pathogenic trypanosomes alive *in vitro* at 37°C for 24 hours. *Ann. Trop. Med. Parasit.* **23**, 601.

467. ZAMAN, V. (1964) Studies of the immobilization reaction on the genus *Balantidium*. *Trans. Roy. Soc. Trop. Med. Hyg.* **58**, 255.
468. ZAMAN, V. (1965) The application of fluorescent antibody test to *Balantidium coli*. *Trans. Roy. Soc. Trop. Med. Hyg.* **59**, 80.
469. ZELEDÓN, R. (1960a) Comparative physiological studies on four species of hemoflagellates in culture. I. Endogenous respiration and respiration in the presence of glucose. *J. Protozool.* **7**, 146.
470. ZELEDÓN, R. (1960b) II. Effect of carbohydrates and related substances and some amino compounds on the respiration. *J. Parasitology* **46**, 541.
471. ZELEDÓN, R. (1960c) III. Effect of the Krebs' cycle intermediates on the respiration. *Rev. Biologia. Trop. San. José, Costa Rica* **8**, 25.
472. ZELEDÓN, R. (1960d) IV. Effect of metabolic inhibitors on the respiration. *Rev. Biologia. Trop. San. José, Costa Rica* **8**, 181.
473. ZELEDÓN, R. (1960e) Transaminases. *Rev. bras. Biol.* **20**, 409.
474. ZUCKERMAN, A. (1964) Autoimmunization and other types of indirect damage to host cells as factors in certain protozoan diseases. *Exptl. Parasitol.* **15**, 138.
475. ZWEIG, A., and SHAFFER, J. G. (1961) Studies on the growth requirements of *Entamoeba histolytica*. VII. Studies on the altered bacterial structures formed in the Shaffer-Frye and related media with a fluorochrome dye and lysozyme. *Amer. J. Trop. Med. Hyg.* **10**, 704.
476. ZWEMER, R. L., and CULBERTSON, J. T. (1939) The serum potassium level in *Trypanosoma equiperdum* infection in rats: the role of potassium in death from this infection. *Amer. J. Hyg.* **29**, Sec. C7.

IMMUNOLOGY OF PROTOZOAN INFECTIONS

WILLIAM H. TALIAFERRO

Division of Biological and Medical Research
Argonne National Laboratory
Argonne, Illinois

and

LESLIE A. STAUBER

Department of Zoology and Bureau of Biological Research
Rutgers University
New Brunswick, New Jersey

CONTENTS

IMMUNOLOGY OF PROTOZOAN INFECTIONS

Interest in all phases of immunology has greatly increased during the past quarter-century. Immunological literature bearing directly on the protozoa and that of potential interest to protozoologists are so extensive that they cannot be reviewed in the present chapter. Instead, an attempt will be made to present some of the newer concepts of antibodies and their formation and to outline some of the basic concepts of the cellular and humoral mechanisms involved in immunity that are or may be of use in studying the protozoa.

The immunological studies on infectious organisms obviously overlap the field of study that Lincicome[104] designates the chemical basis of parasitism. In fact, in 1929, when the structure of antigens and antibodies was still unknown, H. G. Wells[220] wrote: "Immunological reactions, the processes by which the living organism defends itself against the chemical attacks of its enemies and are so able to exist in an environment seething with such enemies, are chemical reactions." And now that we know the structure of certain innate factors, such as the hemoglobin molecules that protect against *Plasmodium falciparum*, and are rapidly learning the structure and much of the biochemical behavior of the antibodies, the titles "Immunology of Parasitic Infections" and "Chemical Basis of Parasitism" can be used almost interchangeably.

I. ANTIGEN-ANTIBODY MECHANISMS

Antibody-mediated mechanisms have generally been characterized as acquired and specific in contrast to innate and nonspecific mechanisms. That antibodies are acquired, however, may be in error. Indeed, the early theories of antibody formation have been questioned, as discussed by Talmage and Cann,[210] since the rise of microbial genetics and the general belief that the production of a protein is under rigid genetic control. Early theories postulated that the antigen not only produces the specific differentiation of the antibody-forming cell, but also becomes an integral part of the template that directs the sequence of the amino acids or the folding of the amino acid chain of the antibody. In 1955, Jerne[96] proposed his natural selection theory of antibody formation which in essence holds that the globulin molecules of an antibody-forming animal include molecular configurations capable of reacting with each antigen to which the animal can form an antibody. The presence of these varieties of gamma globulin molecules is supposed to be the result of natural selection in the development of each species. Next, Talmage[209] suggested that the replicating unit in antibody formation is the cell and not some subcellular particle. Later, in 1959, Burnet[28] developed the clonal theory which assumes that antibody-forming cells represent a heterogeneous population of cells that together have the capacity to form all of the antibodies that an individual is capable of forming. Antigen induces antibody formation by initiating the division of antibody-forming cells—possibly those having a surface structure complementary to the antigen: a clone of cells thus produced forms an antibody that acts specifically with the antigen. Talmage and Pearlman[212] described one model of the antibody response. Some scientists question the fundamental concept that the body can have genetic information to make all of the diverse antibodies that are possible, including some to "unnatural" compounds. These workers generally postulate that the antigen can produce heritable changes in DNA or less permanent changes in cytoplasmic RNA which result in a long-lasting or permanent ability to make a specifically reactive antibody. Before the selection process is discarded, however, it should be noted that evolution has encompassed many statistical miracles.

If Burnet's clonal theory of antibody formation proves to be true, antibody formation will have to be classed, in large measure, as an innate capacity to react to a wide range of antigens that has evolved following contact with specific antigens from parasites or other sources. Such a situation would be similar to the mutual adaptation of certain protozoa and the wood roach in which a specific hormone produced by the prothoracic glands of the infected roach initiates processes which are followed by sexual phenomena in the protozoa.[35] Even if antibodies are eventually shown to be innate, they should be separated from other innate factors because they react specifically and are *acquired* in the biochemical sense of being a new protein synthesized directly from the free amino acids of the amino acid pool. We shall, therefore, designate them or the immunity they provide as specific or acquired in contrast to nonspecific innate factors.

Antibodies arise after immunization by an antigen. They are generally distinguished in two ways. Based on the character of the secondary phase of the antigen–antibody reaction, they are called agglutinins, lysins, etc., or by placing the prefix, anti, before the antigen, they are called antiplasmodial antibodies, etc.

Antigens and antibodies have been discussed by Boyd,[22] Cushing and Campbell,[48] Raffel,[136] Talmage and Cann[210] and Humphrey and White.[87] The immunologically competent cell is considered by Wolstenholme and Knight.[228] Various references to immunochemical specificity are given by Boyd.[23] The book by Sherwood[150] is especially pertinent for those engaged in work on immune reactions against infectious organisms. Various immunological methods are described by Kabat and Mayer,[99] Campbell et al.[29] and Ackroyd.[1]

Host–parasite relationships may be roughly divided into three types according to increasing complexity. (1) The invertebrates and their parasites: neither host nor parasite form antibodies.[17] (2) Vertebrates that form antibodies and their parasites that do not. (3) Vertebrates with a tissue homograft or heterograft, in which the host cells and recipient cells are capable of specific antibody formation and delayed hypersensitivity. In this last situation, the host may reject the graft (homograft rejection) or the graft may reject the host (wasting disease and ultimate death of the host). According to most investigators in the field of transplantation immunity, homograft rejection is in large part closely related to—if not identical with—immunologically specific hypersensitivity, which is classically associated with tuberculosis and other infections. Hypersensitivity to tuberculosis cannot be passively transferred with serum antibody, but can be passively transferred with cells (adoptive transfer), especially lymphocytes, as described in Section II.

Antibodies add specificity to the defense mechanisms. They are particularly valuable in removing various protein antigens. They stimulate phagocytosis, aid in the encapsulation of living and dead antigens by localizing antigens, and neutralize exo- and endotoxins. Large numbers of potential antigens exist in the form of enzymatic proteins involved in each cellular chemical reaction. Potential antigens also include "native" proteins, such as structural elements and food stuffs. In addition, one antigen may induce antibodies of presumably identical specificity that vary in their physical properties. This statement will be amplified later in discussing Table 1.

Typically, the antigen–antibody reaction takes place in two steps: the primary invisible rapid union of antigen and antibody and the secondary visible stage, such as precipitation, phagocytosis or lysis. The variable secondary stage for precipitation and agglutination is dependent upon certain physical factors, such as salt and pH concentration in the diluent, and for lysis and phagocytosis after opsonization is dependent upon cooperative factors, such as complement. In certain cases, the same antibody can be set up to give different secondary reactions. Methods pertaining to antibody–antigen reactions are described by Boyd,[22] Campbell et al.,[29] and Heidelberger and Plescia.[78]

As the initial stage of every antibody-mediated antiparasitic activity presupposes an initial union of antigen and antibody, the surface antigens of unicellular parasites are usually considered to be the chief functional ones. Indeed the beginning of such reactions as opsonization, agglutination, immune adherence, and lysis is frequently pictured as the deposition of a layer of antibody on the surface of the cell as a result of the reaction between surface antigens and antibodies (see especially Refs. 76, 143). It is, however, entirely possible that antibody may be taken into the cell through various organelles or with food.

The injurious nature of antigen–antibody reactions under certain conditions has been stressed in various fields. Many animals die just after an intense number crisis in malaria.[194, 200] Somewhat similarly, various pathological conditions are associated with antigen–antibody complexes.[57, 70, 232]

A. Characterization of Antibodies

The induction of antibody occurs and the antibody-synthesizing mechanism is developed during the latent period, i.e., the time after antigen is received until the time antibody appears in the serum. Thereafter, amino acids are incorporated extremely rapidly into the new antibody protein. Synthesis of antibody is biochemically a *de novo* process from the amino acids of the free amino acid pool. Of considerable importance is the absence during the latent period of long-lived amino acid-containing precursors that later are incorporated into antibody (Taliaferro and Talmage,[208] Taliaferro and Taliaferro[202]). The amount of antibody in the serum at any specified time is the result of two opposing processes, i.e., the synthesis of antibody from the free amino acid pool and the degradation of antibody into its constituent amino acids. The rate of metabolic decay may vary according to species, electrophoretic mobility, and age.[58, 181] The antibody molecule itself, however, is stable in the sense that as long as it retains its immunological characteristics there is no dynamic exchange of its amino acids or atoms with similar amino acids or atoms in other molecules. This was first demonstrated by Heidelberger *et al.*[79] For more extended discussions of the subject, see papers by Taliaferro,[180, 181] Stavitsky,[166] and Haurowitz.[77] These relationships would probably be modified in infections in which considerable antibody is bound in localized antigen–antibody deposits as described by Taliaferro and Sarles[192, 193] and restudied by Jackson[91] using modern fluorescent antibody techniques.

Antibody activity has been found in the following classes of serum globulins: 18 S γ-macroglobulins (γ_1 globulins) and 6.6 S γ globulins (γ_2 globulins). That found in the β_{2A} globulins is probably the result of the overlapping of γ globulins, and it has not been associated with the micro-globulins, i.e., the Bence–Jones proteins.[63] In the following discussion, we shall use the terminology γ_1 antibody for the 18 S macroglobulins and γ_2 antibody for the 6.6 S γ globulins. Readers interested in the designation of immunoglobulins (γ or Ig) according to polypeptide chains, molecular formulae, and notations for genes, genotypes, and allotypes are referred to the reference prepared under the auspices of the World Health Organization.[229] According to this reference, γ_1 and γ_2 immunoglobulins are identified as γM or IgM and γG or IGG, respectively.

The heterogeneity of antibodies with the same or closely related immuno-logic specificity is well illustrated by the Forssman hemolysin response in the rabbit after immunization with heated sheep erythrocyte stromata. The erythrocyte–hemolysin system is a model reaction for complement-dependent cytolysis as its biological activity can be accurately determined by a 50 per cent endpoint using photoelectric colorimetric determinations of hemoglobin liberated from the lysed erythrocytes (see especially Refs. 198, 201). After a latent period of several days following a single injection of the antigen, γ_1 hemolysin appears in the serum, rises to a peak titer of about 3 log units and then falls (see Fig. 3 C, described later). No appreciable γ_2 hemolysin appears during this time. The antigen when repeatedly injected, however, leads to the production of large quantities of γ_2 hemolysin which may eventually represent a major portion of the hemolytic activity of the serum as revealed in Fig. 1 B. Figure 1 A demonstrates that the γ_1 component is more avid than the γ_2 component, i.e., it does not transfer as readily from cell to cell. These and other differences are listed in Table 1. It should be emphasized, however, that these two hemolysins possess closely related if not identical immunological specificity, as shown by cross-blocking experiments.[211]

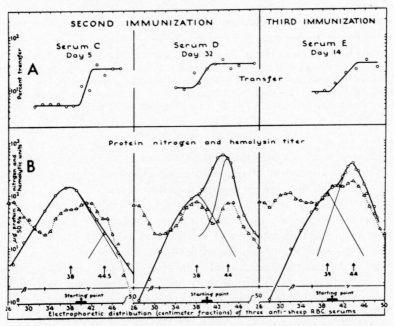

FIG. 1 The peaks of γ_1 and γ_2 components of Forssman hemolysin at 38 and 44.5, respectively, in starch blocks for three antiserums from a rabbit during early(C) and late (D and E) immunization with repeated intravenous injections of heated erythrocyte stromata. Section A gives the per cent of transfer which is inversely related to avidity, and Section B shows hemolysin titers (solid lines) and protein nitrogen (dotted lines). The fine solid lines show the estimated amount of γ_1 and γ_2 hemolysin in those regions containing a mixture of the two components. During early immunization hemolysin predominantly occurred in the γ_1 fraction and later increased markedly in the γ_2 fraction: the γ_1 fraction had a low percent of transfer, i.e., high avidity, as compared to the γ_2 fraction. From Taliaferro and Taliaferro[194] by permission of the authors and the National Academy of Sciences.

TABLE 1. CHARACTERISTICS OF γ_1 AND γ_2 FORSSMAN HEMOLYSINS IN THE RABBIT INJECTED WITH HEATED STROMATA FROM SHEEP RED BLOOD CELLS

	γ_1	γ_2	a, e, g, h, j*
Appearance and peak titer (after immunization)	Early	Late and especially in hyperimmune animals	c, d, g, h, i, j
Molecular weight	1,000,000	165,000	a, d, g
Rate of hemolysis	Varies as the square of the concentration	Varies as the fourth power of the concentration	f
Blood/tissue equilibration	80/20	50/50	b
Half life	2.81 ± 0.12 days	5.56 ± 0.17 days	b
Avidity	High	Moderately low	f, i, j
Action of 2-mercaptopurine	Degraded	Not degraded	g

* Data from: (a) Stelos (1956); (b) Taliaferro and Talmage (1956); (c) Talmage *et al.* (1956a); (d) Talmage *et al.* (1956b); (e) Stelos and Talmage (1957); (f) Weinrach *et al.* (1958) and Weinrach and Talmage (1958); (g) Stelos and Taliaferro (1959); (h) Stelos *et al.* (1961); (i) Taliaferro, Taliaferro and Pizzi (1959); (j) Taliaferro and Taliaferro (1961). These papers may be found in one or more of the following references (167, 180, 183, 203, 206).

The same antibody may manifest differences in avidity or firmness of the antigen–antibody union. High avidity is associated with high reaction rates and low rates of dissociation (see discussion by Jerne[95]). Avidity is usually tested by diluting antigen–antibody complexes: dilution of highly avid complexes has relatively little effect, whereas dilution of nonavid complexes results in marked dissociation of antigen and antibody.[64] In general, a highly avid antibody is considered desirable. Hemolysin, however, is an exception in that the net effect of high avidity is less hemolysis, whereas nonavid hemolysin easily dissociates from one antigenic site and combines with another to initiate a series of lytic injuries as long as sufficient complement is present.[111, 122] Weinrach and Talmage[217] suggested that the greatest amount of hemolysis occurs within a narrow range of optimal hemolysin avidity. Below this optimum, the antibody dissociates before the lytic injury is complete, whereas above this optimum dissociation is too slow to produce many lytic injuries. This suggestion was confirmed by an experiment in which avidity was measured.[206] When, for example, hemolysin from sensitized unlabeled red cells transfers to unsensitized Cr^{51}-labeled red cells, the amount of transfer can be gauged by measuring in a well-type scintillation counter the hemoglobin liberated by the lysed Cr^{51}-labeled red cells after incubation with complement. Figure 2 shows the transfer ability of 20 units of serum hemolysin from one untreated rabbit and from eight rabbits given one injection or after a month or two one reinjection of sheep erythrocyte stromata. The titers of these serums can be approximated by reference to Fig. 3C. As measured by the number of unhemolyzed Cr^{51}-labeled cells surviving the test period, transfer of 20 units of hemolysin was rapid in low-titered normal or 2-day serums and was negligible in the high-titered serums on day 6 and thereafter. In other words, a given amount of a low-titered nonavid hemolysin caused more hemolysis in a much shorter time than the same amount of a high-titered avid hemolysin. These results suggest that, provided complement is maintained in excess, complement–dependent reactions with antibodies of low titer found in animals not intentionally immunized may be active out of all proportion to their titer as measured by conventional methods. Such studies with either parasitic or free-living protozoa are needed to ascertain whether the concepts formulated for the hemolysin model are applicable to the protozoa.

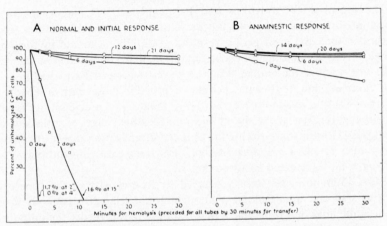

FIG. 2. Differences in avidity of the same number of units (20) of natural and of immune hemolysins, as measured by their ability to dissociate from sensitized unlabeled erythrocytes and to sensitize Cr^{51}-labeled erythrocytes. To five tubes for each serum, complement was added for different lengths of time (2 to 30 minutes) to measure hemolysis of the sensitized Cr^{51}-labeled cells. High avidity was associated with high per cents of unhemolyzed Cr^{51}-labeled cells. Avidity was low in normal serums but increased rapidly after one injection or a later reinjection of sheep red cells. From Taliaferro et al.[206] by permission of the authors and the University of Chicago Press.

II. REAGINIC ANTIBODIES, DELAYED HYPERSENSITIVITY AND ADOPTIVE IMMUNITY

Antibody-mediated activity is tested *in vitro*, or is tested *in vivo* by passive transfer of serum antibody. In addition, lymphocytes, after being induced by an antigen in a donor host, will produce antibody when transferred to a nonimmunized recipient. This type of transfer has been widely used in the study of homograft rejection and in searching for antibody-producing cells (see review by Cochrane and Dixon[36]). It is frequently termed an adoptive transfer. Taliaferro[183] has suggested that lymphocyte-bound antibody may be involved in some crises that simulate an antibody-mediated reaction, as in infections of *Plasmodium cathemerium* in the canary where antibodies have never been unequivocally demonstrated.

Reaginic antibodies of man are ordinarily characterized as being non-precipitating, skin-sensitizing, and relatively heat-labile. They can be demonstrated by the Prausnitz–Küstner method of local transfer of serum from a sensitive to a non-sensitive person.[157] Andrews[13] has pointed out that the protozoan antigens have been surprisingly ineffectual in stimulating reaginic antibodies. This result is in marked contrast to helminth antigens.

The recent work of Kuhns and Pappenheimer[101] may necessitate a revision of the accepted views on the nature of reaginic antibodies. These authors found that most people respond to diphtheria toxoid by forming a classical type of antitoxin that is precipitating, fixes complement in high titer, does not sensitize the human skin and leaves the injected area within about 100 minutes, but that some people—especially those with a history of allergy—form a reagin-type of antibody that is not precipitating, is skin-sensitizing, remains at the site of injection for weeks, fixes complement very weakly and loses its skin-sensitizing property after heating at 56°C for 4 hours. They also found a nonprecipitating, non-skin-sensitizing antibody. Surprisingly, all three acted as antitoxins.

Most immunologists classify delayed hypersensitivity of the tuberculin-type as a specific immunologic phenomenon not related to antibody formation. Some hold that it may be a first response that precedes the outpouring of serum antibody and some believe that it is cell- or lymphocyte-bound antibody (see review by Gell and Benacerraf[68]). It differs from the antibody-mediated mechanisms by the fact that it can be transferred in animals only with cells—chiefly lymphocytes. In man, Lawrence[103] has described its transfer by a factor released from sensitive human leucocytes. Delayed hypersensitivity is generally believed to be largely functional in homograft rejection, but not in immunity to infectious organisms. Recently, however, Neeper and Seastone[125] reported that spleen cells from mice immunized with type 1 pneumococcal polysaccharide conferred an adoptive immunity on normal mice and immunologically paralyzed mice. In marked contrast, spleen cells from the paralyzed mice were ineffective when transferred to normal mice. The authors believe it unlikely that antibody formation played any significant role in these experiments. So far, the production of delayed hypersensitivity with the protozoan antigens has been difficult, if not impossible.[10, 25]

III. CELLULAR REACTIONS IN PROTOZOAN INFECTIONS

The connective tissue cells involved in immune reactions are listed in Table 2. They are classified as predominantly fixed or free cells. Of the fixed cells, the fibroblasts and endothelial cells are functional chiefly in repair of connective tissue and in the encapsulation of foreign material that cannot be readily phagocytosed or digested. Encapsulation is seldom seen in defense

TABLE 2. CONNECTIVE TISSUE CELLS INVOLVED IN IMMUNE REACTIONS AND THE SYSTEM TO WHICH THEY HAVE BEEN ASSIGNED*

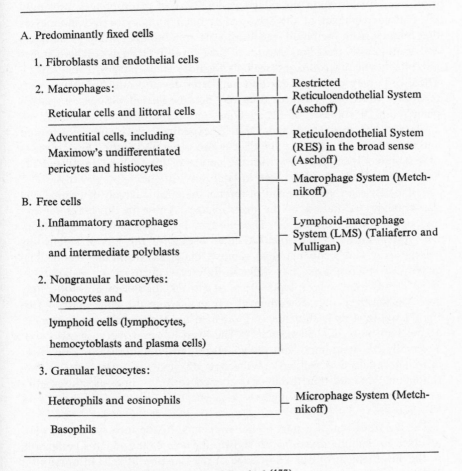

A. Predominantly fixed cells

  1. Fibroblasts and endothelial cells

  2. Macrophages:

    Reticular cells and littoral cells — Restricted Reticuloendothelial System (Aschoff)

    Adventitial cells, including Maximow's undifferentiated pericytes and histiocytes — Reticuloendothelial System (RES) in the broad sense (Aschoff)

Macrophage System (Metchnikoff)

B. Free cells

  1. Inflammatory macrophages

    and intermediate polyblasts

Lymphoid-macrophage System (LMS) (Taliaferro and Mulligan)

  2. Nongranular leucocytes:

    Monocytes and

    lymphoid cells (lymphocytes, hemocytoblasts and plasma cells)

  3. Granular leucocytes:

    Heterophils and eosinophils — Microphage System (Metchnikoff)

    Basophils

* Modified from Taliaferro, *Ann. Rev. Microbiol.* [177]

17 a*

against protozoan infections. From an immunological viewpoint the most important cells are the phagocytic cells and the lymphoid cells that transform into macrophages or into antibody-forming cells. The phagocytic cells, in order of importance, are macrophages, monocytes, heterophils and eosinophils.

Initial cellular activities of the connective tissue can be seen during inflammation that follows a local introduction of foreign material into the skin or from parasites leaving the blood and setting up local inflammatory foci (see Fig. 12C). Heterophils begin to migrate from the local blood vessels within 15 minutes and continue to be recruited from the blood. They represent a first line of phagocytic defense, especially in bacterial infections, but their function is limited as they are end cells and cannot divide. They are not ordinarily active in protozoan infections. The brunt of defense against protozoa depends upon the phagocytic activity of macrophages. Not only are the macrophages of the area active, but lymphocytes and monocytes that migrate from the blood vessels into the area rapidly (within 15 minutes) and continuously over long periods of time develop through polyblast stages into phagocytic macrophages (see inflammatory macrophages, Table 2, B 1). These cells may divide *in situ* and may later develop into fibroblasts with reparative functions. The area thus may become loaded with excess macrophages and fibroblasts of histogenous and hematogenous origin. When antibodies are present, phagocytosis is expedited. Both the cellular and antibody phases of immunity have local and general aspects. They are more or less stereotyped, but vary with the nature of the inciting agent and the location involved, as will be seen in later descriptions.

The localization and removal of foreign material is largely determined by the strategic orientation of the macrophages. Those in the lungs remove material acquired from the air. Those in lymph nodes remove material from the lymph. Those in the so-called filter organs of the blood, chiefly the spleen, liver and bone marrow, remove materials from the blood. The activity of macrophages may differ in different infections. In malaria[184, 188, 200] individual macrophages are most active in the spleen, are moderately active in the liver and are comparatively inactive in the bone marrow (see Fig. 7), but in early leishmaniasis in the hamster, those in the liver are more active than those in the spleen.[160] The liver, however, because of its size, is actually the most important phagocytically in both infections. Thus, after injecting radioactive sulfanil-azo-sheep erythrocyte stromata into rabbits Ingraham[88] found that the liver contained 16 to 70 times as much radioactivity as the spleen, although the *concentration* in the spleen was 1.4 to 5.6 times that of the liver.

The classification of a part of the connective tissue into systems of cells involved in immune reactions, as shown in Table 2, has added significantly to the development of our knowledge of the function of cells in immunity. Parenthetically, it should be noted that many of these cells have additional functions in the intermediary metabolism of the body. In 1901, before tissue staining was adequate, Metchnikoff[117] grouped the phagocytic cells into two systems—the macrophage system, which probably included intermediate polyblasts and monocytes, and the microphage system which included the short-lived heterophils and eosinophils. His concept stressed the essential role of the mesenchymal cells in inflammation and their defense function in immune reactions. He held that small lymphocytes are never phagocytic as such, but become so after acquiring an ample layer of cytoplasm. Later, with improved methods, Maximow[110] demonstrated that hematogenous lymphocytes in the field of inflammation are transformed into macrophages. The best known term, the reticuloendothelial system (RES), was advocated by Aschoff[14] in 1927. He excluded lymphocytes from his system. In 1937, Taliaferro and Mulligan[188] proposed the term lymphoid-macrophage system (LMS) to honor the brilliant pathfinding work of Metchnikoff and Maximow in demonstrating the interrelationships of macrophages, monocytes, lymphocytes and transitional cells. This concept was substantiated by studies of Taliaferro and his associates on the histogenesis of the cells involved in immunity to various parasites.[18, 154, 184, 188, 190, 192, 193, 200] Moreover, the basic ideas clearly evident in the term "lymphoid-macrophage system" have been upheld by much recent work, especially that involving the role of the lymphocyte in antibody formation (see next section) and are implicitly accepted by many investigators under the term "lympho-reticular system" or under the term "reticuloendothelial system" tacitly understood to include lymphoid cells. For recent work on this subject, the reader is referred to papers by White[223] and Rebuck et al.[139]

A. Mesenchymal Reserves in Immunity

The number of phagocytic cells available under normal circumstances is rarely adequate for more than the mildest infections. Extra phagocytes, therefore, are of critical importance, especially when parasite populations are rapidly increasing during innate immunity before opsonins are developed. Macrophages and lymphoid cells, which retain to varying degrees the embryonic capacity to undergo heteroplastic development into other connective tissue cells fill this need. In addition, antibody formation necessitates the proliferation of lymphoid cells.

The increase of lymphocytes, macrophages, and other cells in the spleen during successful immune reactions is often reflected by the relative weight of the spleen. Thus, Moulder and Taliaferro[121] found that the ratio of spleen weight to body weight (0.23 ± 0.006) in uninfected chickens rose steadily until it reached almost 4 times the normal ratio near peak parasitemia in malarious chickens. From this high point it dropped to 1.5 times the normal ratio at 6 weeks. An important finding in this work was that enlargement of the spleen involves a true increase in functional tissue and that the new cells exhibit the same glucose metabolism as the original cells of the uninfected spleen.

Under immunologic stress, the fixed reticular cells may round up and become large basophilic lymphocytes, the so-called lymphoblasts, that may form antibodies and are a source of lymphocytes. Most lymphocytes, however, arise by mitotic division. They then hypertrophy and become macrophages, as was first reported by Maximow in 1902,[110] and develop into plasma cells, as shown by Taliaferro and his co-workers.[184, 188, 190, 200] There has been little question about the mesenchymal potencies of certain fixed cells, and recently investigators are substantiating the validity of the mesenchymal potencies of the lymphocytes, especially with respect to their developing into plasma cells[36, 42, 126, 166, 227] and functioning in the delayed type of hypersensitivity[137] and in homograft rejection.

Counterbalancing the intense activity of the mesenchymal reserves, large numbers of lymphocytes and macrophages are injured and even destroyed during severe infections. This condition is especially true when exotoxin is involved (see the work of Conway[41] on diphtheria toxin) and in severe protozoan infections (see later).

B. Antibody Formation

The liver forms most of the serum proteins, but is not generally active in antibody formation unless it acquires extra lymphatic tissue in the periportal areas. The most active organs in antibody formation are the spleen and lymph nodes. The bone marrow may also form antibody as shown by the transfer of bone marrow cells from an immunized donor to an unimmunized recipient.[202,204] Under these conditions, the induced donor cells form antibody in the recipient. In addition, when Draper and Sussdorf[59] injected antigen directly into the femoral bone marrow of splenectomized rabbits, the serum of the rabbits reached antibody titers not significantly different from those in intact rabbits receiving the same amount of antigen intravenously.

Antibodies are sometimes supplied from the mother through the placenta, as in man and the rabbit; or through the colostrum after birth in many animals, such as the horse, pig, sheep, and cattle.[108] Active antibody formation is not developed until some time after birth (Aitken[11]).

C. Contrast of Lymphoid and Myeloid Functions

The spleen has long interested parasitologists. In many infections its removal is followed by an intensified parasitemia (see Fig. 17) or a relapse. Its functions in innate and acquired immunity are various rather than unique; they include lymphoid and myeloid activities. Jordan[98] believes that the spleen appeared during vertebrate evolution about the time hemoglobin-containing cells appeared; and that in its most primitive form it was the source of erythrocytes, granular leucocytes, and lymphoid cells. During the evolution of the higher vertebrates the spleen shared the function of lymphocyte formation with the bone marrow in the reptiles and birds and with the bone marrow and lymph nodes in mammals. The normal spleens of chickens, rats, mice, and certain other animals probably always form some erythrocytes. Even in man, where the division between lymphoid and myeloid tissue is sharpest, the spleen may form large numbers of myeloid cells in certain diseases, such as myeloid leukemia.

The tendency of the spleen in mice to revert to its primitive condition is well illustrated by the studies of Singer[151-4] on CF_1 mice infected with *Plasmodium berghei* and of Taliaferro and Pizzi[190] on C_3H mice infected with *Trypanosoma cruzi*. In both infections an initial stimulation of lymphopoiesis in the spleen was followed by a loss of lymphoid elements and their replacement by erythroid elements. Associated with the depletion of lymphoid tissue, the lymphatic tissue became hyperplastic in the lymph nodes, and the liver assumed the major phagocytic function lost by the spleen. Moreover at the time of the minor decline in *P. berghei* infections, parasitized erythrocytes were found in the venous sinuses of the spleen and in the sinuses and venules of the liver and bone marrow. These localizations are highly suggestive of the localization of *P. brasilianum* shown in Fig. 6. The substitution of lymphoid tissue by erythroid tissue in *P. berghei* infections might be considered a result of extensive red cell loss. It was, however, about as rapid and as extensive in infections with *T. cruzi* in which comparatively few erythrocytes were lost. This progression, therefore, may be largely an innate response of the mouse to immunological stress in general.

D. Examples of Cellular Activities

The rise and fall of cellular elements during immune reactions are reflected in the spleen (Fig. 3), as shown by Sussdorf's[168] work. Thus, after the intravenous injection of such a small amount of a nonliving antigen as $10^{9.2}$ washed sheep red cells, two transient early waves of increase in both the splenic white and red pulp were associated with the early induction of antibody formation and the peak of antibody synthesis, respectively.

During virulent infections, such as malaria, cellular changes in the lymphoid tissue of the spleen are shown in Figs. 8, 9, and 10 to be described later. Suffice it to say here that immune reactions are much more rapid in birds than in mammals. Thus the sharp decline in parasitemia, which presaged the advent of antibody-mediated acquired immunity, occurred on day 4 in the chicken (Figs. 8 and 9) and on day 16 in the monkey (Fig. 4). The response was also much faster in superinfections than in initial infections (cf. Fig. 10 with Fig. 9).

In his histopathological study of *Theileria parva*, the parasite of fatal East Coast fever of cattle in Africa, Barnett[18] reported that mobilization of

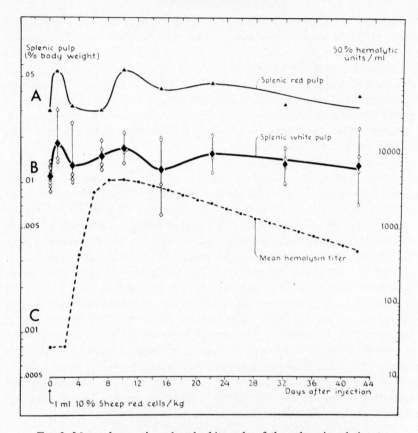

Fig. 3. Mean changes in red and white pulp of the spleen in relation to hemolysin titer in groups of rabbits following a single injection of sheep erythrocytes. The two early red and white pulp peaks were associated with the time of induction and maximum synthesis of antibody formation. From Süssdorf[167] by permission of the author and the University of Chicago Press.

reticular cells and proliferation of lymphocytes in the lymph node adjacent to the site of infection (the ear via infected ticks) "were eventually overshadowed by regressive, degenerating and pathological changes involving depletion of the lymphocytes, disruption and destruction of the lymphocytopoietic centers, a progressive toxicosis associated with cellular destruction especially of the lymphocytes and granulocytes, and terminally a total destruction of heterophils." This fatal outcome is not characteristic of all *Theileria* infections. Barnett[19] has reviewed many aspects of natural and acquired immunity to the *Th. mutans, Th. annulata* and *Th. parva* groups of organisms. Immunity to *Th. parva*, when successfully achieved, is most stable. It is apparently a sterile immunity. In the *Th. annulata* group, strains of reduced virulence have been used for immunization for many years. One of the strains now used in Israel gives only partial protection and is supplemented by a virulent strain.

The cellular aspects of immunity have been reviewed by Rebuck[138] and Taliaferro.[177] Various aspects are also considered in a series of papers edited by Whipple and Spitzer.[222] The comprehensive survey by Goble and Singer[72] is especially valuable because it deals with the malarias and trypanosomiases. Recent reviews on the cellular aspects of antibody formation include those by Cochrane and Dixon,[36] Holub and Jarošková,[83] Nossal,[126] and Stavitsky.[166]

IV. IMMUNE PROCESSES IN PROTOZOAN INFECTIONS

Early work on the immunology of the parasitic protozoa has been reviewed by Taliaferro[171, 173] and Culbertson.[47] Special fields of protozoan immunity have recently been stressed in a series of articles edited by Whipple[221] and by Fulton.[66] Toxoplasmosis has been dealt with by Beatty (in Ref. 67) and Jacobs.[92] The literature on malaria has been covered by Hewitt,[82] Huff,[84] and Taliaferro and his associates.[176, 178, 184, 188, 194, 195, 200] Reviews may also be found in the following periodicals: *Annual Review of Microbiology*, *Advances in Parasitology*, and *Modern Trends in Immunology*.

A recent landmark in the development of the subject was the symposium of the British Society for Immunology in 1961 that resulted in the book edited by Garnham and associates[67] entitled *Immunity to Protozoa*. This volume, the first relating solely to protozoan immunity, consists of a series of papers on concepts of immunity to protozoa followed by descriptions of mechanisms involved in immunity to selected blood- and tissue-inhabiting species. In this volume Robertson[144] presented a fascinating account of the local and general aspects of the formation and action of antibodies in the cow infected with *Trichomonas foetus*. The parasite is transmitted by coitus and infection is localized to the genital tract. The uterus is the preferred site although some parasites occur in the vagina. Infection is minor in the bull, but may cause infertility and abortion in the female. Specific agglutinins seemed to be formed in the uterus and vagina and were found in the serum. They sensitized the skin, as evidenced by skin reactions of the anaphylactic type within 30 minutes. Moreover, like the Forssman hemolysin in the rabbit, a so-called natural serum antibody was present. The specific antibody in the serum seemed to have no prophylactic value and did not modify the disease, that in the vagina freed the vagina of parasites but did not prevent recurrent infection from the uterus, while that in the uterus appeared to terminate mild infections and in acute ones was at times instrumental in the rapid disappearance of large numbers of trichomonads at the time of abortion. The resulting immunity persisted for at least 3.5 months.

Mechanisms in the host comprise all the factors that protect the body from the entrance of foreign materials or rid it of such materials when they penetrate or are carried through the outer barriers.

Nonspecific, i.e., nonantibody, factors are present before the host is infected or otherwise immunized. Together they are probably more important to the host than the antibody-mediated mechanisms. They include a heterogeneous collection of biochemical compounds. Some are used in the host's normal metabolism, others act antibiotically, and still others provide structural features that make infection difficult. Finally, some may be antibodies that are not recognized because the antigen is unknown.

The interactions between parasite and host can be considered as a study in population ecology of the parasite as influenced by its biotope, the host. From an evolutionary viewpoint, once a parasite invades a specific host it becomes more or less isolated in a manner comparable to the geographic isolation of a free-living species on islands or other areas walled off by an ecological barrier.[16] The biotope of the parasite is, however, an organism that may evolve specific adaptations to the parasite. In fact, each parasitic species is not only limited in its power to invade, colonize and reproduce, but is limited in its range of hosts.[55, 109, 145, 163, 164, 178, 218, 219] Whether infection results in death of the host, elimination of the parasite, or chronic infection depends upon the balance between invasiveness of the parasite and counteracting immune mechanisms of the host. This balance is seldom static. In many cases, it seesaws within a narrow range for long periods. During these periods, a higher parasite population may yield more antigen that in time may stimulate the formation of more antibody that in turn may lead to a smaller parasite population.

In an over-all sense, a nonvirulent parasite indicates an immune host: a virulent parasite a nonimmune host. In a general way, factors of invasiveness are ascribed to the parasite and factors of immunity are ascribed to the host. Thus, representative parasitic factors include the secretion of exotoxins that injure cells of the lymphoid-macrophage system while host activities include antibody mechanisms. In a number of situations, however, a factor may be ascribed to either host immunity or parasite invasiveness. A variant host hemoglobin, when unfavorable to the development of plasmodia, can be classified as an athreptic factor of the host or inversely as a lack of certain enzymes and/or a lack of metabolic pathways in the parasite.

Most antibody-mediated mechanisms act quickly to kill and remove protozoa from the host. How then can there be so many mutually adjusted host–parasite associations? Taliaferro[178] has noted a prolongation of the association by the reproduction-inhibiting action of ablastin, by the slowly acting antibodies that stunt helminths, and by the ability of certain trypanosomes to produce heritable variations in their antigens. From a different angle, Damien[52] conceives of molecular mimicry as a sharing of antigens by host and parasite. He terms these antigens eclipsed antigens in that they will not be considered foreign by the host and therefore will not stimulate the formation of antibodies. Such antigens have to be clearly identified as of host and not of parasite and, therefore, are difficult to establish unless the parasite can be grown *in vitro*. The reader is referred to Damien's paper for discussions of the evolutionary origin and importance of these eclipsed antigens. In related papers, Dineen[56] discusses the evolutionary significance of different degrees of host–parasite antigenic disparity.

As the knowledge of protozoan immunity advances, antibodies may be found to act by blocking the parasite from essential metabolic enzymes or necessary food stuffs and accessory factors essential to it. Such an antibody action is suggested by the activity of ablastin in inhibiting nucleic acid and protein synthesis and in modifying the carbohydrate metabolism of *Trypanosoma lewisi* (see section IX).

The interplay of invasiveness of the parasite and immunity of the host can be followed by observing changes in a parasite population over long periods. Especially well fitted for this purpose are the blood-inhabiting species. Blood films of these infections can be studied with respect to (1) the parasitemia and (2) the reproductive rate of the parasites unaffected by their mortality rate.[173, 174] The second component can be measured in the synchronously reproducing plasmodia by determining the mean number of parasites produced by segmenters in a specified time[176, 195] and among the trypanosomes can be approximated by obtaining the coefficient of variation for size or the percent of division forms (dividing plus short forms) in populations.[170, 185, 189]

Non-antibody, i.e., nonspecific, mechanisms are operative before antibodies are produced. The appearance of antibodies can be detected by such phenomena as a sudden drop in parasitemia followed closely by *in vivo* agglutination and greatly enchanced phagocytosis (Fig. 7), by the rapid elimination of parasites when injected into immune animals as seen in some bird infections, and by the development of protective antibodies as in human and simian infections. In infections like the leishmaniases, the presence of antibodies can be assumed when parasites markedly decrease in number. After the crisis-like drop in numbers, the parasitemia is sometimes remarkably constant for long periods, as evidenced by the survival of only one merozoite per segmenter in various malarias (cf. Fig. 5). These statements will be elaborated in the following four sections where the host–parasite relationships will be considered in various malarias, the leishmaniases and the pathogenic and nonpathogenic trypanosomiases. Malaria represents a predominantly phagocytic immunity and shows the role of connective tissue in immunity, the leishmanias invade the macrophage citadel itself, the pathogenic trypanosomiases exemplify a predominantly lytic immunity, and *T. lewisi* infections illustrate ablastic immunity. Finally, in infection with *Theileria parva* which has already been considered in Section III, there is an almost total breakdown of immunity.

V. THE MALARIAS

We selected the experimentally blood-induced infection of *Plasmodium brasilianum* in the cebus monkey as a prototype of the malarias because it has no exoerthyrocytic stages as far as is known and in general reproduces synchronously every 3 days. These characteristics help to delineate certain principles of immunity (see Taliaferro[176]). Some of the factors of pathogenesis and invasiveness of malarial parasites have recently been considered by Maegraith,[106] and some aspects of human malaria are discussed by McGregor.[115]

A. Parasiticidal and Reproduction-inhibiting Factors of Immunity

During the course of the patent quartan malaria shown in Fig. 4, the parasitemia escalated until a peak was reached on day 13. It then decreased precipitously and eventually subsided into a low grade infection.

The relative constancy of the rate of reproduction and death of the parasites indicate that innate factors of immunity were operative during the rise of the patent parasitemia through day 13. Mature and segmenting schizonts, which occurred every 3 days, showed a mean number of about 10 merozoites. Of this number during each 3-day period, only three lived to maturity: four died during segmentation and three died during parasite growth within the erythrocyte. Had all merozoites lived during the five segmentations shown in Fig. 4, 20 parasites would have inhabited every erythrocyte instead of only one parasite occurring in every 25th cell. That this parasiticidal activity is fundamentally the result of nonantibody factors is shown by the failure to modify either merozoite production or the constant death rate either by splenectomy or by blockade of the lymphoid-macrophage system,[69, 72] both of which are known to lower antibody-induced immunity. The ineffectiveness of splenectomy during the early rise of malaria is illustrated by the similarity in the length of the asexual cycle and the number of parasites produced on days 9 through 12 during malaria in intact and splenectomized chickens in Fig. 17A and B. The relatively constant parasite death rate is the result of all adverse factors of innate immunity—some active, some passive—which make the host environment less than a perfect medium for the parasite.[67, 174, 176] These adverse factors vary with the host species[86, 97, 112, 194, 195] or even with individuals of a single host species.[158, 195] Some are athreptic, such as the absence of essential vitamines (e.g., Brackett *et al.*[24]). Others may depend upon the type of hemoglobin or the age of the invaded erythrocyte (see later discussion).

Death of plasmodia free in the blood stream may occur somewhat as follows, as suggested by Moulder.[120] Unless a free merozoite rapidly invades an erythrocyte, it dies. Outside an erythrocyte it can obtain glucose,

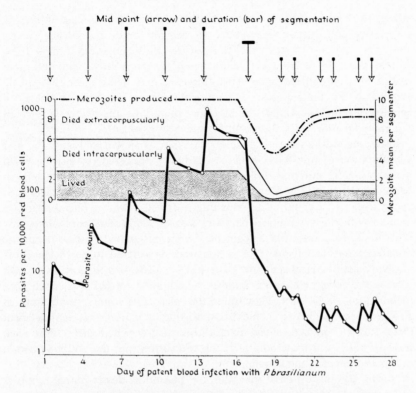

FIG. 4. An initial blood-induced infection of the quartan parasite, *Plasmodium brasilianum*, in a Central American cebus monkey showing the parasite count, number of merozoites produced at each asexual segmentation and the number of plasmodia that lived and died. From data by Taliaferro and Taliaferro[194] by permission of Taliaferro[178] and the Princeton University Press.

methionine, *p*-aminobenzoic acid, and pantothenate, but it suffers from certain deficiences in its synthesis of coenzyme A and folic acid, and in its carbohydrate oxidation. Moulder[120] holds that the plasmodium is restricted to an intracellular existence and that the true reproductive unit is the invaded erythrocyte, the parasite furnishing the enzymes necessary for reproduction and the erythrocyte furnishing the necessary environment.

In *P. falciparum* infections in man, certain hemoglobins that are inherited antimalarial factors can be defined chemically. One of these is the sickle-cell hemoglobin of Southern European, Asian and African populations. Allison,[12] who has studied the subject extensively, gives the following picture of the relation of this abnormal hemoglobin to infection with *P. falciparum*. Children one year of age with the sickle-cell trait are infected with *P. falciparum* to the same extent as children without this trait, but their survival rate as they grow older is higher. Apparently their less intense infections allow time for acquired immunity to develop and to reinforce innate immunity. Ingram[90] reported that sickle-cell hemoglobin differs from normal hemoglobin by the substitution of a valine for a glutamic acid residue in each half-molecule. This difference may make more difficult its metabolism by the parasite. For more details on the role of sickle-cell hemoglobin and other types of inherited mutations, the reader is referred to papers by Allison,[12] Bowman[21] and Motulsky.[118]

Returning to the quartan malarial infection as shown in Fig. 4, the first manifestation of antibody-mediated immunity appeared on day 16 when the parasitemia not only failed to rise as expected, but abruptly fell. In addition, the rate of reproduction was temporarily lowered, as evidenced by an irregular asexual cycle extending over 6 days and by the appearance of many obviously damaged parasites and of segmenters containing only four to six merozoites. Such segmenters were designated "crisis" forms by Taliaferro and Taliaferro[194, 195] and were considered to be the result of antibody action. Huff and his associates[84] question this conclusion and ascribe the lower merozoite number to athreptic factors associated with malnutrition of the host. They found that merozoite counts in infections of *P. gallinaceum* were less in chickens subsisting on pantothenic acid-deficient diets than in chickens given pantothenic acid-enriched diets. This idea, however, does not materially alter the conclusion that the antibody action was predominantly parasiticidal.

During the entire patent infection, the plasmodia destroy large numbers of erythrocytes; flood the blood with foreign material, such as corpuscular debris, free malarial parasites, and malarial pigment; sometimes produce infarctions, especially in the spleen; and damage various tissues. This damage is counterbalanced to varying degrees by hyperplastic and reparative activities of the host.[173, 176, 179, 188, 200]

Again returning to Fig. 4, the 3-day cycle of reproduction was regularly resumed a few days after the abrupt parasite decline, but the action of acquired immunity, superimposed on innate immunity, was evident by the death of eight out of the nine parasites formed. Parenthetically, it should be noted that the disruption of the cycle between days 13 and 19 caused the original brood of parasites to separate into two broods, one of which segmented on the original schedule and the other a day later.

The first clear-cut demonstration of antibody protection in malaria was reported in 1937 by Coggeshall and Kumm[38] in monkeys that had received immune serum by passive transfer. These results have now been amply substantiated by results obtained with antiplasmodial antibodies in man. Cohen and McGregor[40] and McGregor[114] reported that passive transfer of immune serum was followed consistently by clinical recovery and a pronounced reduction in parasitemia. Serum was obtained from the blood of individuals immune to malaria and was purified by chromatography on

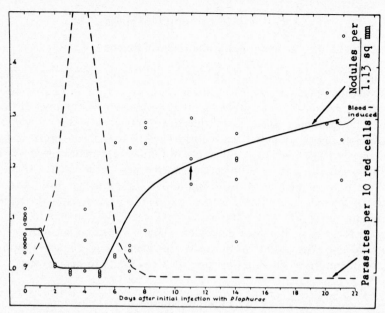

FIG. 9. The number of lymphatic nodules in the spleen of chickens during initial infection of *Plasmodium lophurae*. Lymphocyte depletion was roughly inversely related to parasitemia and reached a high level at 22 days. Modified from Taliaferro and Taliaferro[200] by permission of the authors and the University of Chicago Press.

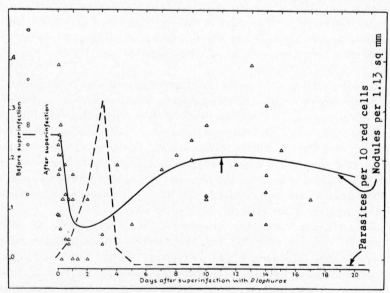

FIG. 10. The number of lymphatic nodules in the spleen of chickens during superinfection of *Plasmodium lophurae*. Changes were somewhat similar to those in Fig. 9, but the number of nodules was high before superinfection (overregeneration retained from the initial infection) and, after reaching a level on day 11 comparable to that in Fig. 9, declined. Modified from Taliaferro and Taliaferro[200] by permission of the authors and the University of Chicago Press.

E. Variations in the Cellular Response

Singer[151-4] described certain interesting variations in the cellular reactions against *P. berghei* when grown in inbred CF_1 mice. The variations apparently depended (1) upon the fact that mice under immunological stress replace the lymphoid tissue of the spleen with erythroid tissue, as noted in Section III, and (2) upon the fact that the parasite is unable to utilize mature erythrocytes. The parasites' preference for immature mouse erythrocytes was shown by the course of infection and the histopathological picture in normal mice as well as in splenectomized, drug-treated, irradiated or cortisone-treated mice. For example, in mice infected with *P. berghei* 20 minutes after 500 R, the mounting parasitemia was similar to that in controls for 6 days, but then decreased sharply while that in controls continued to rise. The radiation-supressed parasitemia was accounted for by a lack of immature erythrocytes because of X-ray injury to hemopoiesis.

VI. LEISHMANIASES

The leishmaniases are a group of infectious diseases of man and certain lower animals, chiefly the Canidae and Rodentia, which are transmitted by sandflies of the genus *Phlebotomus*.[7] The parasites are generally divided into cutaneous and visceral species, most typically *Leishmania tropica* and *L. donovani*, respectively. They exist in the vertebrate host as leishmaniform invaders of macrophages. The localization and disseminating or viscerotropic characteristics, however, can in part be modified — even within the same host.

Adequate methods for counting leishmanias, as developed by Stauber,[160] have made possible the study of many aspects of the immunological reactions in the leishmaniases. Two basic methods have been perfected. The first and simpler one used the determination of the number of parasites per cell nucleus of a given organ in stained impression smears. In the second one parasites were directly counted in a weighed amount of infected organ. This procedure involved staining and counting the parasites in a square centimeter containing 0.005 ml of a suspension derived from 100 mg of a finely ground infected tissue. The two methods showed a high correlation.

Two contrasting immunological situations are found among the leishmaniases (cf. reviews 5, 7, 8, 107, 163, 184). On the one hand, a solid immunity develops against *Leishmania tropica* in typical "oriental sore" and against *L. donovani* in human kala-azar after successful treatment and even occasionally during spontaneous recovery. Here, the leishmanias presumably disappeared—though certainly not in all cases.[169] On the other hand, in some chronic but nonlethal infections of *Leishmania*, the parasite number eventually decreases to a level that suggests the presence of parasiticidal or reproduction-inhibiting processes or both. Such infections were reported to be cutaneous as well as visceral. They occurred in man and animals both naturally and experimentally. In some chronic cutaneous lesions, the parasites could not be found but were probably present in small numbers, as emphasized by Adler.[5]

Cutaneous infections could not be studied quantitatively as well as visceral ones. Because leptomonads are easy to culture and count they would be the obvious choice to initiate test infections, but their initial loss was so great, at least in infections with *L. donovani*, that the fate of the small percentage of survivors was difficult to assess.[165] Even when leishmaniform organisms were injected, presumably with less loss,[162] the parasites were not easy to count in dermal and subdermal areas. For these reasons, the quantitative work to date has dealt mainly with the more easily manageable *L. donovani* infections initiated with splenic parasites injected intravascularly into small rodents.[73, 161] This work has uncovered some interesting phenomena and, although dermal strains may show a different course in the tissues, present information suggests otherwise.

A. Differences between *L. donovani* in Two Hosts

Of the highly susceptible hosts, the cotton rat, like the Chinese hamster, did not succumb to infection with leishmanias as did the golden hamster and the spermophil (Adler[3]). In the spleen and liver of the cotton rat, the parasites initially increased rapidly (10–60-fold in the first 8 days), but subsequently increased less rapidly, especially in the liver. A recalculation of Grun's data[73] showed that the number of parasites in the liver doubled every 30–40 hours during the first 8 days and every 82 days later. The sequence of events during the first week depended upon a variety of nonspecific factors, including athreptic ones, and the kind, number and availability of host cells that destroyed the parasites intracellularly and extracellularly. In fact, splenomegaly during kala-azar is a gross manifestation of the general activation of the lymphoid-macrophage system.[5, 116, 124,182] Such nonspecific factors in the leishmanial infection may have exerted an inhibitory effect on infection of *Plasmodium berghei* in the hamster,[4] but could not account for the mutually inhibitory effects of mycobacterial infection and leishmaniasis.[100] The diminishing rate of parasite increase after the first week, according to accumulating evidence, seems probable dependent on the development of an antibody-mediated immunity. The immunological bases for this infection could not be separated into parasiticidal and reproduction-inhibiting factors because no satisfactory method has been devised to measure reproductive rates of parasites as has been done for plasmodia (Fig. 4) and trypanosomes (Figs. 13, 15 and 16).

The mouse resembled the gerbil and the guinea pig in being more resistant than the cotton rat.[73, 128, 161] Contrary to most claims in the earlier literature, it has more recently been infected intravascularly provided sufficient numbers of leishmaniform organisms are inoculated. The course of the infection was influenced by the strain of mouse[65] and the source,[128] nutritional state[2] and strain of the parasite. One Mediterranean and three African strains capable of producing fatal infections in golden hamsters (Stauber[165] and unpublished data) differed chiefly in the degree to which they parasitized mice.

Early parasitization of mice, following the intravenous injection of parasites, diminished in rate with time even before peak infection was reached. The peak occurred in 10 to 100 days depending upon the strain of parasite and the size of the inoculating dose. In contrast to infections in the cotton rat, a parasitic crisis followed, but did not generally reduce the parasitemia to the subpatent level—at least for several months. This number crisis probably indicates the presence of antibody-mediated parasiticidal factors. "Recovered" animals were resistant, as manifested by a lower parasitization and earlier crisis during superinfection than during the initial infection (for the mouse,[65] gerbil,[161] and guinea pig[128]). When organisms were injected intraperitoneally, parasites were rarely seen microscopically in the spleen or liver, but the mice were infected and showed the same heightened resistance to superinfection.[65] A state of true premunition existed. After the crisis, parasites persisted at a level dependent upon many factors (strain, route, size of the inoculating dose, etc.), but at a level much lower in the mouse (from 1/100 to 1/10,000) than in the cotton rat. Thus, any reproduction of the parasites, which probably occurred, was counterbalanced by parasiticidal factors.

B. Site of Colonization

All tissues of hosts were not equally favorable to the leishmanias, even though the parasites are located within the cytoplasm of a macrophage. Non-viscerotropic cutaneous infections contrast with non-dermotropic visceral infections. Post-kala-azar dermal leishmaniases contrast with metastatic cutaneous leishmaniases. In addition, quantitative studies of visceral infections in rodents indicated not only that rates of parasitic increase differed in different organs but that total and relative parasite burdens varied with the size of the inoculum. These relationships are shown in Table 3. Thus, the liver was more highly parasitized than the spleen throughout the entire dose range; but as the inoculating dose was decreased, the number of parasites decreased faster in the liver than in the spleen. For example, the parasite ratio for the liver and spleen was 7 for the largest dose of inoculum and 1.7 for the smallest one.

The fact that leishmanias live in macrophages, which normally constitute the most active phagocytic cell in immunity to various microbial invaders, suggested that the cellular reactions to them might be greatly modified. Taliaferro,[182] on the contrary, has pointed out that the reactions to them are in general essentially similar to those described for the plasmodia in section V.

The immune mechanisms in the leishmaniases are unknown, and the phrase quoted from Taliaferro and Pizzi[190] on page 542 of this chapter could properly be repeated here. This conclusion gains credence from the fact that the cellular changes in C_3H mice infected with *T. cruzi* were largely paralleled by the cellular changes in hamsters infected with a virulent strain of *L. donovani* (Taliaferro and Stauber, unpublished work). In addition, the greater ability of the liver, as compared to the spleen, to destroy leishmanias during late stages of the infection has suggested differences in the metabolic activity of the macrophages of the two organs or a greater concentration of opsonins. A similar difference between the inflammatory and fixed macrophages has been noted in defense against *T. cruzi*.

TABLE 3. Parasite Distribution in the Liver and Spleen of Hamsters inoculated intracardially with Splenic *Leishmania donovani* as influenced by the Size of the Inoculum. (Values are group medians for the animals remaining after half the animals in the group had succumbed to the infection.)

Inoculum size	Total parasites		Liver/spleen parasite ratio
	In the spleen ($\times 10^8$)	In the liver ($\times 10^8$)	
5×10^6	3·1	21·8	7·0
5×10^5	2·4	11·0	4·5
5×10^4	4·8	14·4	3·0
5×10^3	5·6	4·4	0·8
5×10^2	3·0	6·4	2·1
5×10^1	6·7	8·6	1·3
5×10^0	1·0	1·8	1·7

Adapted from Stauber[161] by permission of the author and Rice University.

C. Antigenic Complexities

Like other organisms, the leishmanias are antigenically complex and their injection into animals may lead to the production of typical agglutinating or precipitating antibodies.[9, 33, 49, 171] Some of these antibodies may be useful for diagnostic purposes when used in the complement fixation test, intradermal tests, and the more recently described hemagglutination[146] and fluorescent antibody reactions.[61, 80, 149] Some may be helpful in the study of antigenic relationships.[6, 102] None has yet been shown to function in acquired immunity. Although many attempts have been made to relate the intradermal reaction to the immune state of the host, only the recent fluorescent antibody reaction of Herman[81] has shown a correlation of serum antibody titer with the progress of the visceral infection.

Changes in serum globulins during visceral leishmaniasis have long been recognized, and some diagnostic procedures (e.g., the formol gel test) were based on them. Much of this work has been reviewed both for natural as well as experimental human infections.[147, 159] Decreased albumin and increased globulins were the characteristic changes noted. While increased globulin would be expected from the greatly accelerated development of plasma cells,[7, 182] increased α_2 globulin seen in the golden hamster and increased γ globulin in the cotton rat probably reflect unresolved aspects of the infection. The γ globulin changes deserve further comment. Cooper et al.[43] first noted that a slow-moving component was present in the γ globulin fraction in the leishmaniases where true recovery did not occur (man, cotton rat, chinchilla). This component differed from the excess γ globulins of normal mobility found in a number of other infections. It may in part be associated either with antibodies formed to unknown antigens or with autoimmune processes according to Taliaferro.[182] Putnam[134] has reviewed the evidence pertaining to the pathological changes in the serum proteins during disease.

There is prime need for further characterizing both the globulins produced during leishmanial infections and the antigenic mosaics of the parasites that elicit their production. Possible autoimmune reactions during infection need to be explored. These phenomena may well reflect the presence of excess γ globulin in the chinchilla and man and of amyloidosis in the hamster.

VII. PATHOGENIC TRYPANOSOMIASES

Some of the earliest work on immunity to protozoan infections was concerned with a study of the mechanisms involved in the relapsing infections of laboratory animals by trypanosomes, including *Trypanosoma brucei*, *T. rhodesiense* and *T. gambiense*.[171] If injected into mice, these parasites increased more or less steadily until the host died. As determined by division forms, the rate of reproduction of the parasites remained constant and fairly high. When these same pathogenic trypanosomes were grown in the guinea pig, dog, or rabbit, alternate increases and decreases in the parasite population took place until the host died. In such relapsing infections, the rate of reproduction of the parasite also remained fairly high. The sharp decreases in parasitemia were associated with the periodic production of trypanolytic crises and the acquisition of resistance to the lysin among some of the survivors. By 1947,[75] it was generally held that the acquisition of resistance was actually a selection of resistant stocks from a number of genetic antigenic variants. The relapse strains differed antigenically from the original passage strain. In fact, Ritz[142] incompletely cured a mouse 20 times and by cross immunity tests found 17 immunologically different relapse strains. These genetic variations were inherited for as many as 400 mouse passages, but were lost in time. Relapse strains of different antigenicity were also produced by drug treatment.[105, 142] This subject is reviewed by Goble.[71]

Figure 11 shows the temporary trypanolytic action of immune guinea pig serum. Following the passive transfer of this serum into an infected mouse, a precipitous parasitic decline occurred, but resistant trypanosomes repopulated the blood stream and the mouse eventually died. The adaptation of trypanosomes to abnormal hosts is reviewed by Desowitz.[55]

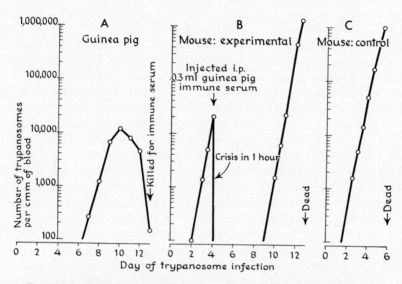

FIG. 11. Antibody-induced lysis in the blood infection of *Trypanosoma equinum* in the mouse. In B vs. C trypanosomes rapidly disappeared from the blood of the infected experimental mouse following injection of immune guinea pig serum but reappeared later with a fatal outcome. Modified from Taliaferro and Johnson[186] by permission of Taliaferro[178] and the Princeton University Press.

The genetic versatility of trypanosomes in changing their lysinogens has been of continuing interest to protozoologists, especially in relation to the production of vaccines. Refined immunological techniques are now being applied to the agglutinogenic exoantigens. These exoantigens were derived from the serums of trypanosome-infected rats and have the same electrophoretic mobility as rat globulins. When used as immunizing agents, rats and mice survived longer after infection with homologous trypanosome strains. In contrast when injected with parasites into mice, they enhanced the resulting infection. Weitz[218] concludes that these results are not brought about by any agressin-like factor in the exoantigens, but by a better preservation of the trypanosomes. He suggests that the exoantigens may act as an "advance guard" in preserving the trypanosomes against the host

18*

defense mechanisms. An important difference between exoantigens and bound antigens is that the former in a broad sense are species-specific, whereas the latter are shared by many species of trypanosomes.[219]

Cantrell and Betts[32] reported that rats infected with *T. equiperdum* and treated with oxophenarsine acquired a rapidly developing highly specific immunity as demonstrated by the disappearance of reinjected parasites. They also concluded that the form of the curve relating antigen dose to the period of protection indicated that the parasite population was composed of a major antigenic type and one or more minor types. Cortisone in large doses, such as 200 mg per kg rat, did not lengthen the period of protection when the dose of antigen was kept well above the threshold value of about 100 trypanosomes per cmm of blood. At threshold doses of antigen, an adverse effect of cortisone on immunization was observed. These data suggest an inverse relationship between the immunity acquired from antigens liberated by the drug and the suppression of immunity by cortisone. In later studies of mutations, Cantrell[31] estimated that two mutations per 10^6 trypanosomes per generation determined specificity in his strain of *T. equiperdum*, that the dissimilar antigenic types were capable of mutating to the same antigenic type, and that one type was capable of giving rise to mutants of more than one kind.

Brown[26] has separated the antigens of the *T. rhodesiense* group into two types: an A group, which was predominantly protein, and a B group, which so far has not been chemically identified. His work not only emphasizes the multiplicity of relapse strains, but indicates that practically all of the antigens were involved in each change in antigenicity. This remarkably detailed attack on the characterization of *T. rhodesiense* antigens was carried out in collaboration with Williamson and Desowitz.[27, 224-6] It involved various chemical, physical and immunological methods.

Interesting modifications of three trypanosome infections have been described by Singer and his associates.[155] Mice injected with *Escherichia coli* endotoxin, prior to inoculation with *T. congolense* or *T. rhodesiense*, lived longer. Similar treatment, using the nonpathogenic *T. duttoni*, resulted in a decreased parasitemia. The effect of the endotoxin was negligible when injected with the parasites. Once all three parasitemias had developed, injection of the endotoxin caused a pronounced reaction and usually resulted in death within 24 hours. The mechanisms involved in these situations are as yet speculative, but are probably connected with both humoral and cellular factors.

The tissue reactions in C_3H mice infected with a reticulotropic strain of *T. cruzi* have been studied by Taliaferro and Pizzi.[190] Early in initial infections, the leishmaniform stages invaded the fixed and inflammatory macrophages of the reticular organs and loose connective tissue. The reactions in the tissues were intense but essentially ineffective. Focal and diffuse inflammatoid activities occurred in the lymphoid-macrophage system, especially in the reticular organs. Most of the virulent parasites apparently developed normally in the macrophages (Fig. 12 A, B and D), but a few were digested, especially in the inflammatory macrophages (Fig. 12 C). As in the highly virulent *P. gallinaceum* infections, depletion of lymphocytes and

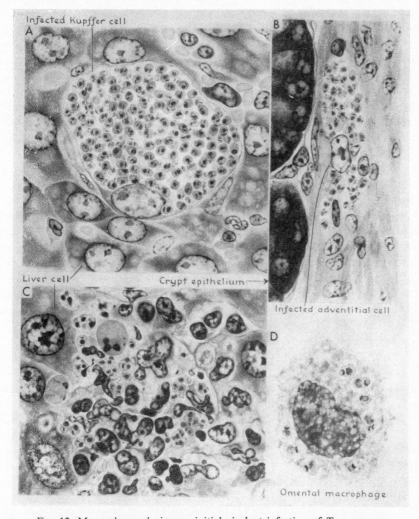

FIG. 12. Macrophages during an initial virulent infection of *Trypanosoma cruzi* in C₃H mice. A, B and D, macrophages in the liver, intestine and omentum infected with apparently healthy parasites. C, inflammatory macrophages in the liver (probably after the rupture of a cell similar to that in A) apparently clearing up debris and parasites. (Some of the latter appeared damaged, especially in the upper left corner.) Camera lucida drawings, × 1500. From Taliaferro and Pizzi[190] by permission of the authors and the University of Chicago Press.

macrophages was accompanied by replacement of macrophages through the mitotic proliferation and mobilization of reticular cells. The destructive processes eventually predominated in nonimmune mice, but marked lymphoid, myeloid and macrophage hyperplasias prevailed in immune mice. In fact, inflammatory activities at times assumed such intensity in the myocardium that they may have accounted for the death of some immune animals which had successfully reduced the challenging infection to a very low grade. As stated by the authors: "One of the central problems in immunity to *T. cruzi* is the mechanism whereby the macrophage changes from a site in which the parasite grows in the nonimmune host to a site in which the parasite is destroyed in the immune host." They concluded from their own and earlier work by Pizzi and his associates[131] that this change is brought about in part by the development of antibodies and in part by the more effective disposal of parasites by the inflammatory macrophages than by the fixed macrophages.

VIII. NONPATHOGENIC TRYPANOSOMIASES

Beginning with Rabinowitch and Kempner,[135] a series of early workers established that the blood of rats infected with *Trypanosoma lewisi* only contains dividing parasites during the early part of the infection. Later, from the tenth day on, it contains nonreproducing "adult" forms. In 1924, Taliaferro[170] demonstrated that a passively transferable serum component inhibits the reproduction of *T. lewisi in vivo*. Thus, adult trypanosomes from the same source remained adults when injected into an experimental rat along with 2 ml of immune rat serum whereas they rapidly divided when injected into a control rat given the same amount of normal rat serum (Fig. 13). Later, Taliaferro[172] termed the component of immune serum "ablastin" and considered it an antibody. It was temporarily suppressed by splenectomy or gestation in association with infection with *Haemobartonella muris*.[140, 185] Taliaferro's co-worker Coventry[45] reported that a large proportion of the parasites were killed early in the infection by a trypanocidal antibody while some resistant ones survived. Later, a second antibody, which terminated the patent infection, was irregularly associated with a lysin *in vitro*.[170, 172] These irregular results may have been due to the binding of Ca^{++} and Mg^{++} by the sodium citrate in the saline solution used to collect and concentrate the trypanosomes.

In an extension of this work, Taliaferro and Pavlinova[189] reported that *T. duttoni* in the mouse, although pursuing a course of infection somewhat similar to that of *T. lewisi* in the rat, showed a lower parasitemia and less reproductive activity. Reproduction was inhibited, but not as early or as completely. Subsequently, Taliaferro[172a] demonstrated a passively transferable ablastin in the mouse similar to that in the rat. The two ablastins cross-reacted. Thus, the rat anti-*lewisi* ablastin inhibited the division of *T. duttoni* in mice and the anti-*duttoni* ablastin inhibited *T. lewisi* in the rat. A terminal, trypanocidal antibody to *T. duttoni* could not be compared with the anti-*lewisi* antibody because normal rat serum is trypanocidal for *T. duttoni*.

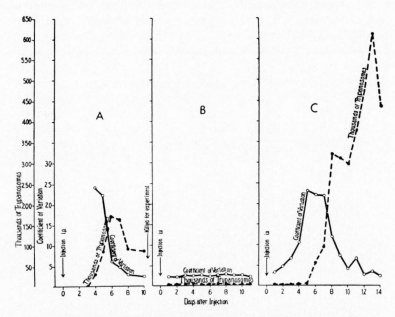

Fig. 13. Ablastin-induced inhibition of reproduction of *Trypanosoma lewisi* in the blood of a rat, as measured by the coefficient of variation for length. Adult trypanosomes from rat A did not divide in rat B when injected with ablastic immune serum from rat A, but divided in rat C when injected with serum from an uninfected rat. Because of the difference in reproductive activity, the number of parasites remained constant in B and rose to a high level in C. From Taliaferro[170] by permission of the author and the Rockefeller Institute.

In 1932, Taliaferro[172] reported that ablastin has no persistent *in vitro* affinity for trypanosomes, and that it and the terminal trypanolysin are associated with the eu- and pseudoglobulins of the serum. These results were confirmed and amplified by D'Alesandro.[50] The nonabsorbability of ablastin may result from an unsatisfactory antigen preparation or a low antigen-antibody avidity or both. D'Alesandro,[50] using modern methods of starch block electrophoresis, found that ablastin and the two trypanocidal antibodies occur in the γ_1 globulins. He further ascertained that ablastin and the early trypanocidal antibody are 7 S proteins and that the terminal trypanocidal antibody is a 17 S protein. These differences in electrophoretic mobility and the nonabsorbability of ablastin make untenable the thesis of Thillet and Chandler[213] that ablastin inhibits reproduction in low titer, but agglutinates and opsonizes the organisms in high titers. D'Alesandro[51] has recently devised a method of titrating ablastin *in vitro* (Fig 14). The metabolic effects of ablastin are considered in Section IX.

It has also been found that there are variable strains in the *lewisi* group[53] and that certain nonsusceptible hosts can be infected with a given strain provided that they are supplied with suitable amounts of serum from susceptible hosts.[55, 104]

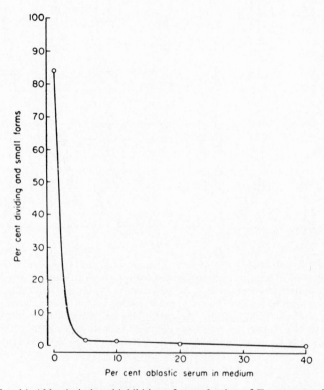

FIG. 14. Ablastin-induced inhibition of reproduction of *Trypanosoma lewisi in vitro*, as measured by the percent of dividing and small forms. Division of the trypanosomes rapidly decreased from 84 to 1 per cent as the concentration of ablastic serum was increased from 0·5 to 40 per cent in cultures incubated overnight at 37 °C. From D'Alesandro[51] by permission of the author and the Society of Protozoologists.

In 1963, Ormerod accepted Coventry's results on the presence of trypanocidal antibodies in *T. lewisi* infections, but discounted the presence of an antibody with the characteristics of ablastin.[127] He advanced what he termed a two-antigens hypothesis involving the early and terminal trypanocidal antibodies (see also Augustine[15]). The early trypanocidal antibody, according to his idea, destroyed young reproducing forms but not the adult stages that had acquired a new antigenicity. The fundamental question not answered by Ormerod's hypothesis is what prevents the adult stages, after acquiring their new antigenicity, from dividing and repopulating the blood stream as they do after splenectomy and gestation or as pathogenic trypanosomes do after a trypanolytic crisis (Fig. 11). Moreover, that reproduction of the trypanosomes is actually inhibited is demonstrated by the *in vivo* and *in vitro* experiments illustrated in Figs. 13 and 14 and by the inhibition of nucleic acid and protein synthesis described in Section IX (Figs. 15 and 16).

IX. METABOLIC EFFECTS OF ANTIBODIES

Most antibody-mediated antiparasitic activities, such as lysis and phagocytosis after opsonization, quickly kill and/or remove the organism from the host. As compared to these activities, the metabolic effects of ablastin on *Trypanosoma lewisi* proceed slowly. Thus, Moulder[119] reported that during the first ten days of the infection the rate of oxygen consumption by the trypanosomes increased and the rate of glucose consumption decreased. The oxygen/glucose ratio of about one in the reproducing forms rose to about 3 in the nonreproducing forms, and the respiratory quotient of about 0·75 in the reproducing forms rose to about 0·9 in the nonreproducing forms. Because of these results, Moulder suggested that ablastin inhibits division and growth by a change in glucose metabolism from one of oxidative assimilation to one of maintenance. Corroborative results were obtained by Ryley[148] and Thurston.[214]

A more direct relation of ablastin to reproduction was established by Taliaferro and Pizzi[191] in a study of protein and nucleic acid synthesis in infections of rats with *T. lewisi*. The rate of protein synthesis of the trypanosomes was determined by the rate of incorporation of S^{35} into protein from S^{35}-labeled amino acids, and the rate of nucleic acid synthesis was determined by the rate of incorporation of C^{14} into nucleic acid from adenine-8-C^{14}. The procedure involved infecting rats with adult trypanosomes, injecting either labeled amino acids or labeled adenine at various intervals and removing the trypanosomes 1 to 3 hours later for radioassay. The rate of protein synthesis was highest in nonreproducing adult trypanosomes injected to start the infection and decreased markedly thereafter (Fig. 15). The high value on day 0 when the parasites were morphologically adult probably represents a rapid and complete release from ablastic inhibition as a result of washing the parasites in a phosphate saline solution prior to their injection. It could not be ascribed to ablastin as the parasites begin to divide a day later. The 3-day reading, when parasites were still rapidly dividing, was used to gauge inhibition of protein synthesis. The radioassay at day 10, as compared to day 3, indicated an approximate inhibition of 63 per cent. During this period, reproduction of the trypanosomes, as indicated by the percent of dividing forms, had decreased markedly.

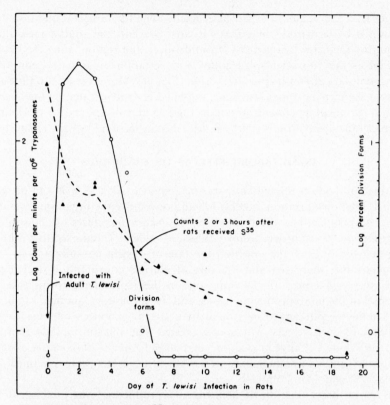

FIG. 15. Incorporation of S^{35} into the protein of *Trypanosoma lewisi*, as measured by radioassay of trypanosomes from groups of infected rats that were injected at various times with S^{35}-labeled amino acids, and the inhibition of reproduction of the trypanosomes as measured by the per cent of division forms. Protein synthesis of the trypanosomes was highest just after injection of adults which had been washed and released from ablastin: after the trypanosomes began to divide protein synthesis decreased as reproduction was inhibited. Redrawn with added data from Taliaferro and Pizzi[190] by permission of the authors and the National Academy of Sciences.

Figure 16 shows the rate of nucleic acid formation in *T. lewisi* during infection. It was highest (392 counts per minute) when adenine-8-C^{14} was injected 2 days after the rats had received "released" adult trypanosomes and decreased rapidly through day 12. Thereafter, it was more or less constant. The value at day 10, as compared to day 3, represented an inhibition of about 90 per cent in nucleic acid formation.

Similar results with respect to the inhibition of protein and nucleic acid synthesis were obtained *in vivo* after the passive transfer of ablastic serum (Table 4) and *in vitro*.

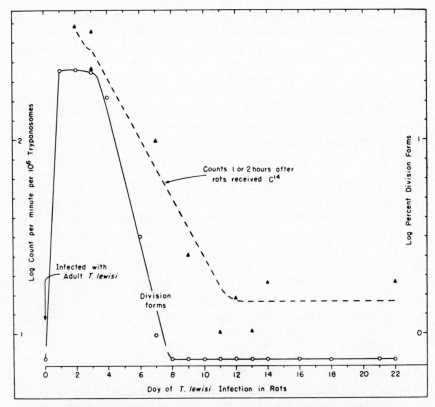

FIG. 16. Incorporation of C^{14} into the nucleic acid of *Trypanosoma lewisi*, as measured by radioassay from groups of infected rats that were injected at various times with adenine-8-C^{14}, and the inhibition of reproduction of the trypanosomes, as measured by the per cent of division forms. Note the essential similarity between the curve of nucleic acid synthesis and that of protein synthesis in Fig. 15. Redrawn with added data from Taliaferro and Pizzi[190] by permission of the authors and the National Academy of Sciences.

There is no definitive explanation of how the synthesis of protein and nucleic acid is blocked. Pizzi and Taliaferro[132] in a study of various trypanosomes, however, found that only small amounts of labeled C^{14} were incorporated in the fraction precipitated by TCA from glycine-2-C^{14}. This result indicates that the parasites cannot synthesize the purine ring and suggests that precursors of the purine ring cannot be absorbed or if absorbed are blocked by some derangement of carbohydrate metabolism. Moulder's work[119] suggests such a derangement. Using *in vitro* methods, Harmon and Callow[74] confirmed the action of ablastin on the incorporation of adenine into nucleic acids. In the case of methionine, they observed an inhibition of uptake in nondividing forms but not in dividing forms.

Inasmuch as the work by Pizzi and Taliaferro[132] showed that ablastin inhibits the uptake of purines, pyrimidines and nucleosides, D'Alesandro[50] tried to bypass this block with preformed nucleotides, but failed to counteract ablastic suppression. If and when the mechanism of ablastic action is known, it will probably be described in terms of a specific action on enzymes in the trypanosomes.

The quantitative measurement of parasiticidal factors by Desowitz's[54] manometric method may also be of value in devising further experiments on antibody effects in protozoan metabolism.

TABLE 4. *In vivo* INHIBITION OF PROTEIN AND NUCLEIC ACID SYNTHESIS IN *Trypanosoma lewisi*, AS GAUGED BY RADIOASSAY OF RADIOACTIVE AMINO ACIDS AND NUCLEIC ACIDS, RESPECTIVELY, IN RATS WHICH RECEIVED TRYPANOSOMES AND IMMUNE ABLASTIC SERUM

Group	0	1	Day 3		
	T. lewisi[a]	Serum[a]	0·01 mc/100 g rat	Radioassay[b,c] Counts per minute per 10^6 trypanosomes	Per cent Inhibition
1	Dividing	Ablastic	S^{35} amino acids	16 ± 4 (4)	66
2	Dividing	Ablastic	Adenine-8-C^{14}	41 ± 8 (3)	87
3	Dividing	None	Controls	47 ± 4 (4) 320 ± 27 (2)	

From data by Taliaferro and Pizzi.[191]

[a] Dividing trypanosomes were injected intravenously into rats and one day later immune serum, after being adsorbed with living trypanosomes to remove any trypanocidal antibody, was injected intraperitoneally in 2·4 to 3·5 ml amounts per 100 g rat.

[b] Trypanosomes for radioassay were collected from rats killed 2 hours after intraperitoneal injection of the isotopes.

[c] Numbers in parentheses indicate the number of rats in each group.

X. IMMUNE MECHANISMS IN CHEMOTHERAPY

Present opinion favors the idea that immune mechanisms are active in the successful drug treatment of infections (review by Goble[71]). Some investigators believe that such mechanisms act as an integral part of the drug action, while others believe that they act as coordinate but independent antiparasitic factors. The latter view appears to hold for the action of quinine in chickens infected with *Plasmodium gallinaceum*, as shown by a series of papers by Taliaferro and his associates.[175, 187, 197] In this work quinine predominantly inhibited reproduction of the parasites by lengthening the asexual cycle and by reducing the number of merozoites formed per segmenter. It did not stimulate phagocytosis by the macrophages of the spleen, liver and bone marrow. On the other hand, innate and acquired immunity predominantly exerted parasiticidal effects, as mentioned earlier in connection with Fig. 4. Further analysis indicated that the spleen played two mutually antagonistic roles during quinine therapy: it decreased drug-parasite contact and increased acquired immunity. Prior nonspecific stimulation of the lymphoid-macrophage system, via injections of sheep serum, or prior stimulation with *P. lophurae* did not appreciably alter the quinine blood levels or more effectively suppress the *P. gallinaceum* infection in quinine-treated chickens as compared to nontreated infected chickens. From these data on the quinine treatment of avian malaria, it was concluded that three relatively independent antiplasmodial factors are operative: quinine, innate immunity, and acquired immunity. The first mainly inhibits growth and reproduction of the parasites, and the last two are mainly parasiticidal. Superficially, there appears to be some basis for the idea that the drug makes the parasite more easily phagocytosed. This sequence, however, only emphasizes the fact that the quinine-induced inhibition of growth and reproduction of the parasites simply precedes the scavenging phagocytosis of injured parasites. Although in a sense acquired immunity is relegated to a secondary role, it is a highly important antiparasitic factor, as shown by the occurrence of frequent and sometimes fatal relapses when quinine is pushed to the point where antigen is insufficient to stimulate acquired immunity.

Figure 17 illustrates the action of quinine when superimposed on acquired immunity against *P. gallinaceum* in intact and splenectomized chickens. Quinine was administered intravenously in three doses of 1.25 mg per 100 g chicken on days 12, 13, and 14 at the peak of the parasitemia in sporozoite-induced infections. In the intact quinine-treated chickens as compared to the intact untreated controls, the rate of parasite reproduction (length of the asexual cycle and number of merozoites) was reduced, with a consequent more abrupt decline in the parasitemia (cf. Fig. 17A and C). The same sequence occurred in the splenectomized quinine-treated chickens as compared to the splenectomized untreated controls (cf. Fig. 17B and D), although the parasitemia was more intense in both groups than in the intact groups.

Soltys and Folkers[156] reported from their own and other work that drug-resistant strains of trypanosomes are more easily obtained after host immunity is lowered by such procedures as splenectomy or RES blockade. They suggested that the development of drug-resistant strains may be avoided by raising the defenses of the host so that the immune mechanism and the drug may act synergistically to control the trypanosome infection better than does the drug alone. Such a synergistic action needs clarification, however, because the two agents act more or less independently in malaria, as just described.

The comprehensive review by Goble[71] should prove invaluable to the reader interested in reactions during chemotherapy of various protozoan and other parasitic infections.

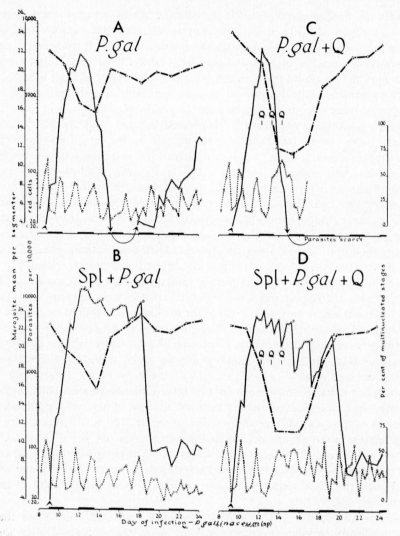

FIG. 17. Parasite count (solid line) and number of merozoites produced (dot and dash line) at each 36-hour asexual segmentation (dotted line and barred baseline) of sporozoite-induced (sp) infections of *Plasmodium gallinaceum* in groups of intact and splenectomized chickens with and without quinine (1.25 mg intravenously per 100 g chicken). Reproduction of the parasites was markedly inhibited in the quinine-treated infections (C vs. A and D vs. B) and fewer parasites were killed in the splenectomized groups (B vs. A and D vs. C). The combined effects of quinine and splenectomy are apparent in D. From Taliaferro and Taliaferro[197] by permission of the authors and the University of Chicago Press.

XI. IMMUNE MECHANISMS IN DIAGNOSIS

Immunological methods for diagnosis may develop from the finding of antibodies that react with parasites and known parasite antigens or, conversely, from the finding of antigens that react with antiparasite antibodies. Many of the immunological reactions of precipitation, agglutination, complement fixation, etc., have been used for immunodiagnosis. Most of them have been carried out *in vitro* but a few, such as skin tests, have been *in vivo*. Such methods for diagnosing protozoan diseases are reviewed by Fulton.[66]

Among the more recently employed methods, not only for diagnostic but for fundamental studies on the antigenic mosaic of the protozoa, are the following: fluorescein-labeling of antibody (see Coons[42]), the detection of antiplasmodial antibodies (Tobie[215]), and the diffusion-in-gel methods including immunoelectrophoresis (Ouchterlony[129, 130]). For an illustration of these methods as applied to malaria, the reader is referred to Zuckerman.[231]

XII. FACTORS THAT INJURE IMMUNE REACTIONS

Mention has already been made of the lowering of immunity by radiation, splenectomy and radiomimetic compounds (cortisone) in mice infected with *P. berghei* and by splenectomy and concomitant infections with bartonella in rats infected with *T. lewisi*. These effects have been widely studied during innate immunity and especially during acquired immunity. Modifications of infections by any of these agents involve a balance of many factors, such as time and dose of the particular agent to be tested with respect to the time of infection; the species, age and amount of immunity of the host; and the host-parasite relationships during innate and acquired immunity that are seldom static. Exact determinations of any of these modifications are further complicated by the fact that the parasite as well as the host may be injured or otherwise affected. The extensive literature on irradiation has been reviewed by Taliaferro and his associates.[176, 199, 205]

Effects of large doses of X-rays are especially pronounced as the following few brief descriptions demonstrate. Young chickens, when irradiated with 500 R at the beginning or during the course of their infection with the virulent parasite, *Plasmodium gallinaceum*, usually died, whereas young chickens when irradiated similarly during infection with the nonpathogenic *P. lophurae* only died when irradiated on the day of infection (Fig. 18). This effect was operative against parasiticidal immunity and not against any reproduction-inhibiting immunity of the host. From these and other data, Taliaferro *et al.*[207] concluded that a radiation-induced decrease in immunity is only detectable when the sum of innate and acquired immunity is at an intermediate level. In the above series, the radiation-induced detectable effect on the intermediate level of immunity is represented by the fatal

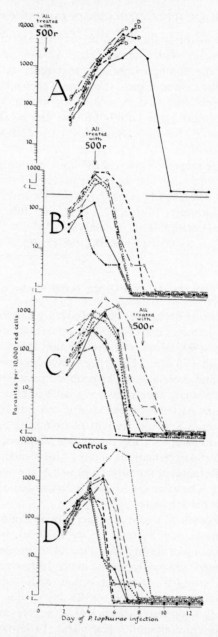

FIG. 18. Parasite counts of *Plasmodium lophurae* in chickens given 500 R on the day of infection (A) and 4 and 8 days after infection (B and C). Control group D was not irradiated. The effect of irradiation was more pronounced during innate immunity (group A) than later when acquired immunity was present. From Taliaferro *et al.*[207] by permission of the authors and the University of Chicago Press.

relapses of *P. gallinaceum* and the fatal initial infections of *P. lophurae* (controls recovered), whereas the radiation-induced inappreciable effects are represented by the fatal initial infections of *P. gallinaceum* (controls also died), on the one hand, and by the nonfatal relapses of *P. lophurae* (controls also recovered), on the other hand.

The effects of irradiation were also studied in rats infected with *T. lewisi* by Naiman[123] and Jaroslow,[94] and in mice infected with *T. duttoni* by Jaroslow.[93, 94] In rats infected with *T. lewisi* one hour before irradiation with 500 R, the prepatent period was lengthened and the parasitemia was higher than in controls, while the reproductive activity of the parasites remained unaltered. Doses of 300 R were less effective. Irradiation also depressed immunity, as tested by a challenging infection. This depression was especially evident in the relatively avirulent infection of *T. duttoni* in mice. The parasitemia and reproductive activity increased rapidly in mixe infected from four days before to 15 days after 500 R. Under these conditions, irradiation evidently delayed antibody formation sufficiently to permit the infection to kill the host. The effects of blockade with India ink and 550 R were additive in mice infected one day after irradiation. Recovery from radiation damage was noted in mice infected 22 days after 500 R.

The depressing effects of X-rays in the foregoing infections are in line with radiation-induced changes of the immune response when other antigens, i.e., foreign erythrocytes and bovine serum albumin, are injected *after* X-rays (reviewed by Taliaferro *et al.*[205]). As far as we are aware, however, no radiation-induced enhancement of immunity against the protozoan infections has been reported comparable to that found when foreign erythrocytes and several other antigens are injected *before* irradiation.[205]

Certain other materials, which are mostly toxic, may at times enhance or depress immunity, depending upon the time of administering the material, as reviewed by Goble and Singer.[72] For example, work with the nitrogen mustard, tris (beta-chloroethyl) amine hydrochloride, a radiomimetic substance,[196] revealed the following two mutually antagonistic effects when tested in chickens infected with *P. gallinaceum* or *P. lophurae*. (1) The drug inhibited reproduction by lowering the number of merozoites and by producing obvious damage to all stages of the parasite. (2) It lowered the parasiticidal effects of acquired immunity. Of these two effects, loss of immunity by the host was more important than injuries inflicted on the parasite.

XIII. REFERENCES

1. ACKROYD, J. F., ed. (1964) *Immunological Methods*, 628 pp. F. A. DAVIS Company, Philadelphia, Pennsylvania.
2. ACTOR, P. (1960) Protein and vitamin intake and visceral leishmaniasis in the mouse. *Exper. Parasitol.* 10, 1–20.
3. ADLER, S. (1947) Cellular reactions in leishmaniasis. *Acta Med. Orientalia* 6, 151–5.

4. ADLER, S. (1954) The behavior of *Plasmodium berghei* in the golden hamster *Mesocricetus auratus* infected with visceral leishmaniasis. *Trans. Roy. Soc. Trop. Med. Hyg.* **48**, 431–40.

5. ADLER, S. (1963a) Immune phenomena in leishmaniasis. In *Immunity to Protozoa*, 235–45, eds. P. C. C. GARNHAM *et al.*, Blackwell Scientific Publications, Oxford.

6. ADLER, S. (1963b) Differentiation of *Leishmania brasiliensis* from *L. mexicana* and *L. tropica. Proc. VIIth Int. Congr. Trop. Med. Malaria (Rio)*, Abstracts, 177–8, and *Rev. Inst. Salub. Enferm. Trop.* **23**, 139–52.

7. ADLER, S. (1964) Leishmania. In *Advances in Parasitology* **2**, 35–96, ed. B. DAWES, Academic Press, Inc., New York.

8. ADLER, S. (1965) Immunology of leishmaniasis. *Israel Jour. Med. Sciences* **1**, 9–13.

9. ADLER, S., and ADLER, J. (1955) The agglutinogenic properties of various stages of the leishmanias. *Bull. Res. Council. Israel* **54**, 396–7.

10. ADLER, S., and NELKEN, D. (1965) Attempts to transfer delayed hypersensitivity to *Leishmania tropica* by leucocytes and whole blood. *Trans. Roy. Soc. Trop. Med. Hyg.* **59**, 59–63.

11. AITKEN, I. D. (1964) Development of natural anti-Forssman hemolysin in young rabbits. *J. Infectious Diseases* **114**, 174–8. (1967) Hemolysin production in young rabbits. *J. Infectious Diseases*, in press.

12. ALLISON, A. C. (1963) Inherited factors in blood conferring resistance to protozoa. In *Immunity to Protozoa*, 109–22, eds. P. C. C. GARNHAM *et al.*, Blackwell Scientific Publications, Oxford.

13. ANDREWS, J. M. (1962) Parasitism and allergy. *J. Parasitol.* **48**, 3–12.

14. ASCHOFF, L. (1924) Das reticulo-endotheliale System. *Ergeb. inn. Med. u. Kinderheilk.* **26**, 1–118.

15. AUGUSTINE, D. L. (1943) Some factors in the defense mechanism against reinfection with *Trypanosoma lewisi. Proc. Amer. Acad. Arts and Sci. U.S.* **75**, 85–93.

16. BAER, J. G. (1951) *Ecology of Animal Parasites*, 224 pp., University of Illinois Press, Urbana, Illinois.

17. BALL, G. H., and CHAO, J. (1963) Contributions of *in vitro* culture toward understanding the relationships between avian malaria and the invertebrate host. *Ann. N.Y. Acad. Sci.* **113**, 322–31.

18. BARNETT, S. F. (1960) Connective tissue reactions in acute fatal East Coast fever (*Theileria parva*) of cattle. *J. Infectious Diseases* **107**, 253–82.

19. BARNETT, S. F. (1963) The biological races of the bovine *Theileria* and their host-parasite relationship. In *Immunity to Protozoa:* 180–95, eds. P. C. C. GARNHAM *et al.*, Blackwell Scientific Publications, Oxford.

20. BECKER, E. L. (1964) Comments on immunization against malaria. *Amer. J. Trop. Med.* **13**, Suppl., 235–6.

21. BOWMAN, J. (1964) Comments on abnormal erythrocytes and malaria. *Amer. J. Trop. Med.* **13**, Suppl., 159–61.

22. BOYD, W. C. (1956) *Fundamentals of Immunology*, 776 pp., Interscience Publishers, Inc., New York.

23. BOYD, W. C. (1962) *Introduction to Immunochemical Specificity*, 158 pp., Interscience Publishers, Inc., John Wiley and Sons, New York.

24. BRACKETT, S., WALETZKY, E., and BAKER, M. (1946) The relation between pantothenic acid and *Plasmodium gallinaceum* infections in the chicken and the antimalarial activity of analogues of pantothenic acid. *J. Parasitol.* **32**, 453–62.

25. BRAY, R. S., and LAINSON, R. (1965) Failure to transfer hypersensitivity to *Leishmania* by injection of leucocytes. *Trans. Roy. Soc. Trop. Med. Hyg.* **59**, 221–2.

26. BROWN, K. N. (1963) The antigenic character of the "*Brucei*" trypanosomes. In *Immunity to Protozoa*, 204–12, eds. P. C. C. CARNHAM *et al.*, Blackwell Scientific Publications, Oxford.

27. BROWN, K. N., and WILLIAMSON, J. (1964) The chemical composition of trypanosomes. IV. Location of antigens in subcellular fractions of *Trypanosoma rhodesiense*. *Exper. Parasitol.* **15**, 69–86.

28. BURNET, M. (1959) *The Clonal Selection Theory of Acquired Immunity*, 209 pp., Vanderbilt University Press, Nashville, Tennessee.

29. CAMPBELL, D. H., GARVEY, J. S., CREMER, N. E., and SUSSDORF, D. S. (1963) *Methods in Immunology*, 263 pp., W. A. BENJAMIN, Inc., New York.

30. CANNON, P. R. (1940) The functional significance of specific agglutinins and precipitins. *Physiol. Rev.* **20**, 89–114.

31. CANTRELL, W. (1958) Mutation rate and antigenic variation in *Trypanosoma equiperdum*. *J. Infectious Diseases* **103**, 263–71. (1959) Cortisone and the course of *Trypanosoma equiperdum* infection in the rat. *J. Infectious Diseases* **104**, 71–77. (1960) The pattern of antigenic variation in *Trypanosoma equiperdum*. *J. Infectious Diseases* **107**, 29–33.

32. CANTRELL, W., and BETTS, G. D. (1956) Effect of cortisone on immunization against *Trypanosoma equiperdum* in the rat. *J. Infectious Diseases* **99**, 283–96.

33. CHAFFEE, E. F. (1963) Preliminary report on the *Leishmania* sp. antigens. *Proc. VIIth Int. Congr. Trop. Med. Malaria (Rio)*, Abstracts, 528–9.

34. CHAO, J., and BALL, G. H. (1964) Cultivation of the insect cycle of plasmodia. *Amer. J. Trop. Med.* **13**, Suppl., 181–92.

35. CLEVELAND, L. R. (1949) Hormone-induced sexual cycles of flagellates. *J. Morphol.* **85**, 197–296.

36. COCHRANE, C. G., and DIXON, F. J. (1962) Antibody production by transferred cells. In *Advances in Immunology* **2**, 205–39, eds. W. H. TALIAFERRO and J. H. HUMPHREY, Academic Press Inc., New York.

37. COGGESHALL, L. T. (1943) Immunity in malaria. *Medicine* **22**, 87–102.

38. COGGESHALL, L. T., and KUMM, H. W. (1937) Demonstration of passive immunity in experimental monkey malaria. *J. Exper. Med.* **66**, 177–90.

39. COGGESHALL, L. T., and KUMM, H. W. (1938) Effect of repeated superinfection upon the potency of immune serum of monkeys harboring chronic infections of *Plasmodium knowlesi*. *J. Exper. Med.* **68**, 17–27.

40. COHEN, S., and MCGREGOR, I. A. (1963) Gamma globulin and acquired immunity to malaria. In *Immunity to Protozoa*, 123–59, eds. P. C. C. GARNHAM *et al.*, Blackwell Scientific Publications, Oxford.

41. CONWAY, E. A. (1939) Hyperplasia and necrosis of lymphatic tissue after diphtheria toxin. *Anat. Rec.* **73**, Suppl. 2, 13–14.

42. COONS, A. H. (1959) Some reactions of lymphoid tissues to stimulation by antigens. *The Harvey Lectures* delivered in 1957-8, 113–29, Academic Press Inc., New York.

43. COOPER, G. R., REIN, C. R., and BEARD, J. W. (1946) Electrophoretic analysis of kala-azar human serum. Hypergammaglobulinemia associated with seronegative reactions for syphilis. *Proc. Soc. Expl. Biol. Med.* **61**, 179–83.

44. CORRADETTI, A. (1964) Comments on passive transfer of malarial immunity. *Amer. Trop. Med.* **13**, Suppl., 240–1.

45. COVENTRY, F. (1930) The trypanocidal action of specific antiserums on *Trypanosoma lewisi in vivo*. *Amer. J. Hyg.* **12**, 366–80.

46. COX, H. W. (1963) A study of the infections of relapse strains of *Plasmodium berghei* in normal mice. In *Progress in Protozoology*, 469, eds. J. LUDVÍK, J. LOM, and J. VÁVRA, Academic Press Inc., New York.

47. CULBERTSON, J. T. (1941) *Immunity against Animal Parasites*, 274 pp., Columbia University Press, New York.

48. CUSHING, J. E., and CAMPBELL, D. H. (1957) *Principles of Immunology*, 344 pp., McGraw-Hill Book Company, Inc., New York.

556 W. H. TALIAFERRO AND L. STAUBER

49. D'ALESANDRO, P. A. (1954) A serological comparison of the leishmaniform and the leptomonad stages of *Leishmania donovani*. M.S. thesis, 42 pp., Rutgers-The State University, New Brunswick, New Jersey.
50. D'ALESANDRO, P. A. (1959) Electrophoretic and ultracentrifugal studies of antibodies to *Trypanosoma lewisi*. *J. Infectious Disease* **105**, 75–95.
51. D'ALESANDRO, P. A. (1962) *In vitro* studies of ablastin, the reproduction-inhibiting antibody to *Trypanosoma lewisi*. *J. Protozool*. **9**, 351–8.
52. DAMIEN, R. T. (1964) Molecular mimicry: antigen sharing by parasite and host and its consequences. *Amer. Naturalist* **98**, 129–49.
53. DAVIS, B. S. (1952) *Studies on the Trypanosomes of some California Mammals*, 249 pp., University of California Press, Berkeley, California.
54. DESOWITZ, R. S. (1959) Studies on immunity and host-parasite relationships. I. The immunological response of resistant and susceptible breeds of cattle to trypanosomal challenge. *Ann. Trop. Med. Parasitol*. **53**, 293–313.
55. DESOWITZ, R. S. (1963) Adaptation of trypanosomes to abnormal hosts. *Ann. N.Y. Acad. Sci*. **113**, 74–82.
56. DINEEN, J. F. (1963) Immunological aspects of parasitism. *Nature* **197**, 268–9. (1963) Antigenic relationship between host and parasite. *Nature* **197**, 471–2.
57. DIXON, F. J. (1963) The role of antigen-antibody complexes in disease. *The Harvey Lectures*, Series 58, 21–52, Academic Press Inc., New York.
58. DIXON, F. J., TALMAGE, D. W., MAURER, P. H., and DEICHMILLER, M. (1952) The half-life of homologous gamma globulin (antibody) in several species. *J. Exper. Med*. **96**, 313–8.
59. DRAPER, L. R., and SUSSDORF, D. H. (1957) The serum hemolysin response in intact and splenectomized rabbits following immunization by various routes. *J. Infectious Diseases* **100**, 147–61.
60. DUTKY, S. R. (1964) Comments on cultivation of the insect cycle of plasmodia. *Amer. J. Trop. Med*. **13**, Suppl., 193–4.
61. DUXBURY, R. E., and SADUN, E. H. (1964) Fluorescent antibody test for the sero-diagnosis of visceral leishmaniasis. *Amer. J. Trop. Med*. **13**, 525–9.
62. EDOZIEN, J. C. (1964) Comments on immunization against malaria. *Amer. J. Trop. Med*. **13**, Suppl., 233–4.
63. FAHEY, J. L. (1962) Heterogeneity of γ-globulins. In *Advances in Immunology* **2**, 42–110, eds. W. H. TALIAFERRO and J. H. HUMPHREY, Academic Press Inc., New York.
64. FARR, R. S. (1958) A quantitative immunochemical measure of the primary inter-action between I*BSA and Antibody. *J. Infectious Diseases* **103**, 239–62.
65. FRANCHINO, E. M. (1959) Factors influencing the course of infection of *Leishmania donovani* in the white mouse. Ph.D. thesis, 74 pp., Rutgers–The State University, New Brunswick, New Jersey.
66. FULTON, J. D. (1963) Acquired immunity: protozoal infections. In *Modern Trends in Immunology* **1**, 145–60, ed. R. CRUICKSHANK, Butterworth and Co., London.
67. GARNHAM, P. C. C., PIERCE, A. E., and ROITT, I. (1963) *Immunity to Protozoa*, 359 pp., Blackwell Scientific Publications, Oxford.
68. GELL, P. G. H., and BENACERRAF, B. (1961) Delayed hypersensitivity to simple protein antigens. In *Advances in Immunology* **1**, 319–43, eds. W. H. TALIAFERRO and J. H. HUMPHREY, Academic Press Inc., New York.
69. GINGRICH, W. (1941) The role of phagocytosis in natural and acquired immunity in avian malaria. *J. Infectious Diseases* **68**, 37–45.
70. GLYNN, L. E. (1963) Auto-immunity. In *Modern Trends in Immunology* **1**, 206–25, ed. R. CRUICKSHANK, Butterworth and Co., London.
71. GOBLE, F. C. (1964) Immunoreactions in antiparasitic chemotherapy. In *Advances in Chemotherapy* **1**, 355–95. Academic Press Inc., New York.

72. GOBLE, F. C., and SINGER, I. (1960) The reticuloendothelial system in experimental malaria and trypanosomiasis. *Ann. N.Y. Acad. Sci.* **88**, 149–71.

73. GRUN, J. (1958) A study of experimental leishmaniasis in the mouse, Mongolian gerbil, hamster, white rat, cotton rat, and chinchilla. Ph.D. thesis, 82 pp., Rutgers–The State University, New Brunswick, New Jersey.

74. HARMON, W. M., and CALLOW, L. L. (1964) The influence of ablastin on the *in vitro* incorporation of adenine and methionine by *Trypanosoma lewisi. J. Protozool.* **11**, Suppl., 16.

75. HARRISON, J. A. (1947) Antigenic variation in protozoa and bacteria. *Ann. Rev. Microbiol.* **1**, 19–42.

76. HARRISON, J. A. (1955) General aspects of immunological reactions with bacteria and protozoa. In *Biological Specificity and Growth*, 141–56, ed. E. G. BUTLER, Princeton University Press, Princeton, New Jersey.

77. HAUROWITZ, F. (1965) Antibody formation. *Phys. Rev.* **45**, 1–47.

78. HEIDELBERGER, M., and PLESCIA, O. S. eds. (1961) *Immunological Approaches to Problems in Microbiology*, 402 pp., Institute of Microbiology, Rutgers–The State University, New Brunswick, New Jersey.

79. HEIDELBERGER, M., TREFFERS, H. P., SCHOENHEIMER, R., RATNER, S. and RITTENBERG, D. (1942) Behavior of antibody protein toward dietary nitrogen in active and passive immunity. *J. Biol. Chem.* **144**, 555–62.

80. HERMAN, R. (1964a) Fluorescent antibody studies with the intracellular form of *Leishmania donovani* in cell culture. *J. Parasitol.* **50** (3, Sec. 2), 18.

81. HERMAN, R. (1964b) Intracellular growth of and fluorescent antibody studies on *Leishmania donovani* in cell culture. Ph.D. thesis. 190 pp., Rutgers–The State University, New Brunswick, New Jersey.

82. HEWITT, R., (1940) Bird malaria. *Amer. J. Hyg. Monograph.* **15**, 228 pp., Johns Hopkins University Press, Baltimore, Maryland.

83. HOLUB, M., and JAROŠKOVÁ, L., eds. (1960) *Mechanisms of Antibody Formation* 385 pp., Czechoslovak Academy of Science, Prague, Czechoslovakia.

84. HUFF, C. G. (1963) Experimental research on avian malaria. In *Advances in Parasitology* **1**, 1–65, ed. B. DAWES, Academic Press Inc., New York.

85. HUFF, C. G. (1964) Cultivation of the exoerythrocytic stages of malarial parasites. *Amer. J. Trop. Med.* **13**, Suppl., 171–7.

86. HUFF, C. G., and COULSTON, F. (1946) The relation of natural and acquired immunity of various avian hosts to the cryptozoites and metacryptozoites of *Plasmodium gallinaceum* and *Plasmodium relictum. J. Infectious Diseases* **78**, 99–117.

87. HUMPHREY, J. H., and WHITE, R. G. (1964) *Immunology for Students of Medicine*, 2nd ed., 498 pp., F. A. Davis Company, Philadelphia, Pennsylvania.

88. INGRAHAM, J. S. (1955) Artificial radioactive antigens. *J. Infectious Diseases* **96**, 105–17.

89. INGRAM, R. L. (1964) Comments on cultivation of exoerythrocytic stages of plasmodia. *Amer. J. Trop. Med.* **13**, Suppl., 178–80.

90. INGRAM, V. M. (1959) Chemistry of the abnormal human haemoglobins. *Brit. Med. Bull.* **15**, 27–32.

91. JACKSON, G. J. (1960) Fluorescent antibody studies of *Nippostrongulus muris* infections. *J. Infectious Diseases* **106**, 20–36.

92. JACOBS, L. (1963) Toxoplasma and toxoplasmosis. *Ann. Rev. Microbiology* **17**, 429–50.

93. JAROSLOW, B. N. (1955) The effect of X-irradiation on immunity of the mouse to *Trypanosoma duttoni. J. Infectious Diseases* **96**, 242–9.

94. JAROSLOW, B. N. (1959) The effects of X or neutron irradiation, India ink blockade, or splenectomy on innate immunity against *Trypanosoma duttoni* in mice. *J. Infectious Diseases* **104**, 119–29.

95. JERNE, N. K. (1951) Study of avidity based on rabbit skin responses to diphtheria toxin-antitoxin mixtures. *Acta Pathol. Microbiol. Scand.* **87**, Suppl., 3–183.

96. JERNE, N. K. (1955) The natural-selection theory of antibody formation. *Proc. Natl. Acad. Sci. U.S.* **41**, 849–57. (1960) Immunological speculations. *Ann. Rev. Microbiol.* **14**, 341–58.

97. JORDAN, H. B. (1957) Host resistance and regulation of the development of *Plasmodium lophurae* in pheasants, coots and domestic pigeons. *J. Parasitol.* **43**, 395–408.

98. JORDAN, H. E. (1938) Comparative hematology. In *Handbook of Hematology* **2**, 699–862, ed. H. DOWNEY, Paul B. Hoeber Inc., New York.

99. KABAT, E. A., and MAYER, M. M. (1961) *Experimental Immunochemistry*, 2nd ed., 905 pp., Charles C. Thomas, Springfield, Illinois.

100. KONOPKA, E. A., GOBLE, F. C., and LEWIS, L. (1961) Effect of prior infection with *Leishmania donovani* on the course of experimental tuberculosis in mice. *Bacteriol. Proc.* 134.

101. KUHNS, W. J. (1959) Certain forms of hypersensitivity in man mediated by antigen–antibody reaction—an experimental approach to the immediate wheal-type allergies. In *Cellular and Humoral Aspects of the Hypersensitive States*, 535–80, ed. H. S. LAWRENCE, Hoeber-Harper, New York.

102. LAINSON, R., and BRAY, R. S. see BRAY, R. S. and LAINSON, R. (1966) The fluorescent antibody technique in leishmaniasis. *Proc. 1st Int. Congr. Parasitol.* **1**, 347–8.

103. LAWRENCE, H. S. (1959) The transfer of hypersensitivity of the delayed type in man. In *Cellular and Humoral Aspects of the Hypersensitive States*, 279–318, ed. H. S. LAWRENCE, Hoeber-Harper, New York.

104. LINCICOME, D. R. (1963) Chemical basis of parasitism. *Ann. N.Y. Acad. Sci.* **113**, 360–80.

105. LOURIE, E. M., and O'CONNOR, R. J. (1937) A study of *Trypanosoma rhodesiense* relapse strains *in vitro. Ann. Trop. Med. Parasitol.* **31**, 319–40.

106. MAEGRAITH, B. G. (1963) Pathogenesis and pathogenic mechanisms in protozoal diseases with special reference to amoebiasis and malaria. In *Immunity to Protozoa*, 48–68, eds. P. C. C. GARNHAM *et al.*, Blackwell Scientific Publications, Oxford.

107. MANSON-BAHR, P. E. C. (1963a) Active immunization in leishmaniasis. In *Immunity to Protozoa*, 246–52, eds. P. C. C. GARNHAM *et al.*, Blackwell Scientific Publications, Oxford.

108. MANSON-BAHR, P. E. C. (1963b) Immunity in the prophylaxis of protozoal diseases. In *Clinical Aspects of Immunology*, 759–74, eds. P. G. H. GELL and R. R. A. COOMBS, Blackwell Scientific Publications, Oxford.

109. MANWELL, R. D. (1963) Factors making for host-parasite specificity, with special emphasis on the blood protozoa. *Ann. N.Y. Acad. Sci.* **113**, 332–42.

110. MAXIMOW, A. A. (1902) Experimentelle Untersuchungen über entzündliche Neubildung von Bindegewebe. *Beitr. z. pathol. Anat.*, Suppl. **5**, 262 pp. See also (1927) Morphology of the mesenchymal reactions. *Arch. Pathol. and Lab. Med.* **4**, 557–606; and (1963) The lymphocytes and plasma cells. In *Special Cytology* **2**, 603–50, ed. E. V. COWDRY, Hafner Publishing Co., Inc., New York.

111. MAYER, M. M., CROFT, C. C., and GRAY, M. M. (1948) Kinetic studies on immune hemolysis. I. A method. *J. Exper. Med.* **88**, 427–44.

112. MCGHEE, R. B. (1957) Comparative susceptibility of various erythrocytes to four species of avian plasmodia. *J. Infectious Diseases* **100**, 92–96.

113. MCGHEE, R. B. (1964) Autoimmunity in malaria. *Amer. J. Trop. Med.* **13**, Suppl., 219–24.

114. MCGREGOR, I. A. (1964) The passive transfer of human malarial immunity. *Amer. J. Trop. Med.* **13**, Suppl., 237–9.

115. MCGREGOR, I. A. (1965) Considerations of some aspects of human malaria. *Trans. Roy. Soc. Trop. Med. Hyg.* **59**, 145–52.

116. MELENEY, H. E. (1925) The histopathology of kala-azar in the hamster, monkey and man. *Amer. J. Pathol.* **1**, 147–68.

117. METCHNIKOFF, E. (1901) *L' immunité dans les maladies infectieuses.* 600 pp. Masson & Cie., Paris. (1905) *Immunity in Infective Diseases*, 591 pp., University Press, Cambridge, England.

118. MOTULSKY, A. G. (1964) Hereditary red cell traits and malaria. *Amer. J. Trop. Med.* **13**, Suppl., 147–58.

119. MOULDER, J. W. (1948) Changes in the glucose metabolism of *Trypanosoma lewisi* during the course of infection in the rat. *J. Infectious Diseases* **83**, 42–49.

120. MOULDER, J. W. (1962) *The Biochemistry of Intracellular Parasitism*, 172 pp., The University of Chicago Press, Chicago.

121. MOULDER, J. W., and TALIAFERRO, W. H. (1955) Reactions of the connective tissue in chickens to *Plasmodium gallinaceum* and *Plasmodium lophurae*. II. Glucose metabolism during initial infections. *J. Infectious Diseases* **97**, 137–42.

122. MUIR, R. (1909) *Studies on Immunity*, 216 pp. Oxford University Press, London.

123. NAIMAN, D. N. (1944) Effect of X-irradiation of rats upon their resistance to *Trypanosoma lewisi*. *J. Parasitol.* **30**, 209–28.

124. NAPIER, L. E. (1946) *The Principles and Practice of Tropical Medicine*, 917 pp., Macmillan and Co., New York.

125. NEEPER, C. A., and SEASTONE, C. V. (1963) Mechanisms of immunologic paralysis by pneumococcal polysaccharide. I. Studies of adoptively acquired immunity to pneumococcal infection in immunologically paralyzed and normal mice. *J. Immunol.* **91**, 374–7.

126. NOSSAL, G. J. V. (1962) Cellular genetics of immune responses. In *Advances in Immunology* **2**, 163–204, eds. W. H. TALIAFERRO and J. H. HUMPHREY, Academic Press Inc., New York.

127. ORMEROD, W. E. (1963) The initial stages of infection with *Trypanosoma lewisi*: Control of parasitaemia by the host. In *Immunity to Protozoa*, 213–27, eds. P. C. C. GARNHAM *et al.*, Blackwell Scientific Publications, Oxford.

128. OTT, K. J. (1964) Aspects of immunity of laboratory rodents to *Leishmania donovani*. Ph.D. thesis, 130 pp., Rutgers–The State University, New Brunswick, New Jersey.

129. OUCHTERLONY, Ö. (1958) Diffusion-in-gel methods for immunological analysis. In *Progress in Allergy* **5**, 1–78, ed. P. KALLÓS, S. Karger, Basel, Switzerland and New York.

130. OUCHTERLONY, Ö. (1962) Diffusion-in-gel methods for immunological analysis. In *Progress in Allergy* **6**, 30–154, eds. P. KALLÓS and B. H. WAKSMAN, S. Karger, Basel, Switzerland and New York.

131. PIZZI, T. (1957) *Immunologia de la Enfermedad de Chagas*, 183 pp., Stanley, Santiago, Chile.

132. PIZZI, T., and TALIAFERRO, W. H. (1960) A comparative study of protein and nucleic acid synthesis in different species of trypanosomes. *J. Infectious Diseases* **107**, 100–7.

133. POWELL, R. D., and BREWER, G. J. (1964) Active immunization against malaria. *Amer. J. Trop. Med.* **13**, Suppl., 228–32.

134. PUTNAM, F. W. (1960) Abnormal serum globulins. In *The Plasma Proteins* **2**, 345–406, ed. F. W. PUTNAM, Academic Press Inc., New York.

135. RABINOWITSCH, L., and KEMPNER, W. (1899) Beitrag zur Kenntniss der Blutparasiten speciell der Rattentrypanosomen. *Ztschr. f. Hyg. u. Infektionskr.* **30**, 251–94.

136. RAFFEL, S. (1961) *Immunity*, 2nd ed., 646 pp., Appleton-Century-Crofts Inc., New York.

137. RAFFEL, S. (1963) Hypersensitivity. In *Trends in Immunology* **1**, 184–205, ed. R. CRUICKSHANK, Butterworth and Co., London.

138. REBUCK, J. W. (1947) The functions of the white blood cells. *Amer. J. Clin. Pathol.* **17**, 614–30.

139. REBUCK, J. W., COFFMAN, H. I., BLUHM, G. B., and BARTH, C. L. (1964) A structural study of reticulum cell and monocyte production with quantitation of lymphocytic modulation of nonmultiplicative type to histocytes. In *Leukopoiesis in Health and Disease*, eds. H. E. WHIPPLE and M. I. SPITZER, *Ann. N.Y. Acad. Sci.* **113**, 595–611.

140. REGENDANZ, P., and KIKUTH, W. (1927) Über die Bedeutung der Milz für die Bildung des vermehrungshindernden Reaktionsproduktes (Taliaferro) und dessen Wirkung auf den Infektionsverlauf der Ratten-Trypanosomiasis (*Tryp. lewisi*). *Ztbl. Bakt. Abt. 1, Orig.* **103**, 271–9.

141. RICH, A. R. (1941) The significance of hypersensitivity in infections. *Physiol. Rev.* **21**, 70–111.

142. RITZ, H. (1914) Neben Rezidive bei experimenteller Trypanosomiasis. *Deutsche Med. Wschr.* **40**, 1355–8. (1916) Über Rezidive bei experimenteller Trypanosomiasis. *Arch. Schiffs- u. Tropenhyg.* **20**, 397–420.

143. ROBERTSON, M. (1939) A study of the reactions *in vitro* of certain ciliates belonging to the Glaucoma-Colpidium group to antibodies in the sera of rabbits immunized therewith. *J. Path. Bact.* **48**, 305–22.

144. ROBERTSON, M. (1963) Antibody response in cattle to infection with *Trichomonas foetus*. In *Immunity to Protozoa*, 336–45, eds. P. C. C. GARNHAM *et al.*, Blackwell Scientific Publications, Oxford.

145. ROSE, M. E. (1963) Some aspects of immunity to *Eimeria* infections. *Ann. N.Y. Acad. Sci.* **113**, 383–99.

146. ROSSAN, R. N. (1959) The serum proteins of animals infected with *Leishmania donovani* with special reference to electrophoretic patterns. Ph.D. thesis, 214 pp., Rutgers–The State University, New Brunswick, New Jersey.

147. ROSSAN, R. N. (1960) Serum protein of animals infected with *Leishmania donovani*, with special reference to electrophoretic patterns. *Exper. Parasitol.* **9**, 302–33.

148. RYLEY, J. F. (1951) Studies on the metabolism of the protozoa. *Biol. Chem.* **49**, 577–85.

149. SHAW, J. J., and VOLLER, A. (1964) The detection of circulating antibodies to kala-azar by means of immunofluorescent techniques. *Trans. Roy. Soc. Trop. Med. Hyg.* **58**, 349–52.

150. SHERWOOD, N. P. (1951) *Immunology*, 3rd ed., 731 pp., C. V. Mosby Co., St. Louis, Missouri.

151. SINGER, I. (1953) The effect of X-irradiation on infections with *Plasmodium berghei* in the white mouse. *J. Infectious Diseases* **92**, 97–104.

152. SINGER, I. (1954a) The effect of splenectomy or phenylhydrazine on infections with *Plasmodium berghei* in the white mouse. *J. Infectious Diseases* **94**, 159–63.

153. SINGER, I. (1954b) The effect of cortisone on infections with *Plasmodium berghei* in the white mouse. *J. Infectious Diseases* **94**, 164–72.

154. SINGER, I. (1954c) The cellular reactions to infections with *Plasmodium berghei* in the white mouse. *J. Infectious Diseases* **94**, 241–61.

155. SINGER, I., KIMBLE, E. T., III, and RITTS, JR., R. E. (1964) Alterations of the host-parasite relationship by administration of endotoxin to mice with infections of trypanosomes. *J. Infectious Diseases* **114**, 243–8.

156. SOLTYS, M. A., and FOLKERS, C. (1963) The effect of immunity on chemotherapy in trypanosomiasis. In *Immunity to Protozoa*, 228–34, eds. P. C. C. GARNHAM *et al.*, Blackwell Scientific Publications, Oxford.

157. STANWORTH, D. R. (1963) Reaginic antibodies. In *Advances in Immunology* **3**, 181–260, eds. F. J. DIXON, JR., and J. H. HUMPHREY, Academic Press Inc., New York.

158. STAUBER, L. A. (1939) Factors influencing the asexual periodicity of avian malaria. *J. Parasitol.* **25**, 95–116.

159. STAUBER, L. A. (1954) Application of electrophoretic techniques in the field of parasitic diseases. *Exper. Parasitol.* **3**, 544–68.

160. STAUBER, L. A. (1955) Leishmaniasis in the hamster. In *Some Physiological Aspects and Consequences of Parasitism*, 76–90, ed. W. H. COLE, Rutgers University Press, New Brunswick, New Jersey.

161. STAUBER, L. A. (1958) Host resistance to the Khartoum strain of *Leishmania donovani*. *Rice Institute Pamphlet* 45, 80–96. The Rice Institute, Houston, Texas.

162. STAUBER, L. A. (1962) Some recent studies in experimental leishmaniasis. *Sci. Repts. Ist. Super. Sanità* 2, 68–75.

163. STAUBER, L. A. (1963a) Immunity to leishmania. *Ann. N.Y. Acad. Sci.* 113, 409–17.

164. STAUBER, L. A. (1963b) Some aspects of immunity to intracellular protozoan parasites. *J. Parasitol.* 49, 3–11.

165. STAUBER, L. A. (1963c) Characterization of strains of *Leishmania donovani*. *Proc. VIIth Int. Congr. Trop. Med. Malaria (Rio)*, Abstracts, 187. Also (1966) *Exper. Parasitol.* 18, 1–11.

166. STAVITSKY, A. B. (1961) *In vitro* studies of the antibody response. In *Advances in Immunology* 1, 211–61, eds. W. H. TALIAFERRO and J. H. HUMPHREY, Academic Press Inc., New York.

167. STELOS, P., and TALIAFERRO, W. H. (1959) Comparative study of rabbit hemolysins to various antigens. *J. Infectious Diseases* 104, 105–18.

168. SUSSDORF, D. H. (1959) Quantitative changes in the white and red pulp of the spleen during hemolysin formation in X-irradiated and nonirradiated rabbits. *J. Infectious Diseases* 105, 238–52.

169. SYMMERS, W. S. C. (1960) Leishmaniasis acquired by contagion. *Lancet*, Jan. 16, 1960, 127–32.

170. TALIAFERRO, W. H. (1924) A reaction product in infections with *Trypanosoma lewisi* which inhibits the reproduction of the trypanosomes. *J. Exper. Med.* 39, 171–90.

171. TALIAFERRO, W. H. (1929) *The Immunology of Parasitic Infections*, 414 pp., Century Company, New York.

172. TALIAFERRO, W. H. (1932) Trypanocidal and reproduction-inhibiting antibodies to *Trypanosoma lewisi* in rats and rabbits. *Amer. J. Hyg.* 16, 32–84.

172a. TALIAFERRO, W. H. (1938) Ablastic and trypanocidal antibodies against *Trypanosoma duttoni*. *J. Immunol.* 35, 303–28.

173. TALIAFERRO, W. H. (1941) The immunology of the parasitic protozoa. In *Protozoa in Biological Research*, 830–89, eds. G. N. CALKINS and F. M. SUMMERS, Columbia University Press, New York.

174. TALIAFERRO, W. H. (1948a) The inhibition of reproduction of parasites by immune factors. *Bacteriol. Rev.* 12, 1–17.

175. TALIAFERRO, W. H. (1948b) The role of the spleen and the lymphoid-macrophage system in the quinine treatment of gallinaceum malaria. Acquired immunity and phagocytosis. *J. Infectious Diseases* 83, 164–80.

176. TALIAFERRO, W. H. (1949a) Immunity to the malaria infections: In *Malariology* 2, 935–65, ed. M. F. BOYD, Saunders Co., Philadelphia, Pennsylvania.

177. TALIAFERRO, W. H. (1949b) The cellular basis of immunity. *Ann. Rev. Microbiol.* 3, 159–94.

178. TALIAFERRO, W. H. (1955) Host-parasite relationships. In *Biological Specificity and Growth*, 157–76, ed. E. G. BUTLER, Princeton University Press, Princeton, New Jersey.

179. TALIAFERRO, W. H. (1956) Functions of the spleen in immunity. *Amer. J. Trop. Med.* 5, 391–410.

180. TALIAFERRO, W. H. (1957) General introduction: Synthesis and degradation of antibody. *J. Cellular Comp. Physiol.* 50, Suppl. 1, 1–26.

181. TALIAFERRO, W. H. (1958) The synthesis and activities of antibodies. *Rice Institute Pamphlet* 45, 114–40, The Rice Institute, Houston, Texas.

182. TALIAFERRO, W. H. (1962) Remarks on the immunology of leishmaniasis. *Sc. Rep. Istituto Superiore di Sanità* 2, 138–42. Elsevier Publ. Co., Amsterdam.

183. TALIAFERRO, W. H. (1963) The cellular and humoral factors in immunity to protozoa. In *Immunity to Protozoa*, 22–38, eds. P. C. C. GARNHAM *et al.*, Blackwell Scientific Publications, Oxford.

184. TALIAFERRO, W. H., and CANNON, P. R. (1936) The cellular reactions during primary infections and superinfections of *Plasmodium brasilianum* in Panamanian monkeys. *J. Infectious Diseases* **59**, 72–125.

185. TALIAFERRO, W. H., CANNON, P. R., and GOODLOE, S. (1931) The resistance of rats to infection with *Trypanosoma lewisi* as affected by splenectomy. *Amer. J. Hyg.* **14**, 1–37.

186. TALIAFERRO, W. H., and JOHNSON, T. L. (1926) Zone phenomena *in vivo* trypanolysis and the therapeutic value of trypanolytic sera. *J. Preventive Med.* **1**, 85–123.

187. TALIAFERRO, W. H., and KELSEY, F. E. (1948) The role of the spleen and the lymphoid–macrophage system in the quinine treatment of gallinaceum malaria. II. Quinine blood levels. *J. Infectious Diseases* **83**, 181–99.

188. TALIAFERRO, W. H., and MULLIGAN, H. W. (1937) The histopathology of malaria with special reference to the function and origin of the macrophages in defence. *Indian Med. Res. Memoirs* **29**, 1–138. Thacker, Spink and Co., Ltd., Calcutta, India.

189. TALIAFERRO, W. H., and PAVLINOVA, Y. (1936) The course of infection of *Trypanosoma duttoni* in normal and in splenectomized and blockaded mice. *J. Parasitol.* **22**, 29–41.

190. TALIAFERRO, W. H., and PIZZI, T. (1955) Connective tissue reactions in normal and immunized mice to a reticulotropic strain of *Trypanosoma cruzi*. *J. Infectious Diseases* **96**, 199–226.

191. TALIAFERRO, W. H., and PIZZI, T. (1960) The inhibition of nucleic acid and protein synthesis in *Trypanosoma lewisi* by the antibody ablastin. *Proc. Natl. Acad. Sci. U.S.* **46**, 733–45.

192. TALIAFERRO, W. H., and SARLES, M. P. (1939) The cellular reactions in the skin, lungs and intestine of normal and immune rats after infection with *Nippostrongylus muris*. *J. Infectious Diseases* **64**, 157–92.

193. TALIAFERRO, W. H., and SARLES, M. P. (1942) The histopathology of the skin, lungs and intestine of rats during passive immunity to *Nippostrongylus muris*. *J. Infectious Diseases* **71**, 69–82.

194. TALIAFERRO, W. H., and TALIAFERRO, L. G. (1934) Morphology, periodicity and course of infection of *Plasmodium brasilianum* in Panamanian monkeys. *Amer. J. Hyg.* **20**, 1–49.

195. TALIAFERRO, W. H., and TALIAFERRO, L. G. (1944) The effect of immunity on the asexual reproduction of *Plasmodium brasilianum*. *J. Infectious Diseases* **75**, 1–32.

196. TALIAFERRO, W. H., and TALIAFERRO, L. G. (1948) Reduction in immunity in chicken malaria following treatment with nitrogen mustard. *J. Infectious Diseases* **82**, 5–30.

197. TALIAFERRO, W. H., and TALIAFERRO, L. G. (1949) The role of the spleen and lymphoid-macrophage system in the quinine treatment of gallinaceum malaria. III. The action of quinine and of immunity on the parasite. *J. Infectious Diseases* **84**, 187–220.

198. TALIAFERRO, W. H., and TALIAFERRO, L. G. (1950) The dynamics of hemolysin formation in intact and splenectomized rabbits. *J. Infectious Diseases* **87**, 37–62.

199. TALIAFERRO, W. H., and TALIAFERRO, L. G. (1951) Effect of X-rays on immunity: A review. *J. Immunol.* **66**, 181–212.

200. TALIAFERRO, W. H., and TALIAFERRO, L. G. (1955) Reactions of the connective tissue in chickens to *Plasmodium gallinaceum* and *Plasmodium lophurae*. I. Histopathology during initial infection and superinfections. *J. Infectious Diseases* **97**, 99–136.

201. TALIAFERRO, W. H., and TALIAFERRO, L. G. (1956) X-ray effects on hemolysin formation in rabbits with the spleen shielded or irradiated. *J. Infectious Diseases* **99**, 109–28.

202. TALIAFERRO, W. H., and TALIAFERRO, L. G. (1957) Amino acid incorporation into precipitin at different stages in the secondary response to bovine serum albumin. *J. Infectious Diseases* **101**, 252–74.

203. TALIAFERRO, W. H., and TALIAFERRO, L. G. (1961) Intercellular transfer of gamma-1 and gamma-2 Forssman hemolysins. *Proc. Natl. Acad. Sci. U.S.* **47**, 713–24.

204. TALIAFERRO, W. H., and TALIAFERRO, L. G. (1962) Immunologic unresponsiveness during the initial and anamnestic Forssman hemolysin response. *J. Infectious Diseases* **110**, 165–200.

205. TALIAFERRO, W. H., TALIAFERRO, L. G., and JAROSLOW, B. N. (1964) *Radiation and Immune Mechanisms.*, 152 pp., Academic Press Inc., New York.

206. TALIAFERRO, W. H., TALIAFERRO, L. G., and PIZZI, A. K. (1959) Avidity and intercellular transfer of hemolysin. *J. Infectious Diseases* **105**, 197–221.

207. TALIAFERRO, W. H., TALIAFERRO, L. G., and SIMMONS, E. L. (1945) Increased parasitemia in chicken malaria (*Plasmodium gallinaceum* and *Plasmodium lophurae*) following X-irradiation. *J. Infectious Diseases* **77**, 158–76.

208. TALIAFERRO, W. H., and TALMAGE, D. W. (1955) Absence of amino acids incorporation into antibody during the induction period. *J. Infectious Diseases* **97**, 88–98.

209. TALMAGE, D. W. (1957) Allergy and immunology. *Ann. Rev. Med.* **8**, 239–56.

210. TALMAGE, D. W., and CANN, J. R. (1961) *The Chemistry of Immunity in Health and Disease*, 178 pp., Charles C. Thomas, Springfield, Illinois.

211. TALMAGE, D. W., FRETER, G. G., and TALIAFERRO, W. H. (1956) The effect of repeated injections of sheep red cells on the hemolytic and combining capacities of rabbit antiserum. *J. Infectious Diseases* **98**, 293–9.

212. TALMAGE, D. W., and PEARLMAN, D. S. (1963) The antibody response: a model based on antagonistic actions of antigen. *J. Theoret. Biol.* **5**, 321–39.

213. THILLET, C. H. JR., and CHANDLER, A. C. (1957) Immunization against *Trypanosoma lewisi* in rats by injections of metabolic products. *Science* **125**, 346–7.

214. THURSTON, J. P. (1958) The oxygen uptake of *Trypanosoma lewisi* and *Trypanosoma equiperdum* with especial reference to oxygen consumption in the presence of aminoacids. *Parasitol.* **48**, 149–64.

215. TOBIE, J. E. (1964) Detection of malarial antibodies—immunodiagnosis. *Amer. J. Trop. Med.* **13**, Suppl., 195–203.

216. TRAGER, W. (1964) Cultivation and physiology of erythrocytic stages of plasmodia. *Amer. J. Trop. Med.* **13**, Suppl., 162–6.

217. WEINRACH, R. S., and TALMAGE, D. W. (1958) The role of antibody in immune hemolysis. *J. Infectious Diseases* **102**, 74–80.

218. WEITZ, B. (1963a) The antigenicity of some African trypanosomes. In *Immunity to Protozoa*, 196–203, eds. P. C. C. GARNHAM et al., Blackwell Scientific Publications, Oxford.

219. WEITZ, B. (1963b) Immunological relationships between African trypanosomes and their hosts. *Ann. N.Y. Acad. Sci.* **113**, 400–8.

220. WELLS, H. G. (1929) *The Chemical Aspects of Immunity*, 2nd ed., 286 pp., The Chemical Catalog Co., Inc., New York.

221. WHIPPLE, H. E., ed. (1963) Some biochemical and immunological aspects of host-parasite relationships. *Ann. N.Y. Acad. Sci.* **113**, 1–510.

222. WHIPPLE, H. E., and SPITZER, M. I., eds. (1964) Leukopoiesis in Health and Disease. *Ann. N.Y. Acad. Sci.* **113**, 511–1092.

223. WHITE, R. G. (1963) Immunological functions of lympho-reticular tissues. In *Clinical Aspects of Immunology*, 213–45, eds. P. G. H. GELL and R. R. A. COOMBS, Blackwell Scientific Publications, Oxford.

224. WILLIAMSON, J. (1963) The chemical composition of trypanosomes. II. Cytoplasmic constituents and drug resistance. *Exper. Parasitol.* **13**, 348–66.

225. WILLIAMSON, J., and BROWN, K. N. (1964) The chemical composition of trypanosomes. III. Antigenic constituents of *brucei* trypanosomes. *Exper. Parasitol.* **15,** 44–68.
226. WILLIAMSON, J., and DESOWITZ, R. S. (1961) The chemical composition of trypanosomes. I. Protein, amino acid and sugar analysis. *Exper. Parasitol.* **11,** 161–75.
227. WOLSTENHOLME, G. E. W., and O'CONNOR, M., eds. (1960) *Cellular Aspects of Immunity,* Ciba Foundation Symposium, 495 pp. Little, Brown and Co., Boston, Massachusetts.
228. WOLSTENHOLME, G. E. W., and KNIGHT, J., eds. (1963) *The Immunologically Competent Cell: Its Nature and Origin.* Ciba Foundation Study Group **16,** 1–110. Little, Brown and Co., Boston, Massachusetts.
229. WORLD HEALTH ORGANIZATION (1964) Nomenclature for human immunoglobulins. *Bull. Wld. Health. Org.* **30,** 447–50.
230. ZUCKERMAN, A. (1963) Immunity in malaria with particular reference to red-cell destruction. In *Immunity to Protozoa,* 78–88, eds. P. C. C. GARNHAM *et al.,* Blackwell Scientific Publications, Oxford.
231. ZUCKERMAN, A. (1964a) The antigenic analysis of plasmodia. *Amer. J. Trop. Med.* **13,** Suppl., 209–13.
232. ZUCKERMAN, A. (1964b) Autoimmunization and other types of indirect damage to host cells as factors in certain protozoan diseases. *Exper. Parasitol.* **15,** 138–83.

ORGANISMS LIVING ON AND IN
PROTOZOA†

Gordon H. Ball

Department of Zoology,
University of California, Los Angeles

† Aided by Grant Zoology 254, University of California, and by Grant 414, National Science Foundation. The assistance of Dr. Jacqueline Hynes, especially in compiling the bibliographic material, is gratefully acknowledged. This manuscript was completed December 20, 1965.

CONTENTS

INTRODUCTION

In 1941, the late Harold Kirby wrote a chapter with the above heading in the volume, *Protozoa in Biological Research*.[166] In the opinion of most protozoologists, Kirby's masterful treatment of the subject cannot be equalled. It was the most complete compilation up to that time dealing with symbiotic relationships between Protozoa and other organisms associated with them. In addition to its completeness, Kirby's paper was almost the only one of its kind ever written, and no similar work has appeared since.

The present writer intended originally to rewrite Kirby's chapter, with the aim of including findings made since 1940. Various circumstances made this plan inadvisable. This was probably a fortunate occurrence, since Kirby's chapter should not be tampered with. Instead, an entirely new chapter has been written, including only work which has appeared since Kirby's manuscript was completed. Because the topics covered are essentially those treated in Chapter XX of *Protozoa in Biological Research*, and because the present writer feels that the original title of this chapter cannot be improved upon, it has also been used in this review.

In many instances, where merely additional examples of types of associations described by Kirby have been found, and where no new facts of an essential nature have been added, reference will be made to the earlier work. In other cases, however, previously unknown associations of organisms have been discovered since 1941 and these will be discussed at greater length. Two examples are the association between a bacterium and *Crithidia oncopelti*, reflected in an altered nutritive pattern, and the discovery of particles in certain ciliates associated with what has come to be known as a "killer" characteristic.

In any discussion of organisms living on or in Protozoa, terminology becomes of great importance. How can we decide whether certain organisms are parasites, commensals, or mutualists? Some associations may be purely phoretic. In other instances, it becomes a matter of semantics whether a relationship is called predation or parasitism, since the two members concerned are of nearly equal size. And although Kirby[165] and others have pointed out that the term symbiosis should be used to include commensalism, mutualism, and parasitism, this view has not been universally accepted, and symbiosis is still used by many workers to mean mutualism.

For a number of associations between Protozoa and other organisms, the exact type of relationship has never been demonstrated. Yet endoplasmic bacteria in Protozoa are often called "endosymbionts" (meaning endomutualists), and fungi or protozoans destroying or "eating" Protozoa smaller than themselves are called "parasites". Since we do not know the type of association in many cases, it would be preferable to use descriptive terms of the above sort only when we are certain of the relationship. However, this procedure may result in awkward terminology, and we may be forced at times to use less precise terms than is desirable, mainly because of lack of information. The writer asks indulgence of purists in terminology where he has chosen what he believes to be clarity over circumlocution.

The following definitions are those preferred by the present author. Like all definitions in biology, they may not be mutually exclusive, but may grade into one another.

Symbiosis—a relatively intimate association of two or more organisms. It includes:

(a) Commensalism—an association maintained because of a common food supply.

(b) Mutualism—an association of benefit to all its members.

(c) Parasitism—an association in which one organism lives on or in another organism at the latter's expense. Usually the parasite is considerably smaller than the other organism, the host.

Predation—an association in which one organism feeds on another organism, which is either smaller than or approximately the same size as the predator.

Phoresy—the presence of one organism on the outside of another organism.

Epibiont—an organism living on the outside of another; in the present context, living on the outside of a protozoan.

Endobiont—an organism living inside a protozoan.

If it is not evident to the reader at the beginning, it will soon become clear how unsatisfactory these definitions frequently are in describing the relationships between Protozoa and the organisms that live on or in them.

The organisms associated with Protozoa in one or more of the ways mentioned above belong to the groups Bacteria and Spirochaetes, Fungi, Algae, Viruses, other Protozoa, and Metazoa. In addition, the nature of some of the associates has not been definitely settled. In this latter group, we would include the particles associated with the killer property in certain ciliates.

The types of association will be considered under the above headings.

BACTERIA AND SPIROCHAETES

Epibionts. Most of the known epibionts live on the flagellates found in termites. After 1940, Kirby added extensively to his previous reports,[167, 169, 170, 172, 174] and dealt especially with those forms found on the devescovinid flagellates, a group of the trichomonads. The Devescovininae are very closely associated with these microorganisms, which may cover the

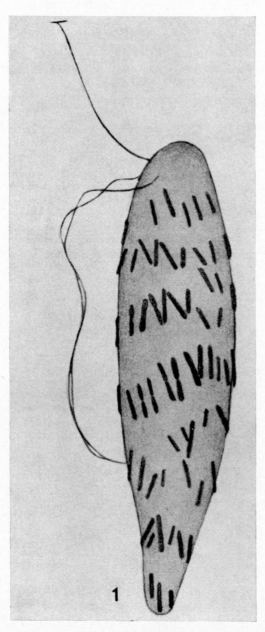

FIG. 1. Bacteria on termite flagellate, *Devescovina elongata*. (From Kirby, 1941.)

entire surface (Figs. 1, 2, 3, 4) or be attached only at the ends of the protozoan's body (Figs. 5, 6). The association is of such a nature that for any one kind of devescovinid, there is a characteristic type of surface microorganism, often found on all individuals of the species. Although this association is probably not a valid taxonomic character, it is useful in recognizing certain genera of devescovinids.[167]

The epibionts are rods, described as fusiformis-like, or are spirochaetes. Figures 1, 2, 5–13 show some of these microorganisms and their patterns of arrangement.[167, 169, 172, 174] In *Macrotrichomonas virgosa*[169] there is a

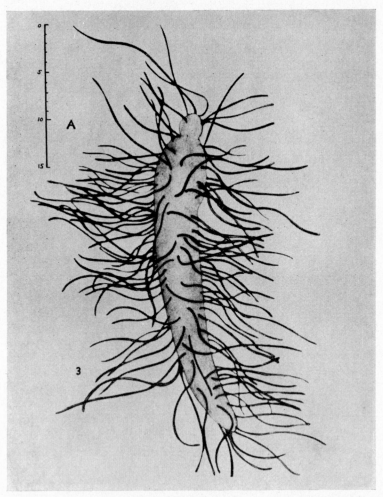

FIG. 2. Adherent spirochaetes on termite flagellate. *Devescovina elongata.* (From Kirby, 1941.)

deep-staining cup-like concavity into which large rod-shaped epibionts fit and from which they readily become detached (Figs. 9–11), and in *Foaina signata*,[170] there are surface rings, occasionally with a spheroidal portion extending into the cytoplasm (Figs. 14–15). These types of attachment are especially interesting in view of the findings of Cleveland and Grimstone[44] that spirochaetes and bacteria on *Mixotricha paradoxa* are also associated with certain structures on the body, and that the spirochaetes play an essential role in the locomotion of the flagellate. This phenomenon will be discussed later.

Various other investigators have reported the presence of bacteria and spirochaetes on termite flagellates from many parts of the world.[42, 80,

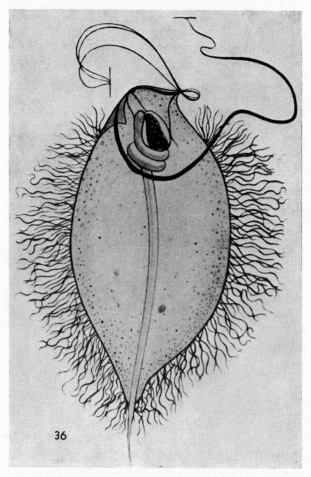

FIG. 3. Spirochaetes adhering to body of termite flagellate, *Devescovina vestita*. (From Kirby, 1941.)

19*

116, 120, 121) These epibionts may also be limited to certain regions of the body; for example they are found only on the posterior end of *Rostronympha magna* or they may be attached along the entire surface as in *Polymastix lineatus*.[80] In some forms, their arrangement is so regular that they were originally mistaken for surface striations, as in *Streblomastix strix*[121] or in *Urinympha* sp. from the wood roach *Cryptocercus*. The bacterial nature of the latter was demonstrated by feeding the roach penicillin, whereupon the surface striations disappeared.[42] The striations on *Streblomastix* were recognized as bacteria when they were examined under the electron microscope.[121, 308]

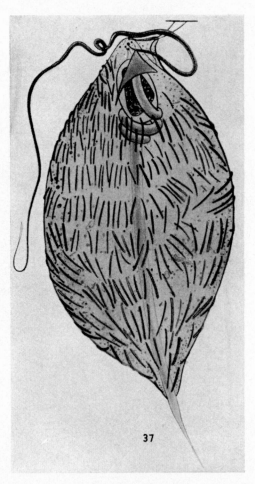

FIG. 4. Rods adhering to body of termite flagellate, *Devescovina vestita*.
(From Kirby, 1941.)

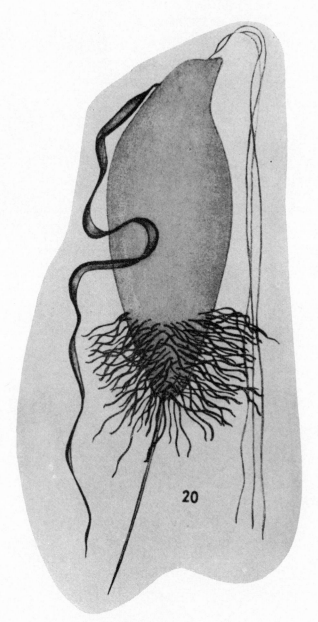

FIG. 5. Spirochaetes attached to posterior end of termite flagellate, *Glypto-termes* sp. (From Kirby, 1945.)

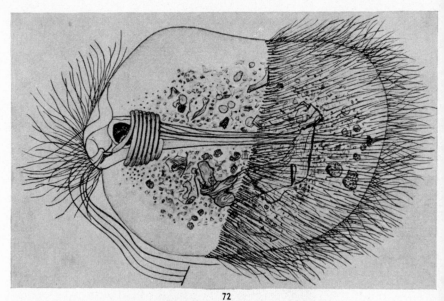

72

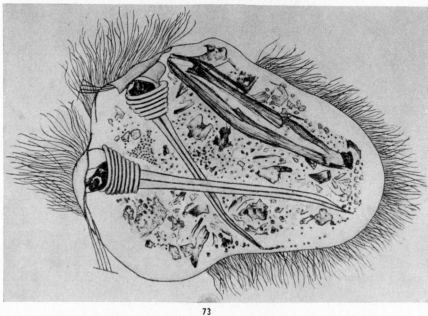

73

FIG. 6. Spirochaetes attached anteriorly and posteriorly to outside of body of termite flagellate, *Hyperdevescovina torquata*, 73—Double flagellate, each mastigont with a group of spirochaetes. (From Kirby, 1949.)

Cross,[47] working in Kirby's laboratory, carried out an extensive study of the subfamily Oxymonadinae in termites belonging to the family Kalotermitidae. She paid considerable attention to the epibionts of four species. In *Oxymonas grandis* (Fig. 16), rods were arranged evenly over the entire body, while spirochaetes were strictly limited to one side of the rostellum, just above the shoulder of the axostyle in a region occupied by one pair of flagella and on the opposite side of the axostyle from the nucleus. In the other species, the flagellate bodies were more or less completely covered by

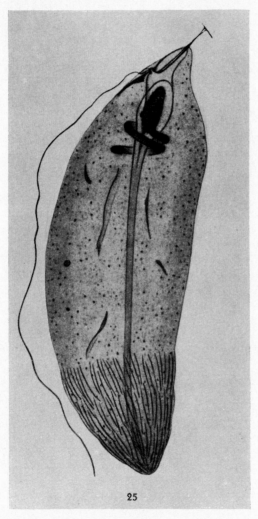

25

FIG. 7. Rodlike bacteria adhering to posterior part of body only, of termite flagellate, *Devescovina tendicula*. (From Kirby, 1941.)

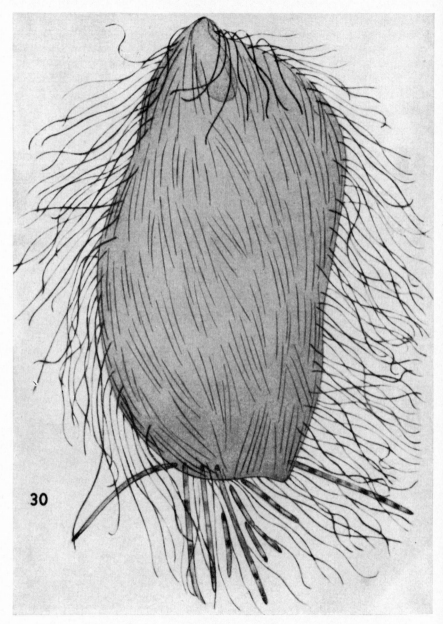

FIG. 8. Spirochaetes and rods adhering to body of termite flagellate, *Devescovina parasoma.* (From Kirby, 1941.)

bacteria and spirochaetes (Fig. 16) which did not show the limited distribution observed for *O. grandis* spirochaetes.

In none of the studies described above, has there been provided any proof, or in most instances even any suggestion, of the function of these epibionts. It remained for Cleveland and Grimstone,[44] using a combination of electron microscopy and cinematography, to demonstrate a vital role of the spirochaetes of *Mixotricha paradoxa* from *Mastotermes darwiniensis* in the locomotion of the flagellate. The outside of the body is covered by a layer of spirochaetes and bacteria. Their general arrangement is shown in Fig. 17. The methods of attachment of these microorganisms to the surface of *Mixotricha* are highly adaptive and complex, and are illustrated in Figs. 18 and 19. Almost the entire surface is drawn out into rows of projecting brackets as shown in Fig. 18. At the anterior face of each bracket is a bac-

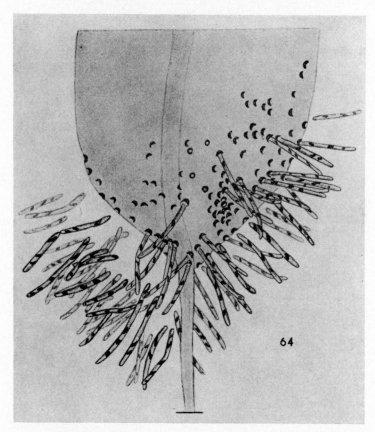

FIG. 9. Rods at posterior end of termite flagellate, *Macrotrichomonas virgosa*. Detached rods show cuplike structures in cytoplasm. (From Kirby, 1942.)

19a   RP III

terium, and attached about half-way up the posterior face are one or more spirochaetes. The spirochaetes fit into depressions in the plasma membrane (Fig. 19). There may be some adhesive material in each depression but bacteria apparently adhere to the plasma membrane by means of an external covering. (In *Streblomastix strix*, Grimstone[121] noted that the epibiotic bacteria were attached to the cell by narrow prolongations into the plasma membrane.)

Mixotricha has four anterior flagella; cinematographic studies[44] indicate that they are probably of no significance in the organism's locomotion except perhaps to change its direction. Locomotion is due to a series of metachronal waves of undulations of the spirochaetes attached to the flagellate's body. These waves pass back rapidly from the anterior end of

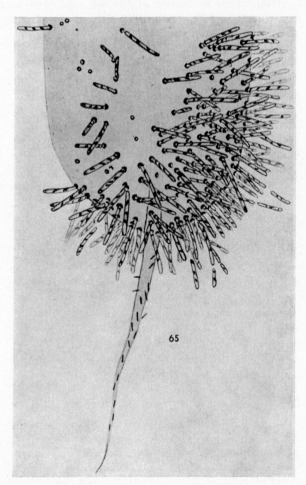

FIG. 10. Rods attached to cup-shaped structures on posterior end of termite flagellate, *Macrotrichomonas virgosa*. (From Kirby, 1942.)

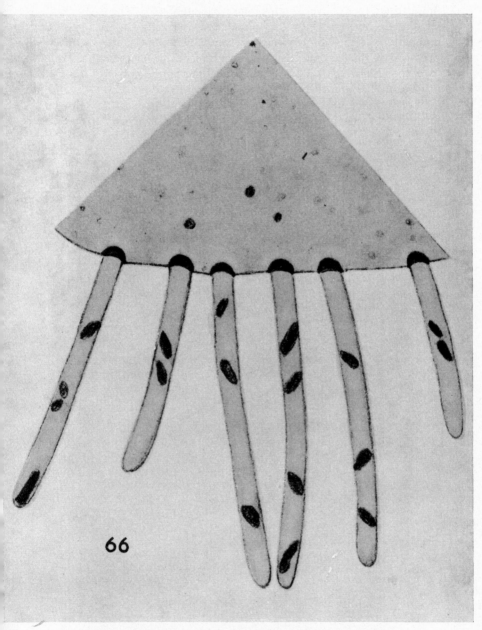

FIG. 11. Semi-diagrammatic view of cuplike structures at posterior end of termite flagellate, *Macrotrichomonas virgosa*. (From Kirby, 1942.)

Mixotricha; their wave length is approximately 10 μ. The high degree of coordinated movement by the spirochaetes is believed to be the result of undulations of the closely placed microorganisms, and not to be due to any structures in the flagellate. This is a very remarkable function to be exhibited by organisms living on a protozoan. The film prepared by Dr. Cleveland[43] is particularly impressive.

It should be noted that in 1945 Nurse[222] suggested that spirochaetes might play a role in the locomotion of the termite flagellate, *Hyperdevesco-*

FIG. 12. Drawings made of living flagellates from termites and showing epibiont bacteria and spirochaetes. 6. *Foaina hilli* from *Glyptotermes iridipennis*. 7. *Metadevescovina debilis* from *Kalotermes hubbardi*. 8. Portion of body of *M. debilis* showing adherent spirochaetes and filamentous microorganisms. (From Kirby, 1945.)

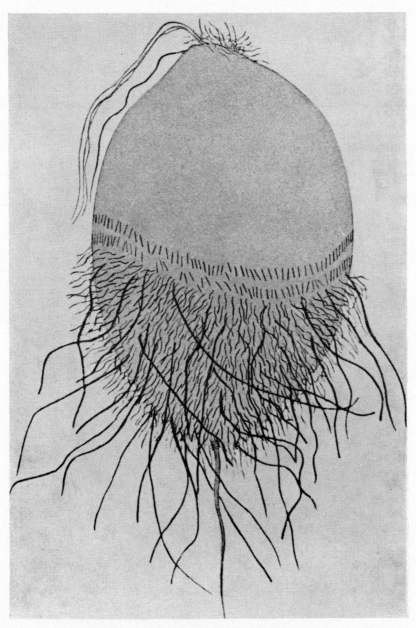

FIG. 13. Adherent microorganisms and belt of peripheral rods in body of termite flagellate, *Hyperdevescovina caudata*. (From Kirby, 1949.)

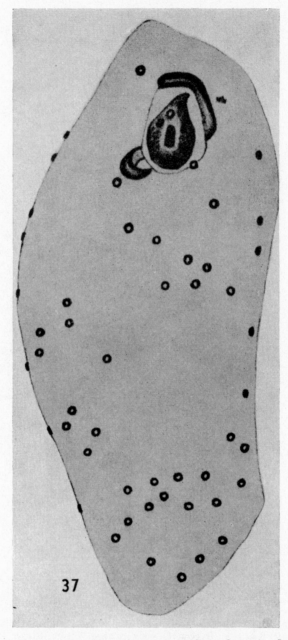

FIG. 14. Disc-shaped bodies adherent to surface of termite flagellate,
Foaina signata. (From Kirby, 1942.)

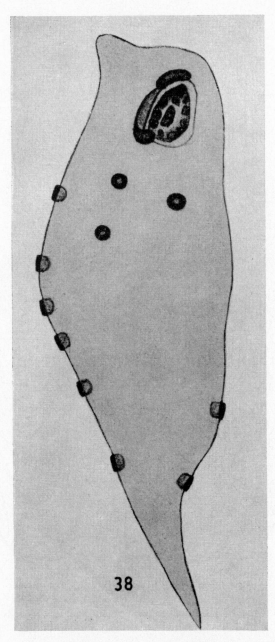

FIG. 15. Disc-shaped bodies adherent to surface of termite flagellate,
Foaina signata. (From Kirby, 1942.)

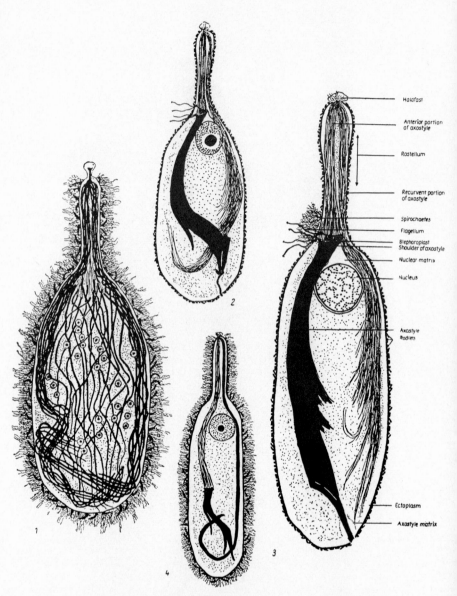

FIG. 16. Oxymonad flagellates showing ectobionts of various kinds. (From Cross, 1946).

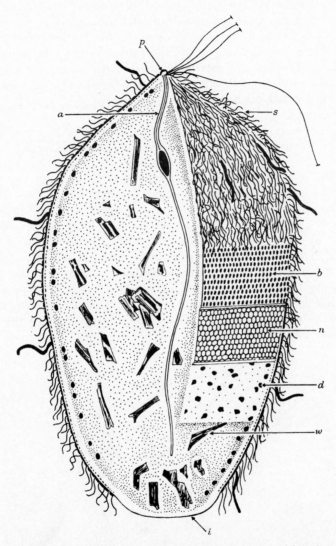

FIG. 17. Diagram of *Mixotricha paradoxa*. Organism in optical section on left; on right surface, structures shown at a series of deeper levels passing backwards. Dimensions of some surface structures slightly exaggerated for clarity. Spirochaetes drawn as they appear in fixed preparations; brackets not shown. a—Axostyle; b—bacterium; d—dictyosome; i—ingestive zone; n—fibrous network; p—papilla; s—spirochaete; w—wood. (From Cleveland and Grimstone, 1964.)

vina calotermitidis. He found that when he removed the surface spirochaetes by feeding the hosts acid fuchsin, the flagellates no longer swam normally, but remained practically motionless. However, Kirby[174] thought that it was "inconceivable that the activity of adherent microorganisms should be so coordinated that they are able to function in the manner of cilia in the locomotion of their host". This would still be the view of most protozoologists, if it had not been for the investigations of Cleveland[43] and of Cleveland and Grimstone[44] referred to above.

Another organism, in which the electron microscope has indicated that structures originally believed to be an integral part of the body of a protozoan are actually epibionts, is *Lophomonas striata,* a flagellate of the cockroach. The so-called body striations have been shown to consist of rods lying on the highly folded surface of this organism[18] (Fig. 20). The rods divide by transverse fission and show structural features of bacteria. Grassé[116] called them *Fusiformis lophomonadis.* They are considered as bacteria by various other investigators.[116, 121, 298, 310] It has been suggested, but without experimental evidence, that a mutualistic relationship involving a nutritive contribution by the bacteria exists between the two kinds of organisms.[18]

Wenrich[310] noted the occurrence of bacteria on various intestinal flagellates of mammals and amphibia. There is no evidence that these are more than casual associates.

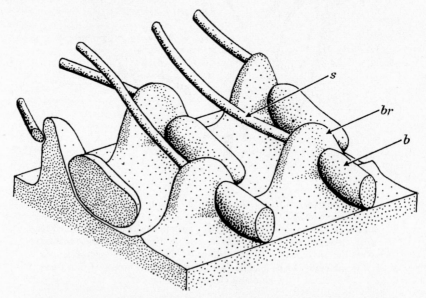

FIG. 18. Reconstruction of small area of cell surface of *Mixotricha paradoxa* to show shape of brackets (br) and the arrangement of the bacteria (b) and spirochaetes (s). (From Cleveland and Grimstone, 1964.)

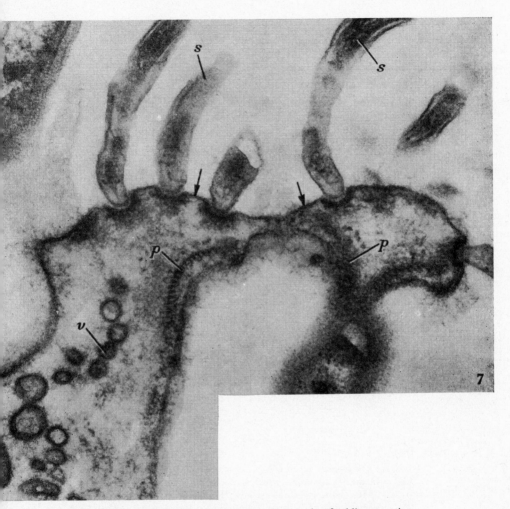

FIG. 19. *Mixotricha paradoxa*—Electron micrograph of oblique section through two brackets from anterior region of cell. Bracket on left with three spirochaetes and trace of fourth attached to it. Bracket on right with at least two spirochaetes. p—striated plates; s—spirochaetes; v—vacuoles. (From Cleveland and Grimstone, 1964.)

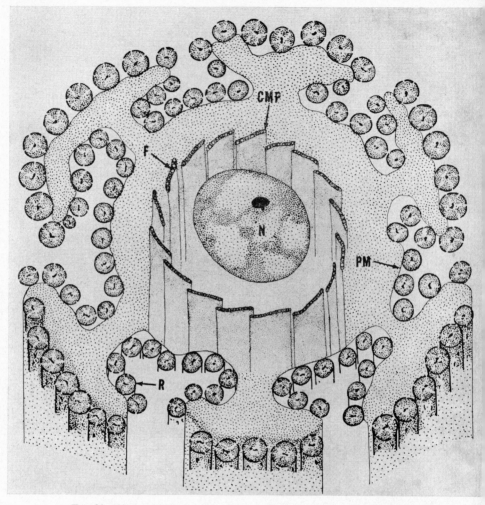

FIG. 20. Diagrammatic cross-section of *Lophomonas striata*, showing its fine structure. Bacteria-like rods (R) located on surface of highly folded body. CMP—calyx membrane plates; F—filaments; N—nucleus; PM—plasma membrane. (From Beams, King, Tahmisian and Devine, 1960).

Among free-living protozoa, chrysomonads,[103] euglenoids,[301] a polytomid,[267] *Volvox*,[127] and psammophilic ciliates[91, 92, 93] have been found to possess epibiotic bacteria.

In the gelatinous sheath of the chrysomonad, *Chrysostephanosphaera globulifera*, Geitler[103] found unicellular "bacteria-like" organisms 0.8 × 1.6 μ (Fig. 21). They multiplied exclusively by budding; some were apparently being digested by the host cells. Similar but smaller forms were seen as epibionts on *Lepochromulina calyx*. Since these organisms were not seen apart from the chrysomonads and since all but the youngest stages of the flagellates were infected, Geitler felt that the relation was one of "symbiosis," i.e., mutualism. He offered no other evidence for his conclusion regarding the type of association.

What may have been similar organisms as well as more typical bacilli were seen by Tschermak-Woess[301] on various colorless euglenoids. They were present in the gelatinous portion of colonies of *Spongomonas discus, S. minima,* and *Phalansterium digitatum,* and in the periplasts of *Petalomonas sphagnicula* and *P. symbiotica.* In the latter species, they may serve as food. These microorganisms are spoken of by the author as ectosymbionts.

Rod-shaped bacteria sometimes completely cover the plasma membrane of *Metapolytoma bacteriferum.*[267] Organisms belonging to two strains of *Pseudomonas fluorescens* were found on colonies of *Volvox aureus* when these were cultured in the laboratory. Since the bacteria could not be removed by washing, bacteria-free colonies were obtained by dissecting out daughter colonies from the interior of a parent colony under sterile conditions. These invariably died unless supplied with both strains of *Pseudo-*

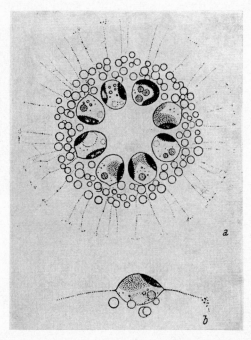

FIG. 21. Bacteria-like organisms in Chrysomonad, *Chrysostephanosphaera globulifera.* (a) Eight-celled colony with symbionts in cytoplasm, one cell with three symbionts. (b) Solitary cell with one symbiont in cytoplasm, five outside of cell. (From Geitler, 1948.)

monas.[127] Although no explanation was offered for the failure of the sterile cultures to survive, it may be that the bacteria provided some essential condition or conditions not present in the artificial culture. A similar situation long prevented the attainment of axenic culture of another protozoan, *Entamoeba histolytica*.

Among the sand-dwelling ciliates, several species of *Centrophorella* have a dorsal covering of bacterial rods.[91, 92, 93] These are arranged so as to form a very close-fitting layer, with the rods giving the appearance of the bristles of a brush (Fig. 22). They are non-motile and may contain dark refractive sulfur granules, so that the host appears black. Rods on other sand-dwelling ciliates may be pink or colorless. Division appears to be longitudinal. The bacteria seem to be closely adapted for living on these ciliates, since they were not found on the sand grains among which *Centrophorella* lives, nor did they appear on glass slides which had been in the sand for several days.[91] Fauré-Fremiet thought they belonged to *Caulobacteria* which he placed among the Thiobacteriaceae. Recent bacterial taxonomy, however, would exclude them from *Caulobacteria*;[22] they probably do belong to the Thiobacteriaceae.

Endobionts. Subsequent to his very complete treatment of the endobiotic bacteria of termite flagellates,[166] Kirby published the results of

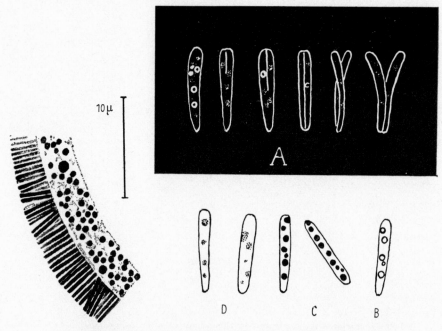

10 μ

A

D   C   B

FIG. 22. Bacterial rods present on outside of psammophilic ciliate, *Centrophorella fistulosa*. Portion of host cell, showing arrangement of rods. Nos. A–D—isolated bacteria. (From Fauré-Fremiet, 1950.)

further studies on parasites of these protozoa. About half of one of his papers[171] is devoted to the nuclear parasites of species of *Trichonympha*. Nuclear parasitism is apparently widespread in *Trichonympha*, although Kirby's observations led him to believe that the incidence in a given population was frequently low. The bacterial parasites ranged in size from less than $1/2 \mu$ to over $1 1/2 \mu$ in diameter. They were placed by Kirby among the Micrococcaceae, in the genus *Caryococcus*. These parasites apparently develop only in the nucleus of the flagellates.

Representative drawings of the genus *Caryococcus* in the nuclei of various species of *Trichonympha* are shown in Fig. 23. In one species, *C. dilator*, the nucleus becomes greatly enlarged, and the chromatin disappears (Fig. 23). These changes were not seen in *Trichonympha* parasitized by other species of *Caryococcus*. Since Kirby's studies were made from fixed material, the effect on living flagellates could not be investigated. From the evident destruction of the nuclei however, there is little doubt that some of these parasites are lethal for their hosts.

In *Trichonympha turkestanica*, Kirby[171] also found some small, spherical granules in the ectoplasm of the anterior portion of the body, and larger, elongated granules in the posterior half. They lay between the flagellar plates. Both of these types of granules were found in all the specimens studied. In addition, a few specimens showed from one to twelve larger spindle-shaped or rod-like structures 3.5μ to 5.5μ in length.

Duboscq and Grassé[80] and Grassé[116] studied the same flagellate under the generic name of *Deltotrichonympha*. They characterized the spherical bodies as micrococci and the elongated ones as bacilli. They figure[80] a dark ring in front of the nucleus (Fig. 24). This is believed to represent a concentration of bacilli, which are prevented from moving further anteriorly by being too large to make their way between the flagellar plates, the latter being tightly packed from this area forward. The term *parasite* is applied to these organisms.

In his studies of the devescovinid flagellates of termites, Kirby reported on the presence of endobionts in numerous species, in addition to the epibionts discussed in the early portion of the present paper. Many of these were rods and sometimes were restricted to certain areas of the body such as the capitulum (Figs. 16, 25, 26), or else they formed a ring of bacilli around the body (Fig. 13).[174] In other instances they were more or less widely distributed (Figs. 26, 27).[169, 174]

In 1946, Kirby[173] described nine kinds of "symbiotes" in the cytoplasm and nucleus of the termite trichomonad *Gigantomonas herculea*. Some of these are evidently bacteria; the organism called Ghl (Fig. 28) is bacillus-like and multiplies by transverse fission; it apparently forms spores. Young stages measure $2.5 - 5 \mu \times 1.5 \mu$, and the spores reach a size of $8.9 \mu \times 6.5 - 7.5 \mu$. These size relationships differ from those of bacilli. The life cycle is depicted in Fig. 28; another bacteria-like "symbiote" about 2.3μ

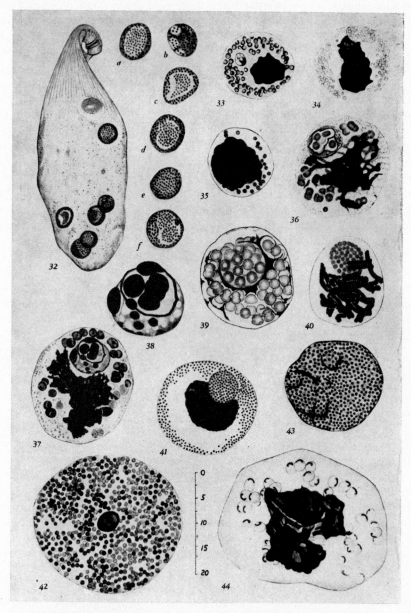

Fig. 23. Nuclear parasites of *Trichonympha*. 32. *T. corbula* with six nuclei parasitized by *Caryococcus nucleophagus*. Enlarged figures of nuclei at right. 33–35. *C. nucleophagus* in nucleus of *T. corbula*. 36–39. *C. invadens* in nuclei of *T. peplophora*. 40–42. *C. dilator* in nucleus of *T. peplophora*. 43. *C. dilator* in nucleus of *T. chattoni*. 44. *C. cretus* in nucleus of *T. corbula*. (From Kirby, 1944.)

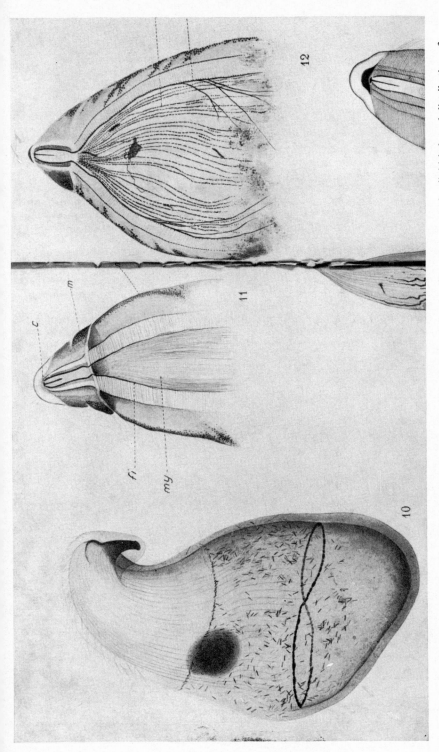

FIG. 24. Bacteria in termite flagellate *Deltotrichonympha numidica.* 10. Shows anterior bacillary ring, posterior lipid belt and distribution of interlamellar bacilli. 11. Longitudinal section, showing centrosome (c.) interlamellar micrococci (m.), internal fibers (fi.) and myonemes (my.) 12. Optical section, showing micrococci laterally. (From Duboscq and Grassé, 1943.)

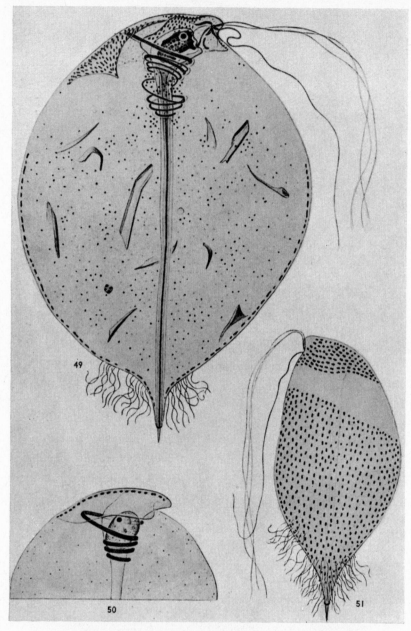

Fig. 25. Adherent spirochaetes, and rods in cytoplasm of termite flagellate, *Hyperdevescovina insignita*. 49 and 50 show distribution of rodlets over capitulum. 51. shows additional rodlets over posterior part of body. (From Kirby, 1949.)

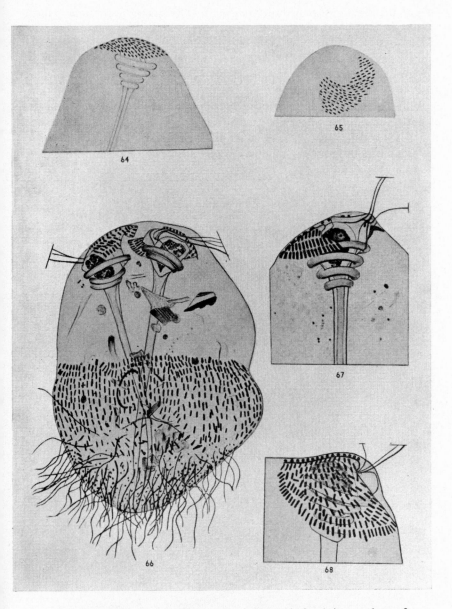

Fig. 26. Distribution of adherent spirochaetes and of rods in cytoplasm of termite flagellate, *Hyperdevescovina falcifera*. 64–65, 67–68, rods over capitular membrane. 66. Double individual, showing also attached spirochaetes. (From Kirby, 1949.)

long in the mature stage is shown in Fig. 29. This organism is found in large vacuoles in the host's cytoplasm.

Hungate[146, 147] discussed the role of some of the intracellular bacteria in termite flagellates, as possibly being responsible for the cellulose digestion carried on by their host protozoans. He concluded that the evidence for this function was not convincing.

With the exception of the studies on endosymbiosis in *Crithidia oncopelti*, there has been little work, since the time of Kirby's review, on bacteria in flagellates other than on those in termites. Wenrich[310] reported rods in the cytoplasm of intestinal mammalian and amphibian flagellates. Davis[52] found a number of bright refringent spherical or rod-shaped bodies in the

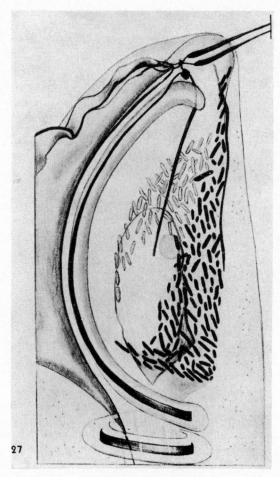

Fig. 27. Endosymbiotes in form of rods in termite flagellate *Macrotricho-monas pulchra*. (From Kirby, 1942.)

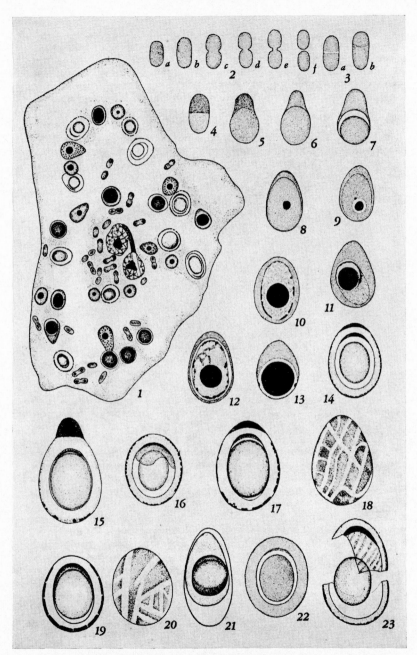

FIG. 28. Symbiote of termite flagellate, *Gigantomonas herculea*. Developmental stages. (From Kirby, 1946.)

cytoplasm of an ectoparasitic flagellate of trout (Fig. 30). These are probably bacteria. In neither paper is there any indication of the role of these intra-cytoplasmic organisms.

In the cytoplasm of *Crithidia oncopelti*, Newton and Horne[220] in 1957 discovered rod-like structures with a marked tendency towards a bipolar appearance (Figs. 31, 32); they contained nucleic acid (Fig. 33).[198] As a result of improved electron microscopy, these bipolar bodies, as they were

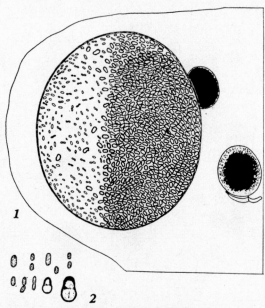

FIG 29. Symbiote of termite flagellate, *Gigantomonas herculea*. 1. Large vacuole showing dividing stages of symbiote at left. 2. Symbiotes of various shapes, some dividing. (From Kirby, 1946.)

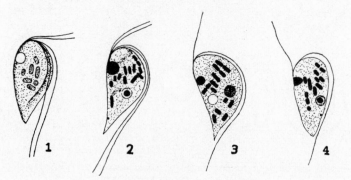

FIG. 30. Rod-shaped bodies in cytoplasm of flagellate, *Costia pyriformis*. (From Davis, 1943.)

first called, were soon found to be bacterial endosymbionts[113, 246] (Fig. 34). Their "symbiotic" or mutualistic nature was determined by comparing the nutritional demands in culture of infected *C. oncopelti* with those of uninfected related flagellates, particularly those belonging to the same genus. Unlike all related organisms, *C. oncopelti* grew on a lysine-free medium.[218, 219] This was due to the lysine-synthesizing ability of the contained bacterium.[112, 113] In addition to obtaining lysine from the activities of its contained bacterium, infected *C. oncopelti* evidently relied on this organism for other nutritional demands since the flagellate could also be cultured on a medium of only four rather than twelve amino acids and did not require haemin as did other members of the lower Trypanosomatidae.[124, 219] The endosymbiont could be removed by the addition of penicillin to the medium,[113] or by taking advantage of the different areas of the culture tube inhabited by infected vs. non-infected *C. oncopelti*.[124] Flagellates lacking the bacterium did not synthesize lysine, or grow in the simple media which formerly supported them. They developed in culture only in the complete medium essential for the growth of other species of crithidia.[124]

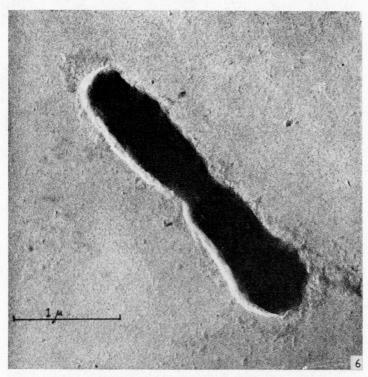

FIG. 31. Electron micrograph of isolated bipolar body from cytoplasm of *Crithidia oncopelti*. (From Newton and Horne, 1957.)

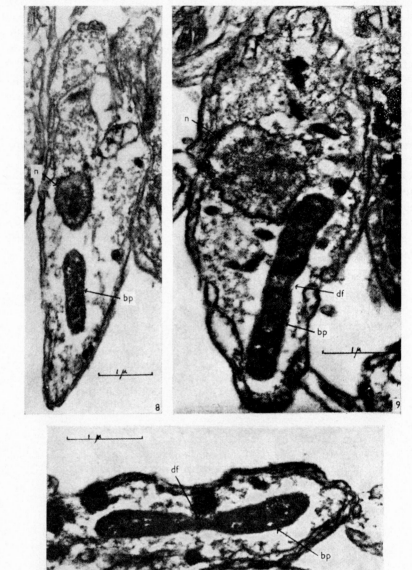

FIG. 32. Electron micrographs of ultra-thin sections of *Crithidia oncopelti* showing variation in size of bipolar bodies (bp) and the development of a central constriction (df). n—nucleus. (From Newton and Horne, 1957.)

There is still considerable discussion about the intracellular bacteria found in the giant amoeba *Pelomyxa palustris*. For a treatment of the subject up to 1940, the reader is referred to Kirby.[166] The large rods present around the nucleus and glycogen masses (Fig. 35) were originally named *Cladothrix* and were so referred to by Hollande[140] in his study of *Pelomyxa* and its associated organisms. However, Keller,[163] who was able to cultivate these bacteria outside the body of the host, thought that *Cladothrix* was really the fruiting body of a *Myxococcus, M. pelomyxae* (Veley) Keller. He also believed that he could recover a second organism from *P. palustris, Bacterium parapelomyxae* Keller.

Leiner and his associates[186, 187, 188] carried on an extensive series of studies with a bacterium in *Pelomyxa*, presumably one of those studied by

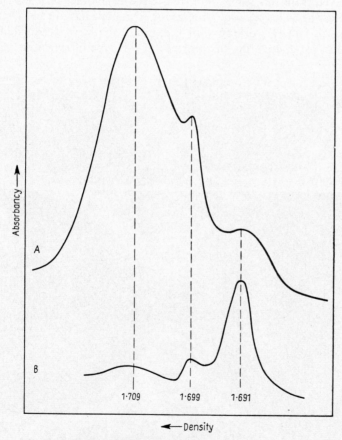

FIG. 33. Banding pattern of DNA from endosymbiote—containing *Crithidia oncopelti* (A) and from isolated cells of endosymbiote (B). (From Marmur, Cahoon, Shimura and Vogel, 1963.)

Hollande[140] and Keller.[163] Leiner's group traced a complicated life history of the organism, involving changes in the morphology, spore formation, etc. (Fig. 36). They did not name the bacterium, and pointed out that it was probably essential for its host, since *P. palustris* did not live without it. The exact nature of the relationship between *P. palustris* and its bacterium has not yet been determined. It has been claimed that the latter plays a role in carbohydrate metabolism, but it will not split cellulose.[187] It has also been suggested that the bacterium is important in the nitrogen metabolism of its host, although it requires some amino acids and is supplied with amides by the *Pelomyxa*.[186] It is unclear how the amoeba regulates the growth of the bacterium.[188]

It has been suggested[261] that the presence of these symbiotic bacteria be made a generic character for *Pelomyxa*, and that forms not showing them be removed from this genus, and transferred to another one; e.g., that *P. carolinensis* be called *Amoeba carolinensis*. This view has not been generally accepted by others working with the group.[116, 179, 322] An additional reason for not considering the presence of this type of symbiont a generic

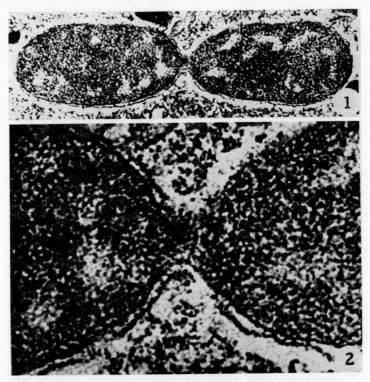

FIG. 34. Electron micrograph of dividing endosymbiote of *Crithidia onco-pelti* No. 2 detail of No. 1. (From Gill and Vogel, 1963.)

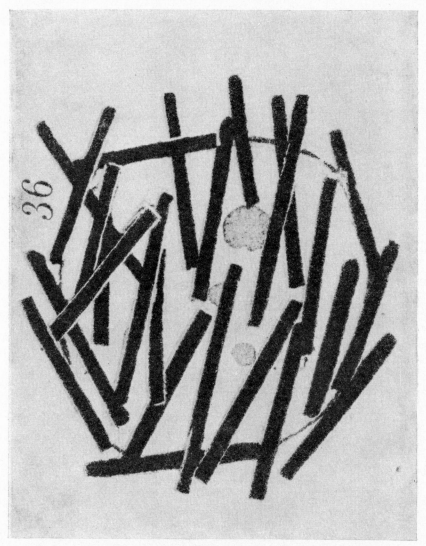

FIG. 35. *Cladothrix* surrounding "bright body" in cytoplasm of *Pelomyxa palustris*. (From Hollande, 1945.)

character is its absence from the cytoplasm of the morphologically similar *P. illinoisensis*. However, this amoeba contains small, membrane-covered, electron-dense bodies $0.2 - 0.5 \mu$ in diameter, which may represent infective organisms in the cytoplasm,[50] and perhaps correspond to the so-called alpha granules described by Andresen.[6]

Closely allied to the report of the presence of these small particles in the cytoplasm of *Pelomyxa*, is the discovery that similar bodies may be present

20*

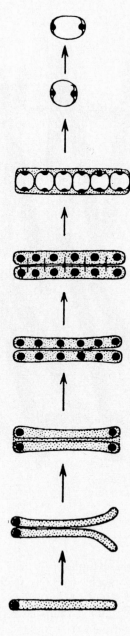

Fig. 36. Schematic life-cycle of symbiontic bacteria of *Pelomyxa palustris*. (From Leiner, Wohlfeil and Schmidt, 1951.)

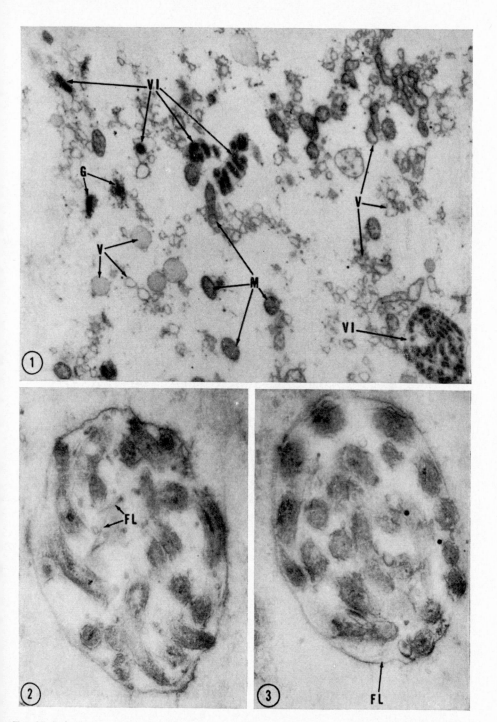

FIG. 37. Infective organisms in cytoplasm of *Amoeba proteus*. Electron micrographs. FL—possible flagella; G—Golgi bodies; M—mitochondria; V—vesicles with no organisms; VI—vesicles with infective organisms. 2 and 3—enlarged views of vesicles with organisms. (From Roth and Daniels, 1961.)

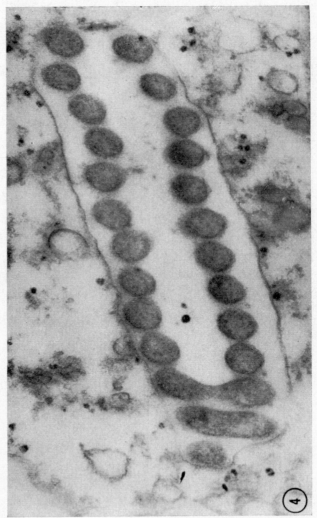

FIG. 38.

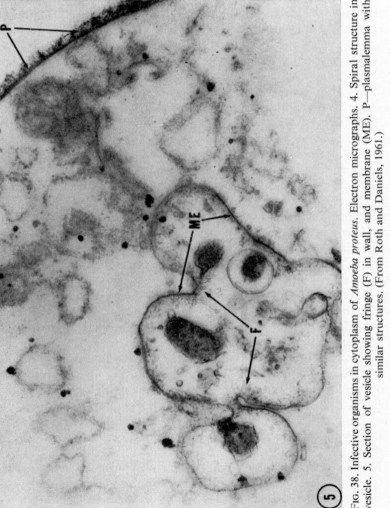

FIG. 38. Infective organisms in cytoplasm of *Amoeba proteus*. Electron micrographs. 4. Spiral structure in vesicle. 5. Section of vesicle showing fringe (F) in wall, and membrane (ME). P—plasmalemma with similar structures. (From Roth and Daniels, 1961.)

in *Amoeba proteus*. Cohen[45] noted the presence of so-called alpha particles, smaller than mitochondria, in the cytoplasm of *A. proteus*. Mercer[201] also observed small particles of unknown nature in the same organism. Later studies indicated that at least some of these particles were infective organisms (0.3 − 0.5 μ in diameter), bacterial, viral, or rickettsial in nature.[49a, 247] They apparently multiply in the body of the host, possibly by binary fission; freshly divided amoebae were estimated to contain about 5400, pre-division stages about 11,000. Roth and Daniels[254] considered them bacteria (Figs. 37, 38); they were present in vesicles and could not be removed by repeated washings or by starving the amoebae. More than one species of endosymbiont may be involved, and infection among amoebae may be widespread. Infection may take place by pinocytosis or by phagocytosis, or perhaps the organisms actively invade the amoeba.

The discovery of these microorganisms in the cytoplasm of *A. proteus* is important in view of the reported presence of DNA synthesis and of RNA and DNA precursors in the cytoplasm of this commonly studied amoeba.[234] It has been suggested that the occurrence of phenomena of this nature in *A. proteus* cytoplasm may be associated with these intracellular symbionts.[234, 247, 254] Hence reports of cytoplasmic DNA or RNA or of cytoplasmic inheritance[133] should probably be viewed with skepticism until the studies have been made in amoebae proved free of these microorganisms.[254]

Drożański[76-79] has reported over several years on the behavior of bacteria parasitizing certain soil amoebae. The bacteria were first seen in *Acanthamoeba castellanii*. They were gram-negative, flagellated cells, 0.5 − 0.6 μ × 3 − 3.5 μ; they could not be grown outside of living organisms; they infected and multiplied in numerous other soil amoebae and in two kinds of Mycetozoa. They did not infect the ciliates exposed to them. The infective bacteria were swallowed by the amoebae, frequently as agglomerations attached to the posterior end. At first, the food vacuoles containing them appeared normal, but later the vacuoles became filled with the bacteria, broke down, and the parasites filled the whole cell, finally bringing about lysis of the host. Apparently they could not be digested by the amoebae. The bacteria which were released into the water attached and agglomerated on the tail end of other susceptible amoebae, and from this area were ingested and entered the food vacuoles.

Bacilli have been reported in the endoplasm of opalinids; in some instances they were found clumped in the posterior region and were possibly involved in certain degenerative changes in the fibrils of this area.[96] It has also been suggested that they are normal symbionts (mutualists) of opalinids.[197]

Several bacterial endobionts have been described in *Paramecium*. These infect either the macro- or the micronucleus, or the cytoplasm. In the macronucleus of *P. caudatum*, Wichterman[312, 318] reported a parasite which apparently belongs to the genus *Holospora*. An infected macronucleus may fill the entire body of the host, and as many as 80 per cent of the animals in a culture may become infected. The earlier work on this organism is discussed by Kirby.[166]

What is apparently another macronuclear parasite was described in the same species of *Paramecium* by Wichterman[319] in 1954. This organism was a small sphere; large numbers were in vacuoles, filling about half the macronucleus. Infected animals had a rather liquid cytoplasm and exhibited from none to four micronuclei and from two to four macronuclei.

Wichterman[315] found zoochlorellae-free *P. bursaria* parasitized by small endoplasmic spheres less than 1 μ in diameter, but aggregated into masses as large as 45 μ. As many as four aggregates might be present in one host. The macronucleus was often pressed upon by these aggregates and showed various abnormalities. Parasitized paramecia showed no cytoplasmic division, and ordinarily did not conjugate.

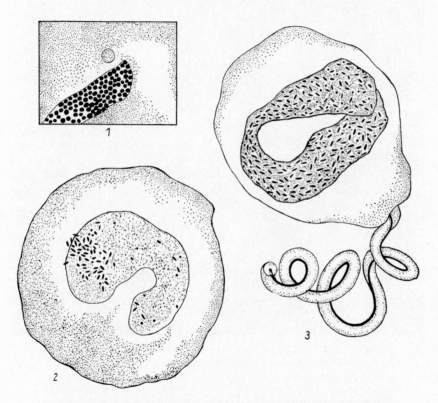

FIG. 39. Bacteria in macronucleus of *Vorticella*. 1. Normal macronucleus with deep-staining chromatin granules. 2. Macronucleus parasitized by bacteria, and hypertrophied mainly in region of greatest number of parasites. A few bacteria in cytoplasm. 3. Macronucleus heavily parasitized with fusiform bacteria. (From Kirby, 1942.)

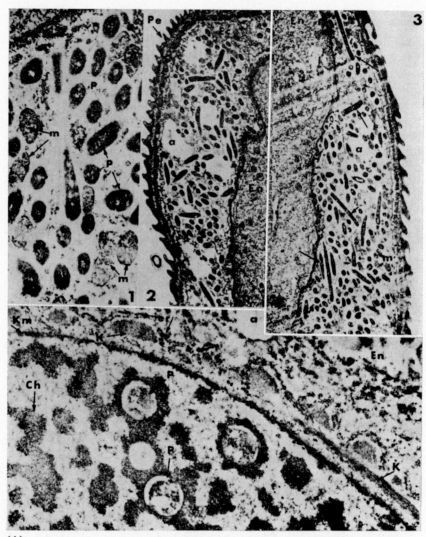

(4.)   Fig. 40. 1, 2, 3—*Entodinium*—showing parasites and mitochondria. 4. *Iso-tricha intestinalis*—parasites inside of nucleus. a—amylopectin; Ch—Chromatin; Ec—ectoplasm; en—endoplasm; er—ergastoplasm; g—granular inclusions; K—Karyophores; KM—nuclear membrane; m—mitochondria; P—parasite; Pe—Pellicle; T—division stage; v—food vacuole. (From Bretschneider and van Vorstenbosch, 1964.)

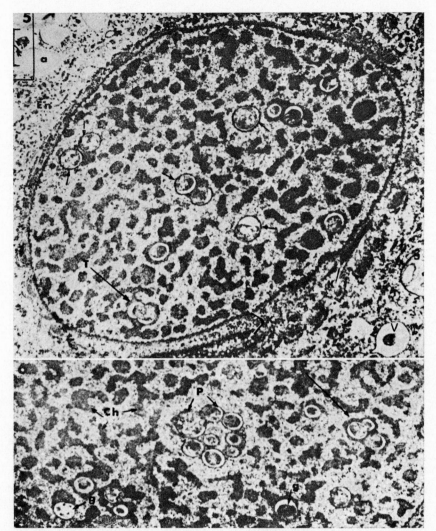

(6.) FIG. 41. 5 and 6. *Isotricha intestinalis*. Parasites inside of nucleus (abbreviations as in Fig. 40). (From Bretschneider and van Vorstenbosch, 1964.)

Diller and Diller have described recently[55] from killerless Kappa mutants of *P. aurelia*, a gram-negative acid-fast pleomorphic bacterium. This resembled *Mycobacteria* or *Nocardia*, and in some respects was similar to the rods obtained by van Wagtendonk and co-workers from killer *P. aurelia*.[305] The paramecia were being grown by the Dillers axenically.

Fauré-Fremiet[94] found 2 species of *Euplotes* taken near Paris to be infected with filamentous bacteria $5 - 12 \mu \times 0.5 \mu$ in size. If the hosts were treated with penicillin, the bacteria were lost, and the *Euplotes* died at

20a*

much lower concentrations of the antibiotic than did normal ciliates. For these reasons, Fauré-Fremiet considered the bacteria to be "symbionts" (mutualists).

Kirby described a bacterial parasite from the macronucleus of a *Vorticella*, probably *V. similis*.[168] The rod-shaped organisms measured 0.5 μ × 1.5 μ; they produced alterations in granules of the nucleus as well as an increase in its size (Fig. 39).

Rod-shaped bodies were found in the body of a suctorian parasitic in *Trichophrya micropteri*, from black bass.[51] Heavy infection of the suctorian was lethal for it.

Bacteria and other microorganisms (Figs. 40, 41) are found in the cytoplasm and nuclei of rumen ciliates.[23] Just as in the case of bacteria found in the bodies of termite flagellates, the question has been raised of the importance of some or all of these in the possible cellulolytic activities of the host ciliates.[146, 147] Hungate[147] who reviewed the published evidence for and against this hypothesis (1955) pointed out that the critical experiments still need to be performed.

Many of the genera of endobiotic bacteria discussed in the preceding paragraphs are unfamiliar to bacteriologists. In the latest edition of *Bergey's Manual of Determinative Bacteriology*,[22] they are placed as an addendum to the class Schizomycetes and are considered not to be intermediate between viruses and Rickettsias. It is pointed out that "the organisms in question are, as yet, best known to protozoologists and are rarely mentioned in textbooks of bacteriology" (p. 927).

FUNGI

The great majority of fungi attacking Protozoa belong to the Chytridiales. In some forms, there seems little doubt that the relationship is one of parasite and host; e.g., in *Sphaerita* and closely related genera, and in *Nucleophaga*. With other Chytrids, however, especially those attacking free-living flagellates or amoebae, it is a question whether the association is one of parasite and host or of predator and prey. It seems to the writer that attempts at defining the type of relationship at this level, are only excursions into semantics, and that the results are essentially meaningless. In fact, some specialists in these groups speak of them as parasites[34, 36] while others call similar or even the same chytrids "predaceous fungi".[68, 74, 81, 84]

Except possibly for the genera *Sphaerita* and *Nucleophaga*, this group of organisms is relatively little known to most protozoologists. Even for the two better known genera listed above, many of the descriptions or reports of infection from protozoologists or parasitologists are based on fixed and stained material. In the absence of diagnostic stages, e.g., the location and number of flagella on the zoospores, it is very difficult to be certain that organisms called *Sphaerita* actually belong in this genus.[230, 233, 287] As for *Nucleophaga*, Kirby[166] pointed out that the nuclear habitat of this

chytrid in the nucleus may not be a sufficient reason for separating it from
Sphaerita. Sparrow[287] says *Nucleophaga* is "a genus of uncertain relationships."

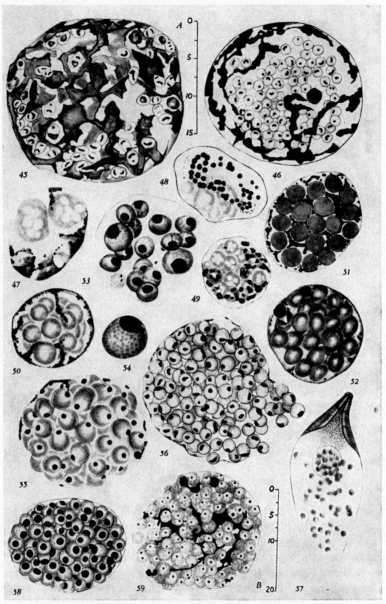

FIG. 42. Nuclear parasites of *Trichonympha*. 45–46. *Caryococcus cretus* in
nucleus of *T. corbula*. 47–59. *Nucleophaga*-like parasites in nucleus of
T. chattoni. (From Kirby, 1944.)

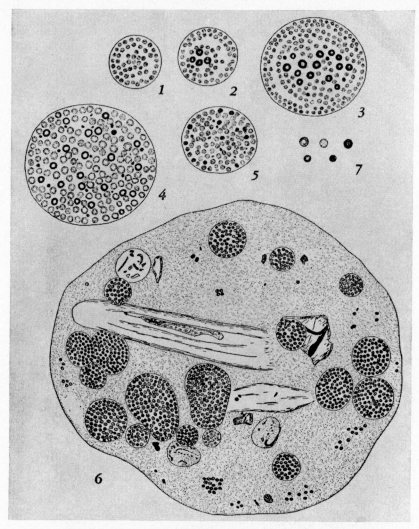

FIG. 43. Symbiote of termite flagellate *Gigantomonas herculea*. (From Kirby, 1946.)

Many of the organisms called *Sphaerita* or *Nucleophaga* have been found in parasitic protozoa, and reference to the fungi has sometimes been a more or less incidental observation.

In addition to the fungi in termite flagellates described in *Protozoa in Biological Research*,[166] Kirby[171, 172, 173] later reported the occurrence of organisms resembling *Nucleophaga* and *Sphaerita* in species of *Trichonympha* (Fig. 42), *Gigantomonas* (Figs. 43, 44) and *Metadevescovina*. Cross[47] found *Oxymonas grandis* parasitized by *Sphaerita*.

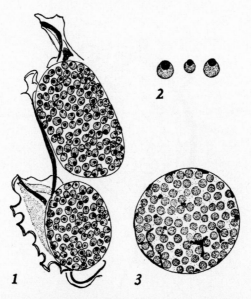

FIG. 44. Symbiote of termite flagellate, *Gigantomonas herculea*. 1. Nuclei of division form of flagellate with contents of nuclei completely replaced by symbiote. 2. Individual symbiotes. 3. Parasitized nucleus with flecks of chromatin remaining. (From Kirby, 1946.)

Crouch[49] recorded the presence of an organism which he called *Sphaerita* in the cytoplasm of all the intestinal protozoa he found in the digestive tract of the woodchuck (*Marmota monax*), except coccidia and *Hexamita*. The hosts were *Chilomastix*, two species of *Trichomonas*, and *Entamoeba*. Crouch believed that two species of *Sphaerita* could be distinguished.

Kirby and Honigberg[175] pictured two parasites in the cytoplasm of *Tritrichomonas muris* from the cecum of a California ground squirrel, *Citellus lateralis chrysodeirus*. One of these (Fig. 45) was supposed to be similar to *Sphaerita trichomonadis* Crouch 1933.[48] The authors point out, however, that since their parasite is apparently solitary and may not form plasmodia, it is possibly not a *Sphaerita*. The other organism in *T. muris* is evidently a different form; it was not classified, but superficially it resembled a *Sphaerita*. *Nucleophaga* has been reported as a pathogenic parasite of *T. augusta*.[256]

In 1940, Wenrich[310] in a brief note reported *Sphaerita* in a number of intestinal amoebae and flagellates. Apparently, he was the first to observe the presence of this parasite in endamoeba cysts as contrasted with trophozoites. The amoebae were *Entamoeba histolytica* and *Endolimax nana*. No other finding of endamoeba cysts being parasitized by *Sphaerita* was made until 1958, when Voge and Kessel found it in *Entamoeba coli* cysts.[309] They reported the number of spores in a sporangium as from four to

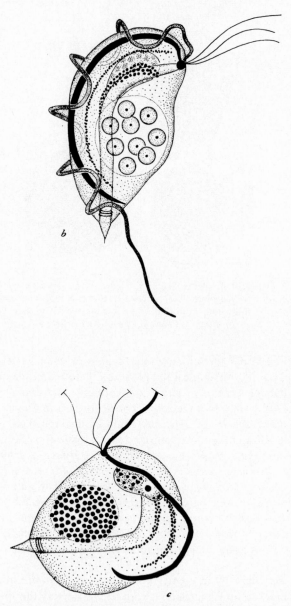

FIG. 45. Microorganisms in *Tritrichomonas muris*. b. *Sphaerita trichomonadis*. c. Granular parasite, different from *S. trichomonadis*. (From Kirby and Honigberg, 1949.)

twenty, and the disappearance on occasion of the sporangial wall (Figs. 46, 47), leaving free spores in the cytoplasm. It is possible that these organisms may therefore be already present in trophozoites when they hatch out from the cysts. Wenrich[311] found *Dientamoeba fragilis* not uncommonly parasitized by *Sphaerita*.

Pérez Reyes,[230] on the basis of failure to find bi-flagellated zoospores in the so-called *Sphaerita* of the intestinal protozoa he examined, proposed that the forms from endozoic protozoa with motionless zoospores be transferred from the genus *Sphaerita* to a new one, *Morella* with *M. endamoebae* (Becker 1926) as the type species. Before this change can be acceptable however, it will be necessary to prove that the motionless zoospores are

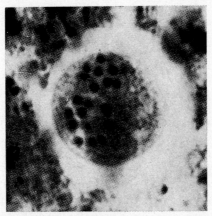

Fig. 46. Binucleate cyst of *Entamoeba coli* showing two sporangia of *Sphaerita*. (From Voge and Kessel, 1958.)

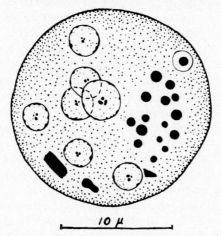

Fig. 47. *Entamoeba coli* cyst showing aggregate of spherical spores. (From Voge and Kessel, 1958.)

mature or that they have not lost any flagella which they may normally possess.

Tuzet and Rouquerol[302] reported that the cytoplasm of *Rizamoeba camariae*, an amoeba parasitizing rice roots, may be inhabited by what is probably a chytrid. The organism develops as a spongy mass, reaching such a size that it pushes the host nucleus to one side.

Ray and Banik[248] believe that so-called "inclusion bodies" they found in the cytoplasm of cysts of *Iodamoeba bütschlii* from the rhesus monkey and the domestic pig represented either a protozoan or a fungal parasite (Fig. 48). This organism appeared to reproduce by budding and to give rise to eight round or oval sporelike bodies; infected cysts were vacuolated and supposedly undergoing degeneration. The parasite resembles at least superficially the organism found in *Tritrichomonas muris* of the ground squirrel.[175]

Lubinsky[194] made a detailed study of *Sphaerita hoari* in several species of rumen ciliates from Pakistan (Fig. 49). Infection was heaviest in *Eremoplastron bovis* from a goat. In the earliest stage, the parasite was in the form of a long band-shaped plasmodial thallus. This later became a spherical sporangium, averaging 12.7 μ in diameter. Two kinds of sporangia, microsporous and macrosporous, were described. Empty sporangia were seen in the ciliate cytoplasm, but unfortunately no sporangia were fixed at the time of discharge. Hence, it was not proved that the zoospores were flagellated. It appears to the present writer that the final generic determination must await a description of the zoospores.

Lubinsky[195] also described another chytrid in Ophryoscolecids from a Pakistan goat. In this parasite, the plasmodial thallus may fill almost the entire body of the ciliate (Fig. 50). The spores are in the shape of arrowheads, with the nucleus at the pointed end (Fig. 51). The host is eventually killed by the parasite, although even heavily infected individuals may continue to grow and divide for a time. Lubinsky pointed out the resemblance of these spores to the peg-shaped organisms found by Kirby in the termite flagellate, *Stephanonympha* (Ref. 166, Fig. 216A); he also noted their similarity to some so-called Microsporidia. Some of the latter may be actually chytrid fungi. Lubinsky[195] placed this parasite, which he named *Sagittospora cameroni*, provisionally in the Olpidiaceae, the family to which most workers assign *Sphaerita* and *Nucleophaga*.

Misra[203] observed a chytrid parasite in the nucleus of an Indian beetle gregarine, *Stylocephalus bahli*. This fungus was fatal to the protozoan host. Rodgi and Ball[253] found a *Sphaerita*-like organism (Figs. 52, 53) in the cytoplasm of gametocysts of a millipede gregarine, *Stenophora falciformis*, from Mysore State, India.

Kirby[173] says of *Sphaerita* diagnoses that "none of the accounts of so-called *Sphaerita* in endozoic protozoa have provided indisputable evidence of the presence of the features necessary for placement in that genus" (p. 203).

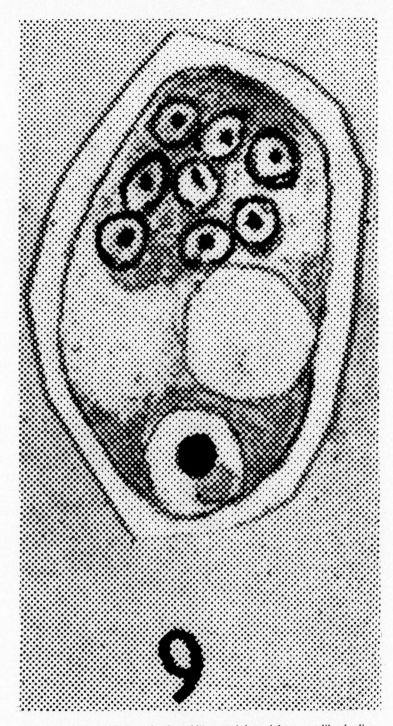

FIG. 48. Cyst of *Iodamoeba bütschlii* containing eight spore-like bodies
(From Ray and Banik, 1965.)

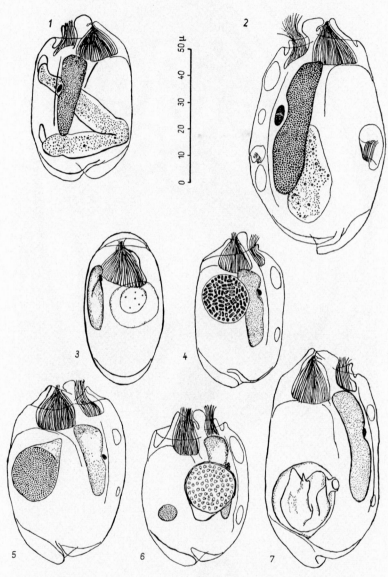

FIG. 49. *Sphaerita hoari* in rumen ciliate, *Eremoplastron bovis*. (From Lubinsky, 1955.)

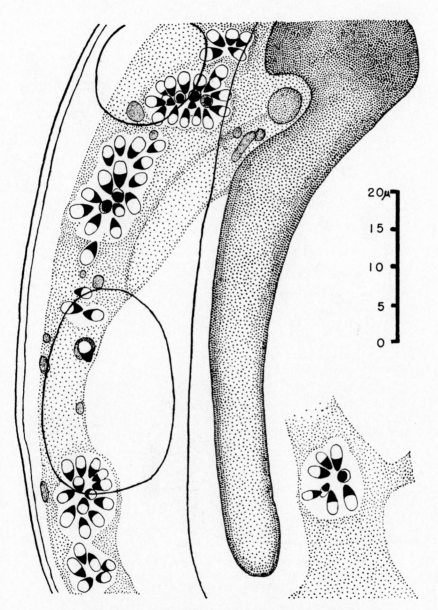

FIG. 50. Chytrid, *Sagittospora cameroni* in *Eudiplodinium maggii*. Enlarged
view of portion of ciliate. (From Lubinsky, 1955.)

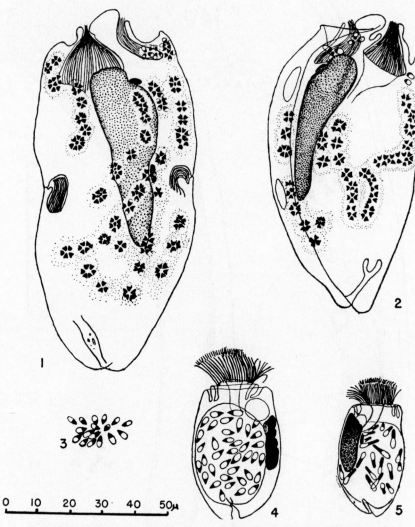

FIG. 51. Chytrids in rumen ciliates. 1–3. *Sagittospora cameroni*, parasite of *Diplodinium minor*. 4–5. Spores similar to those of *S. cameroni* in *Entodinium*. (From Lubinsky, 1955.)

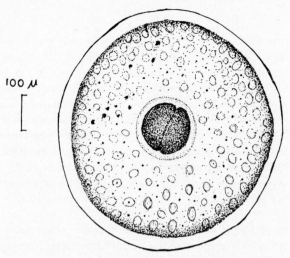

100 μ

FIG. 52. *Sphaerita*-like body in gametocyst of gregarine, *Stenophora falciformis*. (From Rodgi and Ball, 1961.)

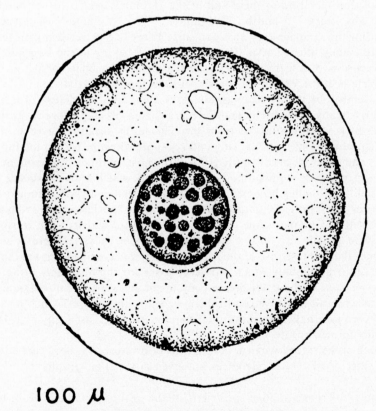

100 μ

FIG. 53. *Sphaerita*-like body in gametocyst of gregarine, *Stenophora falciformis*. (From Rodgi and Ball, 1961.)

The fungi parasitizing or preying upon free-living protozoa have for the most part been studied more thoroughly, especially in recent years, than have those found in the bodies of parasitic protozoa. This is due in part to the fact that often they can be cultivated in the laboratory, and their entire life history studied in detail. They have been investigated mainly by mycologists, and, as noted previously, are relatively unknown to most protozoologists. Their remarkable behavior and the frequently bizarre morphological stages in their life history warrant more than a passing glance by protozoologists, however. A discussion of the life histories of some of the forms living on or in protozoa as well as the inclusion of a representative sample of figures may serve to bring them to the attention of students of Protozoology.

Most of these forms belong to Phycomycetes; a few are found in the Hyphomycetes, which are part of the Fungi Imperfecti. Sparrow's "Aquatic Phycomycetes"[287] includes the fungi found in many protozoa, but does not consider the very interesting Zoopagales of amoebae and testaceans. A general consideration of these and of the Hyphomycetes is to be found in papers by Peach[228] and by Duddington.[82, 83, 84] Those Phycomycetes, excluding the Zoopagales, which parasitize or prey upon free-living protozoa belong mainly to the Order Chytridiales; a few belong to the Lagendiales; one record is of a form placed in the Blastocladiales. Sparrow[287] gives a complete host list, except for the Zoopagales (pp. 1073–1104).

A number of the Phycomycetes attack plant-like flagellated protozoa, although many have been reported parasitizing other protozoan groups. The host is usually attacked from the outside, by means of a tube or of rootlike projections from the encysted zoospore. In some forms, the fungus enters and develops inside of the body of the host; in others, the contents of the host pass into the main body of the fungus, which remains outside the host cell. The thallus becomes multinucleate, forming a sporangium which produces zoospores discharged into the water. The latter are ordinarily flagellated and motile; some may exhibit amoeboid activity. The zoospore can swim usually for only a few hours before it encysts. There is some evidence that the response of the zoospore to stimuli coming from a potential host, or to a stimulus which is also effective for the host, may bring the zoospore close to the latter before encystment and subsequent invasion.

Some chytrids also give rise to thick-walled resting spores, which may be sculptured externally. Resting spores may be produced asexually or from a sexually-formed zygote.

Much of the recent work on the chytrids of protozoa has been carried out by Canter.[33-39] Other references are given in the Bibliography.[12, 20, 46, 105, 130, 137, 140, 142, 143, 149, 150, 151, 155, 162, 225, 226, 232, 233, 257]

Figures of representative specimens of the group, including life history stages, are shown in Figs. 54–63. These fungi, with the possible exception of *Sphaerita*, are eventually lethal to their protozoan hosts.[287]

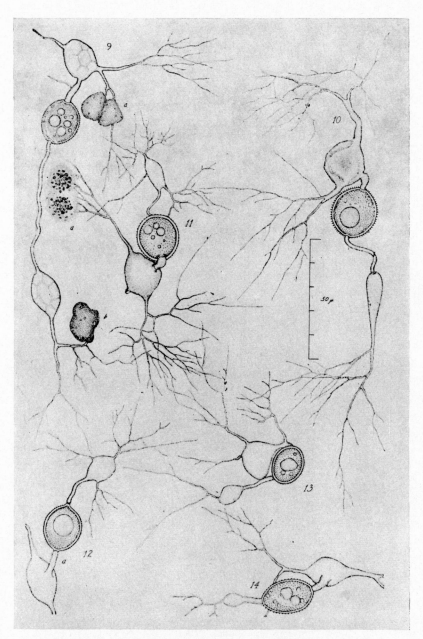

FIG. 54. Chytrid, *Polyphagus euglenae* attacking *Euglena*. a and b—parasitized *Euglena*. (From Bartsch, 1945.)

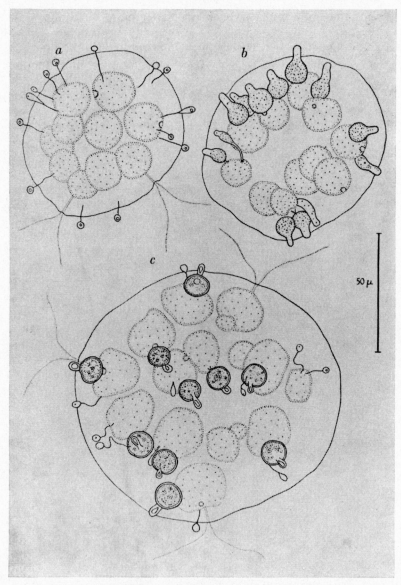

Fig. 55. Chytrid, *Dangeardia mammillata* on *Eudorina elegans*. (From Canter, 1946.)

Although the Zoopagales are not treated in the monograph by Sparrow[287] as proved members of the Phycomycetes, many mycologists consider that they belong to this group. However, there is little agreement as to their ordinal position.[83] Unlike the Phycomycetes discussed above, which are aquatic, the Zoopagales are soil-inhabiting and attack naked and testaceous amoebae found in the soil.

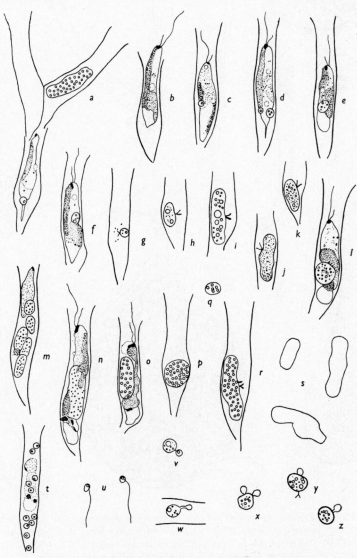

FIG. 56. Chytrid, *Rhizophidium oblongum* developing in *Dinobryon*. (From Canter, 1954.)

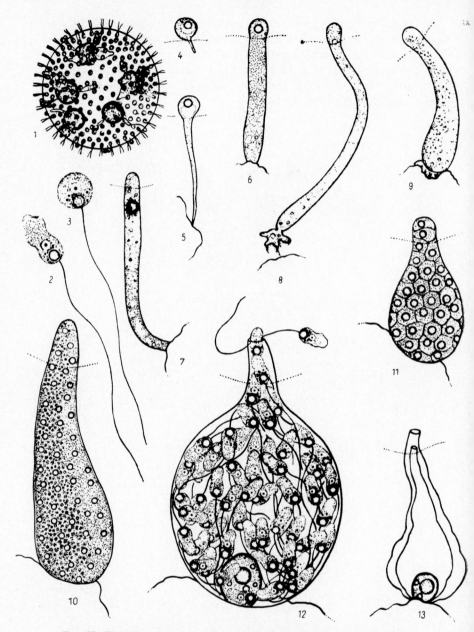

FIG. 57. Chytrid, *Loborhiza metzneri* parasitizing *Volvox carteri*. 1—parasitized daughter colonies of *Volvox*. 2–3—motile zoospores. 4–5—germination of zoospores. 6–11—development of zoosporangium. 12—liberation of zoospores. 13—tertiary sporangium. (From Hanson, 1944.)

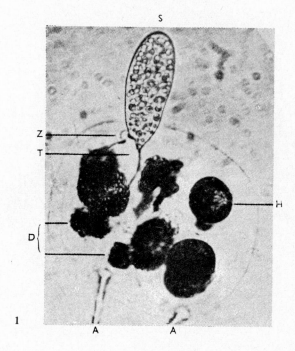

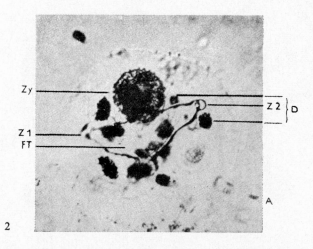

FIG. 58. Chytrid, *Endocoenobium eudorinae* parasitizing *Eudorina elegans*. A—adjacent alga; D—diseased *Eudorina* cells; FT—fusion-thallus; S— zoosporangium; T—thallus; Z—zoospore knob; Zy-zygospore. (From Ingold, 1940.)

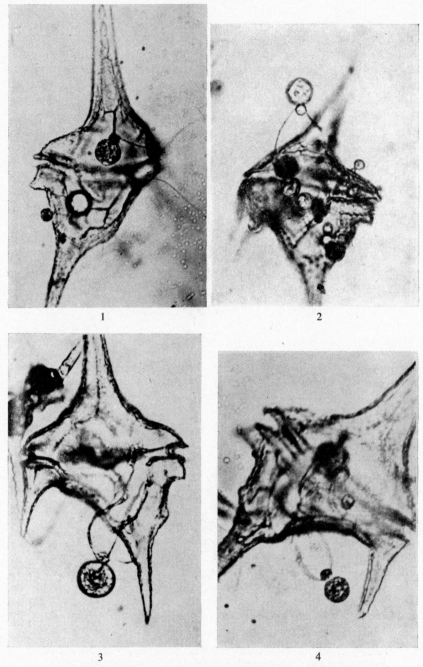

FIG. 59. Chytrid, *Amphicypellus elegans* on *Ceratium hirundinella*. (From Ingold, 1944).

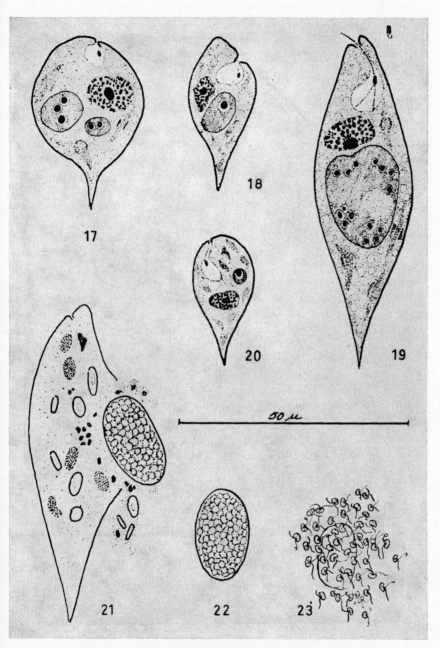

FIG. 60. *Euglena granulata* parasitized by *Sphaerita dangeardi*. (From Pérez-
Réyes and Salas Gómez, 1958.)

Some Zoopagales invade the host cell and reproduce inside of it, eventually destroying it completely (Figs. 64, 65, 67–70). In others, a mycelium is produced which traps the host or the prey by means of an adhesive secretion. Later a set of rootlike hyphae invades the trapped organism and digests it (Figs. 66, 67).

In the former type, the host is attacked by a spore adhering to the outside of the cell, or the host may ingest the spore. The conidia or spores which

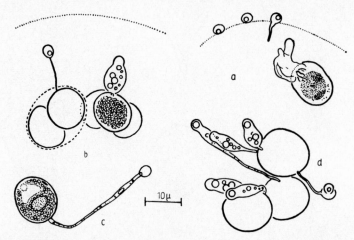

FIG. 61. Chytrid, *Dangeardia sporapiculata* attacking *Chlamydomonas*. (From Geitler, 1962.)

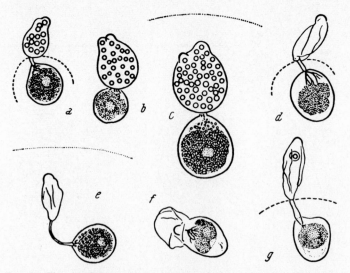

FIG. 62. Chytrid, *Dangeardia sporapiculata* (above) attacking *Chlamydomonas*, showing stages in emptying of sporangia into host. (From Geitler, 1962.)

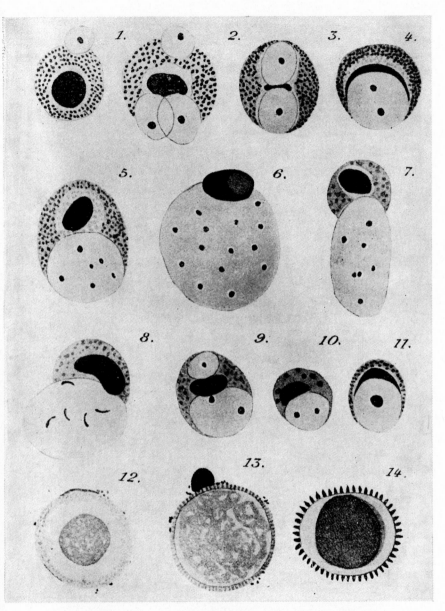

FIG. 63. Chytrid, *Nucleophaga* parasitizing nucleus of *Peranema iricho-phorum*. (From Hollande and Heim, 1942.)

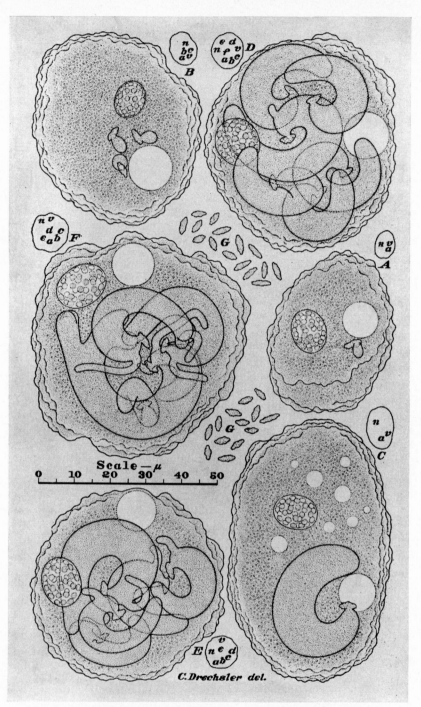

FIG. 64. Zoopagaceous fungus, *Cochlonema euryblastum* attacking unidentified species of amoeba. (From Drechsler, 1942.)

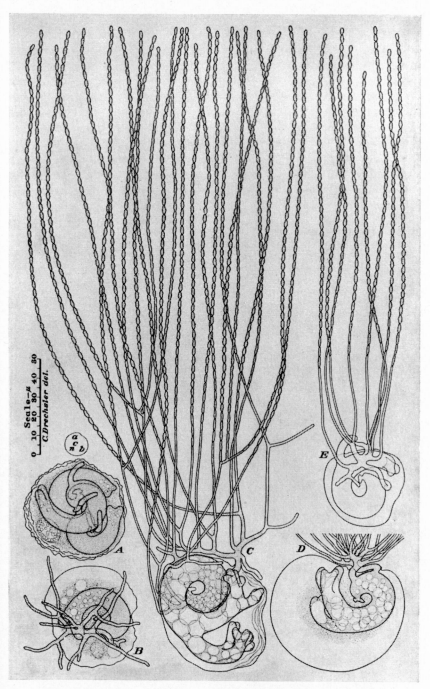

Fig. 65. Zoopagaceous fungus, *Cochlonema euryblastum* in unidentified species of amoeba. Development of spore chains. (From Drechsler, 1942.)

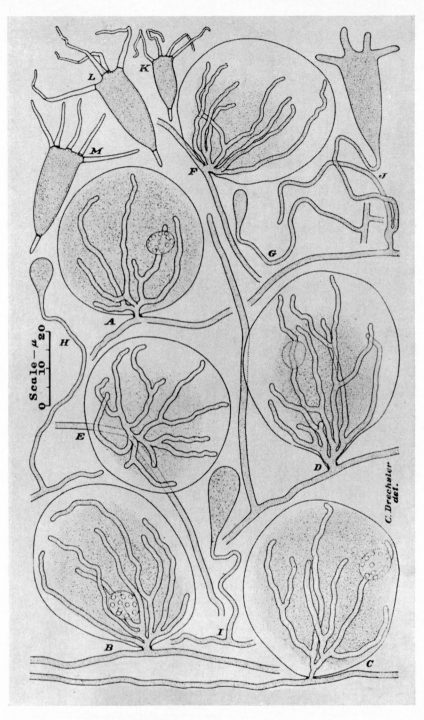

Fig. 66. Zoopagaceous fungus, *Acaulopage tetraceros* parasitizing unidentified species of amoeba. (From Drechsler, 1942.)

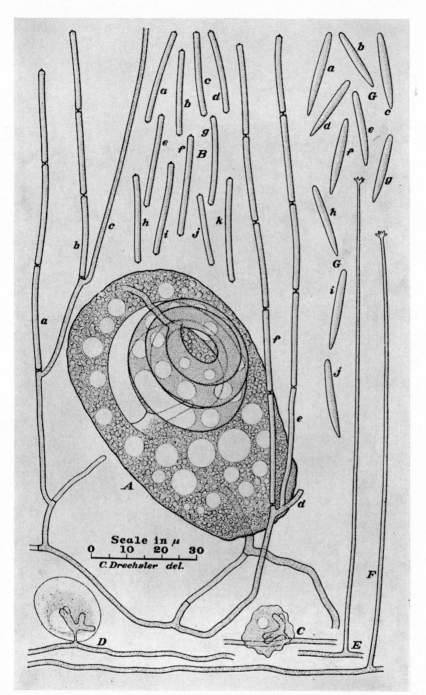

FIG. 67. Zoopagaceous fungi parasitizing amoebae. A, B—*Cochlorema bactrosporum* var. *longius* in rhizopod *Heleopera sylvatica*. C–G—*Stylopage cephalote* parasitic in unidentified species of amoeba. (From Drechsler, 1942.)

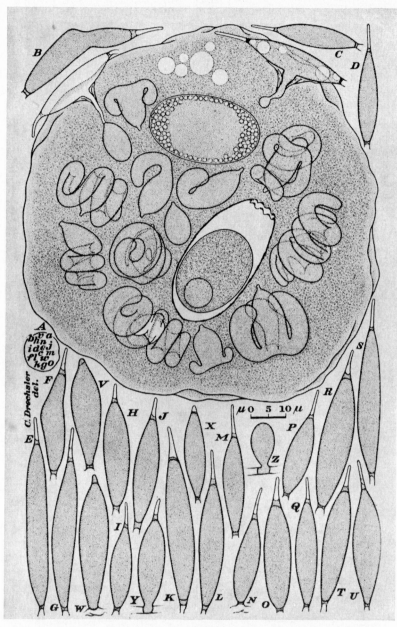

FIG. 68. Zoopagaceous fungus, *Endocochlus binarius* in *Amoeba papyracea* (?) Amoeba contains cyst of *Euglypha*. (From Drechsler, 1949.)

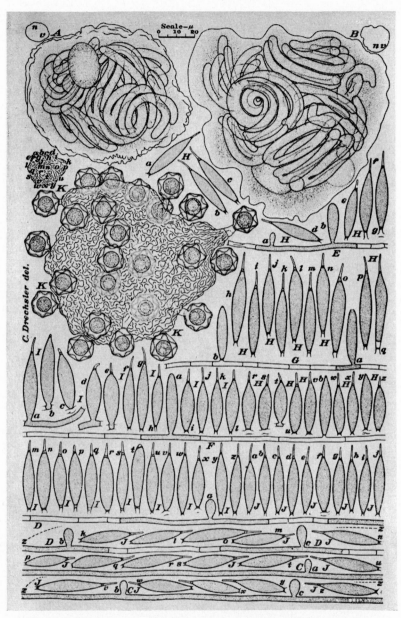

FIG. 69. Zoopagaceous fungus, *Endocochlus binarius* in *Amoeba papyracea* (?) K—collapsed pellicle of amoeba bearing 25 zygosporangia. (From Drechsler, 1949.)

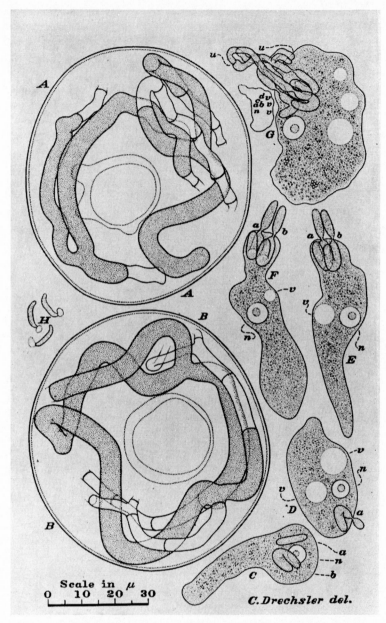

FIG. 70. Zoopagaceous fungus in rhizopods. A, B—in test of *Arcella discoides*. C–G—parasitic in small, unidentified amoeba. (From Drechsler, 1951.)

arise from the thallus are discharged into the soil and ordinarily do not germinate unless they come in contact with a suitable host.[228] The bizarre stages in the life histories are shown in the figures. To the mycelial group belong also those Zoopagales which trap nematodes in the soil.

Some genera of hyphomycetous fungi attack the same type of host as do the Zoopagales. Rhizopods are caught by the adhesive fungal hyphae, the fungus later sending hyphae into the body of the host to destroy it. One species of *Dactyella* makes use of the phagotrophic habit of its host, a testacean, *Geococcus vulgaris*. If attacked by the rhizopod, the fungus sends a branch into the mouth of the shell and blocks it up, preventing the owner from withdrawing and eventually killing it.[82]

Studies on the Zoopagales have been carried on mainly by Drechsler.[63–74] Other papers on the group are listed in the Bibliography.[81–84, 155, 158, 227, 228]

Relatively little work has appeared in recent years on fungal parasites of ciliates. Diller[56] reported, but did not identify, a fungal inhabitant of the macronucleus of *Paramecium calkinsi*. Bomford[21] was able to infect *Chlorella*-free *P. bursaria* with an unidentified yeast, originally discovered in cultures of this ciliate. Infection was established in 100 per cent of the paramecia, with 100–300 cells per host. Budding occurred within the body of the ciliate. Infected alga-free *P. bursaria* required regular feeding with bacterized culture fluid, indicating that the yeasts were not replacing the *Chlorella* as a mutualist. Since paramecia with yeasts lost them subsequents to reinfection with *Chlorella* and starvation for several weeks, it is possible that the relationship was one of commensalism. Under these conditions, yeast-infected *P. bursaria* would not normally be found in animals collected in the wild, which ordinarily contain *Chlorella*.

VIRUSES

The problem of the possible presence of undetected viruses in the bodies of protozoa was raised in 1946 by Altenburg.[1] He suggested that they might be designated as "viroids," and that under certain circumstances they might mutate and produce detectable changes in their host cells. Some of Altenburg's hypotheses became involved in early discussions of the nature of the killer factor in *Paramecium* and other ciliates. Further consideration of the possibility that this factor may be viral or viral-like in nature will be taken up later in this chapter.

In what might be termed the pre-electron microscopy era, various small inclusions in protozoa were referred to as possible viruses or viral inclusions. Since most of these structures were not found again at a later period, when they could have been examined under an electron microscope, it is impossible to determine whether they actually were viral in nature. For example, Brug[25] found that about 25 per cent of *Giardia* (*Lamblia*) *muris* showed granular

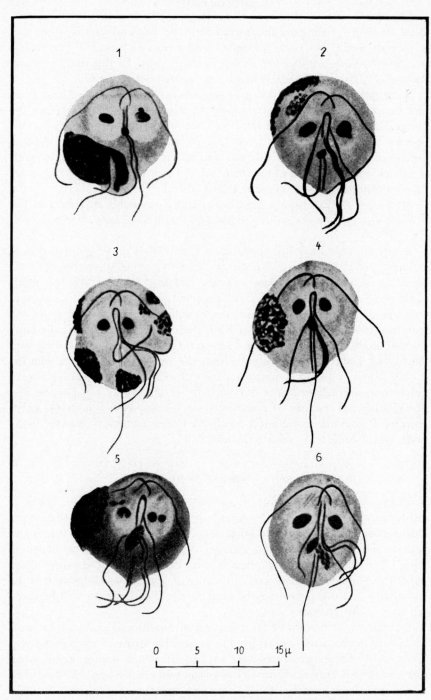

FIG. 71. Inclusion bodies in *Giardia muris*. (From Brug, 1942.)

inclusion bodies, staining purplish red with Giemsa (Fig. 71). In some cases, the inclusions almost filled the body of the flagellate. Brug inclined to the view that this was an infection with a Rickettsia-like virus. Examination of Brug's figures indicates that he may have been dealing with a chytrid fungus.

In *Paramecium caudatum*, Wichterman[316, 319] found a race with a variable number of micronuclei and with extra contractile vacuoles. The cytoplasm showed exceptionally low viscosity, and the macronucleus was sometimes irregularly shaped. The macronucleus, and occasionally the cytoplasm, was parasitized by small, spherical structures believed to represent "perhaps a virus" (p. 405).[318] Wichterman[318, 319] speculated that the induction of micronuclear variation by microorganisms might be of considerable evolutionary significance in *Paramecium*.

More recent work, in which the inclusions have been examined under an electron microscope, has provided much more reliable evidence that viruses may occur in protozoa. Garnham, Bird and Baker[102] pictured bodies they called crystalloids in ookinetes of *Plasmodium gallinaceum* and of *P. cynomolgi bastianellii* (Fig. 72). They saw up to three such bodies in a single ookinete. Each crystalloid was about 1 to 1.5 µ in width and contained many irregular spheres about 35 mµ in diameter. Based on morphological resemblance to known viruses, it is highly probable that the crystalloid is a virus parasitic in the ookinetes of these two species of *Plasmodium*.

Cohen[45] suggested that the so-called alpha particle of *Amoeba proteus* (see p. 608 above) might be a cytoplasmic inclusion indicating a viral infection. He was struck by the resemblance of the alpha particle, when seen under the electron microscope, to cellular inclusions accompanying infection in the Lucké renal adenocarcinoma of frogs.

Miller and Swartzwelder,[202] upon examination of EM pictures of trophozoites of *Entamoeba histolytica*, found in a single section three rows of ovoid or spherical granules 400 Å in diameter in the cytoplasm near the nucleus (Fig. 73). Again, morphologically, these looked like virus particles.

Barker and his co-workers[8-11, 54] have examined the chromatoid body of *Entamoeba invadens* under the electron microscope. The chromatoids consist mainly of RNA and some proteins; they are formed by aggregation of small globular bodies about 70 Å in diameter, with electron transparent centers of about 30 Å diameter. In their early work,[10, 54] these investigators were struck by the resemblance of these small units to virus particles. Later investigations, however, indicated that the units were somewhat larger, 250–300 Å in diameter, and that although they resembled intracellular poliovirus crystals superficially, they were actually ribosomes, which came together to form a crystalline body, the chromatoid. Hence, the explanation of the viral nature of the chromatoids was abandoned.[9] More recently, Siddiqui and Rudzinska[261a] found that a helical structure is characteristic of the chromatoids of *E. invadens*. This is similar to the arrangement of ribosomes in certain metazoan cells. However, the morpho-

21 a*

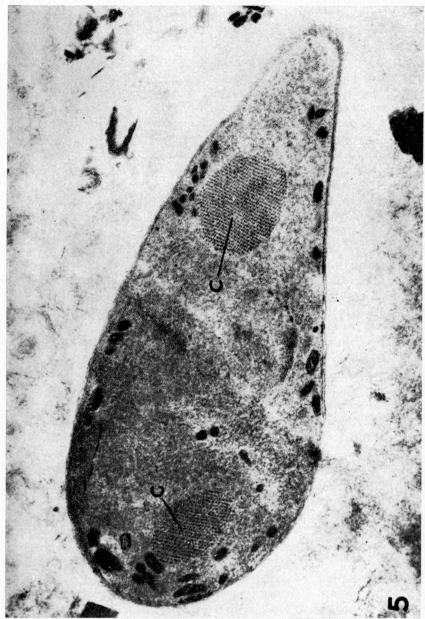

FIG. 72. *Plasmodium cynomolgi bastianellii* ookinete. Electron micrograph of thin section showing crystalloids (C) and lysosomes. (From Garnham, Bird and Baker, 1962.)

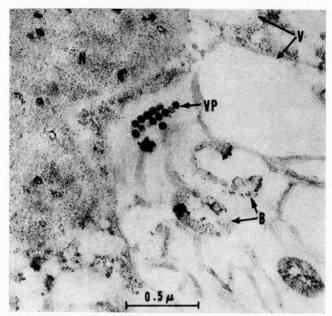

Fig. 73. Electron micrograph of *Entamoeba histolytica* trophozoite showing virus-like particles (VP) near nucleus (N). B—bacteria undergoing digestion; V—food vacuoles. (From Miller and Swartzwelder, 1960.)

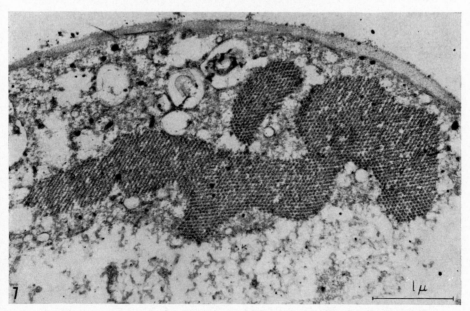

Fig. 74. Electron micrograph of portion of cyst of *Entamoeba invadens* showing aggregation of 200–300 Å particles to form chromatoid bodies. (From Barker and Svihla, 1964.)

logical resemblance of these structures (Fig. 74) to those seen in other protozoa, and interpreted as possible viruses,[45, 102, 202] suggests that the nature
of the inclusions cannot be decided solely on their appearance when seen
under the electron microscope. In addition, as Vickerman[308] points out,
the distinction between infective and cytoplasmic particles is not easy; for
example, those bacteriophages which may be either parasitic or parts of the
genome of the host.

There has been some interest in the possibility that protozoa and other
microscopic organisms might become infected, either by ingestion or by
adsorption with viruses, particularly poliomyelitis virus, in sewage-conta-
minated waters, and that the virus might be protected or might even multiply
in the bodies of the protozoans. Kling and co-workers[176] suggested but
did not demonstrate that species of *Bodo*, which they were able to culture
in stools from poliomyelitis patients, might serve as vectors for the virus.

Other investigators have tested this hypothesis experimentally however,
and the results have indicated that in all cases protozoa cultivated from
sewage have failed to support viruses, usually poliomyelitis virus, to an
extent that would be of any epidemiological significance. The protozoa
tested were *Bodo, Monas, Pleuromonas, Oikomonas, Uronema, Tetrahymena*, and *Amoeba* among the free-living forms,[13, 26, 85, 122, 123, 296]
and *Entamoeba, Trichomonas, Chilomastix, Leishmania*, and *Trypanosoma*
among parasitic protozoans.[26, 327] The last group, of course, included
parasites never found in sewage. There was some indication that virus might
retain its infectivity either in or on the bodies of protozoa for an hour or
so,[296] but no multiplication apparently took place;[26, 327] in fact, there is
evidence that *Tetrahymena*[122, 123] or free-living amoebae[13] feed on and
destroy influenza virus in culture. They may possibly do this also in sewage
disposal plants and in contaminated streams or soil.[122, 123] Electron
microscope pictures showed bacteriophage being destroyed in the body of
an amoeba within 6 hours or less.[13]

Recently, Moewus[204, 205, 206] reported that she was able to infect a
marine hymenostome, *Miamiensis avidus*, with a trout virus in trout-cell
tissue cultures and to infect sea horses with the virus either by injecting them
with the infected ciliates or by exposing the fish to dense suspensions of the
infected protozoa in a small volume of sea water. It has not been shown that
this protozoan serves as a vector of the virus in nature, although the ciliate
does live as a facultative parasite in skin tumors of sea horses.[204]

ALGAE

The association of algae and protozoa has been known for a long time.
Paramecium bursaria and *Chlorella*, or radiolarians or foraminifera and
various zooxanthellae are well-known examples of a more or less continuous
symbiotic association.

Although Kirby[166] did not include the pigmented algae in his discussion of organisms living on and in protozoa, it seems to the present writer that some consideration of them is warranted, especially in view of recent studies on the physiological role of these associates and of their contribution towards understanding the broader question of intracellular symbiosis. There does not seem to be justification, however, for an extensive historical treatment of algal–protozoal relationships. The broad aspects of the problem of symbiosis of plants and animals, with an adequate historical perspective are considered in Buchner.[27] Other general studies of symbiosis are those of Yonge,[326] Füller[101] and Jacob.[153] Grassé's treatise[116] discusses specific examples of alga-protozoan associations.

The algae which have been reported as being symbiotic with protozoa are those believed to be mutualists or perhaps only commensals. They are mainly Cyanophyceae, Chlorophyceae, or Dinophyceae. As intracellular inhabitants in protozoa or metazoa, they are referred to under the headings of Cyanellae, Zoochlorellae or Zooxanthellae, depending upon whether they are blue-green, green, or yellow. There is no precise taxonomic significance to these terms. The Cyanellae are probably all blue-green algae, the Zoochlorellae mainly *Chlorella* or *Pleurococcus*, the Zooxanthellae are dinoflagellates or possibly occasionally cryptomonads.[75]

For the purposes of this discussion, the dinoflagellates and the cryptomonads will be considered along with such organisms as *Chlorella* as being algal. A separate treatment of the Zooxanthellae apart from the Zoochlorellae, on the basis of their classification as protozoa versus algae, would be completely artificial. The writer trusts that the consideration of dinoflagellates and cryptomonads as algae in this section and as protozoa in other sections of the same chapter will not disturb present-day protozoologists, for most of whom this problem should have little or no significance. An alternate solution, proposed by Freudenthal[98] in an attempt to classify a zooxanthellid from a coelenterate, namely, to regard organisms which live holophytically as plants regardless of motility, seems to the present writer to do violence to the view that morphology is of primary importance for taxonomy. This is quite independent of the presence or absence of motile stages. In Freudenthal's paper, which proposes to place a photosynthetic zooxanthellid in the same family as the purely parasitic dinoflagellates, the statement is made that the term "parasitic" for the latter organisms is "probably superficially descriptive rather than truly physiological" (p. 51). The group of parasitic dinoflagellates is discussed in the present review in the following section, headed protozoa. Their parasitism is hardly "superficially descriptive."

Droop[75] (pp. 174–5) gives a table showing those invertebrates (including protozoa) in which symbiosis with algae has been recorded.

The associations of cyanellae with colorless protists are known as Syncyanosen. The most recent complete treatment of the subject is that of Geitler.[104] The algae may be present externally as on *Oikomonas syncyanotica*; it was noted that only those *Oikomonas* well covered with the cyanella continued motility in the absence of free oxygen; movement ceased in the dark, and was resumed again upon illumination.

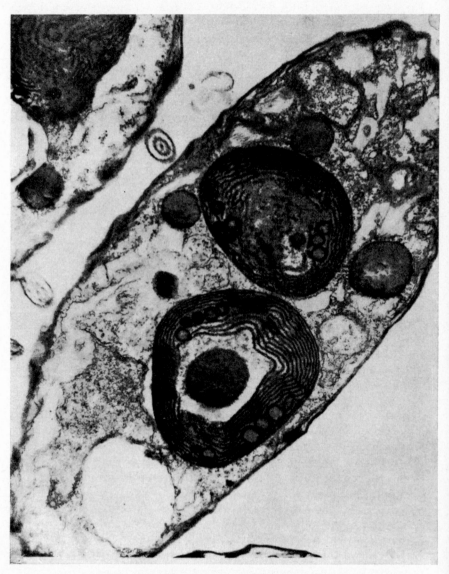

FIG. 75. Electron micrograph of section of flagellate, *Cyanophora paradoxa* with two blue-green algae lying in cytoplasm—*Cyanocyta korschikoffiana*. (From Hall and Claus, 1963.)

Most of the associations are Endocyanosen. Among the protozoa which have been seen to contain cyanellae are a testate amoeba, *Paulinella chromatophora*; a flagellate of uncertain affinity, *Peliaina cyanea*; and a cryptomonad, *Cyanophora paradoxa*. The algae have also been reported to occur in a few other rhizopods and flagellates. The role of the cyanellae is uncertain. In *Peliaina*, only the combination of alga and flagellate can form starch; neither organism is capable of producing it alone;[75] on the other hand, an infected *Cyanophora paradoxa* still requires Vitamin B_{12} *in vitro*.[243] Droop[75] suggests that this is due to the inability of the cyanella to produce enough of this vitamin to meet its own needs in addition to that of its host. Apparently the rhizopod *Paulinella chromatophora* with its cyanellae does not ingest food, relying rather on the photosynthetic activities of its associate.[75]

A very thorough electron microscope study has been made of the cyanella of *Cyanophora paradoxa*.[126] As a result of their investigations, the authors, Hall and Claus, come to the conclusion that the symbiont is a blue-green alga with some special features, and name it *Cyanocyta korschikoffiana*. Geitler[104] previously had been unwilling to accept this as a blue-green. Hall and Claus pictured the lamellated protoplasm with photosynthetic pigments and other inclusions, and a centrally located electron-opaque body surrounded by a fibril-containing halo and believed to be the nucleus. The whole alga was seen to undergo binary fission (Figs. 75, 76). There may be as many as six of these symbionts (1.5×3.7 μ in diameter) in the body of a single flagellate, filling it almost completely. *C. korschikoffiana* has a thin plasma membrane in place of the double-membraned cell wall found in free-living blue-green algae. Possibly this is an adaptation permitting the passage of nutrients in either direction.[126]

As mentioned above, the zooxanthellae are mainly, if not entirely, dinoflagellate in nature. They are associated almost exclusively with marine organisms. Those of the foraminifera and the radiolaria[141] were for many years confused with the life history stages of these protozoa.

In the foraminiferan *Orbitolites duplex*, Doyle and Doyle[62] estimated that an organism 2 mm in diameter contained on the average 16,000 zooxanthellae. Paleontologists have been able to identify associations of this type in sections of fossil foraminifera and to speculate that in some instances the alga may have been destructive to the host's test.[156, 157]

Unfortunately, there is little direct evidence of the role of the zooxanthellae in the economy of the protozoan. Doyle and Doyle[62] noticed that starch grains, calcium oxalate crystals, and pigmented oil droplets in the cytoplasm of *Orbitolites duplex* were identical in appearance with those in the zooxanthella, and that they increased in number only when the alga was distended with these structures. They offered the hypothesis that the particles were transferred to the cytoplasm of the foraminiferan by the bursting of the greatly enlarged alga.

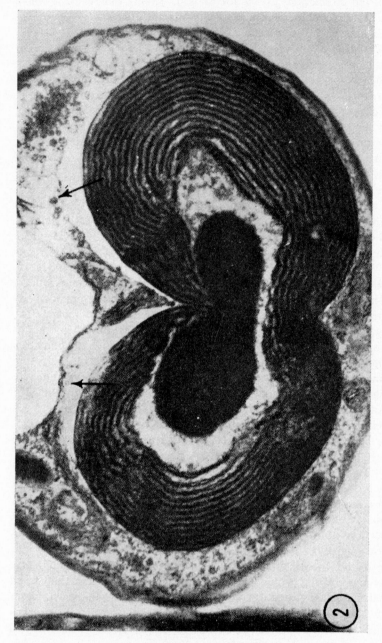

FIG. 76. Electron micrograph of dividing blue-green alga, *Cyanocyta korschikoffiana* in cytoplasm of flagellate, *Cyanophora paradoxa*. Arrows indicate protoplasmic membrane of host. (From Hall and Claus, 1963.)

Wichterman[314] found a ciliate, *Paraeuplotes tortugensis*, which lives on the surface of a coral, to be packed with zooxanthellae. Since no organic food was visible in the body of the ciliate, Wichterman believed that it lived on the food materials synthesized by its symbiont.

In those instances in which zooxanthellae have been grown apart from their partners, they have been isolated from metazoa, usually coelenterates.[99, 199, 200, 328] It is probable, but by no means certain, that those in protozoans behave similarly. In axenic culture, zooxanthellae from coelenterates release free O_2 when exposed to continuous light. Infected hosts are markedly phototactic, but lose this phototaxis when the number of zooxanthellae is drastically reduced.[328] How much O_2 and nutrient is supplied to the host by the zooxanthellae is not known, although there is evidence from the use of isotopes that carbon fixed by zooxanthellae does find its way into the tissue of the coelenterate.[215] This carbon is evidently used by the coelenterate during starvation, in the synthesis of organic compounds necessary to maintain the weight of the host.[213] It may be that the principal advantage of the association accrues to the zooxanthellid and not to the other member, and that the entrance of the alga into a marine animal host enables it to obtain products not easily available to the alga in sea water.[328] However, in the dark the zooxanthellae do not grow as heterotrophs[200] and consequently they cannot obtain all of their essential nutrients from the coelenterate,[75] but must rely, at least in part, on photosynthesis.

Zoochlorellae are found in several groups of protozoa.[135, 136, 181] In some instances they are external; i.e., in the mucilaginous secretions of colonial flagellates such as *Uroglena*.[196] The symbiotic role, if any, of these epibionts has usually not been determined.

Fauré-Fremiet studied possible mutualistic relationships between *Condylostoma tenuis* and a chlamydomonad,[95] and between a marine *Strombidium oculatum*, and a green alga.[89] In the latter case, the ciliate possesses a red eye-spot which it accumulates from stigmas belonging to algae which have disintegrated in its cytoplasm. It is not known if the reconstructed stigma is functional in the ciliate.

The associations which have been examined most thoroughly have been between green algae and ciliates, particularly in *Paramecium bursaria* and to some extent in *Stentor polymorphus*.

In *Stentor polymorphus*, which has *Chlorella* as an associate, there is evidence that particular strains of *Chlorella* are especially adapted for mutualistic existence in this species of *Stentor*. For example, a *Chlorella* strain from *Paramecium bursaria* will live in *S. polymorphus*[260] but infection is less easily established in *Chlorella*-free *Stentor* than it is by *Chlorella* from another *S. polymorphus*.[129] Furthermore, the infection is apt to disappear in those *Stentor* carrying the algae from *P. bursaria*.

Tartar[294] found that in chimeras of *S. coeruleus* and *S. polymorphus* the alga would be rejected unless the graft was predominantly *S. polymorphus*.

This is another indication of the adaptation of the *Chlorella* strain for living in *S. polymorphus* cytoplasm.

There is some indication, although not proved by isolation of the alga, that the *Chlorella* of *S. polymorphus* under certain circumstances may release a lethal ichthyotoxin.[223] One is reminded of the production of fish toxins by various dinoflagellates.

Many of the recent investigations with *Paramecium bursaria* have dealt with the nature of the symbiosis, with the degree of specificity between the members, and with the factors controlling this specificity.

Regarding the nature of the symbiosis, Wichterman,[313, 317, 318] tracing the history of certain crystals in green as compared to colorless *P. bursaria*, came to the conclusion that the paramecia could use the crystalline material for nutrition and that true mutualism did not develop until the crystals were used up by the green *Paramecium* in the light.

As in *Stentor polymorphus*,[129] the presence of chlorellae in the cytoplasm of *P. bursaria* is advantageous for the ciliate, since a higher growth rate and greater maximum population density occur in green as compared to colorless forms. This is most noticeable with optimum illumination and a reduced concentration of bacterial food (Figs. 77, 78). With a high bacterial concentration, the growth rate is not increased by the association with the alga. Consequently, it has been suggested that *P. bursaria* depends on its symbiont when bacterial food is insufficient, so that this association is of survival value in nature in times of nutritive stress.[159] Since well-fed *P. bursaria* show an increased number of chlorellae in the dark, it is possible that the algae acquire their nutrients from their host in the dark[159] although they may also be using suitable organic substances from the medium.[100] Muscatine found that "*Chlorella*-like" symbionts from hydra liberated maltose into the medium when cultivated separately. It is probable that they supply maltose to hydra when the two are associated.[214] It is very possible that *Chlorella* performs a similar function for *P. bursaria*.

A histochemical study of the enzyme systems of *P. bursaria* and of its associated chlorellae showed that the protozoan had all of the enzymes present in the alga. Similarly, all those found in *Paramecium* were present in *Chlorella*, except lipase. It was suggested that this similarity of enzymes facilitated an interchange of metabolites and permitted the protozoan to obtain energy from its algal inhabitants.[148]

Although not every investigator has been successful in producing symbiosis in *P. bursaria* with free-living *Chlorella*,[260] more extensive studies have shown that symbiosis can be established with *Chlorella* drawn from a variety of sources: free-living,[21, 139, 160, 264] from *Stentor polymorphus*,[129, 260] or from the same or different strains of *P. bursaria*.[21, 139, 260, 264, 316] Infection is probably by ingestion; the *Chlorella* then moving from the food vacuole to take up residence in the cytoplasm,[21, 139, 260, 263, 264] but it is possible that occasionally infection occurs by transfer of chlorellae from an

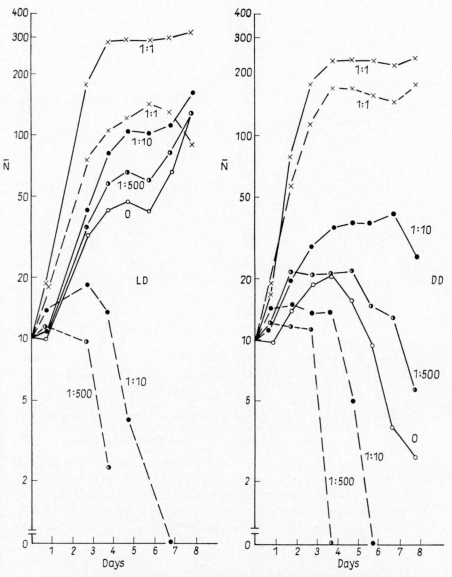

FIG. 77. Effect of bacterial concentration on growth of green and bleached *Paramecium bursaria* in dim light—LD (left graph) and total darkness—DD (right graph). Solid lines—green. Dotted lines—bleached. Dilution factors of bacterial concentrations listed on curves. Ordinate—mean number paramecia per 0.3 ml. (From Karakashian, 1963.)

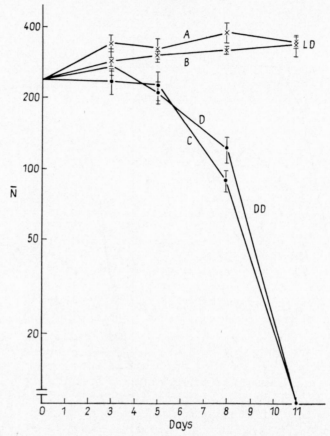

FIG. 78. Growth of green *Paramecium bursaria* in medium with inorganic salts but bacteria-free. LD—illuminated. DD—total darkness. Ordinate— mean number paramecia per ml. (From Karakashian, 1963.)

infected mate at conjugation.[263] Not all combinations of strains of either the ciliate or the alga are equally successful, since in some instances the association is not maintained even when other conditions are favorable.[21] Some combinations have a higher degree of infectivity or a different growth-promoting capacity under stress than do others.[159, 263] This is comparable to the situation in *Stentor* referred to previously.[129]

Since in some of the above associations with normal rates of reproduction, the number of algae present in the cytoplasm is maintained at a more or less constant level through successive divisions, e.g., *Paulinella chromatophora* or *Paramecium bursaria*,[161] the question has been raised as to the distinction between these symbionts and cell organelles.[159, 161] Symbionts of this nature fall into the category of the "plasmids" of Lederberg, i.e., extra-chromosomal intracellular hereditary factors. These may be organelles, plasmagenes, or symbionts.[185] In a recent review, Karakashian and Siegel[161] have considered the problem of endocellular symbiosis from a genetic point of view. They indicate, as have others before them,[185] that hereditary endocellular symbionts may be considered as part of the genetic apparatus of the host and may confer new properties upon it. The association of *P. bursaria* and *Chlorella* is discussed, as well as the genetic behavior of killer factors in *P. aurelia*. Further treatment of this question will be deferred until we consider killer factors in the final portion of this chapter.

It may be noted that *P. bursaria* may be infected not only with *Chlorella* but also with yeasts (see section on fungi above) and with the green alga *Scenedesmus*. The function of the latter organism has not been investigated.[21]

PROTOZOA

Despite the fact that the protozoa are of larger size and frequently more complex than bacteria, fungi, or viruses, there is still considerable doubt about the classification of several "protozoan" parasites of other protozoa. This doubt has resulted in some protozoologists being uncertain as to whether the parasitic organisms they have so described are actually protozoa. In the following discussion, these parasites will be treated along with the group, e.g., Mastigophora, Sarcodina, etc., to which they should probably be assigned. Organisms or structures which cannot be classified suitably in any category will be discussed in the next to the last section of this chapter.

Among the Mastigophora, a species of *Astasia* capable of parasitizing, and in some instances of killing *Stentor coeruleus* (Fig. 79), was reported by Schönfeld.[259] Hungry *Stentor* engulf the flagellates, which are enclosed in food vacuoles. However, many of the *Astasia* are not killed and, after a few hours, wander into the cytoplasm and move about with their characteristic type of locomotion. The host ceases its normal activity, becomes semi-contracted, vacuolated and eventually dies. Apparently, *Stentor* is capable of digesting a few *Astasia*, but the hungry ciliates ingest so many that they are overwhelmed and killed. Since the unidentified species of *Astasia* is capable of growing as a free-living organism, it has been referred to as a facultative parasite although there is no evidence that *Astasia* actually profits from the association. Schönfeld found that the flagellate possibly releases a toxic substance, inasmuch as *Stentor* are rapidly killed in a filtered medium from which *Astasia* has been removed.

A destructive effect by an *Astasia* parasitizing *Amoeba proteus* was also noted by Fox.[97]

A marine euglenoid has been found in *Noctiluca miliaris* in large numbers off Calicut, India. The relationship is probably mutualistic or commensal.[289]

Gillies and Hanson[114, 115] described *Leptomonas karyophilus* from the macronucleus of *Paramecium trichium*. This organism could be transferred to some extent to *P. caudatum, P. bursaria,* and *P. aurelia.* The parasite does not differ morphologically in any essential manner from typical leptomonads; in initial infections, it apparently assumes a leishmanial form before dividing. In established infections, division takes place by longitudinal fission of

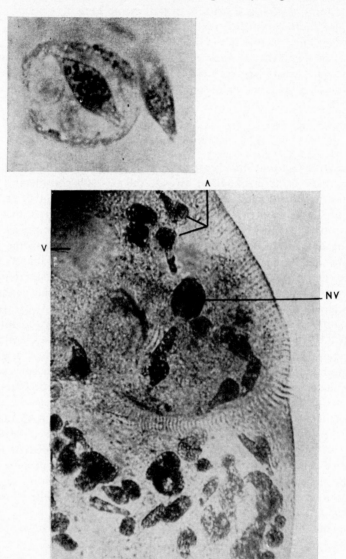

FIG. 79. *Stentor coeruleus* parasitized by *Astasia.* 1. *Astasia* in food vacuole (*left*); escaped from vacuole (*right*). 2. *Astasia* throughout cytoplasm. A—*Astasia* with characteristic shape; NV—intact food vacuole containing two *Astasia*; V—degenerated vacuole with membrane. (From Schönfeld, 1959.)

an elongate flagellated stage, not unlike that described for other lepto-monads.

The paramecia are probably infected by swallowing the leptomonads; the latter move about inside of the food vacuole, later breaking out into the cytoplasm. This behavior occurs also with *Chlorella* in *P. bursaria*[263] and with *Astasia* in *Stentor coeruleus*.[259] The leptomonads swim actively with the flagellar end posterior; when the aflagellar part approaches the macronucleus, it pushes against the nuclear membrane, eventually penetrating into the nucleus itself. The parasites divide inside the macronucleus and, under normal culture conditions, nearly fill the nucleus, eventually killing the host. If the ciliate is starved, the flagellates rapidly outgrow it and kill it. Within 8 days, on the other hand, well-fed paramecia may be able to reproduce as fast as the *Leptomonas* and continue to live with it. If the division rate of the host is kept at the maximum for some time, the *Paramecium* will divide faster than the parasite and eventually some ciliates will be produced free of the leptomonad. Parasitism is apparently obligatory since the flagellate cannot survive more than a few hours outside the body of a *Paramecium*.

The parasitic dinoflagellates are found in the cytoplasm and sometimes in the nucleus of other dinoflagellates, and in the cytoplasm of Radiolaria and of tintinnid ciliates (Fig. 80). These dinoflagellates are highly modified for a parasitic mode of life and display their dinoflagellate character only at the time they are free-living (Fig. 81).[40] The group is discussed thoroughly by Chatton in Grassé,[116] and there seems no need to repeat this treatment here. However, some of the parasites of tintinnids have not been described previously by Grassé; figures of 2 such species are reproduced in Fig. 82.

Since the appearance of Chatton's discussion, life histories of some other dinoflagellates of radiolarians have been published.[31, 141, 145] As many as three species may live in a single host. Stages of these parasites were long considered to belong in the life cycle of the radiolarian host. Some are intra-nuclear; others are limited to the cytoplasm.[31, 145] *Solenodinium* (Fig. 83) is believed to be primitively an intranuclear form which has invaded the endoplasm of the host secondarily. It develops as a plasmodium, pushing out fingerlike lobes until the endoplasm is entirely replaced by the parasite, although the host's nucleus remains intact. Such an intimate mixture of host and parasite illustrates the difficulty of interpreting properly life history stages of either organism.[141]

Hollande[141] reported the presence of a *Bodo* in the gelatinous outer portion of the radiolarian, *Collozoum* sp.

De Puytorac[244, 245] described a protozoan, which he named *Sphaero-suctans emeriti*, from the astomous ciliate *Anoplophrya lumbrici* (?), a parasite of oligochaetes. This organism was classified as a flagellate (sensu latu—Chat-ton) even though it showed no flagellated stage. The free-living stage (Fig. 84) is about 5 × 8 μ; it attacks the posterior end of the ciliate by sink-

Dinoflagellés:		
Peridinium balticum Lemm	Noyau et cytoplasme	*Coccidinium duboscqui* Chatton et Biecheler
P. sociale (Henneguy)	— —	*C. legeri* Chatton et Biecheler
Cryptoperidinium foliaceum Stein	Cytoplasme	*C. mesnili* Chatton et Biecheler
Ostreopsis monotis (Meunier)	—	*C. punctatum* Chatton et Biecheler
Diatomées: Chaetoceras sp.	Surface	*Paulsenella chaetoceratis* (Paulsen)
Radiolaires:		
Collozoum inerme Muller	Cytoplasme intracapsulaire	*Merodinium brandti* Hovasse
— —	— extracapsulaire	— *vernale* Hovasse
— *pelagicum* Haeckel	Cytoplasme	— *insidiosum* Chatton
Myxosphaera coerulea Haeckel	—	— *mendax* Chatton
Sphaerozoum punctatum Müller	—	— *dolosum* Chatton
S. acuferum Müller	—	— *astatum* Chatton
Thalassicolla spumida (Haeckel)	—	*Solenodinium fallax* Chatton
Nbrx genres et espèces	—	Zooxanthelles
Ciliés Cyttarocylis ehrenbergi Cl. et L.	—	*Duboscquella tintinnicola* Lohm
Tintinopsis campanula Cl. et L.	—	— —
Cyttarocylis sp.	—	— *anisospora* Grassé
Tintinnus fraknoii nov.	—	*Duboscquodinium collini* Grassé
Codonella campanula		— *kofoidi* Grassé
Coelentérés:		
Paraweightia robusta Warren	Gonophore	*Syndinium allognosticum* R. Weill
Lizzia blondina Forbes	Ectoderme	*Protoodinium chattoni* Hovasse
Halistemma sergestinum Cl.	Cav. gastro-vase.	*Gymnodinium parasiticum* Poche
Monophyes gracilis Cl.	—	— —
Cuculbalus kochi Will.	—	
Gen. et sp. indet.	Ectod., epicell.	*Oodinium poucheti* Chatton
Velella spirans Lam	Intracellulaire, endod.	*Zooxanthella chattoni* Hovasse
Nbrx genres et espèces	— —	Zooxanthelles
Mollusques: Criseis acicula Rang	Cav. palléale	*Oodinium* sp. Chatton
Ptéropode indét.	Ext.	— Dogiel
Turbellariés: Planaire indét.	Intestin	*Gymmnodinium fuseum* Perty
Annelides: Alciope sp.	Ectoderme	*Oodinium* sp. V. Dogiel
Copepodes: indéterminés	Oeufs	*Chytriodinium roseum* V. Dogiel
		affine V. Dogiel
		parasiticum V. Dogiel
	—	*Trypanodinium ovicola* Chatton
Calanus finmarchicus Gunner	Estomac	*Blastodinium contortum hyalinum* Chatton
	Cavité générale	*Syndinium* sp. Asptein

Paracalanus parvus Cl.	Estomac	*Blastodinium spinulosum* Chatton
— —	—	— *crassum* Chatton
— —	—	— *crassum inormatum* Chatton
— —	—	— *contortum* Chatton
Paracalanus parvus Cl.	Estomac	*Blastodinium contortum hyalinum* Chatton
— —	—	*Syndinium turbo* Chatton
— —	—	— *minutum* Chatton
— —	—	*Synhemidinium rostratum* Chatton
Calocalanus sp.	—	*Blastodinium contortum* Chatton
—	—	— *crassum* Chatton
Clausocalanus furcatus Brady	—	— *spinulosum* Chatton
— *arcuicornis* Dana	—	— *crassum* Chatton
— — —	—	— *crassum inormatum* Chatton
— — —	—	— *contortum* Chatton
— — —	—	— *contortum hyalinum* Chatton
— — —	—	— *pruvoti* Chatton
— — —	—	*Syndinium* sp. Chatton
Scolecithrix bradyi Giesbr.	—	*Blastodinium elongatum* Chatton
— — —	—	— *contortum hyalinum* Chatton
Centropages typicus Kroyer	—	— — —
Temora stylifera Dana	—	— sp. Chatton
Acartia clausi Giesbr.	Estomac (cavité)	— *contortum* Chatton
— — —	— —	— *contortum hyalinum* Chatton
— — —	— (paroi)	*Actinodinium apsteini* Chatton et Hovasse
Oithona helgolandica Cl. = *similis* Cl.	—	*Blastodinium oviforme* Chatton
— — —	Cavité générale	*Syndinium* sp.
— *plumifera* Baird	Estomac	*Blastodinium oviforme* Chatton
— *nana* Giesbr.	—	— — —
Oncaea media —	(Oeufs. cytoplasme	*Trypanodinium ovicola* Chatton
— — —	Estomac	*Blastodinium mangini oncae* Chatton
— *minuta*	—	— — —
Corycella rostrata Cl.	—	— — —
— — —	—	— *navicula* Chatton
Corycoeus giesbrechti Dahl (= *venustus* Dana)	—	*Cochlosyndinium corycaei* Chatton
Décapodes: Carcinus moenas	Sang	*Haematodinium perezi* Chatton et Poisson
Portunus depurator	—	— — —
Platyonychus latipes Penn.	—	— — —
Tuniciers: Fritillaria pellucida Bush.	Ectoderme	*Oodinium fritillaria* Chatton
— —	—	*Apodinium mycetoides* Chatton
Oikopleura dioica Fol.	Ectoderme, queue	*Oodinium poucheti* Chatton
— *cophocerca* Gegenb.	Endoderme	*Apodinium rhizophorum* Chatton

— tortugensis	Ectoderme, queue	Oodinium appendiculariae Brooks et Kell.
Salpa democratica Forskal	Branchie	— amylaceum (Bargoni)
Poissons: Amphiprion percula	Muqueuse branchiale	— ocellatum F. Brown
Lacép et 27 autres espèces.	Peau	— limneticum Jacobs
Poissons d'eau douce (Lebistes. Barbus, Brachydanis etc.)		

FIG. 80. List of parasitic peridinians. (From Grassé, 1952.)

ing structures referred to either as tentacles[244] or as pseudopods[245] into the ectoplasm. It lives as a true ectoparasite, getting nutrients from the host and forming a large plasmodium $25 \times 10 \mu$ in size, which gives rise to small uninucleate cells $2 \times 6 \mu$. The latter presumably grow and become the infective stages. The parasite produces necrosis and local disorganization of the host's infraciliature. The attacked area may hypertrophy and the macronucleus and mitochondria become abnormal. If several parasites are involved, their mass may come to be up to 15 times that of the host. The ciliate may survive light infections, but heavy ones result either in the death of the host or in autotomy of the parasitized region, leaving a viable but truncated anterior portion. This parasite is evidently host specific, since other ciliates living in the oligochaete gut are not attacked.

The organisms parasitizing species of Mallomonas and described by Harris[132] are probably chytrids (Fig. 85). The author inclined to the view that they were protozoa rather than fungi on the basis that the chromatophore of the host is ingested by the parasite. This hardly seems a valid reason for classifying them as protozoa; in other respects, they are typical chytrids.

An unidentified and rapidly multiplying amoeba has been found in Volvox aureus.[221]

A small amoeba was seen in the cytoplasm of Pelomyxa palustris by Hollande and his associates; it had a biflagellated stage and was named Vahlkampfia pelomyxae.[140, 142] Little else about it is known. An endamoeba was found in the same species of Pelomyxa by Leiner et al.[188] This parasite reproduces by plasmotomy and forms cysts inside the body of the host. The active stage is frequently filled with glycogen. Infection is heavier in the warmer months of the year. The method of invasion is not known; infected Pelomyxa may have hypertrophied and vacuolated nuclei, or in some instances may lose them.

Le Calvez described two parasitic Rhizopoda from Foraminifera. One is a Vahlkampfia, V. discorbini, intracytoplasmic in Discorbis mediterranensis.[183] Parasitization of the host occurs in the paired gamont stage and is

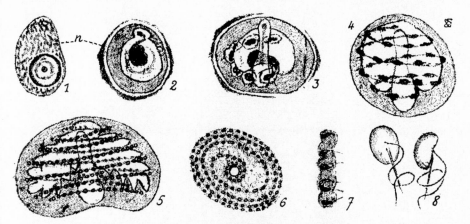

FIG. 81. 1–8. Dinoflagellates parasitic in nucleus of a peridinian. n—host-cell nucleus. (From Chatton and Biecheler, 1935.)

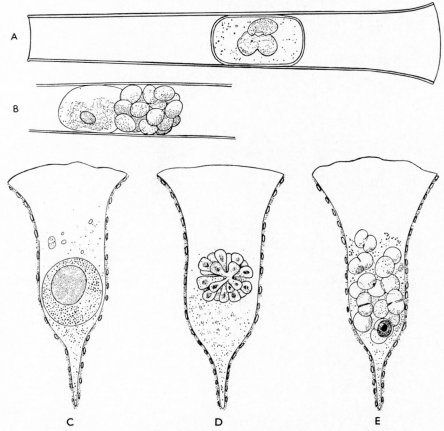

FIG. 82. Parasitic dinoflagellate, *Duboscquodinium* in tintinnoids. A, B—*D.collini* in *Tintinnus fraknoii* C–E—*D*.(?) *kofoidi* in *Codonella campanula*. (From Grassé, 1952.)

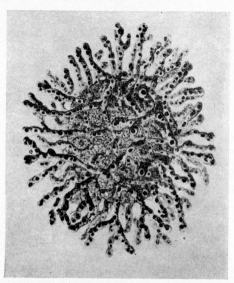

Fig. 83. Radiolarian *Thalassicolla spumida* parasitized by dinoflagellate, *Solenodinium fallax*. Plasmodial prolongations spreading through nuclear membrane into cytoplasm. (From Hollande and Enjumet, 1953.)

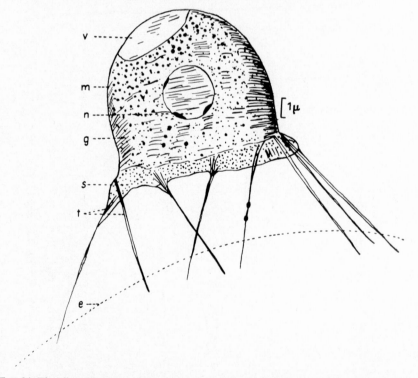

Fig. 84. Flagellate (?) *Spherasuctans emeriti*, parasitic on astomatous ciliate *Anoplophrya*. e—ectoplasmic margin of ciliate; g—lipid globules; m—membrane; n—nucleus; s—basal layer of cytoplasm; t—tentacles; v—vacuole. (From de Puytorac, 1952.)

frequently intense; the mass of the parasite may exceed that of the host. The other parasite is an ectobiont, a foraminiferan *Oolina marginata*; the host is *Discorbis vilardeboanus*.[184] The parasite stretches its pseudopods over the extrathalamic protoplasm with which *D. vilardeboanus* covers its test. It captures granules circulating in this portion of the host's cytoplasm, ingests them, and eventually its own cytoplasm becomes stuffed with them. The parasite is apparently host specific since it does not attack *D. bertheloti*.

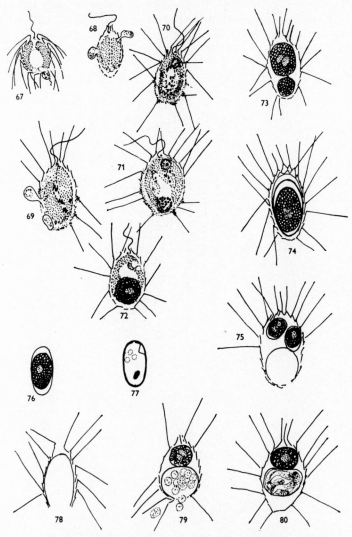

FIG. 85. *Mallomonas intermedia* var. *gesticulans* attacked by parasite. 67, 68—attachment of parasite. 69–72—parasite developing in host cell. 73–80—cyst formation and sporulation. (From Harris, 1953.)

It reproduces after leaving the host, forming asexually two to six "embryos" which shortly develop into infective stages. This is the only known parasitic foraminiferan.

Wolska[324] reported the development of small amoebae in the nucleus of *Amoeba proteus*. These were set free into the water by the bursting of the host's plasma membrane. They remained in culture as free-living amoebae for over two months. She considered these, therefore, to be facultative parasites. Since life histories of free-living amoebae are not known in all cases, and in many instances described life histories are clearly erroneous, involving more than one species of amoeba, this study certainly needs further confirmation.

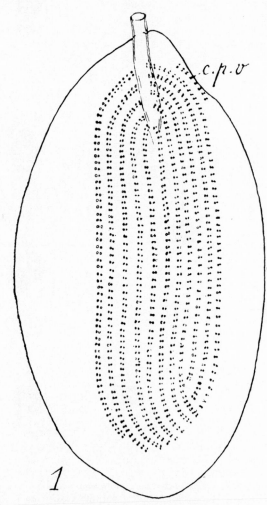

FIG. 86.1. *Hypocoma parasitica* from marine peritrich *Zoothamnium*.

Hazard[134] reported a case of an endomoeba parasitizing an opalinid. As many as 100 were seen in the body of one *Opalina chorophili* from a cricket frog, *Pseudacris triseriata*. Both trophozoites and cysts were seen, and there is evidence that heavily infected opalinids disintegrate on a slide more rapidly than do noninfected individuals. Amaro[4] found a form, which was probably *Entamoeba paulista*, in two species of *Zelleriella* from Brazil. He gave a list of Zelleriellas which had been reported up to 1962 as being parasitized by *Entamoeba*.

The parasitic Ciliatea described in recent years belong to various orders. However, the majority of Ciliophora which are parasites are Suctoria.

Chatton and Lwoff[41] reported protozoan parasitism by two genera of thigmotrichs (Fig. 86), belonging to the family of the Hypocomidae. These thigmotrichs parasitize marine colonial Peritrichs of the genus *Zoothamnium*, as well as suctoria. This last relationship is an interesting one since

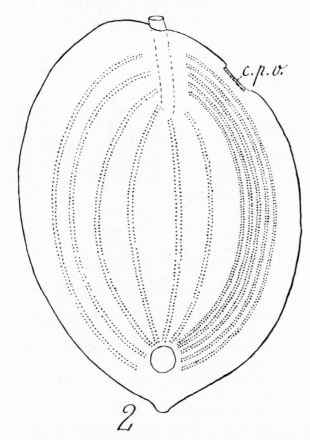

FIG. 86. 2. *Heterocoma hyperparasitica* from marine *Trichophrya salparum*. c.p.v.—vestigial prostomial kinety. (From Chatton and Lwoff, 1939.)

suctorians usually parasitize ciliates, rather than ciliates parasitizing suctoria. These thigmotrichs are apparently true ectoparasites, eventually
killing the protozoan host. The parasites have ciliation restricted to the
dorsal surface, and an anterior-dorsal suctorial tentacle is used to suck out
the host's protoplasm. *Hypocoma parasitica* attacks marine peritrichs; *Heterocoma hyperparasitica* lives on a suctorian attached to a species of *Salpa*.

Penard reported a heliozoan, *Raphidiophrys*, parasitized internally by a
tiny *Blepharisma*-like ciliate 10–12 μ in diameter. Up to 30 per cent of the
heliozoans were infected.[229]

Fauré-Fremiet[87] found a peritrich, *Epistylis lwoffi*, attached to another
peritrich, *Glossatella piscicola*, which was living on a stickleback. The first
form was attached to the second by means of a rigid ring. Also fixed to the
Glossatella was a suctorian *Erastophrya chattoni*. The group provides an
interesting picture of protozoa living in or on other protozoa (Fig. 87).

Nenninger[217] found a peritrich *Rhabdostyla* attached to *Volvox globator*.
She called this apparently one-sided relationship an "irreciprocal sym-
phorium".

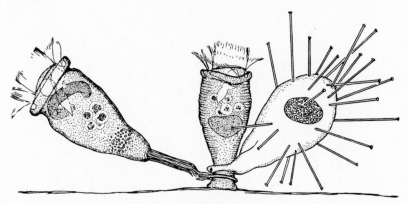

Fig. 87. Vorticellid, *Epistylis lwoffi*, and Suctorian, *Erastophrya chattoni*
attached to Vorticellid *Glossatella piscicola* (center). (From Fauré-Fremiet,
1943.)

Several additional instances of suctorians parasitizing other protozoans
have been reported. The parasitism may be either endobiotic or epibiotic. In
many cases, as was discussed in the introduction to this chapter, the suctorian
may be of the same size or even larger than the protozoan attacked, making
it difficult to determine whether the relationship is one of parasitism or of
predation.

Among the protozoa parasitized or preyed upon are folliculinids by
Pottsia infusorium, with as many as twenty-two suctorians in a single cell;[7]
trichodinids of fish by *Endosphaera engelmanni* (Figs. 88, 89);[180, 224] and
peritrichs by *Tokophrya* (Figs. 90, 91)[90] and *Erastophrya* (Figs. 87, 92),[86,

[87] both of the latter living as epibionts. The peritrichs were attached in turn to the skin of salamanders, to the outer covering of the suctorian, or to the fins of sticklebacks.[86] Fauré-Fremiet remarks of the first two associations that the two organisms act almost as a unit, due probably to the similarity of their ecological habitat.[90] *Erastophrya chattoni* resembles the scyphidian peritrich *Ellobiophrya donacis*, which lies on gill filaments of mussels, in its mode of attachment to the stalk of *Glossatella*. The association is narrowly host specific, since neither trichodinids nor *Gyrodactylus*, a monogenean, both living on the stickleback, are attacked, although another peritrich, *Epistylis*, may provide a substrate for the suctorian (Fig. 87).[86]

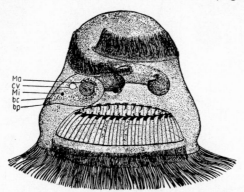

FIG. 88. *Trichodina spheroidesi* parasitized by *Endosphaera engelmanni*. bc—birth canal; bp—birth pore; CV—contractile (?) vacuole; Ma—macronucleus; Mi—micronucleus. (From Padnos and Nigrelli, 1947.)

Podophrya parasitica was the name given by Fauré-Fremiet to a suctorian attacking the gymnostome, *Nassula ornata*.[88] This is an epibiont which apparently feeds on the protoplasm of the ciliate without visible transfer of the host's cytoplasm into the suctorian body (Fig. 93). An interesting phenomenon is the occurrence of temporary chains of *Nassula* attached together by *Podophrya* (Fig. 94). The parasite-host relationship here is more or less specific.

A number of instances of suctoria parasitizing fresh-water ciliates have been found in fresh-water lakes in the vicinity of Mexico City. Among the protozoa attacked are *Epistylis* (Fig. 95),[192, 193, 231] *Stylonychia*,[191] and *Paramecium* (Fig. 95).[231]

Canella[32] has written an extensive monograph on the biology of the suctoria. In this work he discusses possible explanations of choice of host by suctorians. Jankowski[154] has reviewed the life cycles of suctoria parasitizing *Urostyla* and *Paramecium*.

Among the sporozoan parasites of protozoa are Coccidia and Haplosporida; among the Cnidospora, microsporidians have been found in protozoans.

Le Calvez[182] and Myers[216] found an apparent coccidian, *Trophosphaera planorbulinae*, in two genera of foraminiferids. This organism may destroy its host, possibly by mechanically blocking the pores of the test, so that the host eventually starves.[182]

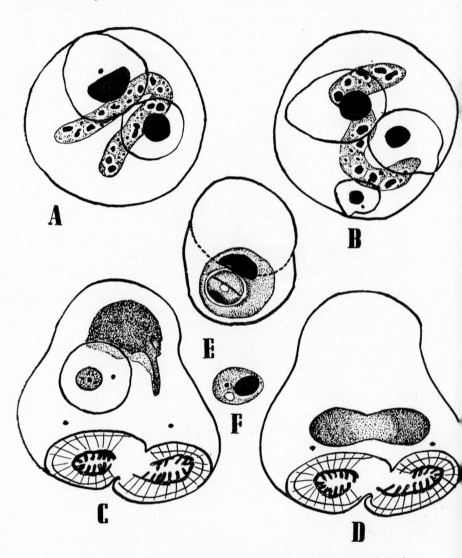

FIG. 89. *Trichodina spheroidesi* parasitized by *Endosphaera engelmanni.* Effects of parasite on host. A and B—host nucleus distorted and vacuolated. C—host nucleus displaced in dividing cell. D—normal position of nucleus in division. E—bud. F—free-living swarmer. (From Padnos and Nigrelli, 1947.)

The members of the next two families are considered by some investigators to be fungi.[116] They are treated here as Haplosporida. Evidence for this classification of the Metchnikovellidae is given by Stubblefield.[288] Recently, however, Vivier[308a] using electron microscope studies offered evidence that the Metchnikovellidae belong to the Microsporida.

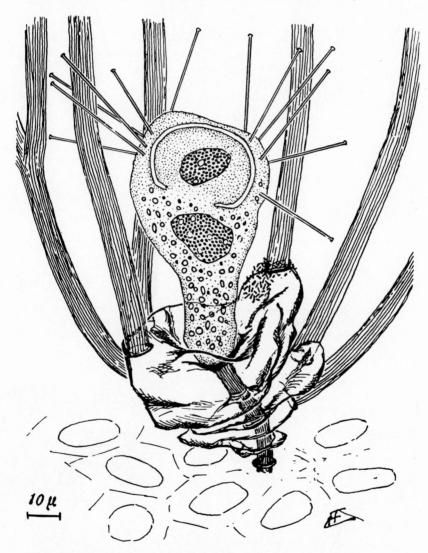

FIG. 90. Suctorian *Tokophrya* sp. attached to skin of *Triturus* with colony of vorticellid *Epistylis trituri* fixed to "molted" cuticle of *Tokophrya*. (From Fauré-Fremiet, 1948.)

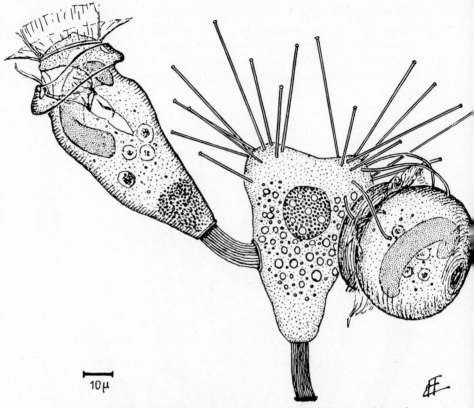

FIG. 91. Suctorian *Tokophrya* sp. attached to skin of *Triturus* with early stage of process of fixation to suctorian of vorticellid *Epistylis trituri*. Form on right held by suctorian tentacles. (From Fauré-Fremiet, 1948.)

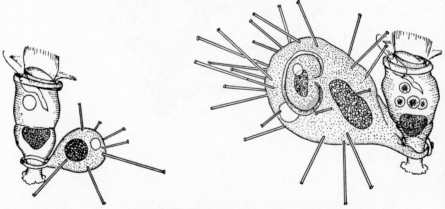

FIG. 92. Suctorian, *Erastophrya chattoni* on vorticellid, *Glossatella piscicola*. (From Fauré-Fremiet, 1943.)

Kirby[171] suggested that some of the nuclear parasites he found in termite flagellates might be haplosporidians (Figs. 96–99) of the family Bertramiidae.

Stubblefield[288] has published a detailed description and life history of the parasites *Amphiacantha ovalis* and *A. attenuata*. These are found in the cytoplasm of the gregarine *Lecudina* living in the gut of two species of the polychaete *Lumbrinereis* (Fig. 100). They belong to the Metchnikovellidae, which are parasites of gregarines. These organisms have been discussed by Kirby[166] on the basis of unpublished work by Stubblefield and little need be added here. Apparently the destructive effects on the host gregarine are

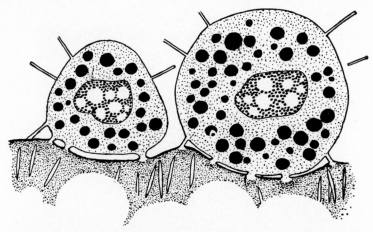

FIG. 93. *Podophrya parasitica* attached to body of *Nassula ornata*. Dark bodies derived from cytoplasm of host. (From Fauré-Fremiet, 1945.)

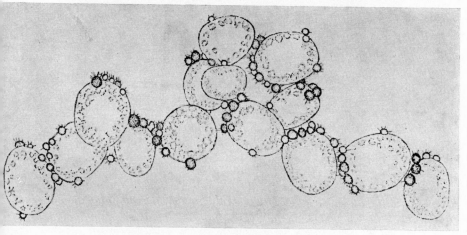

FIG. 94. Chain of *Nassula ornata* attached to one another by tentacles of *Podophrya parasitica*. (From Fauré-Fremiet, 1945.)

the result of the growth and reproduction of the parasite, which practically fills the body of *Lecudina*. Misra[203] found what he believed to be a species of *Metchnikovella* in the cytoplasm of the gregarine *Stylocephalus bahli* in the gut of a coleopteran.

Kudo[177, 178] has made an extensive study of the morphology and development of the microsporidian *Nosema notabilis* living in the cytoplasm of a myxosporidian *Sphaerospora polymorpha*, parasitic in the urinary bladder of the toad fish *Opsanus tau*. *N. notabilis* attacks only the myxosporidian, not the cells of the fish host. Infected cells show definite cytological changes, and in heavy parasitization the host cell's generative nuclei hyper-

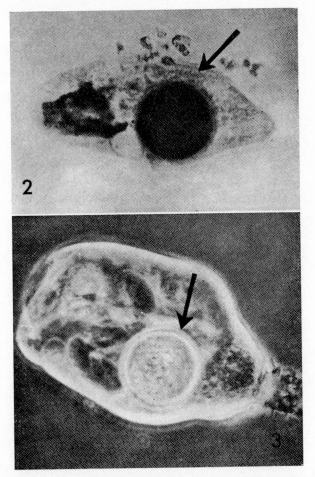

FIG. 95. *Sphaerophrya sol* parasitic in ciliates. 2. In *Paramecium aurelia*. Disorganized host nucleus at left. 3. In *Epistylis plicatus*. Host nucleus at left. (From Pérez-Reyes and Ochoterena, 1963.)

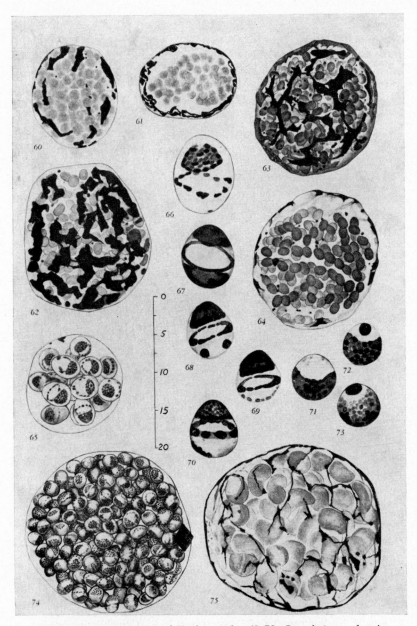

FIG. 96. Nuclear parasites of *Trichonympha*. 60–75. *Caryoletira anulata* in nucleus of *T. corbula*. (From Kirby, 1944.)

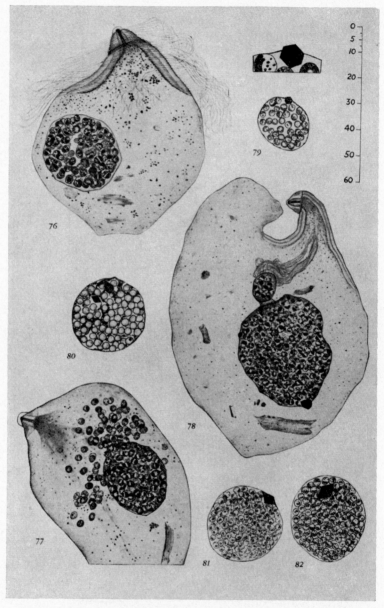

FIG. 97. Nuclear parasites of *Trichonympha*. 76–82. *Caryoletira anulata* in *T. corbula*. (From Kirby, 1944.)

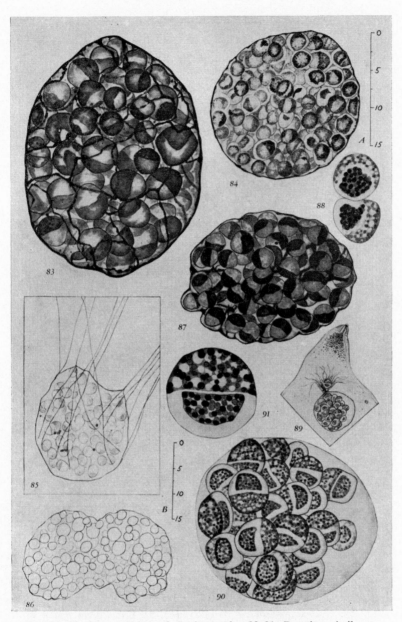

FIG. 98. Nuclear parasites of *Trichonympha*. 83–91. Parasites similar to *Caryoletira anulata*. 83–84. Parasitized nucleus of *T. corbula*. 85–91. Parasites of nucleus of *T. peplophora*. (From Kirby, 1944.)

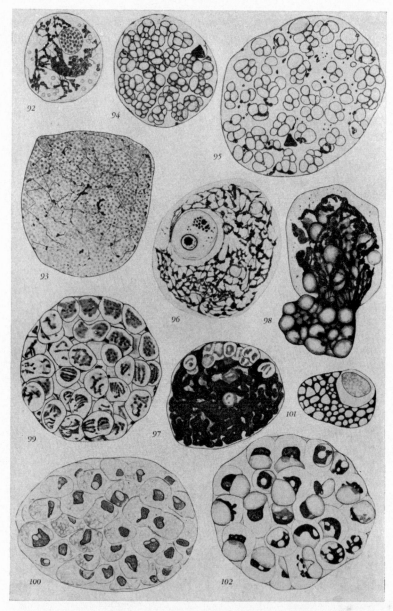

FIG. 99. Nuclear parasites of *Trichonympha*. 92. *Caryococcus dilator* in nucleus of *T. saepicula*. 93. *C. dilator* in nucleus of *T. turkestanica*. 94–95. Parasite in nucleus of *T. saepicula*. 96–101. *Caryoletira magna* in nucleus of *T. turkestanica*. 102. *Caryoletira*-like spores in nucleus of *T. saepicula*. (From Kirby, 1944.)

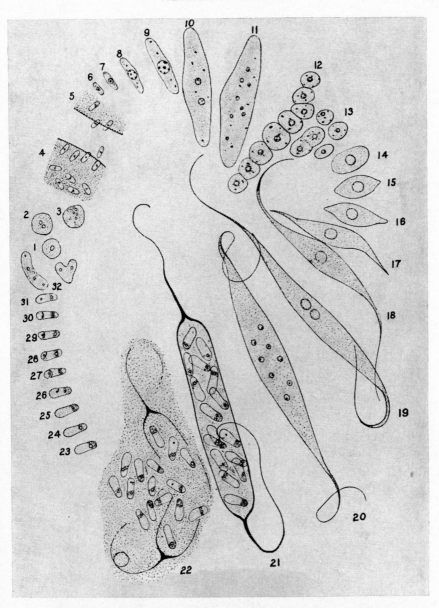

FIG. 100. *Amphiacantha ovalis* from cytoplasm of gregarine, *Lecudina* sp.
1. Zygote. 2–3. Sporonts. 4–5. Sporozoites in host cytoplasm. 6–11. Growth
stages from sporozoites. 12–13. Schizogony producing trophozoites.
14–21. Development of gametocyst. 22. Disintegration of gametocyst within
host cytoplasm. 23–31. Maturation of gametes. 32. Cytoplasmic fusion of
gametes. (From Stubblefield, 1955.)

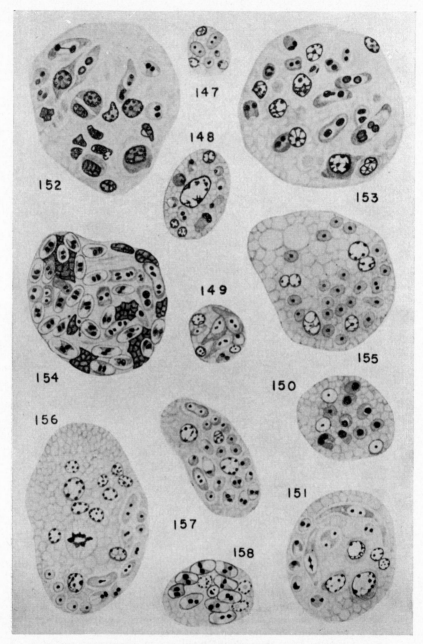

FIG. 101. *Nosema notabilis* in trophozoites of myxosporidian, *Sphaerospora polymorpha*. (From Kudo, 1944.)

trophy and undergo degeneration so that no spore formation takes place (Fig. 101). Eighty-two fish from Maryland and Florida were all infected with both parasites. It may be assumed that the *Nosema* is dependent on the myxosporidian for its continued existence.

Hovasse[144] found a microsporidian *Gurleya nova* in an astomatous ciliate *Spirobütschliella chattoni*, living in the midgut of a polychaetous annelid. *Gurleya* had an amoeboid stage in the ciliate cytoplasm and nucleus; it completed its life cycle in the host cell with the production of two kinds of spores. As long as the parasite remained in the cytoplasm, the ciliate was apparently not disturbed. Invasion of the macronucleus, however, resulted in the disorganization of this structure and, presumably, destruction of the host cell.

Ray and Banik[248] have described a hyperparasite from the cysts of *Iodamoeba bütschlii* (Fig. 48). The parasitic nuclei appear to divide by budding, producing eight spores. Cysts which are attacked are vacuolated and seem to be less viable than are uninfected ones. The parasite may be a protozoan or a fungus; it differs from the chytrid *Nucleophaga* previously described from *I. bütschlii* nuclei.

METAZOA

Nematode worms have been found in the tests of living foraminiferans.[116, 216] In *Iridia lucida*, the worm enters by the test aperture, penetrates the cytoplasm, and produces eggs and larvae, eventually killing the host.[116] The nematode has not been identified. Parasitism of protozoa by metazoans is a rare occurrence. Predation is more common, especially by rotifers. In some instances these associations, however, have been described as parasitic.[166]

STRUCTURES OF UNCERTAIN NATURE

Since 1941, there have continued to be reported in the protoplasm of protozoa particles or structures of which the identity has not yet been settled. Some of these are apparently living organisms, which the investigator was unable to classify; others may be part of the so-called host protozoan; while still others can only be described as enigmatic or equivocal objects found in protozoan bodies. It seems of value to treat briefly these structures since important functions have been assigned to some of them.

Among the Mastigophora, there is considerable uncertainty about the identity of the following:

Bright refringent rods (Fig. 30) were seen in the cytoplasm of *Costia* parasitic on trout.[52] These were not classified by the original investigator, but the present writer believes them to be bacteria and has considered them under that group (see "Bacteria" above).

Kirby,[171, 173] in his exhaustive investigation of the parasites found in the nuclei of termite flagellates, found a number of forms which he did not classify beyond such terms as symbiote GHl (Fig. 28), GH8 (Fig. 29), etc., although in some instances he noted resemblances to bacteria or fungi.

Geitler[103] found very small (0.8–1.0 μ), non-nucleated symbionts (Fig. 21) in the gelatinous sheath of some chrysomonads. He mentions these as budding bacteria-like organisms; they are discussed at length above under the heading of "Bacteria."

Of more importance, from the functional as well as the evolutionary viewpoint, are the suggestions of Ris and his co-workers[251, 252] that such protozoan organelles as the kinetoplast of trypanosomes or the chloroplast of *Chlamydomonas* were actually symbiotic in origin. According to this view, the symbiont in trypanosomes was primitively closely associated with but distinct from the centrioles. Its association with the mitochondrion either would be a later and a secondary connection or else the mitochondrion might be a part of the symbiont. Ris is of the opinion that the DNA portion of the kinetoplast resembles the nucleoplasm of bacteria or blue-green algae. Another and contrary view is that the kinetoplast is a normal organelle of this group of protozoa, conveying genetic information necessary for the synthesis of mitochondrial enzymes and producing and maintaining the mitochondrion.[300, 308] Some investigators consider the kinetoplast itself to be "a highly specialized mitochondrion".[299] DNA has been found in mitochondria of several different kinds of organisms,[290] and hence is not unique to the kinetoplast. The discovery that treatment with acriflavin destroys only the DNA portion of the kinetoplast and severely damages the mitochondria[300] does not seem to offer support for either hypothesis of the origin of the kinetoplast. It does not appear possible at present to solve the question of the origin of kinetoplasts or of mitochondria. These different interpretations only illustrate once again the fact that at this level it is difficult to distinguish between organelles and symbionts.[185]

Ris and Plaut[252] made a similar suggestion regarding the existence of DNA bodies in *Chlamydomonas*. They point out the possibility that these structures, in the shape of microfibrils, may be the genetic system of the chloroplast and that the whole arrangement may represent the surviving condition of an ancestral endosymbiont, possibly a blue-green alga. They refer to Geitler's studies with "Syncyanosen",[104] discussed under "Algae" in the earlier part of this chapter. The presence of blue-green algae in the amoeba *Paulinella chromatophora* endows the cells with photosynthetic ability; since the division of amoeba and its symbiont is regulated in such a way that the number of the latter is kept constant, they point out that there is little real difference between the cyanella and a chloroplast of *Chlamydomonas*.

Herbert[138] suggested that some of the RNA-positive granules in the cytoplasm of *Trypanosoma theileri* are possibly microorganisms, although they were not removed when the trypanosomes were grown in a penicillin-rich

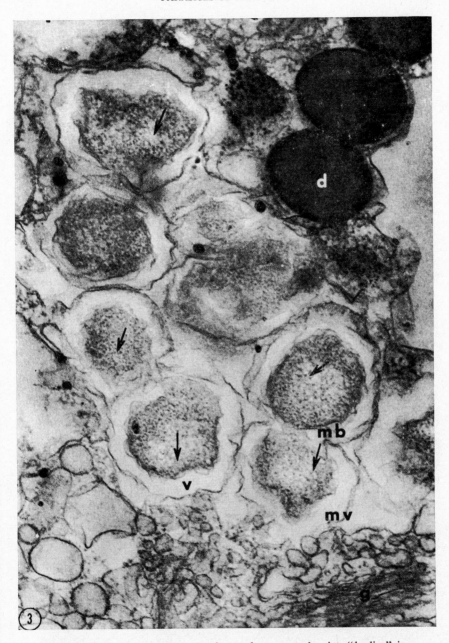

Fig. 102. Electron micrograph of *Amoeba proteus* showing "bodies" in cytoplasm. Fibers and ribosome-like particles within double-limiting membrane of "bodies". Arrows indicate duality of fibers. mb—limiting membrane; v—vacuole; mv—vacuole membrane; d—dense spheres; g—Golgi body. (From Wolstenholme and Plaut, 1964.)

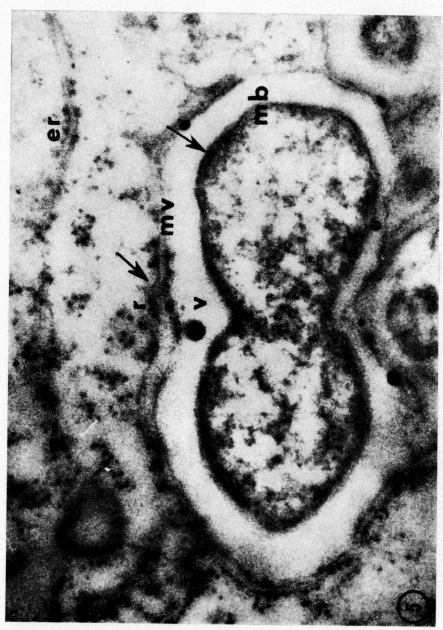

FIG. 103. Electron micrograph of division-like figure of "body" in cytoplasm of *Amoeba proteus*. Arrows indicate double membranes. er—ergastoplasm in amoeba; mb—limiting membrane of "body"; mv—membrane of vacuole; r—ribosomes; v—vacuole. (From Wolstenholme, 1966.)

medium. The particles, frequently called "volutin", are in all probability of a varied nature; hence it is possible that some volutin granules are intracellular symbionts. However, Herbert offers no evidence for this interpretation.

Plaut and Sagan[234] and Wolstenholme and Plaut,[325] in line with similar interpretations for nucleic-acid-containing particles in flagellates,[251, 252] suggest that certain DNA particles in *Amoeba proteus* may be symbionts or on the other hand may have arisen originally from the nucleus. These can be distinguished from ingested bacteria; they show figures suggestive of division (Figs. 102, 103). The authors believe that these particles are different from those described by Roth and Daniels[254] and discussed previously under the heading of "Bacteria".

It is possible that so-called cytoplasmic inheritance in amoebae resulting from injection of portions of the cytoplasm of one species into that of another[133] may be explained by the transfer of nucleic acid particles such as those seen above.[325] There is genetic evidence that hereditary determinants of this nature replicate in the cytoplasm. Under such circumstances, the distinction between gene and symbiont again becomes very blurred. This topic was discussed above under the heading of "Bacteria".

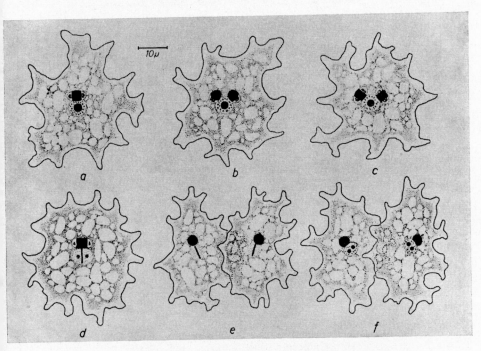

FIG. 104. Division process of *Paramoeba eilhardi* and of Nebenkörper. a–c. Autonomous division of Nebenkörper. d–f. Synchronous division of amoeba nucleus and of Nebenkörper. (From Grell, 1961.)

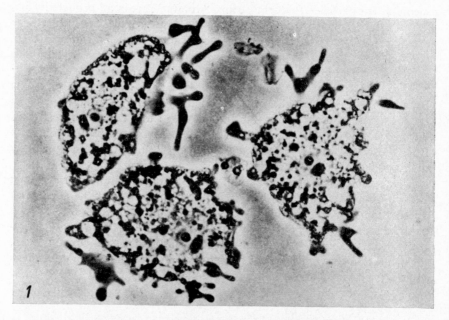

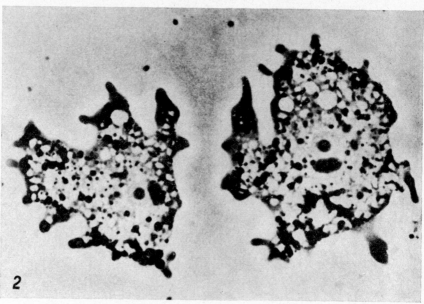

FIG. 105. Microphotographs (phase) of *Paramoeba eilhardi* with Neben-körper adjacent to nucleus. (From Grell, 1961.)

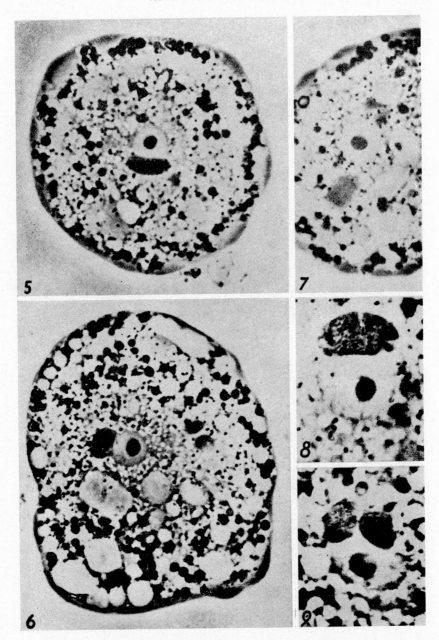

FIG. 106. Microphotographs (phase) of *Paramoeba eilhardi* with Nebenkörper. 7. Nebenkörper destroyed by host cell nucleus. 8–9. DNA granules or fibers in Nebenkörper. (From Grell, 1961.)

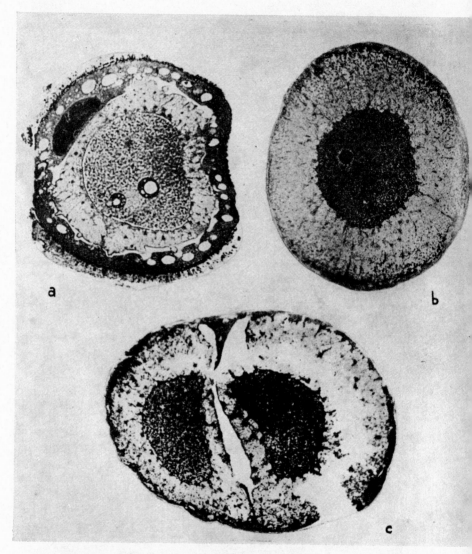

FIG. 107. *Caryotoma bernardi* in nucleus and cytoplasm of radiolarian *Thalassicolla spumida*. c—Two parasites within one central capsule, which has been completely invaded. (From Hollande and Enjumet, 1953.)

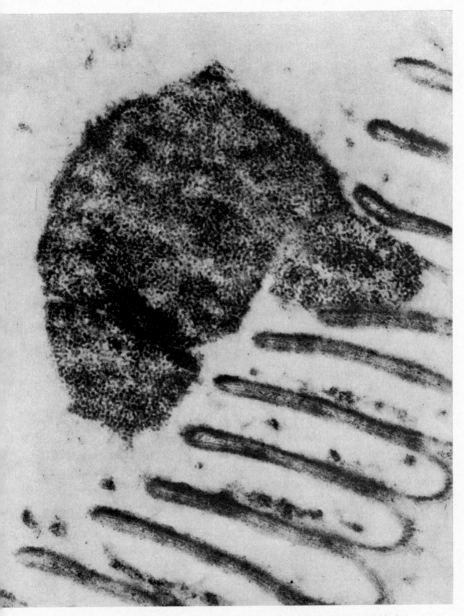

FIG. 108. Unidentified parasite below epicyte of gregarine *Stylocephalus pauliani*. Electron micrograph. (From Grassé and Théodoridès, 1959.)

Grell[118, 119] has investigated the "Nebenkörper" of the marine *Paramoeba eilhardi* (Figs. 104–6). This is a body which lies close to the edge of the nucleus of the amoeba; occasionally there may be as many as four in a single cell. The Nebenkörper has an outer membrane and a central area consisting of DNA. Superficially, it resembles a dinoflagellate nucleus with apparent chromosomes. It may divide independently of the nucleus of the amoeba, especially if more than one Nebenkörper is present. It fulfills all the characteristics of a nucleus but has no genetic relationship to the nucleus of *Paramoeba*. Grell suggests that this may be a "parasitizing" nucleus, but its function, if any, as a possible symbiont is not known.

Hollande and Enjument[141] described an organism which they named *Caryotoma bernardi* (Fig. 107) in the radiolarian, *Thalassicola spumida*. It is a cytoplasmic parasite which lies up against the nucleus, breaks it into two parts, and engulfs one of these. Its systematic position is unknown.

Microorganisms of uncertain taxonomic position have been described in foraminifera[295] and in the testate rhizopod *Quadrula discoides*.[229]

In *Paramecium*, unidentified microorganisms have been found in *P. jenningsi*, in *P. polycarum*,[57] and in *P. caudatum*.[316] Those in the first two species are rodlike and resemble bacteria; those in *P. caudatum* were called "perhaps a virus" (Ref. 318, p. 405). The fact that protein synthesis continues in amacronucleate *P. aurelia* may be explained by various hypotheses, one of which is that RNA is being produced by cytoplasmic symbionts, independent of kappa.[164] A bacterium apart from kappa has recently been discovered by Diller and Diller[55] in the cytoplasm of *P. aurelia*. However, it may be of very limited distribution.

Microorganisms (Figs. 40, 41) have been seen in the ectoplasm of the rumen ciliate, *Entodinium*, and in the macronucleus of *Isotricha intestinalis*, also found in the rumen. The forms in *Entodinium* were considered as either bacteria or *Bartonella*; in *Isotricha* as either *Rickettsia* or *Anaplasma*.[23]

An unknown cytoplasmic parasite of the peritrich *Lagenophrys* appears in the form of spheres, chains, morulae, and plasmodia. It is apparently pathogenic to its host. Rodlike structures appear in the lorica of parasitized and degenerating peritrichs.[53] The appearance of these forms leads one to think that they may be bacteria.

In the Sporozoa, very small spherules 200–240 Å in diameter have been found, associated in masses measuring 2000 × 1400 Å, below the epicyte of the gregarine *Stylocephalus pauliani* (Fig. 108). The masses are surrounded by a membrane, which may indicate that this is not a virus although it is of viral size.[117]

GENETICALLY CONTROLLED CYTOPLASMIC PARTICLES IN CILIATES

The demonstration of what can be called in general a killer factor in ciliates occurred shortly after the appearance of Kirby's chapter[166] in *Protozoa in Biological Research*. Investigations have been carried on mainly but not solely with certain strains of *Paramecium aurelia*. Views as to the nature of this and similar factors have changed considerably since the behavior of killers and sensitives was first described. Without duplicating, we hope, previous reviews,[14, 125, 282, 283, 284, 297] we shall attempt to follow this historical development briefly, placing the main emphasis on the nature of the cytoplasmic particles associated with this type of behavior. These particles at present are considered to be endosymbiotic in nature. So far as possible, we shall not discuss the strictly genetic aspects of their transmission, although, as noted several times previously, it is often difficult to distinguish cytoplasmic constituents from infective agents in unicellular organisms.

It hardly seems necessary to give a detailed description of the killer phenomenon which was discovered by Sonneborn[274] in certain stocks of *Paramecium aurelia*. The original investigations showed that the cells of certain stocks killed paramecia from other stocks when the two were mixed. The former were called killers, the latter sensitives. The ability to kill was the result of the presence of a factor in the cytoplasm known as kappa.[277] While kappa was proved to be self-duplicating, the persistence of the killer character depended upon the presence in the macronucleus, derived, of course, from the micronucleus, of a dominant gene K. The actual killing followed the release into the medium from kappa-containing paramecia of a poisonous substance known as paramecin.[14, 276]

In the context of the present chapter, we are interested in the nature of kappa and of similar particles. Shortly after kappa was discovered[274, 275] and named,[276, 277] the suggestion was made that it was a symbiont, possibly a "viroid"[1, 2] or a virus.[278] Considerable objection to this view was originally raised by Sonneborn,[278, 279] who considered kappa at that time to be a plasmagene.

Discussion on the nature of kappa continued for the next few years.[3, 235, 236, 279, 280] The discovery by Preer in 1948[237] of Feulgen-positive bodies which were uniquely present in the cytoplasm of killers, together with his demonstration that these could not be found in the cytoplasm of sensitives lacking kappa, was the beginning of a series of further investigations which indicated that kappa was not a plasmagene. Van Wagtendonk[303, 304] in the same year also reported the presence of deoxyribonucleoprotein in the cytoplasm of killers. Preer[237, 238] determined the approximate number of particles in each killer paramecium, their approximate size and shape, often double, as well as their rate of multiplication.

Although Sonneborn continued to believe for a time that these particles should be considered plasmagenes,[281] Preer[239] pointed out that they were evidently obligatory symbionts, with Ricksettia-like nuclei, and that they were larger than then-known viruses. Later investigations, however, failed to distinguish discrete nuclei[241] in kappa.

Further studies, such as those showing changes in the oxidative metabolism in killers due to the presence of kappa or directly associated with it,[266] and the demonstrated role of various chemicals and antibiotics in eliminating or damaging kappa,[24, 152, 323] mainly by interfering with its nucleoprotein metabolism, were additional indications of its probable symbiotic nature.

As investigations into the structure of the cytoplasmic factor and the behavior of killers continued, new perspectives, especially on the nature of kappa, became evident. An important discovery was that of Preer and his co-workers based on cytological observations, which showed that the population of kappa from a given cell was not homogeneous.[240, 241] Kappa particles were rod-shaped bodies 0.6–10 μ long, sometimes apparently undergoing binary fission. Some of them contained refractile bodies and were called "brights"; those particles without such refractile bodies were referred to as "non-brights" (Fig. 109). The latter gave rise to the former; only brights possessed killing ability, since they alone were capable of forming the toxic substance, paramecin.[240]

A second important discovery was the existence in various stocks of paramecium of several different kinds of cytoplasmic particles in addition to kappa. Although most of these were like kappa in that they killed other paramecia, they differed either in structure or in the nature of their action. These included mu, responsible for the behavior known as mate-killing,[189, 262] pi,[131] and lambda.[258, 271]

Since these particles seem to be essentially different, they are considered separately in the following paragraphs.

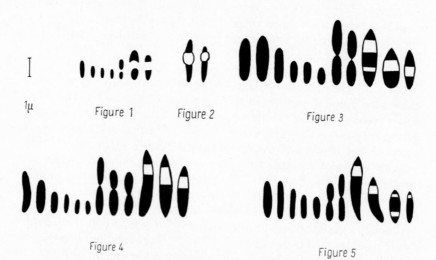

FIG. 109. Kappa from *Paramecium aurelia*—light microscope. 1. From whole animals—Schaudinn fixative. 2. From smears—Schaudinn fixative. 3. From broken animals-phase-unfixed. 4. Osmic fixation before breaking animals-phase. 5. Osmic fixation after breaking animals-phase. (From Preer and Stark, 1953.)

Most of the investigations have dealt with kappa, the first cytoplasmic particle of this nature to be discovered in *Paramecium*. The application of electron microscopy to kappa showed a double membrane on the surface, which is probably the source of specific antibodies.[265] The refractile body in the brights, to which most of the attention was directed, was found to consist of a series of lamellae wound around a central core. The lamellae were described as being wound concentrically[60, 255] (Fig. 110), or as presenting a swiss-roll appearance; this latter structure was called a "toroid"[128] (Fig. 111). Based upon these early electron microscope studies, it was suggested that kappa might be an infected mitochondrion,[128] a pure

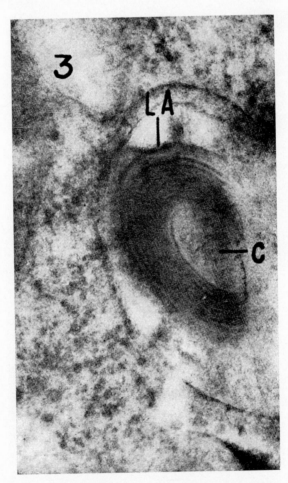

Fig. 110. Kappa body, electron micrograph (slightly oblique section through refractile body of a "bright" particle). LA—concentric lamellae; C—core material. (From Dippell, 1958.)

virus,[128] possibly a bacterium,[61] a degenerate bacterium,[282] or a missing link between viruses and bacteria.[282]

In 1961, Sonneborn[283] reviewed the status of kappa and its bearing on host-parasite relationships. He had come to feel that kappa was not a virus but that the particles were "infectious, intracellular parasites manifesting a more complex level of organization which is close to, if not identical with, that of rickettsiae and bacteria" (p. 5). At this time, he also reported an unfavorable effect of kappa on those paramecia in which it was present. Although kappa was not obviously harmful to its host in a favorable environment, paramecia containing it had less viability under unfavorable

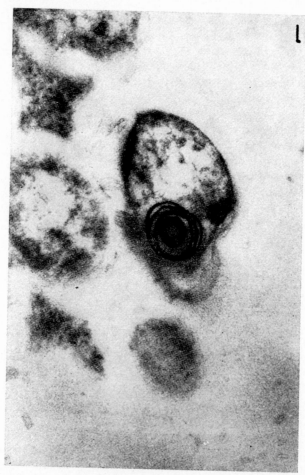

FIG. 111. Kappa body, electron micrograph. Concentric toroids around a central core, wispy, less dense stringy material, and evidence of two limiting outer membranes. (From Hamilton and Gettner, 1958.)

culture conditions than did non-kappa-bearing animals. A similar harmful effect of kappa which had been transferred to the cytoplasm of *Didinium* was later found in one strain of the latter genus.[284]

Soldo[272] was able to grow kappa-bearing paramecia in axenic media; he found that killers, as compared to sensitives, had requirements both for some additional nutritional components and for greater concentrations of those others which were essential for the non-kappa-bearing forms. Burbanck and Martin,[28] however, were unable to grow kappa-bearing paramecia axenically, although animals freed of kappa grew immediately in axenic media.

The more recent studies on kappa have added considerable information on its biochemical and physical nature, but little more is known about its taxonomic position[270] than was summarized by Sonneborn[283] in his 1961 report.

The kappa particles known as brights, containing refractile bodies, were found to be noninfective to other paramecia. Only the non-brights had the capacity to infect.[268, 269, 286] Since the non-brights apparently give rise to brights,[240, 270] a loss of infectivity must occur in this transformation. The mechanism of this loss of infective power is not clear. The refractile bodies themselves are also not infective and the non-bright kappa particles lose their infectivity if they are no longer intact.[209] Apparently the refractile body retains its killing activity, however, even after it is lysed.[242] There is some evidence, from different effects on sensitives, that there is more than one type of refractile body or that a single type may change as the culture ages.[242]

FIG. 112. Sketch of refractile bodies freed from bright Kappa particles (phase contrast). *Paramecium aurelia*. (From Preer and Preer, 1964.)

This duality of the nature of the refractile bodies in kappa has been confirmed in the striking electron microscope studies of Preer and his co-workers.[5, 242] They have shown that the refractile bodies may consist of compact rolls of ribbons 130 Å thick and 5000 Å wide and that these may unroll to form filaments of twisted ribbon from 8–20 μ in length (Figs. 112 to 115). The previously described concentric rings are probably the rolled ribbon which is seen with the electron microscope.[5] The possible role of the sudden unwinding of this ribbon in the killing activity has so far not been demonstrated.[5, 208]

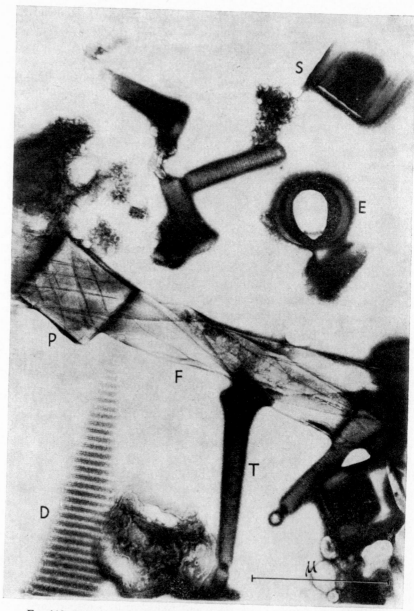

FIG. 113. Electron micrographs of refractile bodies from Kappa in *Paramecium aurelia* killers. E—end view of compact form; S—side view of compact form; P—partly unwound compact form to produce filament F; D—discharged trichocysts; T—trichocyst tip. (From Anderson, Preer, Preer and Bray, 1964.)

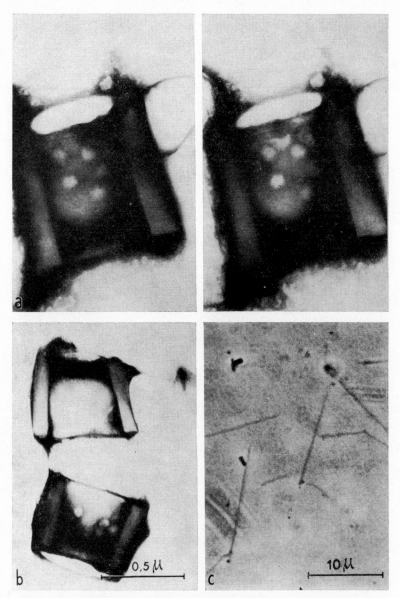

FIG. 114. Electron micrographs of refractile bodies from Kappa in *P. aurelia* killers. a—stereoscopic pair showing cylindrical shape of compact form; overlapping edges of ribbon seen near top. b—double refractile body almost separated into two. c—unwound filaments in phase contrast. Note round objects associated with refractile bodies. (From Anderson, Preer, Preer and Bray, 1964.)

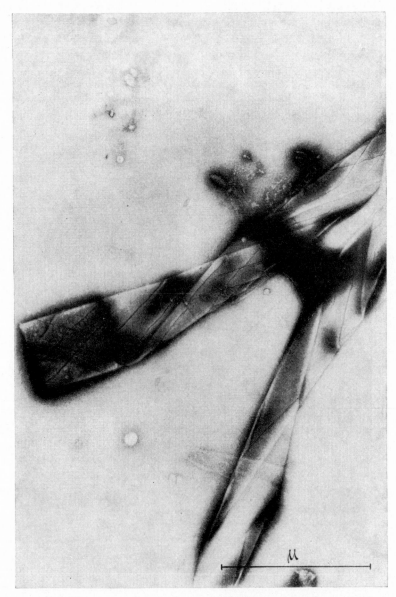

F IG. 115. Electron micrographs of refractile bodies from Kappa in *P. aurelia* killers. Unwound filaments and partially unwound compact form which has collapsed. (From Anderson, Preer, Preer and Bray, 1964.)

Studies on the nature of the infective stage of kappa have resulted in the discovery of a co-factor necessary for infection. [207, 210, 292] If the brei of killer paramecia is centrifuged at 25,000 g, it is possible to separate the co-factor from kappa, the co-factor being recoverable in the supernate (Fig. 116). Since $CaCl_2$ in high concentration may also serva as a co-factor, it is possible that the function of the latter is to aid in the penetration of kappa by altering the physical nature of the paramecium cortex.[210, 292]

Dippell[58, 59] found that kappa mutated spontaneously. Widmayer[320, 321] showed that at least some spontaneous mutations of kappa were associated with the loss of the capacity to form refractile bodies. The presence of the altered, non-refractile or N kappa conferred resistance or immunity to killing action on paramecia carrying these particles. A similar phenomenon was discovered by Mueller [211, 212] in the production of what might be called an induced immunity. If sensitive paramecia are exposed to purified kappa removed from killers, and then transferred to a non-kappa-containing medium with abundant food shortly after the killing effect first appears, some of the transferred paramecia survive. Clones derived from the latter are immune to the killing action of kappa and contain what seem to be altered kappa particles. Such clones lose their immunity when deprived of these latter particles. Needless to say, this type of behavior strongly supports the view that kappa is a symbiont.

The biochemical analysis of kappa[269, 270] has contributed little to the understanding of the biological position of the particle. It has been reported that the chemical composition of kappa resembles that of bacteria[270] and that its DNA is close to that found in certain PPLO organisms or in the polar bodies of *Crithidia oncopelti*. It is not certain if these similarities are fortuitous or if they are indicative of close taxonomic affinity.[269] There is no evidence that kappa contributes to RNA or to protein synthesis in the host paramecium,[164] nor is the development of kappa apparently dependent upon either glycolytic or Krebs TCA cycles or on normal protein synthesis in the cell. On the other hand, if protein synthesis is depressed in sensitive paramecia, those animals exposed to kappa particles are not killed by them. Hence, it would seem that protein synthesis is related to the mechanism of the death of the sensitive cell.[29]

The particles known as mu or mate-killers are different from kappa. They differ in their effects on sensitive paramecia; for example, inlike kappa which does not kill a sensitive mate as a result of contact at conjugation, mu is effective only through contact with a sensitive at the time of conjugation. There is a difference also in the structure of the mu particle. Mate-killers contain from 500–2000 Feulgen-positive particles; these never possess the refractile bodies which produce the "bright" appearance of toxic kappa particles.[190] In appearance, the mu particles are capsulated rods 2–10μ in length by 0.3 μ in diameter.[15, 17] They reproduce by transverse fission and contain a large amount of DNA (Figs. 117, 118). In many ways they resemble

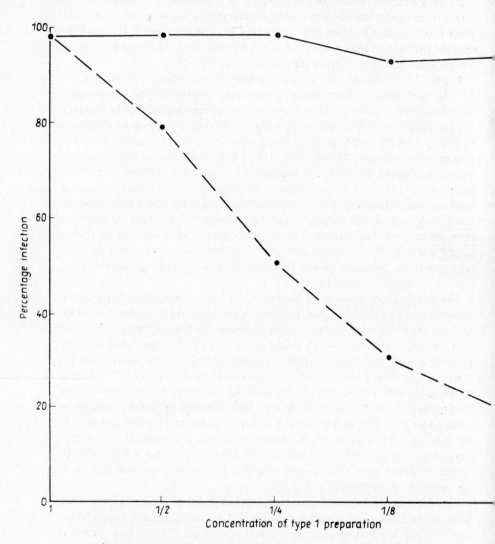

FIG. 116. Comparison of infectivity of brei supernate of killer *Paramecium aurelia* when diluted with co-factor (solid line), as contrasted with dilution with little or no co-factor (broken line). (From Mueller, 1964.)

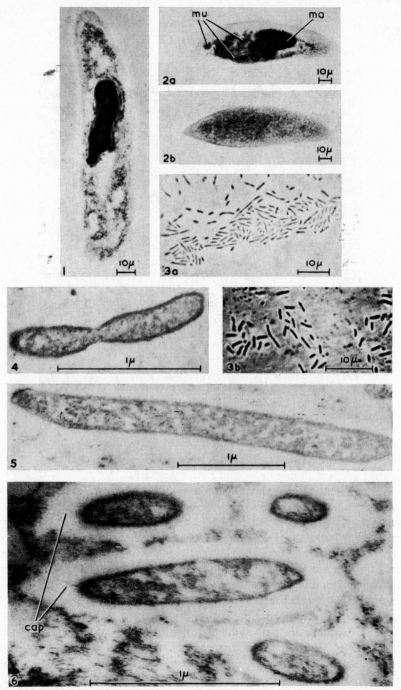

Fig. 117. Mu particles of *Paramecium aurelia*. 1 and 2a. Osmic fixation. 2b. Treated with DNAase before staining. 3a. Unstained mu particles outside *Paramecium*. 3b. Unstained mu particles mounted in india ink, to show capsules. 4–6. Electron micrographs of mu particles. cap—capsule; fv—food vacuole; ma—macronucleus; mu—mu particles. (From Beale and Jurand, 1960.)

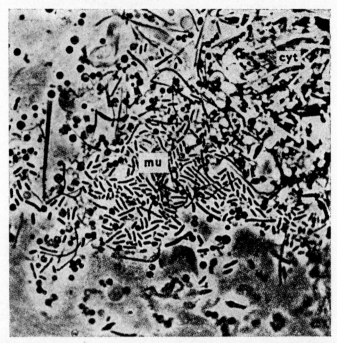

FIG. 118. Clump of mu particles in exudate from a mate-killer *Paramecium*, as seen by phase-contrast microscopy. (Cyt—crushed cytoplasm.) (From Beale, 1964.)

bacteria morphologically; Beale and Jurand[17] suggest that they may be bacteria adapted to live in paramecium cytoplasm.

The persistence of mu particles in the cytoplasm of certain stocks of mate-killers for a considerable number of fissions following loss of the dominant genes known to be necessary for the reproduction of mu led Gibson and Beale[107, 108] to suggest the existence of still another entity called a metagon. According to this theory, the dominant genes release into the cytoplasm factors which are normally nonreplicating. These are called metagons; they mediate the action of a gene on a cell character it specifically controls.[16] A single gene-initiated metagon is sufficient to maintain a large number of mu particles in the cytoplasm. The metagons must be present in the cytoplasm in order for the mu particles to be maintained; they resemble messenger RNA, but differ from it in certain respects, such as infectibility. A paramecium may possibly contain over a thousand metagons, and these may continue to be distributed to cells at division for at least eighteen asexual generations in the complete absence of a dominant gene.[16, 106, 109, 249, 250] When a cell no longer receives a metagon as a result of their gradual dilution by successive fissions, mu particles are lost in a few hours.[109]

The importance of metagons in the context of the present chapter is their reported introduction into *Didinium* by feeding each individual one mate-killer paramecium containing metagons and mu. Following this, the didinia were maintained on sensitive paramecia with neither mu nor metagons for 6 months or about 1000 cell generations. During all this time, both mu and metagons were present in the didinia. It was concluded that the metagons had multiplied during this time, continuing to maintain and to permit the development of mu. Metagons introduced into didinia could even multiply without the presence of mu.[284] All of this was particularly surprising in view of the fact that metagons are apparently incapable of multiplying or do so very slowly in the absence of the dominant gene in their normal resident cell, *Paramecium*.[110]

This type of behavior of the metagon has led Gibson and Sonneborn[110] to suggest that it may behave as a type of messenger RNA in *Paramecium* and as a virus in *Didinium*. A similar persistence and multiplication in the body of *Didinium* was observed for some forms of kappa.[111, 284, 285]

Further investigation of these phenomena is certainly required.[284]

Very little is known about the nature of the particle called pi. It is probably a mutant of kappa;[131] paramecia with pi show Feulgen-positive bodies but are not killers.[14] Pi shows no bright inclusions and apparently is not

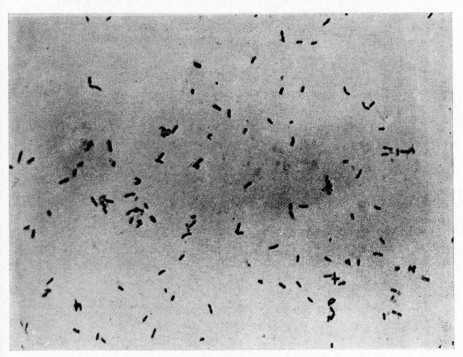

FIG. 119. Lambda particles from *Paramecium aurelia* grown *in vitro*. (From van Wagtendonk, Clark and Godoy, 1963.)

infective through the agency of the medium.[291] If pi and kappa particles are present in the same cytoplasm, pi is displaced by kappa.[14]

The last type of cytoplasmic particle to be discussed is known as lambda.[258, 271] These particles release into the medium a substance which kills sensitive paramecia in a very different manner than does kappa.[30, 258] Several hundred particles are present in a cell; they are about the size of *Escherichia coli* and appear as gram-negative rods or as diplorods[273] (Fig. 119). The fluid from which lambda-bearing paramecia have been removed contains lethal particles 5–10 μ in size, sedimenting at 31,000 g.[30]

Lambda particles contain both RNA and DNA.[19, 272, 273, 293, 306, 307] They stain less heavily with Feulgen stains than do kappa particles.[293] They can be removed from paramecia by various antibiotics; penicillin treatment is very effective in destroying them (Fig. 120).[306] They are apparently capable of synthesizing folic acid and can supply it to the paramecia which they have infected, when the ciliates are grown on axenic media. It is known that *P. aurelia* requires folic acid; paramecia containing lambda do not need it, but if they are treated with penicillin and the lambda

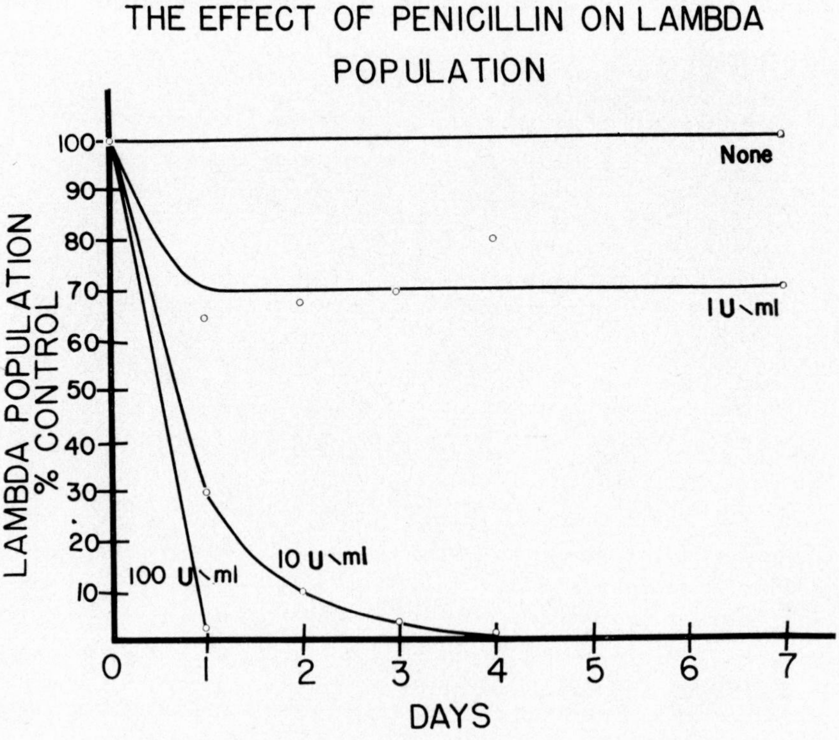

FIG. 120. Effect of penicillin on lambda population in cytoplasm of *Paramecium aurelia*. (From Soldo, 1963.)

particles are removed, the requirement for folic acid is restored. In this respect lambda acts as an endosymbiont.[305, 306]

All this is reminiscent of the role of the bipolar bacterial endosymbiont in the flagellate *Crithidia oncopelti*.[113, 124, 219] One difference is that there is no definite agreement that lambda or the other cytoplasmic particles in paramecia are bacteria. It seems to be accepted that they are all endosymbionts; they may also be considered, at least in some cases, to be an integral part of the cell in which they live. The particular category in which they are placed may be a purely semantic decision. On the other hand, the acceptance of the view that there is no real difference between the consideration of these particles as endosymbionts or as cell organelles may lead investigators to gloss over the problem of distinction as being insoluble, when actually it may be insoluble only in the present state of our knowledge.

Finally, the discovery of these particles in paramecia would lead one to suspect that similar structures are present in other protozoa and perhaps also in cells of multicellular organisms. There is increasing evidence that this may be true.[305, 306]

REFERENCES

1. ALTENBURG, E. (1946) The "viroid" theory in relation to plasmagenes, viruses, cancer and plastids. *Am. Nat.* **80**, 559–67.
2. ALTENBURG, E. (1946) The symbiont theory in explanation of the apparent cytoplasmic inheritance in *Paramecium. Am. Nat.* **80**, 661–2.
3. ALTENBURG, E. (1948) The role of symbionts and autocatalysts in the genetics of the ciliates. *Am. Nat.* **92**, 252–64.
4. AMARO, A. (1962) Observacoes em Zelerielas hiperparasitadas por entamebas (Protozoa, Mastigophora). *Atas. Soc. Biol. Rio de Janeiro* **6**, 21–25.
5. ANDERSON, T. F., PREER, J. R., PREER, L. B., and BRAY, M. (1964) Studies on killing particles from *Paramecium:* The structure of refractile bodies from Kappa particles. *J. Microscopie* **3**, 395–402.
6. ANDRESEN, N. (1956) Cytological investigations on the giant amoeba *Chaos chaos. C.R. Trav. Lab. Carlsberg, Sér. Chim.* **29**, 435–555.
7. ANDREWS, E. A., and REINHARD, E. G. (1943) A folliculinid associated with a hermit crab. *J. Washington Acad. Sci.* **33**, 216–23.
8. BARKER, D. C. (1963) A ribonucleoprotein inclusion body in *Entamoeba invadens. Zeitschrift für Zellforschung und mikroskop. Anat.* **58**, 641–59.
9. BARKER, D. C. (1963) Ribosome structures revealed by negative staining subcellular fractions from a crystalline ribonucleoprotein body. *Exper. Cell Research* **32**, 272–9.
10. BARKER, D. C., and DEUTSCH, K. (1958) The chromatoid body of *Entamoeba invadens. Expt . Cell Res.* **15**, 604–10.
11. BARKER, D. C., and SVIHLA, G. (1964) Localization of cytoplasmic nucleic acid during growth and encystment of *Entamoeba invadens. J. Cell Biol.* **20**, 389–98.
12. BARTSCH, A. F. (1945) The significance of zygospore character in *Polyphagus euglenae. Mycologia* **37**, 553–70.
13. BAUER, L. (1961) Ein Beitrag zur Klärung der Beziehungen zwischen Amöben und Virus im Wasser. *Arch. Hyg. u. Bakteriol.* **145**, 12–20.
14. BEALE, G. H. (1954) *The Genetics of Paramecium aurelia*, Cambridge Monographs in Experimental Biology 2, Cambridge University Press.

15. BEALE, G. H. (1957) A mate-killing strain of *Paramecium aurelia*, variety 1 from Mexico. *Proc. Roy. Phys. Soc. Edinburgh* **26**, 11–14.

16. BEALE, G. H. (1964) Genes and cytoplasmic particles in *Paramecium*. In *Cellular Control Mechanisms and Cancer*, eds. P. EMMELOT and O. MÜHLBOCK, Elsevier Publishing Company, Amsterdam, 8–18.

17. BEALE, G. H., and JURAND, A. (1960) Structure of the mate-killer (mu) particles in *Paramecium aurelia*, stock 540. *J. Gen. Microbiol.* **23**, 243–52.

18. BEAMS, H. W., KING, R. L., TAHMISIAN, T. N., and DEVINE, R. (1960) Electron microscope studies on *Lophomonas striata* with special reference to the nature and position of the striations. *J. Protozool.* **7**, 91–101.

19. BEHME, R. J. (1964) DNA base compositions of serveral symbionts in *Paramecium aurelia*. *Genetics* **50**, 235.

20. BENEKE, E. S., and SCHMITT, J. A. (1961) Aquatic fungi from South Bass and neighboring islands in western Lake Erie. I. Uniflagellate and biflagellate phycomycetes. *Ohio J. Sci.* **61**, 283–5.

21. BOMFORD, R. (1965) Infection of alga-free *Paramecium bursaria* with strains of *Chlorella*, *Scenedesmus*, and a yeast. *J. Protozool.* **12**, 221–4.

22. BREED, R. S., MURRAY, E. G. D., and SMITH, N. R. (1957) *Bergey's Manual of Determinative Bacteriology*, 7th ed., Williams and Wilkins, Baltimore.

23. BRETSCHNEIDER, L. H., and VAN VORSTENBOSCH, C. J. A. H. V. (1964) Das Vorkommen von intraplasmatischen und intranuklearen Mikroorganismen in einigen Pansenciliaten. *Proc. Koninkl. Nederl. Akademie van Wetenschappen, Series C, Biol. and Med. Sci.* **67**, 313–9.

24. BROWN, C. H. (1950) Elimination of kappa particles from "killer" strains of *Paramecium aurelia* by treatment with chloromycetin. *Nature* **166**, 527.

25. BRUG, S. L. (1942) Eigentümliche Einschlüsse in *Lamblia muris*. *Zentralbl. Nakt. I Abt. Orig.* **148**, 166–8.

26. BRUTSAERT, P., JUNGEBLUT, C. W., and KNOX, A. (1946) Attempts to propagate murine Poliomyelitis virus on various intestinal bacteria and Protozoa. *Proc. Soc. Exp. Biol. and Med.* **61**, 265–8.

27. BUCHNER, P. (1952) *Endosymbiose der Tiere mit pflanzlichen Mikroorganismen*, Birkhäuser, Basel.

28. BURBANCK, W. D., and MARTIN, V. L. (1965) The effect of the food of *Paramecium aurelia*, syngen 4, stock 51, mating type VII on its role in symbiosis. In *Progress in Protozoology*, abstracts of papers from Second Internat'l Conf. Protozoology, London, 1965, 114–5.

29. BUTZEL, JR., H. M., and PAGLIARA, A. (1962) The effect of biochemical inhibitors upon the killer-sensitive system in *Paramecium aurelia*. *Exptl. Cell. Res.* **27**, 382–95.

30. BUTZEL, JR., H. M., and VAN WAGTENDONK, W. J. (1963) Some properties of the lethal agent found in cell-free fluids obtained from cultures of lambda-bearing *Paramecium aurelia*, syngen 8, stock 299, *J. Protozool.* **10**, 250–2.

31. CACHON-ENJUMET, M. (1961) Contribution á l'étude des Radiolaires Phaeodariés. *Arch. de Zool. Exp. et Gén.* **100**, 151–237.

32. CANELLA, M. F. (1957) Studi e Richerche sui Tentaculiferi nel quadro della Biologia Generale. *Ann. dell' Univ. Ferrara N. S. III Biol. Anim.* **1**, 259–716.

33. CANTER, H. M. (1946) Studies on British Chytrids. I. *Dangeardia mammillata* Schröder. *Trans. Brit. Mycol. Soc.* **29**, 128–40.

35. CANTER, H. M. (1951) Fungal parasites of the phytoplankton. II. (Studies on British Chytrids. XII.) *Annals of Botany*, N. S., **15**, 129–56.

35. CANTER, H. M. (1953) Annotated list of British aquatic Chytrids. *Trans. Brit. Mycol. Soc.* **36**, 278–301.

36. CANTER, H. M. (1954) Fungal parasites of the phytoplankton. III. *Trans. Brit. Mycol. Soc.* **37**, 111–33.

37. CANTER, H. M. (1955) Annotated list of British aquatic Chytrids (Supplement I). *Trans. Brit. Mycol. Soc.* **38**, 425–30.

38. CANTER, H. M. (1959) Fungal parasites of the phytoplankton. IV. *Rhizophydium contractophilum* sp. nov. *Trans. Brit. Mycol. Soc.* **42**, 185–92.

39. CANTER, H. M. (1963) Studies on British Chytrids. XXIII. New species on Chrysophycean algae. *Trans. Brit. Mycol. Soc.* **46**, 306–20.

40. CHATTON, E., and BIECHELER, B. (1935) Les *Amoebophrya* et le *Hyalosaccus;* leur cycle évolutif. L'Ordre nouveau des *Coelomastigina* dans les Flagellés. *C.R. Acad. Sci.* **200**, 505.

41. CHATTON, E., and LWOFF, A. (1939) Sur la systématique de la tribu des Thigmotriches Rhynchoïdés. Les deux familles des *Hypocomidae* Bütschli et des *Ancistrocomidae n. fam.* les deux genres nouveaux, *Heterocoma* et *Parhypocoma*. *C.R. Acad. Sci.* **209**, 429.

42. CLEVELAND, L. R. (1951) Hormone-induced sexual cycles of flagellates. VII. One-division meiosis and autogamy without cell division in *Urinympha*. *J. Morph.* **88**, 385–439.

43. CLEVELAND, L. R. "Flagellates of Australian Termites". Film.

44. CLEVELAND, L. R., and GRIMSTONE, A. V. (1964) The fine structure of the flagellate *Mixotricha paradoxa* and its associated micro-organisms. *Proc. Royal Soc.*, Ser. B, **159**, 668–86.

45. COHEN, A. I. (1957) Electron microscopic observations of *Amoeba proteus* in growth and inanition. *J. Biophysic, and Biochem. Cytol.* **3**, 859–66.

46. CONRAD, W. (1941) Notes protistologiques. XV. Flagellates d'un mare d'Ardenne. *Bull. Mus. Roy. Hist. Nat. Belg.* **17**, Fasc. 39, 11 pp.

47. CROSS, J. B. (1946) The flagellate subfamily Oxymonadinae. *Univ. Calif. Publ. Zool.* **53**, 67–162.

48. CROUCH, H. B. (1933) Four new species of *Trichomonas* from the woodchuck (*Marmota monax* Linn.). *J. Par.* **19**, 293–301.

49. CROUCH, H. B. (1936) The animal parasites of the woodchuck (*Marmota monax* L.) with special reference to Protozoa. *Iowa St. Coll. J. Sci.* **11**, 48–50.

49a. DANIELS, E. W. (1964) Electron microscopy of centrifuged *Amoeba proteus*. *J. Protozool.* **11**, 281–90.

50. DANIELS, E. W., and ROTH, L. E. (1961) X-irradiation of the giant amoeba, *Pelomyxa illinoisensis*. III. Electron microscopy of centrifuged organisms. *Radiation Res.* **14**, 66–82.

51. DAVIS, H. S. (1942) A suctorian parasite of the small mouth Black Bass, with remarks on other suctorian parasites of fishes. *Trans. Am. Micr. Soc.* **61**, 309–27.

52. DAVIS, H. S. (1943) A new polymastigine flagellate, *Costia pyriformis*, parasitic on trout. *J. Par.* **29**, 385–6.

53. DEBAISIEUX, P. (1959) *Lagenophrys lunatus*, Ima. (Ciliate, Péritriche). *La Cellule* **59**, 361–83.

54. DEUTSCH, K., and ZAMAN, V. (1959) An electron microscopic study of *Entamoeba invadens* Rodhain 1934. *Exptl. Cell Res.* **17**, 310–19.

55. DILLER, I. C., and DILLER, W. F. (1965) Isolation of an acid-fast organism from axenic cultures of *Paramecium aurelia* 139 π. *Trans. Am. Micr. Soc.* **84**, 152–3.

56. DILLER, W. F. (1948) Induction of autogamy in single animals of *Paramecium calkinsi* following mixture of two mating types. *Biol. Bull.* **95**, 265.

57. DILLER, W. F. (1958) Studies on conjugation in *Paramecium polycarum*. *J. Protozool.* **5**, 282–92.

58. DIPPELL, R. V. (1948) Mutations of the killer plasmagene, kappa, in variety 4 of *Paramecium aurelia*. *Am. Nat.* **82**, 43–50.

59. DIPPELL, R. V. (1950) Mutation of the killer cytoplasmic factor in *Paramecium aurelia*. *Heredity* **4**, 165–87.

60. DIPPELL, R. V. (1958) The fine structure of Kappa in killer stock 51 of *Paramecium aurelia*. Preliminary observations. *J. Biophysic. and Biochem. Cytol.* **4**, 125–6.

61. DIPPELL, R. V. (1959) Distribution of DNA in Kappa particles of *Paramecium* in relation to the problem of their bacterial affinities. *Science* **130**, 1415.

62. DOYLE, W. L., and DOYLE, M. M. (1940) The structure of zooxanthellae. *Carnegie Inst. of Washington, Papers from Tortugas Lab.* **32**, 127–42.

63. DRECHSLER, C. (1941) Four phycomycetes destructive to nematodes and rhizopods. *Mycologia* **33**, 248–69.

64. DRECHSLER, C. (1941) Predaceous fungi. *Biol. Rev.* **16**, 265–90.

65. DRECHSLER, C. (1942) New species of *Acaulopage* and *Cochlonema* destructive to soil amoebae. *Mycologia* **34**, 274–97.

66. DRECHSLER, C. (1945) Several additional phycomycetes subsisting on nematodes and amoebae. *Mycologia* **37**, 1–31.

67. DRECHSLER, C. (1947) Three zoöpagaceous fungi that capture and consume soil-inhabiting rhizopods. *Mycologia* **39**, 253–81.

68. DRECHSLER, C. (1947) Three new species of *Zoöpage* predaceous on terricolous rhizopods. *Mycologia* **39**, 379–408.

69. DRECHSLER, C. (1949) An *Endocochlus* having binary helicoid thalli of left-handed rotation. *Mycologia* **41**, 229–51.

70. DRECHSLER, C. (1951) Various zoöpagaceous fungi subsisting on protozoans and eelworms. *Mycologia* **43**, 161–85.

71. DRECHSLER, C. (1955) Additional species of Zoöpagaceae subsisting on rhizopods and eelworms. *Mycologia* **47**, 364–88.

72. DRECHSLER, C. (1959) Several Zoöpagaceae subsisting on a nematode and on some terricolous amoebae. *Mycologia* **51**, 787–823.

73. DRECHSLER, C. (1960) A clamp-bearing fungus using stalked adhesive young chlamydospores in capturing amoebae. *Sydowia* **14**, 246–57.

74. DRECHSLER, C. (1961) Some clampless hyphomycetes predacious on nematodes and rhizopods. *Sydowia* **15**, 9–25.

75. DROOP, M. R. (1963) Algae and invertebrates in symbiosis. In *Symbiotic Associations*, 13th Symp. Soc. Gen. Microbiol., eds. P. S. NUTMAN and B. MOSSE, Cambridge Univ. Press, London, 171–99.

76. DROŻAŃSKI, W. (1956) Fatal bacterial infection in soil amoebae. *Acta Microbiologica Polon.* **5**, 315–7.

77. DROŻAŃSKI, W. (1963) Studies of intracellular parasites of free-living amoebae. *Acta Microbiologica Polon.* **12**, 3–8.

78. DROŻAŃSKI, W. (1963) Observations on intracellular infection of amoebae by bacteria. *Acta Microbiologica Polon.* **12**, 9–24.

79. DROŻAŃSKI, W. J. (1965) Fatal bacterial infection of small free-living amoebae and related organisms. In *Progress in Protozoology*, abstracts of papers from Second Internat'l Conf. Protozoology, London, 1965, 254–5.

80. DUBOSCQ, O., and GRASSÉ, P. (1943) Les flagellés de l'*Anacanthotermes ochraceus* Burm. *Arch. Zool. Exp.* **82**, 401–38.

81. DUDDINGTON, C. L. (1951) Further records of British predacious fungi. II. *Trans. Brit. Mycol. Soc.* **34**, 194–209.

82. DUDDINGTON, C. L. (1955) Fungi that attack microscopic animals. *Bot. Rev.* **21**, 377–439.

83. DUDDINGTON. C. L. (1956) The predacious fungi: Zoopagales and Moniliales. *Biol. Rev.* **31**, 152–93.

84. DUDDINGTON, C. L. (1957) The predacious fungi and their place in microbial ecology. In *Microbial Ecology*, 7th Symp. Soc. Gen. Microbiol., eds. R. E. O. WILLIAMS and C. C. SPICER, Cambridge Univ. Press, London, 218–37.

85. EVANS, C. A., and OSTERUD, K. L. (1946) The failure of Poliomyelitis virus to grow in certain Protozoa of sewage. *Science* **104**, 51–53.
86. FAURÉ-FREMIET, E. (1943) Commensalisme et adaptation chez un Acinétien; *Erastophrya chattoni* n.g.n. sp. *Bull. Soc. Zool. France* **68**, 145–7.
87. FAURÉ-FREMIET, E. (1943) Commensalisme et adaptation chez une Vorticellide: *Epistylis lwoffi*, n. sp. *Bull. Soc. Zool. France* **68**, 154–7.
88. FAURÉ-FREMIET, E. (1945) *Podophrya parasitica* nov. sp. *Bull. Biol. France et Belgique* **79**, 85–97.
89. FAURÉ-FREMIET, E. (1948) Le rhythme de marée du *Strombidium oculatum* Gruber. *Bull. Biol. France et Belgique* **82**, 3–23.
90. FAURÉ-FREMIET, E. (1948) Un cas d'association entre cilié et tentaculifère epizoiques. *Anais da Acad. Brasil de Ciencias* **20**, 117–23.
91. FAURÉ-FREMIET, E. (1950) Caulobactériés epizoiques associées aux *Centrophorella* (Ciliés holotriches). *Bull. Soc. Zool. France* **75**, 134–7.
92. FAURÉ-FREMIET, E. (1950) Écologie des Ciliés psammophiles littoraux. *Bull. Biol. France et Belg.* **84**, 35–75.
93. FAURÉ-FREMIET, E. (1951) The marine sand-dwelling ciliates of Cape Cod. *Biol. Bull.* **100**, 59–70.
94. FAURÉ-FREMIET, E. (1952) Symbiontes bactériens des ciliés du genre *Euplotes*. *C.R. Acad. Sci.* **235**, 402–3.
95. FAURÉ-FREMIET, E. (1958) Le cilié *Condylostoma tenuis* n. sp. et son algue symbiote. *Hydrobiologia* **10**, 43–48.
96. FERNANDEZ-GALIANO FERNANDEZ, D. (1947) Observaciones citológicas sobre las opalinas. *Trab. Inst. Cienc. Nat. José de Acosta* **1**, 353–422.
97. FOX, K. (1946) A possible endo-parasite of *Amoeba proteus*. *Micro Notes* **2**, 3–6.
98. FREUDENTHAL, H. D. (1962) *Symbiodinium* gen. nov. and *Symbiodinium microadriaticum* sp. nov., a zooxanthella: taxonomy, life cycle, and morphology. *J. Protozool.* **9**, 45–52.
99. FREUDENTHAL, H. D., and LEE, J. J. (1963) Further studies on the cytology and life history of the zooxanthella, *Symbiodinium microadriaticum* (Freudenthal). *Proc. Int. Congr. Zool.* **16**, 21.
100. FRITSCH, F. E. (1952) Algae in association with heterotrophic or holozoic organisms. *Proc. Roy. Soc., Ser B*, **139**, 185–92.
101. FÜLLER, H. (1958) *Symbiose im Tierreich*, Ziemsen, Wittenberg.
102. GARNHAM, P. C. C., BIRD, R. G., and BAKER, J. R. (1962) Electron microscope studies of motile stages of malaria parasites. III. The ookinetes of *Haemamoeba* and *Plasmodium*. *Trans. Roy. Soc. Tr. Med. and Hyg.* **56**, 116–20.
103. GEITLER, L. (1948) Symbiosen zwischen Chrysomonaden und knospenden bakterienartigen Organismen sowie Beobachtungen über Organisationseigentümlichkeiten der Chrysomonaden. *Osterreich. Bot. Zeitschr.* **95**, 300–24.
104. GEITLER, L. (1959) Syncyanosen. In *Encyclopedia of Plant Physiology*, ed. W. RUHLAND, Springer Press, Berlin **11**, 530–45.
105. GEITLER, L. (1962) *Dangeardia sporapiculata* n. sp., der Begriff "Apikulus" und die Gattungsabgrenzung bei einigen Chytridialen. *Sydowia* **16**, 324–30.
106. GIBSON, I. (1965) Electrophoresis of extracts of *Paramecium aurelia* containing metagons. *Proc. Roy. Soc., Ser. B* **161**, 538–49.
107. GIBSON, I., and BEALE, G. H. (1961) Genic basis of the mate-killer trait in *Paramecium aurelia*, stock 540. *Genet. Res.* **2**, 82–91.
108. GIBSON, I., and BEALE, G. H. (1962) The mechanism whereby the genes M_1 and M_2 in *Paramecium aurelia*, stock 540, control growth of the mate-killer (mu) particles. *Genet. Res.* **3**, 24–50.
109. GIBSON, I., and BEALE, G. H. (1963) The action of ribonuclease and 8-azaguanine on mate-killer Paramecia. *Genet. Res.* **4**, 42–54.

110. GIBSON, I., and SONNEBORN, T. M. (1964) Is the metagon an *m*-RNA in *Paramecium* and a virus in *Didinium? Proc. Nat. Acad. Sci.* **52**, 869–76.

111. GIBSON, I., and SONNEBORN, T. M. (1964) Killer particles and metagons of *Paramecium* grown in *Didinium. Genet.* **50**, 249–50.

112. GILL, J. W., and VOGEL, H. J. (1962) Lysine synthesis and phylogeny: biochemical evidence for a bacterial-type endosymbiote in the protozoon *Herpetomonas (Strigomonas) oncopelti. Biochim. et Biophys. Acta* **56**, 200–1.

113. GILL, J. W., and VOGEL, H. J. (1963) A bacterial endosymbiote in *Crithidia (Strigomonas) oncopelti:* biochemical and morphological aspects. *J. Protozool.* **10**, 148–52.

114. GILLIES, C., and HANSON, E. D. (1962) A flagellate parasitizing the ciliate macronucleus. *J. Protozool.* **9** (Suppl.), 15.

115. GILLIES, C., and HANSON, E. D. (1963) A new species of *Leptomanas* parasitizing the macronucleus of *Paramecium trichium. J. Protozool.* **10**, 467–73.

116. GRASSÉ, P. P. (1952) *Traité de Zoologie* **1**, parts 1 and 2. Masson et Cie., Paris.

117. GRASSÉ, P. P., and THÉODORIDÈS, J. (1959) Recherches sur l'ultrastructure de quelques grégarines. *Ann. Sci. Nat. Zool.*, 12e sér. **1**, 237–52.

118. GRELL, K. G. (1961) Über den "Nebenkörper" von *Paramoeba eilhardi* Schaudinn. *Arch. f. Prot.* **105**, 303–12.

119. GRELL, K. G. (1962) Morphologie und Fortpflanzung der Protozoen (einschließlich Entwicklungsphysiologie und Genetik). *Fortschritte der Zoologie* **14**, 1–85.

120. GRIMSTONE, A. V. (1961) Fine structure and morphogenesis in Protozoa. *Biol. Rev.* **36**, 97–150.

121. GRIMSTONE, A. V. (1961) The fine structure of *Streblomastix strix.* Abstr., 1st. Int. Conf. Protozoologists, Prague, 121.

122. GROUPÉ, V., HERRMANN, JR. E. C., and RAUSCHER, F. J. (1955) Ingestion and destruction of influenza virus by free-living ciliate *Tetrahymena pyriformis. Proc. Soc. Exp. Biol. and Med.* **88**, 479–82.

123. GROUPÉ, V., and PUGH, L. H. (1952) Inactivation of influenza virus and viral hemagglutinin by the ciliate *Tetrahymena geleii. Science* **115**, 307–8.

124. GUTTMAN, H. N., and EISENMAN, R. N. (1965) "Cure" of *Crithidia (Strigomonas) oncopelti* of its bacterial endosymbiote. *Nature* **206**, 113–4.

125. HAGEMAN, R. (1964) *Plasmatische Vererbung* (No. 4, of *Genetik, Grundlagen, Ergebnisse und Probleme in Einzeldarstellungen*), Gustav Fischer Verlag, Jena, Germany.

126. HALL, W. T., and CLAUS, G. (1963) Ultrastructural studies on the blue-green algal symbiont in *Cyanophora paradoxa* Korschikoff. *J. Cell Biol.* **19**, 551–63.

127. HAMBURGER, B. (1958) Bakteriensymbiose bei *Volvox aureus* Ehrenberg. *Arch. Mikrobiol.* **29**, 291–310.

128. HAMILTON, L. D., and GETTNER, M. E. (1958) Fine structure of kappa in *Paramecium aurelia. J. Biophysics and Biochem. Cytol.* **4**, 122–3.

129. HÄMMERLING, J. (1946) Über die Symbiose von *Stentor polymorphus. Biol. Zentralbl.* **65**, 52–61.

130. HANSON, A. M. (1944) A new chytrid parasitizing *Volvox: Loborhiza metzneri*, gen. nov., sp. nov. *Am. J. Botany* **31**, 166–71.

131. HANSON, E. D. (1954) Studies on kappa-like particles in sensitives of *Paramecium aurelia*, variety 4. *Genetics* **39**, 229–39.

132. HARRIS, K. (1953) A contribution to our knowledge of *Mallomonas. J. Linnean Soc. London, Botany* **55**, 88–102.

133. HAWKINS, S. E., and COLE, R. J. (1965) Studies on the basis of cytoplasmic inheritance in amoebae. *Exptl. Cell Res.* **37**, 26–38.

134. HAZARD, F. O. (1940) An endamoeba parasitic in *Opalina chorophili. J. Parasitol.* **26**, 157–8.

135. HEAL, O. W. (1962) The abundance and microdistribution of testate amoebae (Rhizopoda: Testacea) in Sphagnum. *Oikos* **13**, 35–47.

136. HEAL, O. W. (1964) Observations on the seasonal and spatial distribution of Testacea (Protozoa: Rhizipoda) in *Sphagnum*. *J. Anim. Ecol.* **33**, 395–412.

137. HEIDT, K. (1943) Über eine Wasserblüten bildende *Euglena* und ihre Zerstörung durch einen Parasiten. *Ber. Oberhessischen Gesellsch. f. Natur- u. Heilkunde zu Giessen. N.F., Naturwissensch. Abt.* **20–22**, 9–14.

138. HERBERT, I. V. (1965) Cytochemistry of *in vitro* cultured *Trypanosoma theileri*. *Exptl. Par.* **16**, 348–62.

139. HIRSHON, J. B. (1964) The response of *Paramecium bursaria* to potential endocellular symbionts. *Dissert. Abstr.* **25**, 2187.

140. HOLLANDE, A. (1945) Biologie et reproduction de Rhizopodes des genres *Pelomyxa* et *Amoeba* et cycle évolutif de l'*Amoebophilus destructor* nov. gen., nov. sp., Chrytidinée (sic., Chytridinée) parasite de *Pelomyxa palustris* Greeff. *Bull. Biol. France et Belgique* **79**, 31–66.

141. HOLLANDE, A., and ENJUMET, M. (1953) Contribution a l'étude biologique des Sphaerocollides (Radiolaires collodaires et Radiolaires polycyttaires) et de leurs parasites. Partie I: *Thalassicollidae, Physematidae, Thalassophysidae. Ann. Sci. Nat., Zoologie, Sér. 11*, **15**, 99–183.

142. HOLLANDE, A., and GUILCHER, Y. (1945) Les Amibes du genre *Pelomyxa*: Éthologie, structure, cycle évolutif, parasites. *Bull. Soc. Zool. France* **70**, 53–56.

143. HOLLANDE, A., and HEIM DE BALSAC, H. (1941) Parasitisme du *Peranema trichophorum* par une Chytridinée du genre *Nucleophaga. Arch. Zool. Exptl. et Gén.* **82**, 37–46.

144. HOVASSE, R. (1950) *Spirobütschliella chattoni* nov. gen., nov. sp., Cilié astome, parasite en Méditerranée du Serpulien *Potamoceros triqueter* L. et parasité par la microsporidie *Gurleya nova*, sp. nov. *Bull. Inst. Océanogr. Monaco* **962**, 10 pp.

145. HOVASSE, R., and BROWN, E. M. (1953) Contribution à la connaissance des Radiolaires et de leurs parasites syndiniens. *Ann. Sci. Nat., Sér. 11*, **15**, 405–38.

146. HUNGATE, R. E. (1950) Mutualisms in Protozoa. *Ann. Rev. Microbiol.* **4**, 53–66.

147. HUNGATE, R. E. (1955) Mutualistic intestinal Protozoa. In *Biochemistry and Physiology of Protozoa*, eds. S. H. HUTNER and A. LWOFF, Academic Press, New York **2**, 159–99.

148. HUNTER, N. W. (1963) Histochemical observations of some enzymes in *Paramecium bursaria*. *Trans. Amer. Microscop. Soc.* **82**, 54–59.

149. INGOLD, C. T. (1940) *Endocoenobium eudorinae* gen. et sp. nov., a chytridiaceous fungus parasitizing *Eudorina elegans* Ehrenb. *New Phytol.* **39**, 97–103.

150. INGOLD, C. T. (1944) Studies on British Chytrids. II. A new chytrid on *Ceratium* and *Peridinium. Trans. Brit. Mycol. Soc.* **27**, 93–96.

151. JAAG, O., and NIPKOW, F. (1951) Neue und wenig bekannte parasitische Pilze auf Plankton-Organismen schweizerischer Gewässer. I. *Ber. Schweizer Bot. Ges.* **61**, 478–98.

152. JACOBSON, W. E., WILLIAMSON, M., and STOCK, C. C. (1952) The destructive effec of 2,6-diaminopurine on kappa of stock 51 killers, variety 4, of *Paramecium aurelia*. *J. Exptl. Zool.* **121**, 505–19.

153. JAKOB, H. (1959) Revue de phytosociologie. Associations et symbioses entre algues et animaux. *Bull. Soc., Bot. France* **106**, 155–62.

154. JANKOWSKI, A. W. (1963) (Pathology of Ciliophora. II. Life cycles of suctoria parasiting in *Urostyla* and *Paramecium*.) (in Russian.) *Tsitologiya* **5**, 428–39.

155. JOHNS, R. M. (1964) A new *Polyphagus* in algal culture. *Mycologia* **56**, 441–51.

156. JOHNSON, J. H. (1947) *Nubecularia* from the Pennsylvanian and Permian of Kansas. *J. Paleontol.* **21**, 41–45.

157. JOHNSON, J. H. (1950) A Permian algal-foraminiferal consortium from west Texas. *J. Paleontol.* **24**, 61–62.

158. JONES, F. R. (1958) Three zoopagales from brackish water. *Nature* **181**, 575–6.

159. KARAKASHIAN, S. J. (1963) Growth of *Paramecium bursaria* as influenced by the presence of algae symbionts. *Physiol. Zool.* **36**, 52–68.

160. KARAKASHIAN, S. J., and KARAKASHIAN, M. W. (1965) Evolution and symbiosis in the genus *Chlorella* and related algae. *Evolution* **19**, 368–77.

161. KARAKASHIAN, S. J., and SIEGEL, R. W. (1965) A genetic approach to endocellular symbiosis. *Exptl. Parasit.* **17**, 103–22.

162. KARLING, J. S. (1946) Brazilian Chytrids. IX. Species of *Rhizophydium. Amer. J. Bot.* **33**, 328–34.

163. KELLER, H. (1949) Untersuchungen über die intrazellulären Bakterien von *Pelomyxa palustris* Greeff. *Zeit. f. Naturf.* **4**b, 293–7.

164. KIMBALL, R. F., and PRESCOTT, D. M. (1964) RNA and protein synthesis in amacronucleate *Paramecium aurelia. J. Cell Biol.* **21**, 496–7.

165. KIRBY, JR., H. (1941) Relationships between certain Protozoa and other animals. In *Protozoa in Biological Research*, eds. G. N. CALKINS and F. M. SUMMERS, Columbia University Press, New York, 890–1008.

166. KIRBY, JR., H. (1941) Organisms living on and in Protozoa. In *Protozoa in Biological Research*, eds. G. N. CALKINS and F. M. SUMMERS, Columbia University Press, New York, 1009–1113.

167. KIRBY, JR., H. (1941) Devescovinid flagellates of termites. I. The genus *Devescovina. Univ. Calif. Publ. Zool.* **45**, 1–92.

168. KIRBY, JR., H. (1942) A parasite of the macronucleus of *Vorticella. J. Parasit.* **28**, 311–4.

169. KIRBY, JR., H. (1942) Devescovinid flagellates of termites. II. The genera *Caduceia* and *Macrotrichomonas. Univ. Calif. Publ. Zool.* **45**, 93–166.

170. KIRBY, JR., H. (1942) Devescovinid flagellates of termites. III. The genera *Foaina* and *Parajoenia. Univ. Calif. Publ. Zool.* **45**, 167–246.

171. KIRBY, JR., H. (1944) The structural characteristics and nuclear parasites of some species of *Trichonympha* in termites. *Univ. Calif. Publ. Zool.* **49**, 185–282.

172. KIRBY, JR., H. (1945) Devescovinid flagellates of termites. IV. The general *Metadevescovina* and *Pseudodevescovina. Univ. Calif. Publ. Zool.* **45**, 247–318.

173. KIRBY, JR., H. (1946) *Gigantomonas herculea* Dogiel, a polymastigote flagellate with flagellated and amoeboid phases of development. *Univ. Calif. Publ. Zool.* **53**, 163–226.

174. KIRBY, JR., H. (1949) Devescovinid flagellates of termites. V. The genus *Hyperdevescovina*, the genus *Bullanympha*, and undescribed or unrecorded species. *Univ. Calif. Publ. Zool.* **45**, 319–422.

175. KIRBY, H., and HONIGBERG, B. (1949) Flagellates of the caecum of ground squirrels. *Univ. Calif. Publ. Zool.* **53**, 315–66.

176. KLING, C., OLIN, G., FAHRAEUS, J., and NORLIN, G. (1942) Sewage as a carrier and disseminator of Poliomyelitis virus. *Acta Med. Scandin.* **112**, 217–63.

177. KUDO, R. R. (1941) The development of *Nosema notabilis* Kudo, a microsporidian, and of its host myxosporidian, *Sphaerospora polymorpha* Davis, parasitic in *Opsanus tau. Anat. Rec.* **81** (suppl.), 133 (Abst.).

178. KUDO, R. R. (1944) Morphology and development of *Nosema notabilis* Kudo, parasitic in *Sphaerospora polymorpha* Davis, a parasite of *Opsanus tau* and *O. beta. Univ. Illinois Biol. Monogr.* **20**, 83 pp.

179. KUDO, R. R. (1959) *Pelomyxa* and related organisms. *Ann. New York Acad. Sci.* **78**, 474–86.

180. LAIRD, M. (1953) The Protozoa of New Zealand intertidal zone fishes. *Trans. Roy. Soc. New Zealand* **81**, 79–143.

181. LAZO, W. (1961) Growth of green algae with myxomycete plasmodia. *Amer. Midland Nat.* **65**, 381–3.

182. LE CALVEZ, J. (1939) *Trophosphaera planorbulinae*, n. gen., n. sp., protiste parasite du Foraminifère *Planorbulina mediterranensis* d'Orb. *Arch. Zool. Exptl.* **80**, 425–43.

183. LE CALVEZ, J. (1940) Une amibe, *Vahlkampfia discorbini*, n. sp. parasite du Foraminifère *Discorbis mediterranensis* (d'Orbigny). *Arch. Zool. Exptl. et Gén.* **81**, 123–9.

184. LE CALVEZ, J. (1947) *Entosolenia marginata*, Foraminifère apogamique ectoparasite d'un autre Foraminifère *Discorbis vilardeboanus*. *C.R. Acad. Sci.* **224**, 1448–50.

185. LEDERBERG, J. (1952) Cell genetics and hereditary symbiosis. *Physiol. Rev.* **32**, 403–30.

186. LEINER, M., and WOHLFEIL, M. (1954) Das symbiontische Bakterium in *Pelomyxa palustris* Greeff. III. *Zeit. f. Morph. u. Ökol. der Tiere* **42**, 529–49.

187. LEINER, M., WOHLFEIL, M., and SCHMIDT, D. (1951) Das symbiontische Bakterium in *Pelomyxa palustris* Greeff. I. *Zeit. f. Naturf.* **6**b, 158–70.

188. LEINER, M., WOHLFEIL, M., and SCHMIDT, D. (1954) *Pelomyxa palustris* Greeff. *Ann. Sci. Nat., Zool., Sér. 11*, **16**, 537–94.

189. LEVINE, M. (1953) The diverse mate-killers of *Paramecium aurelia*, variety 8: Their interrelations and genetic basis. *Genetics* **38**, 561–78.

190. LEVINE, M., and HOWARD, J. L. (1955) Respiratory studies on mate-killers and sensitives of *Paramecium aurelia*, variety 8. *Science* **121**, 336–7.

191. LÓPEZ-OCHOTERENA, E. (1962) Protozoarios ciliados de México. I. *Stylonichia mytilus* Ehrenberg, 1838 y *Sphaerophrya sol* Metchnikoff, 1864. Un caso de parasitismo entre protozoarios. *Acta Zool. Mexicana* **6**, 1–6.

192. LÓPEZ-OCHOTERENA, E. (1962) Protozoarios ciliados de México. II. Notas sobre la biología de *Tokophrya quadripartita* (Claparède et Lachmann, 1861) Bütschli, 1889 (Ciliata: Suctorida), en aguas dulces de México. *Rev. Biol. Trop.* **10**, 1–10.

193. LÓPEZ-OCHOTERENA, E. (1964) Mexican ciliated protozoa. III. *Hypophrya fasciculata* gen. nov., sp. nov. (Ciliata: Suctorida). *J. Protozool.* **11**, 222–4.

194. LUBINSKY, G. (1955) On some parasites of parasitic Protozoa. I. *Sphaerita hoari* sp. n.—A chytrid parasitizing *Eremoplastron bovis. Canad. J. Microbiol.* **1**, 440–50.

195. LUBINSKY, G. (1955) On some parasites of parasitic Protozoa. II. *Sagittospora cameroni* gen. n., sp. n.—A phycomycete parasitizing Ophryoscolecidae. *Canad. J. Microbiol.* **1**, 675–84.

196. LUND, J. W. G. (1953) New or rare British Chrysophyceae. II. *Hyalobryon polymorphum* n. sp. and *Chrysonebula holmesii* n. gen. n. sp. *New Phytol.* **52**, 114–23.

197. LWOFF, A., and VALENTINI, S. (1948) Culture du flagellé opalinide *Cepedea dimidiata Ann. Inst. Pasteur* **75**, 1–7.

198. MARMUR, J., CAHOON, M. E., SHIMURA, Y., and VOGEL, H. J. (1963) Deoxyribonucleic acid type attributable to a bacterial endosymbiote in the Protozoa *Crithidia* (*Strigomonas*) *oncopelti. Nature* **197**, 1228–9.

199. MCLAUGHLIN, J. J. A., and ZAHL, P. A. (1957) Studies in marine biology. II. *In vitro* culture of Zooxanthellae. *Proc. Soc. Exptl. Biol. and Med.* **95**, 115–20.

200. MCLAUGHLIN, J. J. A., and ZAHL, P. A. (1959) Axenic Zooxanthellae from various invertebrate hosts. *Ann. New York Acad. Sci.* **77**, 55–72.

201. MERCER, E. H. (1959) An electron microscopic study of *Amoeba proteus. Proc. Roy. Soc., Ser. B.* **150**, 216–32.

202. MILLER, J. H., and SWARTZWELDER, J. C. (1960) Virus-like particles in an *Entamoeba histolytica* trophozoite. *J. Parasit.* **46**, 523–4.

203. MISRA, P. L. (1941) Observations on a new gregarine, *Stylocephalus bahli*, sp. nov. from the alimentary canal of an Indian beetle, *Gonocephalum helopioides* FRM. *Rec. Ind. Mus.* **43**, 43–72.

204. MOEWUS, L. (1963) Studies on a marine parasitic ciliate as a potential virus vector. In *Symposium on Marine Microbiology*, ed. C. H. OPPENHEIMER, C. C. THOMAS, Springfield, Illinois, 366–79.

205. MOEWUS-KOBB, L. (1965) Studies with IPN virus in marine hosts. *Ann. New York Acad. Sci.* **126**, 328–42.

206. MOEWUS-KOBB, L. (1965) Experimental parasitization of fishes with *Miamiensis avidus* (Thompson and Moewus 1964) a holotrichous, marine ciliate. In *Progress*

in Protozoology, abstracts of papers from Second Internat'l Conf. Protozoology, London, 1965, 252–3.

207. MUELLER, J. A. (1961) Further studies on the nature of the "co-factor" required for kappa infection in *Paramecium aurelia*, syngen 4. *Am. Zool.* **1**, 375.

208. MUELLER, J. A. (1962) Induced physiological and morphological changes in the B particle and R body from killer paramecia. *J. Protozool.* **9**, (suppl.), 26.

209. MUELLER, J. A. (1963) Separation of kappa particles with infective activity from those with killing activity and identification of the infective particles in *Paramecium aurelia*. *Exptl. Cell Res.* **30**, 492–508.

210. MUELLER, J. A. (1964) Cofactor for infection by kappa in *Paramecium aurelia*. *Exptl. Cell Res.* **35**, 464–76.

211. MUELLER, J. A. (1964) Paramecia develop immunity against kappa. *Am. Zoologist* **4**, 313–4 (abstract).

212. MUELLER, J. A. (1965) Kappa-affected Paramecia develop immunity. *J. Protozool.* **12**, 278–81.

213. MUSCATINE, L. (1961) Symbiosis in marine and fresh water coelenterates. In *The Biology of Hydra*, eds. H. M. LENHOFF and W. F. LOOMIS, Univ. of Miami Press, Miami, 255–68.

214. MUSCATINE, L. (1965) Symbiosis of hydra and algae. III. Extracellular products of the algae. *Comp. Biochem. and Physiol.* **16**, 77–92.

215. MUSCATINE, L., and HAND, C. (1958) Direct evidence for the transfer of materials from symbiotic algae to the tissues of a coelenterate. *Proc. Nat. Acad. Sci.* **44**, 1259–63.

216. MYERS, E. H. (1943) Life activities of Foraminifera in relation to marine ecology. *Proc. Am. Phil. Soc.* **86**, 439–58.

217. NENNINGER, U. (1948) Die Peritrichen der Umgebung von Erlangen mit besonderer Berücksichtigung ihrer Wirtsspecifität. *Zool. Jahrb., Abst. Syst., Ökol. u. Geogr. Tiere* **77**, 169–266.

218. NEWTON, B. A. (1956) A synthetic growth medium for the trypanosomid flagellate *Strigomonas (Herpetomonas) oncopelti*. *Nature* **177**, 279–80.

219. NEWTON, B. A. (1957) Nutritional requirements and biosynthetic capabilities of the parasitic flagellate *Strigomonas oncopelti*. *J. Gen. Microbiol.* **17**, 708–17.

220. NEWTON, B. A., and HORNE, R. W. (1957) Intracellular structures in *Strigomonas oncopelti*. I. Cytoplasmic structures in *Strigomonas oncopelti*. *Exptl. Cell Res.* **13**, 563–74.

221. NIEBOER, H. J. (1959) *Volvox aureus*, historisch overzicht, kweken, zwemmen, orientatie. *Levende Natuur* **62**, 65–71, 88–94.

222. NURSE, F. M. (1945) Protozoa from New Zealand termites. *Trans. Roy. Soc. New Zealand* **74**, 305–14.

223. OTTERSTRØM, C. V., and LARSEN, K. (1946) Extensive mortality in trout caused by the infusorian *Stentor polymorphus* Ehrenb. *Rept. Danish Biol. Sta.* **48**, 53–57.

224. PADNOS, M., and NIGRELLI, R. F. (1947) *Endosphaera engelmanni* endoparasitic in *Trichodina spheroidesi* infecting the puffer, *Sphaeroides maculatus*. *Zoologica* **32**, 169–72.

225. PATERSON, R. A. (1958) Parasitic and saprophytic phycomycetes which invade planktonic organisms. I. New taxa and records of chytridiaceous fungi. *Mycologia* **50**, 85–96.

226. PATERSON, R. A. (1958) Parasitic and saprophytic phycomycetes which invade planktonic organisms. II. A new species of *Dangeardia* with notes on other lacustrine fungi. *Mycologia.* **50**, 453–68.

227. PEACH, M. (1950) Aquatic predaceous fungi. *Trans. Brit. Mycol. Soc.* **33**, 148–53.

228. PEACH, M. (1955) Soil fungi that prey on Protozoa. In *Soil Zoology*, Proceedings of the Univ. Nottingham Second Easter School in Agricultural Science, eds. D. KEVAN and MCE. KEITH, Academic Press, New York, 302–10.

229. PENARD, E. (1940) Protozooaires et psychologie. *Arch. Sci. Phys. et Nat.* **22**, 160–75, 179–200, 203–26, 265–89.

230. PÉREZ REYES, R. (1963) Algunas consideraciones sobre los parasitos de protozoarios incluidos en el genero *Sphaerita*. *Rev. Soc. Mex. Hist. Nat.* **24**, 1–6.

231. PÉREZ REYES, R., and LÓPEZ-OCHOTERENA, E. (1963) *Sphaerophrya sol* (Ciliata: Suctoria) parasitic in some Mexican ciliates. *J. Parasit.* **49**, 697.

232. PÉREZ REYES, R., and SALAS GÓMEZ, E. (1958) Euglenae de valle de Mexico. I. Algunas especies encontradas en el estanque de Chapultepec. *Rev. Latinoamer. Microbiol.* **1**, 303–25.

233. PÉREZ REYES, R., and SALAS GÓMEZ, E. (1961) Euglenae del valle de Mexico. IV. Descripcion de algunos endoparasitos. *Rev. Latinoamer. Microbiol.* **4**, 53–73.

234. PLAUT, W., and SAGAN, L. A. (1958) Incorporation of thymidine in the cytoplasm of *Amoeba proteus*. *J. Biophysic. and Biochem. Cytol.* **4**, 843–4.

235. PREER, J. R. (1946) Some properties of a genetic cytoplasmic factor in *Paramecium*. *Proc. Nat. Acad. Sci.* **32**, 247–53.

236. PREER, JR., J. R. (1948) A study of some properties of the cytoplasmic factor, "kappa", in *Paramecium aurelia*, variety 2. *Genetics* **33**, 349–404.

237. PREER, JR., J. R. (1948) Microscopic bodies in the cytoplasm of "killers" of *Paramecium aurelia* and evidence for the identification of these bodies with the cytoplasmic factor, kappa. *Genetics* **33**, 625 (abstract).

238. PREER, JR., J. R. (1948) The killer cytoplasmic factor kappa. Its rate of reproduction, the number of particles per cell, and its size. *Am. Nat.* **82**, 35–42.

239. PREER, JR., J. R. (1950) Microscopically visible bodies in the cytoplasm of the "killer" strains of *Paramecium aurelia*. *Genetics* **35**, 344–62.

240. PREER, JR., J. R., SIEGEL, R. W., and STARK, P. S. (1953) The relationship between kappa and paramecin in *Paramecium aurelia*. *Proc. Nat. Acad. Sci.* **39**, 1228–33.

241. PREER, JR., J. R., and STARK, P. (1953) Cytological observations on the cytoplasmic factor "kappa" in *Paramecium aurelia*. *Exptl. Cell Res.* **5**, 478–91.

242. PREER, L. B., and PREER, JR., J. R. (1964) Killing activity from lysed particles of *Paramecium*. *Genetical Res.* **5**, 230–9.

243. PROVASOLI, L., and PINTNER, I. J. (1953) Ecological implications of *in vitro* nutritional requirements of algal flagellates. *Ann. New York Acad. Sci.* **56**, 839–51.

244. DE PUYTORAC, P. (1952) Parasitisme de certains Ciliés astomes par un protozoaire nouveau: *Spherasuctans emeriti* n. g. n. sp., *C.R. Acad. Sci.* **234**, 749–51.

245. DE PUYTORAC, P. (1953) Actions de *Spherasuctans emeriti* de Puytorac, protozoaire parasite, sur un hôte, *Anoplophrya* cf. *lumbrici*, cilié astome. *Bull. Soc. Zool. de France* **77**, 326–30.

246. PYNE, C. K. (1963) Étude de la structure infra-microscopique de *Strigomonas oncopelti* (flagellé, famille Trypanosomidae). In *Progress in Protozoology*, Proc. First Internat'l Conf. Protozoology, Prague, 1961, 396.

247. RABINOVITCH, M., and PLAUT, W. (1962) Cytoplasmic DNA synthesis in *Amoeba proteus*. II. On the behavior and possible nature of the DNA-containing elements. *J. Cell Biol.* **15**, 535–40.

248. RAY, H. N., and BANIK, D. C. (1965) A hyperparasite of *Iodamoeba buetschlii* from the rhesus monkey, *Macaca mulatta*, and the domestic pig. *J. Protozool.* **12**, 70–72.

249. REEVE, E. C. R., and ROSS, G. J. S. (1962) Mate-killer (mu) particles in *Paramecium aurelia*: The metagon division hypothesis. *Genetical Res.* **3**, 328–30.

250. REEVE, E. C. R., and ROSS, G. J. S. (1963) Mate-killer (mu) particles in *Paramecium aurelia*: Further mathematical models for metagon distribution. *Genetical Res.* **4**, 158–61.

251. RIS, H. (1960) The structure of the kinetoplast in trypanosomes. In *10e Congrès int. Biol. Cellulaire, Paris*. Résumé des communications, p. 232. Paris, L'expansion scient. Franc.

252. RIS, H., and PLAUT, W. (1962) Ultrastructure of DNA-containing areas in the chloroplast of *Chlamydomonas. J. Cellular Biol.* **13**, 383–91.

253. RODGI, S. S., and BALL, G. H. (1961) New species of gregarines from millipedes of Mysore State, India. *J. Protozool.* **8**, 162–79.

254. ROTH, L. E., and DANIELS, E. W. (1961) Infective organisms in the cytoplasm of *Amoeba proteus. J. Biophys. and Biochem. Cytol.* **9**, 317–23.

255. RUDENBERG, F. H. (1962) Electron microscopic observations of kappa in *Paramecium aurelia. Tex. Repts. Biol. and Med.* **20**, 105–12.

256. SAMUELS, R. (1941) The morphology and division of *Trichomonas augusta* Alexeieff *Trans. Am. Micr. Soc.* **60**, 421–40.

257. SCHMITT, J. A., and BENEKE, E. S. (1962) Aquatic fungi from South Bass and neighboring islands in western Lake Erie. II. Additional biflagellate and uniflagellate phycomycetes. *Ohio. J. Sci.* **62**, 11–12.

258. SCHNELLER, M. V. (1958) A new type of killing action in a stock of *Paramecium aurelia* from Panama. *Proc. Indiana Acad. Sci.* **67**, 302–3.

259. SCHÖNFELD, C. (1959) Über das parasitische Verhalten einer *Astasia*-Art in *Stentor coeruleus. Arch. Prot.* **104**, 261–4.

260. SCHULZE, K. E. (1951) Experimentelle Untersuchungen über die Chlorellensymbiose bei Ciliaten. *Biol. Generalis* **19**, 281–98.

261. SHORT, R. B. (1946) Observations of the giant amoeba *Amoeba carolinensis. Biol. Bull.* **90**, 8–18.

261a. SIDDIQUI, W. A., and RUDZINSKA, M. A. (1965) The fine structure of axenically-grown trophozoites of *Entamoeba invadens* with special reference to the nucleus and helical ribonucleoprotein bodies. *J. Protozool.* **12**, 448–59.

262. SIEGEL, R. W. (1953) A genetic analysis of the mate-killer trait in *Paramecium aurelia*, variety 8. *Genetics* **38**, 550–60.

263. SIEGEL, R. W. (1960) Hereditary endosymbiosis in *Paramecium bursaria. Exptl. Cell Res.* **19**, 239–52.

264. SIEGEL, R. W., and KARAKASHIAN, S. J. (1959) Dissociation and restoration of endocellular symbiosis in *Paramecium bursaria. Anat. Rec.* **134**, 639.

265. SIEGEL, R. W., and PREER, J. R. (1957) Antigenic relationships among Feulgen positive cytoplasmic particles in Paramecium. *Am. Nat.* **91**, 253–7.

266. SIMONSEN, D. H., and VAN WAGTENDONK, W. J. (1952) Respiratory studies on *Paramecium aurelia*, variety 4, killers and sensitives. *Biochimica et Biophysica Acta* **9**, 515–27.

267. SKUJA, H. (1958) Eine neue vorwiegend sessil oder rhizopodial auftretende synbakteriotische Polytomee aus einem Schwefelgewässer. *Svensk. Bot. Tidskr.* **52**, 379–90.

268. SMITH, J. E. (1961) Purification of kappa particles of *Paramecium aurelia*, stock 51. *Am. Zoologist* **1**, 390.

269. SMITH-SONNEBORN, J., GREEN, L., and MARMUR, J. (1962) Deoxyribonucleic acid base composition of kappa and *Paramecium aurelia*, stock 51. *Nature* **197**, 385.

270. SMITH-SONNEBORN, J. E., and VAN WAGTENDONK, W. J. (1964) Purification and chemical characterization of kappa of stock 51, *Paramecium aurelia. Exptl. Cell Res.* **33**, 50–59.

271. SOLDO, A. T. (1960) Cultivation of two strains of *Paramecium aurelia* in axenic medium. *Proc. Soc. Exptl. Biol. and Med.* **105**, 612–5.

272. SOLDO, A. T. (1961) The use of particle-bearing *Paramecium* in screening for potential antitumour agents. *Trans. New York Acad. Sci.* **23**, 653–61.

273. SOLDO, A. T. (1963) Axenic culture of *Paramecium.* Some observations on the growth behavior and nutritional requirements of a particle-bearing strain of *Paramecium aurelia* 299 λ. *Ann. New York Acad. Sci.* **108**, 380–8.

274. SONNEBORN, T. M. (1943) Gene and cytoplasm. I. The determination and inheritance of the killer character in variety 4 of *Paramecium aurelia. Proc. Nat. Acad. Sci.* **29**, 329–38.

275. SONNEBORN, T. M. (1943) Gene and cytoplasm. II. The bearing of the determination and inheritance of characters in *Paramecium aurelia* on the problems of cytoplasmic inheritance, *Pneumococcus* transformations, mutations and development. *Proc. Nat. Acad. Sci.* **29**, 338–43.

276. SONNEBORN, T. M. (1945) Gene action in *Paramecium. Ann. Missouri Bot. Gard.* **32**, 213–21.

277. SONNEBORN, T. M. (1945) The dependence of the physiological action of a gene on a primer and the relation of primer to gene. *Am. Nat.* **79**, 318–39.

278. SONNEBORN, T. M. (1946) Experimental control of the concentration of cytoplasmic genetic factors in *Paramecium. Cold Spring Harbor Symposia on Quantitative Biology* **11**, 236–55.

279. SONNEBORN, T. M. (1947) Recent advances in the genetics of *Paramecium* and *Euplotes. Advances in Genetics* **1**, 263–358.

280. SONNEBORN, T. M. (1948) Genes, cytoplasm, and environment in *Paramecium. Sci. Monthly* **67**, 154–60.

281. SONNEBORN, T. M. (1950) The cytoplasm in heredity. *Heredity* **4**, 11–36.

282. SONNEBORN, T. M. (1959) Kappa and related particles in *Paramecium. Advances in Virus Res.* **6**, 229–356.

283. SONNEBORN, T. M. (1961) Kappa particles and their bearing on host-parasite relations. *Perspectives in Virology* **2**, 5–12.

284. SONNEBORN, T. M. (1965) The metagon: RNA and cytoplasmic inheritance. *Am. Nat.* **99**, 279–307.

285. SONNEBORN, T. M., GIBSON, I., and SCHNELLER, M. V. (1964) Killer particles and metagons of *Paramecium* grown in *Didinium. Science* **144**, 567–8.

286. SONNEBORN, T. M., and MUELLER, J. A. (1959) What is the infective agent in breis of killer paramecia? *Science* **130**, 1423.

287. SPARROW, JR., F. K. (1960) *Aquatic Phycomycetes*, ed. 2. Univ. Michigan Press, Ann Arbor.

288. STUBBLEFIELD, J. W. (1955) The morphology and life history of *Amphiacantha ovalis* and *A. attenuata*, two new haplosporidian parasites of gregarines. *J. Parasitology* **41**, 443–59.

289. SUBRAHMANYAN, R. (1954) A new member of the Euglenineae, *Protoeuglena noctilucae* gen. et sp. nov., occurring in *Noctiluca miliaris* Suriray, causing green discoloration of the sea off Calicut. *Proc. Indian Acad. Sci., Sect. B* **39**, 118–27.

290. SWIFT, H. (1965) Nucleic acids of mitochondria and chloroplasts. *Am. Nat.* **99**, 201–27.

291. TALLAN, I. (1959) Factors involved in infection by the kappa particles in *Paramecium aurelia*, syngen 4. *Physiol. Zool.* **32**, 78–89.

292. TALLAN, I. (1961) A cofactor required by kappa in the infection of *Paramecium aurelia* and its possible action. *Physiol. Zool.* **34**, 1–13.

293. TANGUAY, R. B., and VAN WAGTENDONK, W. J. (1963) Histological staining and chemical identification of the lambda particle of *Paramecium aurelia*, stock 299 (killers). *Fed. Proc.* **22**, 646.

294. TARTAR, V. (1953) Chimeras and nuclear transplantations in ciliates, *Stentor coeruleus* × *S. polymorphus. J. Exptl. Zool.* **124**, 63–103.

295. THALMANN, H. E. (1949) Mitteilungen über Foraminiferan. VII. *Eclogae Geol., Helvetiae* **41**, 366–72.

296. TOOMEY, J. A., TAKACS, W. S., and SCHAEFFER, M. (1948) Attempts to infect *Amoeba proteus* with poliomyelitis virus. *Am. J. Dis. Children* **75**, 11–14.

297. TRAGER, W. (1960) Intracellular parasitism and symbiosis. In *The Cell*, ed J. BRACHET and A. E. MIRSKY, Academic Press, New York 4, 151–213.

298. TRAGER, W. (1964) The cytoplasm of Protozoa. In *The Cell*, ed. J. BRACHET and A. E. MIRSKY, Academic Press, New York 6, 81–137.

299. TRAGER, W. (1965) The kinetoplast and differentiation in certain parasitic Protozoa. *Am. Nat.* 99, 255–66.

300. TRAGER, W., and RUDZINSKA, M. A. (1964) The riboflavin requirement and the effects of acriflavin on the fine structure of the kinetoplast of *Leishmania tarentolae*. *J. Protozool.* 11, 133–45.

301. TSCHERMAK-WOESS, E. (1950) Über eine Synbacteriose und ähnliche Symbiosen. *Oesterreich. Bot. Zeitschr.* 97, 188–206.

302. TUZET, O., and ROUQUEROL, T. (1962) Sur quelques caractéristiques biologiques de *Rizamoeba camariae*. *Ann. Épiphyties* 13, 259–62.

303. VAN WAGTENDONK, W. J. (1948) The action of enzymes on paramecin. *J. Biol. Chem.* 173, 691–704.

304. VAN WAGTENDONK, W. J. (1948) The killing substance paramecin: Chemical nature. *Am. Nat.* 82, 60–68.

305. VAN WAGTENDONK, W. J., CLARK, J. D., and GODOY, G. A. (1963) The biological status of lambda and related particles in *Paramecium aurelia*. *Proc. Nat. Acad. Sci.* 50, 835–8.

306. VAN WAGTENDONK, W. J., and SOLDO, A. T. (1965) Endosymbionts of ciliated protozoa. In *Progress in Protozoology*, abstracts of papers from Second Internat'l Cong. Protozoology, London, 1965, 244–5.

307. VAN WAGTENDONK, W. J., and TANGUAY, R. B. (1963) The chemical composition of lambda in *Paramecium aurelia*, stock 299. *J. Gen. Microbiol.* 33, 395–400.

308. VICKERMAN, K. (1963) Electron microscopy of parasites. In *Techniques in Parasitology*, First Symposium of the British Society for Parasitology, Blackwell Scientific Publications, Oxford, 69–98.

308 a. VIVIER, E. (1965) Étude, au microscope électronique, de la spore de *Metchnikovella hovassei* n. sp., appartenance des Metchnikovellidae aux Microsporidies. *C.R. Acad. Sci.* 260, 6982–4.

309. VOGE, M., and KESSEL, J. F. (1958) *Sphaerita* in cysts of *Entamoeba coli*. *J. Parasitology* 44, 454–5.

310. WENRICH, D. H. (1940) Observations on parasites and inclusion bodies in certain intestinal protozoa. *Science* 92, 416–7.

311. WENRICH, D. H. (1944) Studies on *Dientamoeba fragilis* (Protozoa). IV. Further observations with an outline of present-day knowledge of this species. *J. Parasit.* 30, 322–38.

312. WICHTERMAN, R. (1940) Parasitism in *Paramecium caudatum*. *J. Parasit.* 26 (Suppl.), 29.

313. WICHTERMAN, R. (1941) Studies on Zoöchlorella-free *Paramedium bursaria*. *Biol. Bull.* 81, 304–5 (abstract).

314. WICHTERMAN, R. (1942) A new ciliate from a coral of Tortugas and its symbiotic Zooxanthellae. *Carnegie Inst. Washington, Papers from Tortugas Lab.* 33, 107–10.

315. WICHTERMAN, R. (1945) Schizomycetes parasitic in *Paramecium bursaria*. *J. Parasit.* 31 (Suppl.), 25.

316. WICHTERMAN, R. (1946) Unstable micronuclear behavior in an unusual race of *Paramecium*. *Anat. Rec.* 94, 94.

317. WICHTERMAN, R. (1948) The presence of optically active crystals in *Paramecium bursaria* and their relationship to symbiosis. *Anat. Rec.* 101, 97–98.

318. WICHTERMAN, R. (1953) *The Biology of Paramecium*, Blakiston, New York.

319. WICHTERMAN, R. (1954) The common occurrence of micronuclear variation during binary fission in an unusual race of *Paramecium caudatum*. *J. Protozool.* 1, 54–59.

320. WIDMAYER, D. (1961) The detection of two new mutations of hump kappa in killer stock 51, syngen 4, *Paramecium aurelia. Am. Zool.* **1**, 398.
321. WIDMAYER, D. J. (1965) A nonkiller resistant kappa and its bearing on the interpretation of kappa in *Paramecium aurelia. Genetics* **51**, 613–23.
322. WILBER, C. G. (1947) Concerning the correct name of the rhizopod, *Pelomyxa carolinensis. Trans. Amer. Microsc. Soc.* **66**, 99–101.
323. WILLIAMSON, M., JACOBSON, W., and STOCK, C. C. (1952) Testing of chemicals for inhibition of the killer action of *Paramecium aurelia. J. Biol. Chem.* **197**, 763–70.
324. WOLSKA, J. (1949) The small amoebas in the plasm of *Amoeba proteus* Pall. *Ann. Univ. Mariae Curie-Sklodowska, Sect. C, Biol.* **4**, 137–47.
325. WOLSTENHOLME, D. R., and PLAUT, W. (1964) Cytoplasmic DNA synthesis in *Amoeba proteus.* III. Further studies on the nature of the DNA-containing elements. *J. Cell Biol.* **22**, 505–13.
326. YONGE, C. M. (1944) Experimental analysis of the association between invertebrates and unicellular algae. *Biol. Rev.* **19**, 68–80.
327. YOUNG, V. M., FELSENFELD, O., and BYRD, C. L. (1949) Behavior of virus of poliomyelitis in a culture of *Endamoeba histolytica. Am. J. Clin. Path.* **19**, 1135–8.
328. ZAHL, P. A., and MCLAUGHLIN, J. J. A. (1959) Studies in marine biology. IV. On the role of algal cells in the tissues of marine invertebrates. *J. Protozool.* **6**, 344–52.

ACKNOWLEDGMENTS

Permission has been granted from the following for use of the figures listed. The figure numbers are those employed in the present chapter. The author expresses his appreciation for these courtesies.

Academic Press, Inc.: Fig. 109 from vol. 5, Figs. 31, 32 from vol. 13, Fig. 116 from vol. 35, *Experimental Cell Research.*

Archiv für Protistenkunde, K. G. Grell, editor: Fig. 79 from vol. 104, Figs. 104–106 from vol. 105.

Blackwell Scientific Publications, Ltd.: Fig. 59 from vol. 39, *The New Phytologist.*

The Royal Society of Tropical Medicine and Hygiene: Fig. 72 from vol. 56, *Transactions of the Royal Society of Tropical Medicine and Hygiene.*

Journal of Parasitology, J. F. Mueller, editor: Fig. 39 from vol. 28, Fig. 30 from vol. 29, Fig. 100 from vol. 41, Figs. 46, 47 from vol. 44, Fig. 73 from vol. 46, Fig. 95 from vol. 49.

Journal of Protozoology, W. Trager, editor: Fig. 20 from vol. 7, Figs. 52, 53 from vol. 8, Fig. 34 from vol. 10, Fig. 48 from vol. 12.

Physiological Zoology, Thomas Park, editor and Dr. S. J. Karakashian: Figs. 77, 78 from vol. 36.

New York Academy of Sciences, Harold E. Whipple, editor: Fig. 120 from vol. 108, *Annals of the New York Academy of Sciences.*

Zentralblatt für Bakteriologie, V. Hoss, editor: Fig. 71 from vol. 148.

University of Illinois Press, D. Jackson, Director: Fig. 101 from vol. 20, *Illinois Biological Monographs.*

Journal de Microscopie: Figs. 113–115 from vol. 3.

Elsevier Publishing Company, Amsterdam, and Dr. G. H. Beale: Fig. 118 from *Cellular Control Mechanisms and Cancer,* P. Emmelot and O. Mühlbock, editors.

The Linnaan Society of London: Fig. 85 from vol. 55, *Journal of Linnaan Society, Botany.*

Masson et Cie., Paris: Figs. 80–82 from vol. 1, p. 11, *Traité de Zoologie,* P. P. Grassé, editor (article by E. Chatton); Figs. 83, 107 from *Ann. Sci. Nat.: Zoologie,* vol. 15, sér. 11 (article by Hollande and Enjumet); Fig. 108 from *Ann. Sci. Nat.: Zoologie,* vol. 1, sér. 12 (article by Grassé and Théodoridès).

Archives de Zoologie expérimentale: Fig. 24 from vol. 82 (article by Duboscq and Grassé); Fig. 63 from vol. 82 (article by Hollande and Heim).

University of California Press: Figs. 1–15, 25–27 from vol. 45, Figs. 23, 42, 96–99 from vol. 49, Figs. 16, 28, 29, 43–45 from vol. 53, *University of California Publications in Zoology*.

The Rockefeller Institute Press: Figs. 75–76 from vol. 19, Fig. 74 from vol. 20, Figs. 102, 103 from vol. 22, *Journal of Cell Biology*; Figs. 110, 111 from vol. 4, Figs. 37, 38 from vol. 9, *Journal of Biophysical and Biochemical Cytology*. The Rockefeller Institute Press has requested the inclusion of the following statement in connection with the reproduction of the above figures: "The photographs here reproduced from halftone copy inevitably show a loss of detail, and the quality of the results is not representative of the originals."

Academia Brasileira de Ciencias, Anais, Rio de Janeiro, Arthur Moses, editor: Figs. 90, 91 from vol. 20.

Zeitschrift für Naturforschung, Tübingen, Dr. Mundinger, editor: Fig. 36 from vol. 6b.

British Mycological Society, Dr. J. G. Manners, editor: Fig. 55 from vol. 29, Fig. 56 from vol. 37, Fig. 59 from vol. 27, *Transactions*.

Cambridge University Press: Fig. 117 from vol. 23 (article by Beale and Jurand, Structure of mate-killer (mu) particles in *Paramecium aurelia*, stock 540), *J. Gen. Microbiol.*

Nature: Fig. 33 from vol. 197.

Mycologia, Clark T. Rogerson, Managing editor: Fig. 54 from vol. 37, Figs. 64–67 from vol. 34, Figs. 68, 69 from vol. 41, Fig. 70 from vol. 43.

Zoologica: Figs. 88, 89 from vol. 32.

Springer-Verlag, editors, *Österreichische Botanische Zeitschrift*: Fig. 21 from vol. 95.

Gauthier-Villars, Paris, editor, *Comptes-rendus Acad. Sci.*: Figs. 81, 84, 86 (Fig. 81 from article by Chatton and Biecheler, *Les Amoebophrya* and le *Hyalosaccus*; leur cycle evolutif, vol. 200, p. 505, 1935, Fig. 84 from article by de Puytorac, Parasitisme de certains Ciliés astomes par un protozoaire nouveau: *Spherosuctans emeriti* n.g.n.sp., vol. 234, pp. 749–751, 1952; Fig. 86 from article by Chatton and Lwoff, Sur la Systématique de la tribu Thigmotriches Rhynchoîdés, vol. 209, p. 429, 1939).

Koninlilijke Nederlandse Akademie van Wetenschappen, *Proceedings*, A. M. Verheggen, editor, Amsterdam: Figs. 40, 41 from vol. 67.

National Research Council of Canada: Figs. 49–51 from vol. 1, 1955 (articles by Lubinsky) *Canadian Journal of Microbiology*, J. A. Morrison, editor-in-chief.

Genetical Research, E. C. R. Reeve, editor: Fig. 55 from vol. 5.

Sydowia, Dr. F. Petrak, editor, Vienna; Figs. 61, 62 from vol. 16.

National Academy of Sciences, *Proceedings*, Mrs. Josephine A. Williams, editorial associate: Fig. 119 from vol. 50.

Revista Latinoamericana de Microbiologia y Parasitologia, Luis Rey, editor; Fig. 60 from vol. 1.

American Journal of Botany, Charles Heimsch, editor: Fig. 57 from vol. 31 (article by Hanson, A new chytrid parasitizing *Volvox*: *Loborhiza metzneri*, gen. nov., sp. nov.)

Council of the Royal Society, London, Dr. D. C. Martin, Executive Secretary; Figs. 17, 18, 19 from *Proceedings* B, vol. 159 (article by Cleveland and Grimstone, pl. 40, fig. 7; text-figs. 1, 11).

Bulletin Biologique de France et de la Belgique, Dr. P. P. Grassé, editor: Fig. 22 from vol. 84; Figs. 35, 93, 94 from vol. 79.

Permission was also obtained from the following authors for use of the above figures: Dr. Ruth V. Dippell, Fig. 110; Dr. W. Plaut, Figs. 102, 103; Dr. W. T. Hall, Figs. 75, 76; Dr. L. D. Hamilton, Fig. 111; Dr. L. E. Roth, Figs. 37, 38; Dr. G. Svihla, Fig. 74; Dr. Hilda Canter Lund, Figs. 55, 56; Professor C. T. Ingold, Fig. 59; Dr. Geoffrey Beale, Fig. 117; Dr. Julius Marmur, Fig. 33; Dr. Ross Nigrelli, Figs. 88, 89; Dr. E. Fauré-Fremiet, Figs. 87, 92; Dr. W. J. van Wagtendonk, Fig. 119; Dr. R. Pérez-Reyes and Dr. E. Salas Gómez, Fig. 60; Dr. L. R. Cleveland, Figs. 17, 18, 19.

INDEX OF SCIENTIFIC NAMES

SUBJECT INDEX

CONTENTS OF VOLUME 1

CONTENTS OF VOLUME 2

Volume 4 in preparation